PFR
combustors
ore roasters
side feed reactors
staged adiabatic fixed beds
turbidostats
reaction bombs
trickle beds
tubes
moving beds
enzyme reactors
absorption towers
fluidized beds
chemostats
piston
tanks
vats
plug
batch
mixed
CFSTR

THE CHEMICAL REACTOR OMNIBOOK

shaft kilns
blast furnaces
semibatch reactors
gas/liquid and gas/solid reactors
bubble tank absorbers
catalytic packed beds
fermentation vats
reactor-regenerators
activated sludge tanks
photochemical reactors
metallurgical reactors
reactors with decaying catalyst
laminar flow reactors
stirred tanks
shrinking & growing particle reactors
polymerization vats and tanks
adiabatic
microbial reactors
cross-flow reactors
recycle reactors
slurry reactors
CSTR
etc.

THE CHEMICAL REACTOR OMNIBOOK

OCTAVE LEVENSPIEL

Chemical Engineering Department
Oregon State University
Corvallis, Oregon 97331-2702

January 1993

Distributed by:

OSU Book Stores, Inc.
Corvallis, Oregon 97339

ISBN: 0-88246-160-5

PREFACE

The OMNIBOOK aims to present the main ideas of reactor design in a simple and direct way. It includes key formulas, brief explanations, practice exercises, problems from experience, and it skims over the field touching on all sorts of reaction systems.

What is the Omnibook good for? Perhaps

- as a reference book for methods in reactor design
- as a supplementary text for a course of study

But most important of all, it tries to show the reader how to approach the problems of reactor design, and what questions to ask. In effect it tries to show that a common strategy threads its way through all reactor problems, a strategy which involves three factors: identifying the flow pattern, knowing the kinetics, and developing the proper performance equation. It is this common strategy which is the heart of Chemical Reaction Engineering and identifies is as a distinct field of study.

I firmly believe that learning comes with doing, and with trying to apply ideas to new situations. Hence this book focuses on solving problems. Try them and if you have trouble then go to the text for help. I have kept most of the problems very simple to emphasize principles.

Regarding the text: I should warn the reader that despite its length the Omnibook's presentation is rather condensed. In most cases, I have avoided details of derivations and have gone from assumptions and starting equations directly to the final useful expressions. This compactness is particularly evident in the first few chapters.

Basic Philosophy: One can approach the characterization of chemical reactors at different levels of sophistication, accuracy and complexity. I have always felt that one should start with the simple model since it is easily solved and usually reasonably approximates the main features of the process. Of course the simple model can always be refined and extended when needed. If its extension gives a very different answer, this is a warning to look into the matter more carefully. Albert Einstein put it nicely, and he could have been looking straight at me when he said, "*Everything should be made as simple as possible, but not simpler.*" In general, I have tried to avoid complex material and methods in the Omnibook since there are so many important elementary ideas to treat on the subject.

Teaching from the Omnibook: Some of this material may be suitable for a first course on reactors, the rest for advanced courses. Here's a suggestion

1. For a broad background course, which is what a first course on the subject should be, I suggest covering chapters 1, 2, 3, 4, 5 to pg 7, 21, 23 to pg 6, 51, 52 to pg 4, 61, 62.

After this one can cover the remaining material in any order desired, for example

2. Gas solids systems: chapters 11, 20's, 30's, 50's
3. Non gas solid systems: chapters 6, 7, 8, 40's, 60's, 80's

Problems: A few words about these since they form such a large part of the Omnibook. First of all let me say that they involve no tricks, all are solvable by the methods and equations in the text, and most are short, few needing more than one page to solve. In learning the material it is a good idea to try one problem of each type.

Problems are grouped according to type by the letters A, B, C, ...; while the symbol * designates harder or longer problems, usually unsuited for quizzes.

References: Books are referred to compactly by the author's name and are listed in the book index. There is also an author index and a subject index.

This Printing: The Omnibook has come in green (1979), pink (1984) and blue (1989) printings. This is the fourth version in which a few new problems have been added, a few others have been changed and all errors found have been removed. I hope that this version is relatively free of these abominations. Bekki Levien, muchos gracias for correcting the typed material.

Also, I welcome back those two whimsical cartoon characters from Ronald Searle's creative pen. I wonder what they are cooking up in their reactor?

Finally, another medal for my wife Mary Jo for her support and good humor. However, she still refuses to let me use the word "omnibook" in Scrabble. Pity, for this one word could be worth over 300 points!!!

Octave Levenspiel

Corvallis, Oregon

CONTENTS

SINGLE PHASE REACTORS

1. Introduction to single phase reactors

Some simple reactor types		1.2
The rate equation		1.3
Terminology, symbols and an example problem		1.5
Converting pressure to concentration and an example		1.10
Problems	after	1.11

2. The batch reactor

Basic performance equation		2.1
Integrated forms for constant volume		2.2
Integrated forms for constant pressure and changing volume		2.7
Comments		2.8
Problems	after	2.9

3. The plug flow reactor

Basic performance equation		3.1
Integrated forms		3.2
Comments		3.3
Problems	after	3.6

4. The mixed flow reactor

Basic performance equation		4.1
Particular forms of the performance equation		4.2
Comments		4.3
Problems	after	4.4

5. More on ideal reactors, and extensions

Recycle reactor		5.1
Comparison of single reactors		5.4
Mixed flow reactors in series		5.5
Any combination of reactors		5.6
Finding the best combination of reactors		5.7
Partial emptying batch reactor--PEBR		5.8
Side entry flow reactors		5.10
Simple economic problems		5.14
Problems	after	5.17

6. Multiple reactions: qualitative

Rule 1: on desirable operating temperatures		6.2
Rule 2: on concentration levels		6.2
Rule 3: on maximizing the production of an intermediate		6.3

Rule 4: on series-parallel reactions		6.4
Rule 5: on optimization in the face of physical restraint		6.6
Comments and other possible rules		6.7
Problems	after	6.8

7. One step reactions: parallel, side-by-side, etc.

Single reactant systems		7.1
Two reactant systems		7.5
Temperature effects		7.6
Problems	after	7.7

8. Potpourri of multiple reactions

$A \rightarrow R \rightarrow S$, both first order		8.1
$A \rightarrow R \rightarrow S$, mixed zero and first order.		8.6
Two step series-parallel reactions		8.8
The Denbigh reaction and its special cases		8.14
Comments, suggestions and extensions		8.17
Problems	after	8.17

INTERLUDE

11. Multiphase reactors, background discussion

Kinetics and six examples		11.1
The general performance equation		11.5
Simplifications leading to practical expressions		11.7

REACTORS WITH SOLID CATALYST

21. Introduction to solid catalysed reactions

Definition of reaction rate		21.2
Performance equations		21.3
Simultaneous homogeneous and heterogeneous reactions		21.4
Types of experimental reactors		21.5
Choosing a commercial scale reactor		21.7
Problems	after	21.7

22. The porous catalyst pellet

The spectrum of kinetic regimes		22.1
Rate equations for each of the regimes		22.2
Effectiveness factor when all resistances enter the picture		22.11
Interpreting data and predicting behavior		22.12
Final thoughts		22.18
Problems	after	22.18

Final thoughts		22.18
Problems	after	22.18

23. Pore diffusion effects in reactors

Single irreversible first order irreaction		23.1
Single reaction other than first order irreversible		23.4
Multiple reactions: shift in product distribution with diffusional effects		23.7
Particles having more than one pore size		23.9
Final comments		23.12
Problems	after	23.12

24. Adiabatic packed bed reactors

Graphical representation		24.1
Design for single reactors		24.3
Design for multistage reactor systems		24.7
The hot spot and temperature runaway		24.15
Problems	after	24.20

25. Fluidized reactors of fine catalyst solids

The single rising bubble		25.3
Flow model for beds of fine particles		25.4
Application to catalytic reactions		25.7
Problems	after	25.20

26. Tube wall, monolith and plate catalytic reactors

Isothermal steady state operation		26.1
Problems	after	26.6

CATALYTIC REACTORS WITH TWO CHANGING PHASES

31. Kinetics of deactivating porous catalyst pellets

Rate forms		31.1
Experimental devices and strategy		31.2
Finding the rate from batch S/flow G experiments		31.4
Finding the rate from batch S/batch G experiments		31.13
Distortion of the rate by pore diffusion effects		31.16
Example having deactivation and pore diffusion		31.19
Problems	after	31.21

32. Reactors with a batch of slowly deactivating catalyst

Batch S/once through G reactors		32.2
Reactors with recycle of unused reactant		32.15
Batch mixed S/batch mixed G reactors		32.20
Problems	after	32.20

33. Reactors with flowing deactivating catalyst

Concentration independent deactivation		33.1
Concentration dependent deactivation		33.5
Deactivation in fluidized beds		33.6
Optimum size ratio of reactor-regenerators		33.7
Problems	after	33.8

34. G/L reactions on solid catalyst: trickle beds, slurry reactors, and 3 phase fluidized beds

General rate equation		34.2
Simplifications of the general rate equation		34.4
Performance equation for an excess of liquid reactant		34.6
Performance equation for an excess of gas reactant		34.10
Choice of contactor		34.11
Applications		34.13
Problems	after	34.17

GAS/LIQUID AND LIQUID/LIQUID REACTIONS

41. Kinetics of G/L and L/L reactions

The rate equation		41.1
How to use the general rate equation		41.9
Problems	after	41.10

42. Design of G/L and L/L reactors

Factors to consider in selecting a contactor		42.2
Design for straight mass transfer		42.6
Design for not very slow reactions		42.13
Problems	after	42.18

REACTION OF SOLIDS

51. Kinetics of G/S reactions. The SCM for constant size particles

The shrinking core model, or SCM		51.1
Clues to the controlling mechanism		51.4
SCM for non spherical particles		51.5
Final comments		51.6
Problems	after	51.6

52. G/S reactors for solids of unchanging size, fixed gas environment, SCM

The discrete size distribution		52.1
Design of single reactors		52.1
Reactors with elutriation, sedimentation, and/or attrition		52.5
Multistage reactors		52.14

Choosing a commercial scale reactor 52.19
Problems after 52.19

53. G/S reactors for solids of unchanging size, changing gas environment, SCM
Single reactors 53.3
Reactor-regenerator systems 53.5
Two examples 53.9
Problems after 53.14

54. Shrinking and growing particles
Kinetics of growth and shrinkage 54.1
Measurement of size distribution 54.2
Single reactor performance equations 54.3
General procedure for shrinking particles 54.18
General procedure for growing particles 54.19
Circulation system with growth and shrinkage 54.19
Mechanism of particle growth and shrinkage 54.22
Problems after 54.26

55. Kinetic models for the reaction of solids
SCM - the shrinking core model 55.2
UCM - the uniform conversion model 55.3
GPM - the grainy pellet model 55.4
CCM - the cracking core model 55.6
CVM - the changing voidage model 55.8
TDM - thermal decomposition models 55.13
PCM - phase change models 55.16
SCM for multistep reactions 55.20
Multistep reactions of porous pellets 55.21
Multistep reactions of pellets which become porous on reaction 55.22
Comments 55.23
An unusual mechanism involving loose atoms 55.24
On the use of reaction order 55.24
Problems after 55.25

FLOW OF MATERIALS THROUGH REACTORS

61. Flow pattern and contacting
Overall picture of non ideal flow 61.1
Conversion for a single phase, single feed reactor 61.6
Experimental methods for finding RTD 61.8
Chemical methods for finding the RTD 61.17
Summary 61.18
Problems after 61.18

62. Compartment models

Physical tracer methods		62.1
Chemical tracer method		62.7
Problems	after	62.7

63. The mean and variance of an RTD

$\bar{t}$ and σ^2 from pulse response data		63.1
$\bar{t}$ and σ^2 from step response data		63.6

64. The dispersion model

The physical picture		64.2
Small deviations from plug flow		64.3
Large deviations from plug flow		64.5
Step input of tracer		64.11
Correlations for axial dispersion		64.15
Chemical conversion		64.20
Problems	after	64.22

66. The tanks in series model

Pulse response experiments and the RTD		66.1
Step response experiments and the F curve		66.6
Chemical conversion		66.7
Problems	after	66.9

68. Convection model

Which model to use--convection, dispersion or diffusion		68.1
Pulse response experiments and the E curve		68.3
Step response experiments and the F curve		68.6
Tracer curves for non newtonians and for non circular channels		68.8
Tracer curves for line measurements		68.12
Chemical conversion		68.13
Problems	after	68.15

ENZYME AND MICROBIAL REACTIONS

81. Enzyme fermentation

Michaelis-Menten kinetics		81.2
Inhibition by a foreign substance		81.9
Substrate inhibition		81.14
Problems	after	81.15

82. Microbial fermentation. Overall picture

Constant environment fermentation		82.2
Batch fermentor		82.2
Mixed flow fermentor		82.4

Product distribution and fractional yields 82.4
Kinetic expressions, the Monod equation and its generalization 82.5
Planned treatment of the subject 82.7

83. Substrate limiting microbial fermentation
Batch fermentor 83.2
Mixed flow fermentor 83.6
Optimum operations 83.10
Concentration and recycle of cells 83.13
Comments 83.15
Problems after 83.15

84. Product poisoning limiting microbial fermentation
Rate equation 84.1
Batch fermentor 84.2
Mixed flow fermentor 84.5
Fermentation with $n \neq 1$ poison limiting kinetics 84.7
Substrate + poison influenced kinetics 84.10
Problems after 84.12

100. Dimensions, units, conversions, order of magnitude and this and that
Newton's law 100.1
Length
Volume
Mass
Pressure
Work, energy, and heat 100.2
Molecular weight
Ideal gas
Viscosity
Density 100.3
Diffusivity
Concentration
Thermal conductivity 100.4
Heat transfer coefficient
Mass transfer coefficient
Rate of reaction 100.5
Dimensionless groups

Name index

Book index

Subject index

1

Chapter 1 INTRODUCTION TO SINGLE PHASE CHEMICAL REACTORS.

Reactors come in all colors shapes and sizes, and are used for all sorts of reactions. As a brief sampling we have the giant cat crackers for oil refining, the monster blast furnaces for iron making, the crafty activated sludge ponds for sewage treatment, the amazing polymerization tanks for plastics, paints and fibers, the so important pharmaceutical vats for aspirin, penicillin and birth control drugs, the happy go lucky fermentation jugs for moonshine, and of course that abomination, the beastly cigarette.

To find what a reactor is able to do we need to know the **kinetics**, the **contacting pattern** and the **performance equation**. Schematically

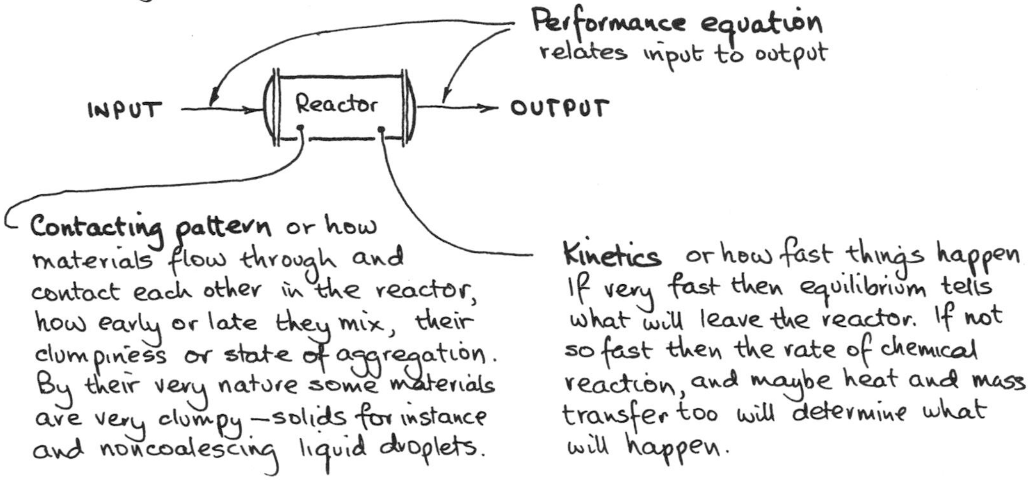
Performance equation
relates input to output
INPUT
Reactor
OUTPUT
Contacting pattern or how materials flow through and contact each other in the reactor, how early or late they mix, their clumpiness or state of aggregation. By their very nature some materials are very clumpy—solids for instance and noncoalescing liquid droplets.
Kinetics or how fast things happen If very fast then equilibrium tells what will leave the reactor. If not so fast then the rate of chemical reaction, and maybe heat and mass transfer too will determine what will happen.

Much of this book deals with finding the expression to relate input to output for various kinetics and various contacting patterns, or

$$\text{output} = f\left[\text{input, kinetics, contacting}\right]$$

This is called the **performance equation**. Why is this important? Because with this expression we can compare different designs and conditions, find which is best, and then scale up to larger units.

We first consider single phase systems. Think of these as a single gas or liquid flowing through the reactor and reacting therein. We treat these systems rather thoroughly (chapters 1~9) since the principles learned there carry over in large part to the much more difficult and important problem of design of heterogeneous reacting systems, those where two or more phases contact each other and react.

A. Some simple reactor types.

We start with the idealized flow patterns shown below and we very often try to make real reactors approach these ideals as closely as possible

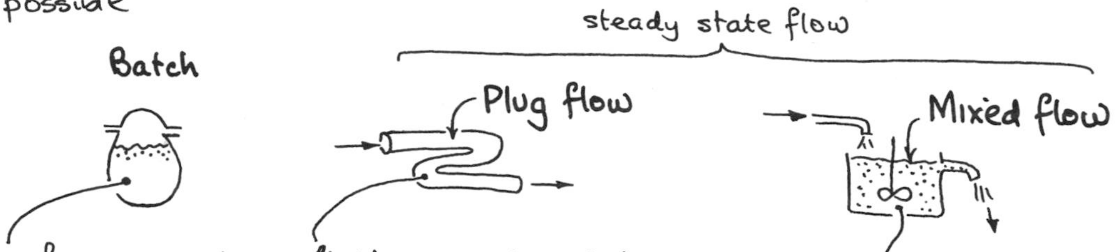

Batch: uniform composition everywhere in the reactor, but of course the composition changes with time

Plug flow: fluid passes through the reactor with no mixing of earlier and later entering fluid, and with no overtaking. It is as if the fluid moved in single file through the reactor

Mixed flow: uniformly mixed, same composition everywhere, within the reactor and at the exit

We particularly like these three flow or reacting patterns because they are easy to treat (it is simple to find their performance equations) and because one of them often is the best pattern possible (it will give the most of whatever it is we want). Later we will consider

recycle reactors 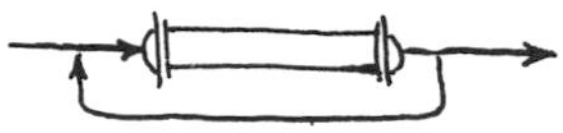

and

staged reactors 

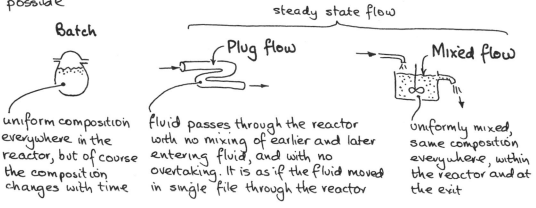

and other flow pattern combinations, including deviations of real reactors from these ideals.

B. The rate equation.

Suppose a single phase reaction $aA + bB \rightarrow rR + sS$. The most useful measure of reaction rate for reactant A is then

$$-r_A = -\frac{1}{V}\frac{dN_A}{dt} = \frac{\text{(amount of A disappearing)}}{\text{(volume)(time)}}, \quad \left[\frac{\text{mol}}{\text{m}^3\cdot\text{s}}\right]$$

rate of disappearance of A (pointing to $-r_A$ and $\frac{1}{V}\frac{dN_A}{dt}$)

note that this is an intensive measure

the minus sign means 'disappearance'

In addition, the rates of reaction of all materials are related by

$$\frac{-r_A}{a} = \frac{-r_B}{b} = \frac{r_R}{r} = \frac{r_S}{s}$$

Experience shows that the rate of reaction is influenced by the composition and the energy of the material. By energy we mean the temperature (random kinetic energy of the molecules), the light intensity within the system (this may affect the bond energy between atoms), the magnetic field intensity, etc. Ordinarily we only need to consider the temperature, so let us focus on this factor. Thus we can write

$$-r_A = f\left[\begin{matrix}\text{temperature} & \text{concentration} \\ \text{dependent} & \text{dependent} \\ \text{terms,} & \text{terms}\end{matrix}\right] \underset{\text{example}}{\overset{\text{as an}}{=\!=}} k C_A^a = k_0 e^{-E/RT} C_A^a$$

$-r_A$: $\frac{\text{mol}}{\text{m}^3\cdot\text{s}}$

rate constant: $\left(\frac{\text{mol}}{\text{m}^3}\right)^{1-a} \text{s}^{-1}$

activation energy: E

reaction order: a

temperature dependent term: $k_0 e^{-E/RT}$

A few words about the temperature dependent and the concentration dependent terms of the rate.

1. How the temperature affects the rate.

The reaction rate usually rises exponentially with temperature, as shown

This dependancy is often well fitted by an Arrhenius law expression

$$k = k_0 e^{-E/RT}$$

E = activation energy $\left[\frac{J}{mol}\right]$

R = gas constant $= 8.314 \frac{J}{mol \cdot K} = 8.314 \frac{Pa \cdot m^3}{mol \cdot K} = 1.987 \frac{cal}{mol \cdot K}$ ... etc...

To fit the temperature dependent term make a semilog plot as shown, at fixed $C_A, C_B, \ldots$

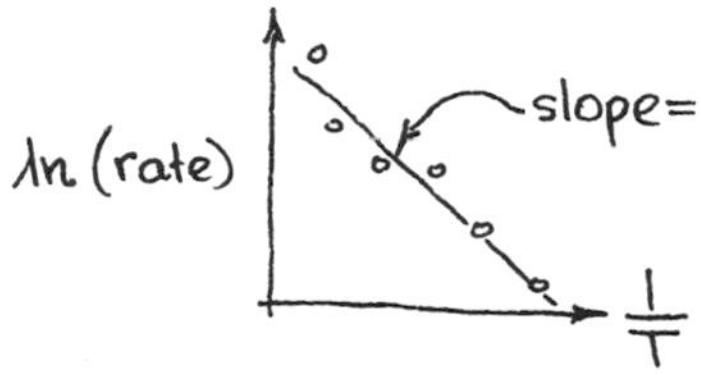

steep slope ⇒ high E, very temperature sensitive reaction

shallow slope ⇒ low E, not very temperature sensitive reaction

At same concentration but at two different temperatures: $\ln \frac{rate_1}{rate_2} = \ln \frac{k_1}{k_2} = \frac{E}{R}\left(\frac{1}{T_2} - \frac{1}{T_1}\right)$

High E values (200~400 kJ/mol) are typical of gas phase reactions which only proceed at high temperature (combustion, free radical reactions)
Low E values (20~80 kJ/mol) are typical of enzyme, cellular and life related reactions, those which occur at around room temperature.

2. <u>How composition affects the rate of reaction.</u> Often a simple expression fits the data, for example

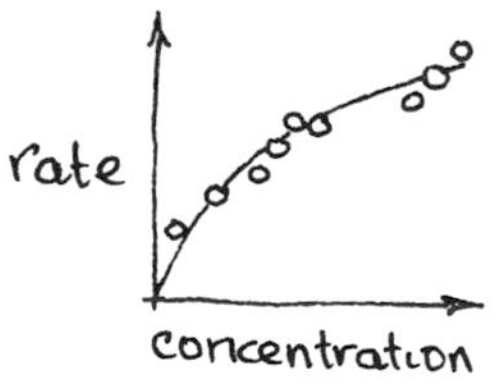

$$-r_A = kC_A$$
$$= kC_A^2$$
$$= kC_A C_B$$
$$= k_1 C_A - k_2 C_R$$

but sometimes we need a more complicated expression. As an example today we recommend

for $N_2 + 3H_2 \rightleftarrows 2NH_3$ ... use $+r_{NH_3} = k_1 \frac{C_{N_2} C_{H_2}^{3/2}}{C_{NH_3}^2} - k_2 \frac{C_{NH_3}}{C_{H_2}^{3/2}}$

The concentration dependent term is only found by guessing. Always try the simpler forms first. Thus you may want to try a specific rate form

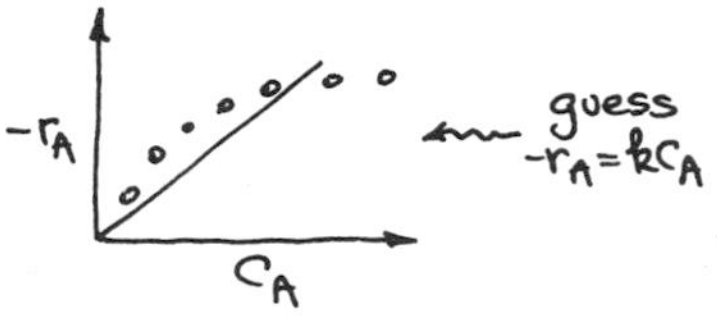

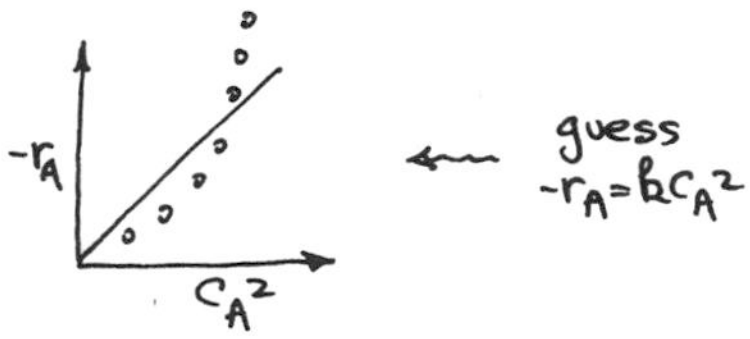

... and so on

or you may want to try a whole class of rate forms. Thus if you wish to try $-r_A = kC_A^n$, n = any number then plot as follows

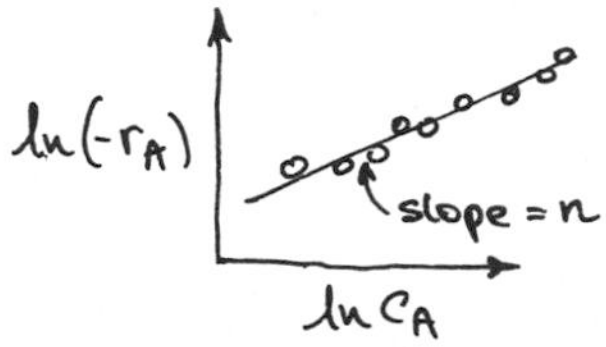

If $-r_A = kC_A^n$ then on taking logs we get

$$\ln(-r_A) = \ln k + n \ln C_A$$

or a straight line with slope n and intercept $= \ln k$

Many other ways are available to test or search for the concentration term, see any chemical engineering kinetics or reactor text.

C. Terminology and symbols.

1. **For batch reactors** we use the following symbols

N_{A0} = moles of A in reactor at time $t=0$

$N_A = N_{A0}(1-X_A)$, moles of A present at time t.

V = volume of reactor. What we really mean is volume of reacting fluid

t = time of reaction

$t_{1/2}$ = half life, or time for C_A to drop from C_{A0} to $C_{A0}/2$.

X_A = fraction of reactant which has reacted away.

A batch reactor may be a **constant volume** reactor (as sketched above) or it may be a **variable volume** reactor, for example a piston-cylinder arrangement

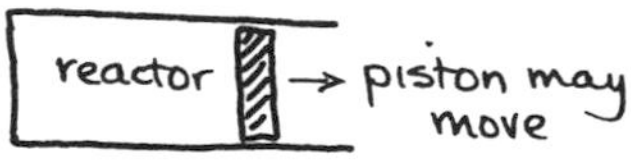

For gases pressure and concentration are related. Thus for an **ideal gas, constant volume** reactor but with changing number of moles during reaction (total pressure π changes with time), or

$$aA + bB \rightarrow rR + sS \qquad \text{with } \Delta n = r + s - (a+b)$$

For any reactant: $$p_A = C_A RT = p_{A0} + \frac{a}{\Delta n}(\pi_0 - \pi)$$

For any product: $$p_R = C_R RT = p_{R0} - \frac{r}{\Delta n}(\pi_0 - \pi)$$

For an **ideal gas, constant pressure, constant temperature**, but with changing number of moles during reaction (reactor volume changes with time)

$$V = V_0(1 + \varepsilon_A X_A) \quad \text{where} \quad \varepsilon_A = \frac{V_{\text{all A reacted}} - V_{\text{no reaction}}}{V_{\text{no reaction}}} = \frac{V_{X_A=1} - V_{X_A=0}}{V_{X_A=0}}$$

2. __For flow reactors__ we have the following

$F_{A0} = \dfrac{\text{moles A fed}}{\text{hr}}$

$v_0 = \dfrac{\text{m}^3 \text{ fluid entering}}{\text{hr}}$

C_{A0} = concentration of A in feed stream

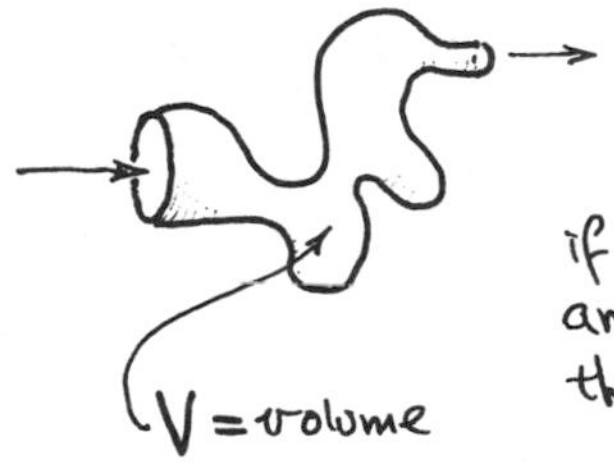

$F_A = F_{A0}(1 - X_A)$

C_A, F_A, X_A

if there is any ambiguity then call these C_{Af}, F_{Af}, X_{Af}

$$\tau = \begin{pmatrix}\text{time needed to treat} \\ \text{one reactor volume} \\ \text{of feed stream}\end{pmatrix} = \frac{V}{v_0} = \frac{C_{A0}V}{F_{A0}}, \ [\text{hr}]$$

: the **space-time**, the capacity measure for the reactor

$$\bar{t} = \begin{pmatrix}\text{mean residence time} \\ \text{of fluid in the reactor}\end{pmatrix}, \ [\text{hr}]$$

- for constant density systems (all liquids and some gases) $\bar{t} = \tau = \frac{V}{v}$
- for changing density systems $\bar{t} \neq \tau$, $\bar{t} \neq V/v$, and it is difficult to find how these two times are related

For flow reactors the relationship between **concentration** and **conversion** of a reacting specie is not obvious, and depends on a number of factors.

Special case 1 Constant density systems. This includes most liquid reactions and also those gas reactions run at constant temperature and pressure and with no change in number of moles during reaction. Here C_A and X_A are related as follows

$$\left. \begin{array}{ll} X_A = 1 - \dfrac{C_A}{C_{AO}} & \cdots \text{and} \quad dX_A = -\dfrac{dC_A}{C_{AO}} \\[2em] \dfrac{C_A}{C_{AO}} = 1 - X_A & \cdots \text{and} \quad dC_A = -C_{AO}\, dX_A \end{array} \right\} \cdots \text{for } \varepsilon_A = 0$$

To relate the changes in B and R to A we have

$$\frac{C_{AO} - C_A}{a} = \frac{C_{BO} - C_B}{b} = \frac{C_R - C_{RO}}{r} \quad \cdots \text{or} \quad \frac{C_{AO} X_A}{a} = \frac{C_{BO} X_B}{b}$$

Special case 2 Gases of changing density but with T and π constant. Here the density changes because of the change in number of moles during reaction. In addition we require that the volume of a fluid element changes linearly with conversion, or $V = V_o(1 + \varepsilon_A X_A)$. In this case

$$\left. \begin{array}{ll} X_A = \dfrac{C_{AO} - C_A}{C_{AO} + \varepsilon_A C_A} & \cdots \text{and} \quad dX_A = -\dfrac{C_{AO}(1 + \varepsilon_A)}{(C_{AO} + \varepsilon_A C_A)^2}\, dC_A \\[2em] \overset{\text{mole fraction}}{\dfrac{y_A}{y_{AO}}} = \dfrac{C_A}{C_{AO}} = \dfrac{1 - X_A}{1 + \varepsilon_A X_A} & \cdots \text{and} \quad \dfrac{dC_A}{C_{AO}} = -\dfrac{1 + \varepsilon_A}{(1 + \varepsilon_A X_A)^2}\, dX_A \end{array} \right\} \cdots \text{for } \varepsilon_A \neq 0$$

To follow changes in the other components we have

between reactants:
$$\begin{cases} \varepsilon_A X_A = \varepsilon_B X_B \\[1em] \dfrac{a \varepsilon_A}{C_{AO}} = \dfrac{b \varepsilon_B}{C_{BO}} \end{cases}$$

for products and inerts:
$$\begin{cases} \dfrac{y_R}{y_{AO}} = \dfrac{C_R}{C_{AO}} = \dfrac{(r/a) X_A + C_{RO}/C_{AO}}{1 + \varepsilon_A X_A} \\[1em] \dfrac{y_I}{y_{IO}} = \dfrac{C_I}{C_{IO}} = \dfrac{1}{1 + \varepsilon_A X_A} \end{cases}$$

Special case 3 Gases in general, (varying ρ, T, π) which react according to

$$aA + bB \rightarrow rR, \quad a+b \neq r$$

Pick one reactant as the basis for determining the conversion. We call this the **key reactant**. Let A be the key. Then for **ideal gas** behavior

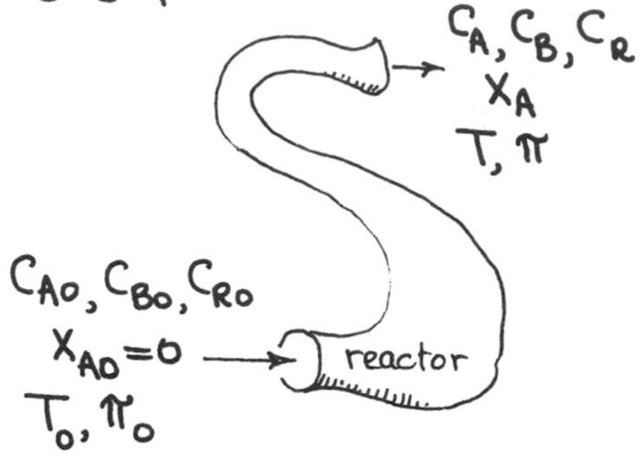

$$X_A = \frac{1 - \dfrac{C_A}{C_{A0}}\left(\dfrac{T\pi_0}{T_0\pi}\right)}{1 + \varepsilon_A \dfrac{C_A}{C_{A0}}\left(\dfrac{T\pi_0}{T_0\pi}\right)} \quad \text{or} \quad \frac{C_A}{C_{A0}} = \frac{1 - X_A}{1 + \varepsilon_A X_A}\left(\frac{T_0\pi}{T\pi_0}\right)$$

$$X_A = \frac{\dfrac{C_{B0}}{C_{A0}} - \dfrac{C_B}{C_{A0}}\left(\dfrac{T\pi_0}{T_0\pi}\right)}{\dfrac{b}{a} + \varepsilon_A \dfrac{C_B}{C_{A0}}\left(\dfrac{T\pi_0}{T_0\pi}\right)} \quad \text{or} \quad \frac{C_B}{C_{A0}} = \frac{\dfrac{C_{B0}}{C_{A0}} - \dfrac{b}{a}X_A}{1 + \varepsilon_A X_A}\left(\frac{T_0\pi}{T\pi_0}\right)$$

$$X_A = \frac{\dfrac{C_R}{C_{A0}}\left(\dfrac{T\pi_0}{T_0\pi}\right) - \dfrac{C_{R0}}{C_{A0}}}{\dfrac{r}{a} - \varepsilon_A \dfrac{C_R}{C_{A0}}\left(\dfrac{T\pi_0}{T_0\pi}\right)} \quad \text{or} \quad \frac{C_R}{C_{A0}} = \frac{\dfrac{C_{R0}}{C_{A0}} + \dfrac{r}{a}X_A}{1 + \varepsilon_A X_A}\left(\frac{T_0\pi}{T\pi_0}\right)$$

evaluate ε_A from the stoichiometry at some constant T and π

for high pressure non ideal gas behavior ...replace $\left(\dfrac{T_0\pi}{T\pi_0}\right)$ by $\left(\dfrac{z_0 T_0 \pi}{z T \pi_0}\right)$

To change to another key reactant, say B, note that

$$\frac{a\varepsilon_A}{C_{A0}} = \frac{b\varepsilon_B}{C_{B0}} \quad \text{and} \quad \frac{C_{A0}X_A}{a} = \frac{C_{B0}X_B}{b}$$

For liquids or isothermal gases with no change pressure and density

$$\varepsilon_A \rightarrow 0 \quad \text{and} \quad \left(\frac{T_0\pi}{T\pi_0}\right) \rightarrow 1$$

and the above expressions simplify greatly.

Example 1. A gas feed enters a reactor at 720K and 2.4 bar with $C_{AO} = 10$, $C_{BO} = 15$, $C_{RO} = 5$ and $C_{io} = 10$ mol/m³ where i stands for an inert material. In the reactor A and B combine as follows

$$A + 3B \longrightarrow 2R$$

The exit gas passes through a cooler and leaves the system at 300K and 2 bar with $C_A = 16$ mol/m³. Find X_A, C_B and C_R in this cool exit stream. Assume ideal gas behavior.

Solution.

First make a sketch
of the system:

$C_{AO} = 10$ mol/m³
$C_{BO} = 15$
$C_{RO} = 5$
$C_{io} = 10$
$T_o = 720K$
$\pi_o = 2.4$ bar

cooler

reactor

$C_A = 16$
$C_B = ?$
$C_R = ?$
$X_A = ?$
$T = 300K$
$\pi = 2$ bar

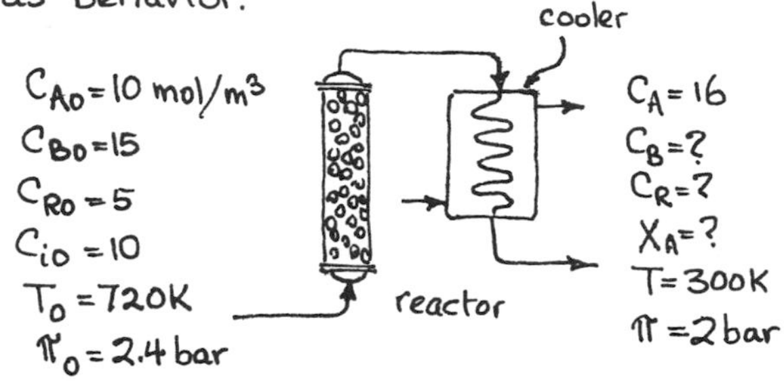

Take 40 volumes of gas at entering conditions as basis for finding ε_A.

At $X_A = 0$ $\quad V = 10A + 15B + 5R + 10i = 40$ volumes
At $X_A = 1$ $\quad V = 0A + (-15B) + (5R + 20R) + 10i = 20$ volumes $\Big\}$ at same T and π

Thus

$$\varepsilon_A = \frac{20 - 40}{40} = -\frac{1}{2}$$

Since A is not the limiting reactant and since we are basing conversions on A we may find ourselves with negative volumes. Don't panic, plunge along, keep track of all numbers and all will be well.

Now from the formulas on
the previous page we find

$$X_A = \frac{1 - \frac{16}{10}\left(\frac{300}{720} \cdot \frac{2.4}{2.0}\right)}{1 + \left(-\frac{1}{2}\right)\frac{16}{10}\left(\frac{300}{720} \cdot \frac{2.4}{2.0}\right)} = \frac{1}{3}$$

$$C_B = 10\left(\frac{\frac{15}{10} - \frac{3}{1} \cdot \frac{1}{3}}{1 + \left(-\frac{1}{2}\right)\frac{1}{3}}\right)\left(\frac{720}{300} \cdot \frac{2.0}{2.4}\right) = 12$$

$$C_R = 10\left(\frac{\frac{5}{10} + \frac{2}{1} \cdot \frac{1}{3}}{1 + \left(-\frac{1}{2}\right)\frac{1}{3}}\right)\left(\frac{720}{300} \cdot \frac{2.0}{2.4}\right) = 28$$

D. Converting pressures to concentrations

In gas reactions the composition term in the rate equation is frequently expressed by the partial pressure of the reacting species. In such situations it is usually best to first transform these pressures to concentration, then proceed with the analysis. Thus

$$-r_A = k_p\, p_A^n \quad \Longrightarrow \quad -r_A = k\, C_A^n$$

Units for $-r_A = k_p p_A^n$: $-r_A$ in $\frac{mol}{m^3 \cdot s}$ or $\frac{mol}{lit \cdot s}$; k_p in $\frac{mol}{m^3 \cdot Pa^n \cdot s}$ or $\frac{mol}{lit \cdot atm^n \cdot s}$; p_A^n in Pa^n or atm^n.

Units for $-r_A = k C_A^n$: $-r_A$ in $\frac{mol}{m^3 \cdot s}$ or $\frac{mol}{lit \cdot s}$; k in $\left(\frac{m^3}{mol}\right)^{n-1} s^{-1}$ or $\left(\frac{lit}{mol}\right)^{n-1} s^{-1}$; C_A^n in $\left(\frac{mol}{m^3}\right)^n$ or $\left(\frac{mol}{lit}\right)^n$.

For ideal gases the transformation is direct because

$$p_A = C_A R T$$

where p_A is in Pa or atm; C_A in $\frac{mol}{lit}$ or $\frac{mol}{m^3}$; $R = 8.314 \frac{m^3\, Pa}{mol \cdot K}$ or $0.082 \frac{lit \cdot atm}{mol \cdot K}$

Example 2. At 610 K and 1 atm an elementary reversible reaction is reported to proceed as follows

$$2A \underset{2}{\overset{1}{\rightleftharpoons}} B, \quad -r_A = k_1 p_A^2 - k_2 p_B \quad \text{with} \quad \begin{cases} k_1 = 10^{-3} \dfrac{mol}{lit \cdot atm^2 \cdot hr} \\ K_p = 0.5\ atm^{-1} \end{cases}$$

Convert this rate expression into concentration units

Solution At 1 atm it is reasonable to assume ideal gas behavior, thus

$$p_A = RTC_A = (0.082)(610)C_A = \left(50 \frac{lit \cdot atm}{mol}\right) C_A$$

So at 610K

$$-r_A = k_1(C_ART)^2 - k_2(C_BRT) = \underbrace{k_1(RT)^2}_{k_1'} C_A^2 - \underbrace{k_2 RT}_{k_2'} C_B \quad \cdots (i)$$

where

$$k_1' = \left(10^{-3} \frac{\text{mol}}{\text{lit}\cdot\text{atm}^2\cdot\text{hr}}\right)\left(50 \frac{\text{lit}\cdot\text{atm}}{\text{mol}}\right)^2 = 2.5 \frac{\text{lit}}{\text{mol}\cdot\text{hr}} \quad \cdots (ii)$$

Now k_2 is not given but can be found from the equilibrium constant, as follows

$$K_c = \frac{k_1'}{k_2'} = \frac{C_{Be}}{C_{Ae}^2} = \frac{p_{Ae}/RT}{(p_{Be}/RT)^2} = K_pRT = (0.5)(50) = 25 \frac{\text{lit}}{\text{mol}}$$

$$\therefore k_2' = \frac{k_1'}{K_c} = \frac{2.5\ \text{lit}/\text{mol}\cdot\text{hr}}{25\ \text{lit}/\text{mol}} = 0.1\ \text{hr}^{-1} \quad \cdots (iii)$$

Replacing (ii) and (iii) in (i)

$$-r_A = \left(2.5 \frac{\text{lit}}{\text{mol}\cdot\text{hr}}\right)C_A^2 - (0.1\ \text{hr}^{-1})C_B \quad \cdots \text{ with } K_C = 25 \frac{\text{lit}}{\text{mol}}$$

Note. Those working with gas phase reactions often write the rate in terms of partial pressures. As an example for a 2nd order reaction they write

$$-r_A = kp_A^2, \text{ or } -\frac{dp_A}{dt} = kp_A^2 \quad \text{in place of} \quad -r_A = kC_A^2$$

They should be aware of the fact that each of these rate forms gives a **different activation energy** for the same data and for the same reaction, see problem 1.33 for an example. Luckily, this difference is only a few kJ, and can be ignored for reactions with reasonably high activation energies.

Chapter 1 Problems

A1 A reaction has the stoichiometric equation A + B = 2R. What is the order of reaction?

A2 Given the reaction $2NO_2 + \frac{1}{2}O_2 = N_2O_5$, what is the relation between the rates of formation and disappearance of the three components of the reaction?

A3 A reaction with stoichiometric equation $\frac{1}{2}A + B = R + \frac{1}{2}S$ has the following rate expression

$$-r_A = 2C_A^{0.5}C_B$$

What is the rate expression for this reaction if the stoichiometric equation is written as A + 2B = 2R + S?

A4 Experiments show that the homogeneous decomposition of ozone proceeds with a rate

$$-r_{O_3} = \frac{k[O_3]^2}{[O_2]}$$

What is the reaction order with respect to O_3, with respect to O_2, and overall?

A5 The decomposition of nitrous oxide is found to proceed as follows

$$N_2O \rightarrow N_2 + \frac{1}{2}O_2, \quad -r_{N_2O} = \frac{k_1[N_2O]^2}{1 + k_2[N_2O]}$$

What is the order of this reaction with respect to N_2O, and overall?

A6 A rocket engine burns a stoichiometric mixture of fuel (liquid hydrogen) in oxidant (liquid oxygen). The combustion chamber is cylindrical, 75 cm long and 60 cm in diameter, and the combustion process produces 108 kg/s of exhaust gases. If combustion is complete find the rate of reaction of hydrogen and of oxygen.

A7 Consider a municipal water treatment plant for a smallish community. Waste water, 32000 m^3/day, flows through the treatment plant with a mean residence time if 8 hours, air is bubbled through the tanks, and microbes in the tank attack and break down the organic material

$$\text{(organic waste)} + O_2 \xrightarrow{\text{microbes}} CO_2 + H_2O$$

A typical entering feed has a BOD (biological oxygen demand) of 200 mg O_2/lit, while the effluent has a negligible BOD. Find the rate of reaction, or decrease in BOD, in the treatment tanks.

Chapter 1 Problems

A8 A human being (75 kg) consumes about 6000 kJ of food per day. Assume that the food is all glucose and that the overall reaction is

$$C_6H_{12}O_6 + \underset{\text{from air}}{6O_2} \rightarrow \underset{\text{breathed out}}{6CO_2} + 6H_2O, \quad -\Delta H_r = 2816 \text{ kJ}$$

Find man's metabolic rate (the rate of living, loving, and laughing) in terms of moles of oxygen used per m^3 of person per second.

A9 Large central power stations (about 1000 MW electrical) using fluidized bed combustors may be built some day. These giants would be fed 240 tons of coal/hr (90%C, 10% H_2), 50% of which would burn within the battery of primary fluidized beds, the other 50% elsewhere in the system. One design would use a battery of 10 fluidized beds, each 20 m long, 4 m wide, and containing solids to a depth of 1 m. Find the rate of reaction within the beds, based on the oxygen used.

B10 A 1100 K n-nonane thermally cracks (breaks down into smaller molecules) 20 times as rapidly as at 1000 K. Find the activation energy for this decomposition.

B11 In the mid-19th century the entomologist Henri Fabre noted that French ants (garden variety) busily bustled about their business on hot days but were rather sluggish on cool days. Checking his results with Oregon ants I find

Running Speed, m/hr	150	160	230	295	370
Temperature, °C	13	16	22	24	28

What activation energy represents this change in bustliness?

B12 Dicyandiamide (DCD), important starting material for pharmaceuticals and explosives, is formed by the aqueous dimerization of cyanamide:

$$2H_2CN_2 \text{ (aq.)} \rightarrow (H_2CN_2)_2 \text{ (aq.)}$$

The dimerization is practically complete in 10 hrs at 40 °C, and in 6 hrs at 60 °C. How long would you expect it to take at 80 °C?

B13 A reaction has E = 400 kJ/mol. By what percentage does the reaction rate change if the temperature is raised (a) from 300 to 310 K, (b) from 2000 to 2010 K?

B14 The maximum allowable temperature for a reactor is 800 K. At present our operating set point is 780 K, the 20 K margin of safety to account for fluctuating feed, sluggish controls, etc. Now, with a more sophisticated control system we would be able to raise our set point to 792 K with the same margin of safety that we now have. By how much can the reaction rate, hence production rate, be raised by this change if the reaction taking place in the reactor has an activation energy of 175 kJ/mol?

Chapter 1 Problems

B15 Every May 22 I plant one watermelon seed. I water it, I fight slugs, I pray, I watch my beauty grow, and finally the day comes when the melon ripens. I then harvest and feast. Of course, some years are sad, like 1980, when a bluejay flew off with the seed. Anyway, six summers were a pure joy and for these I've tabulated the number of growing days versus the mean daytime temperature during the growing season. Does the temperature affect the growth rate? If so, represent this by an activation energy.

Year	1976	1977	1982	1984	1985	1988
Growing days	87	85	74	78	90	84
Mean temp, °C	22.0	23.4	26.3	24.3	21.1	22.7

B16 Milk is pasteurized if it is heated to 63 °C for 30 min, but if it is heated to 74 °C it only needs 15 sec for the same result. Find the activation energy of this sterilization process.

B17 On typical summer days field crickets nibble, jump, and chirp now and then. But at night when great numbers congregate chirping seems to become a serious business and tends to be in unison. In 1897 Dolbear (Am. Naturalist **31** 970) reported that this social chirping rate was dependent on the temperature as given by

(number of chirps in 15 sec) + 40 = (temperature, °F)

Assuming that the chirping rate is a direct measure of the metabolic rate, find the activation energy in kJ/mol of these crickets in the temperature range of 60 to 80 °F.

B18 The pyrolysis of ethane proceeds with an activation energy of about 300 kJ/mol. How much faster is the decomposition at 650 °C than at 500 °C?

C19 On doubling the concentration of reactant the rate of reaction triples. Find the reaction order.

For the reaction stoichiometry $A \rightarrow R$ and the following tabulated data is it reasonable to represent the rate-concentration relationship by an n-th order kinetic expression? If so, find the reaction order.

C20 . . .

C_A	2.3	2.3	2.3	6.7	6.7	6.7
$-r_A$	0.038	0.041	0.041	0.064	0.074	0.072

C21 . . .

C_A	2	5	10	15
$-r_A$	6.2	12.1	14.9	15.1

Chapter 1 Problems

For the stoichiometry $A + B \rightarrow$ (products) find the reaction orders with respect to A and B.

C22 . . .

C_A	4	1	1
C_B	1	1	8
$-r_A$	2	1	4

C23 . . .

C_A	2	2	3
C_B	125	64	64
$-r_A$	50	32	48

The following problems consider an isothermal single phase flow reactor operating at steady state and essentially constant pressure.

D24 . . . Given a gaseous feed, $C_{A0} = 100$, $C_{B0} = 200$, $A + B \rightarrow R + S$, $X_A = 0.8$. Find X_B, C_A, C_B.

D25 . . . Given a dilute aqueous feed, $C_{A0} = C_{B0} = 100$, $A + 2B \rightarrow R + S$, $C_A = 20$. Find X_A, X_B, C_B.

D26 . . . Given a gaseous feed, $C_{A0} = 200$, $C_{B0} = 100$, $A + B \rightarrow R$, $C_A = 50$. Find X_A, X_B, C_B.

D27 . . . Given a gaseous feed, $C_{A0} = 100$, $C_{B0} = 200$, $C_{i0} = 100$, $A + 3B \rightarrow 6R$, $C_A = 40$. Find X_A, X_B, C_B.

D28 . . . Given a gaseous feed, $C_{A0} = C_{B0} = 100$, $A + 2B \rightarrow R$, $C_B = 20$. Find X_A, X_B, C_A.

A continuous stream of fluid enters a vessel at temperature T_0 and pressure π_0, reacts there, and leaves at T and π.

E29 . . . Given a gaseous feed, $T_0 = 400$ K, $\pi_0 = 4$ atm, $C_{A0} = 100$, $C_{B0} = 200$, $A + B \rightarrow 2R$, T= 300 K, $\pi = 3$ atm, $C_A = 20$. Find X_A, X_B, C_B.

E30 . . . Given a gaseous feed, $T_0 = 1000$ K, $\pi_0 = 5$ atm, $C_{A0} = 100$, $C_{B0} = 200$, $A + B \rightarrow 5R$, T= 400 K, $\pi = 4$ atm, $C_A = 20$. Find X_A, X_B, C_B.

E31 . . . Given a gaseous feed, $T_0 = 500$ K, $\pi_0 = 20$ atm, $C_{A0} = 100$, $C_{B0} = 300$, $C_{R0} = 300$, $C_{i0} = 100$, $A + B \rightarrow R$. Find C_A, C_B, X_A, X_B if the reaction goes to completion and the exit stream from the reactor is at 800 K, 16 atm.

E32 * . . . Given a gaseous feed, $T_0 = 400$ K, $\pi_0 = 4$ atm, $C_{A0} = C_{B0} = 100$, $A + 2B \rightarrow R$, T= 700 K, $\pi = 3$ atm, $C_A = 30$. Find X_A, X_B, C_B.

Chapter 1 Problems

F33 A researcher reports the following

at $T_1 = 400$ K $\quad -r_A = 2.3\, p_A^2 \quad$ for $\quad -r_A = [\text{mol/m}^3 \cdot \text{s}]$

at $T_2 = 500$ K $\quad -r_A = 2.3\, p_A^2 \quad$ p_A in atm

Find the activation energy of this reaction (in kJ/mol) if the rate is written

(a) as above

(b) in terms of concentrations, or $-r_A = kC_A^2$

F34* Show that the expansion factor ε_A can be expressed by

$$\varepsilon_A = \frac{C_{A0}}{C_{total.0}} \cdot \frac{\Delta n}{a} = \begin{pmatrix} \text{mole fraction of A} \\ \text{in the feed} \end{pmatrix} \cdot \frac{\Delta n}{a}$$

Problem from M. Colakyan and P. Subramanian

Chapter 2 THE BATCH REACTOR

A material balance over the whole reactor for any reactant A gives

well mixed and uniform in composition at all times

C_A and N_A change with time

C_{A0} at $t=0$

C_A at $t>0$

$$\underbrace{\cancel{\text{Input}}_{=0} - \cancel{\text{Output}}_{=0}}_{\text{for no flow}} = \underset{\frac{dN_A}{dt},\ \text{mol A/s}}{\text{Accumulation}} + \underset{(-r_A)V,\ \text{mol A/s}}{\text{Disappearance}}$$

or...

$$-\frac{dN_A}{dt} = (-r_A)V \quad \cdots(1)$$

where V = constant, or $\varepsilon_A = 0$, the usual situation, we have

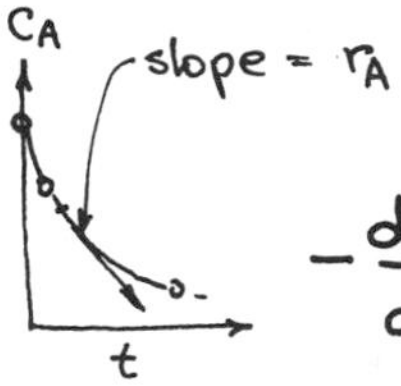

$$-\frac{dC_A}{dt} = (-r_A)$$

$$t = -\int_{C_{A0}}^{C_A} \frac{dC_A}{(-r_A)} = C_{A0}\int_0^{X_A} \frac{dX_A}{(-r_A)} \quad \cdots(2)$$

where V changes linearly with conversion, or $V = V_0(1+\varepsilon_A X_A)$, a rarely met situation, we have

$$-\frac{C_{A0}}{C_{A0}+\varepsilon_A C_A}\frac{dC_A}{dt} = (-r_A)$$

$$t = -\int_{C_{A0}}^{C_A} \frac{dC_A}{\left(1+\varepsilon_A \frac{C_A}{C_{A0}}\right)(-r_A)} \quad \cdots(3)$$

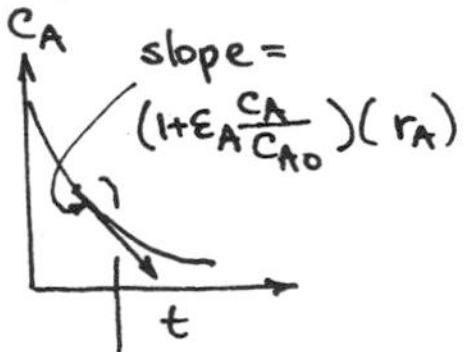

Let us first treat the constant volume case, and let us leave the variable volume case till later. The graphical representation of the constant volume reactor is then

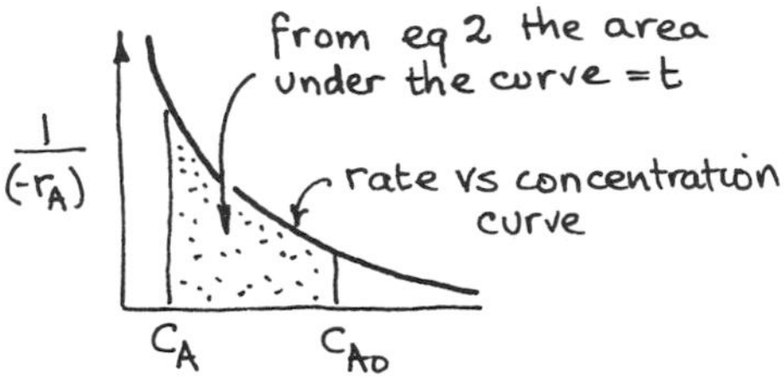

Equation 2 or this figure relate the four quantities C_{A0}, C_A, $-r_A$, t, and knowing any three of them allows you to evaluate the fourth.

If C_{A0} or C_A or t is the unknown simply integrate eq 2 either analytically or graphically. But if $-r_A$ is unknown things become more difficult. In this case we have two general procedures, either the **differential** or the **integral** method. Briefly

Differential method

(a) Plot C_A vs t

(b) Take the slope. This gives $\frac{dC_A}{dt} = r_A$

(c) Search for a relationship between C_A and r_A.

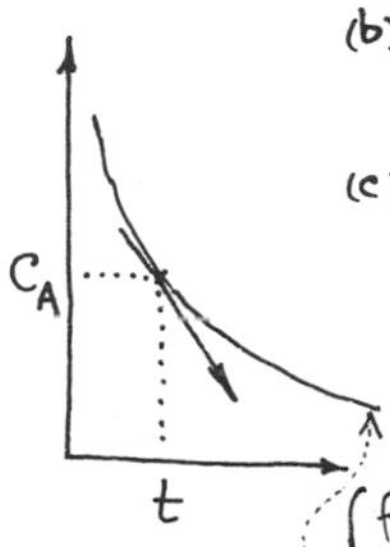

for $n<1$ C_A becomes zero in finite time

for $n \geq 1$ C_A never reaches zero

Integral Method

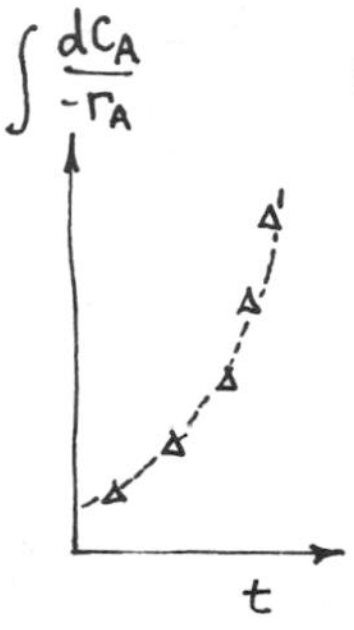

(a) Guess a rate form

(b) Insert in eq 2 and integrate

(c) Plot the concentration term vs the time term. If the data fall on a straight line you've guessed right. If not guess again, and again

Let us evaluate and list some of the more frequently encountered integral forms. For this put the rate expression to be tested into eq 2 or eq 3 and integrate.

I. Integrated Forms for the Constant Volume Batch Reactor.

Zero Order homogeneous, $A \rightarrow \cdots, \; -r_A = k$

For $t \leq \frac{C_{A0}}{k}$ $\quad \cdots \quad \frac{kt}{C_{A0}} = 1 - \frac{C_A}{C_{A0}} = X_A$

For $t \geq \frac{C_{A0}}{k}$ $\quad \cdots \quad C_A = 0$

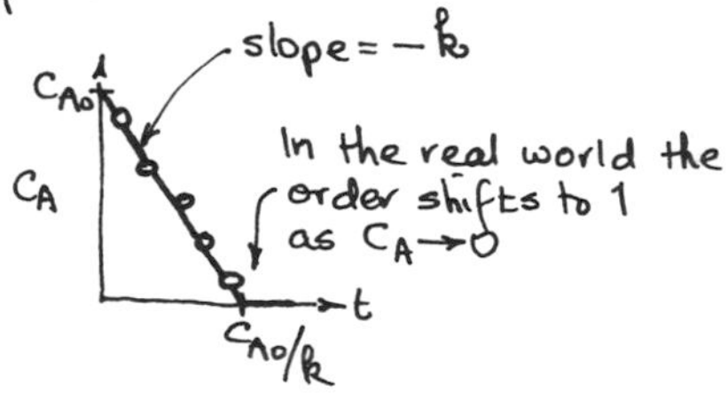

1st order, $A \rightarrow \cdots, \; -r_A = kC_A$

$$kt = \ln \frac{C_{A0}}{C_A} = \ln \frac{1}{1-X_A} \; ; \text{ or } \; \frac{C_A}{C_{A0}} = e^{-kt}$$

$$t_{1/2} = \frac{0.693}{k} = \text{half life}$$

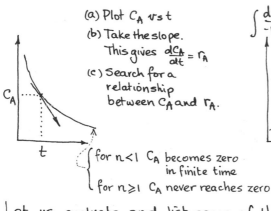

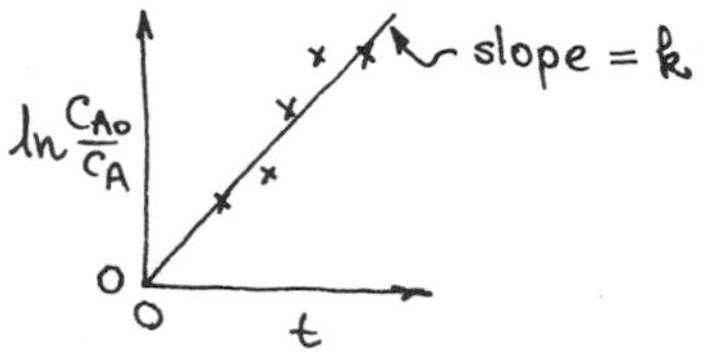

2·3

1st order reversible, $A \underset{k_2}{\overset{k_1}{\rightleftarrows}} rR$, $-r_A = k_1C_A - k_2C_R$, $M = \dfrac{C_{R0}}{C_{A0}}$

X_{Ae}, C_{Ae}: equilibrium

$$k_1t = \frac{M + r\left(1 - \dfrac{C_{Ae}}{C_{A0}}\right)}{M+r} \ln \frac{C_{A0} - C_{Ae}}{C_A - C_{Ae}}$$

or

$$k_1t = \frac{M + rX_{Ae}}{M+r} \ln \frac{X_{Ae}}{X_{Ae} - X_A}$$

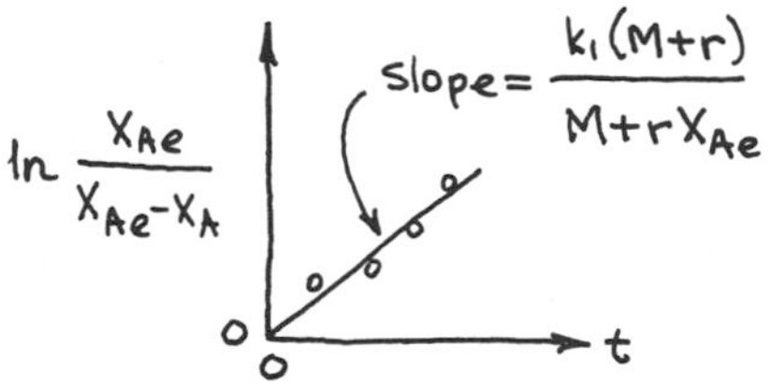

2nd order, $A \xrightarrow{k}$ products, $-r_A = kC_A^2$

$$ktC_{A0} = \frac{C_{A0}}{C_A} - 1 = \frac{X_A}{1-X_A} \quad \text{...or...} \quad \frac{C_A}{C_{A0}} = \frac{1}{1 + kC_{A0}t}$$

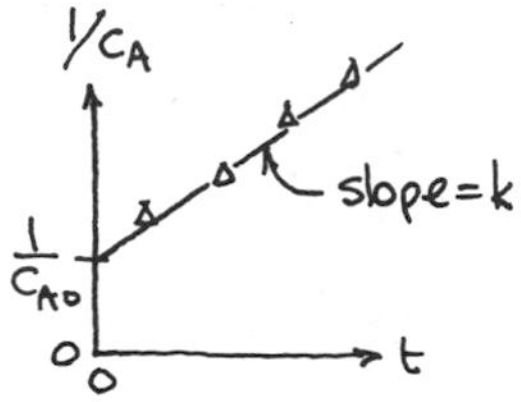

2nd order, $A + bB \xrightarrow{k}$ products, $-r_A = kC_AC_B$

For $M = \dfrac{C_{B0}}{bC_{A0}} \neq 1$ ... $\quad ktbC_{A0}(M-1) = \ln \dfrac{C_B}{bMC_A} = \ln \dfrac{M - X_A}{M(1-X_A)}$

For $M = 1$ ... $\quad ktC_{B0} = \dfrac{C_{A0}}{C_A} - 1 = \dfrac{X_A}{1-X_A} \quad \text{...or...} \quad \dfrac{C_A}{C_{A0}} = \dfrac{1}{1 + ktC_{B0}}$

For M close to 1 ... use the above expressions with C_{B0} replaced by $\dfrac{bC_{A0} + C_{B0}}{2}$

2nd order reversible, $A+B \underset{2}{\overset{1}{\rightleftarrows}} R+S$, $2A \underset{2}{\overset{1}{\rightleftarrows}} R+S$, $2A \underset{2}{\overset{1}{\rightleftarrows}} 2R$, $A+B \underset{2}{\overset{1}{\rightleftarrows}} 2R$
with corresponding rate equations, $C_{A0} = C_{B0}$, $C_{R0} = C_{S0} = 0$, X_{Ae}: equilibrium

$$2k_1\left(\frac{1}{X_{Ae}} - 1\right)tC_{A0} = \ln \frac{X_{Ae} - (2X_{Ae} - 1)X_A}{X_{Ae} - X_A}$$

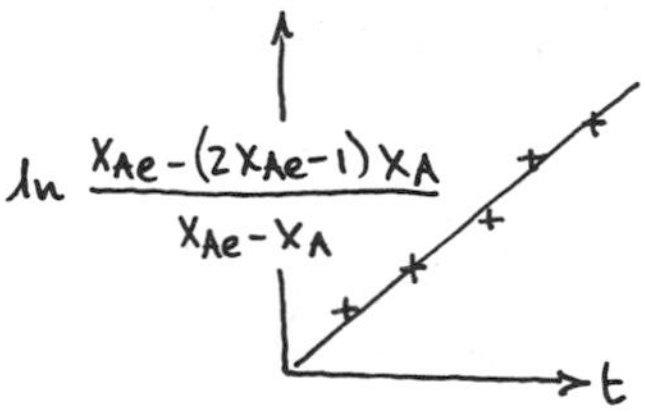

3rd order, $A+B+C \rightarrow \cdots$, $-r_A = k C_A C_B C_C$

For $C_{A0} \neq C_{B0} \neq C_{C0}$

$$kt = \frac{1}{(C_{A0}-C_{B0})(C_{A0}-C_{C0})} \ln \frac{C_{A0}}{C_A} + \frac{1}{(C_{B0}-C_{A0})(C_{B0}-C_{C0})} \ln \frac{C_{B0}}{C_B} + \frac{1}{(C_{C0}-C_{A0})(C_{C0}-C_{B0})} \ln \frac{C_{C0}}{C_C}$$

For $C_{A0} = C_{C0} \neq C_{B0}$

$$kt(2C_{B0}-C_{A0})^2 = \frac{(2C_{B0}-C_{A0})(C_{A0}-C_A)}{C_{A0}C_A} + \ln \frac{C_{B0}C_A}{C_B C_{A0}}$$

For $C_{A0} = C_{B0} = C_{C0}$

$$2kt = \frac{1}{C_A^2} - \frac{1}{C_{A0}^2} \quad \cdots\text{or}\cdots \quad \frac{C_A}{C_{A0}} = \frac{1}{\sqrt{1+2ktC_{A0}^2}}$$

3rd order, $2A+B \rightarrow \cdots$ $-r_A = -2r_B = kC_A^2 C_B$

For $C_{A0} \neq 2C_{B0}$

$$\frac{kt}{2}(2C_{B0}-C_{A0})^2 = \frac{(2C_{B0}-C_{A0})(C_{A0}-C_A)}{C_{A0}C_A} + \ln \frac{C_{B0}C_A}{C_B C_{A0}}$$

For $C_{A0} = 2C_{B0}$

$$kt = \frac{1}{C_A^2} - \frac{1}{C_{A0}^2} \quad \cdots\text{or}\cdots \quad \frac{C_A}{C_{A0}} = \frac{1}{\sqrt{1+ktC_{A0}^2}}$$

3rd order, $3A \rightarrow \cdots$, $-r_A = kC_A^3$

$$2kt = \frac{1}{C_A^2} - \frac{1}{C_{A0}^2} \quad \cdots\text{or}\cdots \quad \frac{C_A}{C_{A0}} = \frac{1}{\sqrt{1+2ktC_{A0}^2}}$$

3rd order, $A+B \rightarrow \cdots$, $-r_A = kC_A^2 C_B$

For $C_{A0} \neq C_{B0}$

$$kt(C_{B0}-C_{A0})^2 = \frac{(C_{B0}-C_{A0})(C_{A0}-C_A)}{C_{A0}C_A} + \ln \frac{C_{B0}C_A}{C_{A0}C_B}$$

For $C_{A0} = C_{B0}$

$$2kt = \frac{1}{C_A^2} - \frac{1}{C_{A0}^2} \quad \cdots\text{or}\cdots \quad \frac{C_A}{C_{A0}} = \frac{1}{\sqrt{1+2ktC_{A0}^2}}$$

nth order, $A \rightarrow \cdots$, $-r_A = kC_A^n$

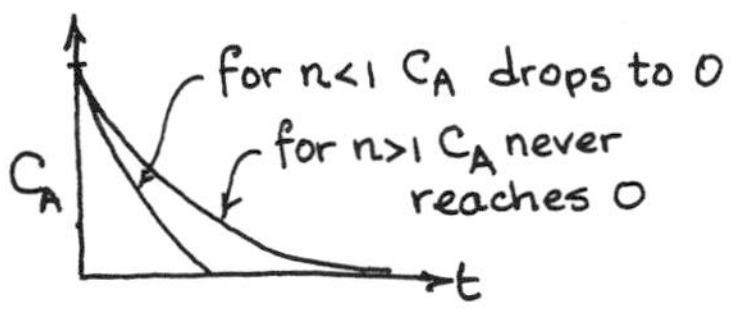

For $n \neq 1$

$$(n-1)C_{A0}^{n-1}kt = \left(\frac{C_A}{C_{A0}}\right)^{1-n} - 1$$

Half life method, see example pg 2.9

$$t_{1/2} = \frac{(1/2)^{1-n}-1}{k(n-1)} C_{A0}^{1-n}$$

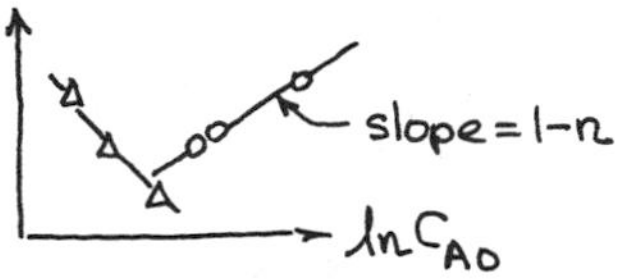

[... see Levenspiel, pg 53, for other stoichiometry, say $aA+bB \rightarrow \cdots$]

Reactions of shifting order,

$$A \rightarrow \cdots, \quad -r_A = \frac{kC_A}{M + C_A} \cdots \begin{cases} 1^{st} \text{ order at low } C_A \\ 0 \text{ order at high } C_A \end{cases}$$

$$kt = M \ln \frac{C_{A0}}{C_A} + C_{A0} - C_A \quad \cdots \text{or} \cdots \quad \frac{C_{A0} - C_A}{\ln C_{A0}/C_A} = -M + k \frac{t}{\ln C_{A0}/C_A}$$

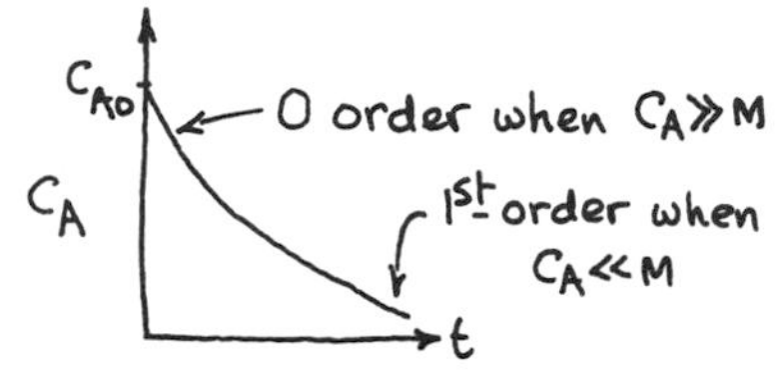

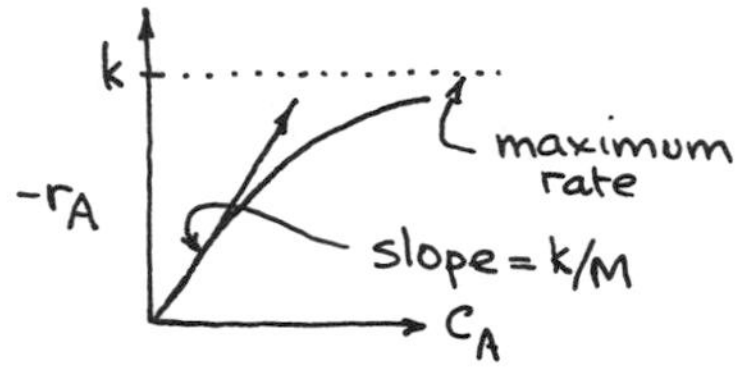

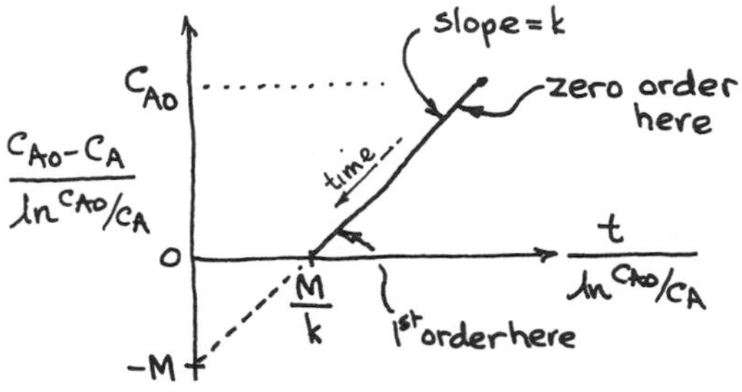

For orders other than between 0 and 1 see Levenspiel, 65.

Reactions in series, 1st order,

$$A \xrightarrow{k_1} R \xrightarrow{k_2} S \cdots \begin{cases} -r_A = k_1 C_A \\ -r_R = k_2 C_R - k_1 C_A \end{cases}$$

For $C_{R0} = C_{S0} = 0$ we have

$$\frac{C_A}{C_{A0}} = e^{-k_1 t}, \quad \frac{C_R}{C_{A0}} = \frac{k_1}{k_2 - k_1}\left(e^{-k_1 t} - e^{-k_2 t}\right), \quad C_S = C_{A0} - C_A - C_R$$

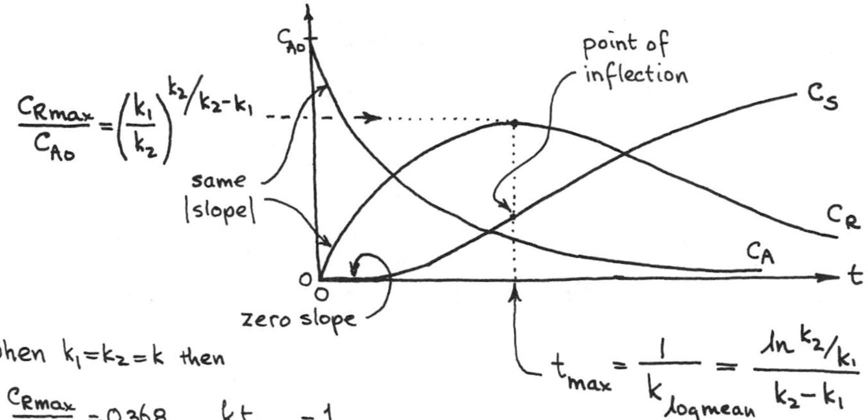

When $k_1 = k_2 = k$ then

$$\frac{C_{R\,max}}{C_{A0}} = 0.368, \quad kt_{max} = 1$$

(2.6)

Uncatalysed and homogeneous catalytic,

$$\left.\begin{array}{l} A \xrightarrow{1} R \\ A + C \xrightarrow{2} R + C \end{array}\right\} \cdots \quad -r_A = k_1 C_A + k_2 C_A C_C$$

$$(k_{observed})t = (k_1 + k_2 C_C)t = \ln \frac{C_{A0}}{C_A} = \ln \frac{1}{X_A}$$

and from a series of runs using different catalyst concentrations make this plot

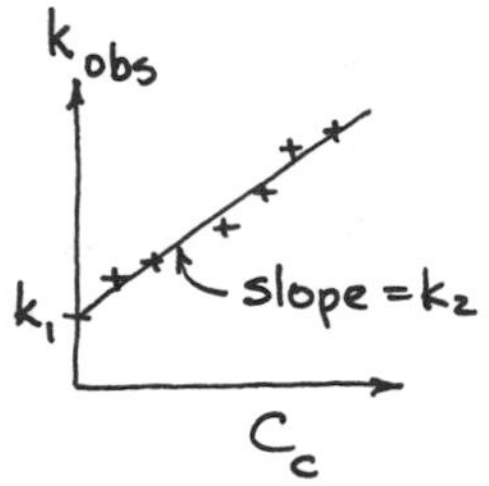

2nd order autocatalytic, $A + R \xrightarrow{k} 2R$, $-r_A = kC_AC_R$, $M = \frac{C_{R0}}{C_{A0}} \neq 0$

$$kt(C_{A0} + C_{R0}) = \ln \frac{C_R/C_{R0}}{C_A/C_{A0}} = \ln \frac{M + X_A}{M(1 - X_A)}$$

or

$$\frac{C_A}{C_{A0} + C_{R0}} = 1 \Big/ 1 + \frac{C_{A0}}{C_{R0}} e^{k(C_{A0} + C_{R0})t}$$

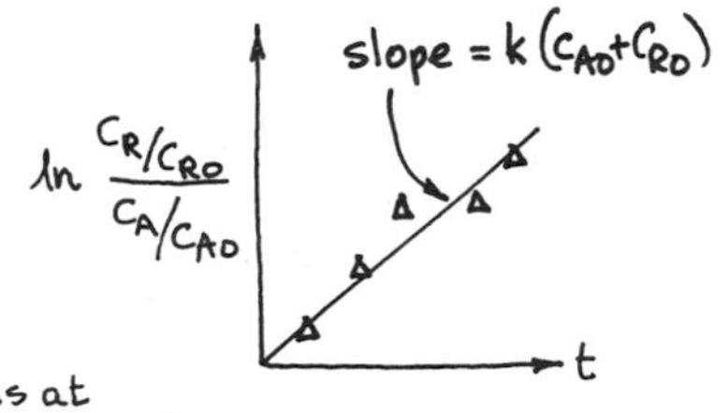

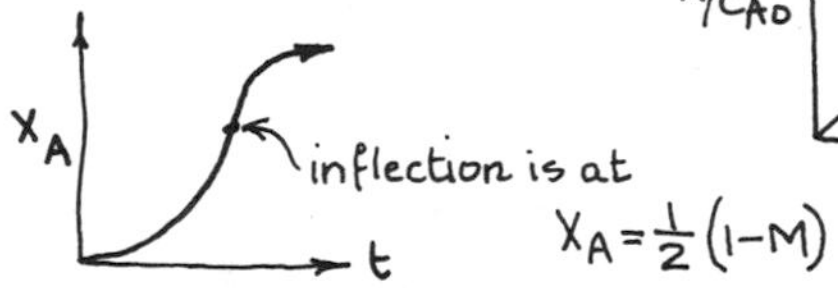

Uncatalysed and 2nd order autocatalytic,

$$\left.\begin{array}{l} A \xrightarrow{1} R \\ A + R \xrightarrow{2} 2R \end{array}\right\} \cdots \quad -r_A = k_1 C_A + k_2 C_A C_R$$

and with $C_{R0} = 0$

$$(k_1 + k_2 C_{A0})t = \ln\left(\frac{1 + \frac{k_2}{k_1} C_{A0} X_A}{1 - X_A}\right)$$

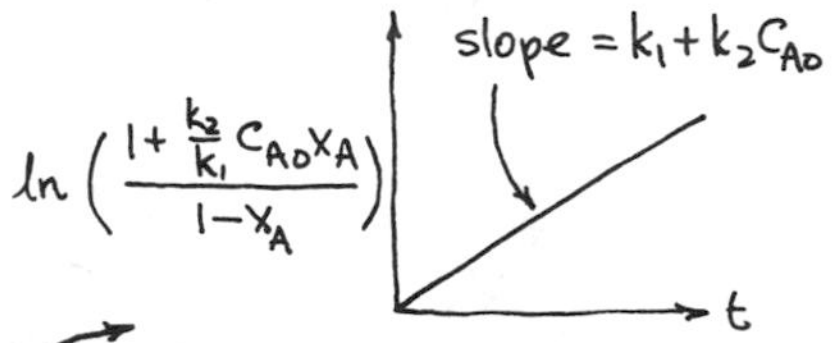

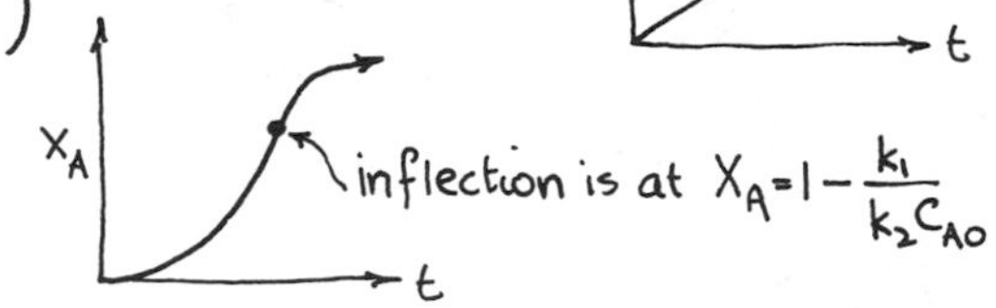

II. Integrated forms for the constant pressure changing volume batch reactor.

Here we integrate eq. 3. This then is for isothermal gas phase systems where $V = V_o(1+\varepsilon_A X_A)$. For example, for a 2nd order reaction eq. 3 gives

$$-r_A = \frac{C_{A0}}{(1+\varepsilon_A X_A)}\frac{dX_A}{dt} = kC_A^2 = kC_{A0}^2\left(\frac{1-X_A}{1+\varepsilon_A X_A}\right)^2$$

integrate

In general

$$\varepsilon_A \cdot \frac{C_A}{C_{A0}} = (1+\varepsilon_A)\frac{V_o}{V} - 1$$

Zero order, $A \rightarrow rR$, with inerts, $-r_A = k$

$$\frac{\varepsilon_A kt}{C_{A0}} = \ln\left(\frac{1+\varepsilon_A}{1+\varepsilon_A C_A/C_{A0}}\right) = \ln\frac{V}{V_o}$$

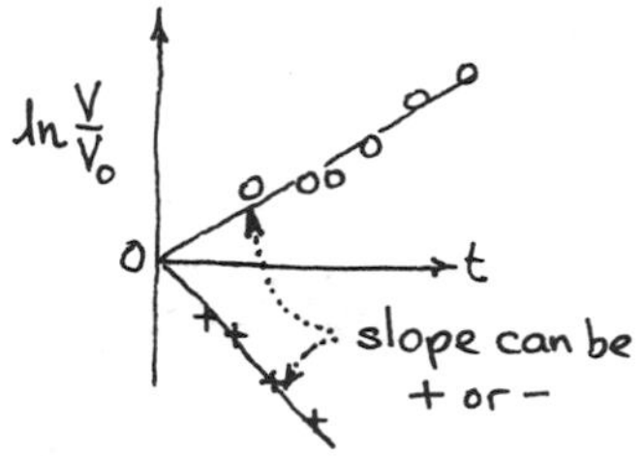

1st order, $A \rightarrow rR$, with inerts, $-r_A = kC_A$

$$kt = \ln\left(\frac{C_{A0}+\varepsilon_A C_A}{(\varepsilon_A+1)C_A}\right) = -\ln\left(1-\frac{\Delta V}{\varepsilon_A V_o}\right)$$

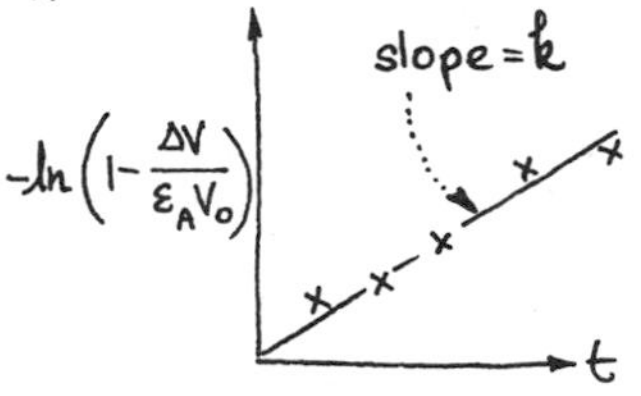

2nd order, $A \rightarrow rR$, with inerts $-r_A = kC_A^2$

$$ktC_{A0} = \frac{C_{A0}-C_A}{C_A} + \varepsilon_A \ln\frac{C_A(1+\varepsilon_A)}{C_{A0}+\varepsilon_A C_A} = \frac{\Delta V}{V_o - \frac{V}{1+\varepsilon_A}} + \varepsilon_A \ln\left(1-\frac{\Delta V}{\varepsilon_A V_o}\right)$$

These integrated forms very soon become cumbersome, so lets not try any others.

III. Comments.

(a) Other integrated forms could be developed, the various textbooks on kinetics have them, but this listing is long enough as it is.

(b) In the above integrated expressions whenever the reactant ratio equals the stoichiometric ratio a special differential equation results and this must be integrated, just for that case.

(c) We have made but brief mention of multiple reactions. We treat these more fully in later chapters.

(d) The listed integrated forms help us in our search for a rate equation by the integral method. But which method should we use in the first place ... integral or differential?

The **integral method** is simple and speedy. Just guess the rate form (please guess the simple ones first ... be a good engineer), make the suggested plot and see if you get a straight line. Malheureusement, if no guess works then you must go to the **differential method**. This is much more time consuming but has the advantage of allowing you to search for real, messy rate forms. For clues and suggestions on how to do this see Levenspiel pgs 67-71.

So to answer our question: try the integral method first. If you can't find a good fit then go to the differential method.

(e) Note that the rate constant k in the performance expressions have a variety of dimensions depending on reaction order. Thus

$$k = \left[s^{-1}\right] \quad \cdots \text{ for } n=1$$

$$k = \left[\frac{m^3}{mol \cdot s}\right] \quad \cdots \text{ for } n=2$$

$$k = \left[\frac{(m^3)^{n-1}}{mol^{n-1} \cdot s}\right] \quad \cdots \text{ for } n^{th} \text{ order reaction}$$

and so on.

Example 1 – the Fractional Life Method. (a simple way to bypass the differential method with its tedious slope-taking, for fitting n^{th} order reactions).

Find an nth order rate equation to represent the following batch data:

C_A, mol/lit	10	8	6	5	3	2	1.4
time, s	0	20	40	60	120	180	240

Solution. Let the time for C_A to drop to any fraction **F** of its original value be Δt_F. Then the half life method generalizes to

$$\Delta t_F = \frac{F^{1-n} - 1}{k(n-1)} C_{A,start}^{1-n} \quad \cdots (i)$$

Now plot the data and draw a smooth line to represent it. It is crucial that you do this wisely. Your answer depends on it

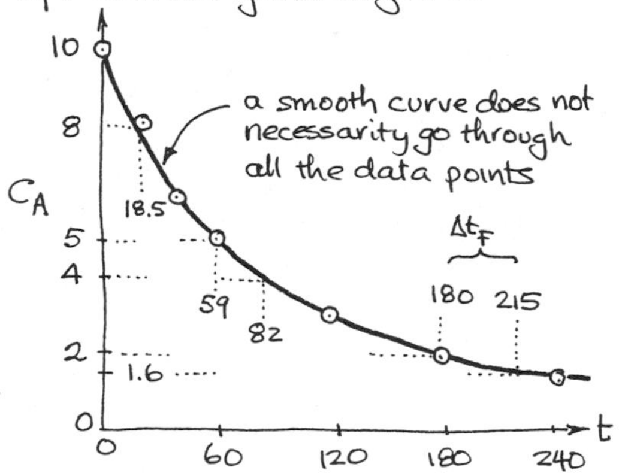

Next choose the fraction F. Let us take F = 0.8. Then select $C_{A,start}$ = 10, 5 and 2. This gives, from the figure

time needed for C_A to drop 20%			$\log \Delta t_F$	$\log C_{A,start}$
0 → 18.5 = 18.5 s	10 → 8 mol/lit	⇝	1.27	1.0
59 → 82 = 23 s	5 → 4 mol/lit		1.36	0.7
180 → 215 = 35 s	2 → 1.6 mol/lit		1.54	0.3

Now plot

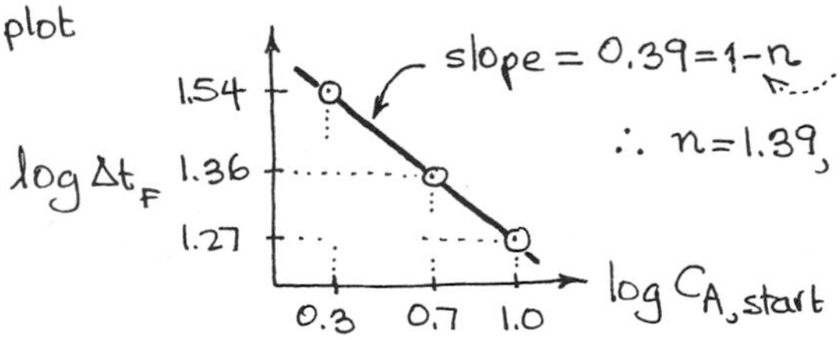

slope = 0.39 = 1 − n ... same as at bottom of pg 2.4

∴ n = 1.39, say 1.4

To evaluate the rate constant k take any point on the C_A vs t curve. Let us pick $C_{A,start}$ = 10, for which Δt_F = 18.5. Replacing these values and n = 1.4 all into eq (i) gives k = 0.005

∴ the rate equation is
$$-r_A = \left(0.005 \frac{lit^{0.4}}{mol^{0.4} \cdot s}\right) C_A^{1.4}, \quad \frac{mol}{lit \cdot s}$$

Chapter 2 Problems

A1 Aqueous A reacts to form R ($A \rightarrow R$) and in the first minute in a batch reactor its concentration drops from $C_{A0} = 2.03$ mol/lit to $C_{Af} = 1.97$ mol/lit. Find the rate equation for the reaction if the kinetics is second order with respect to A.

A2 When a concentrated urea solution is stored it slowly condenses to biuret by the following elementary reaction

$$2NH_2\text{-}CO\text{-}NH_2 \rightarrow NH_2\text{-}CO\text{-}NH\text{-}CO\text{-}NH_2 + NH_3$$

To study the rate of condensation a sample of urea (C = 20 mol/lit) is stored at 100 °C and after 7 hr 40 min we find that 1 mol% has turned into biuret. Find the rate equation for this condensation reaction.

Data from W. M. Butt, Pak. I. Ch. E. **1** 99 (1973).

A3 In a batch reactor 0.4% of A decomposes in 20 seconds when $C_A \approx 4$ mol/lit and the same 0.4% decomposes in 10 seconds when $C_A \approx 16$ mol/lit. Find a rate equation to represent the decomposition of reactant A.

A4 In a constant pressure batch reactor kept a 404 °C and 5 atm the concentration of pure gaseous A drops by 1% in 1 second as it reacts by the elementary reaction $A \rightarrow 2R$. Find the rate equation for this decomposition.

Aqueous A at a concentration $C_{A0} = 1$ mol/lit is introduced into a batch reactor where it reacts away to form product R according to stoichiometry $A \rightarrow R$. The concentration of A in the reactor is monitored at various times as shown below

B5 . . . Find $-r_A$ at $C_A = 250$ mol/m^3 using the differential method

t, min	0	100	200	300	400
C_A, mol/m^3	1000	500	333	250	200

B6 . . . Use the differential method to find the initial rate of reaction for

t, min	0	5	10	15
C_A, mol/m^3	1000	630	310	77

C7 For the reaction of problem 5 and $C_{A0} = 500$ mol/m^3, find the fraction of reactant converted after 5 hours in a batch reactor.

C8 For the reaction of problem 6 and $C_{A0} = 1000$ mol/m^3 find the time needed for 75% conversion of reactant in a batch reactor.

Chapter 2 Problems

Find a rate equation to represent the conversion of reactant to product from the following batch reactor data

D9 . . .

t, hr	0	1	2	3	∞
C_A, mol/m^3	1000	500	300	240	200

D10 . . .

t, hr	0	1/3	1	6
C_A, mol/m^3	1000	430	150	9

Aqueous A and B react to form product in a batch reactor. Find a rate equation to represent the kinetics of the reaction from the following information.

D11 . . . $A + 2B \rightarrow R + S$, $C_{B0} = 2C_{A0}$

t, min	0	10	40	90
C_A, mol/m^3	1000	500	200	100

D12 . . . $A + B \rightarrow R + S$, $C_{B0} = 3C_{A0}$

t, hr	0	1	2	4	6
C_A, mmol/lit	500	225	110	30	10

E13 An ampoule of radioactive Kr-89 (half life = 76 min) is set aside for a day. What does this do to the activity of the ampoule? Note that radioactive decay is a first order process.

E14 Find the time needed for 76% conversion in a batch reactor for

$$A \rightarrow R, \quad -r_A = 0.04\, C_A - 0.01\, C_R \ \frac{\text{mol}}{\text{lit·min}}, \quad C_{A0} = 1 \text{ mol/lit}$$

E15 Enzyme E catalyses the transformation of reactant A to product R as follows

$$A \xrightarrow{\text{enzyme}} R, \quad -r_A = \frac{200\, C_A C_E}{2 + C_A} \ \frac{\text{mol}}{\text{lit·min}}$$

If we introduce enzyme (C_E = 0.001 mol/lit) and reactant (C_{A0} = 10 mol/lit) into a batch reactor and let the reaction proceed find the time needed for the concentration of reactant to drop to 0.025 mol/lit? Note that the concentration of enzyme remains unchanged during the reaction.

Chapter 2 Problems

E16 Find the conversion after one hour in a batch reactor for

$$A \rightarrow R, \quad -r_A = 3\, C_A^{0.5}\ \frac{\text{mol}}{\text{lit·hr}}, \quad C_{A0} = 1 \text{ mol/lit}$$

F17 For the elementary reaction $A \rightarrow R$ reactant A is 50% converted in one hour in a batch reactor. How long will it take for 75% conversion?

F18 For the reaction $A \rightarrow R$, second order kinetics and $C_{A0} = 1$ mol/lit, we get 50% conversion after one hour in a batch reactor. What will be the conversion and concentration of A after one hour if $C_{A0} = 10$ mol/lit?

F19 For the decomposition $A \rightarrow R$, $C_{A0} = 1$ mol/lit, in a batch reactor conversion is 75% after one hour, and is just complete after two hours. Find a rate equation to represent these kinetics.

F20 After 8 minutes in a batch reactor, reactant ($C_{A0} = 1$ mol/lit) is 80% converted; after 18 minutes, conversion is 90%. Find a a rate equation to represent this reaction.

F21 A 10-minute experimental run shows that 75% of liquid reactant is converted to product by a one-half order rate. What would be the amount converted in a half hour run?

F22 In a homogeneous isothermal liquid polymerization, 20% of the monomer disappears in 34 min for initial monomer concentration of 0.04 and also for 0.8 mol/lit. What is the rate of disappearance of the monomer?

In the presence of a homogeneous catalyst of given concentration aqueous reactant A is converted to product at the following rates, and C_A alone determines this rate

C_A, mol/lit	1	2	4	6	7	9	12
$-r_A$, mol/lit·hr	0.06	0.1	0.25	1.0	2.0	1.0	0.5

We plan to run this reaction in a batch reactor at the same catalyst concentration as used in getting the above data.

G23 . . . Find the time needed to lower the concentration of A from $C_{A0} = 10$ mol/lit to $C_{Af} = 2$ mol/lit.

G24 . . . For a feed containing 7 molA/lit, find the concentration of A after 10 hours in the reactor.

Chapter 3   THE STEADY STATE PLUG FLOW REACTOR.

Composition changes progressively through the reactor

C_{AO}
F_{AO}
$X_{AO} = 0$
v_o

fluid flows with a flat velocity profile, in single file, with no overtaking

C_A, X_A
(or C_{Af}, X_{Af})

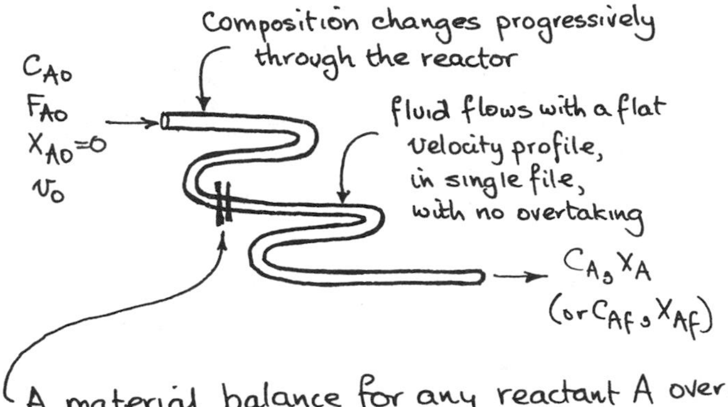

This ideal approximates
· the long tube
· the packed bed
· the multistaged
· the counterflow
and many other types of reactors.

A material balance for any reactant A over a little slice of volume dV gives

$$\underset{\substack{\uparrow \\ F_{Ain}}}{In pot} - \underset{\substack{\uparrow \\ F_{Aout}}}{Output} = \underset{\substack{\uparrow \\ = 0 \text{ for steady flow}}}{Accumulation} + \underset{\substack{\uparrow \\ (-r_A)dV}}{Disappearance \text{ by reaction}}$$

Thus at any point in the reactor

for any ε_A value ... $\left. \begin{array}{l} F_{AO}dX_A = (-r_A)dV \\[2mm] -dC_A = (-r_A)d\tau \end{array} \right\} \cdots (1)$

for $\varepsilon_A = 0$ ...
(special case)

slope = $-r_A$ slope = $+r_A$

X_A C_A

V/F_{AO} τ

(good for any ε_A)   (only good when $\varepsilon_A = 0$)

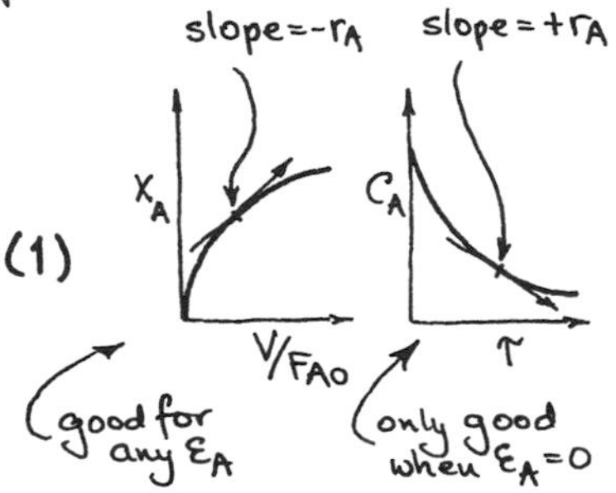

For the reactor as a whole, unconverted feed, any ε_A, integration of eq 1 gives

$$\left. \begin{array}{l} \dfrac{V}{F_{AO}} = \displaystyle\int_0^{X_{Af}} \dfrac{dX_A}{-r_A} \\[4mm] \tau = \dfrac{C_{AO}V}{F_{AO}} = \dfrac{V}{v_o} = C_{AO}\displaystyle\int_0^{X_{Af}} \dfrac{dX_A}{-r_A} \end{array} \right\} \cdots (2)$$

$\frac{1}{-r_A}$

area $= \dfrac{V}{F_{AO}} = \dfrac{\tau}{C_{AO}}$

X_A X_{Af}

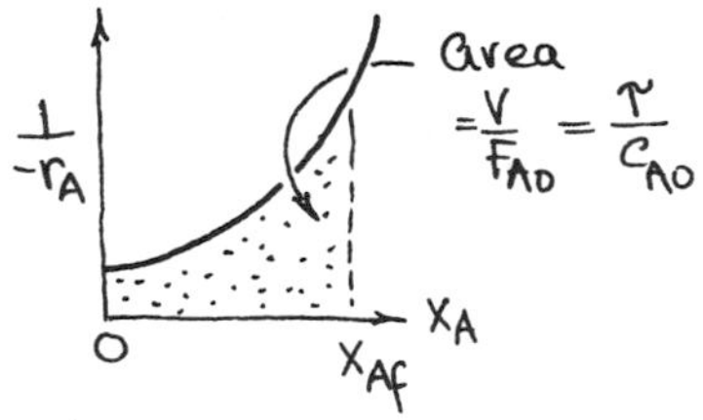

For the special case of $\varepsilon_A = 0$ (all liquids and some isothermal gas systems) we can also write if we wish

$$\tau = \dfrac{C_{AO}V}{F_{AO}} = \dfrac{V}{v_o} = \int_{C_A}^{C_{AO}} \dfrac{dC_A}{-r_A} \quad \cdots (3)$$

$\frac{1}{-r_A}$

area $= \tau = \dfrac{V}{v} = \dfrac{C_{AO}V}{F_{AO}}$

C_{Af} C_{AO} C_A

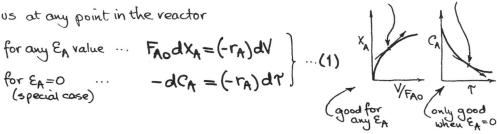

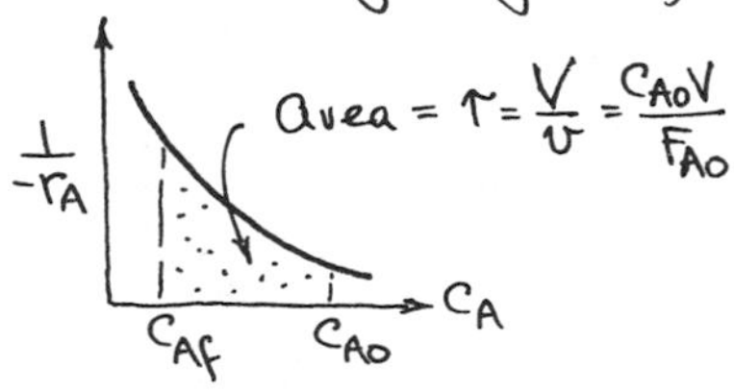

These equations and figures relate … { feed composition, exit composition, reactor size, rate of reaction } … and knowing any three allows you to determine the fourth.

If the rate equation is known then the integral can be evaluated directly. Otherwise use graphical procedures (find areas under curves).

I. Integrated forms for Plug Flow.

In eq 2 replace $-r_A$ by the rate equation being considered, then integrate. For example, for 2nd order kinetics ($A \rightarrow R$, $-r_A = kC_A^2$) use $-r_A = kC_{A0}^2 \left(\frac{1-X_A}{1+\varepsilon_A X_A}\right)^2$ in eq 2 and integrate. The following are some of the simpler integrated forms.

Zero order homogeneous $A \rightarrow \ldots, \quad -r_A = k$

for any ε_A … $\frac{k\tau}{C_{A0}} = X_A = \frac{C_{A0}-C_A}{C_{A0}+\varepsilon_A C_A}$

1st order $A \rightarrow \ldots, \quad -r_A = kC_A$

for $\varepsilon_A \neq 0$ … $k\tau = (1+\varepsilon_A)\ln\frac{1}{1-X_A} - \varepsilon_A X_A$

for $\varepsilon_A = 0$ … $k\tau = \ln\frac{1}{1-X_A} = \ln\frac{C_{A0}}{C_A}$

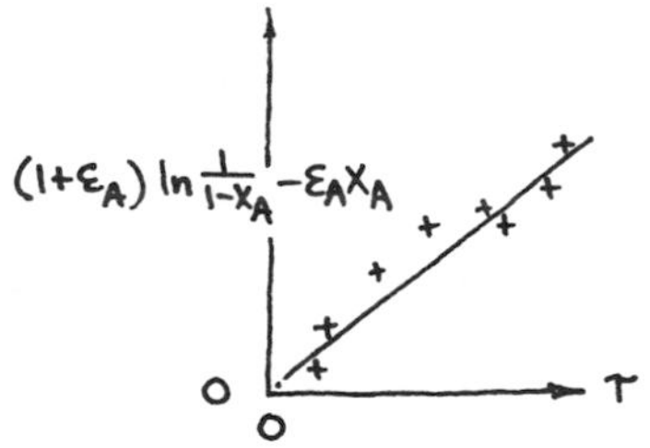

1st order reversible $A \underset{2}{\overset{1}{\rightleftharpoons}} rR, \quad -r_A = k_1C_A - k_2C_R, \quad \frac{C_{R0}}{C_{A0}} = M, \quad X_{Ae}$ = equilibrium

for $\varepsilon_A \neq 0$ … $k_1\tau = \frac{M+rX_{Ae}}{M+r}\left[(1+\varepsilon_A X_{Ae})\ln\frac{X_{Ae}}{X_{Ae}-X_A} - \varepsilon_A X_A\right]$

for $\varepsilon_A = 0$ … $k_1\tau = \frac{M+rX_{Ae}}{M+r}\ln\frac{X_{Ae}}{X_{Ae}-X_A} = \frac{M+r\left(1-\frac{C_{Ae}}{C_{A0}}\right)}{M+r}\ln\frac{C_{A0}-C_{Ae}}{C_A-C_{Ae}}$

2nd order $\begin{cases} 2A \rightarrow \ldots, & -r_A = kC_A^2 \\ A+B \rightarrow \ldots, & -r_A = kC_AC_B, \quad C_{B0} = C_{A0} \end{cases}$

for $\varepsilon_A \neq 0$ … $k\tau C_{A0} = 2\varepsilon_A(1+\varepsilon_A)\ln(1-X_A) + \varepsilon_A^2 X_A + (\varepsilon_A+1)^2\frac{X_A}{1-X_A}$

for $\varepsilon_A = 0$ … $k\tau C_{A0} = \frac{X_A}{1-X_A} = \frac{C_{A0}-C_A}{C_A}$ … or … $\frac{1}{C_A} - \frac{1}{C_{A0}} = k\tau$

II. Comments.

(a) For rate expressions beyond those listed here:

- where $\varepsilon_A \neq 0$ integration gives a messy expression, so we dont bother with these.
- where $\varepsilon_A = 0$ the integrated forms are **identical to those for batch reactors**, except that τ here is replaced by **t** there. So see the long batch reactor listing.

(b) To simplify the algebra where $\varepsilon_A \neq 0$ always use X_A, not C_A, in your calculations. Where $\varepsilon_A = 0$ it doesn't make much difference one way or other what you use, although I happen to prefer using C_A's.

(c) Note that **residence time t** does not appear in any of the plug flow expressions. It is not a useful term. On the other hand, the **space time τ** is the proper time or capacity or performance measure here. Use it or its related quantity V/F_{A0}.

(d) When the feed enters the reactor partly converted it is best to imagine a fictitious stream, completely unconverted, of properties F_{A0} and C_{A0}. Thus

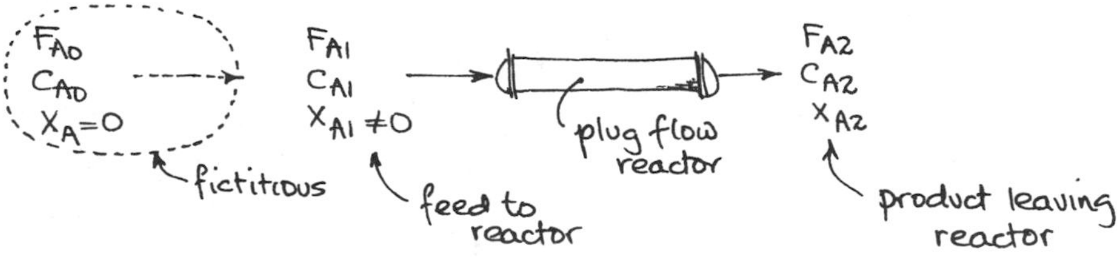

In terms of this fictitious stream and our real stream we have

$$\frac{V}{F_{A0}} = \int_{X_{A1}}^{X_{A2}} \frac{dX_A}{-r_A} \quad \cdots (4)$$

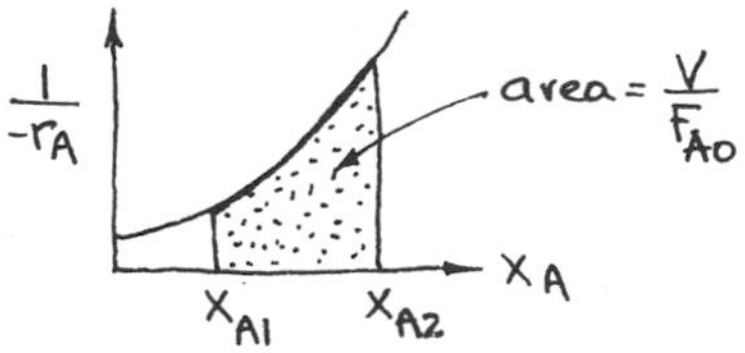

This equation is useful for stagewise operations where fluid is partly converted between stages

(e) **Non isothermal plug flow reactors.** Let us illustrate the performance expression for these reactors with the rather general n^{th} order gas phase reaction

$$A(g) \rightarrow rR(g), \quad -r_A = kC_A^n, \quad k = k^* e^{-E/RT}, \quad \text{ideal gas}$$

Graphically then

Entering stream: C_{A0}, T_0, v_0, k_0, $X_{A0} = 0$

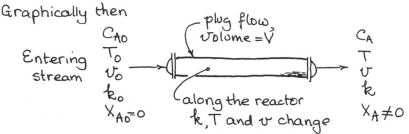

Leaving: C_A, T, v, k, $X_A \neq 0$

The performance equation is then

$$\tau = \frac{V}{v_0} = C_{A0} \int_0^{X_A} \frac{dX_A}{kC_A^n}$$

k changes with T, see pg 1·4 — to write C_A in terms of X_A for non isothermal situations see pg 1·8

Replacing gives

$$k_0 T_0 C_{A0}^{n-1} = \int_0^{X_A} \frac{dX_A}{e^{-\frac{E}{R}\left(\frac{1}{T} - \frac{1}{T_0}\right)} \cdot \left(\frac{1 - X_A}{1 + \varepsilon_A X_A}\right)^{n-1} \cdot \left(\frac{T_0}{T}\right)^n}$$

sub "o" refers to the entering stream; T varies with X_A; solve graphically or numerically; the term $\left(\frac{T_0}{T}\right)^n$ represents ideal gas behavior

For adiabatic operations Chap. 24 shows that T varies linearly with X_A, or nearly so. Thus

$$T \cong T_0 + \frac{(-\Delta H_r)}{C_{p,A}} \cdot X_A = T_0 + (\text{const.}) X_A$$

For other kinetics use the same approach as above.

Example** Pure A (1 kmol/hr, 1 atm) is fed to a plug flow reactor where it reacts reversibly and isothermally at 1219 K with elementary kinetics

$$A \underset{2}{\overset{1}{\rightleftharpoons}} 2R \quad \cdots \quad \begin{cases} k_1 = 200\ \text{hr}^{-1} \\ K_p = 1\ \text{atm} \end{cases}$$

Find (a) the size of reactor needed for 40% conversion.
(b) the equilibrium conversion.

Solution (a) <u>Volume of plug flow reactor</u>

The reaction is elementary, hence 1st order forward, 2nd order reverse, or $-r_A = k_1 C_A - k_2 C_R^2$. Thus the plug flow performance equation becomes

$$\frac{V}{F_{A0}} = \int_0^{0.4} \frac{dX_A}{-r_A} = \int_0^{0.4} \frac{dX_A}{k_1 C_A - k_2 C_R^2} = \int_0^{0.4} \frac{dX_A}{k_1 (N_A/V) - k_2 (N_R/V)^2}$$

we must write these in terms of conversions. Since this is not easy to see straight off let us go back to the definition of concentration.

$$V = F_{A0} \int_0^{0.4} \frac{dX_A}{k_1 \dfrac{N_{A0}(1-X_A)}{V_0(1+\varepsilon_A X_A)} - k_2 \left[\dfrac{N_{A0}(2X_A)}{V_0(1+\varepsilon_A X_A)}\right]^2} = F_{A0} \int_0^{0.4} \frac{dX_A}{k_1 C_{A0}\left(\dfrac{1-X_A}{1+\varepsilon_A X_A}\right) - 4k_2 C_{A0}^2 \left(\dfrac{X_A}{1+\varepsilon_A X_A}\right)^2}$$

Now evaluate all the terms in the above performance expression

$$k_1 = 200\ \text{hr}^{-1}$$

$$C_{A0} = P_{A0}/RT = 1\,\text{atm} \Big/ \left(0.08206\ \frac{\text{lit}\cdot\text{atm}}{\text{mol}\cdot\text{K}}\right)(1219\,\text{K}) = 0.01\ \frac{\text{mol}}{\text{lit}}$$

$$k_{2,\text{conc}} = \frac{k_{1,\text{conc}}}{K_c} = \frac{k_{1,\text{conc}}}{K_p/RT} = \frac{(200\,\text{hr}^{-1})(100\,\text{lit}\cdot\text{atm/mol})}{1\,\text{atm}} = 20000\ \frac{\text{lit}}{\text{mol}\cdot\text{hr}}$$

$$F_{A0} = 1000\ \frac{\text{mol}}{\text{hr}}$$

$$\left.\begin{matrix} A & \rightleftharpoons & 2R \\ 1 & & 0 \\ \underline{0} & & \underline{2} \\ 1 & & 2 \end{matrix}\right\} \cdots \quad \varepsilon_A = \frac{2-1}{1} = +1$$

Replacing all values gives

$$V = 10^3 \int_0^{0.4} \frac{dX_A}{(200)(0.01)\left(\dfrac{1-X_A}{1+X_A}\right) - 4(20000)(0.01)^2\left(\dfrac{X_A}{1+X_A}\right)^2} = 500 \int_0^{0.4} \frac{(1+X_A)^2}{1-5X_A^2}\, dX_A$$

Solve graphically:

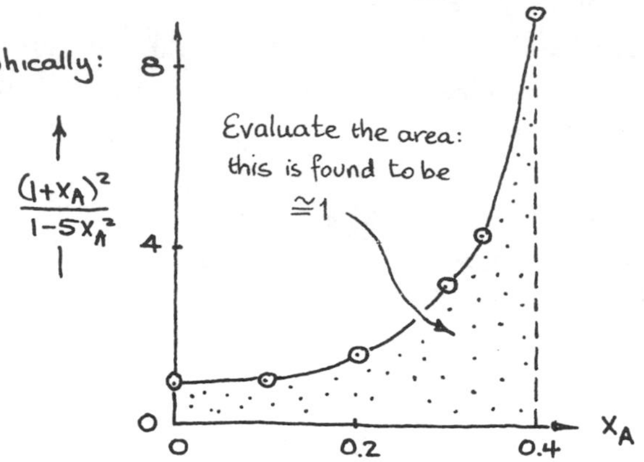

X_A	$\frac{(1+X_A)^2}{1-5X_A^2}$
0	1
0.1	1.27
0.2	1.80
0.3	3.07
0.34	4.25
0.38	6.85
0.4	9.80

$\therefore\ V = (500)(1) = 500\ \text{lit} = 0.5\ m^3$ ← (a)

(b) Equilibrium conversion.

The quickest way to find X_{Ae} is to recognize that this occurs where (forward rate) = (backward rate) ... or where ... $k_1 C_A = k_2 C_R^2$

From the last writing of the performance equation this occurs where

$1 - 5X_A^2 = 0$ ... or where ... $X_{Ae} = 0.45$ ← (b)

Alternatively we can conservatively retreat into formal thermodynamics. Here, for the general ideal gas reaction $aA \rightleftarrows rR + sS$, ... $\Delta n = r + s - a$, we have

$$K = \frac{K_p}{(p^\circ = 1\,atm)^{\Delta n}} = K_c\left(\frac{RT}{p^\circ = 1\,atm}\right)^{\Delta n} = K_y\left(\frac{\pi}{p^\circ = 1\,atm}\right)^{\Delta n}$$

thermodynamic equilibrium constant; $K_p = \frac{p_R^r p_S^s}{p_A^a}$; $K_c = \frac{C_R^r C_S^s}{C_A^a}$; $K_y = \frac{y_R^r y_S^s}{y_A^a}$

For our reaction

	A	$\rightleftarrows 2R$	
	1	0	total = 1
	$1-z$	$2z$	total = $1+z$
Mole fraction:	$\frac{1-z}{1+z}$	$\frac{2z}{1+z}$	

$$\therefore\ K_y = \frac{K_p}{\pi^{\Delta n}} = \frac{K_p}{\pi^{+1}} = \frac{1\,atm}{(1\,atm)^1} = 1 = \frac{y_R^2}{y_A} = \frac{\left(2z/1+z\right)^2}{\left(1-z/1+z\right)} = \frac{4z^2}{1-z^2}$$

From these two

$z = 0.45$ ... but z = mol fraction X_{Ae} $\quad \therefore\ X_{Ae} = 0.45$ ← (b)

Chapter 3 Problems

A1 10 cm^3/sec of aqueous reactant A at 900 mmol/lit enters a five section plug flow reactor (10 cm^3/section, 50 cm^3 total volume), and reacts to form product ($A \rightarrow R + S$). The concentration of A is measured at various locations along the reactor. Find the rate of reaction at C_A = 100 mmol/lit from the following data. No need to find the rate equation.

After section number	1	2	3	4	5
C_A, mmol/lit	625	400	225	100	25

A2 A stream of pure gaseous reactant A at 1000 mmol/lit enters a plug flow reactor (V = 100 cm^3) and decomposes isothermally ($A \rightarrow 4R$). The following data are thereby obtained for various feed rates. From this information find the rate of reaction at a reactant concentration C_A = 100 mmol/lit. No need to find the rate equation.

τ, sec	100	48	25	12	3
C_A, mmol/lit	10	50	100	200	500

A3 Pure gaseous A (1000 mmol/lit) enters a plug flow reactor (V = 10 cm^3) and there reacts isothermally ($2A \rightarrow 3R + S$). For various feed rates the following exit concentrations are measured. From this data find the rate of reaction at C_A = 250 mmol/lit. No need to find the rate equation.

v, cm^3/sec	0.5	3	16	60
C_A, mmol/lit	10	50	200	500

A4 A gaseous mixture of reactant A and inerts (1/3A -2/3 inerts, C_{A0} = 1000 mmol/lit) enters a plug flow reactor (V = 100 cm^3) and reacts isothermally ($A \rightarrow 4R$), and the exit composition is measured at various feed rates. From the following data find the rate of reaction at C_A = 100 mmol/lit. No need to find the rate equation.

v, cm^3/sec	1.5	2.5	4.0	6.5	20
C_A, mmol/lit	10	50	100	200	500

B5 For the reaction of problem 1 find the plug flow space time needed for 75% conversion of an aqueous feed stream of concentration C_{A0} = 0.4 mol/lit.

B6 For the reaction of problem 2 find the volume of plug flow reactor needed for 50% conversion of 3 lit/sec of a C_{A0} = 1 mol/lit feed of pure A.

B7* For the reaction of problem 4 find the volume of plug flow reactor needed for 66.7% conversion of 1 lit/sec of a C_{A0} = 0.5 mol/lit feed of pure A.

Chapter 3 Problems

Find a rate equation to represent the conversion of a reactant to product from the plug flow reactor data

C8 ... of problem 1

C9 ... of problem 2

D10 An aqueous feed containing reactant A (1 mol/lit) enters a 2 liter plug flow reactor and reacts away ($2A \rightarrow R$, $-r_A = 0.05\ C_A^2$ mol/lit·s). Find the outlet concentration of A for a feed rate of 0.5 lit/min.

D11 An aqueous feed of A and B (400 lit/min, 100 mmolA/lit, 200 mmolB/lit) is to be converted to product in a plug flow reactor. The kinetics of the reaction is represented by

$$A + B \rightarrow R, \quad -r_A = 200\ C_A C_B\ \frac{\text{mol}}{\text{lit·min}}$$

Find the volume of reactor needed for 99.9% conversion of A to product.

D12 A plug flow reactor (2 m^3) processes an aqueous feed (100 lit/min) containing reactant A (C_{A0} = 100 mmol/lit). This reaction is reversible and represented by

$$A \leftrightarrow R, \quad -r_A = (0.04\ \text{min}^{-1})C_A - (0.01\ \text{min}^{-1})C_R$$

First find the equilibrium conversion, and then find the actual conversion of A in the reactor.

D13 A specific enzyme acts as catalyst in the fermentation of reactant A. At a given enzyme concentration in the aqueous feed stream (25 lit/min) find the volume of plug flow reactor needed for 95% conversion of reactant A (C_{A0} = 2 mol/lit). The kinetics of the fermentation at this enzyme concentration is given by

$$A \xrightarrow{\text{enzyme}} R, \quad -r_A = \frac{0.1\ C_A}{1 + 0.5\ C_A}\ \frac{\text{mol}}{\text{lit·min}}$$

D14 A gaseous feed of pure A (2 mol/lit, 100 mol/min) decomposes to give a variety of products in a plug flow reactor. The kinetics of the conversion is represented by

$$A \rightarrow 2.5\ (\text{products}), \quad -r_A = (10\ \text{min}^{-1})\ C_A$$

Find the expected conversion in a 22 liter reactor.

Chapter 3 Problems

D15 At 650 °C phosphine vapor decomposes as follows

$$4PH_3 \rightarrow P_{4(g)} + 6H_2, \quad -r_{phos} = (10\ hr^{-1})C_{phos}$$

What size of plug flow reactor operating at 650 °C and 11.4 atm is needed for 75% conversion of 10 mol/hr of phosphine in a 2/3 phosphine -1/3 inert feed?

D16 A stream of pure gaseous reactant A (C_{A0} = 660 mmol/lit) enters a plug flow reactor at a flow rate of F_{A0} = 540 mmol/min and polymerizes there as follows

$$3A \rightarrow R, \quad -r_A = 54\ \frac{\text{mmol}}{\text{lit}\cdot\text{min}}$$

How large a reactor is needed to lower the concentration of A in the exit stream to C_{Af} = 330 mmol/lit.

D17 1 lit/s of a 20% ozone - 80% air mixture at 1.5 atm and 93 °C passes through a plug flow reactor. Under these conditions ozone decomposes by homogeneous reaction

$$2O_3 \rightarrow 3O_2, \quad -r_{ozone} = kC_{ozone}^2, \quad k = 0.05\ \frac{\text{lit}}{\text{mol}\cdot\text{s}}$$

What size reactor is needed for 50% decomposition of ozone?

This problem is a modification of Corcoran & Lacey, pg. 103.

D18 The homogeneous gas phase reaction $A \rightarrow 3R$ has a reported rate at 215 °C

$$-r_A = 0.01C_A^{1/2}\ \frac{\text{mol}}{\text{lit}\cdot\text{s}}$$

Find the space-time needed for 80% conversion of a 50% A - 50% inert feed to a plug flow reactor operation at 215 °C and 5 atm.

D19* The gas leaving an ammonia oxidation plant consists of

10% nitric oxide (NO)
1% nitrogen oxide (NO_2)
8% oxygen

This gas is allowed to oxidize ($NO \rightarrow NO_2$) until the NO_2:NO ratio reaches 8:1. The oxidized gas is then absorbed in water to produce nitric acid ($3NO_2 + H_2O \rightarrow 2HNO_3 + NO$). Calculate the size of tubular reactor (assume plug flow) operating at 20 °C and 1 atm needed for this oxidation for a gas feed rate of 10000 m^3/hr (measured at 0 °C and 1 atm). According to Bodenstein in Z. Phys. Chem. **100** 87 (1922) the reaction proceeds at 20 °C as follows

$$2NO + O_2 \rightarrow 2NO_2, \quad r_{NO_2} = 14000\ C_{NO}^2 C_{O_2}\ \frac{\text{kmol}}{\text{m}^3\cdot\text{s}}$$

This problem is adapted from Denbigh and Turner, pg. 57.

For a given processing rate of pure gaseous feed how many times as large must our plug flow reactor be to raise the conversion of reactant from 1/3 to 2/3, given the following kinetics.

E20 ... $A \rightarrow R, \ -r_A = kC_A^2$

E21 ... $4A \rightarrow R, \ -r_A = kC_A$

E22 The homogeneous gas reaction $A \rightarrow 3R$ follows second order kinetics. For a feed rate of 4 m^3/hr of pure A at 5 atm and 350 °C, an experimental reactor consisting of a 2.5 cm ID pipe 2 m long gives 60% conversion of feed. A commercial plant is to treat 320 m^3/hr of feed consisting of 50% A, 50% inerts at 25 atm and 350 °C to obtain 80% conversion.

(a) How many 2-m lengths of 2.5 cm ID pipe are required?

(b) Should they be placed in parallel or in series?

Assume plug flow in the pipe, negligible pressure drop, and ideal gas behavior.

We wish to raise the conversion of reactant in our plug flow reactor from 60% to 80% by adjusting the feed rate of our 50% A - 50% inert gaseous feed. How should this be done if the decomposition is represented by

E23 ... $A \rightarrow R, \ -r_A = kC_A$

E24 ... $A \rightarrow 3R, \ -r_A = kC_A^2$

In the presence of a homogeneous catalyst of given concentration aqueous reactant A is converted to product at the following rates, and C_A alone influences the rate

C_A, mol/lit	1	2	4	6	8	10
$-r_A$, mol/lit·min	0.05	0.1	0.2	0.33	0.25	0.125

F25 ... What feed rate (lit/min) to a plug flow reactor (66 liters) would yield 66.7% conversion of a $C_{A0} = 6$ mol/lit feed?

F26 ... Find the exit concentration from a 1 liter plug flow reactor treating 40 lit/min of $C_{A0} = 10$ mol/lit feed.

Chapter 3 Problems

F27 Given the following rate-concentration data for a particular gas phase reaction ($A \rightarrow R$) which we plan to run in a plug flow reactor, find the space time needed for 80% conversion of a 10 mol/lit pure A feed.

C_A, mol/lit	1	2	4	6	8	10
$-r_A$, mol/lit·s	0.01	0.02	0.04	0.09	0.16	0.25

G28* In the temperature range between 670 °C and 725 °C 2-pentene thermally cracks in a stainless steel tube to give a variety of products

$$C_5H_{10} \rightarrow (H_2,\ CH_4,\ C_2\text{'s},\ C_3\text{'s},\ C_4\text{'s})$$

and experiments by Kunzru *et al* in IEC/PDD 12 339 (1973) give the following results

T, °C	670	670	700	700	725	725
τ_0, s	0.26	0.87	0.21	1.2	0.18	0.49
X_A	0.088	0.220	0.146	0.503	0.229	0.458
$\dfrac{\text{Moles produced}}{\text{Moles cracked}}$	1.712	1.945	1.852	2.124	2.020	2.206

Most rate equations for thermal cracking follow first order kinetics, so find an equation of this type to fit the data.

Reactant A (10 kmol/hr) enters a plug flow reactor and there dimerizes isothermally at 946 °C by a homogeneous elementary reaction

$$2A \underset{2}{\overset{1}{\leftrightarrow}} R, \qquad \text{where } k_1 = 2\ \text{mol/lit·hr·atm}^2 \text{ and } K_p = 1\ \text{atm}^{-1} \text{ at equilibrium}$$

Find the equilibrium conversion and also the volume of reactor needed

H29* ... for 50% conversion of pure A feed at 10 atm?

H30* ... for 70% conversion of a 50% A - 50% inert feed at 10 atm?

I31* Imagine dilute aqueous A flowing down a tube and decomposing to produce tiny bubbles of product R which flow along with the liquid. In general let the kinetics be

$$A(\ell) \rightarrow R(g)$$

(a) Develop the general performance expression for this situation in terms of $-r_{A\ \text{liquid phase}}$ if the gas-liquid mixture moves as one, at the same velocity and in plug flow down the tube. But note that the velocity of the mixture increases as gas is formed.

(b) What does this expression reduce to if the decomposition in the liquid is second order with respect to A?

(c) Apply the above equations to the decomposition of a dilute aqueous solution of hydrogen peroxide (C_{A0} = 0.08 mol/lit) flowing at 32 °C down a long tube. What volume of tube will give 90% decomposition of the H_2O_2 if the kinetics of this reaction is given by

$$H_2O_2(\ell) \rightarrow H_2O + \frac{1}{2}O_2\,(g), \quad (-r_A)_{liquid} = 2\,C_A^2\ \frac{mol}{lit\cdot s}$$

Chapter 4.   THE STEADY STATE MIXED FLOW REACTOR

C_{AO}
F_{AO}
$X_{AO}=0$
v_0

well mixed and same composition everywhere

C_{Af}, X_{Af}, F_{Af}

This ideal approximates
• real stirred tanks
• sparged vessels
• vessels with large recycle

A material balance for any reactant A over the whole volume V gives

$$\underset{\displaystyle F_{AO}}{In\text{put}} - \underset{\displaystyle F_{Af}=F_{AO}(1-X_{Af})}{Out\text{put}} = \underset{\substack{=0 \text{ because of}\\ \text{steady state}}}{Ac\text{cumulation}} + \underset{\displaystyle (-r_A)V}{Dis\text{appearance by reaction}}$$

For the reactor, for unconverted feed, and for any ε_A the terms in the material balance give

$$\left.\begin{array}{c} \dfrac{V}{F_{AO}} = \dfrac{X_{Af}}{(-r_A)_f} \\[3mm] \tau = \dfrac{V}{v_0} = \dfrac{C_{AO}V}{F_{AO}} = \dfrac{C_{AO}X_{Af}}{(-r_A)_f} \end{array}\right\} \quad \cdots (1)$$

Area $= \dfrac{V}{F_{AO}}$

This point represents the conditions within the reactor. It is the operating point for the reactor

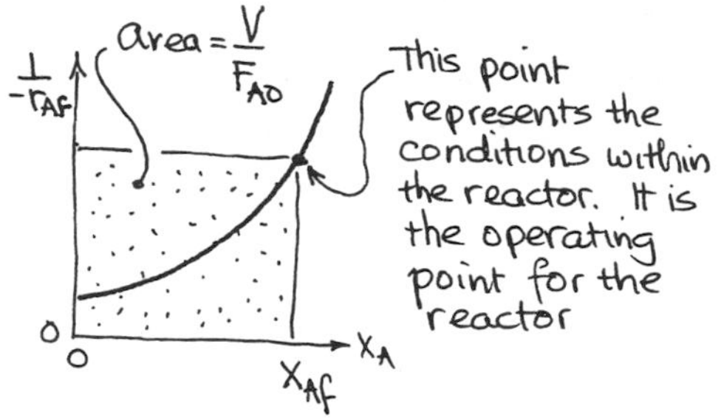

For the special case where $\varepsilon_A=0$ (for practically all liquids & for some gases) we can write eq 1 in terms of concentrations, if we wish

$$\tau = \dfrac{C_{AO}V}{F_{AO}} = \dfrac{V}{v} = \dfrac{C_{AO}-C_{Af}}{(-r_A)_f} \quad \cdots (2)$$

Operating point

Area $=\tau$

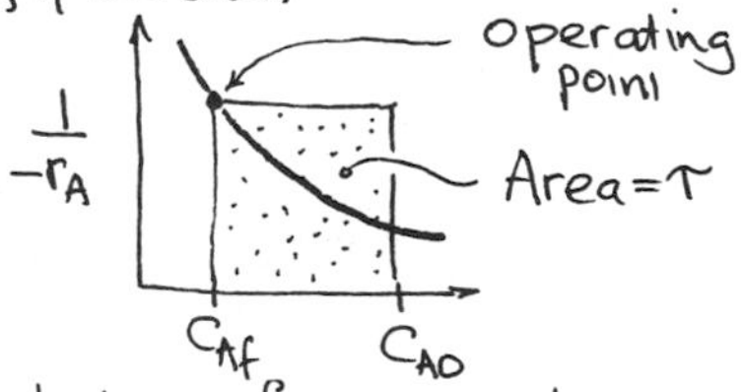

In a similar fashion we can write the material balance for a reaction product. This gives

$$F_{Rf} - F_{RO} = (+r_R)_f V \overset{\varepsilon_A=0}{=\!=\!=} v_0(C_{Rf}-C_{RO}) \quad \cdots (3)$$

These equations and figures relate $\left\{\begin{array}{l}\text{feed composition}\\ \text{exit composition}\\ \text{reactor size \&}\\ \text{rate of reaction}\end{array}\right.$, and knowing any three allows you to calculate the fourth quantity directly without integration or messy mathematics.

I Particular Forms for the Mixed Flow Performance Equation.

If the rate equation is known insert it into the general performance equation (eq. 1, 2, 3 or 4), change everything into concentrations or conversions, and that's it ... no integration, no mathematical complexities. Here are a few final forms, for $\varepsilon_A = 0$ & $C_{Ain} = C_{A0}$.

Zero order homogeneous, $A \rightarrow \cdots, \; -r_A = k$

for any ε_A ...
$$\frac{k\tau}{C_{A0}} = X_A = \frac{C_{A0} - C_A}{C_{A0} + \varepsilon_A C_A}$$

for $\varepsilon_A = 0$ only ...
$$k\tau = C_{A0} - C_A$$

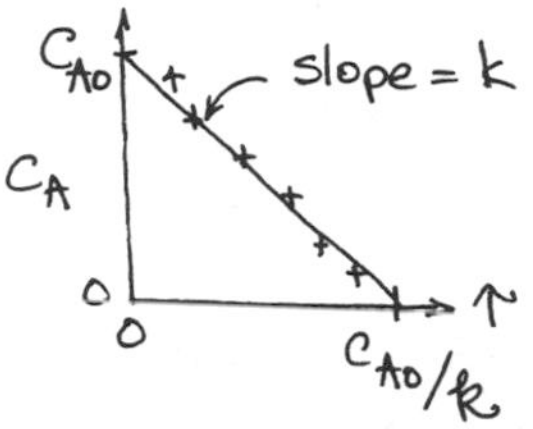

figures are for $\varepsilon_A = 0$ only

1st order, $A \rightarrow \cdots, \; -r_A = kC_A$

for any ε_A ...
$$k\tau = \frac{X_A(1 + \varepsilon_A X_A)}{1 - X_A} = \frac{(C_{A0} - C_A)C_{A0}}{C_A(C_{A0} + \varepsilon_A C_A)}$$

for $\varepsilon_A = 0$ only ...
$$k\tau = \frac{C_{A0} - C_A}{C_A} \quad \ldots \text{or} \ldots \quad \frac{C_A}{C_{A0}} = \frac{1}{1 + k\tau}$$

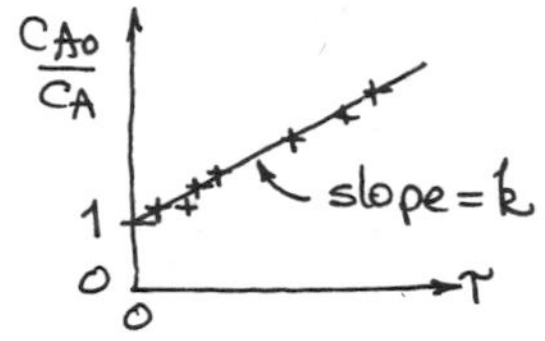

1st order reversible, $A \underset{2}{\overset{1}{\rightleftarrows}} rR, \; -r_A = k_1 C_A - k_2 C_R, \; \frac{C_{R0}}{C_{A0}} = M,$ C_{Ae} & C_{Re} ← equilibrium values

for any ε_A ...
$$k_1\tau = \frac{M + rX_{Ae}}{M + r} \cdot \frac{X_A(1 + \varepsilon_A X_A)}{X_{Ae} - X_A}$$

for $\varepsilon_A = 0$ only ...
$$k_1\tau = \frac{C_{Re}}{C_{A0}(M + r)} \cdot \frac{C_{A0} - C_A}{C_A - C_{Ae}}$$

2nd order $A + bB \rightarrow \cdots, \; -r_A = kC_A C_B, \; \frac{C_{B0}}{C_{A0}} = M$

for premixed feed, any ε_A ...
$$k\tau C_{A0} = \frac{X_A(1 + \varepsilon_A X_A)^2}{(1 - X_A)(M - bX_A)}$$

for premixed feed, $\varepsilon_A = 0$ only ...
$$k\tau = \frac{C_{A0} - C_A}{C_A(C_{B0} - bC_{A0} + bC_A)}$$

for separate feed streams first mix the streams. The above equations then refer to the mixed stream at the reactor T and π

2nd order, $A \to \ldots, \quad -r_A = kC_A^2$

for any ε_A ... $\quad k\tau C_{A0} = \dfrac{X_A(1+\varepsilon_A X_A)^2}{(1-X_A)^2} = \dfrac{(C_{A0}-C_A)C_{A0}^2}{C_A^2(C_{A0}+\varepsilon_A C_A)}$

for $\varepsilon_A = 0$ only ... $\quad k\tau = \dfrac{C_{A0}-C_A}{C_A^2}$ ... or ... $C_A = \dfrac{-1+\sqrt{1+k\tau C_{A0}}}{2k\tau}$

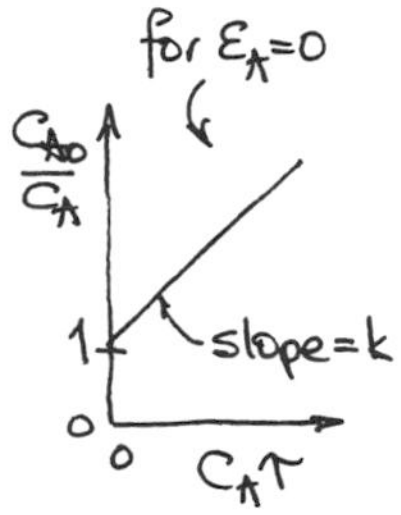

nth order $\quad A \to \ldots, \quad -r_A = kC_A^n$

for any ε_A ... $\quad k\tau C_{A0}^{n-1} = \dfrac{X_A(1+\varepsilon_A X_A)^n}{(1-X_A)^n} = \dfrac{C_{A0}^n(C_{A0}-C_A)}{C_A^n(C_{A0}+\varepsilon_A C_A)}$

for $\varepsilon_A = 0$ only ... $\quad k\tau = \dfrac{C_{A0}-C_A}{C_A^n}$

II. Comments.

(a) First note that each steady state run gives directly a value for the rate of reaction at reactor conditions, C_{Af}. No need to integrate differentiate or use curve fitting procedures.

(b) Even if a whole lot of reactions are occurring in the reactor at the same time mixed flow will let you find the rates for all of them, all at one time, as long as you can measure C_{in} and C_{out} for the component of interest

(c) With mixed flow we can ask a number of questions
- If rate-concentration data from a series of runs is known then

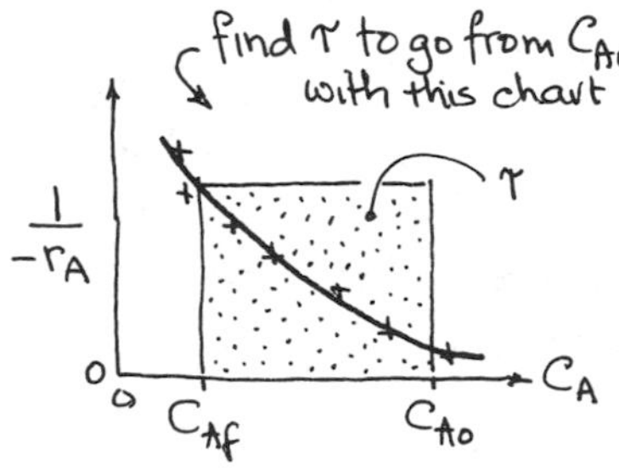

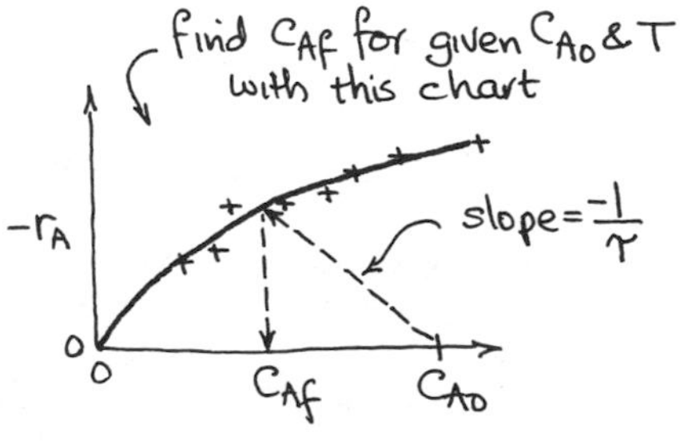

- if a rate equation is known then eq 1 or its special forms, see above, will allow you to determine τ, C_{Af}, or whatever quantity is unknown.

- to test a rate equation make the appropriate plot and see if you get a straight line. As examples

$\dfrac{C_{A0}-C_A}{C_A}$ vs τ

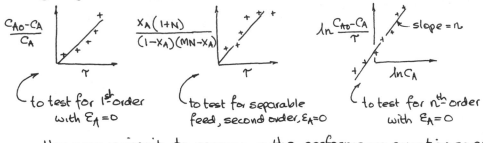

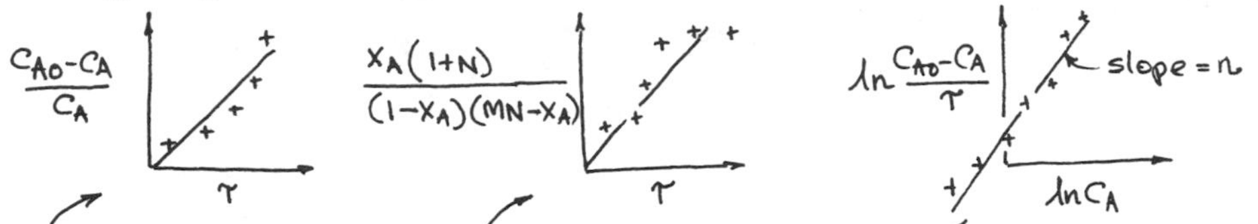

to test for 1st order with $\varepsilon_A = 0$

$\dfrac{X_A(1+N)}{(1-X_A)(MN-X_A)}$ vs τ

to test for separable feed, second order, $\varepsilon_A = 0$

$\ln\dfrac{C_{A0}-C_A}{\tau}$ vs $\ln C_A$ — slope = n

to test for n^{th} order with $\varepsilon_A = 0$

Use your ingenuity to rearrange the performance equation so as to get a straight line plot.

(d) Whenever $\varepsilon_A = 0$ (all liquid systems and some gases) use concentrations, not conversions. This simplifies the algebra.

(e) In the general case where feed enters the reactor partly converted it is best to imagine a fictitious stream, completely unconverted, with properties F_{A0}, C_{A0}. Thus

F_{A0}
C_{A0}
$X_{A0}=0$
← fictitious

F_{A1}
C_{A1}
$X_{A1}\neq 0$
← actual feed

F_{A2}
C_{A2}
X_{A2}
← outlet stream

base the conversion on this fictitious feed stream F_{A0}, C_{A0}

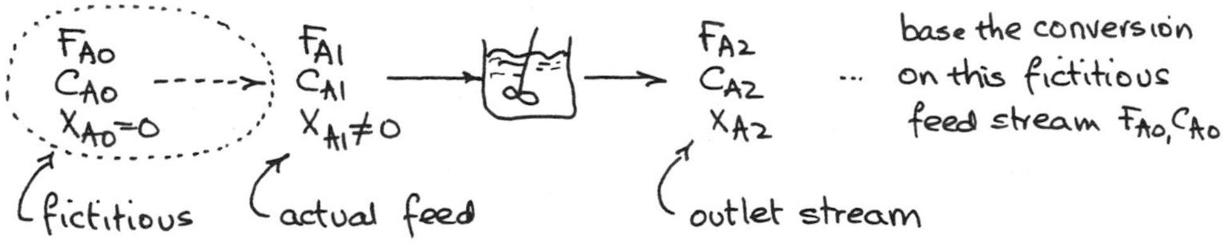

In terms of this fictitious stream and our real incoming stream

or

$$\left.\begin{array}{l} F_{A1}-F_{A2}=(-r_A)_2\, V \\[2mm] F_{A0}\left(X_{A2}-X_{A1}\right)=(-r_A)_2 V \end{array}\right\} \dots (4)$$

← use this form

$\dfrac{1}{-r_A}$ vs $X_{A1}\ \ X_{A2}$ — Area $= \dfrac{V}{F_{A0}}$

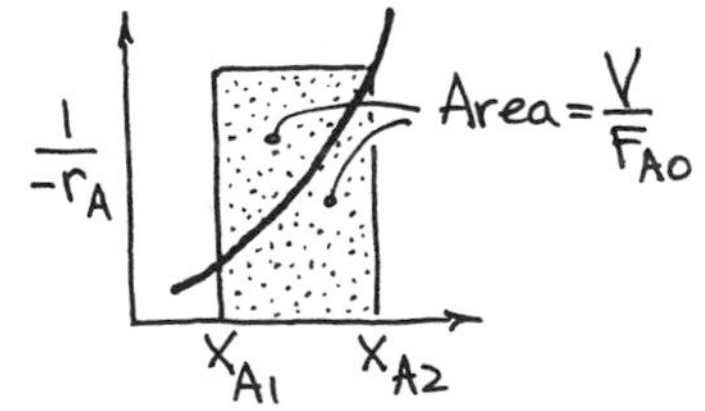

This equation is useful for staged operations. Here the feed to stages 2, 3, ... is partly converted

$F_{A0}, C_{A0} \rightarrow \boxed{\large\circlearrowright} \rightarrow \boxed{\large\circlearrowright} \rightarrow \boxed{\large\circlearrowright} \rightarrow \boxed{\large\circlearrowright} \rightarrow$

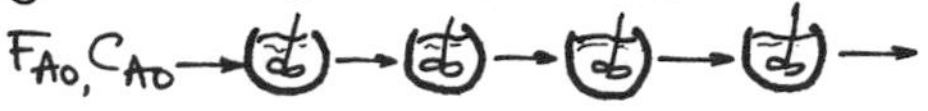

Chapter 4 Problems

A1 A stream of aqueous monomer A (1 mol/lit, 4 lit/min) enters a 2 liter mixed flow reactor, is radiated therein, and polymerizes as follows

$$A \xrightarrow{+A} R \xrightarrow{+A} S \xrightarrow{+A} T \ldots$$

In the exit stream C_A = 0.01 mol/lit, and for a particular reaction product W, C_W = 0.0002 mol/lit. Find the rate of reaction of A, and the rate of formation of W.

A2 At high pressure and temperature (about 8 atm and 200 °C) a gaseous stream of A (0.06 lit/min at 0.2 mol/lit) enters a mixed flow reactor (0.4 liters) and polymerizes isothermally to form products R, S, T, ... with uncertain stoichiometry. The exit stream (0.04 lit/min) has a composition $C_A = C_S$ = 0.05 mol/lit. Find $-r_A$ and r_S. Also find the mean residence time $\bar{t}$, and space time t of fluid in the reactor under these conditions.

B3 The off gas from a boiling water nuclear power reactor contains a whole variety of radioactive trash, one of the most troublesome being Xe -133 (half life = 5.2 days). This off gas flows continuously through a large holdup tank in which its mean residence time is 30 days, and where we can assume that the contents are well mixed. Find the fraction of activity removed in the tank.

B4 A mixed flow reactor (2 m^3) processes an aqueous feed (100 lit/min) containing reactant A (C_{A0} = 100 mmol/lit). The reaction is reversible and represented by

$$A \leftrightarrow R, \quad -r_A = 0.04\, C_A - 0.01\, C_R \; \frac{\text{mol}}{\text{lit·min}}$$

What is the equilibrium and actual conversion in the reactor?

B5 Enzyme E catalyses the fermentation of substrate A (the reactant) to product R. Find the size of mixed flow reactor needed for 95% conversion of reactant in a feed stream (25 lit/min) of reactant (2 mol/lit) and enzyme. The kinetics of the fermentation at this enzyme concentration are given by

$$A \xrightarrow{\text{enzyme}} R, \quad -r_A = \frac{0.1\, C_A}{1 + 0.5\, C_A} \; \frac{\text{mol}}{\text{lit·min}}$$

B6 An aqueous feed of A and B (400 lit/min, 100 mmolA/lit, 200 mmolB/lit) is to be converted to product in a mixed flow reactor. The kinetics of the reaction are represented by

$$A + B \rightarrow R, \quad -r_A = 200\, C_A C_B \; \frac{\text{mol}}{\text{lit·min}}$$

Find the volume needed for 99.9% conversion of A to product.

Chapter 4 Problems

B7 A gaseous feed of pure A (1 mol/lit) enters a mixed flow reactor (2 liters) and reacts as follows

$$2A \rightarrow R, \quad -r_A = 0.05\, C_A^2 \frac{\text{mol}}{\text{lit·sec}}$$

Find what feed rate (lit/min) will give an outlet concentration $C_A = 0.5$ mol/lit.

B8 Gaseous reactant A decomposes as follows

$$A \rightarrow 3R, \quad -r_A = (0.6\ \text{min}^{-1})C_A$$

Find the conversion of A in a 50% A - 50% inert feed ($v_0 = 180$ lit/min, $C_{A0} = 300$ mmol/lit) to a 1 m^3 mixed flow reactor.

B9* A hot gas stream containing reactant A (2 lit/min, 2 atm, 677 K, 1/6 A -5/6 inerts) and a cold gas stream consisting of pure B (0.5 lit/min, 1.95 atm, 330 K) flow into a mixed flow reactor (0.75 lit) kept at 440 K and 1.3 atm where A and B react as follows

$$A + 2B \rightarrow 6R, \quad -r_A = -r_B = kC_AC_B$$

The partial pressure of A in the reactor and in the exit stream is 0.02899 atm. From this information determine

(a) the fractional conversion of A and of B in the reactor

(b) the rate constant (m^3/mol·min) of the reaction.

C10 We are running a first order reversible liquid phase reaction in our mixed flow reactor $A \leftrightarrow R, \ -r_A = k_1C_A - k_2C_R, \ C_{A0} = 1, \ C_{R0} = 0, \ X_{Ae} = 0.667$ and the conversion at present is 33.3%. How must I adjust the feed rate to raise the conversion to 50%?

C11 We plan to replace our present mixed flow reactor with one having double the volume. For the same aqueous feed (10 molA/lit) and the same feed rate find the new conversion. The reaction kinetics are represented by

$$A \rightarrow R, \quad -r_A = kC_A^{1.5}$$

and present conversion is 70%.

In the presence of an enzyme of fixed concentration aqueous reactant A decomposes into product R at the following rates, and C_A alone affects the rate

C_A, mol/lit	1	2	3	4	5	6	8	10
$-r_A$, mol/lit·min	1	2	3	4	4.7	4.9	5	5

We plan to effect this decomposition in a mixed flow reactor at the same fixed enzyme concentration.

D12 . . . Find the volumetric feed rate which can be 80% converted in a 250 lit mixed flow reactor for a feed where C_{A0} = 10 mol/lit.

D13 . . . Find the exit C_A from a 3 m^3 mixed flow reactor whose feed is v = 1000 lit/min of C_{A0} = 8 mol/lit fluid.

A mixed flow reactor is being used to determine the kinetics of a reaction whose stoichiometry is A → R. For this purpose various flow rates of an aqueous solution of 100 mmolA/lit are fed to a 1 liter reactor, and for each run the outlet concentration of A is measured. Find a rate equation to represent the following data. Also assume in these problems that reactant alone affects the rate.

E14 . . .

v, lit/min	1	6	24
C_A, mmol/lit	4	20	50

E15 . . .

v, lit/min	1.5	2.5	12	32
C_A, mmol/lit	25	30	50	65

E16 A combined aqueous feed of A and B is fed to a 1 liter mixed flow reactor and the following data are obtained

Input (mol/lit)	Flow rate (lit/min)	Output (mol/lit)
$C_{A0} = C_{B0} = 100$	v = 1	$C_A = 50$
$C_{A0} = C_{B0} = 200$	v = 9	$C_A = 150$
$C_{A0} = 200,\ C_{B0} = 100$	v = 3	$C_A = 150$

If the stoichiometry of the reaction is A + B → R + S find a rate equation to represent these kinetics.

Pure gaseous A at about 3 atm and 30 °C (120 mmol/lit) is fed into a 1 liter mixed flow reactor at various flow rates. There it decomposes and the exit concentration of A is measured for each flow rate. From the following data find a rate equation to represent the kinetics of the decomposition of A. Assume that reactant A alone affects the rate.

E17 . . . A → 3R

v_0, lit/min	0.06	0.48	1.5	8.1
C_A, mmol/lit	30	60	80	105

Chapter 4 Problems

E18 . . .

v_0, lit/min	0.175	0.45	0.80	2.4
C_A, mmol/lit	30	60	80	105

$2A \rightarrow R$

E19 A high molecular weight hydrocarbon stream A is fed continuously to a heated high temperature mixed reactor where it thermally cracks (homogeneous gas reaction) into lower molecular weight materials, collectively called R, by a stoichiometry approximated by $A \rightarrow 5R$. By changing the feed rate different extents of cracking are obtained as follows

F_{A0}, mmol/hr	300	1000	3000	5000
C_{Aout}, mmol/liter	16	30	50	60

The internal void volume of the reactor is V = 0.1 liter, and at the temperature of the reactor the feed concentration is C_{A0} = 100 mmol/liter. Find a rate equation to fit the cracking reaction.

E20* From the following data find a satisfactory rate equation for the gas phase decomposition $A \rightarrow R + S$ taking place isothermally in a mixed flow reactor using a pure A feed.

Run Number	1	2	3	4	5
τ based on inlet feed conditions, s	0.423	5.10	13.5	44.0	192
X_A (for C_{A0} = 0.002 mol/lit)	0.22	0.63	0.75	0.88	0.96

F21 For the aqueous reaction of problem 14 find the volume of mixed flow reactor needed for 96% conversion of 40 lit/min of C_{A0} = 100 mmol/lit feed. The rate is dependent on C_A alone.

F22 For the aqueous reaction of problem 15 find the molar flow rate of a 150 mmolA/lit feed which can be 80% converted in an 800 liter mixed flow reactor . The rate is dependent on C_A alone.

F23 For the gas reaction of problem 17 what volumetric inflow rate v_0 and outflow rate v_f of a C_{A0} = 320 mmol/lit pure A feed can be 50% converted in a 560 liter mixed flow reactor .

F24 For the gas reaction of problem 18 find the space time in a mixed flow reactor needed for 96% conversion of 1 mol/min of pure A feed at C_{A0} = 520 mmol/lit.

Chapter 4 Problems

G25 A constant density liquid is fed at a number of different temperatures to a mixed flow reactor and there decomposes. The flow rate is adjusted to keep the composition of the exit stream constant. From the following results find the activation energy of the reaction

T, °C	19	27	31	37
v, arbitrary	1	2	3	5

$A \rightarrow R$, first order reaction

G26 The liquid reaction of $A \rightarrow R$ is run at a number of temperature levels in a 1 liter mixed flow reactor . The feed is introduced at v = 1 lit/min at a concentration 100 mmolA/lit and the outlet concentration is measured. Find the complete rate equation for the reaction from the following data.

T, °C	7	76	104	136
C_A, mmol/lit	29	8	5	3

second order reaction

Chapter 5 MORE ON IDEAL REACTORS, AND EXTENSIONS.

Here we introduce the recycle reactor, compare the performance of different reactor types, and see how to treat a series of ideal reactors.

I Recycle Reactors (or Plug Flow with Recycle of Product)

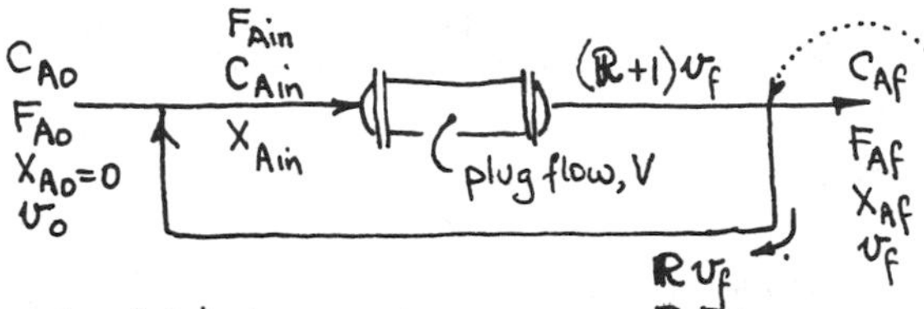

the flow split here defines the **recycle ratio, R**

$$R = \left(\frac{\text{volume returned}}{\text{volume leaving}}\right)$$

A material balance gives

$$\frac{V}{F_{A0}} = (R+1)\int_{X_{Ain}}^{X_{Af}} \frac{dX_A}{-r_A} \qquad \ldots \text{ and for } \varepsilon_A = 0 \text{ only} \qquad \tau = \frac{C_{A0}V}{F_{A0}} = (R+1)\int_{C_{Af}}^{C_{Ain}} \frac{dC_A}{-r_A}$$

$$X_{Ain} = \frac{RX_{Af}}{R+1} \quad \text{this becomes } \frac{X_{A0}+RX_{Af}}{R+1} \text{ when } X_{A0} \neq 0 \qquad C_{Ain} = \frac{C_{A0}+RC_{Af}}{R+1}$$

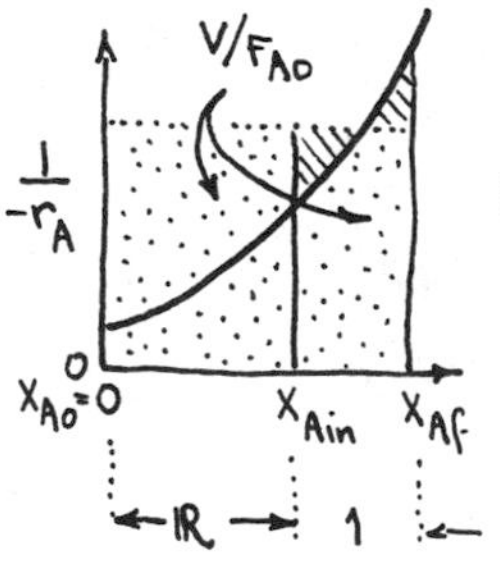

In general:

$$R = \frac{X_{Ain} - X_{A0}}{X_{Af} - X_{Ain}}$$

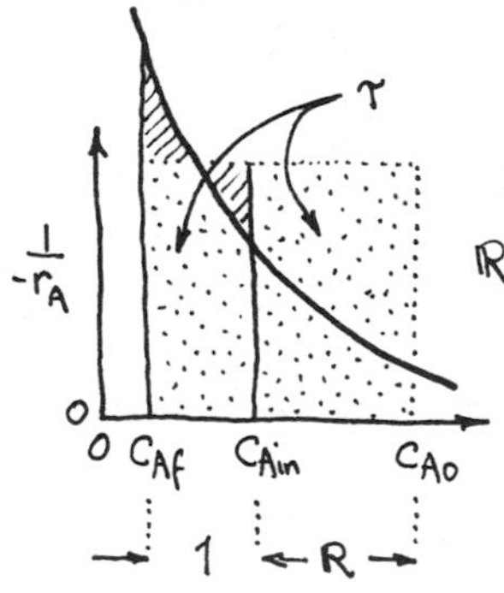

For $\varepsilon_A = 0$

$$R = \frac{C_{A0} - C_{Ain}}{C_{Ain} - C_{Af}}$$

As $R \to 0$ you get plug flow; as $R \to \infty$ you get mixed flow, as shown:

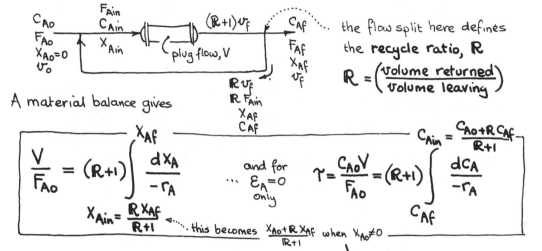

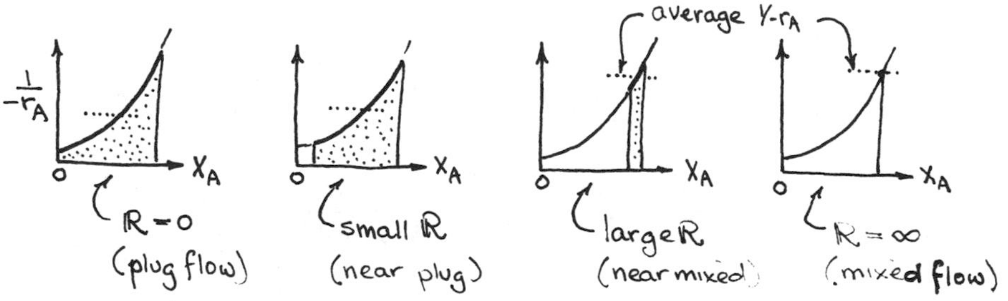

Recycle reactors are a way of getting a plug flow reactor to behave all the way to mixed flow. Just increase $\mathbb{R}$. The recycle reactor is particularly important in catalytic reactor design where we want to use a packed bed (plug flow) but would like it to behave somewhere close to mixed flow.

1. Integrated performance equations for recycle reactors.

(... for $X_{A0}=0$)

1st order $\quad A \rightarrow \cdots, \quad -r_A = k C_A$

for $\varepsilon_A = 0$

$$k\tau = (\mathbb{R}+1)\ln\left[\frac{C_{A0}+\mathbb{R}C_{Af}}{(\mathbb{R}+1)C_{Af}}\right] = (\mathbb{R}+1)\ln\left[\frac{1+\mathbb{R}(1-X_{Af})}{(\mathbb{R}+1)(1-X_{Af})}\right]$$

for $\varepsilon_A \neq 0$

$$k\tau = (\mathbb{R}+1)(1+\varepsilon_A)\ln\left[\frac{1+\mathbb{R}(1-X_{Af})}{(\mathbb{R}+1)(1-X_{Af})}\right] - \varepsilon_A X_{Af}$$

1st order reversible $\quad A \rightleftarrows rR, \quad \varepsilon_A \neq 0, \quad -r_A = k_1 C_A - k_2 C_R, \quad M = \frac{C_{R0}}{C_{A0}}$

$$k_1\tau = \frac{M + rX_{Ae}}{M+r}\left[(\mathbb{R}+1)(1+\varepsilon_A X_{Ae})\ln\frac{X_{Ae}+\mathbb{R}(X_{Ae}-X_{Af})}{(\mathbb{R}+1)(X_{Ae}-X_{Af})} - \varepsilon_A X_{Af}\right]$$

2nd order $\quad 2A \rightarrow \cdots, \quad -r_A = kC_A^2$

for $\varepsilon_A = 0$

$$C_{A0}k\tau = (\mathbb{R}+1)\cdot\frac{C_{A0}(C_{A0}-C_{Af})}{C_{Af}(C_{A0}+\mathbb{R}C_{Af})}$$

for $\varepsilon_A \neq 0$

$$C_{A0}k\tau = 2\varepsilon_A(1+\varepsilon_A)(\mathbb{R}+1)\ln\left[\frac{(\mathbb{R}+1)(1-X_{Af})}{\mathbb{R}+1-\mathbb{R}X_{Af}}\right] + \varepsilon_A^2 X_{Af}$$
$$+\frac{(1+\varepsilon_A)^2(\mathbb{R}+1)X_{Af}}{(1-X_{Af})(\mathbb{R}+1-\mathbb{R}X_{Af})}$$

2. What R to use so as to minimize reactor size, or τ.

This only depends on the shape of the rate-concentration curve.

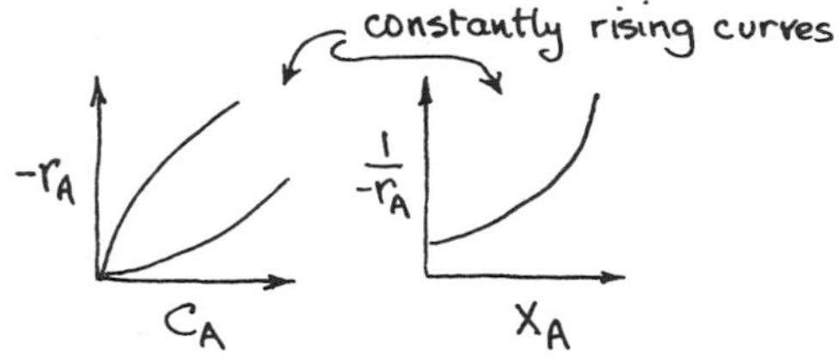

for this form of rate curve, and this includes all n^{th} order reactions we find that

$$R_{opt} = 0$$

Thus use straight plug flow with no recycle.

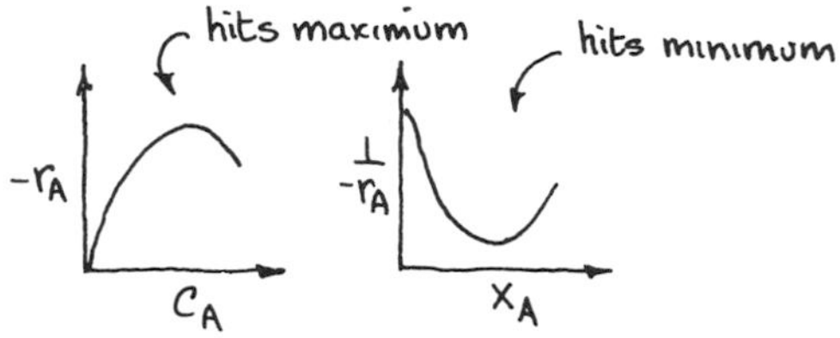

for this form of rate curve some particular R value between 0 and ∞ is best. Reactions of this type include all microbial fermentations, adiabatic packed bed reactors for exothermic reactions and all other autocatalytic-type reactions.

The optimum R value to use for these reactions is best found graphically

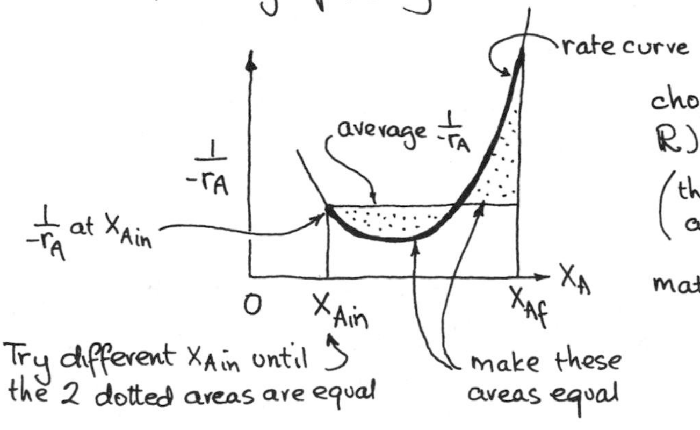

choose X_{Ain} (and the corresponding R) so that

$$\begin{pmatrix}\text{the rate}^{-1} \\ \text{at } X_{Ain}\end{pmatrix} = \begin{pmatrix}\text{average rate}^{-1} \\ \text{in the reactor}\end{pmatrix}$$

mathematically

$$\left.\frac{1}{-r_A}\right|_{X_{Ain}} = \frac{\int_{X_{Ain}}^{X_{Af}} \frac{dX_A}{-r_A}}{X_{Af} - X_{Ain}}$$

3. A graphical comparison with plug flow is given in Levenspiel pgs 148 and 149

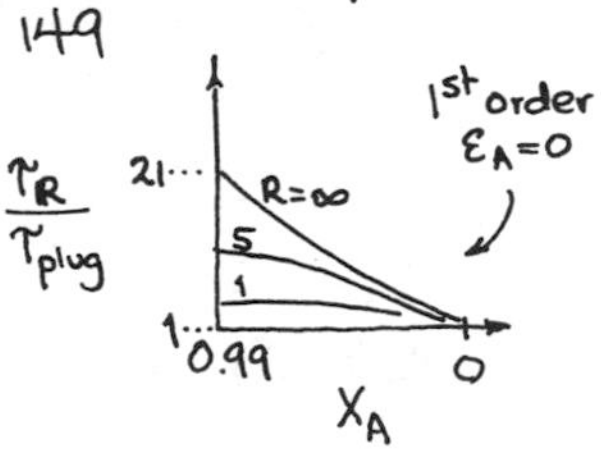

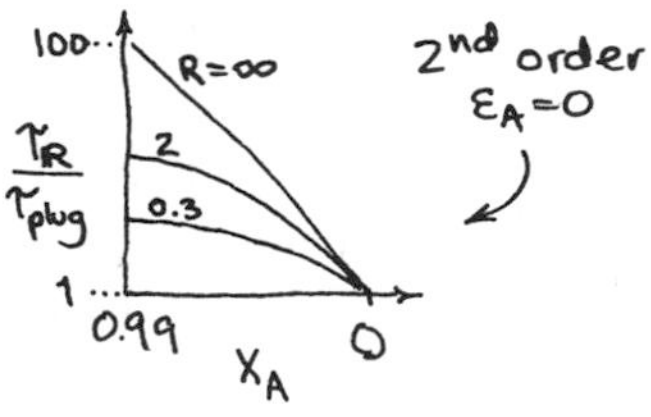

II Comparison of Single Reactors: Plug, Mixed and Recycle.

- For all reactions where the rate increases with concentration (and this includes all n^{th} order reactions)

$$Area = \frac{V_m}{F_{AO}} = \frac{\tau_m}{C_{AO}} : \text{for mixed flow}$$

$$Area = \frac{V_p}{F_{AO}} = \frac{\tau_p}{C_{AO}} : \text{for plug flow}$$

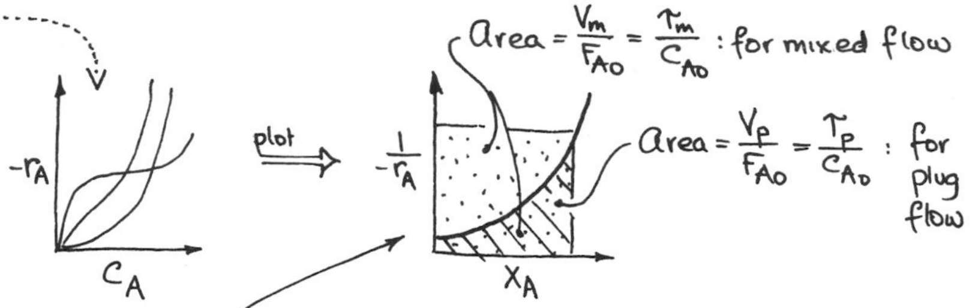

this graph shows that for this rate form plug flow **always requires a smaller volume than mixed flow** (and also recycle)

- For the special case of nth order reactions the size comparison can be given in charts, see Levenspiel pgs. 127, 332

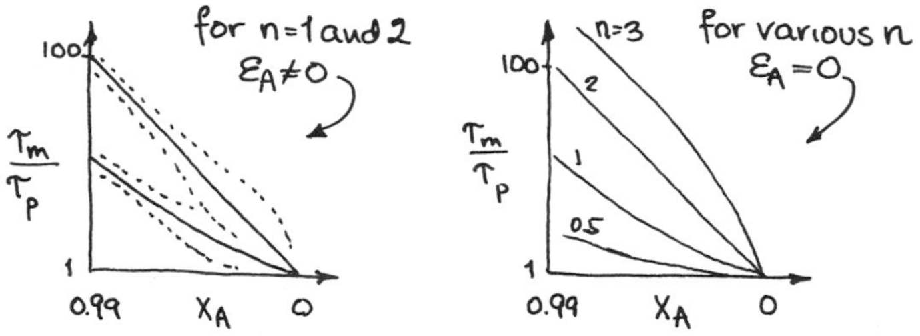

these graphs verify the general conclusion that plug flow is best

- For autocatalytic rate forms the best contacting pattern depends on the conversion level

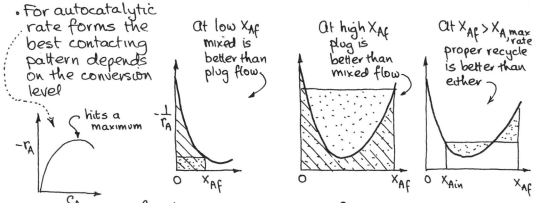

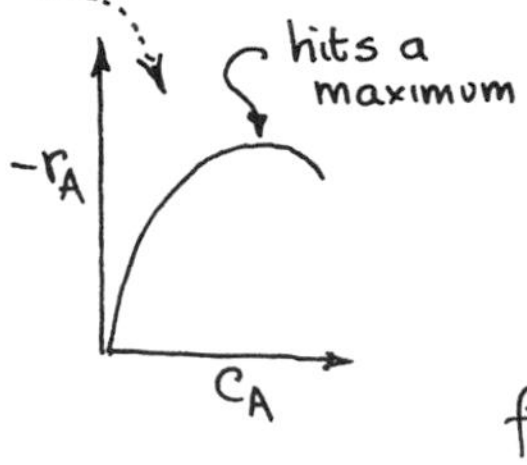

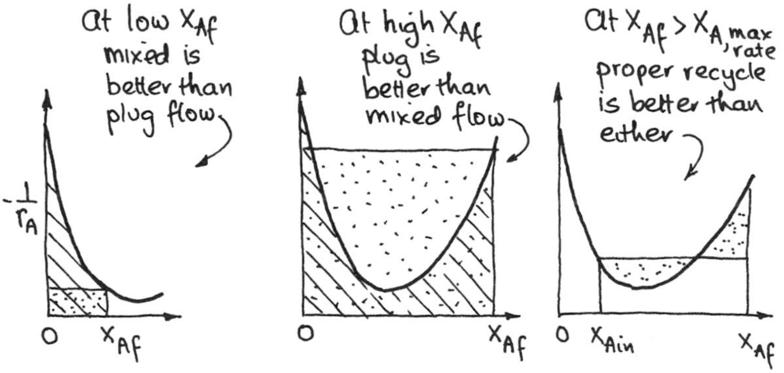

for this rate form **mixed flow is best at low X_{Af}** while **recycle flow is best for higher X_{Af}**

III. Mixed Flow Reactors in Series.

Solving the mixed flow performance equation for stage after stage gives

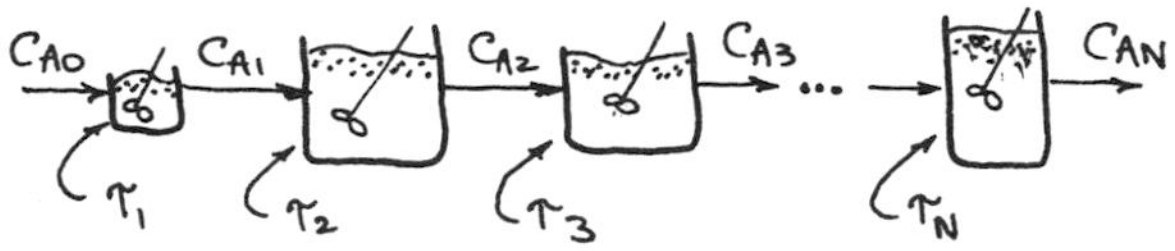

for **1st order**:

$$\frac{C_{AN}}{C_{A0}} = \frac{1}{(1+k\tau_1)(1+k\tau_2)\cdots(1+k\tau_N)}$$

for **2nd order**: equal size tanks only

$$\frac{C_{AN}}{C_{A0}} = \frac{1}{4k\tau_i C_{A0}}\left(-2+2\sqrt{-1+\cdots+2\sqrt{-1+2\sqrt{1+4C_{A0}k\tau_i}}}\right)$$

(τ_i of each tank; N nested roots)

a graphical size comparison of N-tanks vs plug flow is shown in Levenspiel, 136 and 137.

for any **kinetics** use a graphical procedure

To find τ_1, τ_2, τ_3 given X_{A1}, X_{A2}, X_{A3} or C_{A1}, C_{A2}, C_{A3} use these charts ⟹

for any ε_A

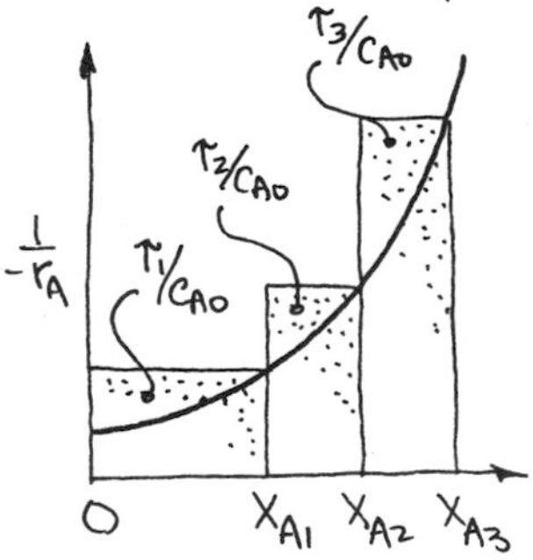

use this chart only when $\varepsilon_A = 0$

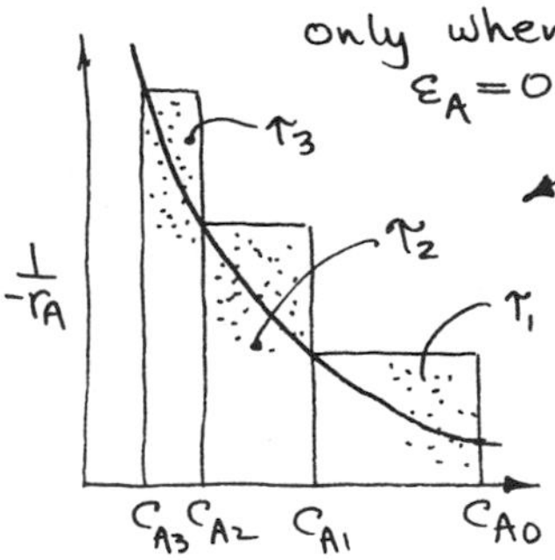

To find C_{A1}, C_{A2}, C_{A3} given τ_1, τ_2, τ_3 use this chart ⟹ (only when $\varepsilon_A = 0$)

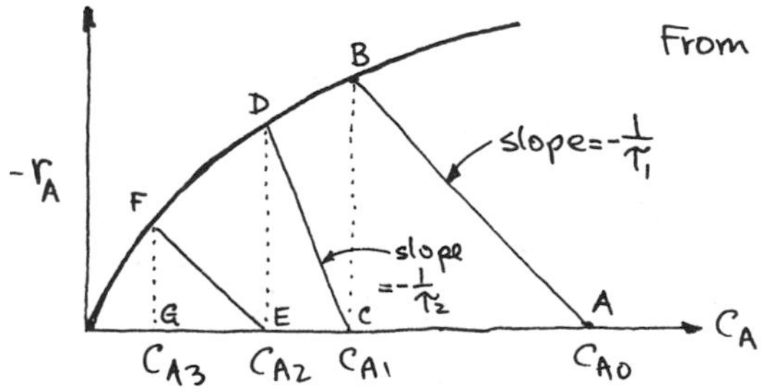

From point A go to B then C, D, E, ···

The **best size ratio** of mixed reactors in series is found graphically for any kinetics by using the method of **maximization of rectangles**

For **2 reactors in series** calculus shows that one should choose X_{A1} such that

$$\begin{pmatrix}\text{diagonal}\\ AB\end{pmatrix} = \begin{pmatrix}\text{slope at}\\ C\end{pmatrix}$$

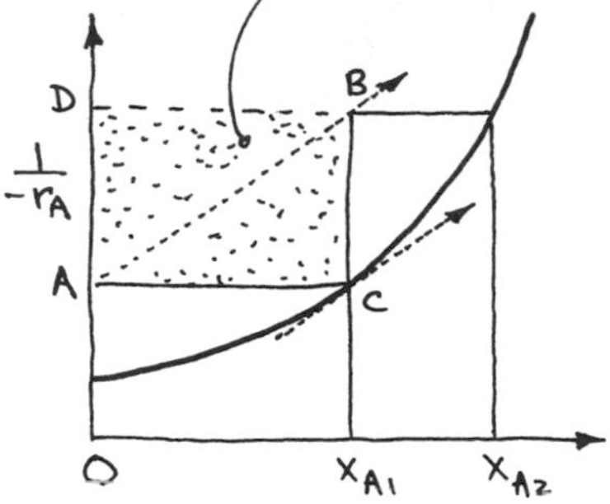

if the 2 slopes are equal then the area of rectangle ACBD is maximized, thus the reactor sizes are minimized

For **3 or more reactors in series** extend the method by guessing X_{A1}. This allows you to construct X_2, X_3 ··· X_{Af}.

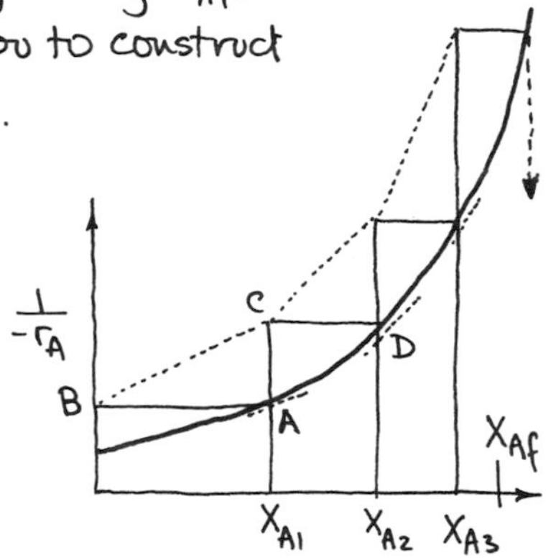

Procedure

- guess X_{A1}
- find the slope at A
- find C (note, the slope BC = the slope at A)
- locate D
- find slope at D

etc.

Keep on going. If you do not find the right number of stages to reach X_{Af} guess a new X_{A1} and repeat

For **1st order reactions** the optimum is to use equal sized reactors; for most other kinetics the improvement (volume decrease) over equal sized systems is rarely over 10%.

IV For Any Arbitrary Reactor Combination.

Treat graphically, for example

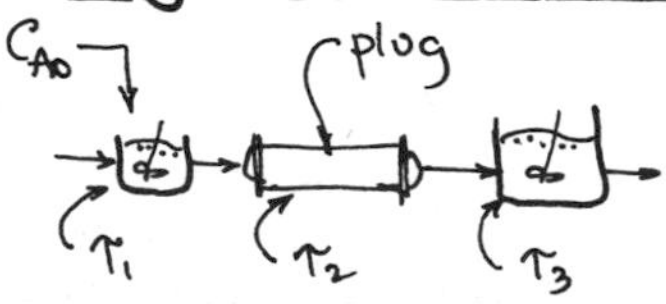

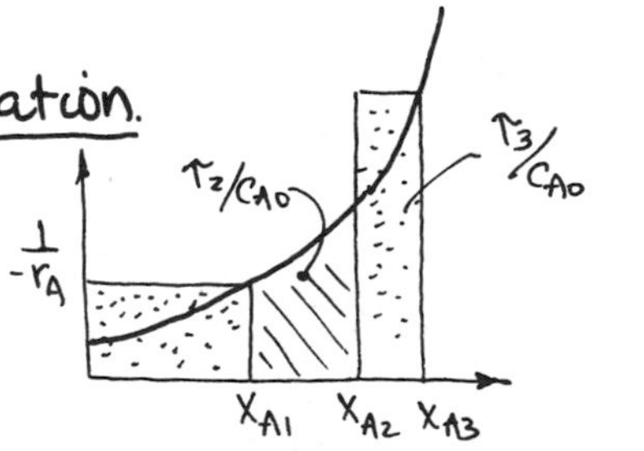

for the special case of $\varepsilon_A = 0$ we can, if we wish, use concentrations. Thus

for example:

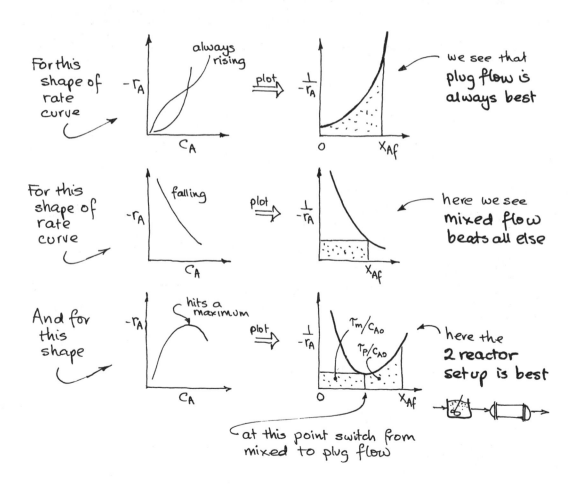

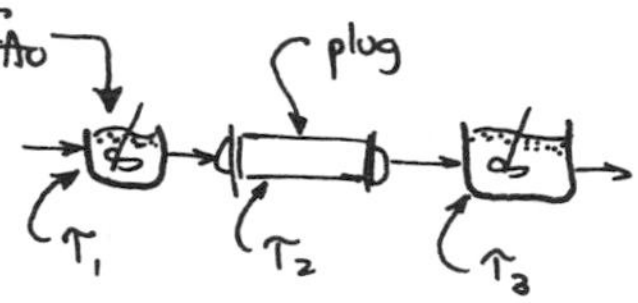

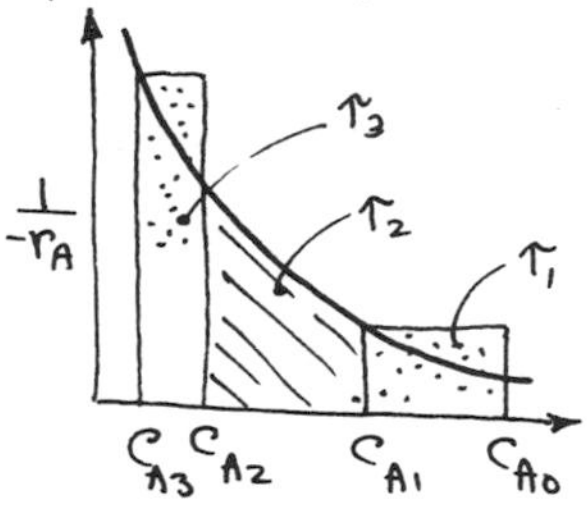

V What Setup (single or multiple reactors - your choice) Gives Minimum Total Volume, Hence is Best.

For this shape of rate curve

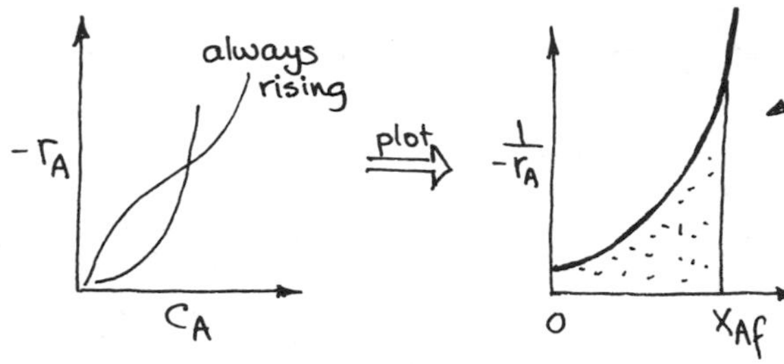

we see that plug flow is always best

For this shape of rate curve

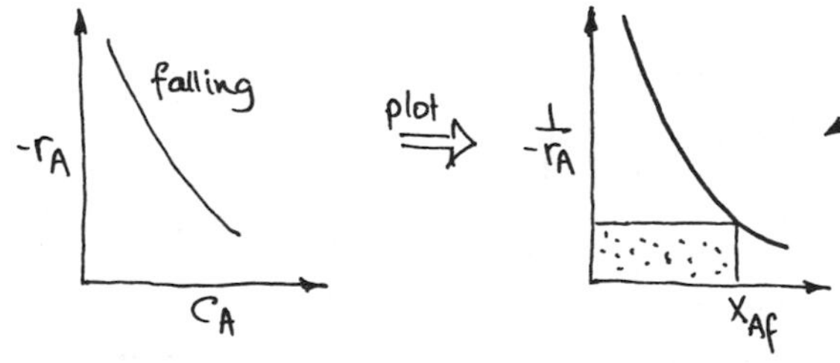

here we see mixed flow beats all else

And for this shape

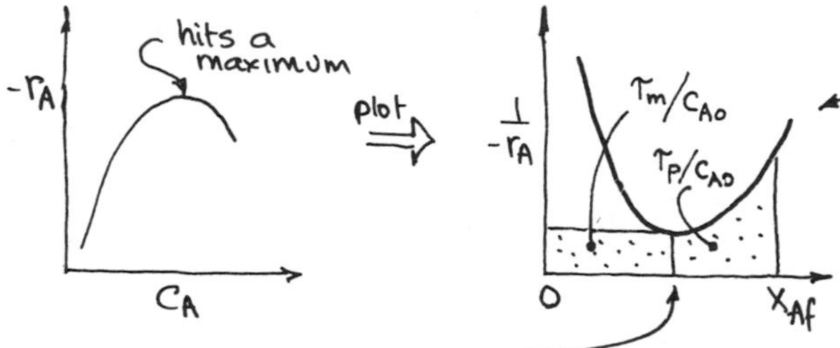

here the 2 reactor setup is best

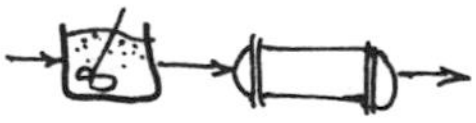

at this point switch from mixed to plug flow

VI Partial Emptying Batch Reactor - PEBR.

In wastewater treatment reaction is autocatalytic and very slow. Hence in steady state operations continual mixing is necessary, and in the large scale this can be costly.

An alternative way of operating is shown in the sketch below. Here you add feed all at one time, stir just long enough to get everything well mixed, let sit for a time t_{PEBR} to allow reaction to take place, remove a fraction "g" of the vessel's contents, then refill and repeat the cycle of operations. This way you only need to stir once every few days, whenever fresh feed is added.

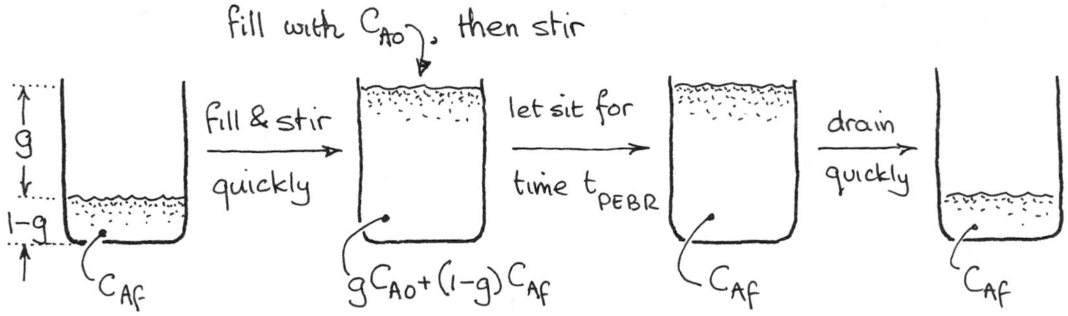

The general performance expression for this kind of operation is then ...

$$t_{PEBR} = -\int_{gC_{A0}+(1-g)C_{Af}}^{C_{Af}} \frac{dC_A}{-r_A} \qquad \cdots \quad (1)$$

For **first order** kinetics, $-r_A = kC_A$, $\varepsilon_A = 0$, this becomes

$$\frac{C_{Af}}{C_{A0}} = \frac{g}{g-1+e^{kt}} \qquad \cdots \text{ or } \cdots \qquad kt = \ln\left(g\frac{C_{A0}}{C_{Af}} + 1 - g\right)$$

For **second order** kinetics, $-r_A = kC_A^2$, $\varepsilon_A = 0$, we have

$$kt = \frac{g(C_{A0} - C_{Af})}{C_{Af}[gC_{A0} + (1-g)C_{Af}]}$$

For other kinetics more appropriate to biochemical reactions (see chapter 83) insert the proper expression into eq 1 and integrate

(a) When $g \to 1$ the performance of the PEBR approaches batch operations

(b) When $g \to 0$ as $t_{PEBR} \to 0$ the PEBR approaches ordinary mixed flow with $\tau_{mixed} = t_{PEBR}/g$.

(c) Partial emptying operations are attractive for very slow autocatalytic type operations which have a maximum rate at some intermediate concentration

(d) It turns out that this operation is directly analogous to the recycle reactor in which the fraction remaining in the PEBR represents the recycle stream. The correspondence is given by

$$R = \frac{1-g}{g} \quad \ldots \text{or} \ldots \quad g = \frac{1}{1+R} \qquad \ldots \text{where } R = \text{recycle ratio}$$

and

$$t_{PEBR} = g \cdot \tau_{recycle}$$

Thus the graphical constructions for the recycle reactor, presented at the beginning of this chapter — to find the optimum recycle ratio, etc. — carry over directly to give the optimum amount of fluid to leave in the PEBR.

(e) For more on partial emptying batch reactors plus their use in waste water treatment, see Wood, J. Wat. Poll. Control Fed. 58 937 (1986).

VII Side Entry Flow Reactors.

There are many ways of feeding flow reactors besides front entry alone, as in plug and in mixed flow. For example:

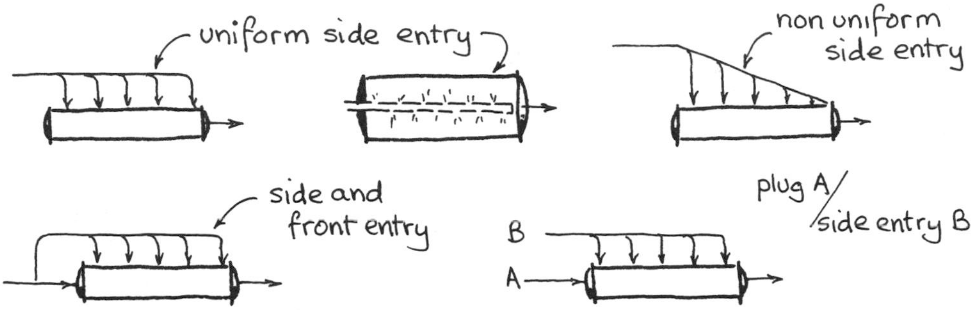

Similarly, with mixed flow reactors in series we may have

In general the performance equations are cumbersome for these operations. However, an important special case is easily solved. Let us consider this case first.

A. One feed stream, uniform side entry, $\varepsilon_A = 0$.

Let us see how to introduce the feed so that $C_A = C_{Af}$ everywhere in the reactor. For this consider a differential slice of reactor, as shown below

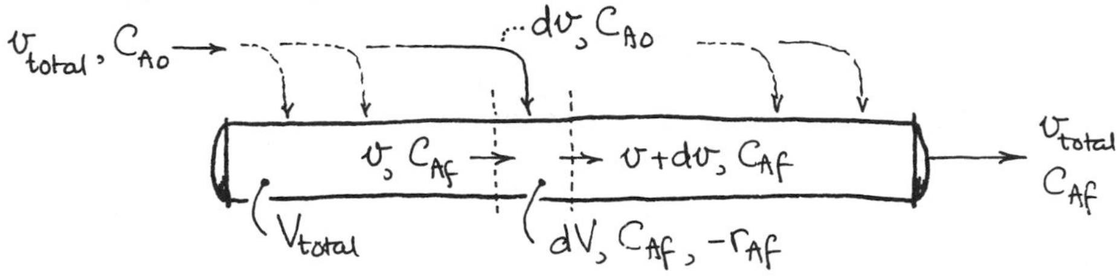

An accounting for reactant A gives

$$\underbrace{C_{A0}\,d\upsilon + C_{Af}\,\upsilon}_{\text{input}} = \underbrace{C_{Af}(\upsilon + d\upsilon)}_{\text{output}} + \underbrace{(-r_{Af})\,dV}_{\text{disappearance}}$$

Combining and rearranging shows that

$$\frac{dV}{d\upsilon} = \underbrace{\frac{C_{A0}-C_{Af}}{-r_{Af}}}_{\text{a constant}} \qquad \therefore \quad \frac{dV}{d\upsilon} = \text{constant}$$

Integrating across the whole reactor gives

$$\tau = \frac{V_{total}}{\upsilon_{total}} = \frac{C_{A0}-C_{Af}}{-r_{Af}} \quad \text{... or mixed flow}$$

Thus ... **uniform side entry gives mixed flow.**

(a) Uniform side entry into a series of mixed flow reactors is also equivalent to mixed flow. For example

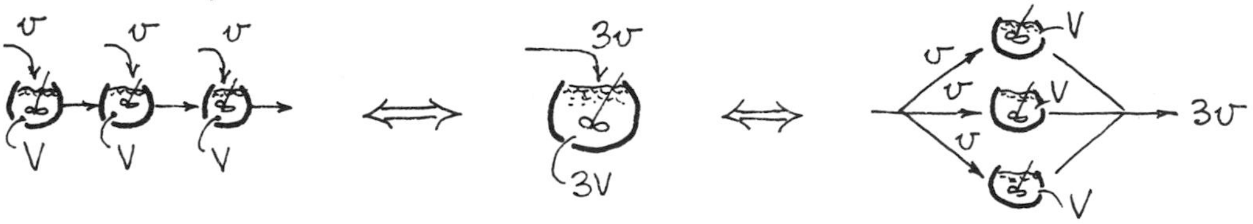

(b) With side entry one can approximate mixed flow followed by plug flow, a scheme which can be optimum for autocatalytic type reactions

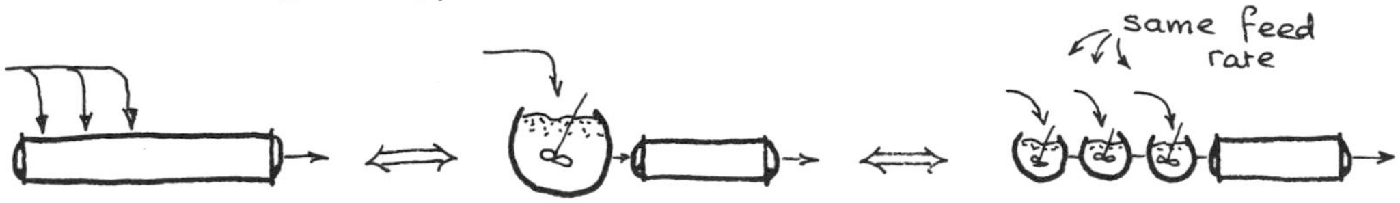

(c) Do you want mixed flow behavior without continual stirring or recycle pumps? Consider side entry.

B. Plug flow A / side entry B, $\varepsilon_A = 0$.

This contacting scheme is useful when one reactant is to be kept at low concentration, the other at high concentration. To develop the performance expressions for this reactor make an accounting, in turn, for A, for B, and for the changing flow rate of fluid through the reactor

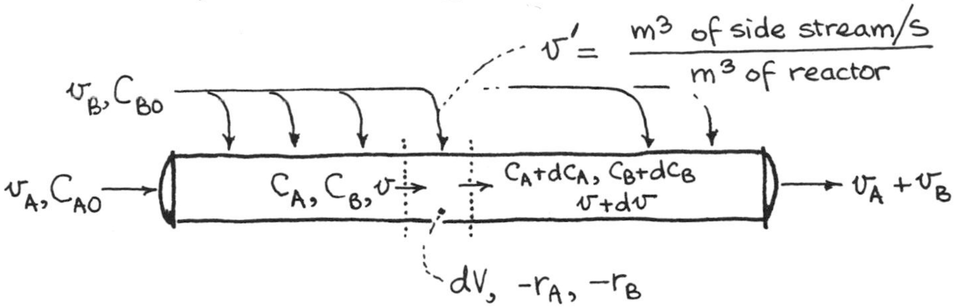

A material balance for reactant A in element dV gives

$$\underbrace{C_A v}_{\text{input}} = \underbrace{(C_A + dC_A)(v + dv)}_{\text{output}} + \underbrace{(-r_A)\,dV}_{\text{disappearance}}$$

or

$$-d(C_A v) = (-r_A)\,dV \qquad \ldots (1)$$

Similarly a material balance for reactant B gives

$$C_B v + C_{B0}(v' dV) = (C_B + dC_B)(v + dv)$$

or

$$C_{B0} v' dV - d(C_B v) = (-r_B)\,dV \qquad \ldots (2)$$

For the flow along the reactor

$$v + v' dV = v + dv \quad \ldots \text{or} \ldots \quad \frac{dv}{dV} - v' = 0 \qquad \ldots (3)$$

Equations 1, 2, and 3 represent the general performance expressions for reactors with both front and side entry of feed. In general their solution is not easy. However, look for special cases

- Is C_B constant along the reactor?
- Is the side feed introduced uniformly ($v' = \text{constant}$)?
- Is $v_A = v_B$?
- Is $v_A \gg v_B$ or is $v_B \gg v_A$ because the feed concentrations are very different, or because one component is in great excess?

These may lead to simplifications in the equations.

VIII Batch Recirculation Systems.

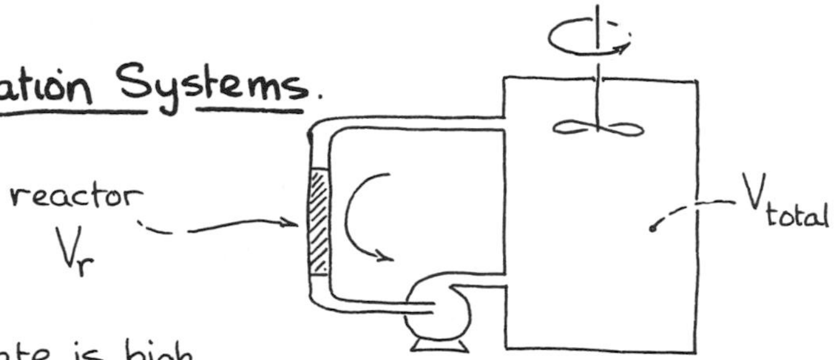

If the recirculation rate is high enough so that conversion per pass is low then the system acts as an ordinary batch reactor where

$$\therefore \quad t = \frac{V_{total}}{V_r} \int_{C_{Af}}^{C_{A0}} \frac{dC_A}{-r_A}$$

If conversion per pass is large then analysis becomes more complicated.

The batch photochemical reactor is an example of such a set up. This type of contactor is also sometimes useful as an experimental reactor for solid catalysed gas phase reactions.

IX Simple Economic Problems.

1. **Flow reactors.** Large reactors cost more, but they can treat more feed or give higher conversion, hence produce a more valuable product. On an hourly basis we can write:

$$\underbrace{\begin{pmatrix}\text{Profit rate}\\ \$/\text{hr}\end{pmatrix}}_{} = \overbrace{\begin{pmatrix}\text{value of}\\ \text{product}\\ \text{stream,}\\ \$/\text{hr}\end{pmatrix}}^{\text{Income, \$/hr}} \overbrace{- \begin{pmatrix}\text{cost of}\\ \text{feed}\\ \text{stream,}\\ \$/\text{hr}\end{pmatrix} - \begin{pmatrix}\text{cost}\\ \text{of}\\ \text{equipment,}\\ \$/\text{hr}\end{pmatrix} - \begin{pmatrix}\text{other costs,}\\ \text{overhead,}\\ \text{labor, etc.}\\ \$/\text{hr}\end{pmatrix}}^{\text{Total cost, \$/hr}} \quad \cdots (1)$$

- value of product stream: depends on composition F_{A0}, C_{A0}, X_A
- cost of feed stream: depends on composition F_{A0}, C_{A0}
- cost of equipment: depends on reactor type and size, V
- other costs: often constant or a weak function of V

With costs known we can write this as a mathematical expression.

Now for a flow reactor the performance equation and material balance relate

$$F_{A0},\ C_{A0},\ X_A,\ F_R,\ -r_A \text{ and } V \quad \cdots (2)$$

As an example for the first order reaction $A \rightarrow rR$ these relationships are:

$$\left.\begin{array}{ll} \text{material balance:} & F_R = r F_{A0} X_A \\ \text{performance equation:} & \dfrac{VC_{A0}}{F_{A0}} = (1+\varepsilon_A)\ln\dfrac{1}{1-X_A} - \varepsilon_A X_A \end{array}\right\} \quad \cdots (3)$$

At this point we want to optimize some **economic criterion**. This can be of various forms depending on the problem at hand. As examples:

- For given feed rate determine V, X_A and F_R so as to maximize the **profit**, \$/hr. For this put

$$\frac{d(\text{profit rate})}{dX_A} = 0 \quad \text{or } dV \text{ or } dF_R$$

- For given reactor size determine F_{A0}, X_A and F_R so as to maximize the **profit**, \$/hr. For this put

$$\frac{d(\text{profit rate})}{dX_A} = 0 \quad \text{or } dF_{A0} \text{ or } dF_R$$

- For given production rate of product F_R determine V, F_{A0} and X_A so as to minimize the **cost**, \$/hr. For this put

$$\frac{d(\text{cost})}{dX_A} = 0 \quad \text{or } dV \text{ or } dF_{A0}$$

With complications such as recycle of unused reactant, multiple feed, separators, etc. the cost and profit expressions must be modified accordingly. The problems at the end of this chapter treat some of these extensions.

In principle we should always optimize the chemical plant as a whole. Fortunately, however, we can often treat the reactor and its recycle unit alone, and analyse them separately.

2. **Batch systems for long term operations.** Here you run the reaction, then you empty, clean and refill, and so on. Thus in the long term you make a batch V of product X_A in time

$$t_{total} = t_{run} + t_{refill} \qquad \cdots (4)$$

and in the long term the profit on an hourly basis is given by the expression

$$\begin{pmatrix}\text{Profit rate,}\\ \$/\text{hr}\end{pmatrix} = \overbrace{\begin{pmatrix}\text{value of}\\ \text{product,}\\ \$/\text{batch}\end{pmatrix}\left(\frac{1\ \text{batch}}{t_{total}}\right)}^{\text{Income, \$/hr}} - \overbrace{\begin{pmatrix}\text{cost of}\\ \text{reactant,}\\ \$/\text{batch}\end{pmatrix}\left(\frac{1\ \text{batch}}{t_{total}}\right) - \begin{pmatrix}\text{cost of}\\ \text{equipment,}\\ \$/\text{hr}\end{pmatrix}}^{\text{Total cost, \$/hr}} - \begin{pmatrix}\text{other costs}\\ \text{overhead, labor}\\ \text{etc., \$/hr}\end{pmatrix} \quad \cdots(5)$$

- value of product: depends on V, C_{A0}, X_A
- cost of reactant: depends on V, C_{A0}
- other costs: often constant or a weak function of V
- cost of equipment: depends on V

The performance equation and material balance for batch reactors relate

$$C_{A0},\ X_A,\ -r_A,\ C_R \text{ and } V \quad \cdots(6)$$

As an example, for the first order reaction $A \rightarrow \text{product}$, $\varepsilon_A = 0$, these relationships are

material balance: $\bar{F}_R = \bar{F}_{A0} X_A = \dfrac{C_{A0} X_A V}{t_{total}}$, $\quad \dfrac{\text{moles R produced in the long run}}{\text{hr}}$

($\bar{F}_R$: long term production rate; $\bar{F}_{A0}$: long term feed rate)

performance equation: $t_{total} = -\dfrac{1}{k} \ln(1 - X_A) + t_{refill}$ $\quad \cdots(7)$

From the above equations we can solve a variety of economic problems. As examples:

- To find the **maximum profit rate** in a given reactor V take

$$\frac{d(\text{profit rate})}{dX_A} = 0 \quad \cdots \text{or} \quad \frac{d(\text{profit rate})}{dt} = 0$$

Here we take account of the cost of the unused, hence the wasted reactant.

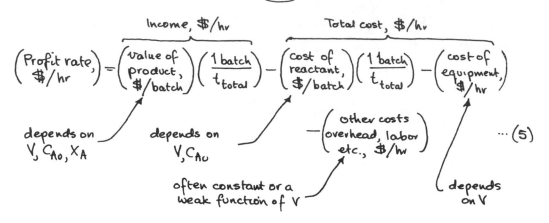

- To find the maximum production rate in a given reactor take

$$\frac{d\bar{F}_R}{dX_A} = 0 \quad \cdots \text{ or } \quad \frac{d\bar{F}_R}{dt} = 0$$

This is the economic criterion to use when the cost of reactant is of no concern.

This approach can be extended to account for the cost of reprocessing unconverted reactant, to prepare it for reuse.

Chapter 5 Problems

A1 A liquid reactant stream (1 mol/lit) passes through two mixed flow reactors in a series. The concentration of A in the exit of the first reactor is 0.5 mol/lit. Find the concentration in the exit stream of the second reactor. The reaction is second order with respect to A and $V_2/V_1 = 2$.

A2 Water containing a short lived radioactive species flows continuously through a well mixed holdup tank. This gives time for the radioactive material to decay into harmless waste. As it now operates the activity of the exit stream is 1/7 of the feed stream. This is not bad, but we'd like to lower it still more.

One of our office secretaries suggests that we insert a baffle down the middle of the tank so that the holdup tank acts as two well mixed tanks in series. Do you think this would help? If not, tell why; if so, calculate the expected activity of the exit stream compared to the entering stream.

A3 An aqueous reactant stream (4 molA/lit) passes through a mixed flow reactor followed by a plug flow reactor. Find the concentration at the exit of the plug flow reactor if in the mixed flow reactor $C_A = 1$ mol/lit. The reaction is second order with respect to A and the volume of the plug flow unit is 3 times that of the mixed flow unit.

Reactant A ($A \rightarrow R$, $C_{A0} = 125$ mol/m^3) passes in steady flow through four equal sized mixed flow reactor in series ($\tau_{total} = 2$ min). When steady state is achieved the concentration of A is found to be 18, 5, 2, 1 mol/m^3 in the four units.

A4 . . . What size of single mixed flow reactor will do the same job as the present four stage unit?

A5 . . . For this reaction what must be τ_{plug} so as to reduce C_A from $C_{A0} = 125$ to $C_{Af} = 1$ mol/m^3?

A6 . . . Find an expression to represent the rate of disappearance of A.

A7 Originally we had planned to lower the activity of a gas stream containing radioactive Xe-138 (half life = 14 min) by having it pass through two holdup tanks in series, both well mixed and of such size that the mean residence time of gas is 2 weeks in each tank. It has been suggested that we replace the two tanks with a long tube (assume plug flow). What must be the size of this tube compared to the two original stirred tanks, and what should be the mean residence time of gas in this tube for the same extent of radioactive decay?

Chapter 5 Problems

A8 At 100 °C pure gaseous A reacts away with stoichiometry $2A \rightarrow R + S$ in a constant volume batch reactor as follows

t, sec	0	20	40	60	80	100	120	140	160
p_A, atm	1.00	0.96	0.80	0.56	0.32	0.18	0.08	0.04	0.02

What size of plug flow reactor operating at 100 °C and 1 atm can treat 100 moles A/hr in a feed consisting of 20% inerts to obtain 95% conversion of A?

A9 We wish to treat 10 lit/min of liquid feed containing 1 molA/lit to 99% conversion. The stoichiometry and kinetics of the reaction are given by

$$A \rightarrow R, \quad -r_A = \frac{C_A}{0.2 + C_A} \; \frac{\text{mol}}{\text{lit}\cdot\text{min}}$$

Suggest a good arrangement for doing this using two mixed flow reactors, and find the size of the two units needed. Sketch the final design chosen.

A10 From steady state kinetic runs in a mixed flow reactor we obtain the following data on the reaction $A \rightarrow R$.

τ sec	C_{A0} mmol/lit	C_A mmol/lit
60	50	20
35	100	40
11	100	60
20	200	80
11	200	100

Find the space time needed to treat a feed of C_{A0} = 100 mmol/lit to 80% conversion
(a) in a plug flow reactor
(b) in a mixed flow reactor

A11 At present we have 90% conversion of a liquid feed ($n = 1$, C_{A0} = 10 mol/lit) to our plug flow reactor with recycle of product (**R** = 2). If we shut off the recycle stream, by how much will this lower the processing rate of our feed to the same 90% conversion?

A12 Aqueous feed containing reactant A (C_{A0} = 2 mol/lit) enters a plug flow reactor (10 lit) which has a provision for recycling a portion of the flowing stream. The reaction kinetics and stoichiometry are:

$$A \rightarrow R, \quad -r_A = 1 C_A C_R \; \frac{\text{mol}}{\text{lit}\cdot\text{min}}$$

and we wish to get 96% conversion. Should we use the recycle stream? If so, at what value should we set the recycle flow rate so as to obtain the highest production rate, and what volumetric feed rate can we process to this conversion in the reactor?

Chapter 5 Problems

In the presence of a specific enzyme E which acts as a homogeneous catalyst a harmful organic A present in industrial waste water degrades into harmless chemicals. At a given enzyme concentration C_E tests in a laboratory mixed flow reactor give the following results

C_{A0}, mmol/m^3	2	5	6	6	11	14	16	24
C_A, mmol/m^3	0.5	3	1	2	6	10	8	4
τ, min	30	1	50	8	4	20	20	4

We wish to treat 100 lit/min of this waste water having C_{A0} = 10 mmol/m^3 to 90% conversion with this enzyme at concentration C_E.

A13 ... One possibility is to use a long tubular reactor (assume plug flow) with possible recycle of exit fluid. What design do you recommend? Give the size of the reactor, tell if it should be used with recycle, and if so determine the recycle flow rate in lit/min. Sketch your recommended design.

A14 ... Another possibility is to use one or two stirred tanks (assume ideal). What two-tank design do you recommend, and how much better is it than the one-tank arrangement?

A15 ... What arrangement of plug flow and mixed flow reactors would you use to minimize the total volume of reactors needed? Sketch your recommended design and show the size of units selected.

A16 At 5 °C the reaction of ketene to diketene

$$2CH_2 = CO \rightarrow (CH_2 = CO)_2, \quad \text{second order kinetics}$$

occurs rather slowly in the liquid phase. We wish to design a flow process to treat a ketene feed (v = 0.8 m^3/hr) to 98% conversion in 2 horizontal tanks in series, each mechanically agitated and having 3 well mixed compartments. In a batch reactor this conversion would require a 12 hour reaction time. What tank volume is needed? Take the volume of internals to be 10% of the tank volume.

Consider the autocatalytic reaction A → R, with $-r_A = 0.001\, C_A C_R$ mol/lit·s. We wish to process 1.5 lit/s of a C_{A0} = 10 mol/lit feed to the highest conversion possible in the reactor system described below. Sketch your recommended design and feed arrangement and determine C_{Af} from this system.

A17 ... The reactor set up consists of four 100 lit mixed flow reactors connected as you wish, and any feed arrangement.

Chapter 5 Problems

A18 . . . The reactor is a 600 lit plug flow reactor, with side feed, side withdrawal, or recycle -- if you so desire.

A19 We desire 90% conversion of A to R in a batch reactor for which partial emptying is allowed. Find the smallest reactor size and frequency of refilling, etc. which will process an average flow of 0.50 m^3/hr of a $C_{A0} = 10$ mol/m^3 and $C_{R0} = 0$ feed. The reaction is autocatalytic and is approximated by $A \rightarrow R$, $-r_A = 0.01\, C_A C_R$ $mol/m^3 \cdot hr$.

A20 Liquid containing chemical A ($C_{A0} = 12$ mol/lit) is to be treated so as to convert 75% of this reactant into product. The reaction proceeds rather slowly, as shown below, so we are considering using a batch reactor system

$A \rightarrow R$								
	C_A, mol/lit	1	2	4	6	8	10	12
	$-r_A$, mol/lit·hr	0.125	0.333	1	1	0.25	0.10	0.05

(a) Determine the smallest size of reactor which would process 100 lit/hr of feed, on the average, and tell how we should operate the reactor cycle time, partial emptying maybe, etc. Assume that the time for emptying and refilling the reactor is negligible compared to the reaction time.

(b) If you recommend a partial emptying operation, how much smaller would that reactor be than if ordinary batch operations were used.

B21 We wish to produce 1000 mol R/hr from an aqueous feed of A ($C_{A0} = 1$ mol/lit) in a mixed flow reactor. The reaction is

$$A \rightarrow R, \quad -r_A = 1\, C_A \, \frac{\text{mol}}{\text{lit}\cdot\text{hr}}$$

The cost of reactant stream is \$0.40/mol A, and the cost of reactor including installation, auxiliary equipment, instrumentation, overhead, labor, depreciation, etc. is \$0.10/lit· hr. Unused A is discarded. Find V, X_A, F_{A0} for optimum operations (minimum cost for R), and find the unit cost of producing R under these conditions.

B22 A plug flow reactor is to produce 1000 mol R/hr from an aqueous feed of A ($C_{A0} = 1$ mol/lit). The reaction is

$$A \rightarrow R, \quad -r_A = 2\, C_A^2 \, \frac{\text{mol}}{\text{lit}\cdot\text{hr}}$$

The cost of reactant stream is \$0.40/molA and the cost of reactor, complete, comes to \$0.20/lit· hr. Unused A is discarded. Find V, X_A, F_{A0} for optimum operations. What is the unit cost of R produced under these conditions?

Chapter 5 Problems

B23 We wish to design a mixed flow reactor system to produce 1000 mol R/hr from a feed of aqueous A (1 molA/lit) which reacts away with stoichiometry $A \rightarrow R$. The cost of reactant is \$1/mol A, the cost of reactor, complete, is \$0.10/lit·hr, and the unused A is discarded. Find V, F_{A0}, X_A for optimum operations and find the cost of R produced under these conditions. The rate of reaction is tabulated as follows

C_A, mol/lit	0.1	0.2	0.3	0.4	0.5	0.6	1
$-r_A$, mol/lit·hr	0.03	0.05	0.075	0.1	0.125	0.1	0.01

B24 Aqueous feed ($C_{A0} = 1$ mol/lit, v = 1000 lit/hr) is available to us at \$1.00/mol A from our friendly neighbor. We could react it as follows

$$A \rightarrow R, \quad -r_A = 2\,C_A \frac{\text{mol}}{\text{lit}\cdot\text{hr}}$$

and sell the product at \$1.60/mol R. A mixed flow reactor plus product purification unit costs \$0.20/lit·hr of reactor, complete (labor, utilities, value of money). Unused A is destroyed when the product is purified. Find the best way to operate such a system (V, X_A, F_R, hourly profit $\$_t$) and then recommend a course of action.

B25 Substance A, present in a waste stream (1000 lit/hr, 1 molA/lit) can be converted into material R by the reaction $A \rightarrow R$. This product is useful and can be sold at \$1.00/mol R. The cost of mixed flow reactor, including all charges, comes to \$0.20/lit·hr. What is the best way of running this recovery operation (find V, X_A, F_R, hourly profit $\$_t$) and then decide whether to proceed with this venture. The rate of reaction of A to R given by

C_A, mol/lit	0.1	0.2	0.3	0.4	0.6	0.8	1.0
$-r_A$, mol/lit·hr	0.15	0.5	1	1.7	3.6	6	9.1

and we will have to pay \$0.10/lit to get rid of the waste stream.

B26 At room temperature the reversible liquid reaction of unknown kinetics

$$A \leftrightarrow R, \quad C_{A0} = 1, \quad C_{R0} = 0$$

proceeds as follows

% of equilibrium conversion	10	30	50	70
time, min	8	18	42	162

After a batch of feed has reacted it takes 100 min. to empty, clean and refill the reactor for the next batch. This is done again and again, day and night.

How should we operate the reactor (reaction time and conversion level) so as to produce the most product per day?

A27* We plan to run the liquid reaction

$$A \rightarrow R, \qquad k = 3\ hr^{-1}$$

in a 1.0 m^3 reactor as follows:

- With the tank full of liquid run the reaction for half an hour, giving C_{A2}.
- Then quickly pour in 0.5 m^3 of fresh feed at C_{A0} = 1 mol/lit while mixing constantly and letting fluid overflow into the collection tank. This brings the concentration to C_{A1}.
- Run for another half hour.
- Again pour in fresh feed.

... Repeat again and again ...

If no reaction occurs in the collection tank what will be its average concentration, C_{A3}, after long time operations.

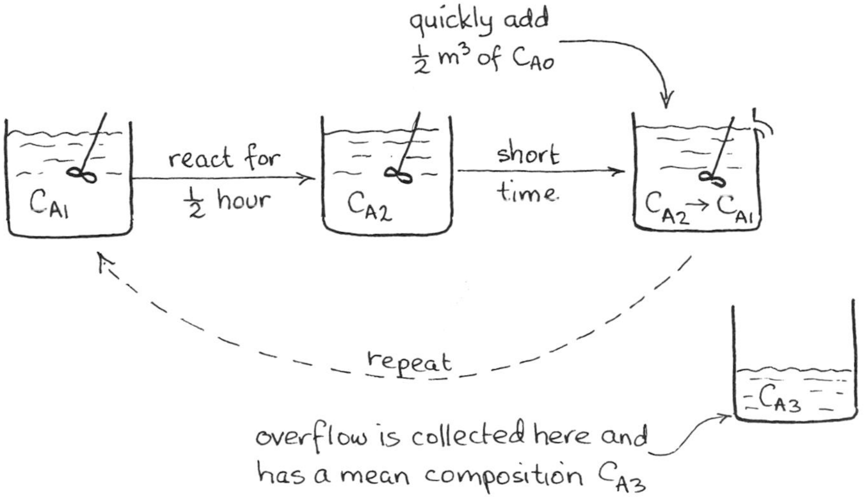

Chapter 6 MULTIPLE REACTIONS; QUALITATIVE.

Suppose we want to contact a mixed dichlorobenzene feed with chlorine so as to maximize the formation of one of the many reaction products, say 1,3,4 trichlorobenzene

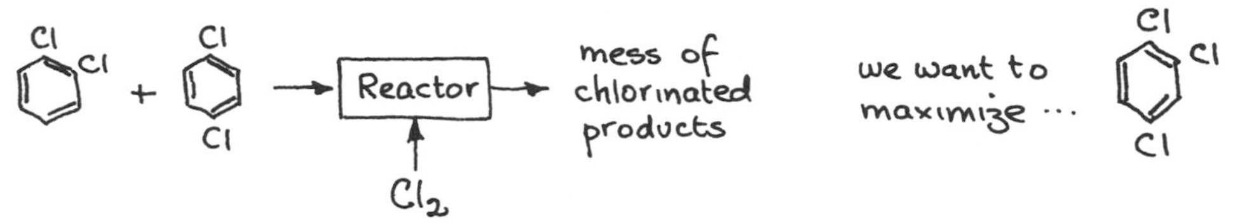

The reactions are

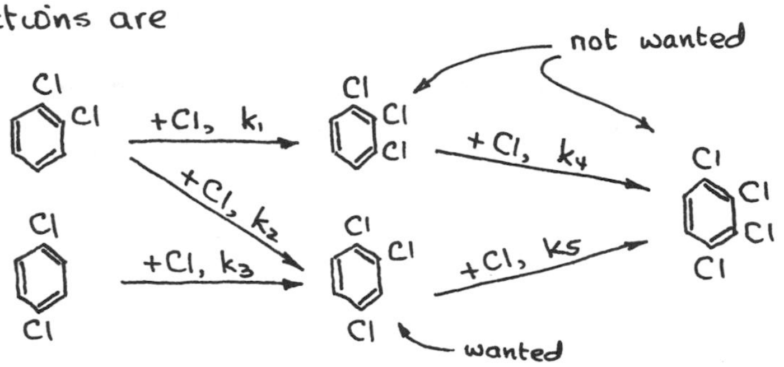

Should we use a plug flow reactor, mixed flow, fast chlorine addition, slow addition, countercurrent column, stirred tank? With k values all known we can tediously search for the contacting pattern which gives the best product distribution ... by guesswork. However there are general rules of behavior which often tell us right away, independent of k values, which contacting pattern is best. These generalizations are our concern here.

Single reactions are those which can be represented by a single stoichiometric equation (eg $A \rightarrow R+S$), hence the products form in fixed proportion. The concern there is to choose conditions where the reaction goes as fast as possible, hence requires minimum reactor volume. In **multiple reactions** two or more reactions occur at the same time, often competing for the same reactant. The main concern with such systems is to find the **best contacting pattern** and temperature progression so as to promote formation of one of the products and not the other. The question of minimizing reactor size is secondary (it is of little use to have a small cheap reactor which very speedily and efficiently produces the wrong product).

Multiple reactions are of the following types

series	parallel	independent or side by side	combined, or mixed, or what have you.		
$A \rightarrow R \rightarrow S$	$B \nearrow R$, $B \searrow S$	$A \rightarrow R$, $B \rightarrow S$	$A+B \rightarrow R$, $R+B \rightarrow S$	$A+D \rightarrow R$, $B+D \rightarrow S$	etc.

It is convenient in our discussions to represent reactions by n^{th} order kinetics and an Arrhenius temperature dependency, thus

$$A + B \xrightarrow{1} R, \qquad r_R = k_{10} e^{-E_1/RT} C_A^a C_B^b$$

We then have the following rules of behavior

Rule 1 **On T levels and relative rates of reaction.**

High T favors the reaction having larger E. Low T favors the reaction having smaller E. The T level has no effect on relative rates and product distribution if $E_1 = E_2$.

Rule 2 **On C level and relative rates of reaction**

High C_A favors the reaction having higher reaction order with respect to C_A. Low C_A favors the reaction having lower reaction order with respect to C_A. The C_A level has no effect on relative rates and product distribution if both reactions are of the same order with respect to C_A.

With two reactant streams here's how to independently maintain high and low concentration of each of the reactants.

Non continuous systems (start with two beakers C_{A0} C_{B0})

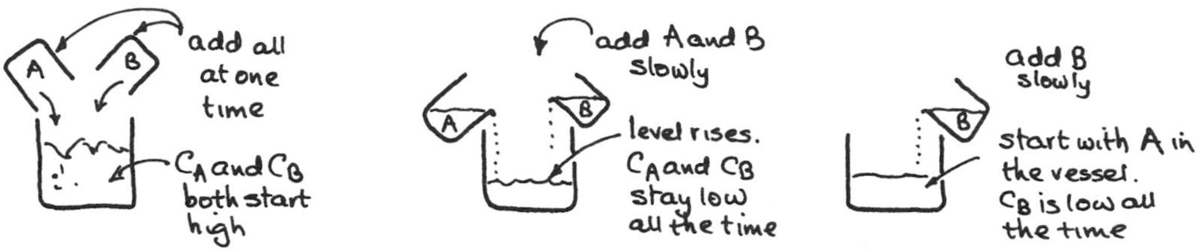
A
B
add all at one time
C_A and C_B both start high
add A and B slowly
level rises. C_A and C_B stay low all the time
add B slowly
start with A in the vessel. C_B is low all the time

For C_A & C_B both high — For C_A & C_B both low — For C_A high, C_B low

Continuous system (let streams of C_{A0} and C_{B0} enter the reactor)

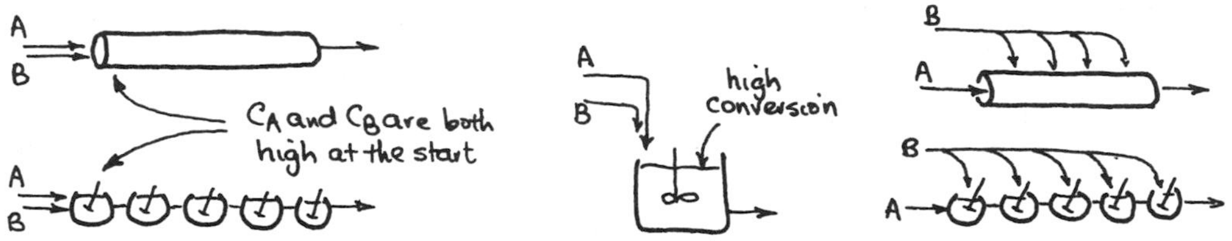
A
B
C_A and C_B are both high at the start
high conversion

For C_A & C_B both high — For C_A & C_B both low — For C_A high, C_B low

Rule 3 <u>On maximizing a reaction intermediate, say "R" in the reaction $A \rightarrow R \rightarrow S$.</u>

To obtain the highest value of C_{Rmax} do not allow fluids having different ratios of A to R (reactant to intermediates) to mix.

For this requirement plug flow is always better than mixed flow (where fresh feed mixes with partly reacted fluid), and straight batch is better than semibatch operations (where fresh reactant is added during reaction). In fact plug flow and straight batch operations always give highest $C_{R\,max}$.

This mixing rule applies to any and all of the intermediates of a whole series of reactions, $A \rightarrow R \rightarrow S \rightarrow T \rightarrow U \cdots \rightarrow Z$

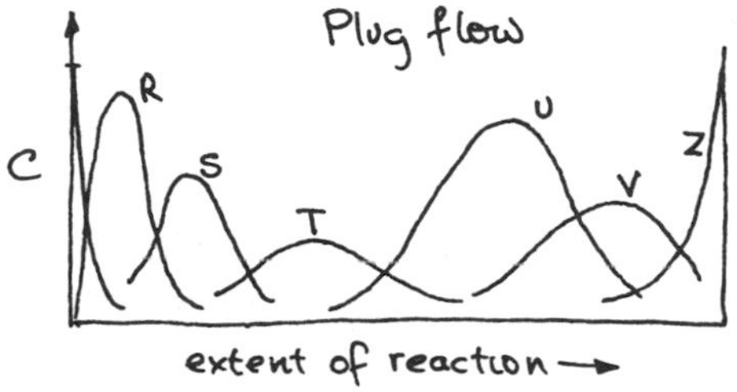

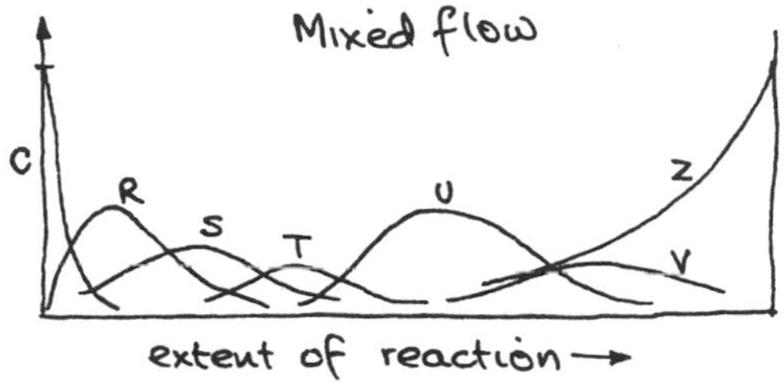

This rule is also important in homogeneous polymerizations where one can control the spread in molecular weight of polymer with proper contacting

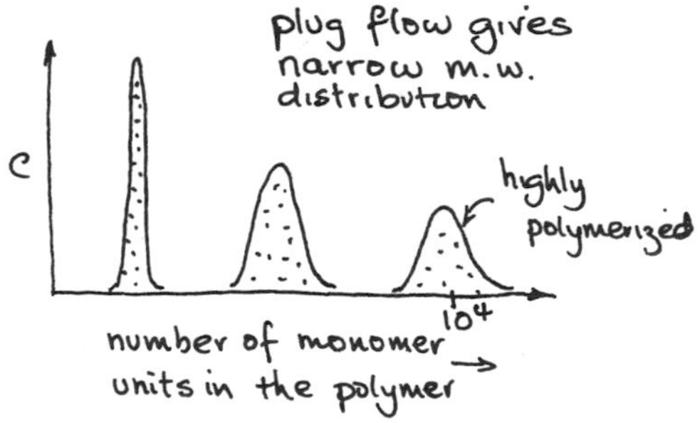

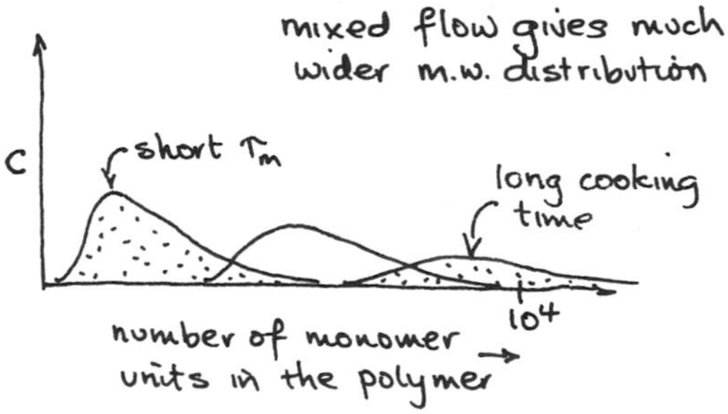

Rule 4 On combined reactions.

These can frequently be analysed in terms of their constituent series reactions and parallel reactions. Thus

$$\left.\begin{array}{l} A+B \xrightarrow{1} R \\ R+B \xrightarrow{2} S \end{array}\right\} \xRightarrow[\text{analyse as}]{\text{equivalent to,}} \begin{array}{l} A \xrightarrow{1} R \xrightarrow{2} S \\ B \begin{array}{l} \nearrow^{1} R \\ \searrow_{2} S \end{array} \end{array}$$

Example 1 Find the contacting pattern which favors formation of R for the following reactions

$$A+B \begin{cases} \xrightarrow{1} 2R \\ \xrightarrow{2} S+T \end{cases} \quad \cdots \begin{cases} r_1 = k_{10} e^{-80000/RT} C_A C_B^{0.3} \\ r_2 = k_{20} e^{-40000/RT} C_A^{0.5} C_B^{1.8} \end{cases}$$

Solution From the above rules

- use high C_A, low C_B
- use high T

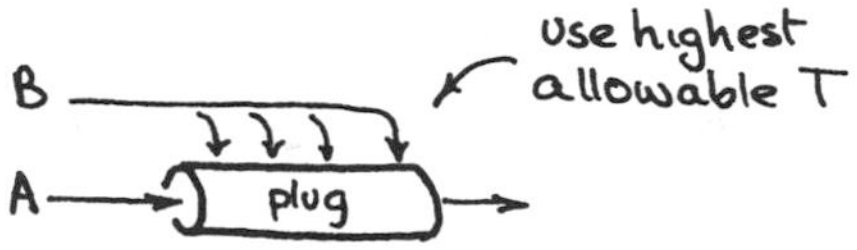
B
A
plug
use highest allowable T

Example 2 Find the contacting pattern to maximize R for the following reactions

$$A \xrightarrow{1} R \xrightarrow{2} S \quad \cdots \begin{cases} r_1 = k_{10} e^{-60000/RT} C_A \\ r_2 = k_{20} e^{-60000/RT} C_R^2 \end{cases}$$

Solution From the above rules

- use low C_{A0}
- use plug flow of A
- use any temperature

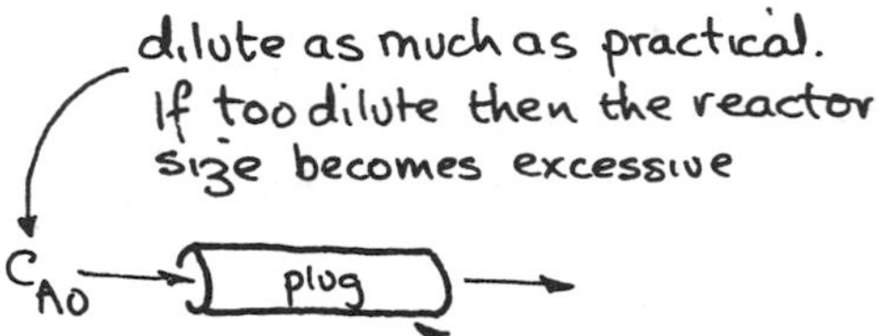
dilute as much as practical.
If too dilute then the reactor size becomes excessive
C_{A0}
plug

although $C_{R\,max}$ is unaffected by the T level, the higher the T the faster everything goes. So use the highest allowable T

Example 3 Find a favorable contacting pattern to form R for

$$A+B \longrightarrow R \quad \cdots \quad r_1 = k_{10} e^{-30000/RT} C_A^2 C_B$$

$$R+B \longrightarrow S \quad \cdots \quad r_2 = k_{20} e^{-40000/RT} C_R C_B$$

Solution.

For A: $A \xrightarrow{n=2} R \xrightarrow{n=1} S$

∴ plug flow A, high C_{A0}

For B: $B \begin{cases} \xrightarrow{n=1} R \\ \xrightarrow{n=1} S \end{cases}$ ∴ any C_B is ok

For T: Use low T

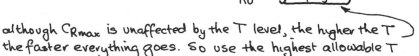

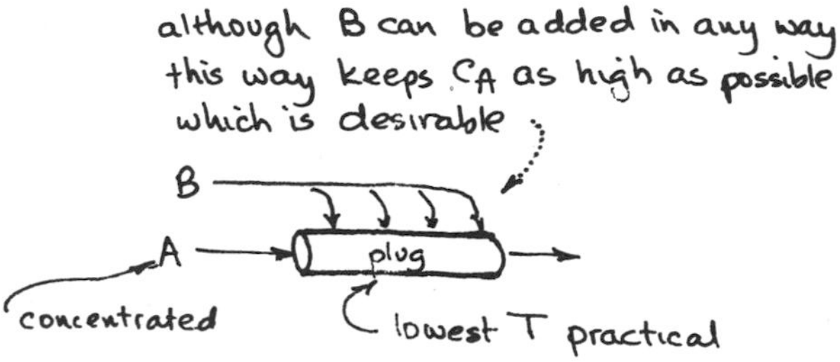
although B can be added in any way this way keeps C_A as high as possible which is desirable
B
A
plug
concentrated
lowest T practical

Rule 5 On optimization in the face of physical restraint.

When optimization requires a low T or a low C this leads us to ask for a reactor of infinite size. But this can't be so we end up fixing the maximum allowable size of a flow reactor or the maximum processing time in a batch reactor. In the face of such restraints analysis becomes quite complicated. However, we do come up with some qualitative generalizations. Consider these

Reactions in parallel: Suppose

$$A \xrightarrow{1} R_{desired}, \quad A \xrightarrow{2} S \qquad n_1 = n_2 \qquad \cdots \text{ and } \tau_{flow} \text{ or } t_{batch} \text{ fixed.}$$

If $E_1 \geq E_2$ we have no problem deciding what to do, operate at the highest allowable T. But with $E_1 < E_2$ the best product distribution is gotten at lowest T, hence using τ or $t \to \infty$. However with τ or t restricted a **rising T is optimum**

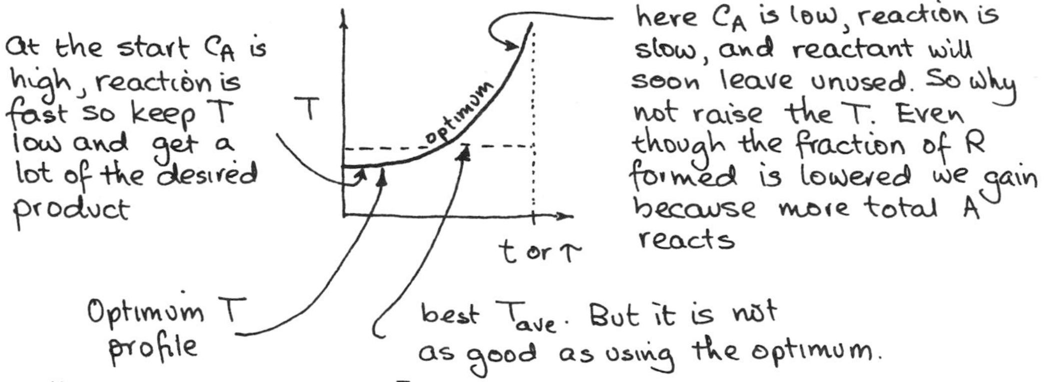
At the start C_A is high, reaction is fast so keep T low and get a lot of the desired product
T
optimum
t or τ
here C_A is low, reaction is slow, and reactant will soon leave unused. So why not raise the T. Even though the fraction of R formed is lowered we gain because more total A reacts
Optimum T profile
best T_{ave}. But it is not as good as using the optimum.

[see Husain & Gangiah 245, 276]

Reactions in series, intermediate desired: Suppose

$$A \xrightarrow{1} R_{desired} \xrightarrow{2} S \qquad n_1 = n_2 \qquad \cdots \text{ and } \tau_{flow} \text{ or } t_{batch} \text{ fixed}$$

Again, if $E_1 \gg E_2$ then the highest allowable T is optimum. However, if $E_1 < E_2$ then the lowest T gives highest $C_{R\,max}$ but in a reactor of infinite size. With a restriction on τ or t a falling temperature is best

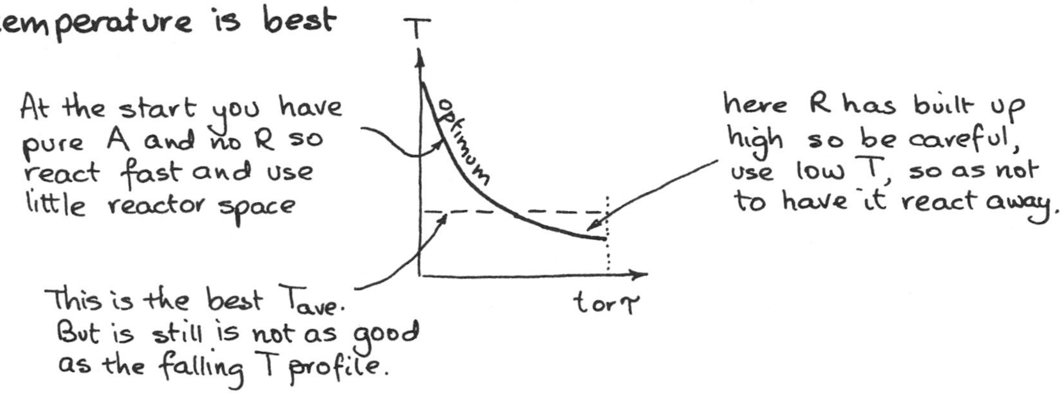
T
optimum
t or τ
At the start you have pure A and no R so react fast and use little reactor space
here R has built up high so be careful, use low T, so as not to have it react away.
This is the best T_{ave}. But is still is not as good as the falling T profile.

[see Husain and Gangiah 53, 275; Fan 85]

Comments

(a) Often it becomes clear from the qualitative treatment alone what type of system is best. However, to find numerical values for concentrations and reaction times requires quantitative analysis.

(b) Sometimes we end up with conflicting demands on a variable such as "use high T" and "use low T". In this case an intermediate temperature always is best, and quantitative analysis will tell its precise value.

(c) At other times two different variables may demand special treatment. But which is more important and should have priority? In such cases there are few generalizations. Here is an example

Given $A \xrightarrow{1} R_{required}$, $A \xrightarrow{2} S$ $\quad \left.\begin{matrix} n_1 < n_2 \\ E_1 < E_2 \end{matrix}\right\}$ ...and τ_{flow} or t_{batch} are fixed

Ideally we want both low T and low C_A. But each leads to $\tau \to \infty$.

- Should we take the temperature effect as dominant thus use plug flow (high C_A) with rising T?
- Should we take the concentration effect as dominant and thus use high T with mixed flow (low C_A) of fluid?
- Or is the answer dependent on how different are $(n_1 - n_2)$ and $(E_1 - E_2)$?

I don't know the answer, I think it depends on Δn & ΔE, however in the few cases I have examined I have found that the T effect dominates. I think that this usually is the case.

(d) On mixing of streams: for a single reaction, say $A \rightarrow R$, and two feed streams at different C_{A0} we can show that to get minimum τ_{flow} or t_{batch}

- if $n > 1$ react the streams separately, then mix.
- if $n < 1$ mix the streams first, then react.

But what of reactions such as $A \xrightarrow{1} R \xrightarrow{2} S$, $n_1 \neq n_2$ and two feeds? For highest $C_{R\,max}$ should we mix first, then react or should react separately? I don't know the answer to that either.

(e) The rules presented in this chapter are useful qualitative generalizations which can be verified quantitatively. However there are other proposed rules as yet speculative and some rather controversial. We do not use these directly in our problems, but it may be of interest to note them.

<u>Rule 6</u> For homogeneous reactions the best steady state flow operations cannot be improved upon by cyclic unsteady state operations.

<u>Rule 7</u> With respect to product distribution every non continuous scheme, batch or semibatch, has its continuous analog, and vice versa. Thus if I can produce that perfect beer by a batch process you should be able to duplicate it by using a continuous process.

Chapter 6 Problems

Consider the following scheme of elementary reactions:

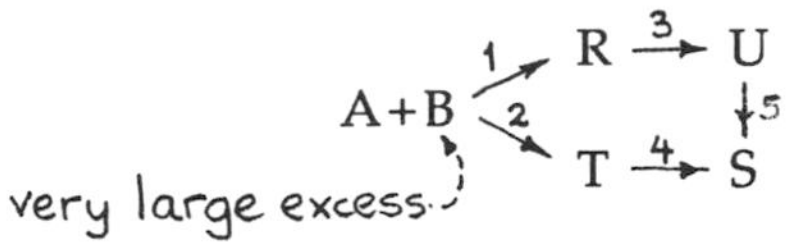

$E_1 = 79$ kJ
$E_2 = 113$ kJ
$E_3 = 126$ kJ
$E_4 = 151$ kJ
$E_5 = 0$

What type of flow reactor system and temperature progression would you recommend if the desired product is

A1 . . . R

A2 . . . S

A3 . . . T

A4 . . . U

This industrially important reaction scheme is reported by Binns *et al* in Trans. I. Chem. E. **47** T53 (1969) and is used by Husain and Gangiah, page 245. In this problem we interchanged two of the reported E values to make the problem more interesting.

For a given feed stream of reactant A what reactor type (plug or mixed flow) or combination of two reactors, and what temperature (high, low, intermediate, rising or falling) will favor the formation of the product indicated. You may dilute the feed but you may not recycle or reuse any unreacted materials

	n_1, E_1	n_2, E_2	n_3, E_3
A5 . . .	1, 25	1, 15	2, 35
A6 . . .	0, 35	2, 15	1, 20
A7 . . .	1, 15	2, 35	0, 25
A8 . . .	2, 25	1, 35	0, 15

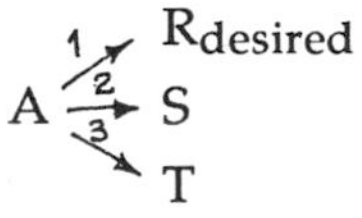

	n_1, E_1	n_2, E_2	n_3, E_3	n_4, E_4
A9 . . .	2, 15	1, 35	1, 45	0, 25
A10 . . .	1, 35	0, 25	2, 15	2, 45
A11 . . .	1, 25	2, 15	0, 45	1, 35
A12 . . .	1, 45	2, 35	0, 15	2, 25

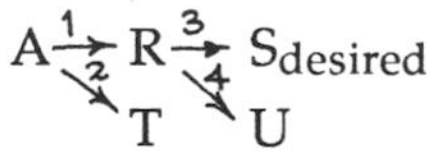

A13 . . .	1, 25	1, 35	0, 25	1, 35
A14 . . .	2, 25	1, 15	1, 45	0, 35
A15 . . .	2, 30	1, 20	1, 40	1, 20
A16 . . .	1, 35	2, 45	1, 25	2, 15
A17 . . .	1, 15	2, 25	2, 35	1, 45
A18 . . .	1, 45	0, 35	1, 25	2, 15

Chapter 6 Problems

Under the action of mixed enzymes reactant A is converted to products as follows

$$A \xrightarrow[k_1]{+\text{enzyme}} R \xrightarrow[k_2]{+\text{enzyme}} S, \quad n_1 = n_2$$

where the rate constants are dependent on the pH of the system.

(a) What reactor set-up (plug flow, mixed flow, or staged mixed flow units) and what uniform pH level would you use?

(b) If it were possible to change the pH level along the plug flow reactor, or from stage to stage in mixed flow units, in what direction would you change the pH level?

A19 . . . $k_1 = pH^2 - 8\,pH + 23$ with $2 < pH < 6$, and R the desired product
$k_2 = pH + 1$

A20 . . . $k_1 = pH + 1$ with $2 < pH < 6$, and S the desired product
$k_2 = pH^2 - 8\,pH + 23$

For a different approach and solution to this type of problem see Husain and Gangiah, 227.

Using separate feeds of A and B sketch the contacting pattern and reactor conditions which would best promote the formation of product R for the following systems of elementary reactions

B21 . . . $\left.\begin{array}{r} A + B \rightarrow R \\ A \rightarrow S \end{array}\right\}$ Flow system

B22 . . . $\left.\begin{array}{r} A + B \rightarrow R \\ 2A \rightarrow S \\ 2B \rightarrow T \end{array}\right\}$ Batch system

B23 . . . $\left.\begin{array}{r} A + B \rightarrow R \\ A \rightarrow S \end{array}\right\}$ Batch system

B24 . . . $\left.\begin{array}{r} A + B \rightarrow R \\ 2A \rightarrow S \end{array}\right\}$ Flow system

---

Chapter 6 Problems

Starting with separate feeds of reactants (C_{A0} and C_{B0} can be made high or low, as you wish) sketch the contacting pattern (plug, mixed or side entry, etc.) which best promotes the formation of intermediate R in the consecutive competitive reactions below. Separation and reuse of unconverted materials is not allowed.

$$\left.\begin{array}{lll} A + B \xrightarrow{1} R_{desired} & \ldots & r_1 = k_1 C_A^{n_1} C_B^{n_2} \\ R + B \xrightarrow{2} S & \ldots & r_2 = k_2 C_R^{n_3} C_B^{n_4} \end{array}\right\}$$

where the reaction orders are given by

	n_1	n_2	n_3	n_4	Type of operation
B25 . . .	2	1	1	1	Batch
B26 . . .	1	2	1	1	Batch
B27 . . .	1	1	2	1	Flow
B28 . . .	1	1	1	2	Flow
B29 . . .	2	2	1	1	Flow
B30 . . .	2	1	2	1	Batch
B31 . . .	2	1	1	2	Batch
B32 . . .	1	2	2	1	Batch
B33 . . .	1	2	1	2	Flow
B34 . . .	1	1	2	2	Flow

Chapter 7. ONE STEP REACTIONS: PARALLEL, SIDE BY SIDE, etc.

Here we treat quantitatively the following sorts of reactions

$$A \begin{matrix} \nearrow R \\ \searrow S \end{matrix} \qquad \left.\begin{matrix} B \rightarrow R \\ D \rightarrow S \end{matrix}\right\} \qquad \left.\begin{matrix} A+B \rightarrow R \\ A+D \rightarrow S \end{matrix}\right\}$$

competing or parallel reactions (same reactant decomposes two ways)

side by side or independent reactions (different reactants for each reaction)

what should we call this type of reaction? ... we have no name for it.

In these reactions no product reacts further, these are all one step reactions. In this chapter we do not treat reactions where the product reacts further, such as

$$A \rightarrow R \rightarrow S \qquad \left.\begin{matrix} A \rightarrow R \\ A+R \rightarrow S \end{matrix}\right\} \qquad \left.\begin{matrix} A+B \rightarrow R \\ R+B \rightarrow S \end{matrix}\right\}$$

These reactions are treated in the next chapter.

I Single Reactant Systems, say $A \begin{matrix} \nearrow R \\ \searrow S \end{matrix}$.

A. Fractional yield φ.

The instantaneous fractional yield φ is a useful tool for evaluating reactor performance, finding optimum operations, etc. for one step reactions. If R is the product of interest we define the instantaneous fractional yield at concentration C_A as

$$\varphi(R/A) = \frac{\text{moles R formed}}{\text{moles A used}} = -\frac{dC_R}{dC_A}$$

where φ is obtained from rate expressions

Example 1. Find an expression for $\varphi(R/A)$ and evaluate φ at $C_A = 1$ for the reaction

$$A \begin{array}{l} \nearrow R \quad \cdots r_R = 3C_A \\ \searrow S \quad \cdots r_S = 6C_A^2 \end{array} \Big\}$$

Solution.

$$\varphi(R/A) = \frac{r_R}{-r_A} = \frac{r_R}{r_R + r_S} = \frac{3C_A}{3C_A + 6C_A^2} = \frac{1}{1 + 2C_A}$$

at $C_A = 1$ $\quad \varphi(R/A) = \frac{1}{3}$; that is at $C_A = 1$ we form 1 mol R for each 3 mols of A decomposed.

B. Reactor Performance Expressions.

In a reactor the fraction of reacted A which transforms into the desired product R depends on φ and the vessel flow pattern. Thus

For plug flow: $\quad C_R = \int_{C_{Af}}^{C_{A0}} \varphi(R/A)\, dC_A$ — we often just write φ if there is no ambiguity or chance of misunderstanding

For mixed flow: $\quad C_R = \varphi_f (C_{A0} - C_{Af})$ (φ_f: at C_{Af})

For mixed flow reactors in series: $\quad C_R = \varphi_1 (C_{A0} - C_{A1}) + \varphi_2 (C_{A1} - C_{A2}) + \cdots$ (φ_2: in vessel 2)

Graphically, we represent these expressions as follows

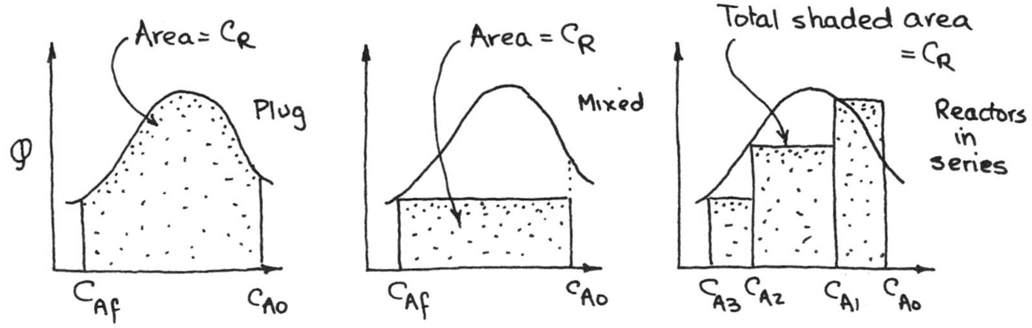

C. Best reactor type for isothermal operations.

By "best" we mean that type of reactor which gives most of the desired product R. The type depends on the shape of the φ vs C_A curve. Consider various shapes

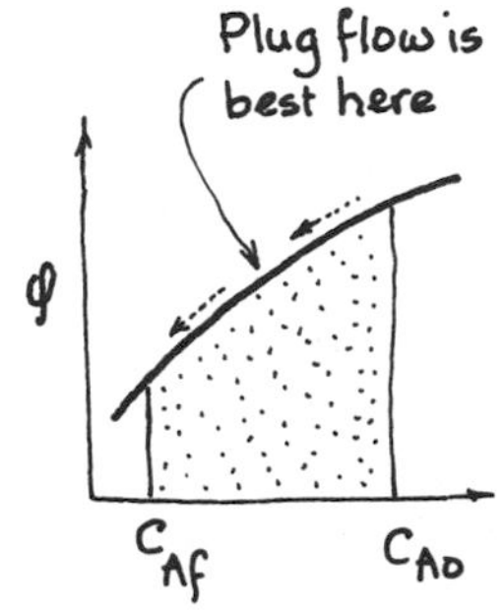

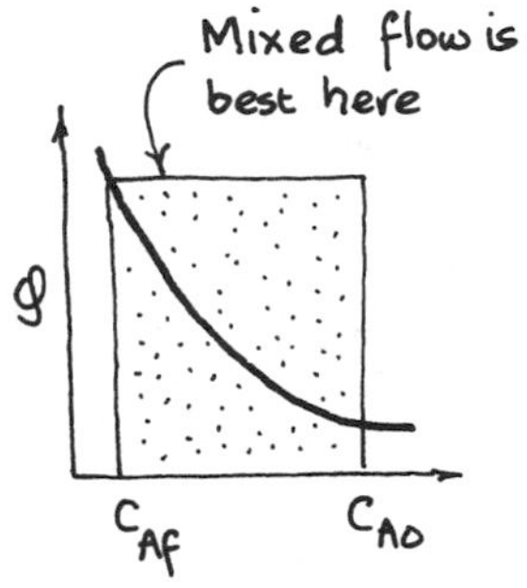

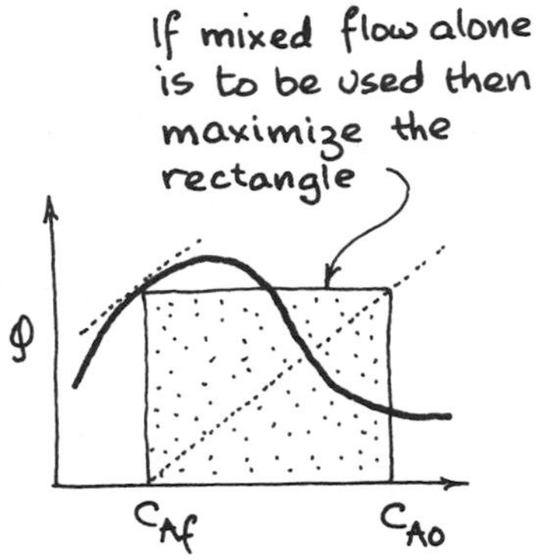

This solution is equivalent to finding C_A for which

$$\frac{d}{dC_A}\left[(\varphi)(C_{A0}-C_A)\right]=0$$

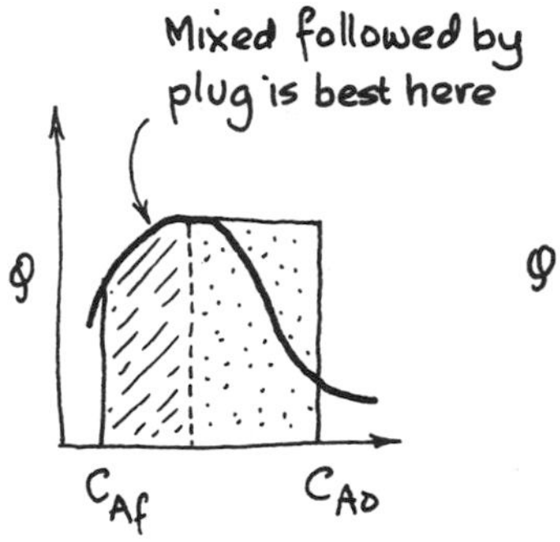

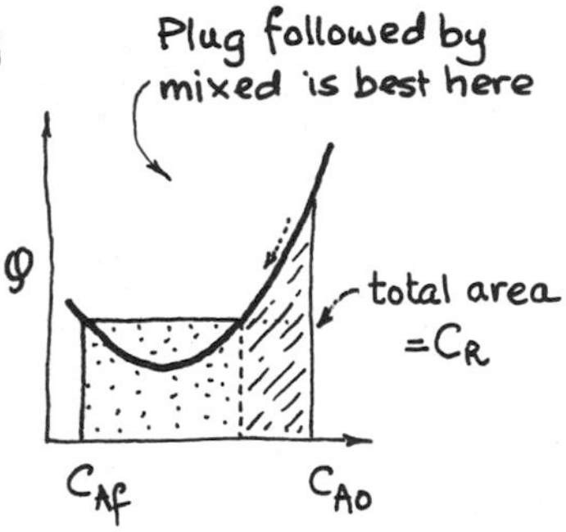

If recycle of unused reactant is possible without cost then operate at that C_A which gives the highest φ. Thus use a mixed flow reactor with recycle, as follows

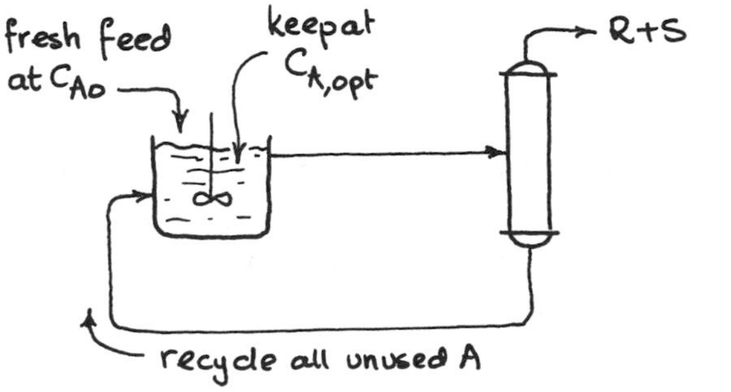

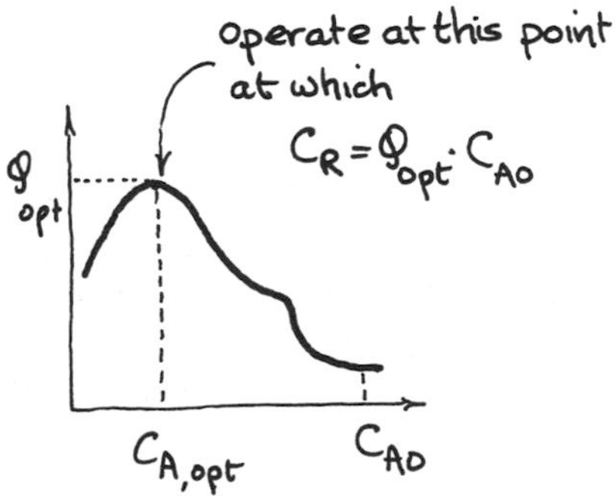

Comments

(a) There are other ways of defining the fractional yield, for example $\varphi(R/R+S)$ or $\varphi(R/\text{sum of products})$. These definitions are not necessarily identical, for example

- if $A \begin{smallmatrix} \nearrow R \\ \searrow S \end{smallmatrix}$ then $\varphi(R/A) = \varphi(R/R+S)$
- if $A \begin{smallmatrix} \nearrow R \\ \searrow 2S \end{smallmatrix}$ then $\varphi(R/A) \neq \varphi(R/R+S)$

(b) If rate expressions are available then all problems can be solved analytically. If rate expressions are not available we must construct the φ vs C_A curve from experiment and solve everything graphically. Thus we have two procedures depending on the type of information available.

(c) We obtain the φ vs C_A curve from experiment as follows:

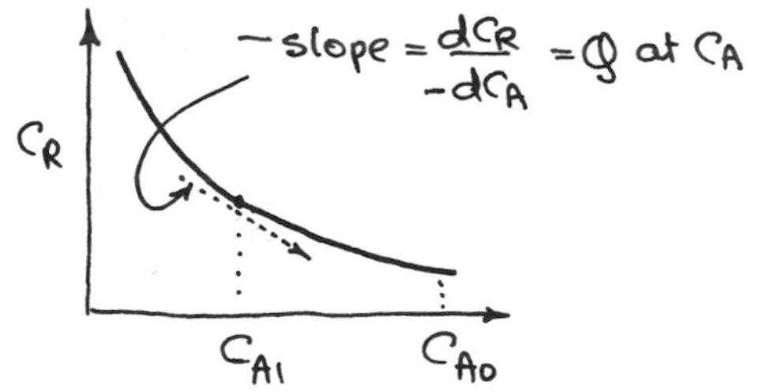

For plug flow or batch reactors measure C_R at various C_A, then plot as shown, and find the slope at various C_A

For mixed flow reactors make runs at various C_{Af}, and at each measure the amount of R formed. Then

$$\varphi_{\text{at } C_{Af}} = \frac{C_{Rf}}{C_{A0} - C_{Af}}$$

then plot... φ

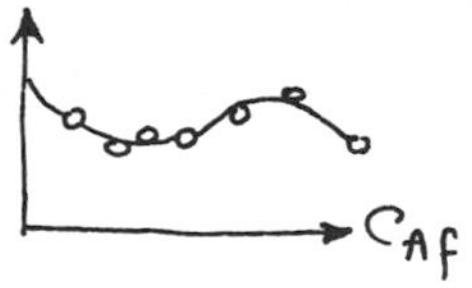

(d) The particular usefulness of the φ function is that it allows us to predict the behavior in one kind of reactor from information taken in another. But beware, you can only use this simple procedure if you are sure that you are dealing with one step reactions. To tell whether this is so add products to the feed. If this does not change φ then you are safe.

(e) It is not essential to use the fractional yield, however it is a convenient auxiliary variable. At times it is easier to use the rate equations directly.

(f) By the quantitative analysis of this chapter we can prove the qualitative generalizations of chapter 6, that high C_A may favor one reaction, low C_A another, and so on. The problems at the end of this chapter verify these generalizations.

II Two Reactant Systems, say. $\left.\begin{array}{l} A+2B \rightarrow R \\ A+B \rightarrow S \end{array}\right\}$

Here we have a variety of contacting patterns to choose from, for example

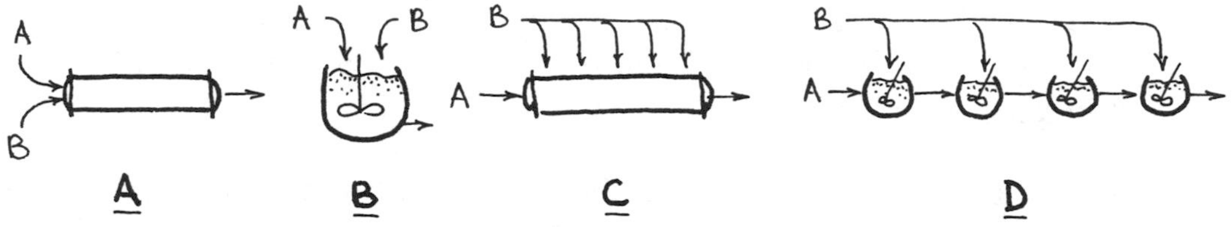

The fractional yield is not a very useful concept with these two reactant systems. It usually is best to first decide by the qualitative considerations of chapter 6 which contacting pattern is best to use, and then apply the rate equations directly to find the optimum conditions for this best contacting pattern.

The performance equations for the contacting patterns of the above sketches are given in earlier chapters

- chapter 3 for pattern **A**,
- chapter 4 for pattern **B**,
- chapter 5 for patterns **C** and **D**.

IV Temperature Effects.

Suppose we have a set of parallel reactions, all of the same order but with different activation energies

$$A \xrightarrow{1} R \quad \cdots \quad r_R = k_1 C_A = k_{10} e^{-E_1/RT} C_A$$
$$A \xrightarrow{2} S \quad \cdots \quad r_S = k_2 C_A = k_{20} e^{-E_2/RT} C_A$$
$$A \xrightarrow{3} T \quad \cdots \quad r_T = k_3 C_A = k_{30} e^{-E_3/RT} C_A$$

with $E_1 < E_2 < E_3$

In optimizing operations two situations should be clearly distinguished

(a) Fluid is allowed to pass through the reactor just once, and so we want to maximize the **production rate** of a given product. For a given flow rate of a given feed this means finding the maximum concentration of desired product.

(b) The product stream from the reactor can be separated and part of it can be recycled, all at no cost. In this situation low conversion per pass is no problem. Here we want to maximize the **fractional yield** of desired product.

In general separation and recycle costs money so an economic optimization must be used

Case (a) One pass operations... maximize $C_{desired}$.

- If the desired reaction has the highest activation energy then use the highest temperature in the largest allowable reactor size.

- If the desired reaction does not have the highest activation energy then choose the largest allowable reactor size τ_{max}, then maximize $C_{desired}$ with temperature.

So if ② is the desired reaction the optimum temperature is that which satisfies

$$(E_3-E_2)k_3\tau_{max} + (E_1-E_2)k_1\tau_{max} = E_2$$

the desired T is buried here $k_3 = k_{30}e^{-E_3/RT_{opt}}$ — and here

This condition also holds if the desired reaction has the lowest of all the E values.

- In the case of only two reactions where ① is desired

$$A \begin{cases} \xrightarrow{1} R \\ \xrightarrow{3} T \end{cases} \quad E_1 < E_3$$

the above condition reduces to

$$T_{opt} = \frac{E_3}{R \ln\left[k_{30}\tau_{max}\left(\frac{E_3-E_1}{E_1}\right)\right]}$$

Case (b) Separation & recycle ... maximize $\varphi_{desired}$.

- If the desired reaction, say ③, has the highest E value then operate at the highest allowable temperature
- If the desired reaction, say ②, has an intermediate E value then φ is maximized when T satisfies

$$\frac{1}{T_{opt}} = \frac{R}{E_3-E_1}\ln\left[\frac{E_3-E_2}{E_2-E_1}\cdot\frac{k_{30}}{k_{10}}\right]$$

- If the desired reaction, say ①, has the lowest E value use the lowest allowable temperature. Although this means very low conversion per pass φ will be very high. In practice some compromise will be arrived at between φ and conversion based on economic considerations.

Chapter 7 Problems

A1 Substance A in the liquid phase produces R and S by the following reactions:

$$A \begin{cases} \nearrow R, & r_R = k_1 C_A^2 \\ \searrow S, & r_S = k_2 C_A \end{cases}$$

The feed ($C_{A0} = 1.0$, $C_{R0} = 0$, $C_{S0} = 0.3$) enters two mixed reactors in series ($\tau_1 = 2.5$ min, $\tau_2 = 10$ min). Knowing the composition in the first reactor ($C_{A1} = 0.4$, $C_{R1} = 0.2$, $C_{S1} = 0.7$), find the composition leaving the second reactor.

A2 An organic A either isomerizes or dimerizes as follows

$$A \rightarrow R, \quad r_R = k_1 C_A$$

$$2A \rightarrow S, \quad r_S = k_2 C_A^2$$

Reactant A ($C_{A0} = 1$ mol/lit) in a solvent is charged to a batch reactor and there reacts away. What can you say about the kinetics of the reaction if $C_R = 0.24$ when reaction is complete.

Liquid reactant A decomposes as follows

$$A \begin{cases} \nearrow R, & r_R = k_1 C_A^2, & k_1 = 0.4\ \text{m}^3/\text{mol·min} \\ \searrow S, & r_S = k_2 C_A, & k_2 = 2\ \text{min}^{-1} \end{cases}$$

A feed of aqueous A ($C_{A0} = 40$ mol/m^3) enters a reactor, decomposes, and a mixture of A, R and S leaves.

A3 . . . Find C_R, and C_S and τ for $X_A = 0.9$ in a mixed flow reactor.

A4 . . . Find C_R, and C_S and τ for $X_A = 0.9$ in a plug flow reactor.

A5 . . . Find the operating condition (X_A, τ and C_S) which maximizes C_S in a mixed flow reactor.

A6 . . . Find the operating condition (X_A, τ and C_R) which maximizes C_R in a mixed flow reactor.

A7 . . . Select the reactor system (plug, mixed or any combination) and operating condition (X_A, τ and C_R) to maximize C_R. Separation and recycle of product is not permitted.

A8 . . . What reactor system will maximize C_R if separation, reconcentration (to $C_A = 40$) and recycle of unused A is possible. Find $C_{R\max}$ and τ for this case, and sketch the system selected.

Chapter 7 Problems

A9 In a reactive environment chemical A decomposes as follows:

$$A \nearrow R, \quad r_R = C_A \text{ mol/lit·s}$$
$$A \searrow S, \quad r_S = 1 \text{ mol/lit·s}$$

For a feed stream $C_{A0} = 4$ mol/lit what size ratio of two mixed flow reactors will maximize the production rate of R? Also give the composition of A and R leaving these two reactors.

Consider the parallel decomposition of A of different orders

$$A \nearrow R, \quad r_R = 1$$
$$A \rightarrow S, \quad r_S = 2\,C_A$$
$$A \searrow T, \quad r_T = C_A^2$$

Determine the maximum concentration of desired product obtainable in

(a) plug flow

(b) mixed flow

(c) in your choice of reactor where separation and recycle of unused reactant is possible

A10 . . . R is the desired product and $C_{A0} = 2$

A11 . . . S is the desired product and $C_{A0} = 4$

A12 . . . T is the desired product and $C_{A0} = 5$

Under ultraviolent radiation reactant A at $C_{A0} = 10$ kmol/m^3 in a process stream decomposes as follows.

$$A \nearrow R, \quad r_R = 16\,C_A^{.5}$$
$$A \rightarrow S, \quad r_S = 12\,C_A$$
$$A \searrow T, \quad r_T = C_A^2$$

We wish to design a reactor setup to maximize formation of a specific product. Any reactor combination will be considered, as well as separation, reconcentration to C_{A0}, and reuse of unconverted reactant. Sketch the scheme selected, calculated the fraction of feed transformed into desired product, and the volume of reactor needed.

Chapter 7 Problems

A13 . . . Product R is the desired material.

A14 . . . Product S is the desired material.

A15 . . . Product T is the desired material.

The stoichiometry of a liquid phase decomposition is known to be

$$A \begin{matrix} \nearrow R \\ \searrow S \end{matrix}$$

In a series of steady-state flow experiments ($C_{A0} = 100$, $C_{R0} = C_{S0} = 0$) in a laboratory mixed flow reactor the following results are obtained:

C_A	90	80	70	60	50	40	30	20	10	0
C_R	7	13	18	22	25	27	28	28	27	25

Further experiments indicate that the level of C_R and C_S have no effect on the progress of the reaction.

A16 . . . With a feed $C_{A0} = 100$ and exit concentration $C_{A1} = 20$, find C_R at the exit from a plug flow reactor.

A17 . . . With $C_{A0} = 200$ and $C_{Af} = 20$, find C_R at the exit from a mixed flow reactor.

A18 . . . How should we operate a mixed flow reactor so as to maximize the production of R? Separation and recycle of unused reactant is not practical and $C_{A0} = 150$.

Reactant A decomposes in an isothermal batch reactor ($C_{A0} = 100$) to produce wanted R and unwanted S and the following progressive concentration readings are recorded:

C_A	(100)	90	80	70	60	50	40	30	20	10	(0)
C_R	(0)	1	4	9	16	25	35	45	55	64	(71)

Additional runs show that adding R or S does not affect the distribution of products formed and that only A does. Also it is noted that the total number of moles of A, R, and S is constant.

With $C_{A0} = 100$ and $C_{Af} = 10$ find C_R

A19 . . . from a mixed flow reactor.

A20 . . . from a plug flow reactor.

Chapter 7 Problems

When aqueous A and aqueous B $(C_{A0} = C_{B0})$ are brought together they react in two possible ways

$$A + B \begin{cases} \nearrow R + T, & r_R = 50\, C_A \ \dfrac{\text{mol}}{\text{m}^3\cdot\text{hr}} \\ \searrow S + U, & r_S = 100\, C_B \ \dfrac{\text{mol}}{\text{m}^3\cdot\text{hr}} \end{cases}$$

to give a mixture whose concentration of active components (A, B, R, S, T, U) is $C_{total} = C_{A0} + C_{B0} = 60\ \text{mol/m}^3$. Find the size of reactor needed and the R/S ratio produced for 90% conversion of an equimolar feed $F_{A0} = F_{B0} = 300$ mol/hr

B21 . . . in a mixed flow reactor.

B22 . . . in a plug flow reactor.

B23 . . . in a reactor which gives highest C_R. Chapter 6 tells that this should be plug flow for A and side entry of B. In such a reactor introduce B in such a way that C_B is constant throughout the reactor.

B24 A and B react with each other as follows

$$2A \rightarrow R, \quad r_R = k_1 C_A^2$$
$$A + B \rightarrow S, \quad r_S = k_2 C_A C_B$$
$$2B \rightarrow T, \quad r_T = k_3 C_B^2$$

Find what ratio of A to B should be maintained in a mixed flow reactor so as to maximize the fractional yield of desired product to S.

B25 A liquid feed stream $(C_{A0} = 10\ \text{mol/lit},\ C_{B0} = 10\ \text{mol/lit})$ enters a mixed flow reactor $(\tau = 1\ \text{min})$ and reacts as follows

$$A + B \rightarrow R, \quad r_R = k_1 C_A C_B, \quad k_1 = 10\ \text{lit/mol}\cdot\text{min}$$
$$B + B \rightarrow S, \quad r_S = k_2 C_B^2, \quad k_2 = 20\ \text{lit/mol}\cdot\text{min}$$

Find the composition of the exit stream.

B26 A and B react as follows

$$A + 2B \rightarrow R, \quad r_R = k_1 C_A C_B^2$$

$$A + B \rightarrow S, \quad r_S = k_2 C_A C_B$$

Chapter 7 Problems

Reactants are charged into a batch reactor ($C_{A0} = 1$, $C_{B0} = 1$) and are left to react to completion. What can you say about the rate constants if analysis of the resulting mixture shows that $C_A = 0.3$?

B27 A combined feed of A and B ($v = 12$ lit/hr, $C_{A0} = C_{B0} = 1$ mol/lit) enters a mixed flow reactor ($V = 1$ lit) and there react away to form products R and S. What can you say about the kinetics of the reaction from the following information

$$A + 2B \rightarrow R, \quad r_R = k_1 C_A C_B^2$$

$$C_{Bf} = C_{Rf} = 0.2$$

$$A + B \rightarrow S, \quad r_S = k_2 C_A C_B$$

A and B react as follows

$$A + 2B \rightarrow R, \quad r_R = C_A C_B^2$$

$$A + B \rightarrow S, \quad r_S = C_A C_B$$

From a combined feed of $C_{A0} = C_{B0} = 1.5$ determine the exit composition which yields

B28 . . . the highest C_R from a plug flow reactor.

B29 . . . the highest C_R from a mixed flow reactor.

B30 Waste gas from a chemical factory present a pollution problem because of the presence of chemical A (50 parts/million) and chemical B (5 parts/million). Because they interact undesirably B must not exceed 1% of A and, in any case, the level of A must not exceed 30 parts/million for this to be acceptable. The laboratory has discovered that additive D will react by elementary second order reaction with both A and B to produce harmless R and S, with relative rates,

$$\frac{r_R}{r_S} = 0.16 \frac{C_A}{C_B}$$

However, unreacted D is not acceptable in the treated effluent. Assuming the treatment conditions are such that the reactions proceed to completion, how much D must be added to meet all the acceptable conditions?

Problem prepared by J. S. Ratcliffe.

Chapter 7 Problems

The decomposition of gaseous A gives a variety of products and can be represented by

$$A \rightarrow R \qquad r_R = 4.95 \times 10^4\, e^{-44\,000/RT}, \quad \text{mol/m}^3\cdot\text{min}$$

$$A \rightarrow S \qquad r_S = 1.04 \times 10^9\, e^{-126000/RT} C_A$$

$$A \rightarrow T \qquad r_T = 1.33 \times 10^6\, e^{-100000/RT} C_A^2$$

With a pure A feed at 7 atm, F_{A0} =1600 mol/min, and operations anywhere between 480°C and 580°C develop a flow sheet for producing S, the desired product in a single reactor. On it show the flows, temperatures and stream compositions the reactor type and size, and the moles of S produced/min.

C31 . . . Assume that the products of reaction are not easily separated, hence we must use a one pass reactor system.

C32 . . . Assume that the unconverted reactant can easily and cleanly be separated, brought back to 7 atm and recycled.

Reactant A decomposes as follows

$$A \rightarrow R, \qquad r_R = k_1 C_A, \quad k_1 = 2\ \text{hr}^{-1}$$

$$A \rightarrow S, \qquad r_S = k_2 C_A, \quad k_2 = 1\ \text{hr}^{-1}$$

The cost for reactants and products are as follows:

Reactant A costs \$0.2/mol at C_A = 1 mol/lit

Product R sells for \$1/mol when separated from A to S

Product S has no value

We are considering buying 600 mol/hr or A at C_{A0} = 1 mol/lit, reacting it in a mixed flow reactor, separating product R from the leaving stream, and selling it.

D33* . . . Determine the best reactor size and conversion of A to use. What profit do we make with this operation?

Data: Cost of mixed flow reactor and R-separator = \$0.1/lit of reactor·hr
Operating cost of reactor and separator = \$1 for each 7.5 lit of fluid treated/hr.

D34* . . . Another possibility is to also use a stripper which cleanly separates and recycles unused A from the product stream and brings it back to C_{A0} = 1 mol/lit. With this recycle stream what reactor size and X_A should be used and what is our profit with this arrangement?

Data: Cost of stripper = \$0.05 for each mol of product stream treated/hr.

Chapter 8. POTPOURRI OF MULTIPLE REACTIONS

This includes all sorts of reactions where the products react further. Here are some examples:

$$A \rightarrow R \rightarrow S \rightarrow T \rightarrow \cdots$$

series

$$\begin{aligned} A+B &\rightarrow R \\ R+B &\rightarrow S \\ S+B &\rightarrow T \\ &\vdots \end{aligned}$$

series-parallel, or consecutive-competitive

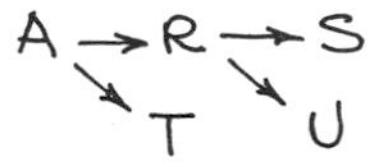

Denbigh system

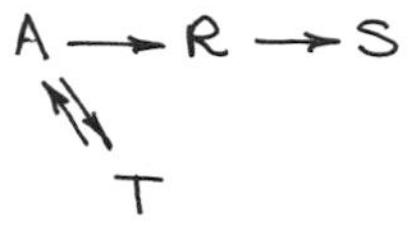

reversible and irreversible

$$A \rightleftarrows R \rightleftarrows S$$

reversible

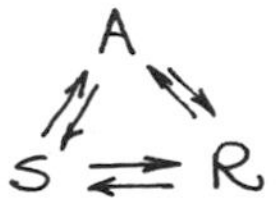

reversible network

We present the performance equations of some simple multiple reactions, and point out some of their special features such as maxima of intermediates. This should tell:

- the value of the rate constants
- what reactor type is best to use.

I. Two Step Reactions in Series (irreversible & first order)

$$A \xrightarrow[n_1=1]{k_1} R \xrightarrow[n_2=1]{k_2} S \quad \cdots \quad \begin{cases} -r_A = k_1 C_A & \cdots (1) \\ r_R = k_1 C_A - k_2 C_R & \cdots (2) \\ r_S = k_2 C_R & \cdots (3) \end{cases}$$

A material balance then gives $-\Delta C_A = \Delta C_R + \Delta C_S$ ... (4)

Let us consider, in turn,

- plug flow or batch operations with time $t_b = \tau_p$; call this t
- mixed flow with space time τ_m; call this τ
- how to do better than the best plug flow or best mixed flow.

A. Batch or plug flow.

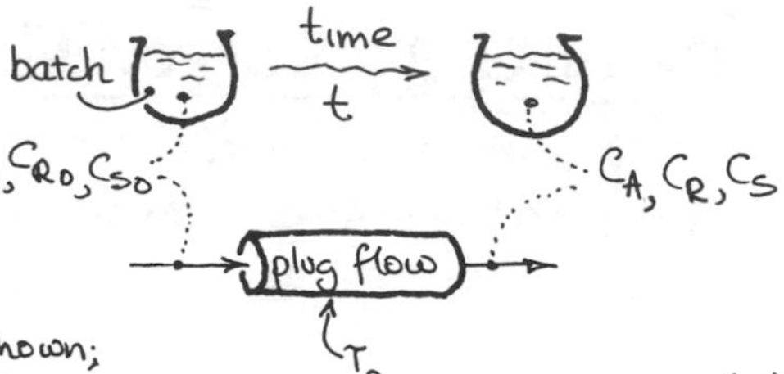

The performance equations for these operations are

$$\frac{C_A}{C_{A0}} = \exp(-k_1 t) \qquad \text{for batch use } t\text{, as shown; for plug flow use } \tau_p \qquad \cdots (5)$$

$$\frac{C_R}{C_{A0}} = \frac{k_1}{k_2-k_1}\left[\exp(-k_1 t) - \exp(-k_2 t)\right] + \frac{C_{R0}}{C_{A0}}\exp(-k_2 t) \qquad \cdots (6)$$

$$C_S = C_{A0} + C_{R0} + C_{S0} - C_A - C_R \qquad \cdots (7)$$

Graphically, for $C_{R0} = C_{S0} = 0$, here's how C_A, C_R and C_S change with time

$$\frac{C_{R,max}}{C_{A0}} = \left(\frac{k_1}{k_2}\right)^{k_2/k_2-k_1} \qquad \cdots (8)$$

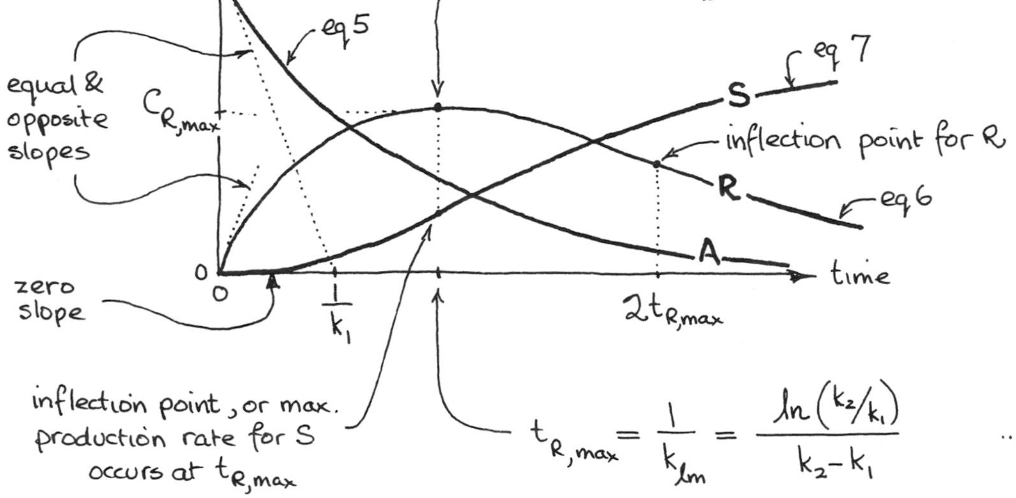

$$t_{R,max} = \frac{1}{k_{lm}} = \frac{\ln(k_2/k_1)}{k_2-k_1} \qquad \cdots (9)$$

Taking the ratio of concentrations (divide eq 6 by eq 5) eliminates the time variable and is useful for finding rate constants. The resulting equations and design chart are given on the next page.

$$\frac{C_R}{C_{A0}} = \frac{1}{1-K}\left[\left(\frac{C_A}{C_{A0}}\right)^K - \frac{C_A}{C_{A0}}\right] + \frac{C_{R0}}{C_{A0}}\left(\frac{C_A}{C_{A0}}\right)^K, \quad K = \frac{k_2}{k_1} \neq 1 \qquad \cdots (10)$$

$$= \frac{C_A}{C_{A0}}\left(\frac{C_{R0}}{C_{A0}} - \ln\frac{C_A}{C_{A0}}\right), \quad K = \frac{k_2}{k_1} = 1 \qquad \cdots (11)$$

From experiment locate a point on the design chart below. This will give the rate constants for the two step reaction.

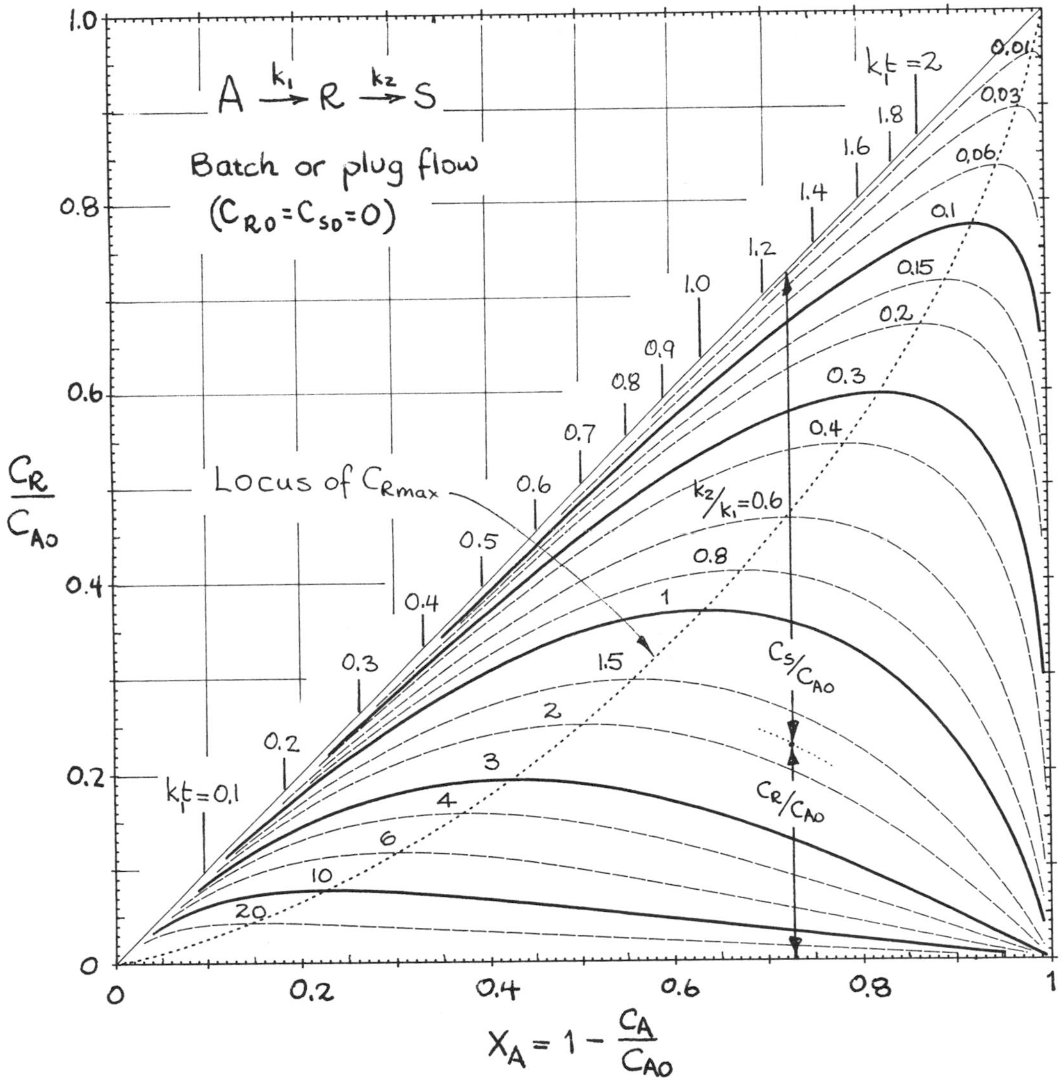

B. Mixed flow

From the rates (eqs 1, 2, 3) and performance eqs. ($\tau_m = (C_{io}-C_i)/(-r_i)$) we find

$$\frac{C_A}{C_{A0}} = \frac{1}{1+k_1\tau_m} \qquad \cdots (12)$$

$$\frac{C_R}{C_{A0}} = \frac{k_1\tau_m}{(1+k_1\tau_m)(1+k_2\tau_m)} + \frac{C_{R0}}{C_{A0}}\cdot\frac{1}{(1+k_2\tau_m)} \qquad \cdots (13)$$

$$C_S = C_{A0} + C_{R0} + C_{S0} - C_A - C_R \qquad \cdots (14)$$

Graphically, for $C_{R0} = C_{S0} = 0$ here's how C_A, C_R and C_S change with time

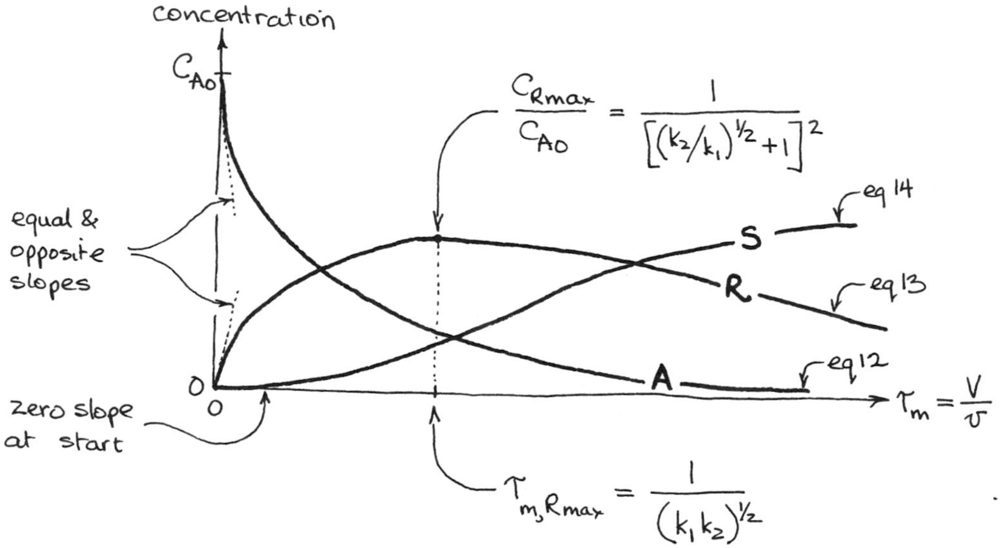

$$\frac{C_{R\,max}}{C_{A0}} = \frac{1}{\left[(k_2/k_1)^{1/2}+1\right]^2} \qquad \cdots (15)$$

$$\tau_{m,R\,max} = \frac{1}{(k_1k_2)^{1/2}} \qquad \cdots (16)$$

Dividing eq 13 by 12 gives C_R in terms of C_A

$$C_R = \frac{C_A(C_{A0}-C_A-C_{R0})}{C_A-(k_2/k_1)(C_{A0}-C_A)} \qquad \cdots (17)$$

The plot on the next page is a graphical representation of all the above equations for mixed flow.

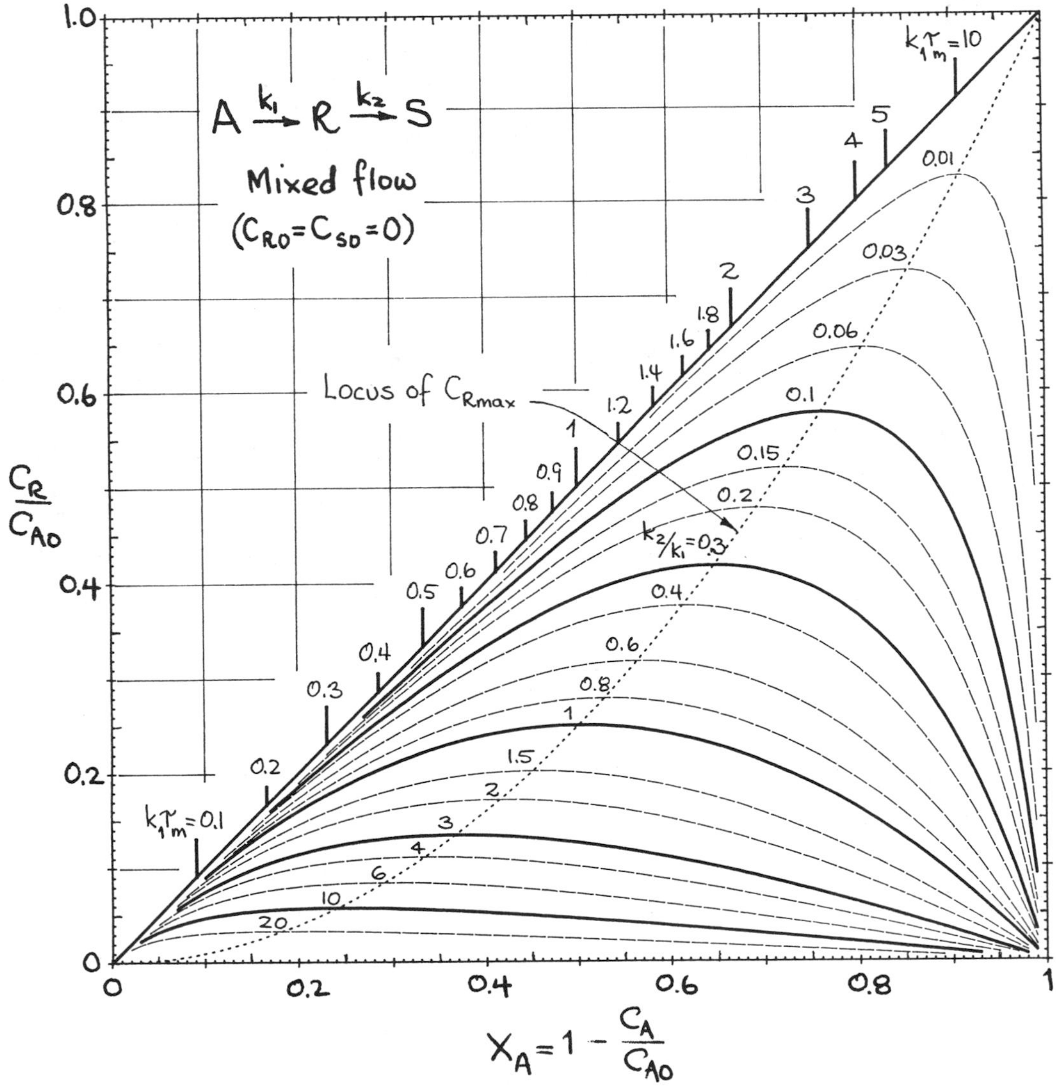

In principle, a single run measuring τ_m and two concentrations should give k_1 and k_2. In practice make a number of runs at different τ_m.

These graphs show that plug flow always gives a higher C_{Rmax}.

For reactions with different stoichiometry, such as $aA \rightarrow rR \rightarrow sS$ simply replace as follows:

$$\frac{C_R}{C_{A0}} \Rightarrow \frac{C_R}{rC_{A0}} \quad , \quad \frac{C_S}{C_{A0}} \Rightarrow \frac{C_S}{sC_{A0}}$$

II Two Step Reactions (mixed orders)

A. First order followed by zero order.

$$A \xrightarrow[n_1=1]{k_1} R \xrightarrow[n_2=0]{k_2} S \qquad \left.\begin{aligned} -r_A &= k_1 C_A \\ r_R &= k_1 C_A - k_2 \end{aligned}\right\} \quad \text{let } K = \frac{k_2/C_{A0}}{k_1} \qquad \cdots (18)$$

For **batch or plug flow** with $C_{R0} = C_{S0} = 0$

$$\frac{C_A}{C_{A0}} = e^{-k_1 t} \qquad \cdots (19)$$

$$\frac{C_R}{C_{A0}} = 1 - e^{-k_1 t} - \frac{k_2}{C_{A0}} t \qquad \cdots (20)$$

Graphically,

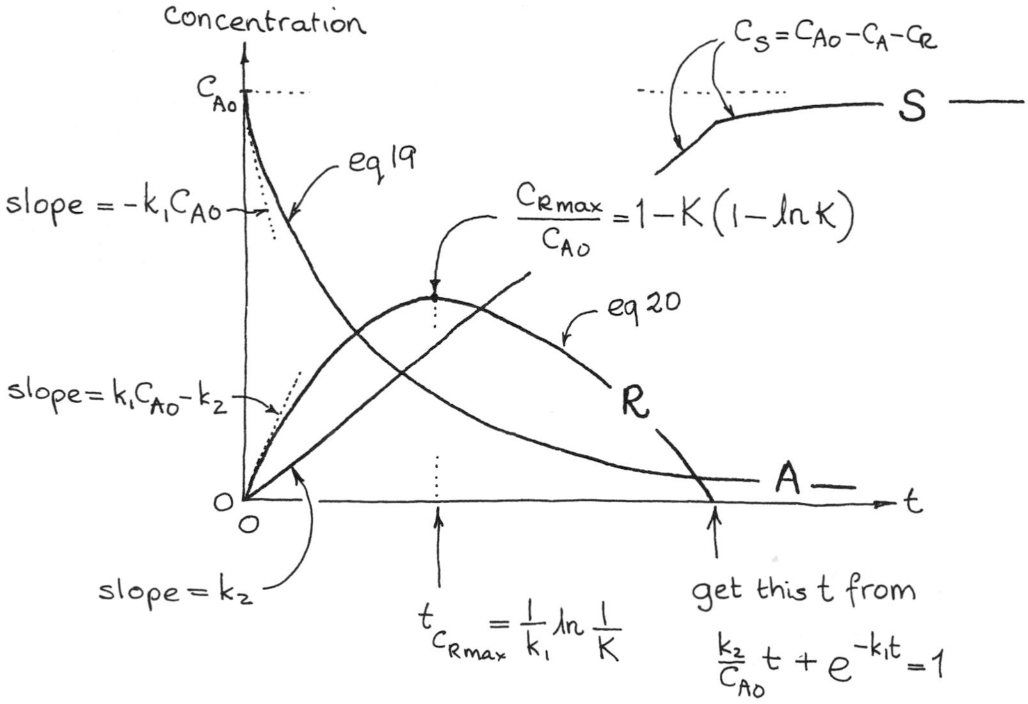

B. Zero order followed by first order.

$$A \xrightarrow[n_1=0]{k_1} R \xrightarrow[n_2=1]{k_2} S \qquad \left.\begin{aligned} -r_A &= k_1 \\ r_R &\begin{cases} = k_1 - k_2 C_R & \cdots A \text{ present} \\ = -k_2 C_R & \cdots A \text{ absent} \end{cases} \end{aligned}\right\} \quad K = \frac{k_2}{k_1/C_{A0}} \quad \cdots (21)$$

For **batch and plug flow** with $C_{R0} = C_{S0} = 0$

$$\frac{C_A}{C_{A0}} = 1 - \frac{k_1 t}{C_{A0}} \qquad \cdots (22)$$

$$\frac{C_R}{C_{A0}} \begin{cases} = \dfrac{1}{K}\left(1 - e^{-k_2 t}\right) & \cdots \; t < \dfrac{C_{A0}}{k_1} & \cdots (23) \\ = \dfrac{1}{K}\left(e^{K - k_2 t} - e^{-k_2 t}\right) & \cdots \; t > \dfrac{C_{A0}}{t} & \cdots (24) \end{cases}$$

Graphically

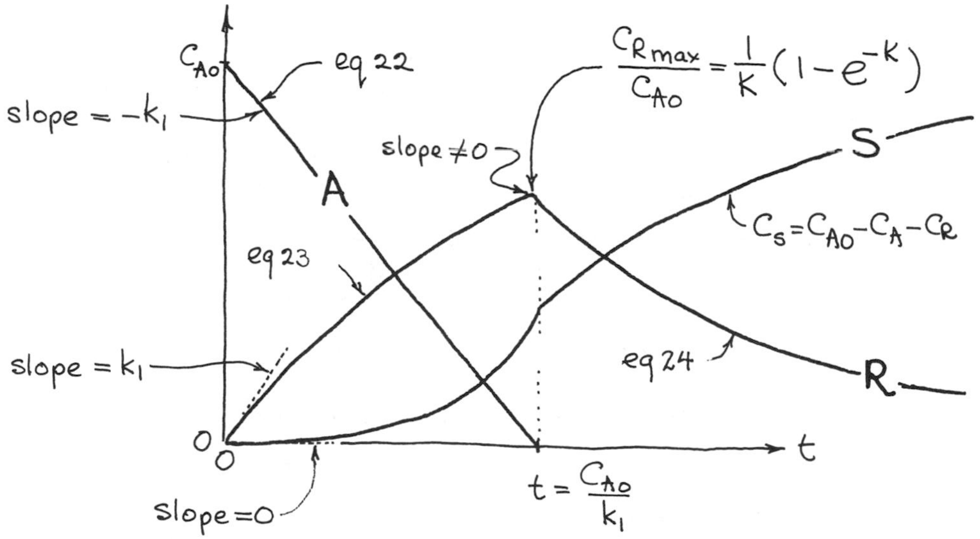

C. Other combination of reaction orders.

Solutions to all other combinations are complicated

III. Two Step Series - Parallel Reactions (irreversible, elementary)

$$A + B \xrightarrow[n_1=2]{k_1} R \qquad\qquad -r_A = k_1 C_A C_B$$
$$R + B \xrightarrow[n_2=2]{k_2} S \qquad\qquad \left.\begin{array}{l} r_R = k_1 C_A C_B - k_2 C_R C_B \\ r_S = k_2 C_R C_B \\ -r_B = k_1 C_A C_B + k_2 C_R C_B \end{array}\right\} K_2 = \frac{k_2}{k_1} \qquad \cdots (25)$$

A material balance for any flow pattern gives

for A $\qquad (-\Delta C_A) = \Delta C_R + \Delta C_S \qquad \cdots (26)$

where $-\Delta C_A = C_{A0} - C_A$, $\Delta C_R = C_R - C_{R0}$, $\Delta C_S = C_S - C_{S0}$

for B $\qquad (-\Delta C_B) = \Delta C_R + 2\Delta C_S \qquad \cdots (27)$

The progress of this reaction looks as follows

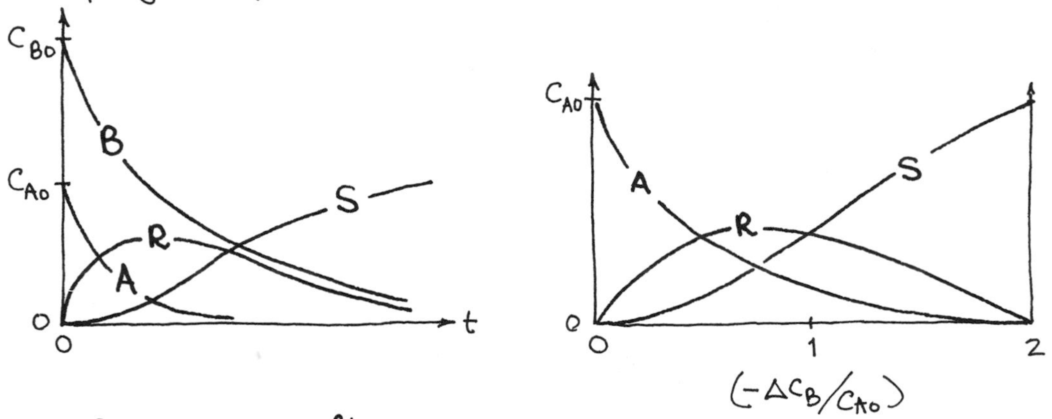

A. Batch or plug flow

Unfortunately, simple expressions telling how C_A, C_R, C_S & C_S change with time, analogous with eqs 5, 6 & 7 cannot be developed. Numerical methods are needed. However the time-independent distribution of C_A, C_R and C_S are identical to that for $A \to R \to S$. So we already have equations for

$$\frac{C_R}{C_{A0}} = f\left(\frac{C_A}{C_{A0}}\right) \cdots \text{eqs 10 \& 11}, \qquad \frac{C_{R\,max}}{C_{A0}} \cdots \text{eq 8}$$

At $C_{R\,max}$, with $C_{R0}=C_{S0}=0$, we also have

$$\left.\frac{C_A}{C_{A0}}\right|_{at\ R\,max} = K_2^{1/1-K_2}$$

$$\left.\frac{C_R}{C_{A0}}\right|_{at\ R\,max} = K_2^{K_2/1-K_2} \quad \text{... eq 8}$$

$$\left.\frac{C_S}{C_{A0}}\right|_{at\ R\,max} = 1 - K_2^{1/1-K_2} - K_2^{K_2/1-K_2}$$

$$\left.\frac{C_B}{C_{A0}}\right|_{at\ R\,max} = \frac{C_{B0}}{C_{A0}} - 2 - 2K_2^{1/1-K_2} - K_2^{K_2/1-K_2}$$

$$K_2 = \frac{k_2}{k_1} \quad \text{... (28)}$$

Graphical representation. The time-independent relationship between all the reaction components can be shown directly by the graph on the next page, as explained below

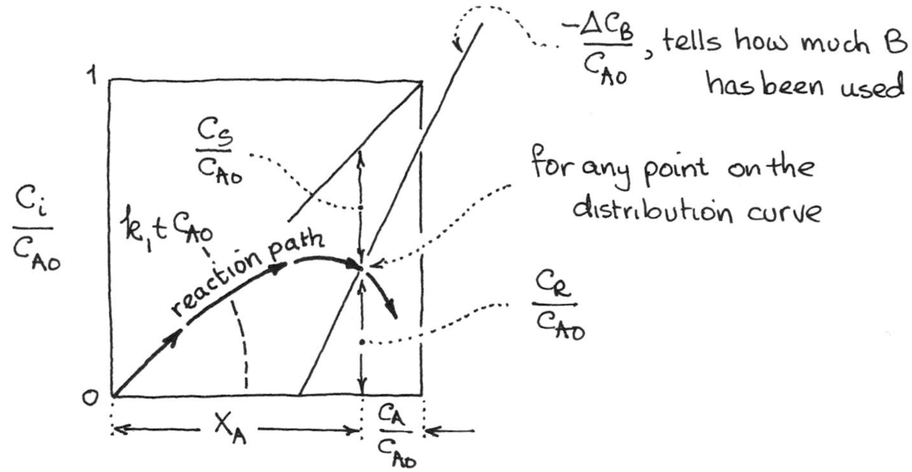

Following the concentration changes of any 2 of the 4 reaction components with time gives k_1 and k_2. Also, if C_B is large enough (in great excess) then this reaction system reduces to first order kinetics.

(8.10)

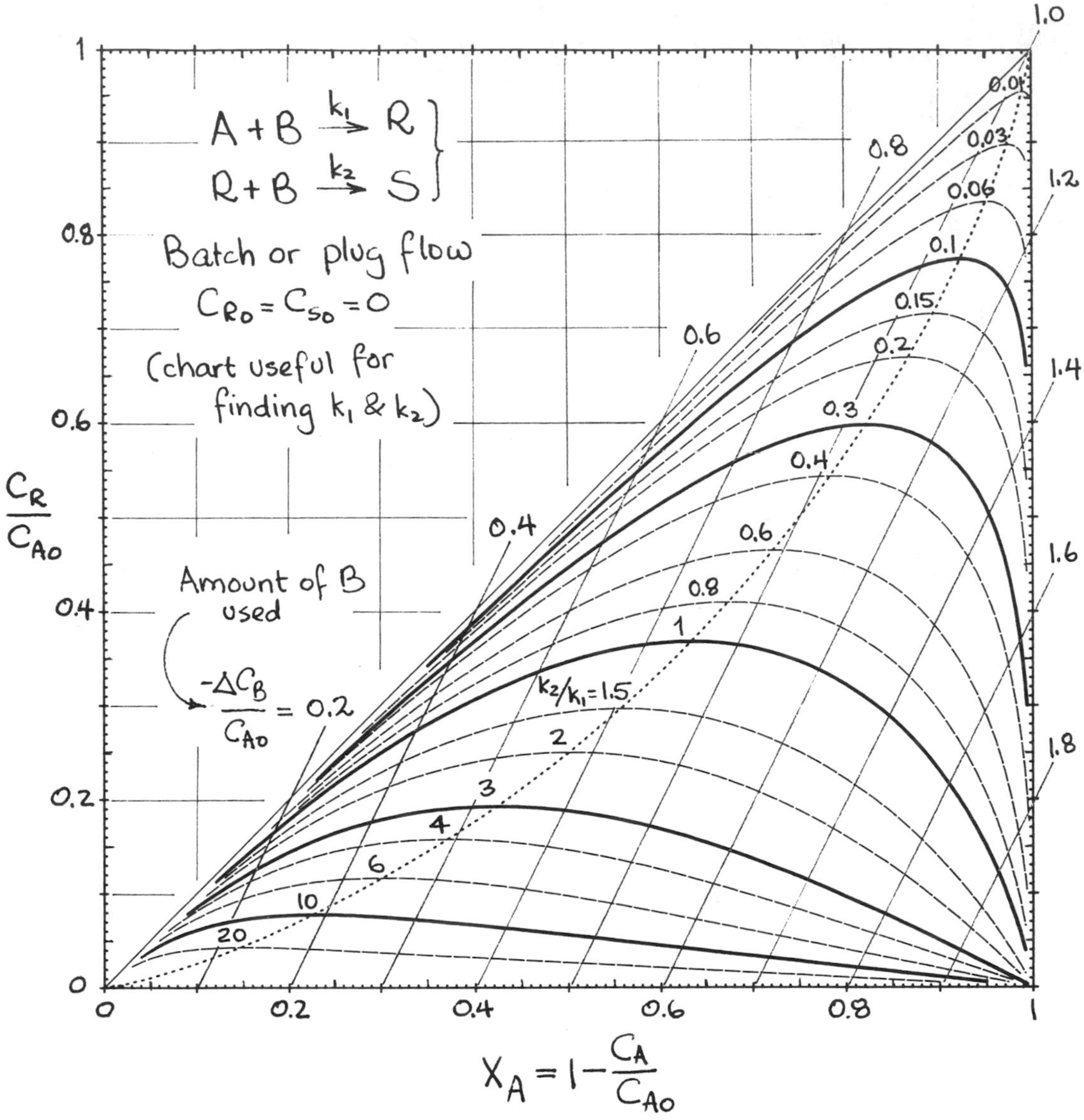

A very simple way to evaluate k_2/k_1 is as follows: add a little bit of B to a batch of A, let the reaction run to completion, then analyse and locate a point on the above graph. Then add a bit more B and repeat, so on. The attractiveness of this method is that no measurements need be made during a run. Just wait and then analyse concentrations at leisure.

B. Mixed Flow.

The performance equation for mixed flow combined with the rate expressions of eq. 25 give

$$\tau_m = \frac{C_{A0}-C_A}{k_1 C_A C_B}, \quad \tau_m = \frac{C_R - C_{R0}}{k_1 C_A C_B - k_2 C_R C_B}, \quad \tau_m = \frac{C_{B0}-C_B}{k_1 C_A C_B + k_2 C_R C_B} \quad \cdots (29)$$

C_S and C_B are given by eqs 26 and 27, and C_R is related to C_A by eq 17.

For the special case where $C_{R0}=C_{S0}=0$ we obtain simple expressions for the conditions where C_R is maximum, or

$$\left.\frac{C_A}{C_{A0}}\right)_{\text{at } R\,max} = \frac{N}{N+1}$$

$$\left.\frac{C_R}{C_{A0}}\right)_{\text{at } R\,max} = \frac{1}{(N+1)^2} \quad \cdots \text{eq } 15$$

$$\left.\frac{C_S}{C_{A0}}\right)_{\text{at } R\,max} = \frac{N}{(N+1)^2}$$

$$\left.\frac{C_B}{C_{A0}}\right)_{\text{at } R\,max} = \frac{C_{B0}}{C_{A0}} - \frac{2N+1}{(N+1)^2}$$

$$N = \left(\frac{k_2}{k_1}\right)^{1/2} \quad \cdots (30)$$

The general relationship between τ_m and all the concentrations is given in the figure on the next page. This is useful for testing the assumptions of this kinetic scheme and for evaluating the constants k_1 & k_2.

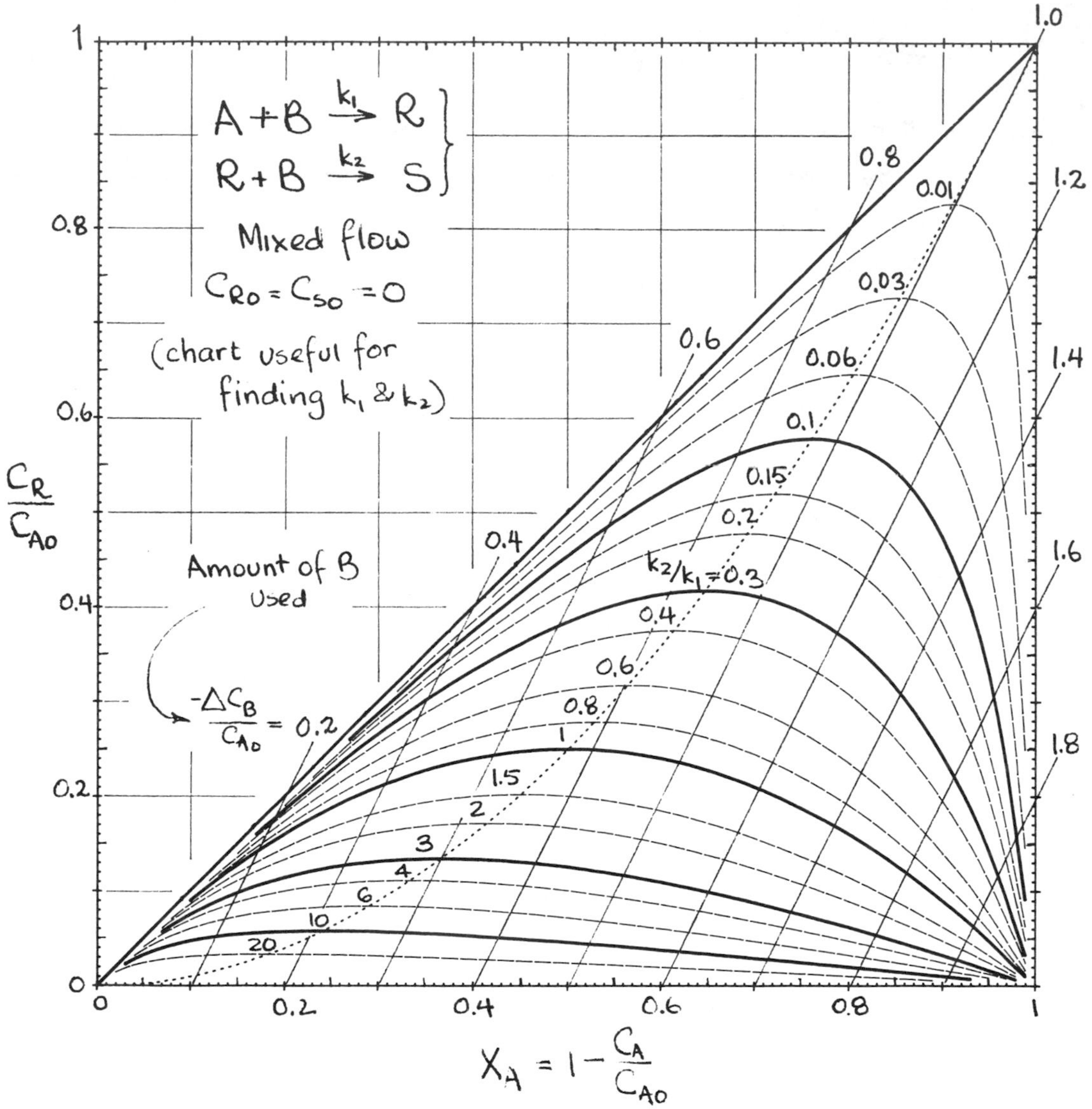

Rate constants from experiments. These can be found in a number of ways

(a) In principle any one steady state run with eq 29 should give k_1 and k_2 directly.

(b) Better still, make a series of runs at different C_A, C_B & C_A/C_B, and see if the data all fall on a line of constant k_1/k_2 in the chart above.

(c) One can also rearrange eqs 29 to get straight line plots from which k_1 and k_2 can be evaluated. Thus

$$\frac{C_{A0}}{C_A} = 1 + k_1 C_B \tau_m \Rightarrow k_1 \qquad \cdots (31)$$

$$\frac{(C_{B0} - C_{A0} + C_A)C_A}{(C_{A0} - C_A)C_R} = \frac{k_2}{k_1} + \frac{1}{k_1} \cdot \frac{1}{C_B \tau_m} \Rightarrow k_1 \text{ and } k_2 \qquad \cdots (32)$$

$$\frac{C_R}{C_A} = -\frac{k_1}{k_2} + \frac{1}{k_2} \frac{C_{B0} - C_B}{C_A C_B \tau_m} \Rightarrow k_1 \text{ and } k_2 \qquad \cdots (33)$$

C. Comments on series-parallel reactions.

- When separation and recycle of components is practical one can do better than plug flow. Which component you plan to recycle depends on the cost of materials.

When A is expensive, B cheap then recycle A.

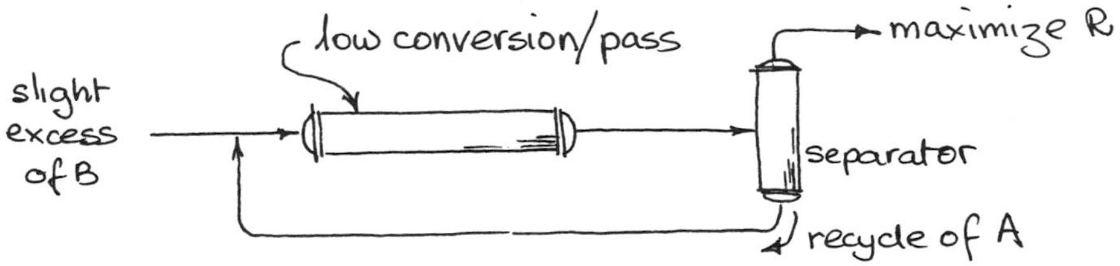

When B is expensive, A cheap then recycle B.

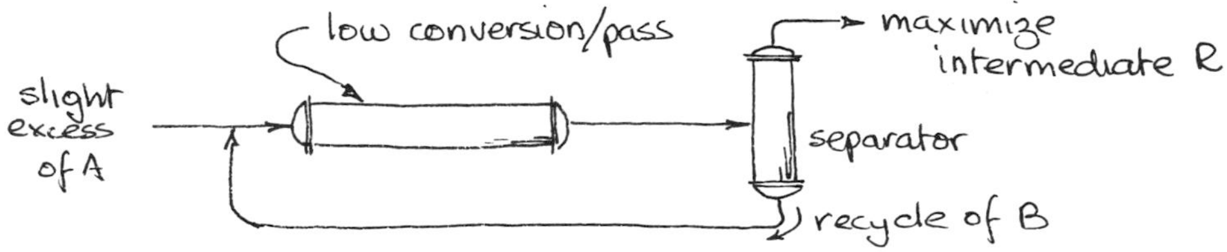

- In analysing data here is a useful approximation in calculating the capacity or time measure t, τ, V or v whenever $C_{B0} \gg C_{A0}$. Simply take C_B as a constant at $\overline{C_B}$ throughout the run and treat the system as pseudo first order.

IV The Denbigh Reaction and its Special Cases.

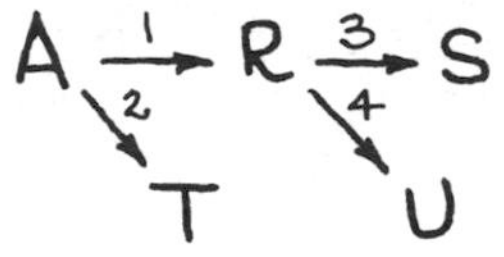

$$A \xrightarrow[2]{1} R \xrightarrow[4]{3} S$$
$$\quad\searrow \quad \searrow$$
$$\quad T \qquad U$$

$$\left.\begin{array}{l} -r_A = k_{12} C_A \\ r_R = k_1 C_A - k_{34} C_R \\ r_S = k_3 C_R \\ r_T = k_2 C_A \\ r_U = k_4 C_R \end{array}\right\} \quad \begin{array}{l} k_{12} = k_1 + k_2 \\[2mm] k_{34} = k_3 + k_4 \end{array} \qquad \cdots (34)$$

with

$$C_{Ao} + C_{Ro} + C_{So} + C_{To} + C_{Uo} = C_A + C_R + C_S + C_T + C_U \qquad \cdots (35)$$

The performance equations for this reaction scheme reduce directly to all the special cases, for example

$$A \to R \to S, \quad A \to R \begin{array}{c}\nearrow S\\\searrow U\end{array}, \quad A \to R \to S, \quad A \xrightarrow{\nearrow R} S, \quad A \begin{array}{c}\nearrow R\\\searrow T\end{array}$$
$$\qquad\qquad\qquad\qquad\qquad\qquad\quad\searrow T$$

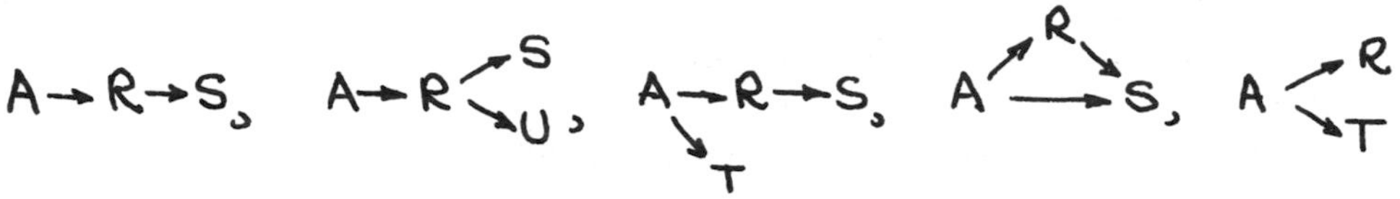

A. Batch or plug flow.

Integration gives the performance equations for this system

$$\frac{C_A}{C_{Ao}} = \exp(-k_{12} t) \qquad \cdots (36)$$

$$\frac{C_R}{C_{Ao}} = \frac{k_1}{k_{34} - k_{12}} \left[\exp(-k_{12} t) - \exp(-k_{34} t) \right] + \frac{C_{Ro}}{C_{Ao}} \exp(-k_{34} t) \qquad \cdots (37)$$

$$\frac{C_S}{C_{Ao}} = \frac{k_1 k_3}{k_{34} - k_{12}} \left[\frac{\exp(-k_{34} t)}{k_{34}} - \frac{\exp(-k_{12} t)}{k_{12}} \right] + \frac{k_1 k_3}{k_{12} k_{34}}$$

$$\qquad\qquad + \frac{C_{Ro}}{C_{Ao}} \frac{k_3}{k_{34}} \left[1 - \exp(-k_{34} t) \right] + \frac{C_{So}}{C_{Ao}} \qquad \cdots (38)$$

$$\frac{C_T}{C_{A0}} = \frac{k_2}{k_{12}}\left[1 - \exp(-k_{12}t)\right] + \frac{C_{T0}}{C_{A0}} \quad \ldots (39)$$

$\frac{C_U}{C_{A0}}$ ... same as $\frac{C_S}{C_{A0}}$ but with $k_3 \leftrightarrow k_4$ and $C_{S0} \leftrightarrow C_{U0}$

For the special case where $C_{R0} = C_{S0} = C_{T0} = C_{U0} = 0$ the above expressions simplify. We also can find $C_R = f(C_A)$, thus

$$\frac{C_R}{C_{A0}} = \frac{k_1}{k_{12} - k_{34}}\left[\left(\frac{C_A}{C_{A0}}\right)^{k_{34}/k_{12}} - \frac{C_A}{C_{A0}}\right]$$

or

$$\ln\frac{C_{A0}}{C_A} = \frac{k_{12}}{k_{12} - k_{34}} \ln\left(1 - \frac{k_{34} - k_{12}}{k_1}\frac{C_R}{C_A}\right) \quad \ldots (40)$$

Graphically we have

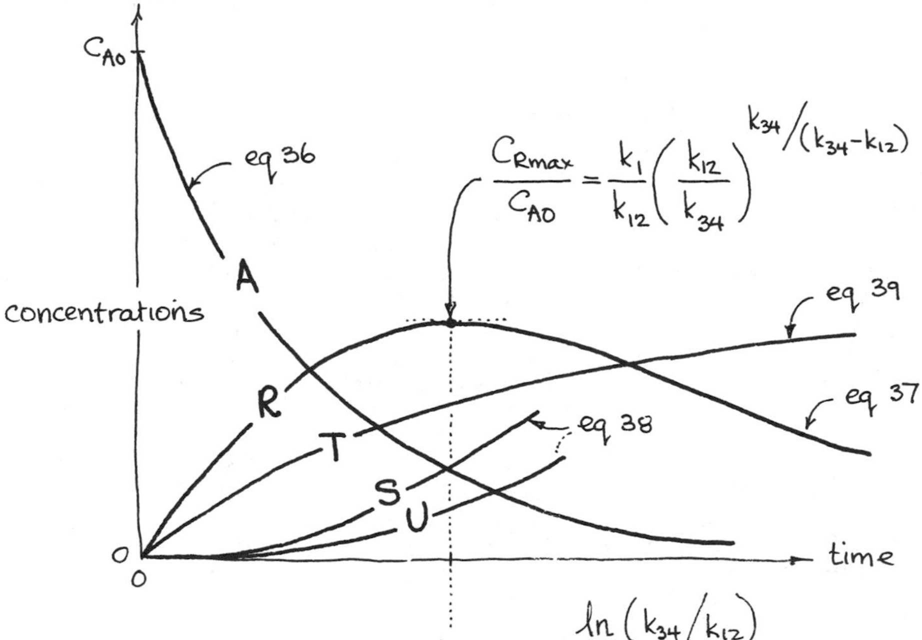

$$\frac{C_{R\max}}{C_{A0}} = \frac{k_1}{k_{12}}\left(\frac{k_{12}}{k_{34}}\right)^{k_{34}/(k_{34} - k_{12})} \quad \ldots (41)$$

$$t_{R\max} = \frac{\ln(k_{34}/k_{12})}{k_{34} - k_{12}} \quad \ldots (42)$$

B. Mixed flow.

Using the mixed flow performance equation with these rates gives

$$\frac{C_A}{C_{A0}} = \frac{1}{(1+k_{12}\tau_m)} \quad \cdots (43)$$

$$\frac{C_R}{C_{A0}} = \frac{k_1\tau_m}{(1+k_{12}\tau_m)(1+k_{34}\tau_m)} + \frac{C_{R0}}{C_{A0}}\frac{1}{(1+k_{34}\tau_m)} \quad \cdots (44)$$

$$\frac{C_S}{C_{A0}} = \frac{k_1k_3\tau_m^2}{(1+k_{12}\tau_m)(1+k_{34}\tau_m)} + \frac{C_{R0}}{C_{A0}}\cdot\frac{k_3\tau_m}{(1+k_{34}\tau_m)} + \frac{C_{S0}}{C_{A0}} \quad \cdots (45)$$

$$\frac{C_T}{C_{A0}} = \frac{k_2\tau_m}{(1+k_{12}\tau_m)} + \frac{C_{T0}}{C_{A0}} \quad \cdots (46)$$

$\frac{C_U}{C_{A0}}$ ... same as $\frac{C_S}{C_{A0}}$ but with $k_3 \leftrightarrow k_4$ and $C_{S0} \leftrightarrow C_{U0}$ ... (47)

Graphically, for $C_{R0} = C_{S0} = C_{T0} = C_{U0} = 0$.

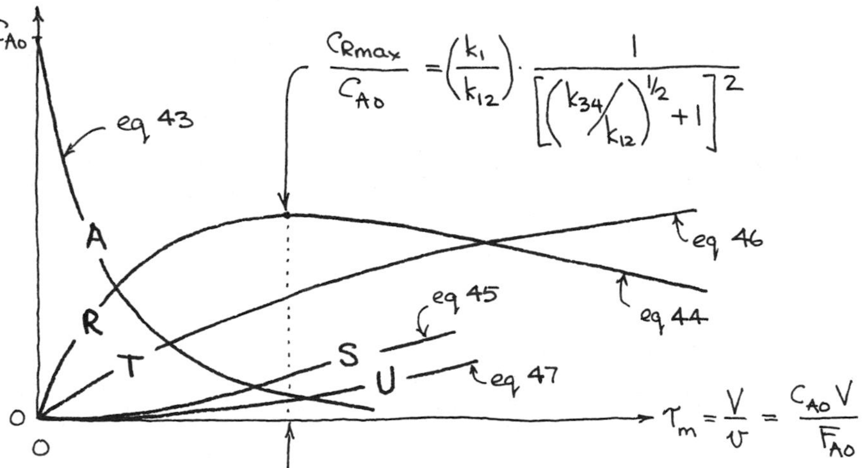

$$\frac{C_{R\,max}}{C_{A0}} = \left(\frac{k_1}{k_{12}}\right)\cdot\frac{1}{\left[\left(\frac{k_{34}}{k_{12}}\right)^{1/2}+1\right]^2} \quad \cdots (48)$$

$$\tau_{m,R\,max} = \frac{1}{(k_{12}/k_{34})^{1/2}} \quad \cdots (49)$$

V Comments, Suggestions and Extensions.

The equations of this chapter can be extended and applied directly to many other reaction schemes, for example

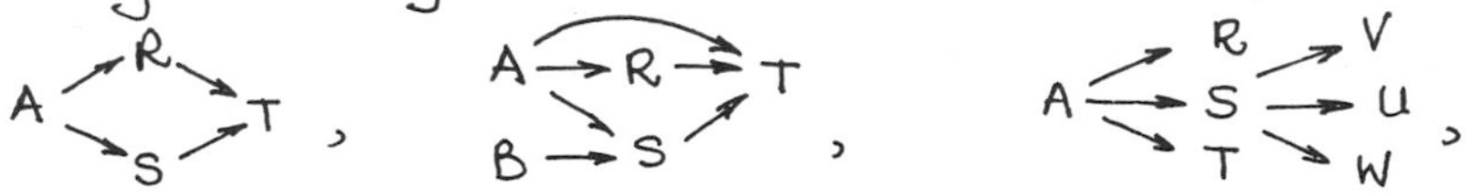

and so on.

Some problems at the end of this chapter consider these extensions.

A careful examination of the shape of the C vs t curves gives much useful information on the rate constants. Here are some clues:

- Look at the initial slope of the curves; measure the slopes; are the slopes of produced materials zero or not?
- Measure the final concentration of all the reaction components.
- Find when an intermediate reaches its maximum concentration, and measure this concentration.
- In searching for a model or mechanism for the reaction scheme make runs at different C_{A0} and different C_{B0}/C_{A0}.
- If possible also make runs starting with intermediate. For example, for $A \rightarrow R \rightarrow S$ start with R alone and follow its disappearance.

If two steps in series have very different values for their rate constants we can approximate the overall behavior as follows:

$$A \xrightarrow{k_1=100} R \xrightarrow{k_2=1} S \quad \Longrightarrow \quad A \xrightarrow{k} S, \text{ where } k = \frac{1}{\frac{1}{k_1}+\frac{1}{k_2}} = 0.99$$

For schemes involving different reaction orders, for reversible reactions, and for a very many step scheme typical of polymerizations analysis becomes complicated. For example see Chien JACS 70 2256 (1948) for the treatment of various 1st & 2nd order combinations.

Chapter 8 Problems

A1 We want to produce R from A in a batch reactor with a run time no greater than two hours and at a temperature somewhere between 5 and 90 °C. The kinetics of this liquid first order reaction system is as follows

$$A \xrightarrow{1} R \xrightarrow{2} S, \quad \begin{matrix} k_1 = 30\, e^{-20000/RT} \\ k_2 = 1.9\, e^{-15000/RT} \end{matrix} \qquad \begin{matrix} k = [\text{min}^{-1}] \\ R = 8.314\ \text{J/mol}\cdot\text{K} \end{matrix}$$

Determine the optimum temperature and run time to use, and the corresponding conversion of A to R.

A2 Chemical A reacts away by first order reactions as follows

$$A \xrightarrow{1} R \xrightarrow{2} S, \quad \begin{matrix} k_1 = 2\ \text{s}^{-1} \\ k_2 = 1\ \text{s}^{-1} \end{matrix}$$

We want to process two feed streams of A ($v_{0,1} = 1$ $C_{A0,1} = 1$ and $v_{0,2} = 2$, $C_{A0,2} = 2$) in a single flow reactor so as to produce as much R as possible. How should this be done (side feed and/or recycle is allowed) and what concentrations of A and R and conversion X_A will exit from the reactor?

A3 Ultraviolet irradiation of ergosterol produces active vitamin D. However, this radiation also attacks the vitamin D formed transforming it into an inactive form. Thus

$$\text{ergosterol} \xrightarrow[\text{radiation}]{\text{u.v.}} \begin{matrix} \text{active form} \\ \text{of vitamin D} \end{matrix} \xrightarrow[\text{radiation}]{\text{u.v.}} \begin{matrix} \text{inactive form} \\ \text{of vitamin D} \end{matrix}$$

Clumsy Chemical Company has the following set up for production of vitamin D. A large vat is first filled with ergosterol solution. Then a small stream of this solution is continually removed, irradiated, and returned to the vat. Conversion per pass is small and the vat is kept well mixed and isothermal at all times. After 36 hours the operation is stopped, the vat discharged and its contents sent to the product separation unit. An analysis of the vat's contents shows that 95% of the ergosterol has reacted but the resulting vitamin D is only 21% active.

Have you any recommendations for improving the process? If so, what are they?

B4 Chemicals A and B react to form desired R and unwanted S by the following elementary reactions

$$\begin{matrix} A + B \xrightarrow{1} R \\ R + B \xrightarrow{2} S \end{matrix} \qquad k_1 = 2k_2$$

From the following information find the minimum cost of producing R in a flow system. Also give the feed ratio to use, the conversion of feed materials and the cost of R produced.

<u>Data:</u> A costs \$3/mol, B costs \$10/mol, reactor costs can be ignored and reaction is quite fast. Also assume that separation and recycle of materials is not practical.

Chapter 8 Problems

B5 The liquid phase reaction of aniline with ethanol produces wanted monoethylaniline and unwanted diethylaniline

$$C_6H_5NH_2 + C_2H_5OH \xrightarrow[H_2SO_4]{k_1} C_6H_5NHC_2H_5 + H_2O$$

$$k_1 = 1.25\ k_2$$

$$C_6H_5NHC_2H_5 + C_2H_5OH \xrightarrow[H_2SO_4]{k_2} C_6H_5N(C_2H_5)_2 + H_2O$$

(a) An equimolar feed is introduced into a batch reactor and reaction is allowed to proceed to completion. Find the concentration of reactants and products at the end of the run.

(b) Find the ratio of mono- to diethylaniline produced in a mixed flow reactor for an alcohol to aniline feed ratio of 2 to 1 for 70% conversion of alcohol.

(c) For an equimolar feed to a plug flow reactor what will be the conversion of the two reactants when the concentration of monoethylaniline is at its highest.

B6 Monoethylaniline can also be produced in the vapor phase in a fluidized bed using natural bauxite as the solid catalyst. The elementary reactions are shown in the previous problem. Using an equimolar feed of aniline and ethanol the fluidized bed produces 3 parts monoethylaniline to 2 parts diethylaniline for a 40% conversion of aniline. Assuming mixed flow of gas in the fluidized bed

(a) find the rate constants for the two reaction steps, and

(b) find the concentration of reactants and products at the exit of the reactor

B7 We suspect that A and B combine by the following elementary reactions

$$A + B \xrightarrow{1} R$$
$$R + B \xrightarrow{2} S$$

To check this we mix different proportions of A and B in three test tubes and leave them standing overnight. Next morning we analyze for S and find the following

Initial feed C_{A0}	Initial feed C_{B0}	After an overnight wait C_S/C_{A0}
20	50	~ 1.00
80	80	~ 0.43
50	30	~ 0.21

(a) Have we waited long enough for the reaction to go to completion?

(b) Is the reaction mechanism consistent with the data?

(c) If so, what can you say about the rate constants?

Chapter 8 Problems

B8 To cleanse ethylene feed streams (99% ethylene) of traces of acteylene (1%) we react the feed with H_2 over an appropriate catalyst. During this operation the following elementary reactions occur

$$C_2H_2 + H_2 \xrightarrow{1} C_2H_4$$

$$C_2H_4 + H_2 \xrightarrow{2} C_2H_6$$

and if we are not careful we may lose more ethylene than we make. If $k_1 = 10\ k_2$ how much ethylene do we lose by converting 99% of the acetylene into ethylene?

B9 In grinding pigments for paint or ink our company feeds a continuous stream of too-large particles to a well mixed grinder. A multistage grinder, approximating plug flow, could also have been used, but isn't. Anyway, in either type of grinder the pigments are progressively ground into smaller and smaller particles.

At present, the exit stream from our well mixed grinder contains 10% too-large (d_p>147μm), 32% just-right (d_p = 38 -147μm), and 58% too-small particles (d_p<38μm).

(a) Can you suggest a better grinding scheme for our present processor, and what would it give?

(b) How about the multistage grinder, how would it do?

By "better" we mean giving more just-right sized pigment in the product stream. Also, separation and recycle of the size cuts is not practical.

C10 When oxygen is bubbled through a high temperature batch of A-containing liquid material A oxidizes slowly to give R, as follows

t, min	C_A, mol/m³	C_R, mol/m³
0	100	0
0.1	95.8	1.4
2.5	35	26
5	12	41
7.5	4.0	52
10	1.5	60
20	negligible	80
∞	0	100

This data suggests that some slowly decomposing intermediate X may be involved or may be formed during the reaction. However, we have no way of analyzing for it.

What can you say about the mechanism and kinetics of this oxidation?

Chapter 8 Problems

C11 Consider the following first order decompositions with rate constants as shown

(a)
$$A \xrightarrow{30} R \xrightarrow{10} S$$
$$\downarrow 10 \quad \downarrow 0.01$$
$$T \qquad U$$

(b)
$$A \xrightarrow{0.02} R \xrightarrow{10} S$$
$$\downarrow 0.01 \quad \downarrow 30$$
$$T \qquad U$$

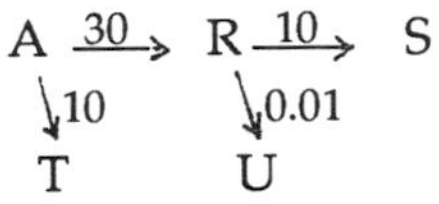

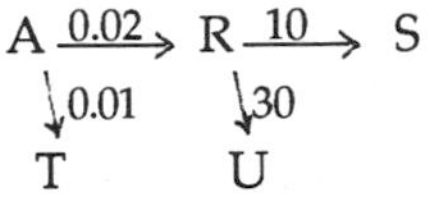

If a colleague reports that $C_S = 0.2 C_{A0}$ in the exit stream of a plug flow reactor what can you say about the concentration of the other reaction components, A, R, T, and U in the exit stream?

C12 Chemicals A and B are thrown into a vat and react away according to the following elementary reactions

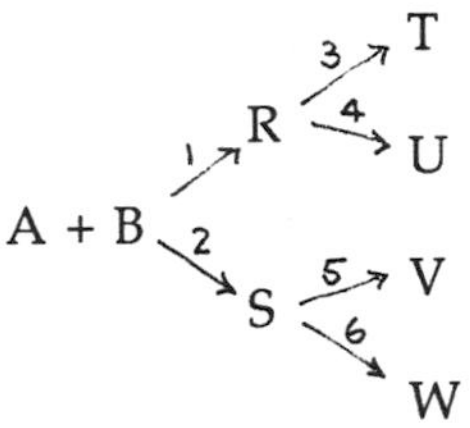

with $C_{A0} = C_{B0}$

What can you say about these six rate constants if an analysis of the mixture shows that

$$C_T = 5 \text{ mol/lit} \qquad C_U = 1 \text{ mol/lit}$$
$$C_V = 9 \text{ mol/lit} \qquad C_W = 3 \text{ mol/lit}$$

at the time

(a) when the reactants in the vat have half reacted?

(b) when reaction is complete?

C13 With a particular catalyst and at a given temperature the oxidation of naphthalene to phthalic anhydride proceeds as follows

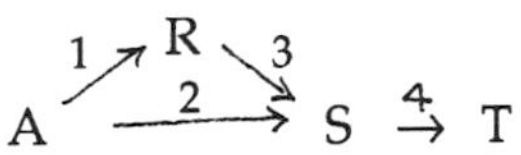

A = naphthalene	$k_1 = 0.21 \text{ s}^{-1}$
B = naphthaquinone	$k_2 = 0.20 \text{ s}^{-1}$
S = phthalic anhydride	$k_3 = 4.2 \text{ s}^{-1}$
T = oxidation products	$k_4 = 0.004 \text{ s}^{-1}$

What reactor type gives the maximum yield of phthalic anhydride? Roughly estimate this yield and the fractional conversion of naphthalene which will give this yield.

Chapter 8 Problems

C14 The progressive chlorination of *o*- and *p*-dichlorobenzene proceeds as shown below, with second order rate constants,

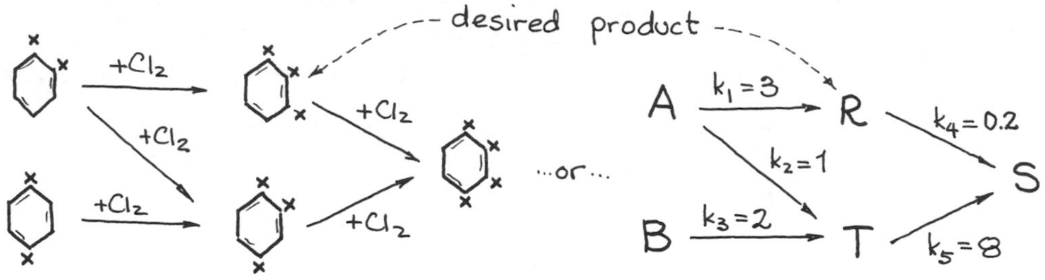

For a single feed stream having $C_{A0} = 2\,C_{B0} = 1$ and 1, 2, 3-trichlorobenzene as the desired product

(a) tell which kind of flow reactor is best.

(b) In this reactor find $C_{R\max}$.

See Corrigan, Chem. Eng. 201, March 1956, for discussion of this process.

Pure A ($C_{A0} = 100$) is fed to a mixed flow reactor, R and S are formed, and the following outlet concentrations are recorded. Find a kinetic scheme to fit this data

D15 ...

Run	C_A	C_R	C_S
1	75	15	10
2	25	45	30

D16 ...

Run	C_A	C_R	C_S
1	50	$33\frac{1}{3}$	$16\frac{2}{3}$
2	25	30	45

D17 ...

Run	C_A	C_R	C_S	t, min
1	50	40	10	5
2	20	40	40	20

D18* ...

Run	C_A	C_R	C_S
1	75	15	10
2	25	25	50

If you were able to fit this data with a series mechanism, try a parallel mechanism as well, and vice versa.

Chapter 8 Problems

D19 The kinetics of the reaction of A to R is studied in a mixed flow reactor, with the following results

τ, sec	25	90	200	1270
C_A, mol/m^3	24	12	6	1

$C_{A0} = 30$ mol/m^3
$C_{R0} = 0$

It is suspected that one or more of the following kinetic forms fits the data.

(a) $A \rightarrow R$

(b) $A + R \rightarrow 2R$

(c) $A \rightarrow R$
$A + R \rightarrow 2R$

See if any of these forms does, and if so then evaluate the rate constants. If none does, then try to come up with a rate form which does fit the data.

D20 Upper Slobbovians and Lower Slobbovians are always at it..., crushing skulls, slitting throats, and so on... . At any gathering the rate at which Upper Slobs are killed is directly proportional to the number of Lower Slobs around, and vice versa. And, at the end of any meeting of these friendly people either Upper Slobs leave, or Lower Slobs ... but never both.

Last week ten Upper Slobs happened upon three Lower Slobs, and when it was all over eight Upper Slobs lived to tell of their exciting victory.

(a) From this encounter how would you rate Upper and Lower Slobs as fighters? For example, would you say that they are equally good, or that one Upper Slob is as good as 2.3 Lower Slobs, or what?

(b) What would be the outcome of a friendly meeting of ten Upper Slobs with ten Lower Slobs?

D21 Chemical X, a powdered solid, is slowly and continuously fed for half an hour into a well stirred vat of water. The solid quickly dissolves and hydrolyses to Y which then slowly decomposes to Z as follows

$$Y \rightarrow Z, \quad -r_Y = kC_Y, \quad k = 1.5\ \text{hr}^{-1}$$

The volume of liquid in the vat stays close to 3 m^3 throughout this operation, and if no reaction of Y to Z occurred the concentration of Y in the vat would be 100 mol/m^3 at the end of the half hour addition of X.

(a) What is the maximum concentration of Y in the vat and at what time is this maximum reached?

(b) What is the concentration of product Z in the vat after one hour?

Problem prepared by Bhaskar Chandan.

Chapter 8 Problems

D22 A large fully automated municipal incinerator is being designed. A survey estimates the garbage load to be 1440 tons/day. This will be harvested by a fleet of compaction trucks which will disgorge their 6-ton loads into an underground storage bin. A conveyor will then feed the garbage to the incinerator.

The proposed daily collection route is such that at the beginning of the working day (6 a. m. sharp!) relatively large quantities of garbage are returned from nearby commercial areas. Subsequently, the supply will diminish as more remote suburban areas are serviced. It is assumed that the collection rate is proportional to the amount of garbage still to be collected, the initial rate being one truckload/min. The conveyer, on the other hand, will transport garbage at a uniform 1 ton/min to the incinerator. At the beginning of the working day, the trucks will work faster than the conveyer; later in the day slower. Thus, each day the bin will accumulate material, then lose material.

To evaluate this operation we need information. Please help us with this.

(a) At what time of day will the trucks have collected 95% of the day's garbage?

(b) How much garbage should the storage bin be designed for?

(c) At what time of day will the bin be fullest?

(d) At what time of day will the bin be empty?

D23* Chemical A decomposes in water (B) to give a variety of products. The elementary reactions are

$$A + B \overset{1}{\nearrow} R \xrightarrow{3} S$$
$$A + B \overset{2}{\searrow} T \xrightarrow{4} U$$

To study the kinetics A is introduced into a water-filled batch reactor (C_{A0} = 1 mol/lit, C_{B0} = 54 mol/lit) and the following concentration-time data are recorded.

t, min	C_A	C_R	C_T, mol/lit
3	0.49	0.41	0.08
6	0.24	0.59	0.11
9	0.12	0.65	0.12
12	0.06	0.66	0.11
15	0.03	0.65	0.11

What can you say about the second order rate constants k_1 and k_2 and the first order rate constants k_3 and k_4?

The idea for this problem came from Binns *et. al.* Trans. I. Chem. E. **47** T53 (1969) and the above data are close (with artistic license) to their reported values.

Chapter 8 Problems

D24* Japanese researchers followed the oxidation of sodium sulfide, Na_2S, in a batch reactor, and found results somewhat as sketched below

(a) Think up a simple network of reactions, all of first order, to represent this oxidation.

(b) Evaluate the constants of this network.

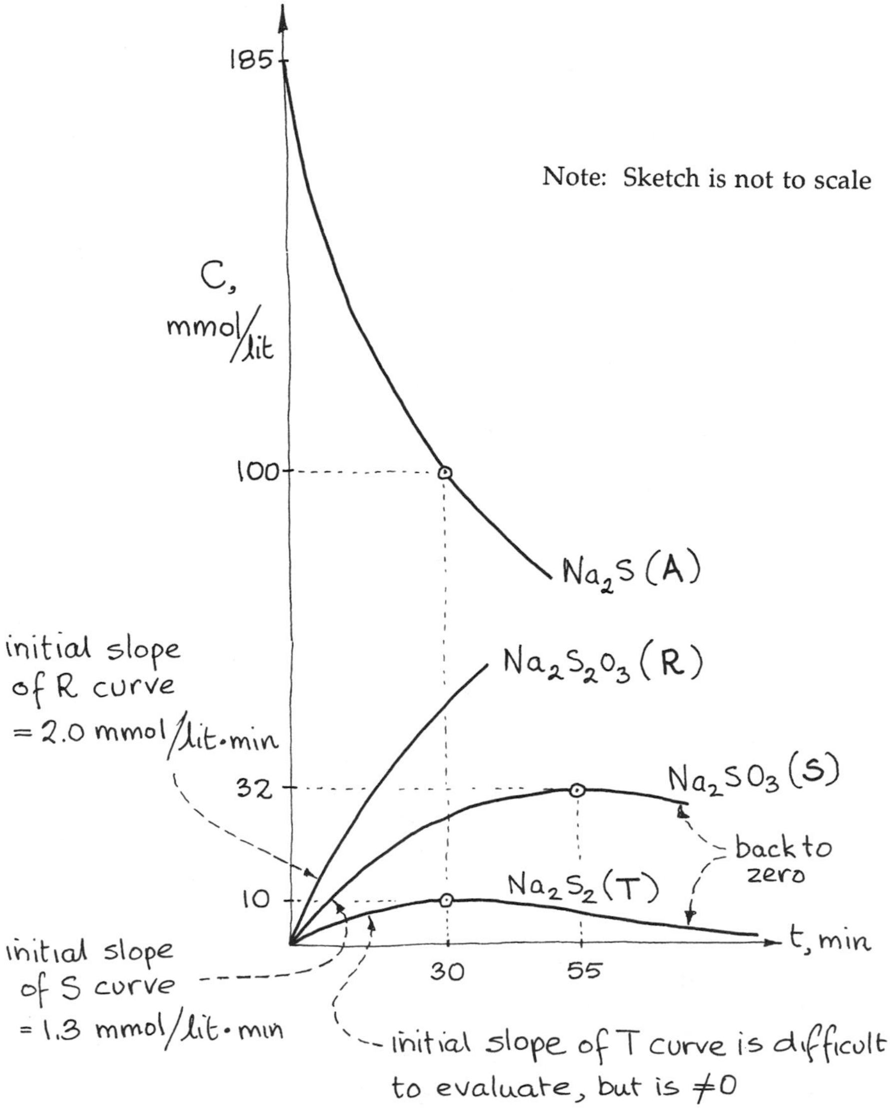

This problem was prepared by David L. Cates

Chapter 11. MULTIPHASE REACTORS, BACKGROUND DISCUSSION.

Multiphase reactors require the presence contact and interaction of more than one phase for the reactions to proceed as they do. They include fluid-fluid (G/L and L_1/L_2), fluid-solid (G/S and L/S) and three or more phase systems. For example, the blast furnace has at least five phases (G, L_1, L_2, S_1, S_2). In this chapter we discuss, in general terms, the factors which influence the behavior of these systems.

I Kinetics.

For reaction to take place material must move from the main body of a phase to its boundary or into another phase. Hence mass transfer kinetics must also be included in the overall rate.

Example 1. Burning of a carbon particle. For simplicity ignore the formation of CO.

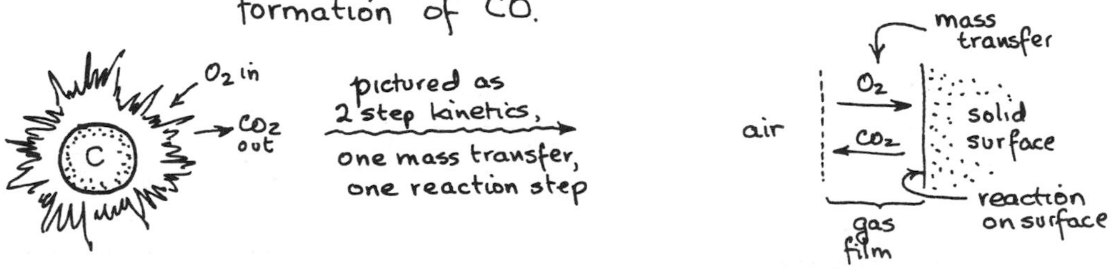

Example 2. Aerobic fermentation. Here the microbes "breathe" oxygen.

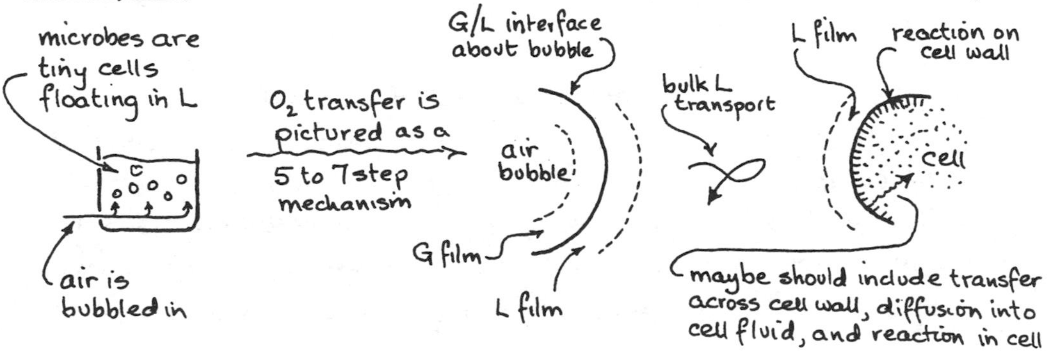

To get an **overall rate expression**

- write the individual rate steps on the same basis (unit surface of burning particle, unit volume of fermenter, unit volume of cells, etc). Now define

$$-r_A = -\frac{1}{V}\frac{dN_A}{dt} = \frac{\text{mol A reacted}}{\text{volume of reactor fluid} \cdot \text{time}}$$

$$-r_A' = -\frac{1}{W}\frac{dN_A}{dt} = \frac{\text{mol A reacted}}{\text{mass of solid} \cdot \text{time}}$$

$$-r_A'' = -\frac{1}{S}\frac{dN_A}{dt} = \frac{\text{mol A reacted}}{\text{surface} \cdot \text{time}}$$

then convert from one definition to another by putting

$$\frac{\text{mol A reacted}}{\text{time}} = (-r_A)V = (-r_A')W = (-r_A'')S$$

Thus

$$r = \frac{W}{V}r', \quad r'' = \frac{V}{S}r, \quad \text{etc.}$$

- if steps are in series

$$r_{overall} = r_1 = r_2 = \cdots$$

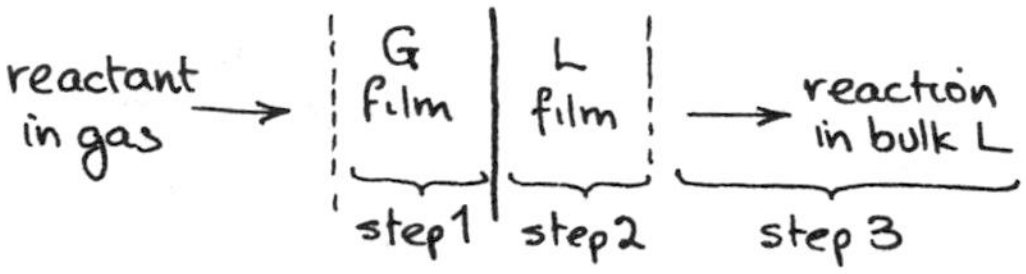

- if steps are in parallel

$$r_{overall} = r_1 + r_2 + \cdots$$

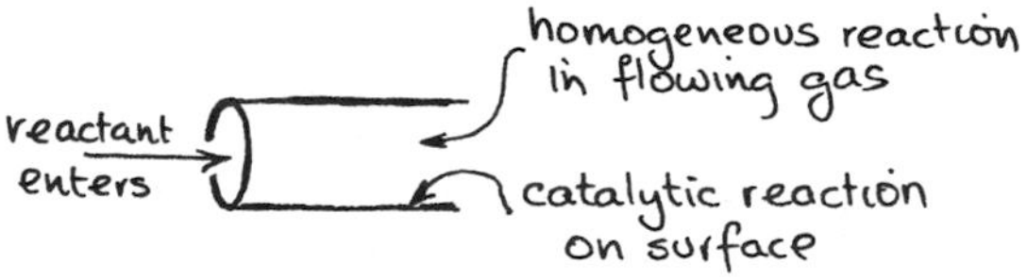

In chapter 41 G/L reactions are treated as 3 steps in series. In chapter 22 reactions on porous catalyst pellets are represented by the complex interaction of 5 heat, mass and reaction steps. In chapter 25 reactions in fluidized beds are represented by 5 to 13 steps in series-parallel arrangement, and so on. For each type of system we must develop the appropriate kinetics.

In general, if all the resistance steps are linear in concentration then it is easy to combine rates. However, if any of the steps is non linear then you get a messy overall rate expression. Since the mass transfer steps are all linear in ΔC, hence concentration, it is the reaction step alone which may be non linear and can cause difficulties.

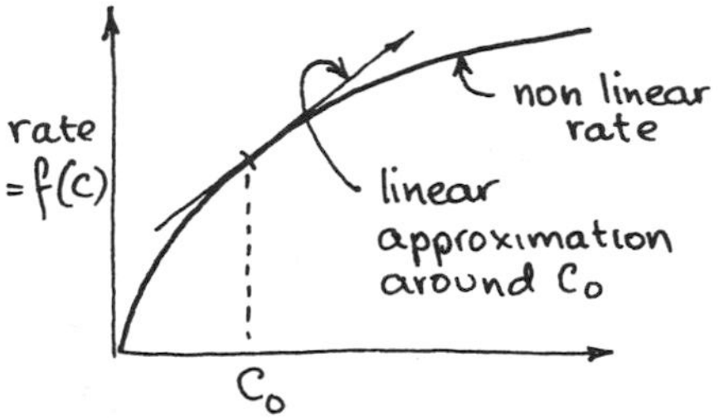

We may try to bypass the messy exact expression by replacing the non linear step with a linear approximation. To linearize about C_0 use a Taylor expansion

$$\underbrace{f(C)}_{\text{non linear}} \cong \underbrace{f(C_0) + (C - C_0) f'(C_0)}_{\text{linear approximation}} + \underbrace{\text{higher terms}}_{\text{ignore}}$$

Better still, often the resistance of one or other of the steps in series dominates and can be taken as rate controlling. Thus the other steps can be ignored. In series - parallel systems we must be careful about which terms to ignore and how to combine terms.

Example 3. Develop the overall rate expression for the following G/S reaction

$$A(g) + B(s) \longrightarrow R(g)$$

taking place on a flat plate. Reaction on the surface is 1st order with respect to A, and account for mass transfer through the film.

Solution

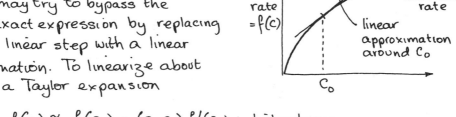

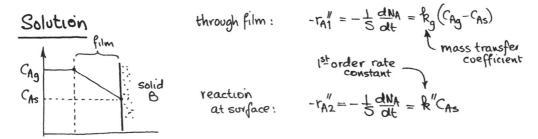

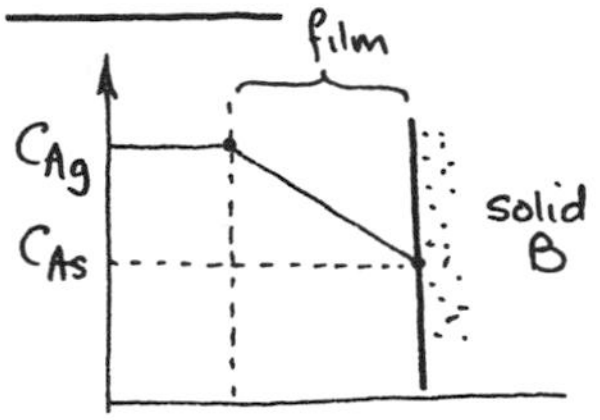

through film: $-r''_{A1} = -\frac{1}{S}\frac{dN_A}{dt} = k_g (C_{Ag} - C_{As})$ ← mass transfer coefficient

reaction at surface: $-r''_{A2} = -\frac{1}{S}\frac{dN_A}{dt} = k'' C_{As}$ ← 1st order rate constant

For resistances in series $-r_A'' = -r_{A1}'' = -r_{A2}''$, so eliminating the intermediate (and unknown) concentration C_{As} gives

$$-r_A'' = \frac{1}{\frac{1}{k_g} + \frac{1}{k''}} C_{Ag}$$

Example 4. For mass transfer followed by a 2nd order surface reaction $-r_{A2}'' = k'' C_{As}^2$ combining the two rate steps as in example 3 gives

$$-r_A'' = \frac{k_g}{2k''}\left(2k''C_{Ag} + k_g - \sqrt{k_g^2 + 4k''k_g C_{Ag}}\right)$$

Example 5. Find a linear approximation to a second order rate $-r = f(C) = k''C^2$ in the vicinity of $C = 5$.

Solution. Here
$$f(C) = k''C^2$$
$$f'(C) = 2k''C$$

and for $C_0 = 5$ ...
$$f(C_0) = k''(5)^2 = 25k''$$
$$f'(C_0) = 2k''(5) = 10k''$$

From the Taylor expansion about $C_0 = 5$
$$f(C) \cong 25k'' + (C-5)\,10k''$$

Therefore in the neighborhood of $C = 5$

$$-r = 10k''(C - 2.5)$$

Example 6. For mass transfer followed by 2nd order reaction at a flat plate linearize the non linear term and then find the overall rate expression in the concentration range around $C = 5$

Solution. From examples 3 and 5 we have

$$\left.\begin{aligned} -r''_{A1} &= k_g(C_{Ag}-C_{As}) \\ -r''_{A2} &= 10k''(C_{As}-2.5) \end{aligned}\right\} \quad \text{and also} \quad r''_{A1} = r''_{A2}$$

Combining to eliminate C_{As} gives

$$\boxed{-r''_A = \frac{1}{\dfrac{1}{k_g}+\dfrac{1}{10k''}}(C_{Ag}-2.5)}$$

note the simplicity of this expression compared to the rigorous one of example 4. However this expression is only good when $C_{As} \cong 5$, a rather severe restriction.

Rate forms for various reaction systems are developed in the appropriate chapters.

II. The General Performance Equation.

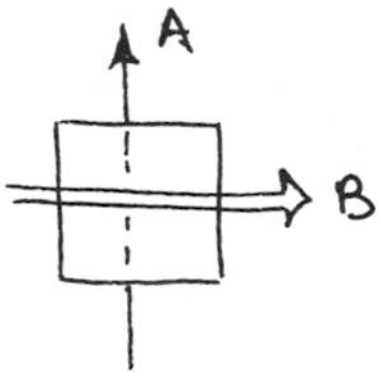

For two changing phases we develop the performance equation (input-output-accumulation-disappearance) by using

- the kinetics
- the material balance, either for the reactor as a whole or for a differential slice of reactor. This relates the consumption of A to the consumption of B.

Sometimes stoichiometry relates A used to B used (e.g. $A+B \rightarrow R$) sometimes it does not, for example

$$A \xrightarrow[\text{catalyst}]{\text{deactivating}} R$$

Here the catalyst activity can be looked upon as a reactant, and the loss in activity can depend on many factors besides the amount of A converted to product; for example the conversion level and the temperature of operations. In general then there is no proportionality relationship between the A converted and the extent of deactivation.

Another complication which may enter concerns the interphase solubility. Upflowing A may dissolve in the liquid and be carried downward without reaction, or downflowing B may vaporize and be carried upward. This sort of thing makes it very difficult to develop the material balance expression.

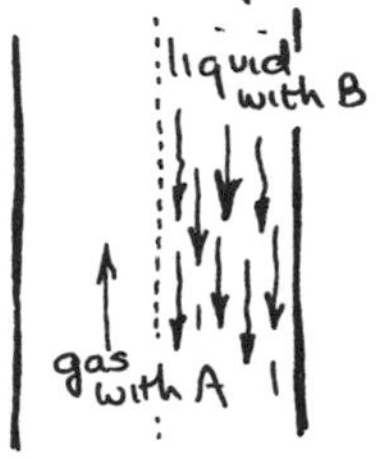

Still another factor, the heat accompanying reaction may be so severe that we may have to include non isothermal effects right from the start. For example, in the highly exothermic solid catalysed gas phase reaction if heat cannot flow to the walls fast enough then the reactor core will get very hot.

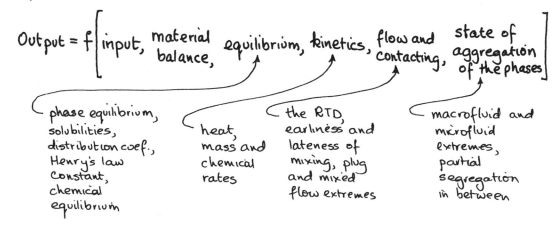

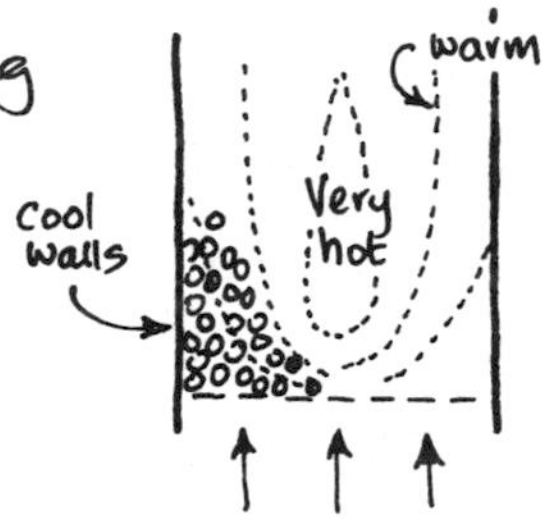

With all these factors included the general performance equation can be written as

$$\text{Output} = f\left[\text{input},\ \text{material balance},\ \text{equilibrium},\ \text{kinetics},\ \text{flow and contacting},\ \text{state of aggregation of the phases}\right]$$

- equilibrium: phase equilibrium, solubilities, distribution coef., Henry's law constant, chemical equilibrium
- kinetics: heat, mass and chemical rates
- flow and contacting: the RTD, earliness and lateness of mixing, plug and mixed flow extremes
- state of aggregation of the phases: macrofluid and microfluid extremes, partial segregation in between

III. Simplifications Leading to Practical Performance Equations.

Since the development of a general performance equation is quite impractical we **always** search for simplifying approximations. Certain simplifications occur naturally with G/S reactors, others with G/L systems, and so on. Here are some important ones which we should always try to use.

A. Simple contacting models and states of aggregation.

All performance equations and reactor predictions are based on some model for flow, contacting and segregation, and as a first approximation we select a combination of **plug flow** and/or **mixed flow** of **micro** and/or **macro fluids** (chapters 60's define these last two terms). Thus we use for flow models

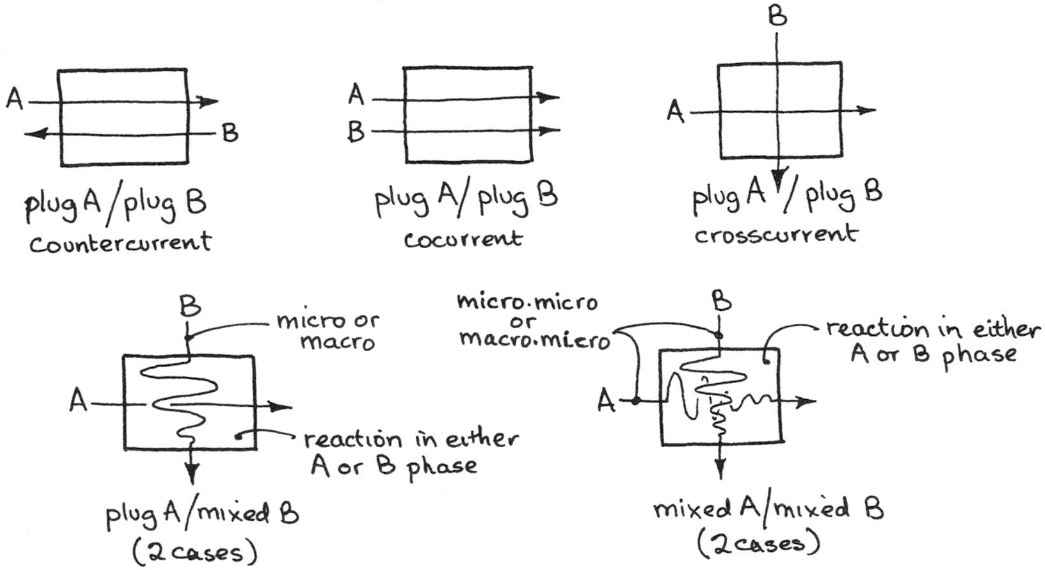

We rarely go beyond these simplest of models to intermediate flow patterns or partial segregation

- because of poor knowledge of the actual flow pattern.

- because of the complexity in analysis for any but the ideal patterns
- because the difference in predictions between the ideals and the more complicated models are usually not that great

One exception is the fluidized bed reactor for fine particles which has a most weird gas flow pattern and therefore needs its own special flow model.

B. Reduction to one phase systems.

Since the performance equations for two changing phases are much more complex than for one changing phase we always look for this simplification. We can use it whenever **at least one phase is in mixed flow**, or whenever **a batch phase is uniform throughout the reactor and only changes slowly with time.**

Example of uniform batch solids – deactivating catalyst.

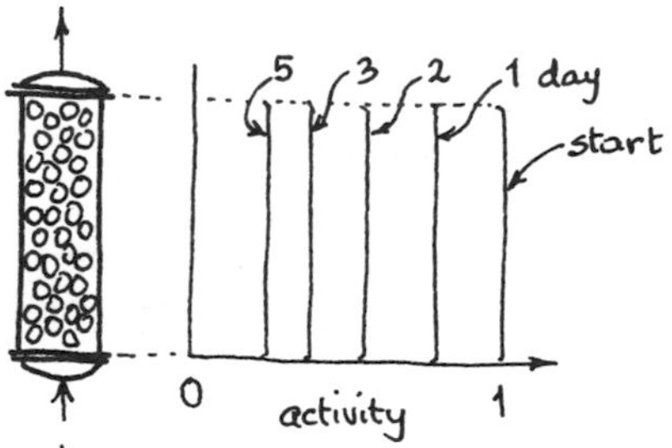

If catalyst activity stays unchanged or if it changes at the same rate throughout the reactor then we have a uniform phase.

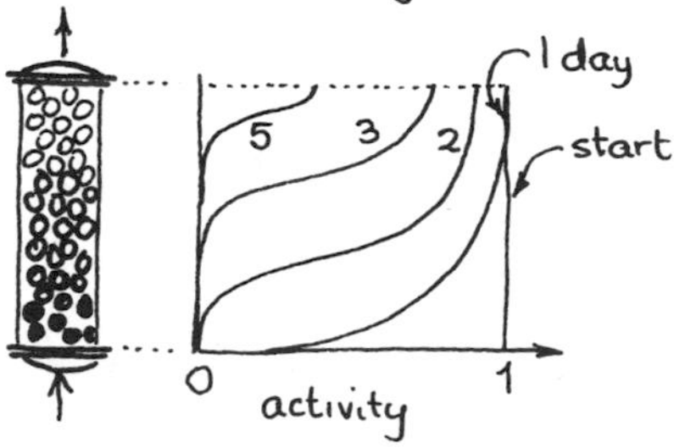

If catalyst decay is concentration dependent or if the reactor is non isothermal then the activity at the front end of the reactor may drop more rapidly, thus a non uniform phase.

There are various ways of transforming a reactor with non-uniform solids into one with uniform solids.

- every so often, say every hour, fluidize the solids briefly with an extra spurt of gas. The solids redistribute throughout the bed however in the long run you still have packed bed behavior
- use a fluidized bed. Here the solids are well mixed, however with this contactor you completely change the flow pattern of gas, hence of reactor behavior.

Example of both phases in mixed flow — agitated G/L contactor

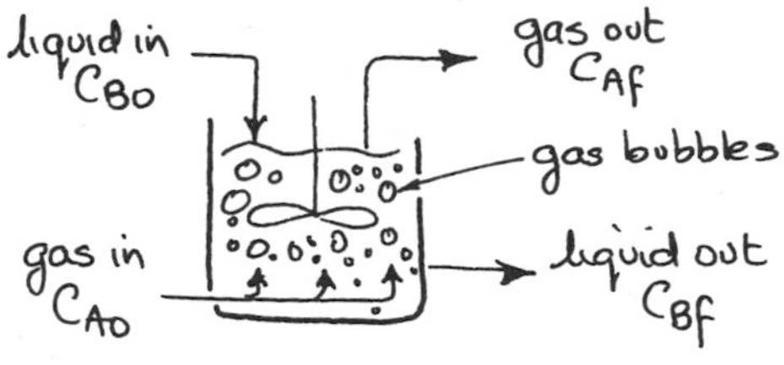

What does the gas see?
Since L is a microfluid G sees and reacts everywhere with exit L of concentration C_{Bf}.

But what does the liquid see?
Since G can be either a microfluid (with a lot of bubble breakup and coalescence) or a macrofluid (no bubble breakup) L either sees exit G at C_{Af} (if G is a microfluid) or it sees G at some proper intermediate concentration $\overline{C}_A$ (if G is a macrofluid). Chapter 42 treats this situation.

Example of one phase in mixed flow — fluidized G/S reactor

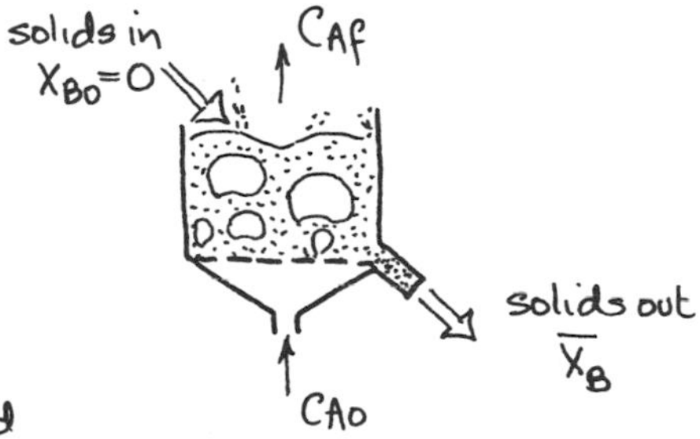

What does the gas see?
Since the solids are in mixed flow the G sees the average solid mixture everywhere, thus the exit composition $\overline{X}_B$.

What do the solids see?
Since the particles wander all over the bed and sample all the gas in the bed they see the average composition within the bed $\overline{C}_A$.
Solids do not see the exit gas C_{Af}

21

C. Final thoughts on flow modeling.

In reactor design and scale up it is essential to select a flow model which reasonably represents our set-up. Too often we put too little thought here, carelessly picking a poor model and then doing computer calculations to the nth degree of accuracy. And then we are surprised when design and scale up do not agree with our predictions. A simple reasonable model is much better than a precise and detailed model which does not represent the contacting. Often the choice of a good flow model and the knowledge of how the flow pattern changes with scale up spells the difference between success and failure.

Chapter 21 SOLID CATALYSED REACTIONS, INTRODUCTION.

The way we treat these systems depends on the number of flowing or changing phases in the system. If only one, then the methods of homogeneous reactions extends directly and simply, the only complication being the intrusion of all sorts of mass and heat transfer effects ... but this is a big complication. If two or more phases are changing in the system then the performance equation and everything else becomes much more difficult.

Here are examples of reactors with only one changing phase

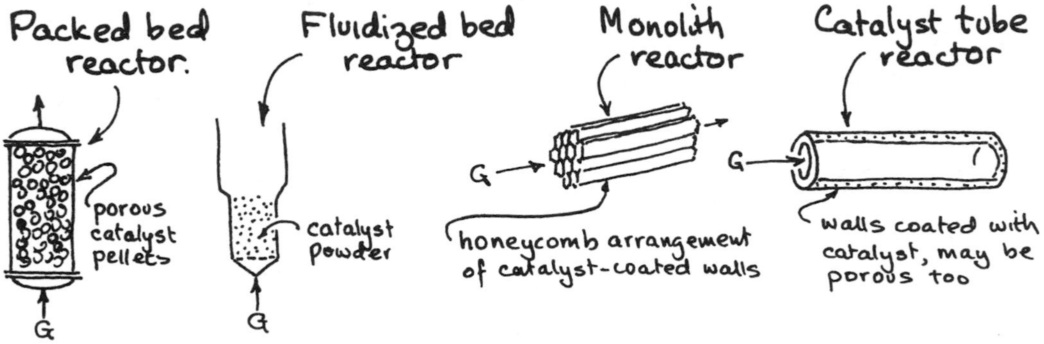

Here are some examples of reactors having two or more changing phases

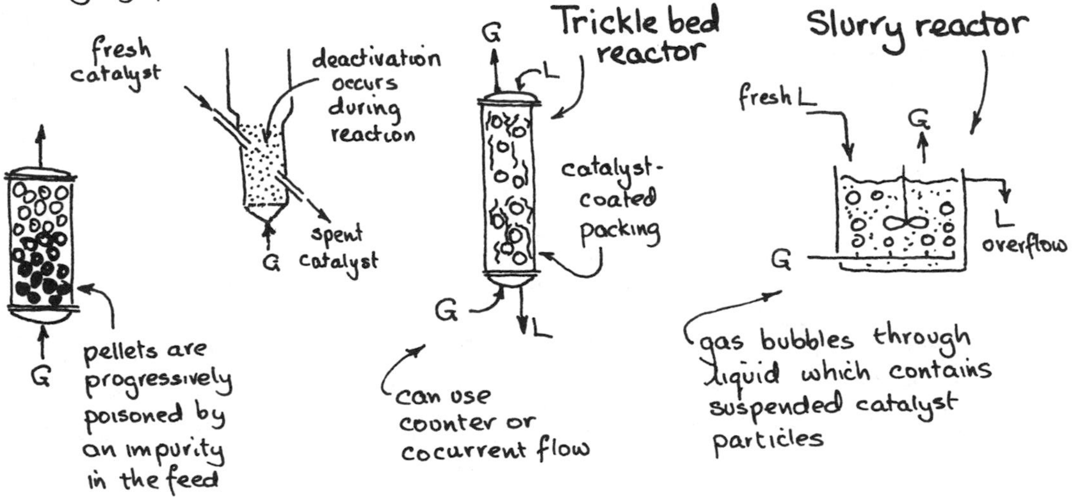

The twenties chapters treat the simple system of one changing phase. The thirties treat two changing phases. We start in this chapter by looking at the various forms of the rate and performance equations, the different ways of obtaining data, and in general by getting acquainted with the "language" of catalytic systems

I Definition of Reaction Rate.

In catalytic systems the rate of reaction can be expressed in one of many equivalent ways. For example, for first order kinetics

Based on volume of voids in the reactor $$-r_A = -\frac{1}{V}\frac{dN_A}{dt} = kC_A, \quad \left[\frac{\text{mols reacted}}{m^3\,\text{voids}\cdot s}\right]$$

Based on weight of catalyst pellets $$-r_A' = -\frac{1}{W}\frac{dN_A}{dt} = k'C_A, \quad \left[\frac{\text{mol reacted}}{\text{kg cat.}\cdot s}\right]$$

Based on catalyst surface $$-r_A'' = -\frac{1}{S}\frac{dN_A}{dt} = k''C_A, \quad \left[\frac{\text{mol reacted}}{m^2\,\text{cat.surf.}\cdot s}\right]$$

Based on volume of catalyst pellets $$-r_A''' = -\frac{1}{V_p}\frac{dN_A}{dt} = k'''C_A, \quad \left[\frac{\text{mol reacted}}{m^3\,\text{solid}\cdot s}\right]$$

Based on total reactor volume $$-r_A'''' = -\frac{1}{V_r}\frac{dN_A}{dt} = k''''C_A, \quad \left[\frac{\text{mol reacted}}{m^3\,\text{reactor}\cdot s}\right]$$

In converting from one basis to another we have

$$rV = r'W = r''S = r'''V_p = r''''V_r$$

and

$$kV = k'W = k''S = k'''V_p = k''''V_r$$

For first order reaction ... s^{-1}, $\frac{m^3\,\text{gas}}{\text{kg}\cdot s}$, $\frac{m^3\,\text{gas}}{m^2\,\text{surface}\cdot s}$, $\frac{m^3\,\text{gas}}{m^3\,\text{solid}\cdot s}$, $\frac{m^3\,\text{gas}}{m^3\,\text{reactor}\cdot s}$ (for other reaction orders use the proper k units)

Use whichever definition is convenient. We can always convert from one to the other. Sometimes however a particular definition is not appropriate. For example for catalyst coated tubes it makes no sense to use r' and r''', and r'' is the only useful definition.

II Performance Equations.

By taking: INPUT = OUTPUT + ACCUMULATION + DISAPPEARANCE BY REACTION, as with homogeneous reactions, we find:

For a **batch** reactor

$$\frac{t}{C_{A0}} = \int \frac{dX_A}{-r_A} = \frac{V}{W}\int \frac{dX_A}{-r_A'} = \frac{V}{S}\int \frac{dX_A}{-r_A''} = \frac{V}{V_p}\int \frac{dX_A}{-r_A'''} = \frac{V}{V_r}\int \frac{dX_A}{-r_A''''}$$

For a **differential** reactor (small slice of a plug flow reactor)

$$F_{A0}\,dX_A = -r_A dV = -r_A' dW = -r_A'' dS = -r_A''' dV_p = -r_A'''' dV_r$$

For a **plug flow** reactor

$$\frac{W}{F_{A0}} = \int_0^{X_{Af}} \frac{dX_A}{-r_A'} \quad ; \quad \frac{S}{F_{A0}} = \int \frac{dX_A}{-r_A''} \quad ; \quad \frac{V_p}{F_{A0}} = \int \frac{dX_A}{-r_A'''} \quad ; \quad \text{etc.} \dots$$

For a **mixed flow reactor**

$$F_{A0}(X_{Af} - X_{A0}) = -r_{Af} V = -r_{Af}' W = -r_{Af}'' S = -r_{Af}''' V_p = -r_{Af}'''' V_r$$

For packed bed design we usually find it convenient to use the W vs r_A' units (underlined above); for monolith reactors S vs r_A'' units; for studying porous pellet kinetics, or for fluidized beds V_p vs r_A''' units.

Note the similarity with the equations for homogeneous reactions. For example

For homogeneous plug flow ... (Space-time)

$$\tau = \frac{VC_{A0}}{F_{A0}} = \frac{V}{v_0} = C_{A0}\int \frac{dX_A}{-r_A} \quad \dots\text{and} \quad k\tau = (1+\varepsilon_A)\ln\frac{1}{1-X_A} - \varepsilon_A X_A$$

(for first order only)

for catalytic plug flow ... (Weight-time)

$$\tau' = \frac{WC_{A0}}{F_{A0}} = \frac{W}{v_0} = C_{A0}\int \frac{dX_A}{-r_A'} \quad \dots\text{and} \quad k'\tau' = (1+\varepsilon_A)\ln\frac{1}{1-X_A} - \varepsilon_A X_A$$

We can use various forms of the capacity measure "τ". These are related as follows

$$k\tau = k'\tau' = k''\tau'' = k'''\tau''' = k''''\tau''''$$

where τ is in s, τ' in $\frac{kg \cdot s}{m^3\ fluid}$, τ'' in $\frac{m^2 surface \cdot s}{m^3\ fluid}$, τ''' in $\frac{m^3 solid \cdot s}{m^3\ fluid}$, τ'''' in $\frac{m^3 reactor \cdot s}{m^3\ fluid}$

III Performance Equation when both Homogeneous and Heterogeneous (Catalytic) Reaction Occurs.

Suppose A disappears on catalyst pellets and in the gas stream itself by both types of reaction. Then

$$\left(\frac{dN_A}{dt}\right)_{total} = \left(\frac{dN_A}{dt}\right)_{homog} + \left(\frac{dN_A}{dt}\right)_{\text{heterogeneous, on catalyst pellet}}$$

(the homog term: represent by r_A; the heterogeneous term: represent by r_A')

By dividing all terms by V, then W, gives in turn

$$(-r_A)_{total} = (-r_A)_{homog} + \frac{W}{V}(-r_A')_{cat} \qquad \cdots (1)$$

$$(-r_A')_{total} = \frac{V}{W}(-r_A)_{homog} + (-r_A')_{cat} \qquad \cdots (2)$$

To evaluate the two rate contributions vary W/V in a set of experiments, then plot as shown

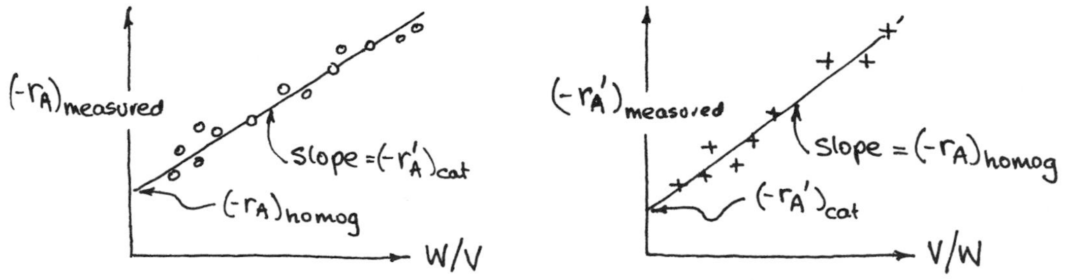

IV Types of Experimental Reactors.

Batch reactor:

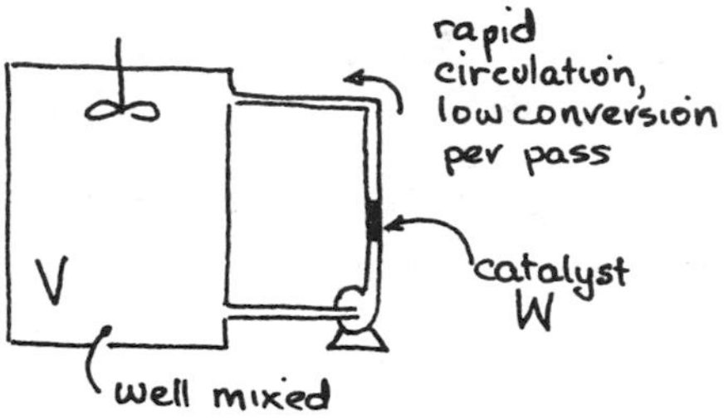

$$t = \frac{C_{A0} V}{W} \int_0^{X_{Af}} \frac{dX_A}{-r_A'}$$

(upper limit X_{Af}: at time t; lower limit 0: at time zero)

Differential reactor:

ΔX should be small enough so that the average rate can be used throughout the reactor, with but little error

$$\tau' = \frac{C_{A0} W}{F_{A0}} = \frac{C_{A0}\,\Delta X_A}{-\overline{r}_A'}$$

($\overline{r}_A'$: average)

Plug flow reactor:

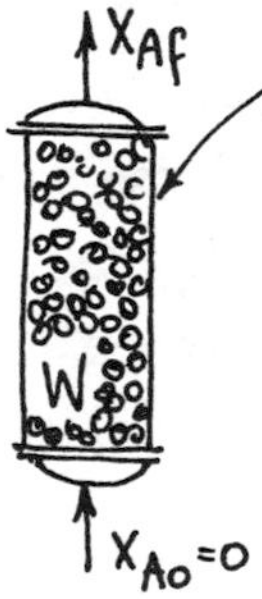

packed bed; always build vertical so that gas will not bypass settled solids

$$\tau' = \frac{C_{A0} W}{F_{A0}} = C_{A0} \int_0^{X_{Af}} \frac{dX_A}{-r_A'}$$

Mixed flow reactor:

Basket type reactor

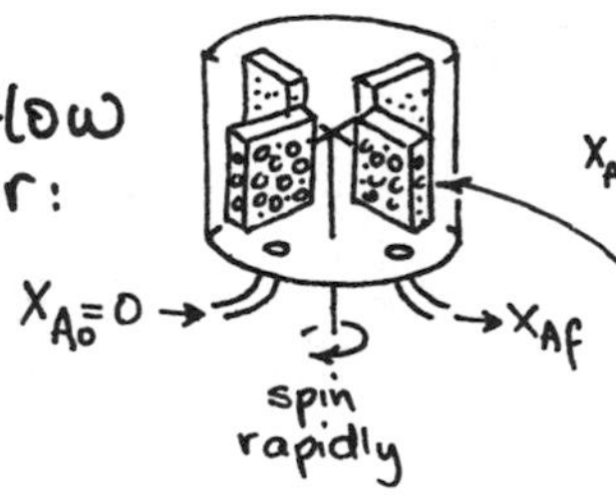

paddles contain catalyst

Recirculating type reactors

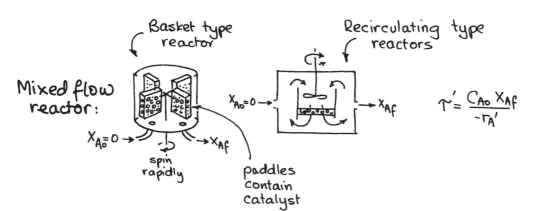

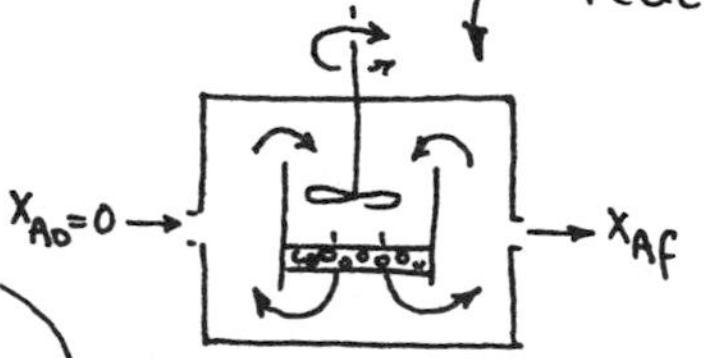

$$\tau' = \frac{C_{A0} X_{Af}}{-r_A'}$$

Recycle reactor:

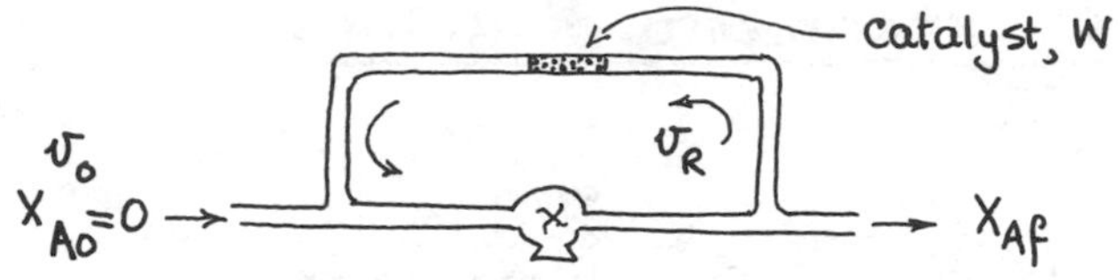

- If circulation of fluid is rapid enough then the conversion/pass becomes small and this reactor approaches mixed flow, in which case

$$\tau' = \frac{W C_{A0}}{F_{A0}} = \frac{C_{A0} X_{Af}}{-r'_{Af}}$$

- If the circulation rate is not high enough then we must use the equations for recycle reactors

$$\tau' = (R+1) C_{A0} \int_{\left(\frac{R}{R+1}\right) X_{Af}}^{X_{Af}} \frac{dX_A}{-r'_A}$$

- In practice, if you assume mixed flow, make your series of runs at fixed recycle ratio R, otherwise you will obtain incorrect kinetics. Thus for constant v_R use the same v_0 for all runs, while changing the feed composition from run to run.

  Wadel and Villadsen [CES 38 1346 (1983)] and Broucek [CES 38 1349 (1983)] amplify on this point

Reflections.

Why all the emphasis in this chapter on the many different forms of rate equations such as r'_A r''_A r'''_A r''''_A with their related k and τ values? Because a proper understanding of the distinction between these forms will help you avoid some of the commonly made errors, and also will allow you to properly relate and compare operations in different types of reactors such as packed beds with pure and with diluted catalysts, fluidized beds, etc.

V What Kind of Reactor to Use on the Commercial Scale

The choice depends on a number of factors, primarily

- the reaction rate
- the catalyst stability
- product distribution considerations

These factors interact as follows

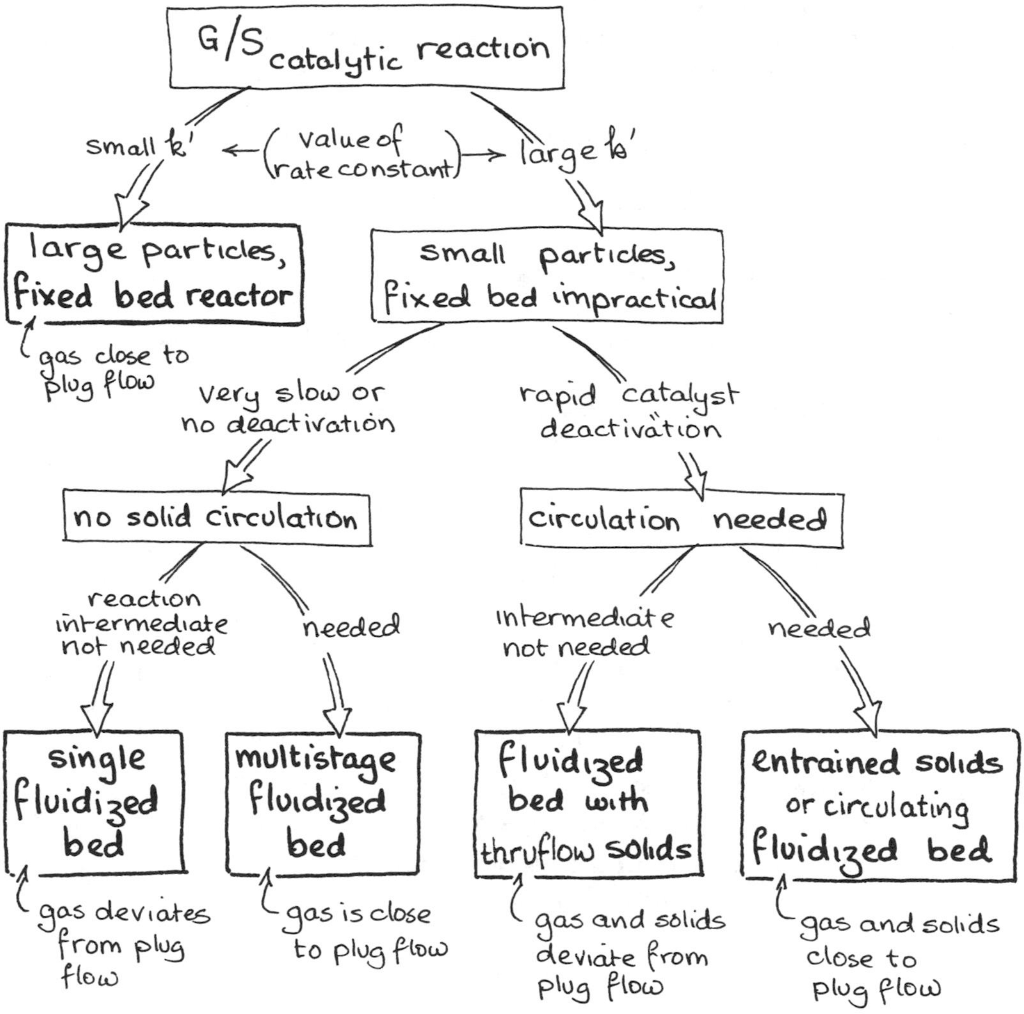

Chapter 21 Problems

A1 The rate of removal of carbon monoxide from cigarette smoke by an efficient packed bed filter (ρ = 1500 kg/m^3) can be represented by

$$-r'_{CO} = 10^{-5} C_{CO} \frac{\text{mg CO removed}}{\text{gm catalyst·s}}, \quad \text{when } C_{CO} \approx 25000 \frac{\text{mg}}{\text{m}^3}$$

How does this value compare with typical gas phase reactions of porous catalyst pellets (see Chapter 100)?

A gas containing A (2 mol/m^3) is fed (1 m^3/hr) to a plug flow reactor with recycle loop (0.02 m^3 loop volume, 3 kg of catalyst), and the output composition from the reactor system is measured (0.5 mol A/m^3). Find the rate equation for the decomposition of A for the following cases. Be sure to give the units of $-r'_A$, C_A, and k' in your final expression.

A2 . . . No recycle, A $\leftrightarrow$ R, first order reversible, K = 7

A3 . . . Very large recycle, A$\rightarrow$ R, n =1/2

A4 . . . Recycle ratio **R** = 1, A $\rightarrow$ R, n = 1

A5 . . . Very large recycle, A $\rightarrow$ 3R, n = 1, 50% A - 50% inerts in feed

A6 . . . No recycle, A $\rightarrow$ 3R, n=2, 25% A - 75% inerts in feed

---

A7* A West Texas gas oil is cracked in a tubular reactor packed with silica-alumina cracking catalyst. The liquid feed (mw=255) is vaporized, heated, enters the reactor at 630 °C and 1 atm, and with adequate temperature control stays close to this temperature within the reactor. The cracking reaction follows first order kinetics and gives a variety of products with mean molecular weight mw = 70. Half the feed is cracked for a feed rate of 60 m^3 liquid/m^3 reactor·hr. In the industry this measure of feed rate is called the liquid hourly space velocity. Thus LHSV = 60 hr^{-1}. Find the first order rate constants k' and k''' for this cracking reaction.

Data: Density of liquid feed: ρ_ℓ = 869 kg/m^3

Bulk density of packed bed: ρ_b = 700 kg/m^3

Density of catalyst particles: ρ_s = 950 kg/m^3

This problem is prepared from Satterfield, page 143.

Chapter 21 Problems

A8 Ethylene and hydrogen react in a packed bed experimental reactor to give ethane, as follows

$$\underset{(A)}{C_2H_4} + \underset{(B)}{H_2} \rightarrow \underset{(R)}{C_2H_6}, \quad r''''_R = [5.96 \times 10^6 e^{-6703/T}]C_B \ \frac{\text{mol}}{\text{m}^3 \text{ reactor}\cdot\text{s}}$$

Find the length of 1 cm ID packed bed reactor needed to give 100% conversion of A for a flow rate of 2×10^{-5} total moles of feed per second consisting of 49% A - 51% B. The whole system is isothermal at 67 °C, and the pressure throughout is close to 10^5 Pa.

This problem is adapted from Tarhan, pg 102-106.

B9* Find an nth order rate equation to represent the kinetics of decomposition of gaseous A from the following data obtained in a differential reactor using W = 0.01 kg of catalyst

$C_{A,\,in}$	0.100	0.080	0.060	0.040
$C_{A,\,out}$	0.084	0.070	0.055	0.038

All runs use a feed of partially converted product of 20 lit/hr of pure unreacted A at C_{A0} =0.1 mol/lit. The stoichiometry of the decomposition is given by A → 4R.

Gaseous A reacts (A → R) in an experimental packed bed reactor (assume plug flow with possible recycle). From the following conversion data at various conditions find a rate equation to represent the reaction

B10 ...

v_0, m³/hr	3	2	1.2	Mixed flow, A → R
X_A	0.2	0.3	0.5	C_{A0} = 10 mol/m³
				W = 4 gms

B11 ...

W, gm	0.5	1.0	2.5	Plug flow, A → R
C_A	30	20	10	C_{A0} = 60 mmol/lit
				v = 3 lit/min

B12 ...

W, gm	90	200	370	Plug flow, A → 2R, pure A feed
X_A	0.5	0.75	0.9	C_{A0} = 0.1 mol/lit
				v_0 = 3 lit/min

A closed loop reactor is used for catalytic rate studies. For this purpose feed gas with reactant is introduced into the system and is rapidly circulated through the catalyst loop. From the following composition-time data find a kinetic equation in units of mol/gm·min to represent this reaction.

Chapter 21 Problems

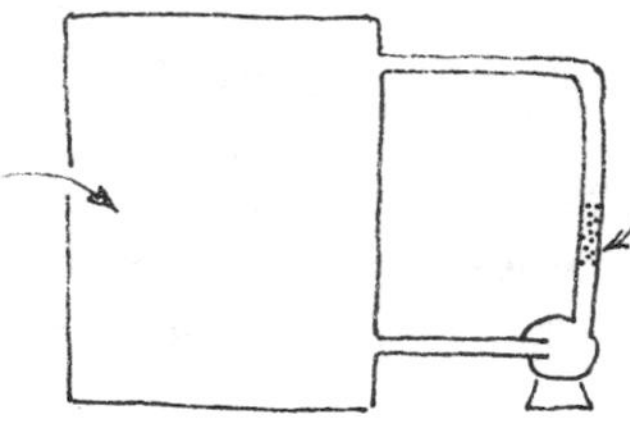

B13 . . .

t, min	0	3	6	9	12	Pure A at 32 °C
π, mm Hg	760	240	130	90	65	$A(g) \rightarrow R(s)$

B14 . . .

t, min	0	4	8	16	36	Pure A at 609 K
π, atm	1	0.75	0.67	0.6	0.55	$2A \rightarrow R$

B15 A packed bed micro reactor ($V = 0.31\ cm^3$, $W = 25$ mg) is tested with the hydrosulfurization of a feed mixture of 0.066 wt% dibenzothiophene in a carrier liquid of n-hexadecane. This feed at 104 atm and 300 °C is passed at various flow rates over the catalyst, reaction is first order and the following results are obtained

τ', kg·hr/m^3	6.8	10.4	14.0	20.4
X_A	0.45	0.59	0.70	0.83

Find whether the flow pattern in this reactor is closer to mixed flow of plug flow, and then calculate the rate constant for this reaction.

Data squeezed from Eliezer *et al*, IEC/F **16** 380 (1977).

B16 Barnett *et al* in AIChE J **7** 211 (1961) reported on the kinetics of catalytic dehydrogenation of cyclohexane in an experimental tubular reactor,

$$C_6H_{12} \rightarrow C_6H_6 + 3H_2$$

One set of runs was made at 1.48 MPa and 627 K on 7.5 gm of 30-40 mesh catalyst using a feed consisting of four parts hydrogen to one part cyclohexane, with the following results

Feed to reactor, cm^3/s	31.0	13.6	7.1
Fraction of cyclohexane converted	0.011	0.020	0.037

Find the rate constant for the dehydrogenation at this temperature, assuming first order reaction.

Chapter 21 Problems

How much catalyst is needed in a packed bed reactor for 80% conversion of 1000 m^3/hr of pure gaseous A (C_{A0} = 100 mol/m^3) if the stoichiometry and rate are given by

C17 . . . $A \rightarrow R, \quad -r'_A = \dfrac{50\, C_A}{1 + 0.02\, C_A} \; \dfrac{mol}{kg \cdot hr}$

C18 . . . $A \rightarrow 2R, \quad -r'_A = 8\, C_A^2 \; \dfrac{mol}{kg \cdot hr}$

C19 Gaseous feed with A and B (v_0 = 10 m^3/hr) pass through an experimental reactor packed with catalyst (W = 4 kg). Reaction occurs as follows

$$A + B \rightarrow R + S, \quad -r'_A = 0.6\, C_A C_B \; \frac{mol}{kg \cdot hr}$$

Find the conversion of reactants if the feed contains C_{A0} = 0.1 mol/m^3 and C_{B0} = 10 mol/m^3.

A tubular pilot plant reactor packed with two kg of catalyst is fed with 2 m^3/hr of pure A at 300 °C and 20 atm. Conversion of reactant is 60%. In a larger plant we wish to treat 100 m^3/hr of feed gases at 40 atm and 300 °C containing 60% A and 40% inerts to 80% conversion. Find the amount of catalyst needed for the following stoichiometry and rate

C20 . . . $A \rightarrow R, \quad -r'_A = k' C_A^2$

C21 . . . $A \rightarrow R + S, \quad -r'_A = k' C_A$

C22 At 700 °C the rate of decomposition $A \rightarrow 3R$ on a specific catalyst of given size is found to be well represented by the expression

$$-r'_A = 10\, C_A \; \frac{mol}{gm \cdot hr}$$

A pilot plant is to be built. This is to be a tubular packed bed 2 cm ID using 25% of these active catalyst pellets evenly mixed with 75% inert pellets to insure isothermal operations. For 400 mol/hr of feed consisting of 50% A-50% inert gas at 8 atm and 700 °C what must be the length of reactor so that $p_{A,out}/p_{A,\,in}$ = 0.111.

<u>Data:</u> Catalyst and inert pellets are porous, 3 mm in diameter, particle density ρ_s = 2 gm/cm^3, bulk voidage of packed bed = 50%.

Chapter 21 Problems

The following kinetic data are obtained in an experimental Carberry type basket reactor using 100 gm of catalyst in the paddles and different flow rates from run to run

$A \rightarrow R$

$C_{A0} = 10\ mol/m^3$

F_{A0}, mol/min	0.14	0.42	1.67	2.5	1.25
C_A, mol/m³	8	6	4	2	1

D23 . . . Determine the amount of catalyst needed in a packed bed reactor for 75% conversion of 1000 mol A/min of a $C_{A0} = 8\ mol/m^3$ feed.

D24 . . . Find W for mixed flow, $X_A = 0.90$, $C_{A0} = 10\ mol/m^3$, $F_{A0} = 1000\ mol/min$.

D25 Find the weight of catalyst needed to treat 4 kmol/hr of pure A at 117 °C and 3.2 atm to 94% conversion in a packed bed reactor given the following rate-concentration data obtained in a Berty type mixed flow reactor

C_A, mol/m³	10	20	40	60	90
$-r'_A$, mol/kg·hr	0.4	2	10	30	80

$4A \rightarrow R$,

The following kinetic data on the reaction $A \rightarrow R$ are obtained in an experimental packed bed reactor using various amounts of catalyst and a fixed feed rate $F_{A0} = 10$ kmol/hr. Keep C_{A0} fixed throughout.

W, kg catalyst	1	2	3	4	5	6	7
X_A	0.12	0.20	0.27	0.33	0.37	0.41	0.44

D26 . . . In designing a large packed bed reactor with feed rate of 400 kmol A/hr how much catalyst would be needed for 40% conversion?

D27 . . . How much catalyst would be needed to treat $F_{A0} = 400$ kmol/hr to $X_A = 0.4$ if the reactor employed a very large recycle of product stream?

D28 A small experimental packed bed reactor (W = 1 kg) using very large recycle of product stream gives the following kinetic data

$A \rightarrow R$,

$C_{A0} = 10\ mol/m^3$,

C_A, mol/m³	1	2	3	6	9
v_0, lit/hr	5	20	65	133	540

Find the amount of catalyst needed for 75% conversion for a flow rate of 1000 mol A/hr of a $C_{A0} = 8\ mol/m^3$ feed stream.

(a) in a packed bed reactor with no recycle of exit fluid

(b) in a packed bed reactor with very high recycle

Chapter 21 Problems

D29 In an attempt to achieve isothermal operating conditions (the catalytic reaction is very exothermic) a single pass heat exchanger with catalyst on the shell side, coola7nt on the tube side, is used as reactor. If the shell side is filled with catalyst conversion of reactant would be 99%, however, we only need 90% conversion. As a result we can add inert pellets to dilute the active pellets and to distribute the heat load. For stoichiometry and rate given by

$$A \rightarrow R, \quad -r_A' = kC_A$$

(a) Determine what fraction of pellets should be active, what fraction inert for $X_A = 0.9$.

(b) We would like to distribute the inerts for a uniform heat release. To solve for this in general would be an interesting problem which we do not consider. Here we simply want to know the amount of inerts to be put at the front end compared to the amount at the back end of the reactor.

D30 "El jefe" (the chief) decided to do something to improve the low conversion ($X_A = 0.95$) of our first order solid-catalyzed liquid phase reaction. Instead of ordering more of the expensive catalyst to fill the half empty reactor he decided to save money by adding some tricky piping to the present vertical packed bed reactor. When I saw what the mechanics were putting together for him (see sketch below), I told "el jefe" that it all didn't seem right. I could sense right away that my saying this annoyed him, but all he said was, "All right young lady, why don't you tell me what conversion to expect with this arrangement?" Please do this.

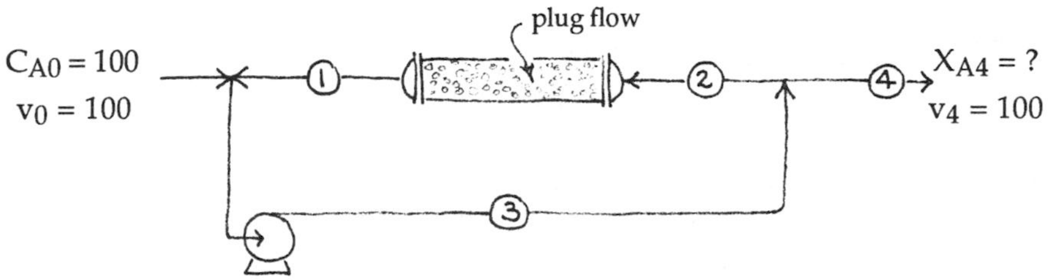

Homogeneous and Catalytic Rates. The homogeneous decomposition of $A \rightarrow R$ is studied in a stainless steel recirculating -type mixed flow reactor ($C_{A0} = 100$ mol/m^3, volume of voids on the reactor V = 0.8 lit, total surface in the reactor S = 800 cm^2) with results shown in series A. We suspect that the stainless steel surface catalyses the reaction. To verify this suspicion additional surface is added to the reactor (C_{A0} = 100 mol/m^3, S = 1500 cm^2, V = 0.75 lit) and more runs are made, see series B.

Find the kinetics of this decomposition, and if homogeneous and catalytic reactions are occurring simultaneously, give a rate expression (including all units) which accounts for both processes.

Chapter 21 Problems

	Series A			Series B		
E31 . . .	τ, sec	26.7	10	τ, sec	16	6
	C_A	20	40	C_A	20	40
E32 . . .	τ, sec	40	10	τ, sec	15	5
	C_A	20	50	C_A	40	66.7
E33 . . .	τ, sec	20	5	τ, sec	22.5	3.75
	C_A	20	50	C_A	10	40
E34 . . .	τ, sec	40	10	τ, sec	26.7	7.5
	C_A	20	40	C_A	20	40

F35 Reactant A decomposes on the surface of a catalyst at 100 °C as follows

$$A \rightarrow 4R, \quad -r_A' = \frac{0.3\,C_A}{0.0002 + C_A} \frac{\text{mol}}{\text{kg}\cdot\text{hr}}, \quad C_A = [\frac{\text{mol}}{\text{m}^3}]$$

600 mol R/hr are to be produced in a packed tubular reactor and any pressure from atmospheric to 20 atm may be used. Naturally, the cost of reactor and supporting equipment will depend not only on its size but also on the pressure selected. The cost on an hourly basis is

$$\$20 + (\$0.04\,W)(\text{pressure in atm})^{0.6}, \pi > 1 \text{ atm}, \quad W = [\text{kg catalyst}]$$

For optimum conditions find π, X_A, W and the unit cost of producing R from a pure A feed which costs \$0.40/mol A.

F36 From a feed containing reactant A at 1 mol/lit, 100 mol/hr of R are to be produced in a catalyst-packed tubular reactor. The reaction in the packed bed can be taken as zero order, or

$$A \rightarrow R, \quad -r_A' = 1 \frac{\text{mol}}{\text{kg cat}\cdot\text{hr}} \quad \text{at all } C_A$$

The cost of feed stream is \$1/mol A, the cost of reactor and catalyst is \$1/kg cat·hr, and unreacted A cannot be recovered.

(a) What is the optimum conversion and the cost of R at this conversion?

(b) Repeat part (a) if the packed bed reactor is operated with a large recycle stream.

Chapter 21 Problems

D37 The following data on the decomposition of A on a solid catalyst is obtained in a recirculating type of mixed flow reactor

W, kg	C_{A0}, mol/lit	v, lit/s	X_A
0.36	4	0.01	0.75
0.36	5	0.02	0.60
0.36	5	0.05	0.40
0.36	6	0.075	0.33
0.20	10	0.02	0.50
0.21	14	0.0125	0.50
0.14	12	0.0125	0.33
0.20	15	0.01	0.33

$A(\ell) \rightarrow R(\ell)$

We want to process F_{A0} = 400 mol/s of liquid feed stream which contains C_{A0} = 20 mol/lit to 95% conversion in a packed bed reactor system (any number of reactors, with or without recycle) which uses the minimum amount of catalyst, because catalyst is very expensive. Make your calculations and sketch your recommended design. On the sketch show how much catalyst is located where, and also show C_A in the various flow streams.

Chapter 22. THE POROUS CATALYST PELLET — IDENTIFYING THE RATE REGIME.

I. The Spectrum of Kinetic Regimes.

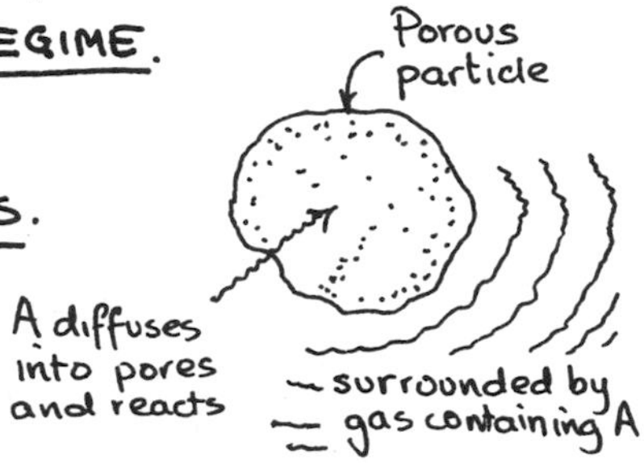

The rate of reaction for the particle as a whole may depend on

① **Surface kinetics**, the intrinsic rate, which may change as the particle deactivates.

② **Pore diffusion resistance** which sets up internal concentration gradients and causes the particle interior to be starved for reactant.

③ **Particle ΔT** or temperature gradients within the particle. This is caused by large heat release or absorption during reaction

④ **Film ΔT** between outer surface of the particle and the main gas stream. For example the particle may be uniform in temperature throughout but hotter than the surrounding gas.

⑤ **Film diffusion resistance** or concentration gradients across the gas film

In gas systems slow reactions are influenced by ① alone, in faster reactions ② intrudes to slow the rate, then ③ and/or ④ enter the picture, and finally for very fast high temperature reactions ⑤ may limit the overall rate. In liquid systems the order in which these effects intrude is ①, ②, ⑤, and rarely ③ and/or ④.

The porous catalyst pellet or particle illustrates this whole range of interaction of heat-mass-reaction kinetics. This type of behavior can be found in many other systems, particularly biological (metabolism of cells, yeast, tissues, microbes, action of enzyme flocs, etc.).

As **characteristic size** of tissue cell or catalyst particle (let us talk of catalyst particle from now on) take

$$L = \left(\frac{\text{volume of particle}}{\text{exterior surface of particle}}\right) \cdots \begin{cases} = \frac{\text{thickness}}{2}, & \text{for flat plate} \\ = \frac{R}{2}, & \text{for cylinder} \\ = \frac{R}{3}, & \text{for sphere} \end{cases}$$

Also, in this chapter the rate of reaction is most conveniently expressed in terms of **volume of particle**. Thus for n^{th} order reaction

$$-r_A''' = \frac{W}{V_s}(-r_A') = k'''C_A^n$$

where $-r_A'''$ has units $\frac{\text{mol}}{\text{m}^3\,\text{solid}\cdot\text{s}}$, and k''' has units

$$\begin{cases} \frac{(\text{m}^3\,\text{gas})^n}{(\text{mol})^{n-1}(\text{m}^3\,\text{solid})\cdot\text{s}} & \cdots \text{for } n^{th} \text{ order reaction} \\ \frac{(\text{m}^3\,\text{gas})}{\text{m}^3\,\text{solid}\cdot\text{s}} & \cdots \text{for } 1^{st} \text{ order reaction} \end{cases}$$

II Rate Equations for the Various Kinetic Regimes

We give, in turn, expressions for these 5 regimes, then show how to interpret experiments to tell where you're at in a given situation

Regime ① The rate for surface kinetics alone.

All sorts of rate equations have been derived from theory. These are useful for studying mechanisms, suggesting extrapolating limits, etc., however we usually have to fall back on the simplest kinetic form, **first order kinetics**, when treating the interplay of heat and mass transfer resistances, otherwise things get too complicated to analyse. Because of this we will treat the intrusion of heat and mass transfer resistances with first order reactions.

Surface kinetics and their proper equations can only be studied with confidence in experiments which are free of physical resistance effects.

Regime ② The rate when pore diffusion effects intrude.

Surface kinetics and pore diffusion cannot be treated as steps in series, they enter the rate equation together. So for 1st order reaction on flat plate particles (not much difference for spherical and other shaped particles) analysis gives

rate without any diffusion effects

=1 for no diffusion resistance

this flat plate expression is a good approximation for all particle shapes. The next chapter gives precise expressions for other shapes.

$$-r_A''' = k''' C_{As}\, \mathcal{E} \quad \cdots with \cdots \quad \mathcal{E} = \frac{\tanh M_T}{M_T}$$

characteristic length

effective diffusion coefficient in porous solids; m³gas/m solid·s

observed rate; mol/m³solid·s

where $\quad M_T = L \sqrt{\dfrac{k'''}{\mathcal{D}_{eff}}} \quad \cdots and\ also \quad M_W = M_T^2\, \mathcal{E} = \dfrac{-r_A''' L^2}{C_{As}\, \mathcal{D}_{eff}}$

$\mathcal{E}$ = effectiveness factor
a sort of fudge factor which varies between 0 and 1, and which accounts for the resistance to pore diffusion

M_T = Thiele modulus
useful for predicting reactor behavior from known kinetic information, thus known k'''.

M_W = Weisz modulus
useful for interpreting experiments since it only includes observables

We have **no resistance** to pore diffusion when:

$\quad M_T < 0.4 \quad or \quad M_W < 0.15 \qquad \cdots here \; \mathcal{E} = 1 \; and \; -r_A''' = k''' C_{As}$

We have **strong pore diffusion effects** when

$\quad M_T > 4 \quad or \quad M_W > 7 \qquad \cdots here \; \mathcal{E} = \dfrac{1}{M_T} = \dfrac{1}{M_W} \; and \; -r_A''' = \dfrac{(k''' \mathcal{D}_{eff})^{1/2}}{L} C_{As}$

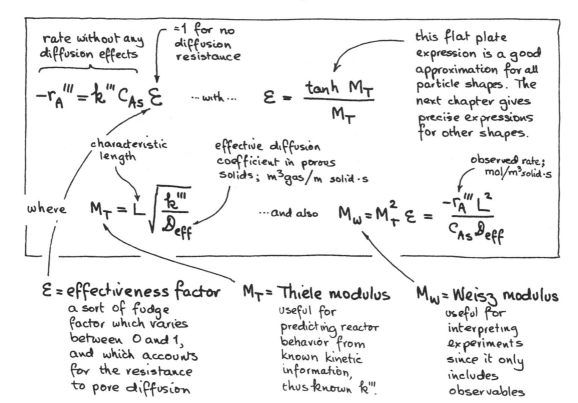

Graphically the effectiveness factor and these two moduli are related as follows ⟶

$\varepsilon = \frac{1}{M_W}$

ε

no pore diffusion resistance ⟸

strong pore diffusion resistance ⟹

M_W

take these values as the limits between regimes. For all shapes of particles the error < 10%

$\varepsilon = \frac{1}{M_T}$

ε

no resistance by pore diffusion

intermediate regime

strong resistance by pore diffusion

M_T

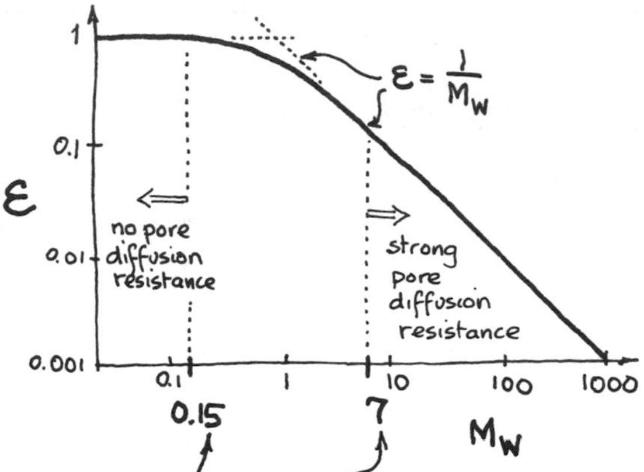

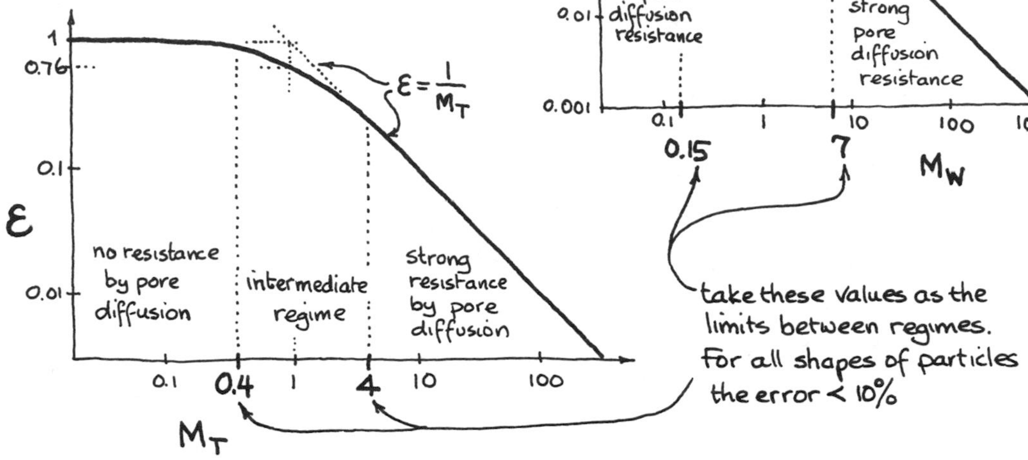

(a) To find how pore diffusion effects influence the rate
- evaluate M_T or M_W
- find ε from the figures above
- insert ε into the rate equation

This gives the rate of reaction and tells to what extent does the resistance of pore diffusion slow the reaction rate.

(b) **Concentration of reactant within the particle.** When diffusional effects intrude the particle interior becomes starved for reactant, and it is this which lowers the rate. Here are some sample C_A values within particles of all shapes

M_T	$\varepsilon = \overline{C_A}/C_{As}$		$C_{A,center}/C_{As}$		
0.1	0.99	~1.00	0.98	~1.00	reactant penetrates to the center of the particle with no difficulty
0.4	0.92	~0.95	0.79	~0.92	
1	0.67	~0.76	0.30	~0.65	reactant concentration at the center of the particle is zero for all practical purposes
4	0.23	~0.25	0	~0.04	
10	0.097	~0.10	0		
	↑ sphere	↑ flat plate	↑ sphere	↑ flat plate	Note: all depends on the M_T value

(c) **Desirable processing range.** Fine solids are free of diffusional effects ($M_T \ll 1$) but are difficult to use (imagine the pressure drop through a packed bed of face powder). On the other hand large solids have a small Δp but are likely to be in the regime of strong pore diffusion. For most effective operations what we usually want is **the largest particle size which is still free of pore diffusion resistance**, or

$$M_T \cong 0.4 \quad \ldots \text{or} \quad M_W \cong 0.15$$

as suggested by the problems in the next chapter this is old stuff to mother nature who sizes her biological building blocks (cells, simple creatures, etc) precisely according to this criterion.

(d) The next chapter treats pore diffusion effects (other than 1st order kinetics, distortion of product distribution, experimental methods, etc.) in more detail.

Regime ③ The effect of temperature gradients within particles.

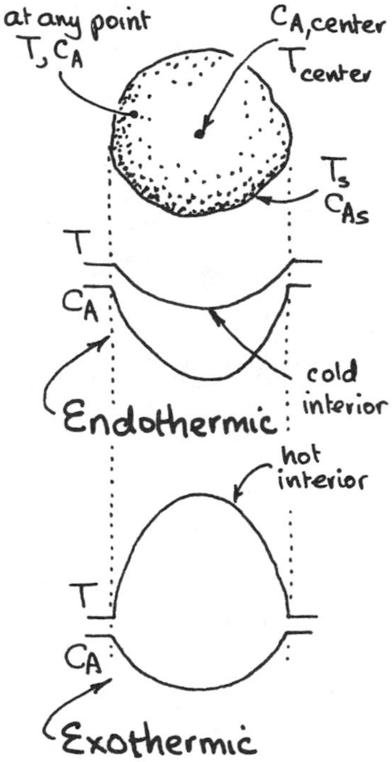

The temperature gradient reflects the concentration gradient and has the same shape. Thus at any point

$$T_{\substack{\text{any point}\\ \text{within}}} - T_s = \frac{\mathscr{D}_{eff}\,(C_{As} - C_{A,\text{same point}})(-\Delta H_r)}{k_{eff}}$$

($-\Delta H_r$: heat of reaction; k_{eff}: thermal conductivity of solid)

At the center

$$\Delta T_{part} = T_{center} - T_s = \frac{\mathscr{D}_{eff}\,(C_{As} - C_{Acenter})(-\Delta H_r)}{k_{eff}}$$

This ΔT becomes maximum in strong pore diffusion because here $C_{Acenter} \cong 0$. Thus

$$\Delta T_{max} = \frac{\mathscr{D}_{eff}\, C_{As}\,(-\Delta H_r)}{k_{eff}}$$

($-\Delta H_r$ in J/mol; k_{eff} in W/m solid·K)

For negligible pore diffusion resistance $\Delta T \to 0$

$\mathcal{E}_{non\,isothermal}$ depends on M_T (or M_W) and the thermal factors, ΔT_{max} and E, the activation energy of the reaction, as shown below:

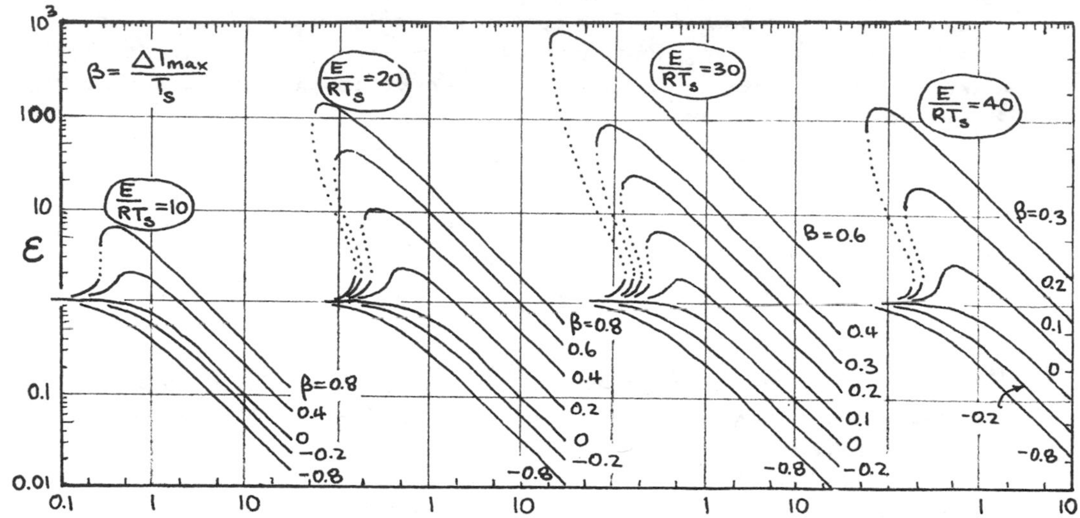

Thiele modulus: $M_T = L\sqrt{\frac{k_s'''}{\mathcal{D}_{eff}}}$ ← evaluated at T_s

These figures were adapted from Weisz and Hicks CES 17 265 (1962)

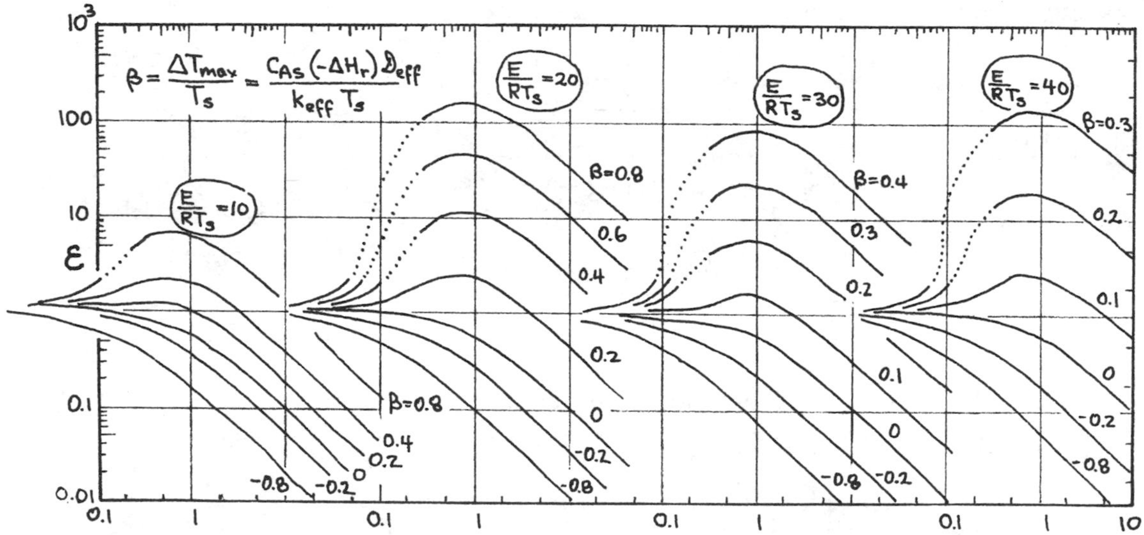

Weisz modulus: $M_W = \frac{(-r_A''')L^2}{C_{As}\mathcal{D}_{eff}}$ ← measured or observed

(a) **To use these figures** first calculate M_T or M_W, E/RT_s and β. Then estimate $\mathcal{E}$ from the figures. Finally determine

$$-r_A''' = k''' C_{As}\,\mathcal{E}_s$$

evaluated at T_s (for k''') — this value ($\mathcal{E}_s$) is based on the assumption that the whole particle is at T_s

(b) **These figures show** that for exothermic reactions ($\beta > 0$) the effectiveness factor and rate are higher than for isothermal reactions occurring at T_s. For endothermic reactions ($\beta < 0$) the rate is lower than for isothermal reactions at T_s.

(c) **For exothermic reactions** the M_T vs $\mathcal{E}$ curve can show S-shaped behavior. Thus coming from the left (for example raise T progressively) you **J·U·M·P** ... the reaction all of a sudden takes off, ignites, and can speed up 100 times or more. But going to the left you **P·L·O·K**, the reaction fizzles, extinguishes and dies on you. Thus you get **hysteresis** behavior with the dotted portion of the curve L·U being unstable and physically unattainable.

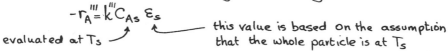

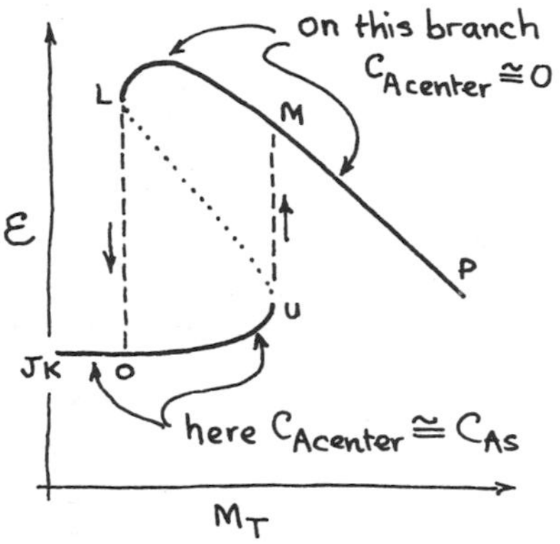

We do not find such behavior with **endothermic** reactions.

(d) On the upper section L·M·P of the S-shaped $\mathcal{E}$ vs M_T curve the particle interior is hot, the rate is fast, reactant is depleted in the interior, and $C_{A,center} \cong 0$. On the lower section J·O·U·K of this curve the particle is practically isothermal throughout, $\mathcal{E} \cong 1$, and $C_{A\,center} \cong C_{As}$.

(e) **The temperature jump** (hot particle interior) in exothermic reactions with its increased rate of reaction is not necessarily desirable. Often it isn't, and it could well be disastrous, giving the wrong product, deactivating the catalyst or shattering the particle by thermal shock and thermal stress (imagine a 100°C temperature rise). So don't cheer when your design calculations suggest that this may happen. Be on guard.

Regime 4 Rate with temperature gradients in gas film only.

Suppose the resistance to the transfer of heat through the particle is negligible compared to the resistance to transfer across the surrounding gas film. Then we can assume a uniform particle temperature, and a heat balance about the particle will give

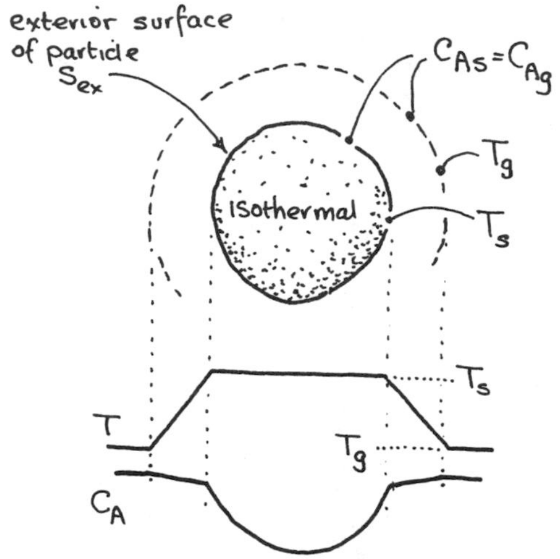

$$Q_{generated} = (-r_A''')V_p(-\Delta H_r) \quad \leftarrow \text{J/mol}$$

$$Q_{\substack{transferred \\ out}} = -h\,S_{ex}(T_g - T_s)$$

where h is in W/m² solid·K (film heat transfer coefficient).

Combining gives

$$\Delta T_{film} = T_s - T_g = \frac{(-\Delta H_r)(-r_A''')L}{h} \quad \text{... or} \quad -r_A''' = \frac{\Delta T_{film}\,h}{(-\Delta H_r)L}$$

where $-r_A''' = k_s''' C_{As} \mathcal{E}_s$

(k_s''' and $\mathcal{E}_s$ evaluated at T_s, not T_g, since the particle is at T_s.)

(a) Film ΔT can occur with or without pore diffusion resistance.

(b) **For exothermic reactions** the particle becomes hotter than the surrounding fluid hence $\mathcal{E}$ and the rate become higher than for a particle at T_g. The opposite holds for **endothermic reactions**.

(c) Evaluating ΔT_{film}, T_s and the rate is done by solving the above boxed equations simultaneously

- For **endothermic reactions** the boxed equations give just one solution. Thus we find one T_s value, somewhat lower than T_g.

- **For exothermic reactions** we find either 0 or 2 mathematical solutions to the boxed equations. At line A·B in the curves below we see 2 solutions. However physical considerations can show that only one of these solutions, the lower one is stable and physically realizable. At line C·D we have no solution. This means that the particle gets so hot that another factor (film mass transfer) becomes controlling... see next section.

(d) The $\mathcal{E}$ vs M_T curves are shown below for two cases, first where pore diffusion effects do not intrude, and then for the case where pore diffusion effects are present.

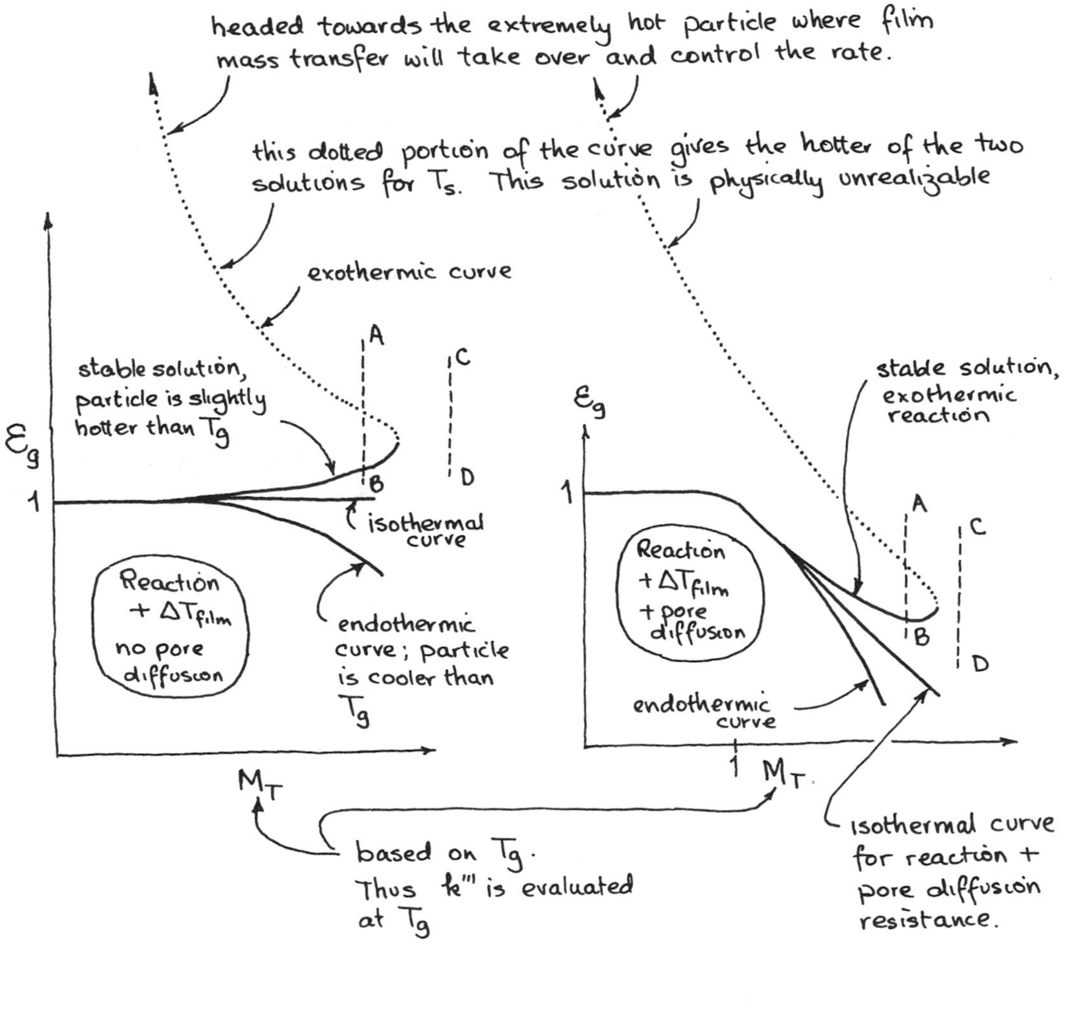

Regime ⑤ Rate when mass transfer to particle is limiting:

Here reactant is so rapidly consumed in the particle that mass transfer to its surface controls the overall rate of reaction. Thus

$$-r_A''' = -r''_{A,ex}\left(\frac{S_{ex}}{V_p}\right) = \frac{-r''_{Aex}}{L} = \frac{k_g(C_{Ag}-\overset{\approx 0}{C_{As}})}{L} = \frac{k_g C_{Ag}}{L} = k''' C_{Ag}\,\mathcal{E}_g$$

and so for film mass transfer control

$$\mathcal{E}_g = \frac{k_g/L}{k'''} = \frac{k_g L}{\mathcal{D}_{eff}} \cdot \frac{1}{M_T^2}$$

- k''': chemical rate constant, m^3 gas/m^3 solid · s
- k_g: film mass transfer coefficient, m^3 gas/m^2 solid · s

$\frac{k_g/L}{k'''}$ and $\frac{k_g L}{\mathcal{D}_{eff}}$: these are equivalent, the second expression being in terms of M_T

Here is what the resulting $\mathcal{E}_g$ vs M_T curves look like.

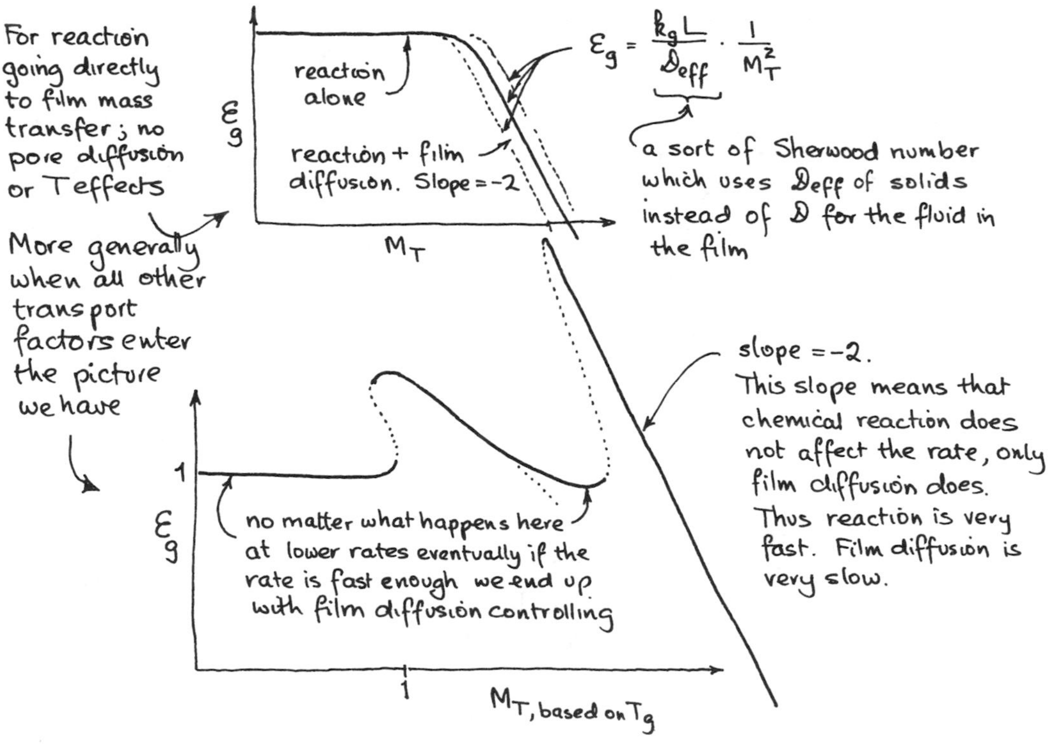
For reaction going directly to film mass transfer; no pore diffusion or T effects
More generally when all other transport factors enter the picture we have
$\mathcal{E}_g$
reaction alone
reaction + film diffusion. Slope = −2
M_T
$\mathcal{E}_g = \frac{k_g L}{\mathcal{D}_{eff}} \cdot \frac{1}{M_T^2}$
a sort of Sherwood number which uses $\mathcal{D}_{eff}$ of solids instead of $\mathcal{D}$ for the fluid in the film
slope = −2. This slope means that chemical reaction does not affect the rate, only film diffusion does. Thus reaction is very fast. Film diffusion is very slow.
1
no matter what happens here at lower rates eventually if the rate is fast enough we end up with film diffusion controlling
1
$M_{T,\text{based on } T_g}$

III $\mathcal{E}$ vs M Curves when all Resistances enter the Picture.

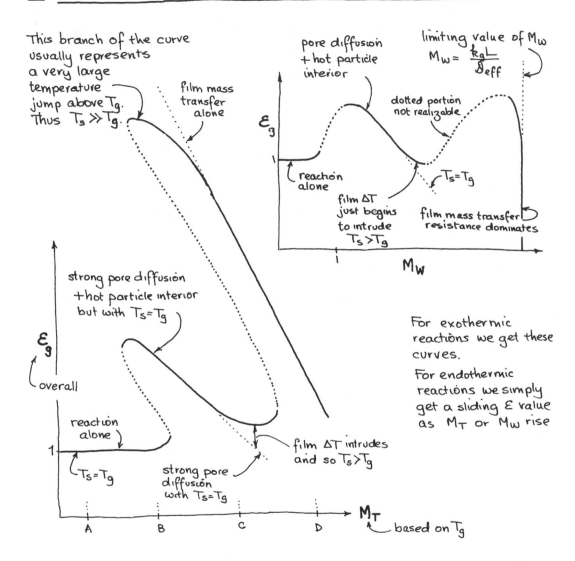

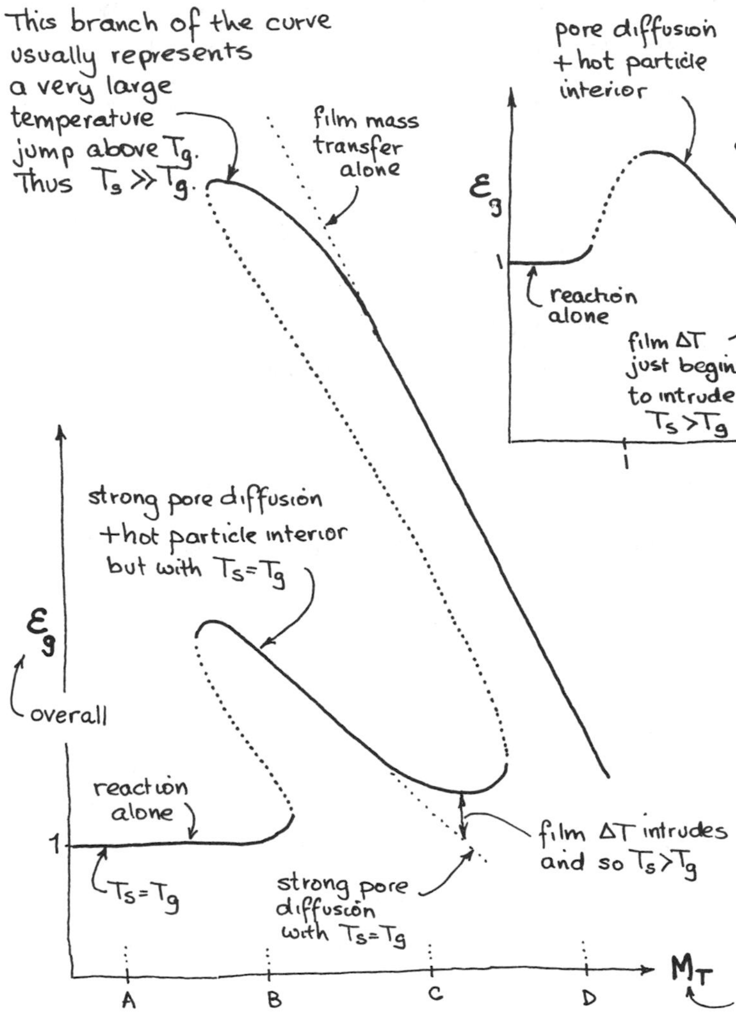

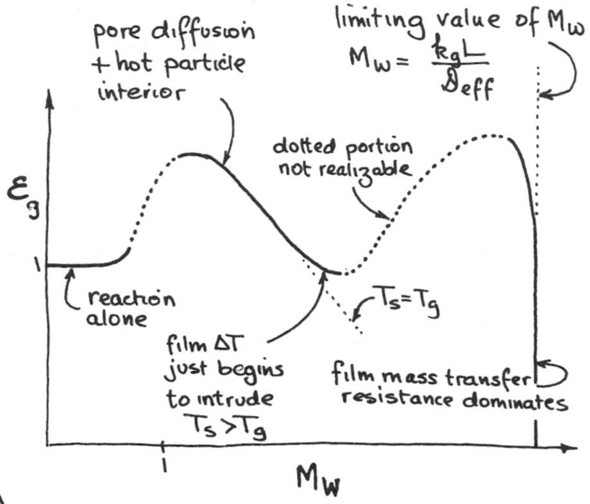

For exothermic reactions we get these curves.

For endothermic reactions we simply get a sliding $\mathcal{E}$ value as M_T or M_W rise

The $\mathcal{E}$ vs M_T curve shows that a particle can exist in one of a number of possible states ... in certain environments. For example only one state in locations A and D above, but 3 states at B, and 2 states at C. When multiple states are possible the actual state that a particle is in depends on its history ... did it start hot, or cold, and so on.

These sketches should help us visualize how the different physical factors enter the picture. Normally we do not operate in a wide enough range of conditions to observe all these regimes. In fact taking typical values for physical quantities of a vigorous highly exothermic reaction Smith [CES 32 1023 (1977)] finds the possibility remote of having multiple steady states in an industrial reactor

IV Interpreting Data and Predicting Behavior.

We encounter two types of situations: either we measure the rate and ask what is happening, or we are given the kinetics of a system and want to know what to expect in an operating reactor. These questions are answered in quite different ways: in essense with r''' known and k''' unknown we use the Weisz modulus as our tool, with k''' known and r''' to be found we use the Thiele modulus.

A. Measure r''' and try to figure out what is happening.

Suppose we measure $-r_A'''$ (in an experimental reactor, by the methods of the previous chapter) for a particular reaction (known E and $-\Delta H_r$) on a given catalyst (known $\mathscr{D}_{eff}$, k_{eff}, L) for a particular reactant stream and system (known C_{Ag}, T_g, h, k_g). Here is the simplest way to find the controlling regime, kinetic constant, temperature, etc.

Step 1. Calculate $\Delta T_{film} = T_s - T_g = \dfrac{(-\Delta H_r)(-r_A''')L}{h}$ and find T_s.

Step 2. Since the particle is bathed by fluid at T_s find

$$C_{As} = C_{Ag}\left(\frac{T_g}{T_s}\right)$$

... this assumes constant pressure and ideal gas behavior.

Step 3. Now see if C_{As} should be corrected for film diffusion

$$\begin{pmatrix}\text{Fraction of resistance}\\ \text{due to film mass transfer}\end{pmatrix} = \frac{(-r'''_{A\,obs})L}{k_g C_{Ag}} \quad \cdots \begin{cases}\text{if} \ll 1 \text{ ignore this effect}\\ \text{if significant then correct as shown}\end{cases}$$

$$C_{As,\,\text{with film resistance}} = C_{As,\,\text{without film resistance}}\left(1 - \frac{(-r'''_{A\,obs})L}{k_g C_{Ag}}\right)$$

We now have the corrected C_{As}, the proper concentration of A bathing the particles. We will use this corrected value from now on.

Step 4 Calculate $M_W = \dfrac{(-r'''_{A\,obs})L^2}{\mathcal{D}_{eff} C_{As}}$

Step 5 Find $\mathcal{E}_s$ (based on the rate at T_s)

- if M_W is small ($M_W \overset{?}{<} 0.15$) then

$C_{A\,center} \cong C_{As}$

$\Delta T_{part} = 0$

$\mathcal{E}_s = 1$

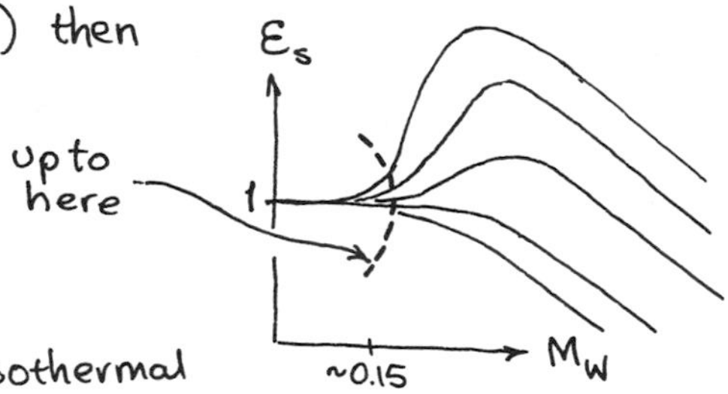

and the whole particle is isothermal and free of pore diffusion resistance.

- if M_W is not small ($M_W \overset{?}{>} 0.15$) calculate

$$\Delta T_{max} = \frac{\mathcal{D}_{eff}(-\Delta H_r)C_{As}}{k_{eff}}, \quad \beta = \frac{\Delta T_{max}}{T_s}, \quad \frac{E}{RT_s}$$

and find $\mathcal{E}_s$ from the non isothermal $\mathcal{E}$ vs M_W charts.

Step 6. Estimate T_{center} and $C_{Acenter}$

to the left ($M_W \overset{?}{<} 0.15$)

$C_{Acenter} \cong C_{As}$

$T_{center} \cong T_s$

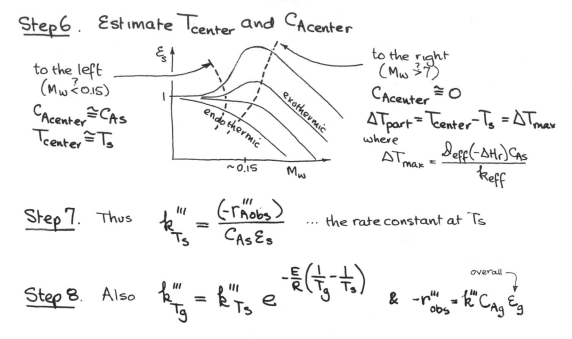

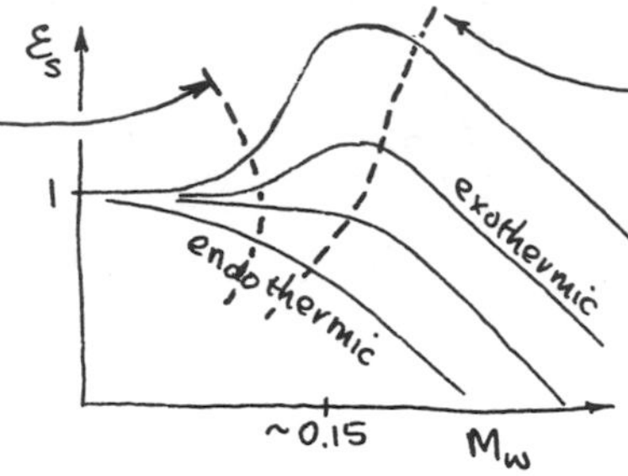

to the right ($M_W \overset{?}{>} 7$)

$C_{Acenter} \cong 0$

$\Delta T_{part} = T_{center} - T_s = \Delta T_{max}$

where

$$\Delta T_{max} = \frac{\mathcal{D}_{eff}(-\Delta H_r)C_{As}}{k_{eff}}$$

Step 7. Thus $$k'''_{T_s} = \frac{(-r'''_{Aobs})}{C_{As}\mathcal{E}_s}$$ ... the rate constant at T_s

Step 8. Also $$k'''_{T_g} = k'''_{T_s}\, e^{-\frac{E}{R}\left(\frac{1}{T_g} - \frac{1}{T_s}\right)} \quad \& \quad -r'''_{obs} = k''' C_{Ag}\, \mathcal{E}_g$$ (overall → $\mathcal{E}_g$)

Thus we have all the information needed: temperatures, rate constants, etc.

B. Given k''', predict what will happen.

Suppose we plan to run a reaction of known kinetics with given catalyst, feed and set up. Will pore diffusion effects intrude? For exothermic reaction will the particle burn up? For endothermic reaction will the rate be unduly slowed by freezing of the heart of the particle? These questions are not so easy to answer, and as mentioned earlier the past history of the particle can be important. Anyway let us see how to go about the search systematically.

First of all we must find the temperature of the fluid bathing the surface of the particle. Unfortunately this requires a trial and error search. The first two steps which follow are concerned with this.

Step 1. Guess $T_s = T_g$, then

- calculate $M_T = L\sqrt{\dfrac{k'''_{T_s}}{\mathcal{D}_{eff}}}$

- evaluate $\mathcal{E}_s$ see pg 22·6

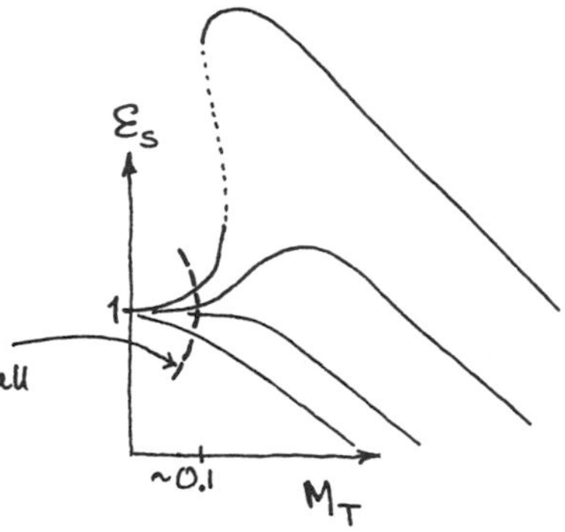

  – if M_T is small ($\overset{?}{<}0.1$) then

  $C_{Acenter} \cong C_{As}$

  $\Delta T_{part} \cong 0$

  $\mathcal{E}_s \cong 1$

  – if M_T is not small ($\overset{?}{>}0.1$) evaluate

  $$\Delta T_{max} = \frac{\mathcal{D}_{eff}(-\Delta H_r)C_{As}}{k_{eff}}, \quad \beta = \frac{\Delta T_{max}}{T_s}, \quad \frac{E}{RT_s}$$

  and from these values find $\mathcal{E}_s$ from the nonisothermal $\mathcal{E}_s$ vs M_T charts.

- calculate $\Delta T_{film} = \dfrac{-\Delta H_r\left[k'''_{T_s} C_{As}\,\mathcal{E}_s\right]L}{h}$

  if $=0$ then our original guess for T_s was right. Go to step 3.

  if $\neq 0$ then our original guess for T_s was wrong. Go to step 2.

Step 2. Guess a new $T_s \neq T_g$, then calculate

- $k'''_{T_s} = k'''_{T_g}\, e^{-\frac{E}{R}\left(\frac{1}{T_s}-\frac{1}{T_g}\right)}$
- $C_{As} = C_{Ag}\left(\dfrac{T_g}{T_s}\right)$

- M_T, $\mathcal{E}_s$, ΔT_{film} as in step 1.
- $T_s = T_g + \Delta T_{film}$

  see if this agrees with the guessed T_s. If not then repeat step 2 with another T_s.

Step 3 When the right T_s is found we then have

$$T_g,\ T_s,\ T_{center},\ \mathcal{E}_s \text{ and } -r_A''' = k'''_{T_s} C_{As} \mathcal{E}_s$$

In exothermic reactions beware because you will find either two solutions for T_s (be sure to take the lower one) or none, in which case you will have to guess higher or higher T_s values until film mass transfer enters the picture.

Step 4. **Test for film mass transfer resistance.** To estimate whether you have to consider this factor evaluate

$$\begin{pmatrix}\text{Fraction of resistance}\\ \text{contributed by the film}\end{pmatrix} = 1 \Big/ 1 + \frac{k_g}{k'''_{T_s} \mathcal{E}_s L} = \frac{C_{Ag} - C_{As}}{C_{Ag}}$$

If this is significant and must be considered we have a messy problem, and how we proceed depends on whether $\Delta T_{film} = 0$ or not. Film mass transfer with $\Delta T_{film} = 0$ is characteristic of **liquid-solid** systems, $\Delta T_{film} \neq 0$ of **gas-solid** systems.

- if $\Delta T_{film} = 0$, $T_s = T_g$. Thus equate $-r_{A②}''' = -r_{A⑤}'''$ to give

$$-r_A''' = k'''_{T_g} C_{Ag} \mathcal{E}_{overall} \quad \ldots\text{where } \mathcal{E}_{overall} = \frac{1}{\dfrac{1}{\mathcal{E}_{pore}} + \dfrac{1}{\mathcal{E}_{film}}} = \frac{1}{\begin{pmatrix}\text{Particle}\\ \text{resistance}\end{pmatrix} + \begin{pmatrix}\text{Film}\\ \text{resist}\end{pmatrix}}$$

($\mathcal{E}_{pore}$ from M_T vs $\mathcal{E}_s$ chart; $\mathcal{E}_{film} = k_g / L k'''_{T_g}$)

From this we find

$$C_{As} = C_{Ag} \Big/ 1 + \frac{k'''_{T_g} \mathcal{E}_s L}{k_g}$$

Then back to step 1 with this C_{As}, recalculate ΔT_{part}, etc. ... eventually getting $-r_A''' = k'''_{T_g} C_{As} \mathcal{E}_s$

- if $\Delta T_{film} \neq 0$ we must calculate a new T_s, one which includes the effect of film mass transfer. The value we need to find must satisfy the relationships

$$\begin{pmatrix}\text{flow of} \\ \text{reactant in}\end{pmatrix} = \begin{pmatrix}\text{flow of} \\ \text{heat out}\end{pmatrix} = \begin{pmatrix}\text{disappearance} \\ \text{by reaction}\end{pmatrix}$$

or... $$-r'''_{A③} = -r'''_{A④} = -r'''_{A⑤}$$

Combining and replacing terms gives

$$-r'''_A = k'''_{T_s} C_{As,\,\text{no film resistance}}\, \mathcal{E}_{overall} \quad \text{...where } \mathcal{E}_{overall} = \frac{1}{\frac{1}{\mathcal{E}_{pore}} + \frac{1}{\mathcal{E}_{film}}}$$

$\mathcal{E}_{pore}$: from M_T vs $\mathcal{E}_s$ chart; $\mathcal{E}_{film} = k_g / L k'''_{T_s}$

$$-r'''_A = \frac{(T_s - T_g)h}{(-\Delta H_r)L}$$

in essense we must guess T_s until these two rates agree.

The procedure is as follows

- guess T_s
- find $k'''_{T_s} = k'''_{T_g}\, e^{-\frac{E}{R}\left(\frac{1}{T_s} - \frac{1}{T_g}\right)}$
- find $C_{As,\,\text{no film resistance}} = C_{Ag}\left(\frac{T_g}{T_s}\right)$
- **find M_T and $\mathcal{E}_{overall}$**
- **compare the above two rates.** If they agree then we are done, we have all the required information including $-r'''_A$! If they don't agree guess again, ... and again.

By experiment we can try to find whether film mass transfer intrudes **by changing the flow rate of fluid past the particle.** Although this may well change k_g it would also change h, hence ΔT_{film} and T_s. And usually the heat effects will dominate. To distinguish between these effects, to unravel their interaction, to come up with the proper interpretation is very tricky, if not hopeless.

V Final Thoughts

This chapter considered the general problem of the porous catalyst pellet with all possible contributing kinetic factors. The real world is never that exciting. Only a couple of factors influence the rate in any given situation, and matters are usually much much simpler.

In different areas of application (outside of catalytic kinetics too) different combinations of these five factors enter the picture. The table below shows what we normally encounter.

	Porous catalyst particle	Catalyst coated surface	Burning of a droplet of fuel	Cells and simple living creatures
Surface reaction	Yes	Yes	No	Yes
Pore diffusion	Yes	No	No	Maybe
Particle ΔT	Not too likely	No	No	No
Film ΔT	Sometimes	Rare	} all important	No
Film mass transfer	No	Yes		Could be

So this chapter provides a general framework for a variety of phenomena.

This chapter may be hard to read with all its steps, cases and sub-cases. Dont try to read it in detail ... skim. Only when solving problems will you see what it all means.

Chapter 22 Problems

The first order catalytic reaction A → R (activation energy E = 167 kJ/mol) is carefully measured at a point where C_{Ag} = 100 mol/m³ and T_g = 500 K in an experimental reactor containing 6 mm catalyst pellets (L = 10^{-3} m).

- Find what factors influence the observed rate (pore diffusion, film mass transfer, particle and film ΔT) find T_s, and find what fraction of resistance is in film mass transfer.
- Find e based on the isothermal pellet at T_g free of physical transport effects.
- Find the reaction rate constant k''' at 500 K. Give complete units of k'''.

The following thermodynamic, system, and rate values are reported for this system. cat

		$-r_A'''$, mol/m³cat·s	ΔH_r, kJ/mol	$\mathcal{D}_{eff}$, m³/m cat·s	k_{eff}, W/m cat·K	h, W/m²cat·K	k_g, m³/m²cat·s
A1	...	10^2	1	10^{-8}	10^{-2}	10^3	1
A2	...	10^2	-10	10^{-4}	1	10	0.1
A3	...	10^2	10	10^{-8}	0.1	10	1
A4	...	10^3	-10	10^{-6}	10^{-2}	10^5	1
A5	...	10^4	-10	10^{-6}	10^{-2}	10^3	1
A6	...	10	0.04	10^{-5}	1	100	1.25×10^{-4}
A7	...	1	-10	10^{-10}	0.1	100	2×10^{-5}
A8	...	10^4	-1	10^{-7}	10^{-2}	20	0.2

Note: To illustrate the points in this chapter some of the above numerical values are deliberately chosen outside their normally observed ranges.

A9 In the catalytic cracking of hydrocarbons free carbon is formed and deposited on the surface of the catalyst causing deactivation. The deactivated catalyst is then regenerated by burning off the deposit with air. It is desirable that the burnoff occur evenly throughout the catalyst particle. For this, oxygen must have ready access to the particle interior. For silica-alumina cracking catalyst take

$\mathcal{D}_{eff} = 4.6 \times 10^{-7}$ m³/m cat·s, for oxygen penetration.

ΔH_r = -198.4 kJ/mol, for the reaction $C + O_2 \rightarrow CO_2$

r''' = 0.4 mol/m³cat·s, at the burnoff temperature of 760 °C

k_{eff} = 0.36 W/m cat·K

Air to the regenerator is at 1 atm

How large a particle can we use and still be free of uneven burnoff and hot particle hearts?

Chapter 22 Problems

A West Texas gas oil is cracked catalytically at 903 K and 1 atm in a bed of silica-alumina cracking catalyst from 8 to 14 mesh in size (d_p = 1.62 mm). For this system we have the following information

For the catalyst: $\mathcal{D}_{eff} = 8 \times 10^{-8}$ $m^3/mcat{\cdot}s$
k_{eff} = 0.36 W/m cat·K

For the reaction: ΔH_r = 1.67 kJ/mol (strongly endothermic)
$-r'''_A$ = 92.7 $mol/m^3cat{\cdot}s$ (at reactor entrance, from problem 21.11)
E = 167 kJ/mol (estimated)

For the gas film: $k_g = 1$ $m^3/m^2cat{\cdot}s$ (estimated)
h = 400 $W/m^2cat{\cdot}K$ (estimated)

A10 ... Find the effectiveness factor for this operation.

A11 ... What pellet size would be free of heat and mass transfer resistances?

See Satterfield 143, 173.

A12 Goto and Morita in J. Chem. Eng. Japan **3** 67 (1970) studied the hydrogenation of ethylene on a single bugged catalyst pellet (d_p = 1.53 cm)

$$C_2H_4 + H_2 \rightarrow C_2H_6, \quad \Delta H_r = -138 \text{ kJ}$$

In run 15 they used a feed of 20% C_2H_4 and 80% H_2 at 75 °C and 1 atm, and they found

ε = 0.132 (effectiveness factor)
T_s = 113 °C (averaged over the surface)
T_{center} = 151 °C

Do these values agree with theory, and if not could film resistance be the cause of the disagreement?

Data: $-r'''_A$ = 3.64 $mol/m^3cat{\cdot}s$

$\mathcal{D}_{eff} = 5.3 \times 10^{-7}$ m^3/m cat·s, for ethylene, the limiting component

k_{eff} = 0.162 W/m cat·K

$h = h_{conv} + h_{radiation}$ = 31.2 + 10.1 = 41.3 $W/m^2cat{\cdot}K$

k_g = 0.1 $m^3/m^2cat{\cdot}s$ (estimated)

With hydrogen in large enough excess we can take the overall reaction to be first order with respect to C_2H_4.

Chapter 22 Problems

A13 Hill developed an example problem from the reported data of Cunningham *et al* in AIChE Journal **11** 642 (1965) on the catalytic hydrogenation of ethylene

$$C_2H_4 + H_2 \rightarrow C_2H_6, \quad \Delta H_r = -136800 \text{ J}$$

Experiments were made on fine powders (to give the true rate of reaction) and on large consolidated pellets (mass and heat transfer resistances could well intrude here), and the ratio of rates of pellet to powder then gave the overall effectiveness factor. For a specific pellet and powder and reaction condition

Cunningham *et al* calculate	$\mathcal{E} = 20$	(their table 2)
Hill calculates	$\mathcal{E} = 1$	(his example, pg 462)
Experiment shows	$\mathcal{E} = 2.0$	(table 2, Cunningham)

What do you find for $\mathcal{E}$?

Data: (from Hill, except where noted)

$d_p = 0.0127$ m cat, spherical pellet

$\rho_s = 1160 \text{ kg/m}^3\text{cat}$, for porous pellet

$\mathcal{D}_{eff} = 3 \times 10^{-6} \text{ m}^3\text{/m cat·s}$, for both H_2 and C_2H_4 in the pellet

$k_{eff} = 0.146$ W/m cat·K, for the porous pellet

$k_g = 0.2 \text{ m}^3\text{/m}^2\text{cat·s}$, an estimate

$h = 57.3 \text{ W/m}^2\text{cat·K}$, estimated by taking $Nu = (hd_p/k_{eff}) = 4$

$T_g = 80$ °C and $p = 1$ atm

Feed: 14% ethylene - 86% H_2, see Cunningham page 639.

$E = 74500$ J/mol, from powder runs

$-r' = 1.8 \times 10^{-3}$ mol C_2H_4/kg cat·s, observed for the pellet

Fractional conversion of ethylene < 2%

The reaction is first order with respect to hydrogen and nearly first order with respect to ethylene, and since hydrogen is in large excess you may want to approximate the overall reaction as simply first order with respect to ethylene.

B14 McGreavy and Thornton in Can. J. Chem. Eng. **48** 187 (1970) give the following data for a packed bed reactor

$d_p = 2.1 \times 10^{-3} \text{ m}^d$	$E = 111$ kJ/mol
$h = 787 \text{ W/m}^2\text{cat·K}$	$C_{A0} = 4.45 \text{ mol/m}^3$
$k_g = 0.0436 \text{ m}^3\text{/m}^2\text{cat/s}$	$k''' = 0.1953 \text{ m}^3\text{gas/m}^3 \text{ cat·s}$
$\mathcal{D}_{eff} = 3.66 \times 10^{-7} \text{ m}^3\text{/m cat·s}$	$T_g = 500$ K
$\Delta H_r = -2.1$ MJ/mol	$k_{eff} = 0.335$ W/m cat·K, estimated, not given.

Evaluate the effectiveness factor and the pertinent temperatures associated with a catalyst particle at the reactor entrance.

Chapter 22 Problems

We plan to run a first order reaction $A \rightarrow R$ in a reactor filled with 6 mm porous catalyst pellets ($L = 10^{-3}$ m). At a point in the reactor where $C_A = 100\ \text{mol/m}^3$ find

- whether pore and/or film diffusion effects are likely to intrude to affect the rate
- whether nonisothermal effects are likely to intrude; in effect, estimate the temperature at the surface and at the center of catalyst pellets
- the rate of reaction, $-r_A'''$
- the effectiveness factor e based on an isothermal particle at T_g free of mass transfer effects

Thermodynamic tables, physical property and rate measurements reported by the catalyst manufacturer, and estimated transfer coefficients for the expected operating conditions are as follows.

	T_g, K	ΔH_r, $\frac{\text{kJ}}{\text{mol}}$	E, $\frac{\text{kJ}}{\text{mol}}$	k''', $\frac{\text{m}^3}{\text{m}^3\text{cat·s}}$	$\mathscr{D}_{eff}$, $\frac{\text{m}^3}{\text{m cat·s}}$	k_{eff}, $\frac{\text{W}}{\text{m cat·K}}$	h, $\frac{\text{W}}{\text{m}^2\text{cat·K}}$	k_g, $\frac{\text{m}^3}{\text{m}^2\text{cat·s}}$
B15 ...	500	-10	167	100	10^{-8}	10^{-2}	10^4	10
B16 ...	1000	-100	335	100	10^{-6}	0.1	10^7	3
B17 ...	500	20	167	100	10^{-6}	10^{-2}	10^5	1
B18 ...	1000	0	251	10^3	10^{-5}	10^{-2}	10	0.1
B19* ...	1000	10	167	10^4	10^{-8}	0.1	10	1
B20* ...	500	20	167	10^4	10^{-6}	10^{-2}	10^2	1
B21* ...	1000	-10	167	100	10^{-8}	0.1	9	0.02
B22* ...	500	-1	167	100	10^{-8}	10^{-2}	9	0.09
B23 ...	1000	-1	167	10^4	10^{-8}	10^{-2}	10^2	1

In the following problem can you find more than one solution?

B24* ...	500	-1	167	100	10^{-8}	10^{-2}	12.5	0.27

Chapter 22 Problems

B25* Consider a porous pellet catalyzing a first order gas phase reaction $A \rightarrow R$. It has been claimed by some that in general there can exist at most two stable conditions for the pellet, as shown in the sketches of pgs 22.6 or 22.9. With the following data show that there are in fact three stable solutions, just as sketched on pg 22.11.

Data: Conditions bathing the pellet:	$T = 500$ K $C_A = 1$ mol/m^3
For the reaction:	$\Delta H_r = -100$ J/mol $k''' = 1$ m^3/m^3 cat·s, at 500K $E = 167000$ J/mol
Pellet properties:	$L = 10^{-2}$ $\mathcal{D}_{eff} = 2.5 \times 10^{-3}$ m^3/m cat·s $k_{eff} = 2.5 \times 10^{-3}$ W/m cat·K
Transport properties:	$h = 10$ W/m^{2}cat·K $k_g = 100$ m^3/m^{2}cat·s

Chapter 23. Pore Diffusion Effects in Reactors.

The previous chapter took up the problem of identifying the various kinetic regimes for porous catalyst pellets when all the heat and mas mass transfer resistances intrude. Often pore diffusion is the only physical factor which affects the rate. So in this chapter let us consider this effect alone for catalyst pellets bathed by fluid C_A.

I. Single Irreversible First Order Reaction.

For pellets of any shape we have

from Thiele, IEC 31 916 (1939) and Aris, CES 6 262 (1957)

$$\left.\begin{array}{l} A \rightarrow R \\ -r_A''' = k'''C_A\mathcal{E} \end{array}\right\} \quad \cdots \text{ where } \mathcal{E} \begin{cases} = \dfrac{1}{M_T}\cdot \tanh M_T \\[2ex] = \dfrac{1}{M_T}\cdot \dfrac{I_1(2M_T)}{I_0(2M_T)} \\[2ex] = \dfrac{1}{M_T}\cdot\left(\dfrac{1}{\tanh 3M_T} - \dfrac{1}{3M_T}\right) \end{cases} \quad \cdots (1)$$

$-r_A'''$ in mol/m³ cat·s

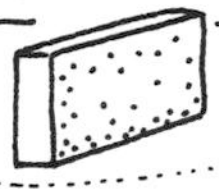

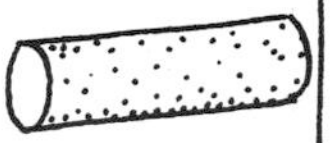

Bessel function (for the cylinder expression)

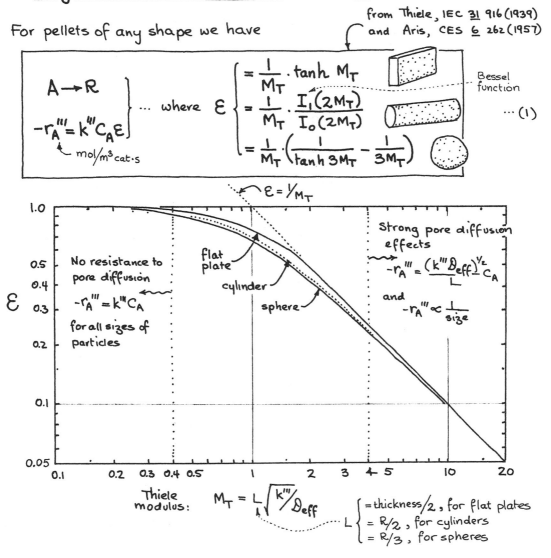

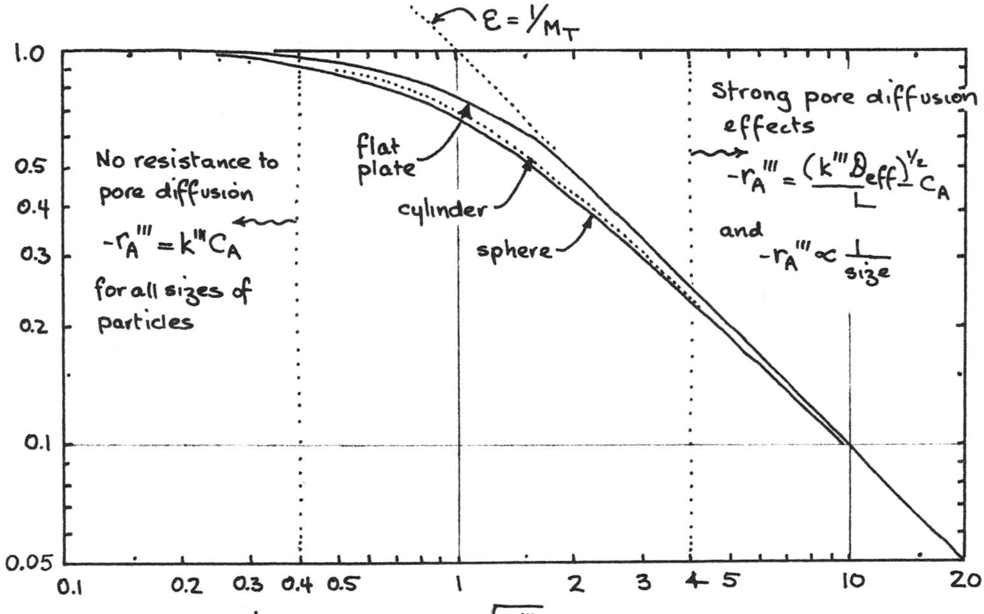

Thiele modulus: $M_T = L\sqrt{k'''/\mathcal{D}_{eff}}$

$$L \begin{cases} = \text{thickness}/2, \text{ for flat plates} \\ = R/2, \text{ for cylinders} \\ = R/3, \text{ for spheres} \end{cases}$$

Experimental consequences.

(a) **Factors influencing $\mathcal{E}$.** The effectiveness factor $\mathcal{E}$ represents the slowdown in rate caused by diffusional resistance. It is dependent on the Thiele modulus M_T. Factors affecting M_T are

- particle size (affects L)
- temperature (affects k''' strongly, $\mathcal{D}_{eff}$ slightly)
- total pressure ($\mathcal{D} \propto \frac{1}{\pi}$ for bulk diffusion, $\mathcal{D}$ is independent of π in Knudsen diffusion)

(b) **Temperature level.** In the strong pore resistance regime

$$-r_A''' = \frac{(k'''\mathcal{D}_{eff})^{1/2}}{L} C_A \quad \cdots \text{ where } \begin{cases} k''' = k_0''' e^{-E/RT} \\ \mathcal{D}_{eff} = \mathcal{D}_{eff,0}\, e^{-E_{diff}/RT} \end{cases}$$

From this we find that the observed activation energy in this regime is

$$E_{obs} = \frac{E_{rx} + E_{diff}}{2} \cong \frac{E_{rx}}{2} \qquad \cdots (2)$$

(E_{diff}: usually very small)

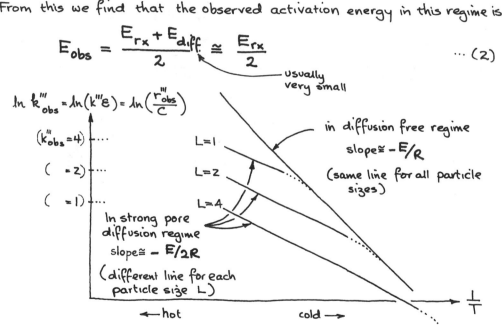

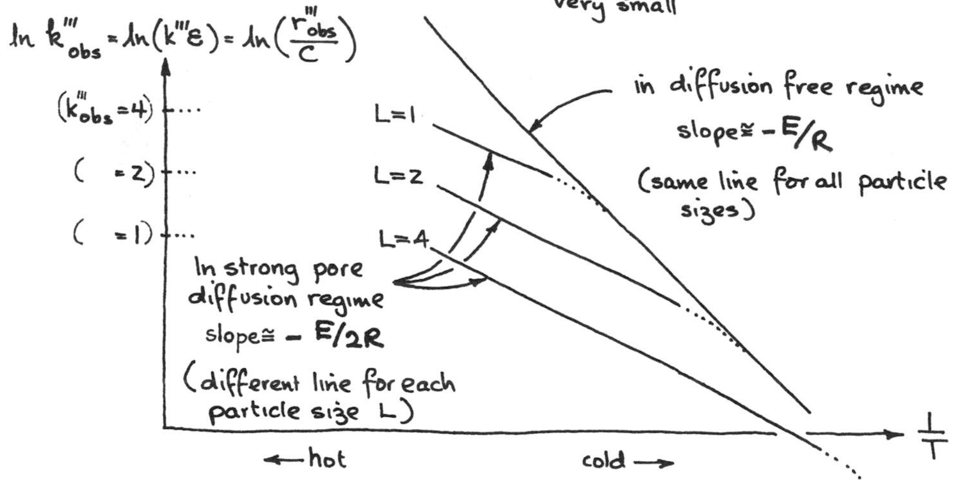

Raise the temperature and you enter the pore diffusion regime (the rate speeds up so much that reactant can't penetrate the particle).

Lower the temperature and you leave the pore diffusion regime.

(c) **Particle size effect.**

Where $M_T < 0.4$ ... $\mathcal{E} = 1$ (see figure) and the observed rate is the same for all sizes of particles

Where $M_T > 4$ ... $\mathcal{E} = 1/M_T$ and $-r'''_{A,obs} \propto \frac{1}{L}$

Thus for any two sizes of solid R_1 and R_2:

$$\frac{\left(-r'''_{Aobs}/C_A\right)_2}{\left(-r'''_{Aobs}/C_A\right)_1} = \left(\frac{k'''_2}{k'''_1}\right)_{obs} \begin{cases} = 1 & \text{for no pore diffusion resistance} \\ = \dfrac{R_1}{R_2} & \text{for strong pore diffusion resistance} \end{cases}$$

(d) **To find the rate equation from data** you need at least three good data points, 2 at different temperatures in one regime, 1 in the other. From these three points draw the two lines (one slope double the other) and find their intersection (Y^*, T^*) for particles of size L^*. We then have

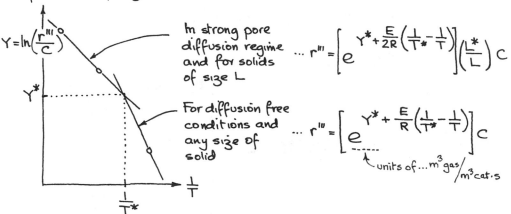

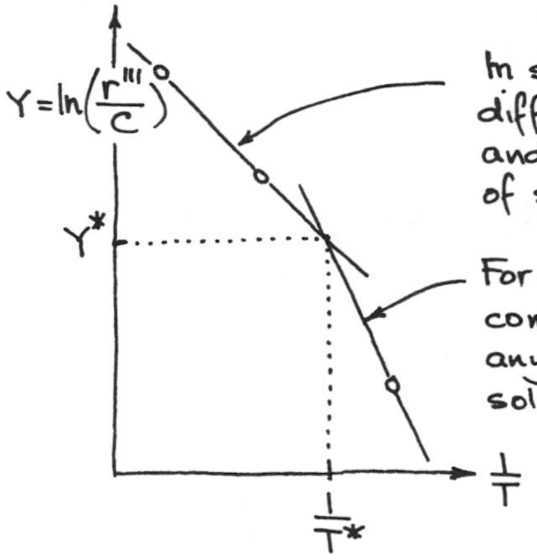

In strong pore diffusion regime and for solids of size L ... $r''' = \left[e^{Y^* + \frac{E}{2R}\left(\frac{1}{T^*} - \frac{1}{T}\right)}\right]\left(\frac{L^*}{L}\right) C$

For diffusion free conditions and any size of solid ... $r''' = \left[e^{Y^* + \frac{E}{R}\left(\frac{1}{T^*} - \frac{1}{T}\right)}\right] C$

(units of ... m^3 gas/m^3 cat·s)

The complete rate equation for all regimes, all sizes of solid, and all temperatures can be written in terms of T^* and Y^*. Thus

$$-r'''_A = \left[e^{Y^* + \frac{E}{2R}\left(\frac{1}{T^*} - \frac{1}{T}\right)}\right]\left(\frac{L^*}{L}\right) \cdot \tanh\left\{\frac{L}{L^*} \cdot e^{\frac{E}{2R}\left(\frac{1}{T^*} - \frac{1}{T}\right)}\right\} C_A \qquad (3)$$

(tanh: strictly only for flat plates)

(e) To sum up: The existence of strong pore diffusion effects can be determined:

- by calculating M_T or M_W if $\mathcal{D}_{eff}$ is known
- by comparing the rate for different pellet sizes
- by noting the drop in observed activation energy with rise in temperature, coupled with a possible change in reaction order, see next section

Additional comments on desirable operating regimes, etc., are given in chapter 22. Please look there.

II Single Reaction other than First Order Irreversible.

These can be treated in a way similar to first order irreversible reactions if M_T and M_W are properly defined. Considering the flat plate approximation to apply we have

1. First order reversible reaction.

$$A \underset{k'''/K}{\overset{k'''}{\rightleftarrows}} R \qquad K = \frac{C_{Re}}{C_{Ae}}$$

$$-r_A''' = \left(k'''C_A - \frac{k'''}{K}C_R\right)\mathcal{E} = k'''\left(\frac{K+1}{K}\right)(C_A - C_{Ae})\mathcal{E}$$

$$C_{A0} + C_{R0} = C_{Ae} + C_{Re} \quad \cdots \quad \mathcal{E} = \frac{\tanh M_T}{M_T}$$

$$M_T = L\sqrt{\frac{k'''(K+1)}{\mathcal{D}_{eff}\,K}} = L\sqrt{\frac{k'''(C_{A0}+C_{R0})}{\mathcal{D}_{eff}(C_{A0}+C_{R0}-C_{Ae})}}$$

$$M_W = \frac{-r_A'''L^2}{\mathcal{D}_{eff}(C_A - C_{Ae})}$$

Use the same curves as for irreversible first order reaction

2. n^{th} order irreversible reaction.

$$A \rightarrow R \quad \cdots \quad n \neq 0$$

$$-r_A''' = k'''C_A^n\,\mathcal{E} \quad \cdots \quad \mathcal{E} = \frac{\tanh M_T}{M_T}$$

$$M_T = L\sqrt{\frac{(n+1)\,k'''C_A^{n-1}}{2\,\mathcal{D}_{eff}}}$$

$$M_W = \frac{n+1}{2}\cdot\frac{-r_A'''L^2}{\mathcal{D}_{eff}\,C_A}$$

For the special case of **zero order** kinetics

$$A \rightarrow R \quad \cdots \quad n=0$$

$$-r_A''' = k'''\mathcal{E} \quad \cdots \quad \mathcal{E}\begin{cases} =1 & \text{for } M_T \leq 1 \\ =\dfrac{1}{M_T} & \text{for } M_T \geq 1 \end{cases}$$

$$\begin{cases} M_T = L\sqrt{\dfrac{k'''}{2C_A\mathcal{D}_{eff}}} \\ M_W = \dfrac{-r_A'''L^2}{2C_A\mathcal{D}_{eff}} \end{cases}$$

Graphically for all n values

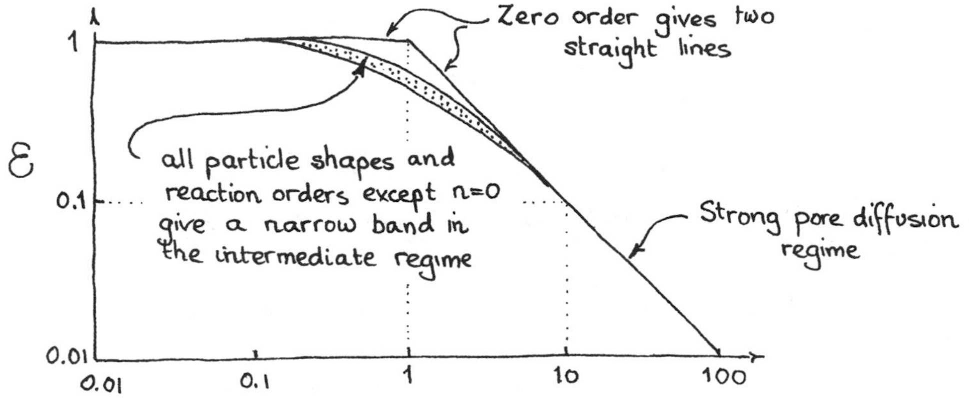

$$M_T = L\sqrt{\frac{n+1}{2}\cdot\frac{k'''C_A^{n-1}}{\mathcal{D}_{eff}}}$$

In the strong pore diffusion regime for all n^{th} order reactions

$$-r_A''' = \left(\frac{2}{n+1}\cdot\frac{k'''\mathcal{D}_{eff}}{L^2}\right)^{1/2} C_A^{(n+1)/2}$$

Thus the observed reaction order is:

$$n_{obs} = \frac{n_{true}+1}{2}$$

The observed activation energy is:

$$E_{obs} = \frac{E_{true}+E_{diff}}{2} \cong \frac{E_{true}}{2}$$

3. Change in number of moles, $A \rightarrow rR$, $r \neq 1$, $\varepsilon_A \neq 0$. This causes a shift with negligible change in shape of the ε vs M_T curve: to the right if $r<1$ (bulk flow into pellet, reaction rate rises), to the left if $r>1$. The extent of this shift is given by

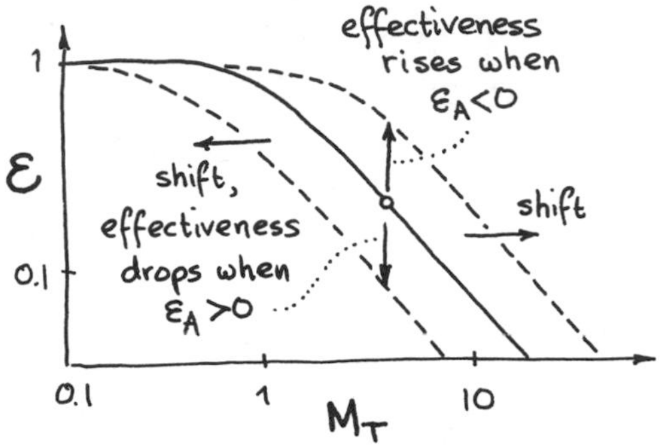

$$M_{T,\varepsilon_A \neq 0} \cong (1+\varepsilon_A)^m \cdot M_T$$

(use this) — put $m = 0.35$ when $\varepsilon_A > 0$

$m = 0.30$ when $\varepsilon_A < 0$

For other reaction orders see:
Weekman & Gorring, J. Catal. 4 260 (1965)

4. Langmuir adsorption or Michaelis-Menten equation form.

$$A \rightarrow R \quad \ldots \quad -r_A''' = \frac{k''' C_A}{C_M + C_A} \cdot \varepsilon \quad \ldots \text{where } C_M \text{ is a constant}$$

for $C_M \gg C_A$ this equation approaches 1st order kinetics and

$$-r_A''' = \frac{k'''}{C_M} \cdot C_A \varepsilon \quad \ldots \text{and} \ldots \quad M_T = L\sqrt{\frac{k'''}{C_M \mathscr{D}_{eff}}}$$

for $C_M \ll C_A$ this equation approaches zero order kinetics and

$$-r_A''' = k''' \varepsilon \quad \ldots \text{and} \ldots \quad M_T = L\sqrt{\frac{k'''}{2 C_A \mathscr{D}_{eff}}}$$

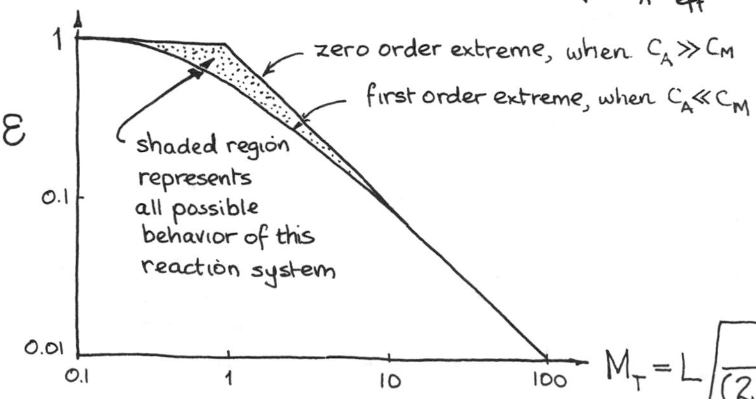

$$M_T = L\sqrt{\frac{k'''}{(2C_A + C_M)\mathscr{D}_{eff}}}$$

<u>III</u> Multiple Reactions: how Pore Diffusion Resistance affects the Distribution of Products.

See Wheeler, Advances in Catalysis **3** 250 (1951) for an excellent treatment of this subject.

1. Parallel reactions.

$$A \overset{1}{\underset{2}{\displaystyle\mathrel{\mathop{\rightrightarrows}}}} \begin{array}{l} R \\ S \end{array} \quad \begin{array}{l} \cdots\ r_1''' = k_1''' C_A^{a_1} \\[2mm] \cdots\ r_2''' = k_2''' C_A^{a_2} \end{array} \qquad \left. \begin{array}{l} \cdots\ r_1''' = \left(\dfrac{2}{a_1+1} \cdot \dfrac{k_1''' \mathcal{D}}{L^2} \right)^{1/2} C_A^{(a_1+1)/2} \\[4mm] \cdots\ r_2''' = \left(\dfrac{2}{a_2+1} \cdot \dfrac{k_2''' \mathcal{D}}{L^2} \right)^{1/2} C_A^{(a_2+1)/2} \end{array} \right\}$$

no intrusion of pore resistance $\qquad\qquad$ with strong resistance to pore diffusion

No resistance to pore diffusion:
$$\frac{dC_R}{dC_S} = \frac{k_1'''}{k_2'''} C_A^{a_1-a_2} \qquad\qquad \mathcal{G}\left(\frac{R}{R+S}\right) = 1 \bigg/ 1 + \frac{k_2'''}{k_1'''} C_A^{a_2-a_1}$$

With strong pore resistance:
$$\frac{dC_R}{dC_S} = \left(\frac{a_2+1}{a_1+1} \cdot \frac{k_1'''}{k_2'''} C_A^{a_1-a_2} \right)^{1/2}, \qquad \mathcal{G}\left(\frac{R}{R+S}\right) = 1 \bigg/ 1 + \left(\frac{a_1+1}{a_2+1} \cdot \frac{k_2'''}{k_1'''} C_A^{a_2-a_1} \right)^{1/2}$$

In both diffusion regimes the higher order reaction is favored at high C_A, however the diffusion-free regime more strongly favors the higher order reaction. Thus

- if the higher order reaction is desired use plug flow and small enough solids to be free of diffusional resistance effects.
- if the lower order reaction is desired use mixed flow and large enough particles to be in the strong diffusion resistance regime.

2. Side by side reactions.

no pore resistance $\qquad\qquad$ strong diffusion resistance

$$A \overset{1}{\rightarrow} R \quad \cdots\ r_1''' = k_1''' C_A^{a} \qquad \left. \begin{array}{l} \cdots\ r_1''' = \left(\dfrac{2}{a+1} \cdot \dfrac{k_1''' \mathcal{D}_A}{L^2} \right)^{1/2} C_A^{(a+1)/2} \\[4mm] \end{array} \right.$$

$$B \overset{2}{\rightarrow} S \quad \cdots\ r_2''' = k_2''' C_B^{b} \qquad \left. \begin{array}{l} \cdots\ r_2''' = \left(\dfrac{2}{b+1} \cdot \dfrac{k_2''' \mathcal{D}_B}{L^2} \right)^{1/2} C_B^{(b+1)/2} \end{array} \right\}$$

No resistance to pore diffusion: $\frac{C_R}{C_S} = \frac{k_1''' C_A^a}{k_2''' C_B^b}$; $\qquad \varphi\left(\frac{R}{R+S}\right) = 1 \Big/ 1 + \frac{k_2''' C_B^b}{k_1''' C_A^a}$

With strong pore resistance: $\frac{C_R}{C_S} = \left(\frac{k_1'''}{k_2'''} \cdot \frac{b+1}{a+1} \cdot \frac{\mathcal{D}_A C_A^{a+1}}{\mathcal{D}_B C_B^{b+1}}\right)^{1/2}$; $\qquad \varphi\left(\frac{R}{R+S}\right) = 1 \Big/ 1 + \left(\frac{k_2'''}{k_1'''} \cdot \frac{a+1}{b+1} \cdot \frac{\mathcal{D}_B C_B^{b+1}}{\mathcal{D}_A C_A^{a+1}}\right)^{1/2}$

Since A and B change independent of each other C_R/C_S depends on everything, reactor type, conversion level, k_2'''/k_1''', a/b, concentration level and pore diffusion effects. No simplification occurs when $a = b$. Actually it is best to calculate C_R and then C_S independently, and not deal with φ values.

3. __Series first order reactions.__ $A \xrightarrow{1} R \xrightarrow{2} S$ ... with $\begin{cases} K = \frac{k_2'''}{k_1'''} \\ \gamma = \left(\frac{k_2'''}{k_1'''}\right)^{1/2} \end{cases}$

For plug flow:

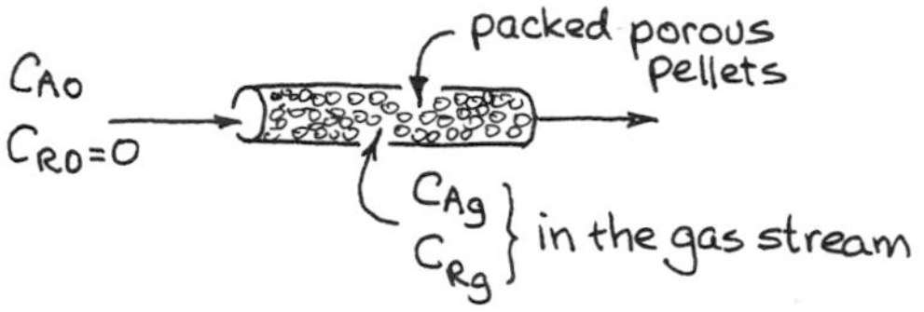

No pore resistance: $\frac{C_{Rg}}{C_{A0}} = \frac{1}{1-K}\left[\left(\frac{C_{Ag}}{C_{A0}}\right)^K - \frac{C_{Ag}}{C_{A0}}\right]$; $\qquad \cdots \left(\frac{C_{Rg}}{C_{A0}}\right)_{max} = K^{K/1-K}$

Strong pore resistance: $\frac{C_{Rg}}{C_{A0}} = \frac{1}{1+\gamma} \cdot \frac{1}{1-\gamma}\left[\left(\frac{C_{Ag}}{C_{A0}}\right)^\gamma - \frac{C_{Ag}}{C_{A0}}\right]$; $\qquad \cdots \left(\frac{C_{Rg}}{C_{A0}}\right)_{max} = \frac{1}{1+\gamma} \cdot \gamma^{\gamma/1-\gamma}$

For mixed flow:

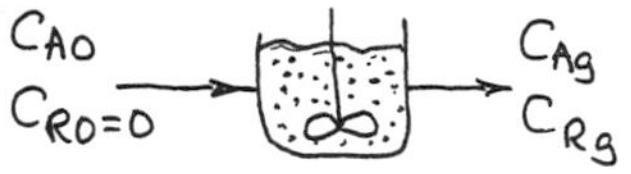

No pore resistance: $C_{Rg} = \frac{C_{Ag}(C_{A0} - C_{Ag})}{C_{Ag} + K(C_{A0} - C_{Ag})}$; $\qquad \cdots \left(\frac{C_{Rg}}{C_{A0}}\right)_{max} = \frac{1}{(K^{1/2}+1)^2}$

Strong pore resistance: $C_{Rg} = \frac{1}{1+\gamma} \cdot \frac{C_{Ag}(C_{A0} - C_{Ag})}{C_{Ag} + \gamma(C_{A0} - C_{Ag}}$ $\qquad \cdots \left(\frac{C_{Rg}}{C_{A0}}\right)_{max} = \frac{1}{1+\gamma} \cdot \frac{1}{(\gamma^{1/2}+1)^2}$

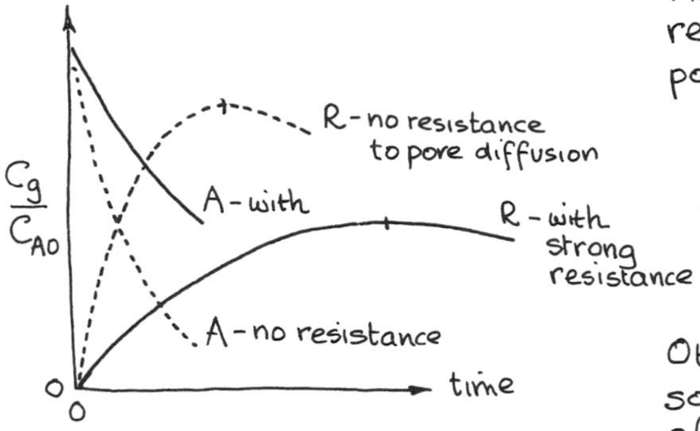

These equations for first order reactions show that with strong pore diffusion resistance

- reaction is slowed (longer time is needed to reach $C_{R,max}$)
- the amount of R formed is less (see table below)

Other reaction orders give the same sort of result. Thus pore diffusion affects product distribution in the same way for all reactions in series.

k_2'''/k_1''' for $A \xrightarrow{1} R \xrightarrow{2} S$	$\left(\frac{C_{Rg}}{C_{A0}}\right)_{max}$ for plug flow			$\left(\frac{C_{Rg}}{C_{A0}}\right)_{max}$ for mixed flow		
	No resistance	strong resistance	% decrease	No resistance	strong resistance	% decrease
1/64	0.936	0.650	30.6	0.790	0.486	38.5
1/16	0.831	0.504	39.3	0.640	0.356	44.5
1/4	0.630	0.333	47.6	0.444	0.229	48.5
1	0.368	0.184	50	0.250	0.125	50
4	0.157	0.083	47.2	0.111	0.057	48.5
16	0.051	0.031	38.2	0.040	0.022	44.5

up to 50% drop in C_{Rmax}

IV. Particles having more than One Pore Size.

Real porous particles can have a rather uniform pore size, a wide spread of sizes, or in some cases, two rather distinct sizes

Compacted pelletized grains are an example of particles having two pore sizes

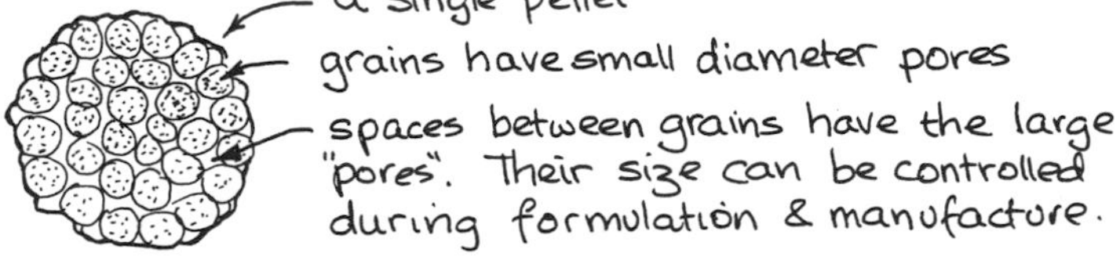

So far, in this chapter we have only considered one size of pore. Here we look at diffusion effects in particles which have two distinct pore sizes as well as particles with a wide size distribution of pores.

1. The macro·micropore model for two distinct pore sizes.

Let us use the following nomenclature for this simple model

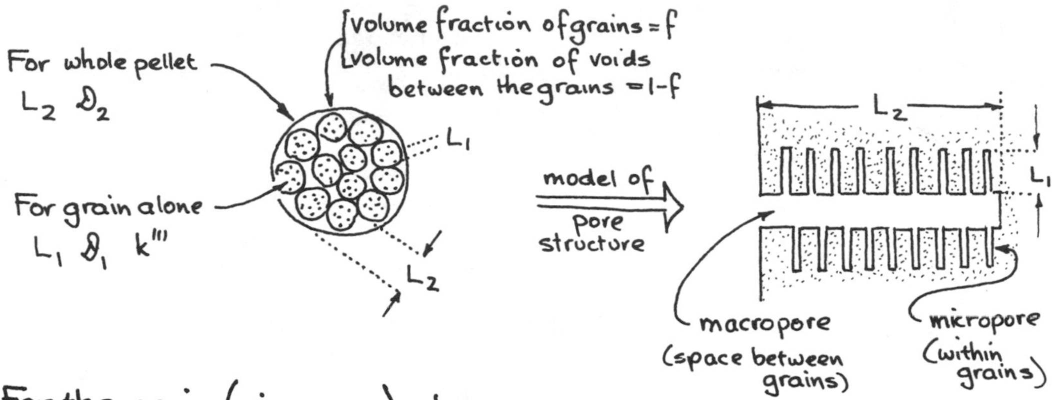

For the grain (micropore) alone

No pore diffusion:
$$-r_A''' = k''' C_A \mathcal{E}_1 = k''' C_A$$

Strong pore diffusion:
$$-r_A''' = k''' C_A \mathcal{E}_1 = \frac{(k''' \mathcal{D}_1)^{1/2}}{L_1} C_A \quad \text{...where } M_1 = L_1 \sqrt{\frac{k'''}{\mathcal{D}_1}}$$

(Thiele modulus for grain)

For the whole pellet (micro·macropore)

No pore diffusion anywhere:
$$-r_A''' = (f k''') C_A$$

Strong pore diffusion in grains only:
$$-r_A''' = (f k''' \underset{1/M_1}{\mathcal{E}_1}) C_A \underset{1}{\mathcal{E}_2} = \frac{f}{L_1} (\mathcal{D}_1 k''')^{1/2} C_A$$

Strong pore diffusion everywhere:
$$-r_A''' = (f k''' \underset{1/M_1}{\mathcal{E}_1}) C_A \underset{1/M_2}{\mathcal{E}_2} = \sqrt{\frac{f(1-f)}{\sqrt{2}} \cdot \frac{\mathcal{D}_1^{1/2} \mathcal{D}_2 (k''')^{1/2}}{L_1 L_2^2}} \cdot C_A$$

$$\text{...where } M_2 = L_2 \sqrt{\frac{f k''' \mathcal{E}_1}{(\mathcal{D}_2/\sqrt{2})(1-f)}}$$

Catalyst chefs have developed these catalysts so as to get easy access into the interior of large particles, thus no diffusion resistance in the macropores. If we have strong diffusional resistance in both macro and micropores then we are defeated and this represents a poor design. One possible exception to this conclusion is when product distribution is helped. This only happens with certain parallel decompositions.

2. <u>For a wide spectrum of pore sizes</u> define

$$\alpha = \begin{pmatrix}\text{degree of branching} \\ \text{in the} \\ \text{porous material}\end{pmatrix} \quad \ldots \text{where} \begin{cases} \alpha = 0 & \text{for non porous particle} \\ \alpha = 1 & \text{for particle with one size of pore} \\ \alpha = 2 & \text{for micro-macro porous material} \\ \text{etc.} & \end{cases}$$

For $\alpha = 1$ and strong pore diffusion everywhere

$$\ldots \begin{cases} E_{obs} = \frac{1}{2} E_{diff} + \frac{1}{2} E_{rx} \\ n_{obs} = 1 + \frac{n-1}{2} \\ \left(\frac{k_2}{k_1}\right)_{obs} = \left(\frac{k_2}{k_1}\right)^{1/2}, \quad \text{for parallel reactions, same order.} \end{cases}$$

For $\alpha = 2$, strong pore diffusion everywhere, but reaction in micropore only (very large surface there).

$$\ldots \begin{cases} E_{obs} = \frac{3}{4} E_{diff} + \frac{1}{4} E_{rx} \\ n_{obs} = 1 + \frac{n-1}{4} \\ \left(\frac{k_2}{k_1}\right)_{obs} = \left(\frac{k_2}{k_1}\right)^{1/4}, \quad \text{for parallel same order reaction} \end{cases}$$

For any α, strong pore diffusion everywhere, but reaction only in smallest size pore (very large surface there)

$$\ldots \begin{cases} E_{obs} = \left(1 - \frac{1}{2^\alpha}\right) E_{diff} + \frac{1}{2^\alpha} E_{rx} \\ n_{obs} = 1 - \frac{n-1}{2^\alpha} \\ \left(\frac{k_2}{k_1}\right)_{obs} = \left(\frac{k_2}{k_1}\right)^{1/2^\alpha}, \quad \text{for parallel same order reaction.} \end{cases}$$

As α increases $E_{obs} \rightarrow E_{diff}$ and $n_{obs} \rightarrow 1$, and the overall process approaches pore diffusion control.

By working backwards, in effect by comparing E_{obs} and E_{rx} or n_{obs} and n, we can find α and say something about the pore structure geometry.

Probably α is the best single parameter to describe the spread of pore sizes in porous materials.

V Final Comments.

Again let us point out that we usually wish to operate at the boundary where pore diffusion resistance just begins to intrude, or $M_T \cong 0.4$ (see comments at the end of chapter 22). We do this:

- by choosing the largest size of pellet which does not show pore diffusion resistance
- by trying to control pore size by proper selection of catalyst support material.
- by clever formulation of pelletized grains with their macro-micropores.
- by coating the outside skin or shell of carrier pellets with catalyst. Per unit volume of pellet the rate of reaction is reduced somewhat, however sometimes hardly at all. On the other hand, per unit mass of catalyst used the rate can be greatly speeded

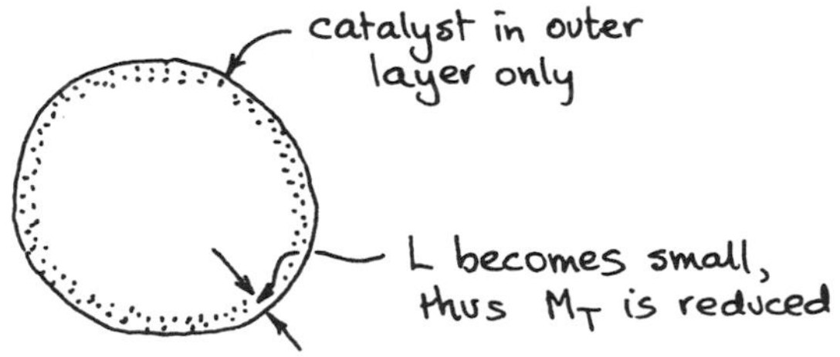

This procedure can be very helpful for very fast reactions where pore diffusion resistance intrudes strongly, or $M_T \gg 1$, $\mathcal{E} \ll 1$.

Chapter 23 Problems

A1 Our packed bed reactor runs the gas phase reaction A → R at 10 atm and 336 °C, and gives 90% conversion of a pure A feed. However, the catalyst salesman guarantees that in the absence of pore diffusion resistance our reaction will proceed on his new improved porous catalyst ($\mathcal{D}_{eff} = 2 \times 10^{-6}$ m³/m cat·s) with a rate given by

$$-r_A''' = 0.08\, C_A \; \frac{\text{mol}}{\text{m}^3\,\text{cat}\cdot\text{s}}$$

which is much better than what we now can do. The catalyst is rather expensive since it is formulated of compressed kookaburra droppings and it is sold by weight. Still, we'll try it when we next replace our catalyst. What diameter of catalyst balls should we order?

A2 A reaction A → R is to take place on a porous catalyst pellet (d_p = 6 mm, $\mathcal{D}_{eff} = 10^{-6}$ m³/m cat·s). How much is the rate slowed by pore diffusional resistance if the concentration of reactant bathing the particle is 100 mol/m³ and the diffusion-free kinetics are given by

$$-r_A''' = 0.1\, C_A^2 \; \frac{\text{mol}}{\text{m}^3\,\text{cat}\cdot\text{s}}$$

A3 If nature does things right, and it usually does, then the size of cells should not be too large (diffusion limitation within the cell, hence inefficient operation) or too small (needs too much surface area). Weisz considers this phenomenon in Nature **195** 772 (1962) somewhat as follows.

Imagine the biochemical action of a cell as a sequence of reactions catalyzed by the different enzymes present in the cell, and where the limiting step in this sequence is a particular reaction **x** at one location in the cell followed by diffusion to a second location where the next reaction **y** occurs.

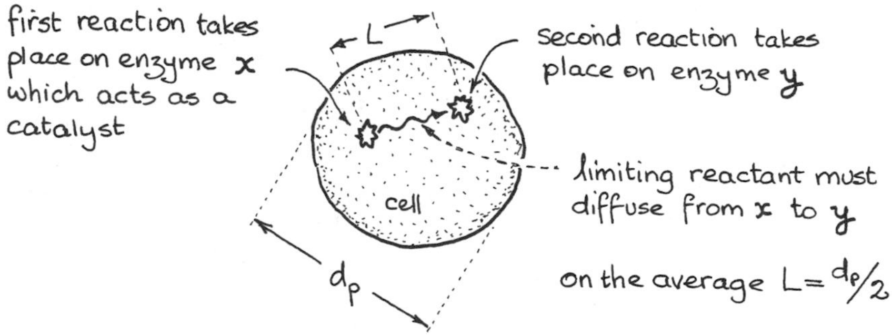

Weisz proposes the following order of magnitude estimates for the pertinent qualities:

- For the rate of oxygen uptake and reaction by various organs, cells and bacteria, 10^{-8} cm³ O_2 measured at 1 atm/gm of cell·min.

- For the concentration and diffusion coefficient within the cell of the limiting component in oxygen metabolism, most likely a large molecule, take $C = 10^{-8}$ mol/cm^3 and $\mathcal{D} = 10^{-6}$ cm^2/s.

From these values estimate the size of a typical cell. How does your value compare with the actual size of these cells, which ranges from 5 μm to 50 μm?

A4 A sperm cell consists of a head, a midpiece and a tail. The head contains the payload, while the midpiece and tail make up the propulsion system. Consider the propulsion system. ATP, the fuel for tail action, is produced in the midpiece. It then diffuses into the tail and is consumed there. If the tail is too long then its end is starved for ATP and it becomes flaccid and a drag. On the other hand if the tail is too short the sperm cell will be a laggard. In either case, the short tailed or long tailed wiggler will lose out in its struggle for immortaility, while the cell with just the right length of tail has the best chance of survival.

Nevo and Rikmenspoel in Theor. Biol. **26** 11 (1970) give the following information for a bull sperm

- Volume of midpiece = 1.3×10^{-18} m^3/sperm
- Oxygen consumption by midpiece = 4.35×10^{-18} mol/s·sperm
- Each mole of oxygen consumed produces 6 moles of ATP
- Volume of tail = 1.5×10^{-18} m^3/sperm
- Diffusion coefficient for ATP along the tail = 3.6×10^{-10} m^2/s
- Total ATP in midpiece = 220×10^{-18} mol/sperm

From the above data estimate the tail length of a bull sperm, and compare this value with the measured value of $\approx 5 \times 10^{-5}$ m. (Hint: first calculate the rate of production of ATP in the midpiece.)

For a completely different view of the mechanism of tail action, see Scientific American, pg. 36, August 1975.

The liquid phase of hydrogenation of unsaturated hydrocarbon is accomplished by bubbling hydrogen gas (A) through liquid containing suspended porous catalyst particles. The gas dissolves in the liquid, diffuses into the catalyst pores and reacts there. Reaction is approximately first order with respect to the limiting reactant, hydrogen, with a diffusion-free rate constant $k''' = 0.1$ m^3/m^3 cat·s and we hope to achieve useful reaction rates in the reactor of the order of

$$-r_A''' = k'''C_A = 1\,\frac{\text{mol}}{\text{m}^3\,\text{cat·s}}$$

From vapor-liquid equilibrium data Henry's law constant for the solubility of hydrogen in this hydrocarbon liquid is estimated to be

$$H_A = p_A/C_A = 0.1\ \text{m}^3\text{liquid·atm/mol}\ H_2$$

and the effective diffusivity of hydrogen in the porous catalyst particles is estimated to be

$$\mathcal{D}_{eff} = 2 \times 10^{-9}\ m^3/m\ cat{\cdot}s$$

A5 . . . If we wish to insure that pore diffusion effects do not intrude to cause inefficient use of the catalyst and if the operation is to be performed at atmospheric pressure what size of suspended catalyst particles should be used?

A6 . . . What hydrogen pressure must we use if we want to get the required rate of reaction with 3 mm catalyst pellets?

These problems were developed by Weisz, CEP Symp. Series **55 (25)** 29 (1959).

The first order decomposition of A is run in an experimental mixed flow reactor. Find the role played by pore diffusion in these runs; in effect determine whether the runs were made under diffusion-free, strong resistance, or intermediate conditions.

B7 . . .

d_p	W	C_{A0}	v	X_A	
3	1	100	9	0.4	$A \rightarrow R$
12	4	300	8	0.6	

B8 . . .

d_p	W	C_{A0}	F_{A0}	X_A	
4	1	300	60	0.8	$A \rightarrow R$
8	3	100	160	0.6	

B9 . . .

d_p	W	C_{A0}	F_{A0}	X_A	
2	4	75	10	0.2	$A \rightarrow 2R$
1	6	100	5	0.6	gas phase, pure A feed

B10 What is the most reasonable interpretation, in terms of controlling resistances, of the following isothermal kinetic data obtained in a basket type mixed flow reactor.

Pellet Diameter	Leaving Concentration of Reactant	Spinning Rate of Baskets	Measured Reaction Rate $-r'_A$
1	1	high	3
3	1	low	1
3	1	high	1

(a) It is known that the catalyst is porous.

(b) It is known that the catalyst is non-porous.

B11 What can you tell about the controlling resistances (film or pore diffusion) and about catalyst porosity from the data below obtained in a recycle type mixed flow reactor. In all runs the leaving stream has the same composition, and conditions are isothermal throughout.

Quantity of catalyst	Pellet Diameter	Flow Rate of Given Feed	Recycle Rate	Measured Reaction Rate, $-r'_A$
1	1	1	high	4
4	1	4	higher still	4
1	2	1	higher still	3
4	2	4	high	3

A packed bed reactor converts A to R by a first order catalytic reaction. With 9 mm pellets the reactor operates in the strong pore diffusion regime and gives 63.2% conversion.

C12 ... If these pellets were replaced by 18 mm pellets (to reduce pressure drop) how would this affect the conversion?

C13 ... If the original pellets were replaced by 3 mm pellets, half active and half inert, and if we still expect to remain in the strong pore diffusion regime, find the conversion.

In aqueous solution, and in contact with the right catalyst, reactant A is converted to product R by the elementary reaction $A \rightarrow 2R$. Find the mass of catalyst needed in a packed bed reactor for 90% conversion of 10^4 mol A/hr of feed having $C_{A0} = 10^3$ mol/m^3. For this reaction

C14 ... $k'''' = 8 \times 10^{-4}$ m^3/m^3 bed·s

C15 ... $k'''' = 2$ m^3/m^3 bed·s

Additional data:

Diameter of porous catalyst pellets = 6 mm

Effective diffusion coefficient of A in the pellet = 4×10^{-8} m^3/m cat·s

Voidage of packed bed = 0.5

Bulk density of packed bed = 2000 kg/m^3 of bed

Chapter 23 Problems

C16 In an experimental mixed flow reactor with 10 gm of 1.2 mm catalyst particles and a feed of 4 cm^3/s of pure A at 1 atm and 336 °C we get 80% conversion for the first order reaction

$$A \rightarrow R, \quad \Delta H_r \approx 0$$

We want to design a commercial sized reactor to treat large amounts of feed to 80% conversion at the above temperature and pressure. Our choice is between a fluidized bed of 1 mm particles (assume mixed flow of gas) and a packed bed of 1.5 cm particles. Which should we choose so as to minimize the amount of catalyst needed. How much advantage is there in this choice?

Additional Data: For the catalyst particles:

$$\rho_s = 2000 \text{ kg/m}^3 \qquad \mathcal{D}_{eff} = 10^{-6} \text{ m}^3\text{/m cat·s}$$

C17 Chemical R is to be produced by the catalytic decomposition of reactant A, and reaction proceeds at 539°C and 2 atm with negligible heat effects as follows

$$A(g) \xrightarrow{\text{catalyst}} R(g), \quad -r_A' = k'C_A, \quad k' = 10^{-2} \text{ m}^3\text{/kg cat·s}$$

We want 90% conversion of reactant to product. Catalyst is very expensive and comes in two sizes, as a 120 μm powder or as 1.2 cm pellets, both at the same cost per kg. The properties of the catalyst are

Particle density = 2500 kg/m^3

Effective diffusivity of gas in the pellet, $\mathcal{D}_{eff} = 10^{-6}$ m^3/m cat·s

We have two choices, to use a packed bed of the large pellets, or a fluidized bed of powder.

(a) How many kg of catalyst powder would be needed for a fluidized bed reactor (assume mixed flow of gas)?

(b) How many kg of catalyst pellets would be needed for a packed bed reactor (assume plug flow of gas)?

D18 Find the activation energy of the first order reaction from the following data

d_p	C_A	$-r_A'$	T, K
1	20	1	480
2	40	1	480
2	40	3	500

$A \rightarrow R$

$C_{A0} = 50$

Chapter 23 Problems

Reactant A at about 50 atm decomposes by a first order reaction $A \rightarrow R$ on both a fine catalyst powder (assume no pore diffusion resistance) and on catalyst pellets with the following results (density of catalyst = 1000 kg/m³).

C_A, mol/m³	1	1	1
$-r_A'''$, mol/m³cat·s	20	1	1
T, K	667	625	667
Catalyst	powder	powder	6 mm pellets

D19 . . . Determine the activation energy of the reaction, find the cross-over temperature at which diffusion slows the reaction for d_p = 6 mm pellets, and find the rate of reaction (mol/kg·s) at 625 K on d_p = 12 mm catalyst pellets.

D20 . . . Develop separate rate equations for all sizes of catalyst particles at all temperatures, first for the diffusion free regime, and then for the strong pore diffusion regime. Express the rate as mol/m³ cat·s and radius of pellets in mm.

D21 . . . Develop the complete rate equation for all particle sizes, temperatures and diffusion regimes, expressing the rate as mol/kg·s and the radius of pellet in mm.

The following data are obtained for the first order catalytic decomposition, $A \rightarrow R$ using 18 mm spherical catalyst particles (density of solid catalyst = 1000 kg/m³).

C_A, mol/m³	0.01	100	5	1	0.1
$-r_A'''$, mol/m³cat·hr	30	270	100	400	110
T, K	400	286	303	345	370

D22 . . . Determine the activation energy of the reaction and find the temperature regime where pore diffusion slows the rate of reaction for particles of this size.

D23 . . . Develop separate rate equations for all sizes of catalyst particles at all temperatures, first for the diffusion free regime, and then for the strong diffusion regime. Let the reaction rate be expressed in moles/kg·s and the particle radius in mm.

D24 . . . Develop the complete rate equation for all particle sizes and diffusion regimes. Give the reaction rate as moles/m³cat·s, and the particle radius in mm.

D25 What can you tell about the influencing resistances (film or pore diffusion) and activation energy for the reaction from the following data obtained in a basket type mixed flow reactor? Assume a uniform temperature throughout the pellet, equal to that of the surrounding gas.

Flow Rate of gas	$C_{A,in}$	$C_{A,out}$	Amount of Catalyst	Pellet Diameter	Spinning Rate of Baskets	T, °C
5	5	1	10	1	low	344
2	4	1	6	2	high	344
8	2	1	4	2	high	372
9	3	1	9	2	low	372

Experiments at 300° C in a packed bed reactor with recycle stream give the results shown below for the first order catalytic decomposition $A \to R \to S$. Under the best possible conditions (always at 300° C) what C_{Rmax}/C_{A0} may we expect, and how do you suggest we get this (what flow pattern and particle size, large or small)?

E26 . . .

d_p	W/F_{A0}	C_{Rmax}/C_{A0}
4	1	0.5
8	2	0.5

No recycle

E27 . . .

d_p	W/F_{A0}	C_{Rmax}/C_{A0}
1	1	0.17
3	1	0.17

Very large recycle

E28 The following table summarizes the results of three runs in an experimental packed bed reactor on the solid-catalyzed first order decomposition $A \to R \to S$.

Size of Porous Catalyst, mm	Temperature of Run, °C	W/F_{A0}	C_{Rmax}/C_{A0}
3	300	27	0.50
6	300	54	0.50
6	320	21	0.50

Further experiments anywhere between 240 and 340 °C are planned to search for conditions where production of R is maximized. What catalyst size (from 1 mm to 8 mm) and temperature should we explore, and what C_{Rmax}/C_{A0} may we expect to find?

Chapter 23 Problems

Reactant A at $C_{A0} = 10\ \text{mol/m}^3$ is to be passed through a packed bed catalytic reactor where it will decompose into either R or S. To maximize the formation of R and for 90% decomposition of A determine

- whether to operate in the strong pore diffusion regime or in the diffusion free regime
- whether to use plug flow or mixed flow (high recycle)
- C_R expected in the exit stream.

The kinetics of the decomposition, when free of pore diffusion resistance, is given by

E29 . . . $A \nearrow R \quad r'_R = C_A^2$; $A \searrow S \quad r'_S = 12$

E30 . . . $A \nearrow R \quad r'_R = 2\,C_A$; $A \searrow S \quad r'_S = 3\,C_A^2$

E31 The solid-catalyzed first order decomposition $A \rightarrow R \rightarrow S$ is studied in a recycle reactor in which the recycle rate of fluid is at least 50 times the throughput rate. The results are summarized below. From these data an installation is planned to produce as much R as possible from a feed identical to that used in the experiments.

Size of Porous catalyst, mm	Temperature of Runs, °C	τ'	$C_{R\max}/C_{A0}$
3	300	30	0.17
6	300	60	0.17
6	320	30	0.17

(a) Choose between a packed bed and a fluidized bed reactor.

(b) Choose between 3 mm and 6 mm catalyst pellets.

(c) In the range between 300 and 320 °C select an operating temperature.

(d) Determine the weight time $\tau' = WC_{A0}/F_{A0}$ to be used.

(e) Predict the expected $C_{R\max}/C_{A0}$.

Chapter 23 Problems

E32 Gaseous A contacts a porous catalyst and there decomposes to R and S by the reactions

$$A \begin{cases} \nearrow R & r'_R = 3 \\ \searrow S & r'_S = C_A^2 \end{cases}$$

At $C_A = 12$ find the ratio of R to S formed for:

(a) no pore diffusion resistance in the catalyst particles

(b) strong pore diffusion resistance in catalyst particles which have one size of pore

(c) pelletized grain catalyst with strong pore diffusion resistance in the micropores, no diffusion resistance in the macropores.

(d) pelletized grain catalyst with strong pore diffusion resistance in both micro and macropores. A rough estimate is sufficient.

F33 At present we are running our catalytic first order reaction in the strong pore diffusion regime in a packed bed reactor filled with platinum impregnated 6 mm particles of uniform size. A catalyst manufacturer suggests that we replace our catalyst with 6 mm pellets consisting of fused 0.06 mm grains. The voidage between grains in the pellet would be about 25%. If these new pellets were free of pore diffusion resistance in their large voids (between grains), but if the grains were still in the strong diffusional resistance regine, how would this change affect the weight of catalyst needed and the reactor volume?

F34 Instead of impregnating the whole porous particle uniformly with platinum (see problem 33), suppose we only impregnate the outer layer of the spherical particle to a thickness of 0.3 mm. How much platinum do we save by this change? Assume that we are in the strong pore diffusion regime throughout.

F35 10^{-5} m^3/s of pure gaseous reactant A at 336 °C and 1 atm are fed to a recirculating mixed flow reactor which contains 0.01 kg of 1.0 mm porous catalyst pellets (ρ_s = 1800 kg/m^3, $\mathcal{D}_{eff} = 2 \times 10^{-6}$ m^3/m cat·s). Reactant decomposes on contact with the catalyst as follows

$$A \rightarrow R, \quad \text{first order}$$

and an analysis of the product stream shows that 80% of reactant has decomposed.

(a) What is the rate constant k' for the reaction?

(b) What size of packed bed (W) of 12.65 mm particles will give 90% conversion of 10^{-3} m^3/s of the above feed?

Chapter 23 Problems

F36 We want to build a packed bed reactor filled with 1.2 cm porous catalyst particles (ρ_s = 2000 kg/m^3, $\mathcal{D}_{eff} = 2 \times 10^{-6}$ m^3/m cat·s) to treat 1 m^3/s of feed gas (1/3 A, 1/3 B, 1/3 inert) at 336 °C and 1 atm to 80% conversion of A. Experiments with fine catalyst particles which are free from diffusional resistance show that

$$A + B \rightarrow R + S, \quad n = 2, \quad k' = 0.01 \text{ m}^6/\text{mol}\cdot\text{kg}\cdot\text{s}$$

How much catalyst must we use?

F37 Our porous wall tubular catalytic reactor is being replaced with a reactor having twice the wall thickness. Assuming first order reaction $A \rightarrow R$, 90% conversion and plug flow of gas through the tube, what will be the conversion in the new reactor if both reactors operate isothermally

(a) in the regime of strong resistance to pore diffusion?

(b) in the regime of negligible resistance to pore diffusion?

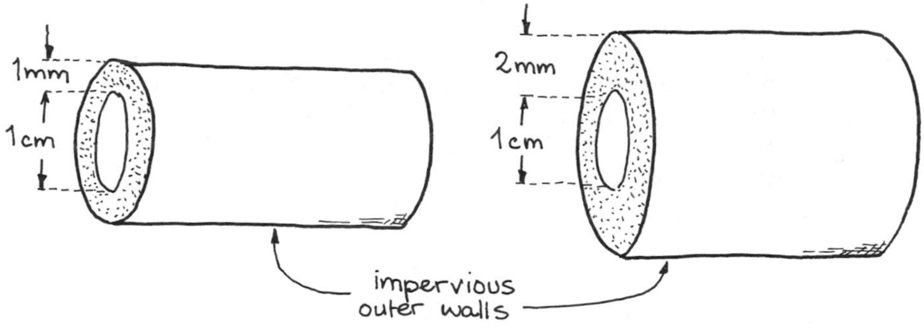

F38 Our first order reaction $A \rightarrow R$ is run in a packed bed of 6 mm porous catalyst particles consisting of platinum deposited uniformly throughout a silica-alumina support structure $\mathcal{D}_{eff} = 10^{-8}$ m^3/m cat·s). To save on catalyst cost it has been suggested that we only impregnate the outer 100 μm layer of the pellet with catalyst. For the same processing rate and conversion of gaseous reactant how would this change affect

(a) the amount of platinum needed?

(b) the size of reactor to be used?

The kinetics and concentrations in our present operations are given by

$$-r'''_{A,obs} = 1 \frac{\text{mol}}{\text{m}^3\,\text{cat}\cdot\text{s}}, \quad \text{at } C_A \approx 10 \frac{\text{mol}}{\text{m}^3}$$

Chapter 23 Problems

F39 A first order catalytic reaction $A(\ell) \rightarrow R(\ell)$ is run in a long narrow vertical reactor with upflow of liquid through a fluidized bed of catalyst particles. Conversion is 95% at the start of operations when the catalyst particles are 5mm in diameter.

The catalyst is friable and slowly wears away, particles shrink and the fine powder produced washes out of the reactor. After a few months each of the 5mm spheres has shrunk to 3mm spheres. What should be the conversion at this time?

(a) Particles are smooth and non porous.

(b) Particles are porous and allow easy access for reactants (no resistance to pore diffusion).

(c) Particles are porous and at all sizes provide a strong resistance to pore diffusion.

F40 The following two experiments with porous catalyst particles were designed to give information for reactor design for the reaction

$$A(g) \rightarrow R(g), \qquad \text{first order}$$

<u>Run 1</u> 98% of entering reactant A is converted to product as feed gas flows continuously through a well mixed reactor containing finely powdered suspended catalyst.

<u>Run 2</u> The same conversion is obtained for the same gas feed rate through a tubular reactor packed with the same mass of 10mm particles as in run 1.

From this information we want to design a packed bed reactor to run this reaction to 99% conversion. What particle size should we use noting that we want to use the catalyst most effectively?

Chapter 24 ADIABATIC PACKED BED REACTORS.

Here we develop a graphical design method based on the use of the **temperature–conversion chart**. The method is simple to use, gives a visual display of the characteristics of the reaction system, and allows a quick evaluation of the many design alternatives, such as

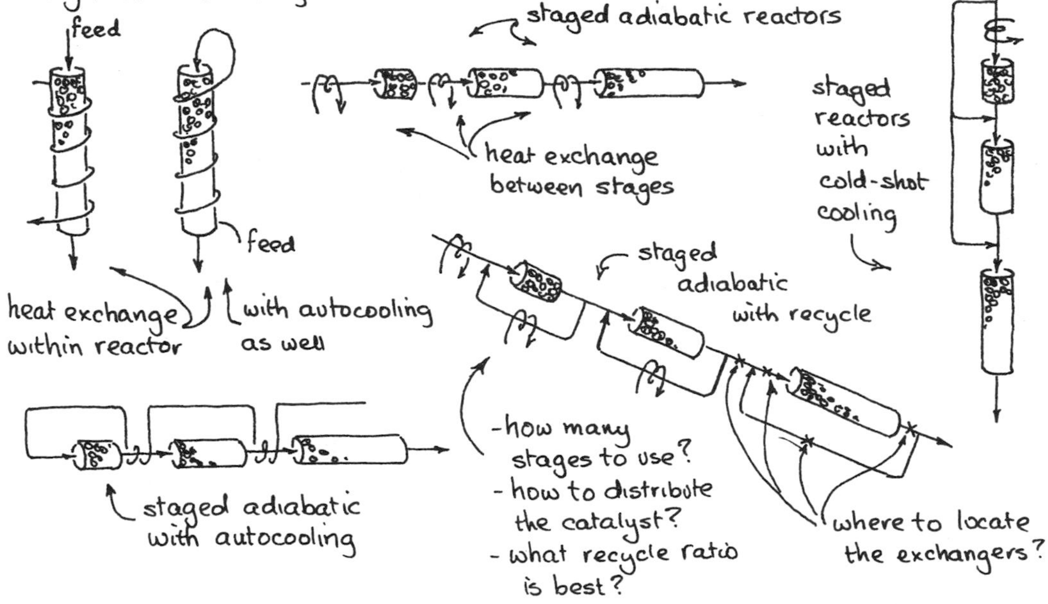

I Graphical Representation.

For a single reaction (take first order as an example) we have

$$A \rightleftarrows R \quad \ldots \Delta H_r, \qquad -r_A' = k_1' C_A - k_2' C_R \quad \ldots \text{with } K = \frac{k_1'}{k_2'}$$

heat of reaction: + for endothermic, − for exothermic

let us write this in terms of conversions. We get this from chapter 1. Thus for $C_{R0} = 0$

$$-r_A' = C_{A0}\left(\frac{T_0 \pi}{T \pi_0}\right)\left[k_{10}' e^{-E_1/RT}\left(\frac{1-X_A}{1+\varepsilon_A X_A}\right) - k_{20}' e^{-E_2/RT}\left(\frac{X_A}{1+\varepsilon_A X_A}\right)\right]$$

Thus for a feed at C_{A0}, π_0 and T_0 we obtain a graph which looks like this:

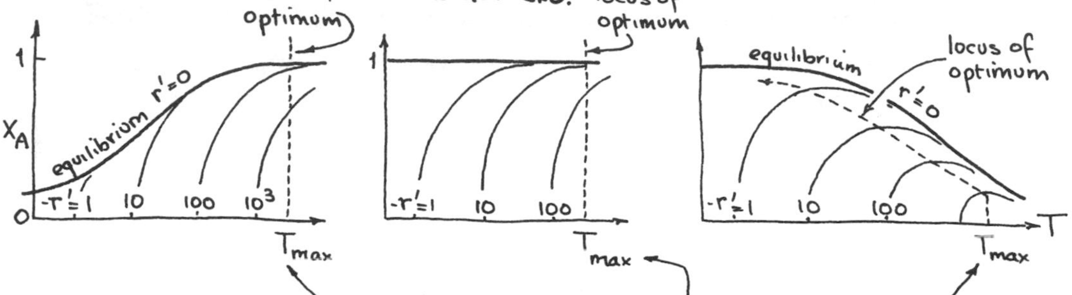

(a) These graphs show the rate of reaction as a function of temperature and conversion. For other kinetics we get graphs of similar general shape.

(b) **For optimum operations** pick (at each X_A) that T where $-r_A'$ is highest. Thus run the reactor at T_{max} for endothermic reversible, and for irreversible reactions; but follow a falling temperature for reversible exothermic reactions.

(c) This graph can also represent the **energy balance**. So for adiabatic operations for any single reaction in any kind of reactor we have

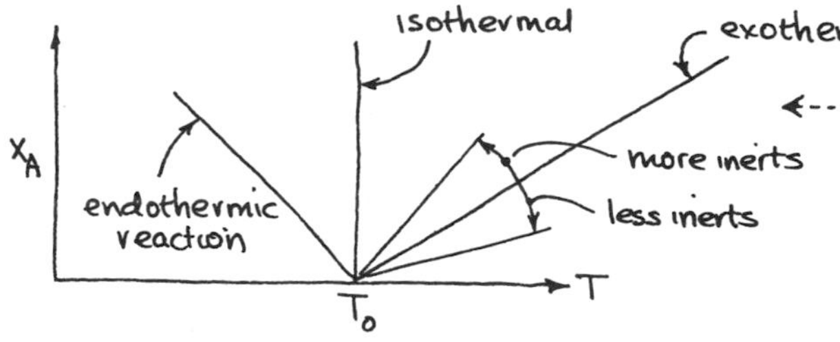

For adiabatic operations these lines have the following equation

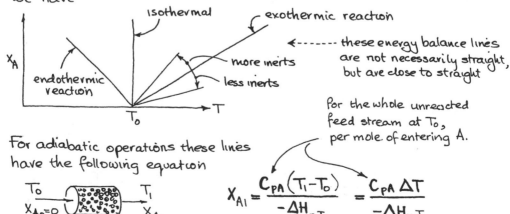

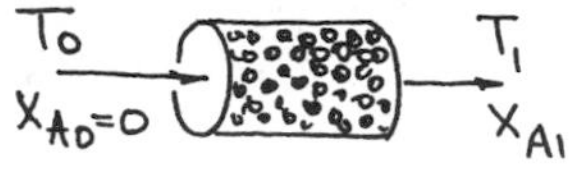

for the whole unreacted feed stream at T_0, per mole of entering A.

$$X_{A1} = \frac{C_{pA}(T_1 - T_0)}{-\Delta H_{r,T_1}} = \frac{C_{pA}\,\Delta T}{-\Delta H_{r,T_1}}$$

(d) The X_A vs T graph is essentially an **enthalpy-composition** diagram. Thus to represent the mixing of two streams use the lever rule, or

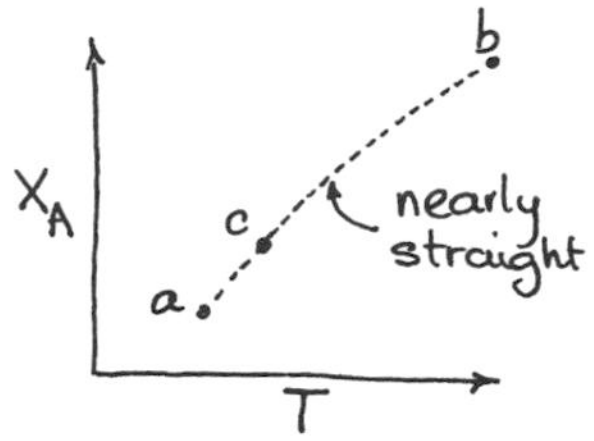

$$\frac{\text{flow } a}{\text{flow } b} = \frac{\text{length } \overline{bc}}{\text{length } \overline{ac}}$$

II Design for a Single Reactor

1. For a given **exothermic reaction**, given rate and entering feed conditions, $X_A = 0.8$ (for illustrative purposes) and any flow pattern — plug, recycle or mixed flow (infinite recycle) — here is how we determine the reactor size.

For any T-X_A progression in the packed bed, and any heat removal arrangement

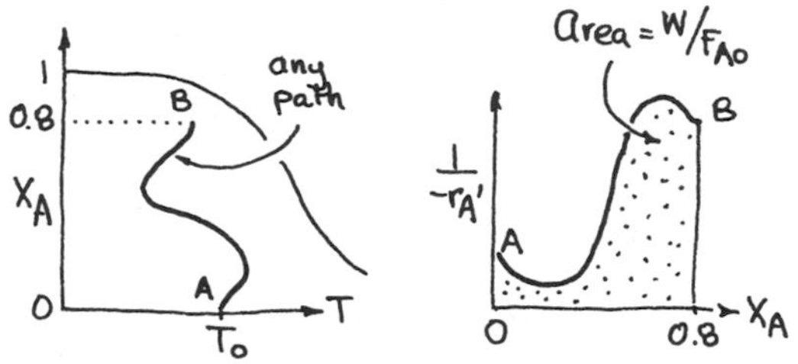

Simply move along curve AB, plot the rate onto the $1/-r_A'$ vs X_A graph, and then evaluate the area. This gives W/F_{A0}.

Remove heat in such a way as to follow the optimum temperature progression

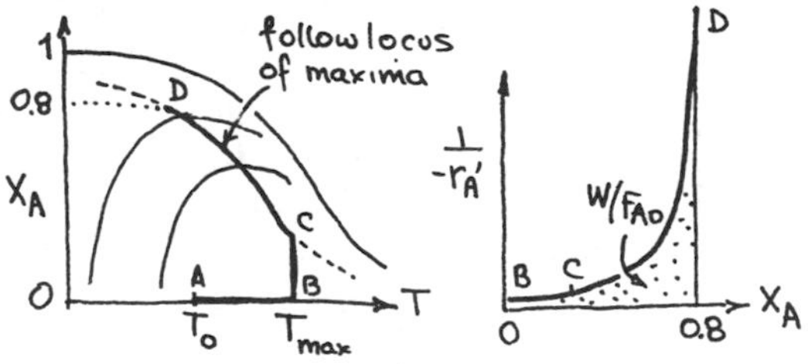

Path ABCD requires the minimum amount of catalyst.

Adiabatic packed bed (plug flow)

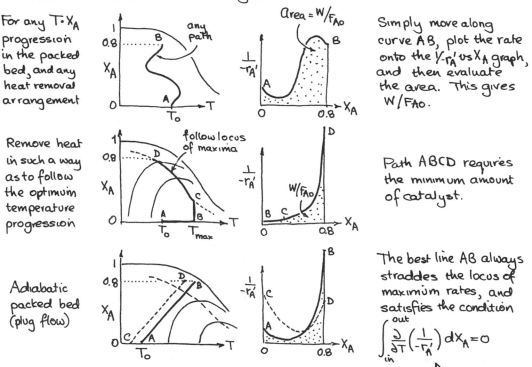

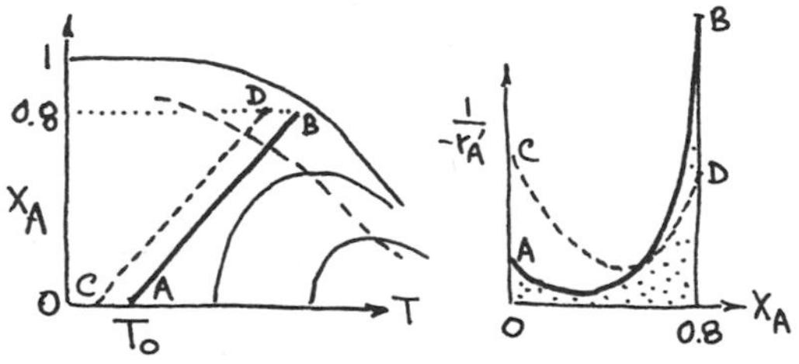

The best line AB always straddles the locus of maximum rates, and satisfies the condition

$$\int_{in}^{out} \frac{\partial}{\partial T}\left(\frac{1}{-r_A'}\right) dX_A = 0$$

In practice it is not useful to try to use this condition. Just try a few lines AB, CD, ... and find which gives the smallest W/F_{A0}.

For adiabatic with recycle

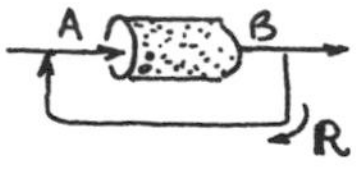

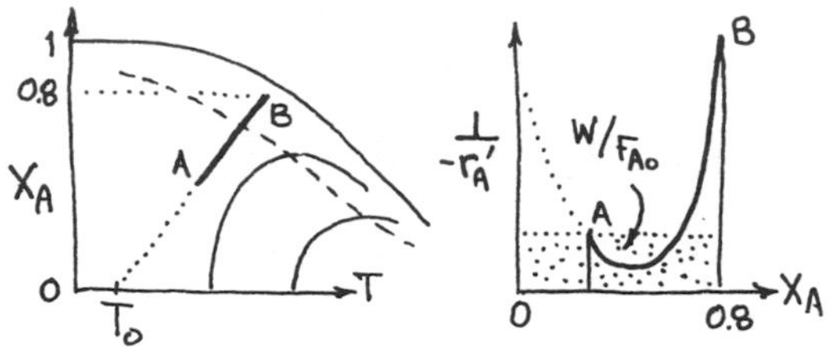

Line AB representing the conditions within the reactor always straddles the locus of maxima. The best recycle rate is given by chapter 5.

Adiabatic with ∞ recycle, or mixed flow

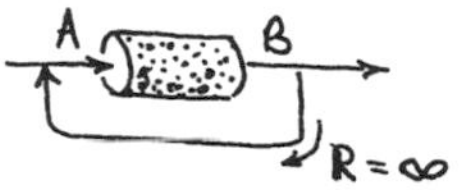

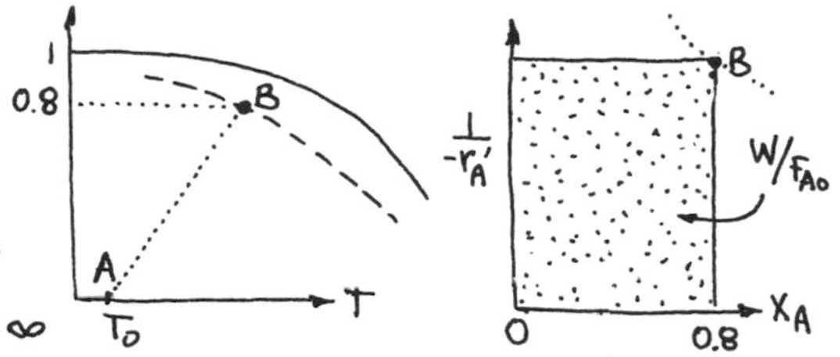

Always locate point B on the locus of maximum rate because at X_{Af} the rate is highest here.

2. **The best type of adiabatic reactor for exothermic reactions** depends primarily on the slope of the operating line (the adiabatic). The sketch below shows two widely different slopes.

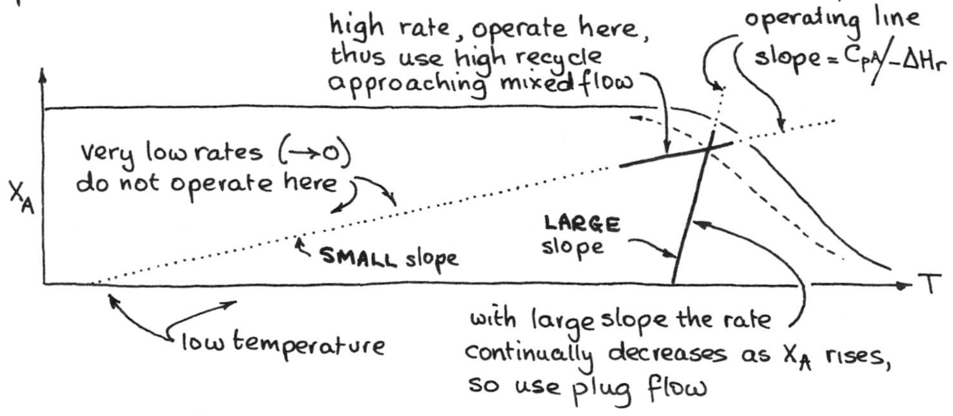

For **small** $C_{pA}/-\Delta H_r$ (pure gaseous reactant large heat of reaction) ... mixed flow (high recycle) is best.

For **large** $C_{pA}/-\Delta H_r$ (gas diluted with inert or liquid systems) ... straight plug flow is best.

3. For non adiabatic operations of exothermic reactions let Q be the heat addition rate [W or J/s] to the reactor or section of reactor. An energy balance then gives

$$\Delta X_A = \frac{C_{pA}\,\Delta T}{-\Delta H_r} + \frac{Q}{F_{A0}\,\Delta H_r}$$

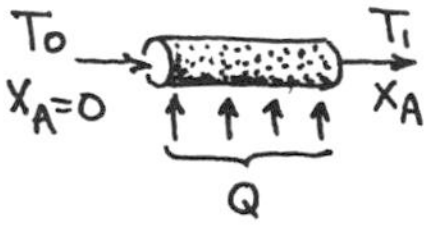

positive for removal of heat

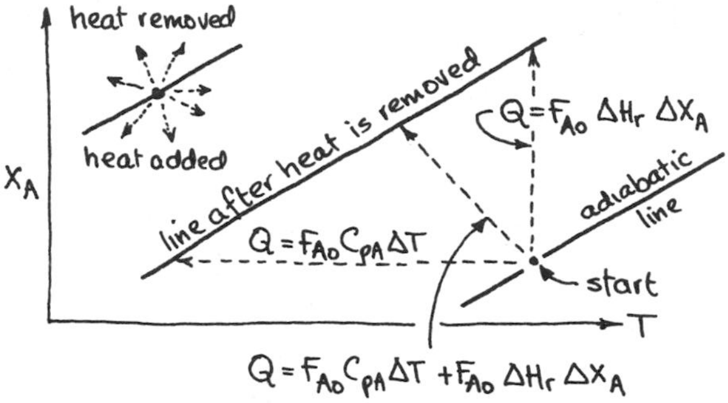

With proper heat removal we can get a plug flow reactor to closely follow the best of temperature profiles, the locus of maximum rates. For example

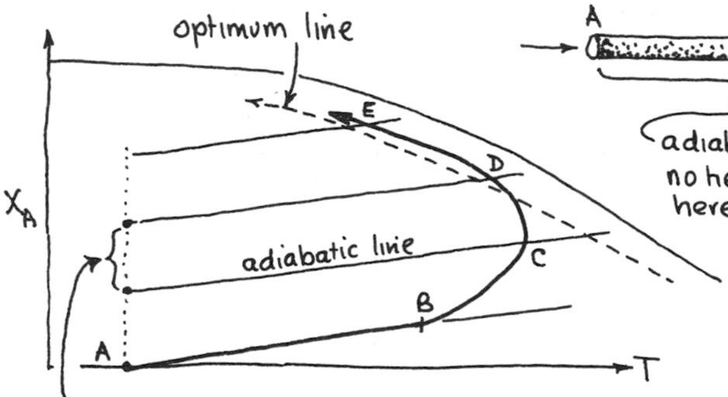

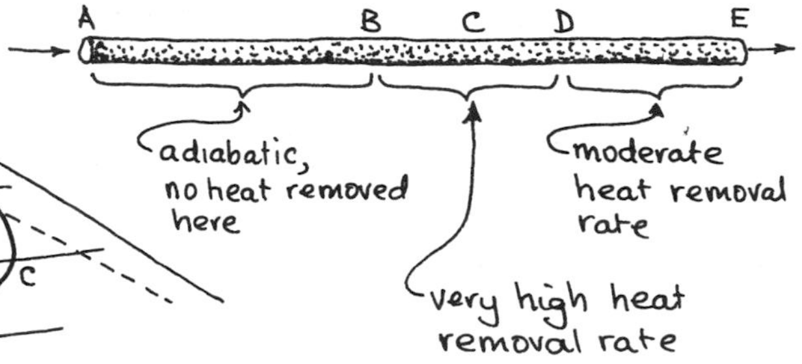

heat removal between points C & D in reactor is given by $Q = F_{A0}\,\Delta H_r\,\Delta X_A$

4. For adiabatic operations of endothermic reactions the rate starts high and continually decreases. Thus plug flow with no recycle of any kind is always best.

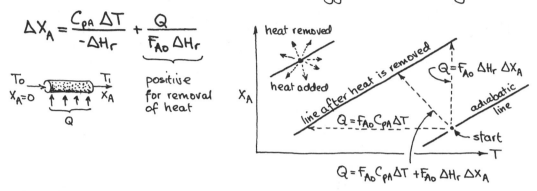

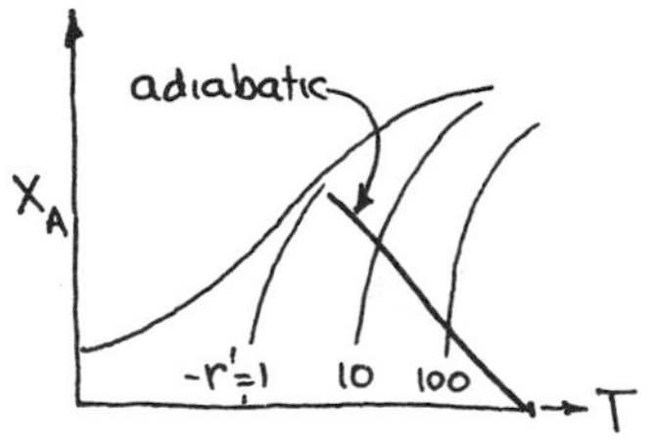

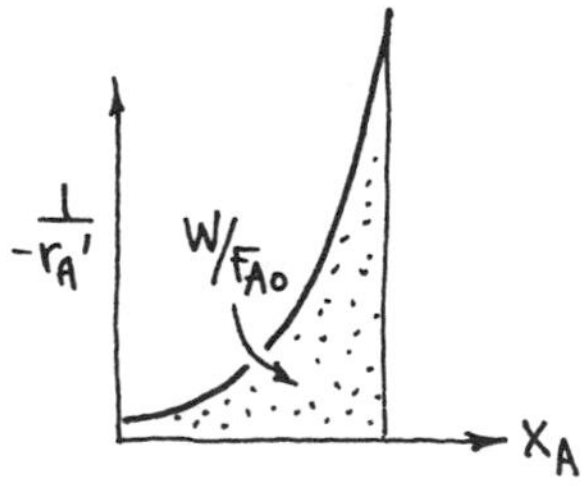

5. **For best operations of endothermic reactions** we want to be at the highest rate, hence highest allowable temperature. Hence run as close to T_{max} as possible by proper heat addition.

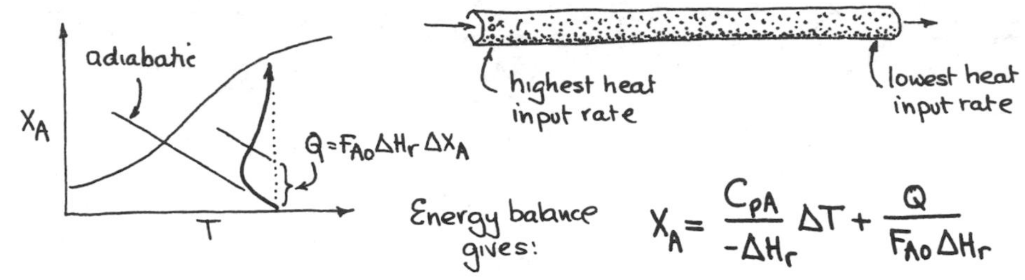

Energy balance gives:

$$X_A = \frac{C_{pA}}{-\Delta H_r}\Delta T + \frac{Q}{F_{A0}\Delta H_r}$$

6. **For adiabatic operations of exothermic or endothermic reactions** the adiabatic operating line and the optimum have opposite slopes.

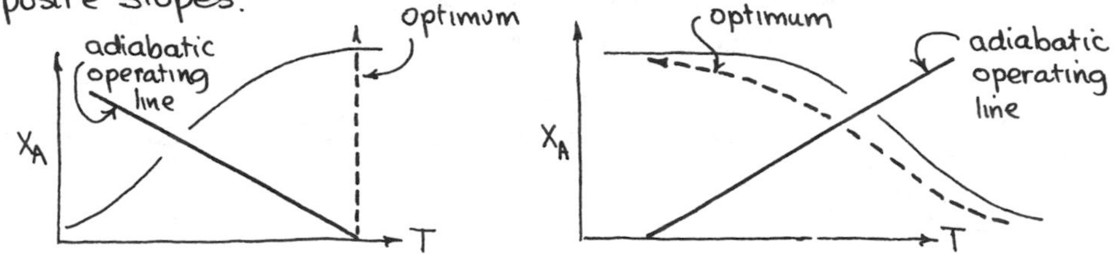

This is not good and here are some of the methods of overcoming this poor operation

- **Proper heat removal or addition.** This is difficult to do and to design for, especially for large reactors. All sorts of terribly complicated mathematical analyses have been tried but the physical parameters are not well enough known to make reliable predictions. This is an especially serious problem for exothermic reactions where the catalyst can be ruined, or the reactor blow up with a temperature runaway.

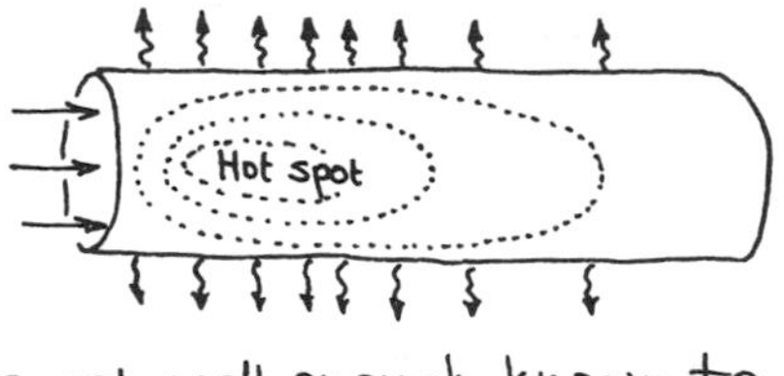

- **Multistaging with interstage cooling, etc.** This is a good way out of the difficulty of strongly non isothemal systems. We treat multistaging in the next section.

III Design of Multistage Reactor Systems.

A series of adiabatic plug flow reactors with interstage heat transfer will approach the optimum temperature progression (for minimum weight of catalyst), the more stages the closer to ideal,

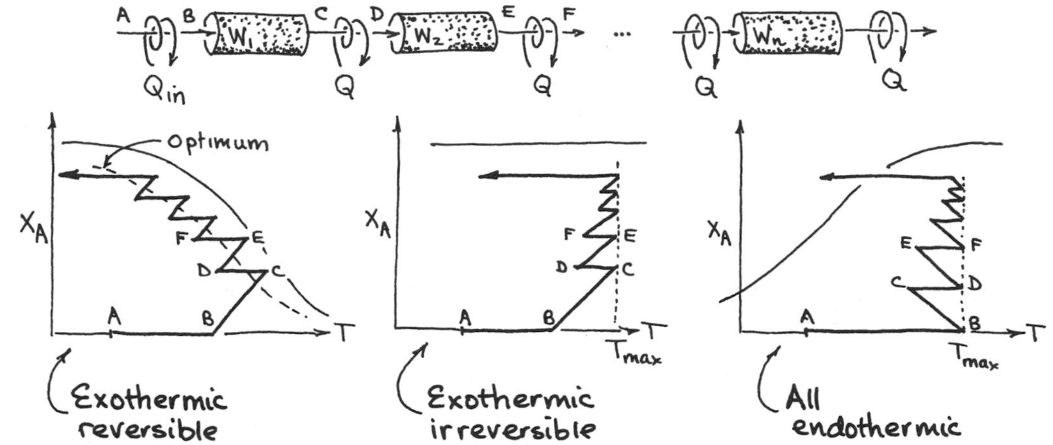

Economic considerations will tell how many stages to use. Remember, heat exchangers cost money too.

Let us show how to find the minimum amount of catalyst for two stages with various flow patterns. The extension to three or more stages should then suggest itself.

A. Exothermic reactions.

1. Plug flow, optimum 2 stage.

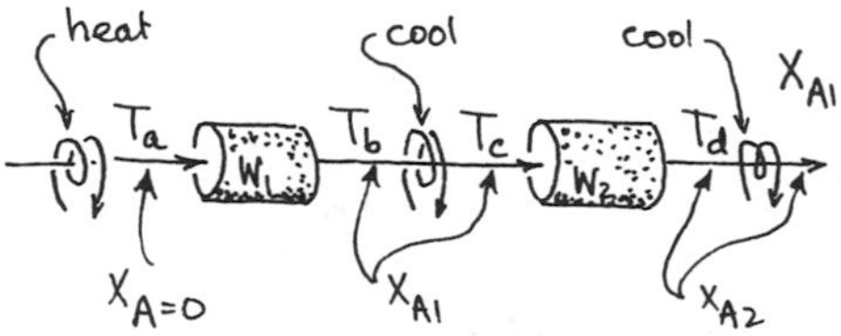

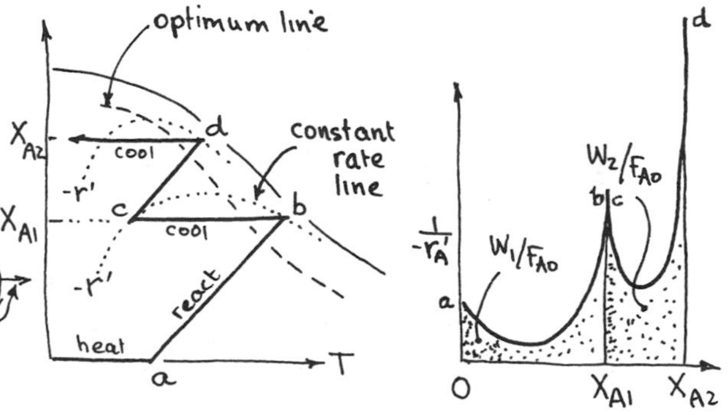

For the best distribution of temperature and of catalyst among the stages

- lines ab and cd must straddle the locus of maximum rates
- points b and c must be on the same rate curve
- ab (and also cd) must satisfy

$$\int_a^b \frac{\partial}{\partial T}\left(\frac{1}{-r_A'}\right) dX_A = 0$$

This tells how long line ab should be, i.e. it tells where b should be.

Procedure:

- guess a
- find b by trial and error. It is impractical to use the above equation without resort to computers.
- then locate c, d, ...
- repeat the procedure with a few different a values. Find which trial gives the smallest W_{total}/F_{A0} (area under the curve).

see Konoki, Chem. Eng. Japan 21 408 (1957); Horn, Z. Electrochemie 65 295 (1961).

2. Plug flow, optimum 2 stage with T_{max} restriction.

- points b and d must be on the T_{max} line
- the precise criterion relating b and c is

$$\frac{\Delta H_r}{C_p}\int_a^b \frac{\partial}{\partial T}\left(\frac{1}{-r_A'}\right) dX_A = \left(\frac{1}{-r_{Ac}'} - \frac{1}{-r_{Ab}'}\right)$$

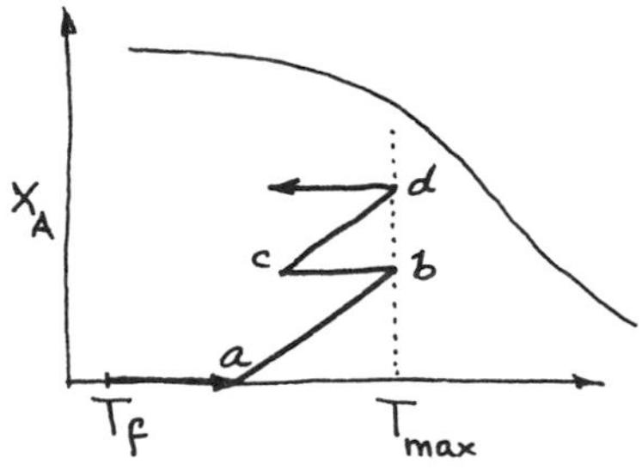

This case is not particularly practical because when you have a T_{max} limitation with an exothermic reaction the plug flow reactor is rarely recommended. Mixed flow is usually simpler, better and safer.

3. Mixed flow, optimum 2 stage.

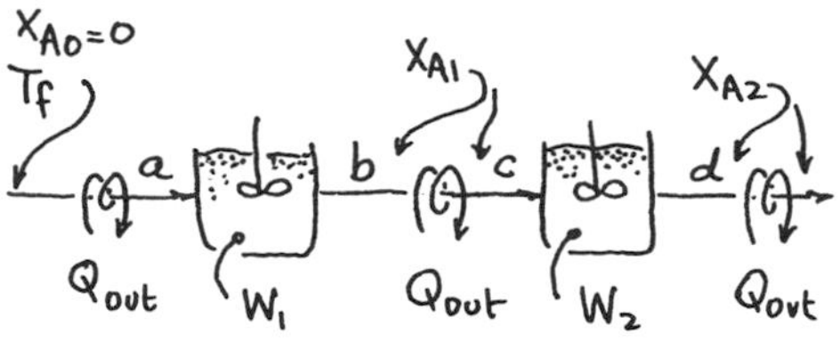

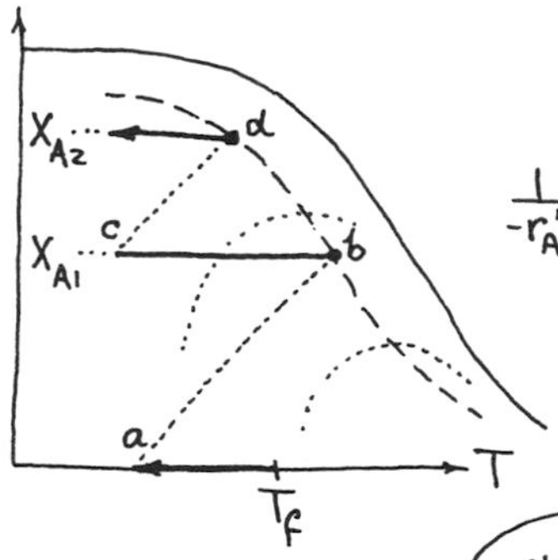

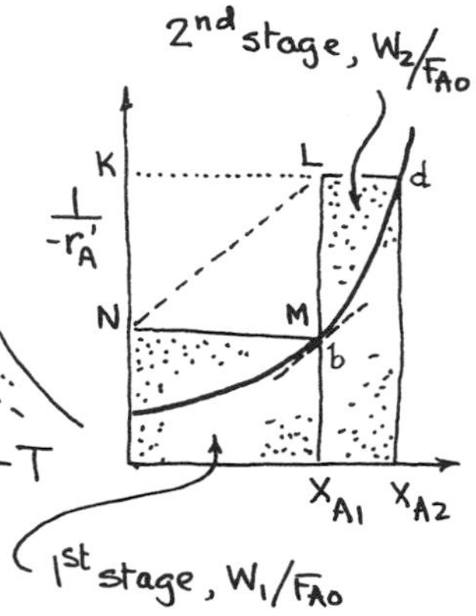

- points b and d should be on the locus of maximum rates
- the location of point b is found by the **maximization of rectangles**. Thus maximize rectangle KLMN.

4. Recycle flow, optimum 2 stage.

For this sketch R = 1 is best for both stages.

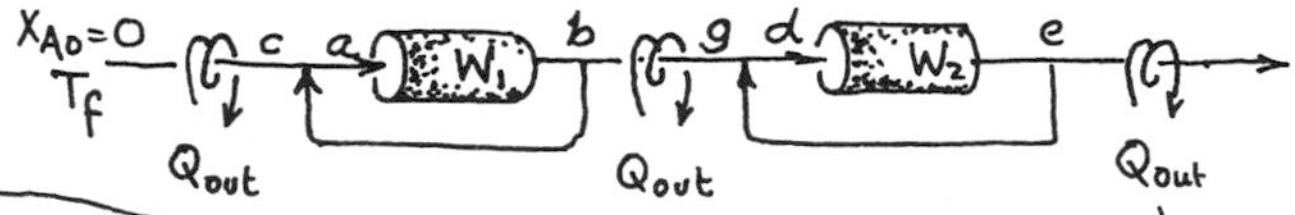

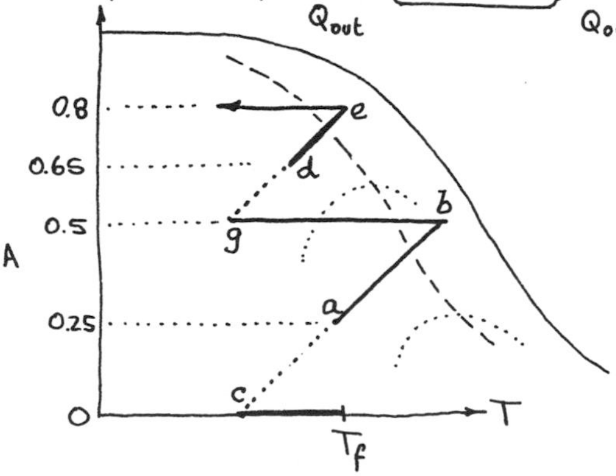

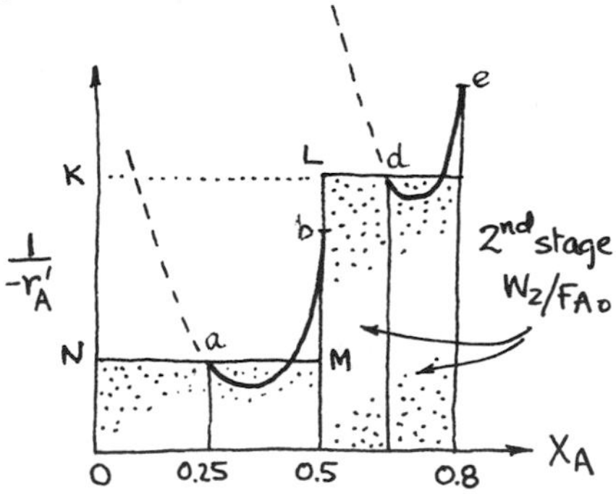

- ab and de straddle the locus of maximum rates.
- the best recycle rate is given in chapter 5.
- the size ratio of stages is guessed. For large R the maximization of rectangles can help find the best size ratio

Konoki, Chem. Eng. Japan 25 31 (1961) gives the precise equation relating points $a, b, \ldots$, but it is not often practical to use it.

5. Cold shot cooling.

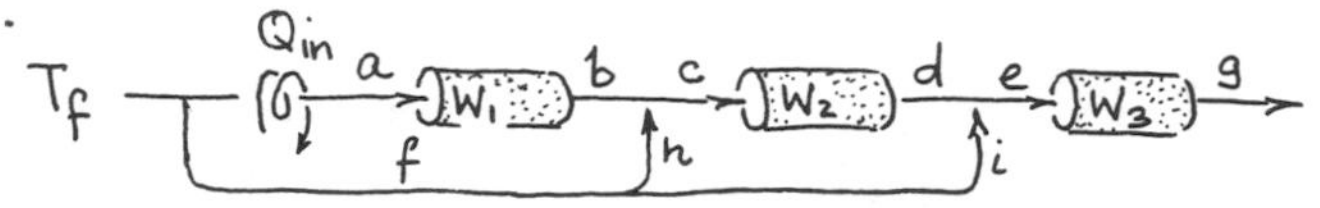

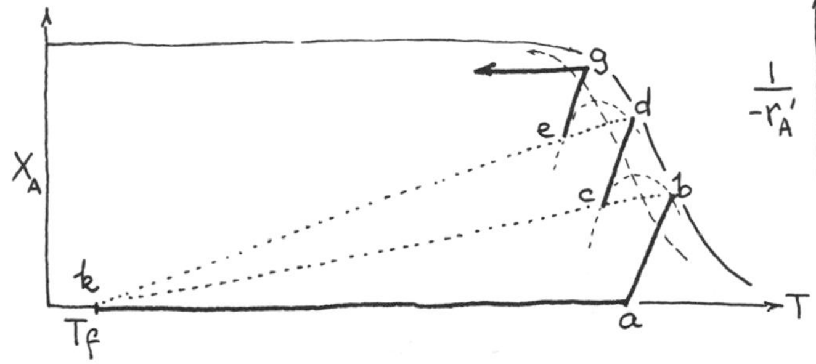

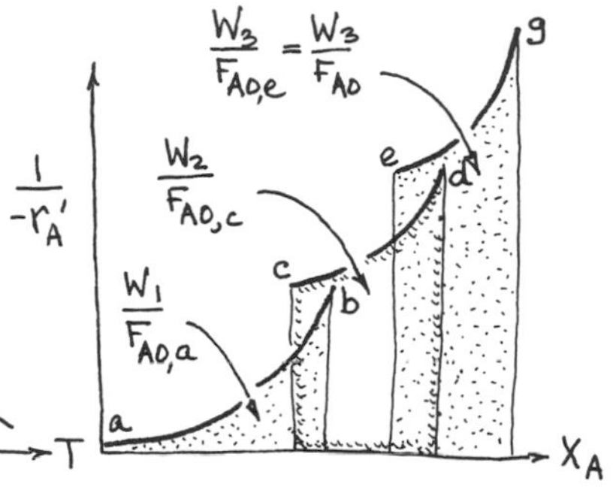

- lines ab, cd, eg should straddle the locus of maximum rates
- points b and c should be on the same rate curve, d and e also on the same curve
- stream b and h join to form stream c. Similarly d and i give e. The flow rates of these joining streams relate to the lengths of the lines on the X_A vs T graph. Thus

$$F_{A0,b} : F_{A0,c} : F_{A0,h} = \overline{kc} : \overline{kb} : \overline{bc}$$

$$F_{A0,d} : F_{A0,e} : F_{A0,i} = \overline{ke} : \overline{kd} : \overline{de}$$

Procedure

- guess a, b, d, then locate c, e
- calculate the flow rates of streams through the reactors and bypassing the reactors.
- determine W_1, W_2, W_3 from the $1/-r_A'$ vs X_A plot
- repeat with new guesses for a, b, d and find which gives the smallest $W_{total} = W_1 + W_2 + W_3$

Konoki, Chem. Eng. Japan 24 569 (1960) gives the equation relating points a, b, ..., but for this graphical solution it is not useful.

Cold shot cooling eliminates all but one heat exchanger, sometimes with very little extra catalyst needed.

Cold shot cooling **is useful** when the feed is much colder than the temperature in the reactor, or when $(T_{rx} - T_f) > \frac{C_p}{-\Delta H_r}$

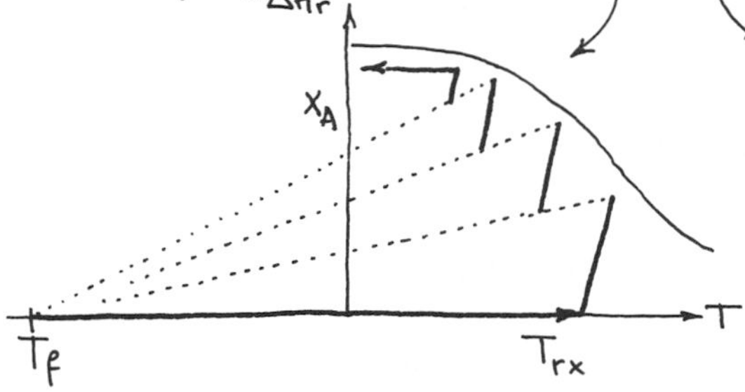

Cold shot cooling **is not useful** when the feed temperature is close to the temperature at which reaction occurs

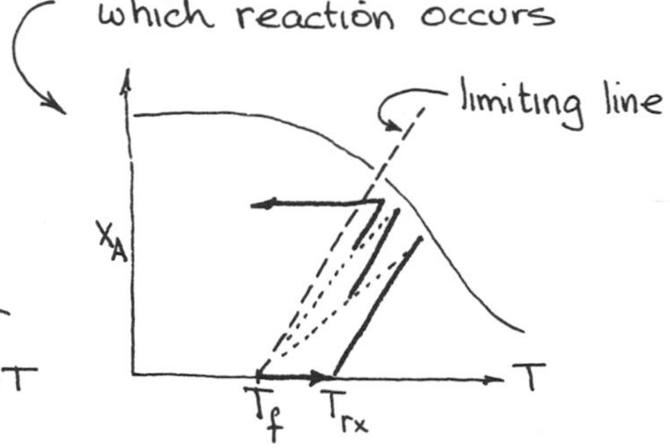

6. Cold inert injection

Inert: $M = \frac{\text{moles inert}}{\text{moles feed}}$

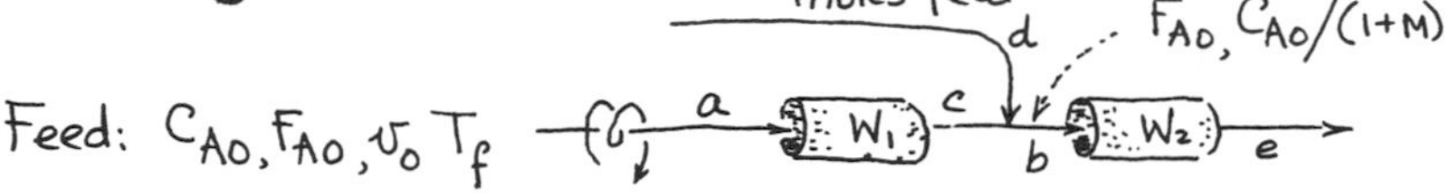

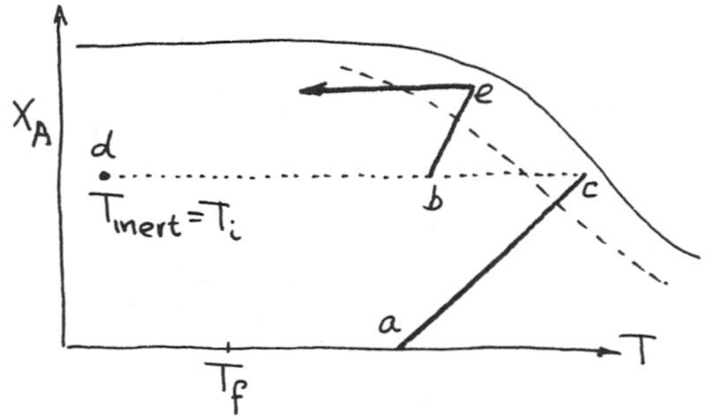

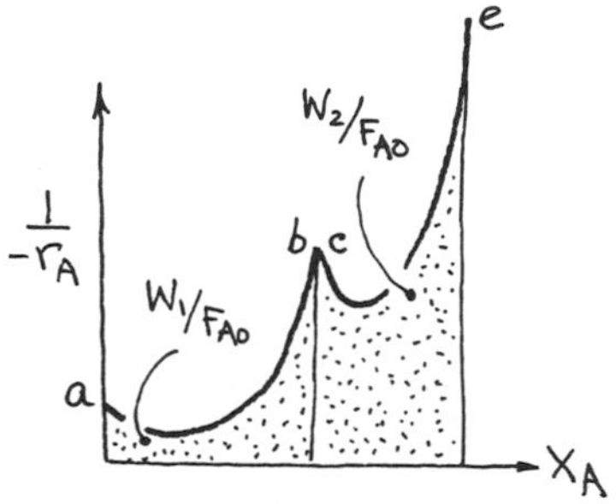

- The rate changes from the chart value because of dilution, and becomes $1/(1+M)$ the original value for first order reaction. For other orders the whole X_A vs T curve changes, including the equilibrium.
- The slope of the adiabatic also changes as inert is added. It becomes $(C_{p,\text{feed+inert}}/\text{mol A} / -\Delta H_r)$ in each reactor.
  For the special case of C_p's all equal: ··· $\left(\frac{\text{slope for reactor 2}}{\text{slope for reactor 1}}\right) = 1 + M$
- For addition of liquid inert which vaporizes use a fictitious entering temperature of inert gas which has the same enthalpy as the entering liquid
- On the X_A vs T graph $\frac{db}{bc} = \frac{1}{M} = \frac{\text{moles through first reactor}}{\text{moles of inert added}}$

7. Comparison of cold feed injection and cold inert injection.

- cold inert injection does not lower X_A between stages.
- if the inert is a liquid a small amout added will do much cooling with but little dilution and little lowering in rate.
- cold inert injection can be used even when the feed temperature is not much lower than the reaction temperature

All in all **cold inert injection** has many advantages over cold feed injection.

Without trouble we can combine both forms of cooling

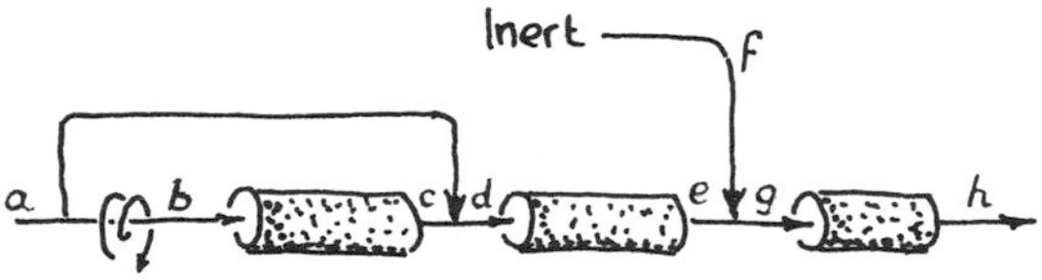

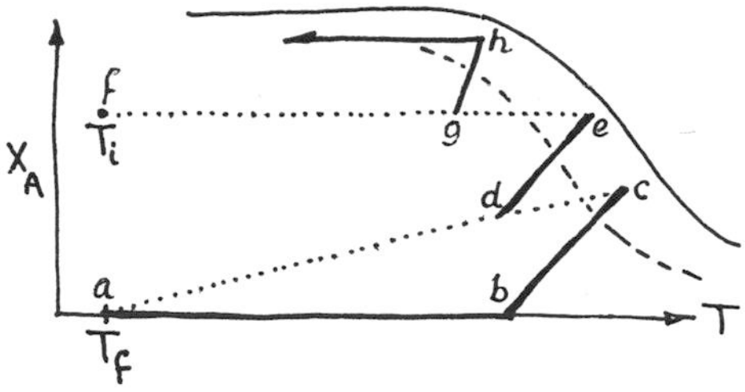

Overall, the attractiveness of cold injection of either type is that it means using **fewer heat exchangers.**

8. Best staged reactor type for exothermic reactions.

Let us illustrate our findings with the typical case of :

$$C_{pA} = 40 \text{ J/mol A·K} \quad \text{and} \quad \Delta H_r = -120000 \text{ J/mol A}$$

Then referring to the figures below we find

(a) **For pure gaseous reactant** $\left(\frac{C_{pA}}{-\Delta H_r} = \frac{40}{120000} = \frac{1}{3000}\right)$ use high recycle approaching **mixed flow**

(b) **For dilute gaseous reactant**, say 1%, or **for liquid reactant** $\left(\frac{C_{pA}}{-\Delta H_r} = \frac{4000}{120000} = \frac{1}{30}\right)$ not needing a large preheat of heat use **plug flow or cold inert injection**

(c) **For dilute gas** or **for liquid** $\left(\frac{C_{pA}}{-\Delta H_r} = \frac{1}{30}\right)$ which requires considerable preheating to bring the reactant stream up to reaction temperature use **cold feed or inert injection, or plug flow**

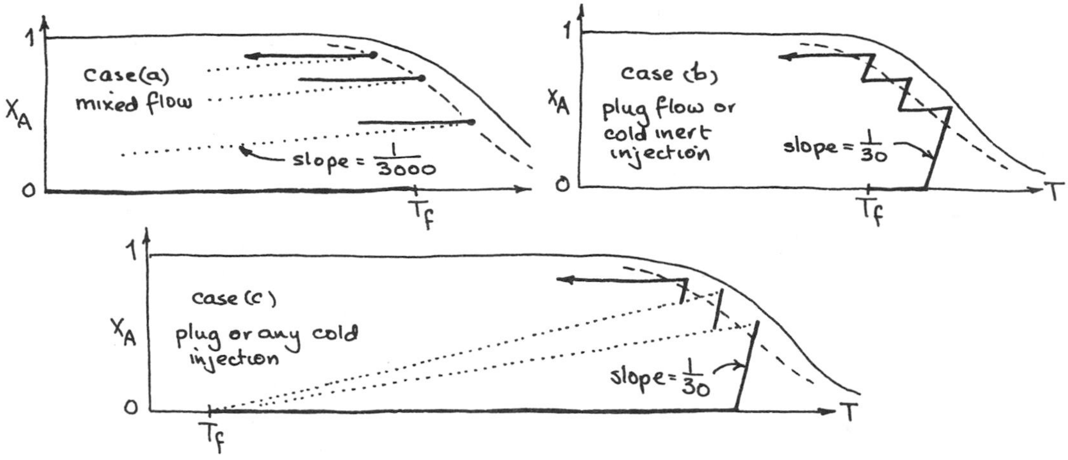

9. <u>**About heat exchangers.**</u> Multistaging leads to a lot of heat exchanger alternatives. Let us look at some of these.

Suppose we have a **cold feed to plug flow** reactors. We can then eliminate much cooling and heating using external sources and sinks by a proper arrangement of flows. For example

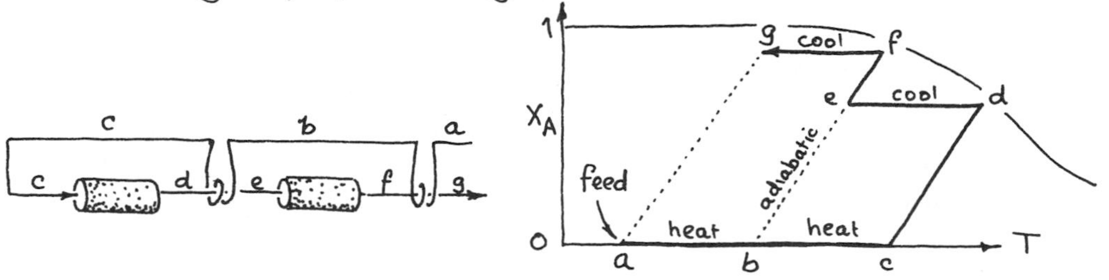

Of course **cold fluid injection** is another possibility with systems of this kind if T_f is low enough. This will allow elimination of all but one heat exchanger

For a reactor with recycle the exchanger can be put in a number of places, see sketch pg 1 chapter 24. Various factors influence our choice of location

- the desire to maximize ΔT across the exchanger, from fluid to fluid

- The desire for high flow rate through the exchanger (gives large h).
- Avoidance of start-up problems (feed may have to be heated initially).

The sketches below show the T vs X_A diagram for various exchanger locations. Note when two streams mix, say x and y, then the resultant is on a point joining x and y.

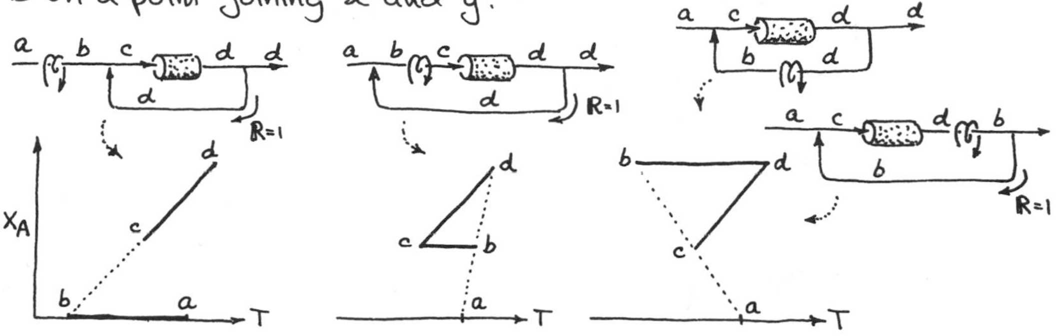

B. Endothermic reactions.

Always heat the feed to T_{max}, then use plug flow. Between stages reheat to T_{max}. No other arrangement, mixed recycle, etc. is better.

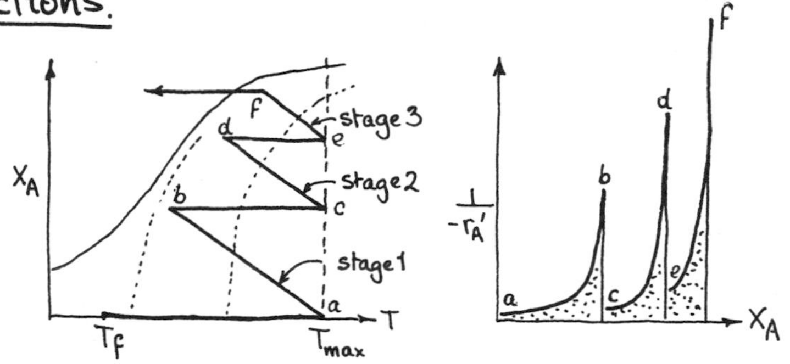

Also, hot inert injection (usually steam) can be used ... but again is accompanied by dilution and lowering of the rate.

C. Comments for the successive trial search.

In adjusting the inlet temperature to the individual stages it is more important to **raise the lowest rate** than it is to raise an already high rate. Thus avoid the regions of lowest rate.

IV The Hot Spot and Temperature Runaway.

These are a specialty of gas phase reactions in packed beds of catalyst, and they are most unwelcome. Side products may be formed, the catalyst may be destroyed, and the reactor may fail, sometimes rapidly and spectacularly. There are three types of temperature excursions:

- those in plug flow reactors with internal cooling.
- those in adiabatic plug flow reactors.
- those in adiabatic packed bed reactors with large recycle (mixed flow).

Consider these three types in turn.

A. Temperature excursions in packed beds with internal cooling.

Here a hot spot can move as a sharp wave down the reactor, ruining the catalyst as it sweeps by. It is caused by inadequate heat removal

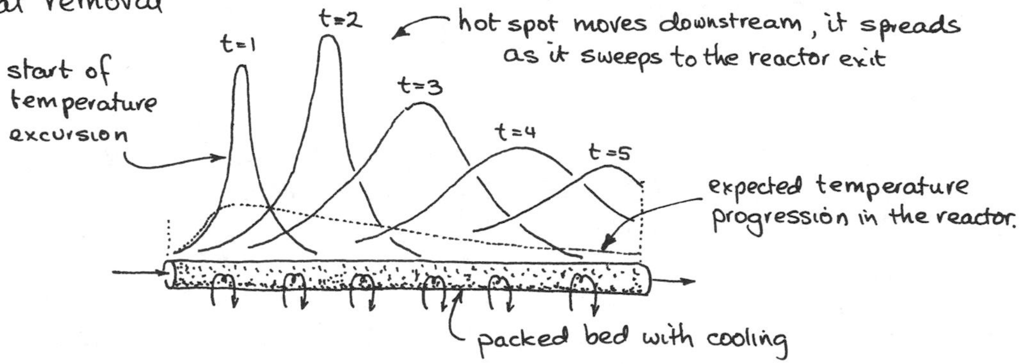
t=1
t=2
hot spot moves downstream, it spreads as it sweeps to the reactor exit
start of temperature excursion
t=3
t=4
t=5
expected temperature progression in the reactor.
packed bed with cooling

This kind of temperature runaway occurs when the adiabatic is shallow (large adiabatic temperature rise, or small $C_{pA}/-\Delta H_r$), in which case a large heat removal is needed. This instability is difficult to calculate, account for and control. Adding inerts to the catalyst or to the reactant stream helps. Often it is prudent to go to staged adiabatic operations.

B. Temperature excursions in adiabatic packed beds with plug flow of gas.

note: we only use plug flow when the adiabatic line is steep

Here a hot spot usually is not mobile and is caused by deviation of flow from the ideal of plug flow, some fluid going faster, some slower. To illustrate this phenomenon imagine a packed bed reactor operating in two different ways: plug flow in one case, and two parallel flow velocities in the other.

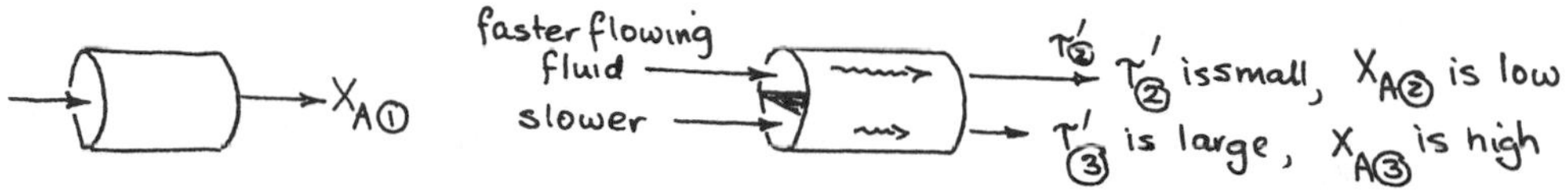

Here is what happens in a bad situation, shown on an X_A vs T graph:

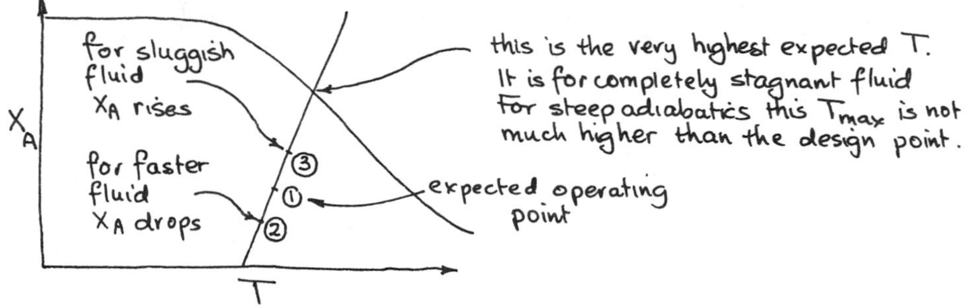

The actual hot spot temperature reached (point ③) depends on the size of the stagnancy and the rate of heat transfer to the surrounding faster moving fluid.

This type of hot spot is likely to occur at some obstruction in the packed bed, a baffle, an inserted tube and so on. Note that a temperature probe could well create its own hot spot. Luckily, hot spots of this kind are localized and not malignant. Also, since the packing density of catalyst is lower near the walls of the reactor, flow is faster there, conversion is lower, so the fluid is cooler at the walls of the reactor.

C. Temperature excursions in beds with large recycle of gas.

Note: we only use mixed flow for shallow adiabatic lines, thus for large adiabatic temperature rise

The material balance curve, or the locus of constant τ values is S-shaped, as shown

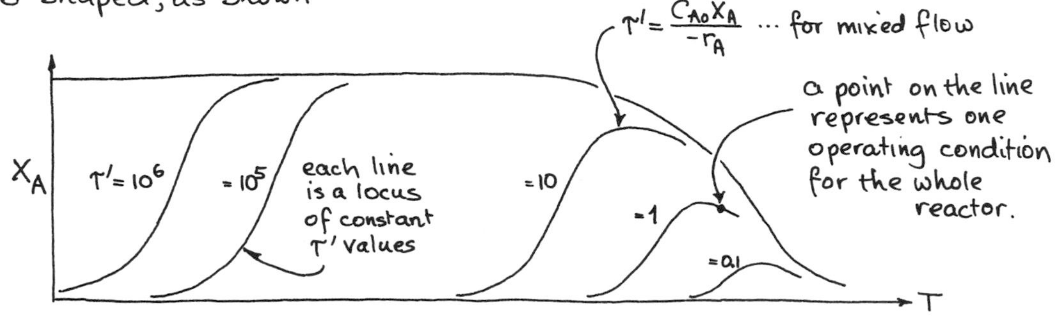

The material balance and energy balance curves intersect at either one or three points

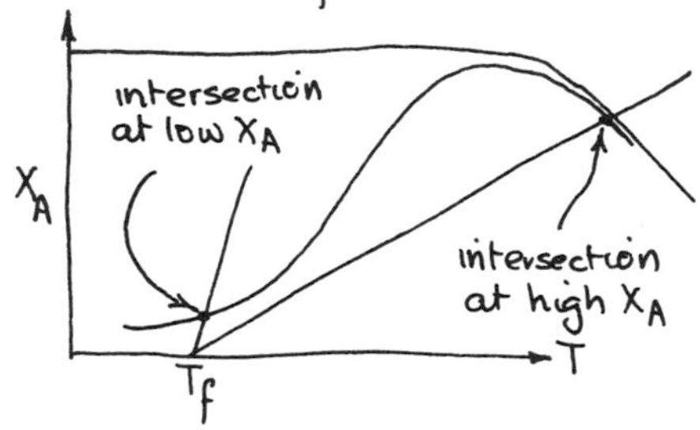

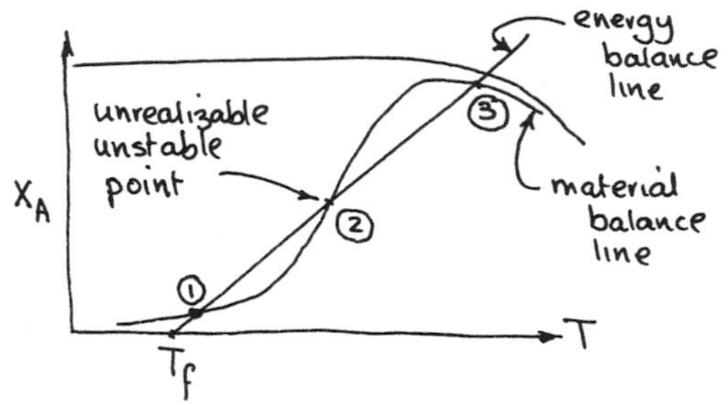

In the three solution case points ① and ③ are realizable physically while point ② is unstable. At this unstable point

$$\begin{pmatrix}\text{slope of}\\ \text{material balance}\\ \text{curve}\end{pmatrix} > \begin{pmatrix}\text{slope of}\\ \text{energy balance}\\ \text{curve}\end{pmatrix}$$

or

$$\begin{pmatrix}\text{slope of the}\\ \tau' \text{ line}\end{pmatrix} > \left(\frac{C_{pA}}{-\Delta H_r}\right)$$

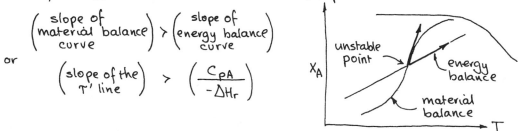

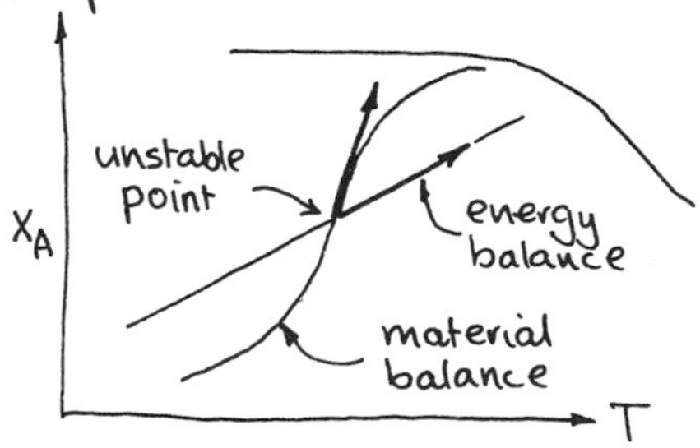

We use this property of point ② to distinguish between stable and unstable operating points. Our procedure is as follows.

1. To construct the constant τ' line on the T vs X_A diagram note for mixed flow that

$$\frac{X_{Af}}{-r'_{Af}} = \frac{\tau'}{C_{A0}} = \text{constant}$$

So pick a point on the chart, say where $r'=1$ and $X=0.1$. Then go to $r'=2$ and $X=0.2$, then $r'=5$ and $X=0.5$, and so on. Join these points with a smooth curve.

2. To see whether a given proposed operating point on the chart is stable

- evaluate X_1 and r'_1 for this point M
- go to the nearest neighboring r' line and on it locate point N such that

$$\frac{X_2}{-r'_2} = \frac{X_1}{-r'_1} \quad \cdots \text{or} \quad X_2 = \left(\frac{X_1}{-r'_1}\right)(-r'_2)$$

- join MN. This is the slope of the material balance line. Now compare this with the slope of the adiabatic.

The sketches below summarize the procedure:

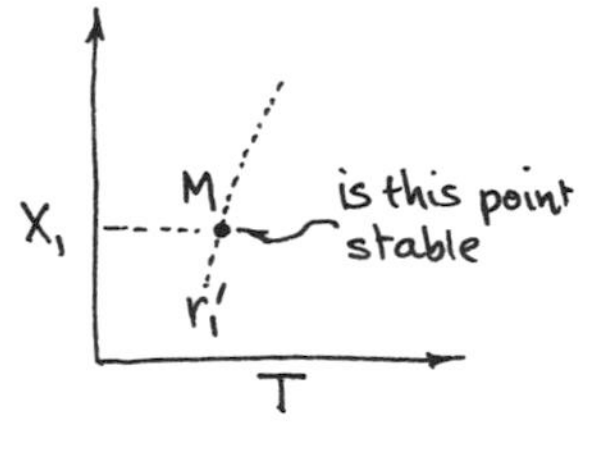

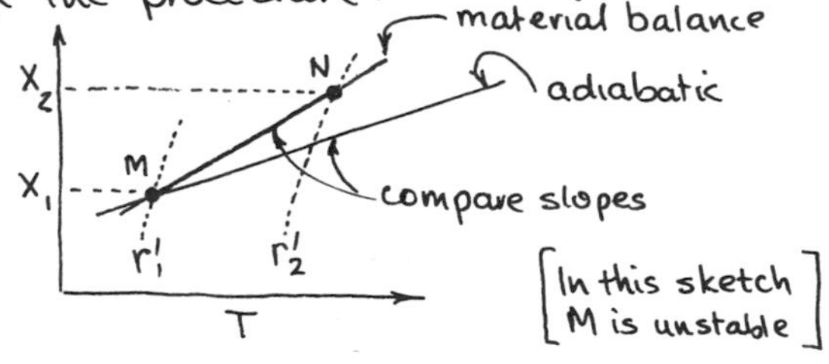

3. To find the stable points corresponding to an unstable point simply continue the τ' line until it again intersects the adiabatic.

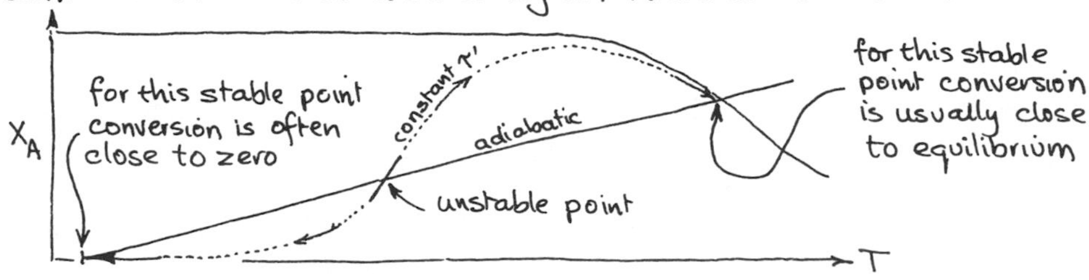

4. The region of instability can be constructed on the T vs X_A chart. First draw a number of constant τ' lines. Then proceed as shown:

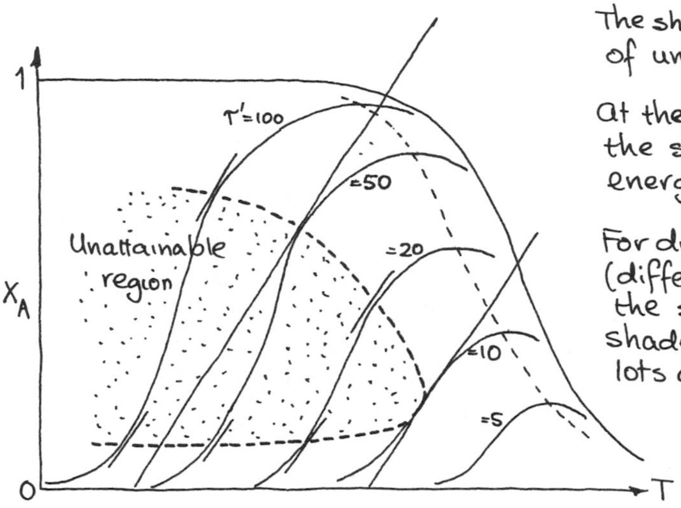

The shaded area shows the region of unstable operating points.

At the boundary of this region the slopes of the material and energy balance lines are equal.

For different adiabatics (different concentrations of inert) the shape and location of the shaded region changes. For lots of inert it disappears.

In general the unstable region is far from equilibrium, and it is **always** to the left of the optimum rate line. So in operations where you plan to straddle the optmum (see left sketch below) you need not worry about unstable points, or temperature runaways. On the other hand, with a temperature limitation this problem will have to be considered (see right sketch):

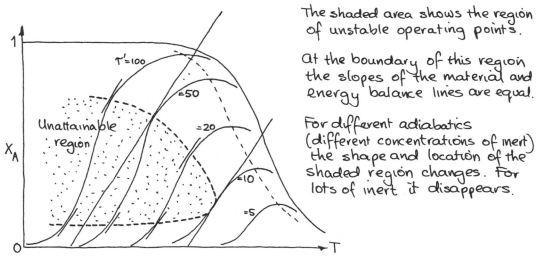

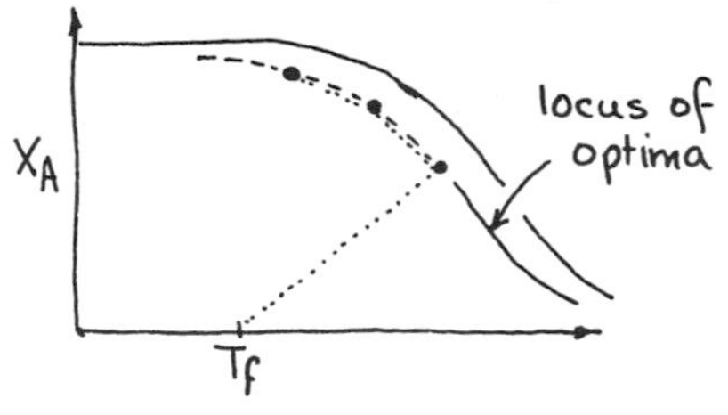

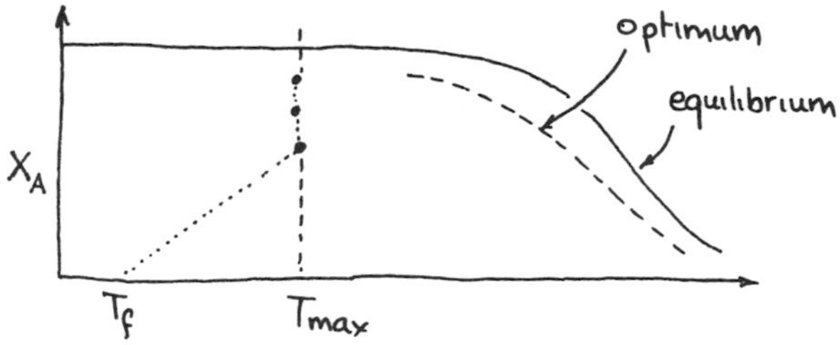

5. For first order reversible kinetics

$$A \rightleftarrows R, \quad -r_A' = k_1' C_A - k_2' C_R = k_{10}' e^{-E_1/RT} C_A - k_{20}' e^{-E_2/RT} C_R$$

we can find an analytical expression for the unstable region. Thus a point is unstable if:

$$\frac{k_1' \tau' \left[E_1 + (E_1 - E_2) k_2' \tau' \right]}{R T^2 \left[1 + (k_1' + k_2') \tau' \right]^2} \geq \frac{C_{pA}}{-\Delta H_r}$$

D. Comments.

When $C_{pA}/-\Delta H_r$ is large (dilute systems) the hot spot is not particularly dangerous because the adiabatic temperature rise is small. Here one uses staged packed bed reactors or packed bed reactors with modest internal cooling. One does not encounter temperature runaways or unstable operating points.

When $C_{pA}/-\Delta H_r$ is small (large adiabatic temperature rise) then things can get dangerous, for reactors with internal cooling are difficult to control, are liable to be in unstable operating regimes. The consequences could be catastrophic. Stay away from internal cooling. However, with staged reactors having large recycle (approaching mixed flow) we can predict the unstable conditions and we can design to avoid them. In this situation we can design with confidence.

This graphical procedure comes from Kimura and Levenspiel, IEC/PDD 16 145 (1977). See this paper for a bit more on the subject (analytical solutions and the behavior in the strong pore diffusion regime.

Chapter **24** Problems

Sketch the flow sheet for the two reactor system represented by the X_A vs T diagram below, and on the sketch show

- the flow rate of all streams for each 100 mols of entering fluid, and where pertinent give the recycle ratios.
- the location of the heat exchangers and indicate whether they cool or heat

A1 . . .

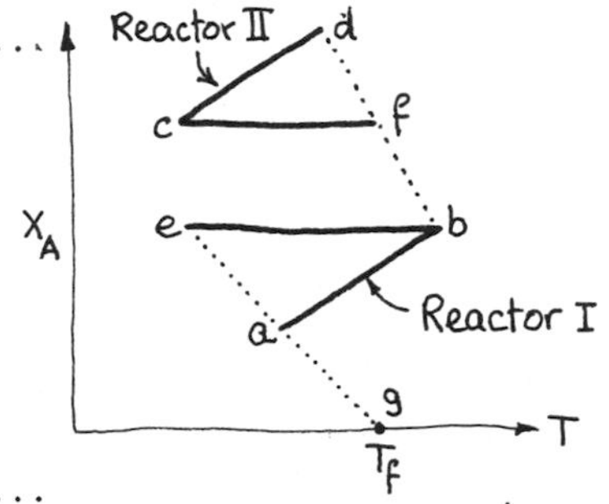

A2 . . .

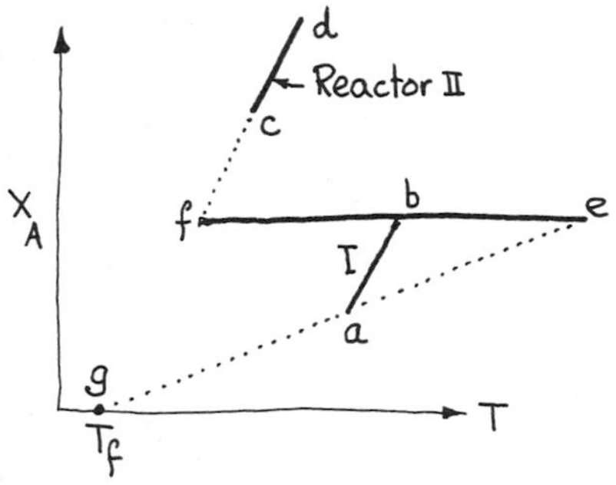

A3 . . .

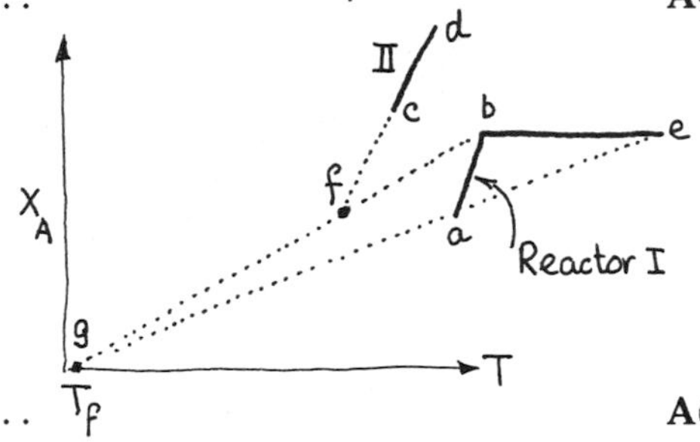

A4 . . .

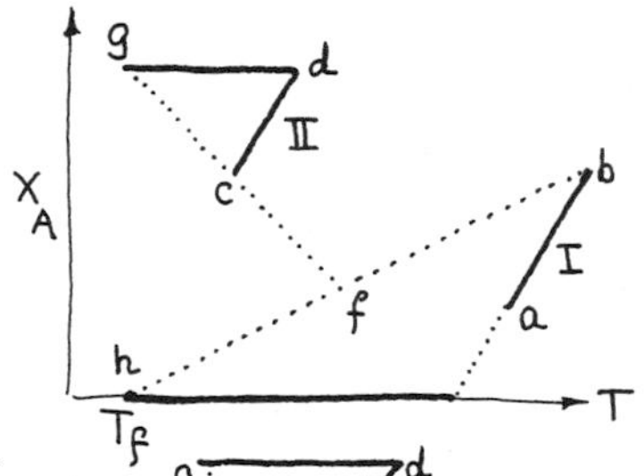

A5 . . .

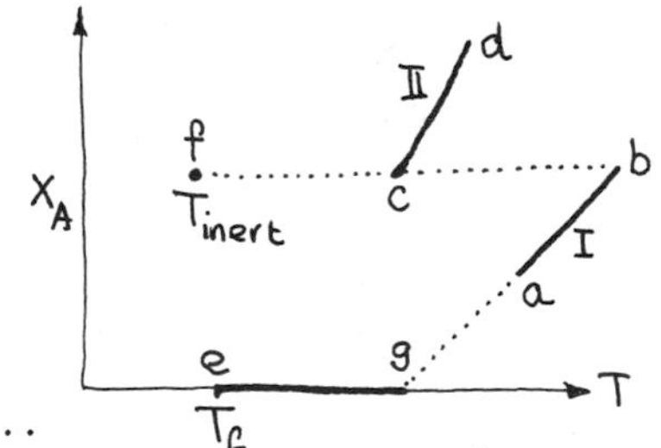

A6 . . .

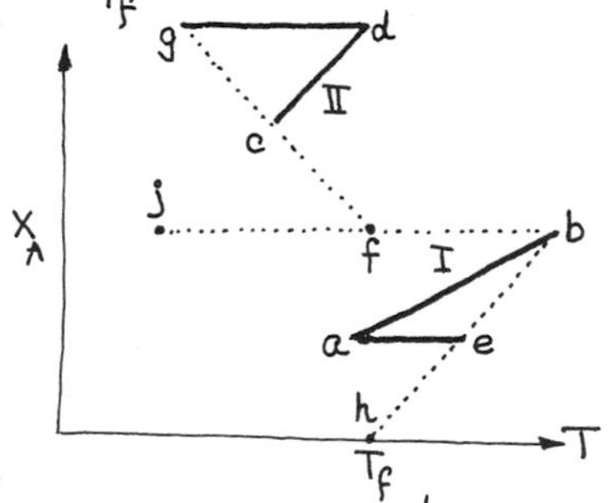

A7 . . .

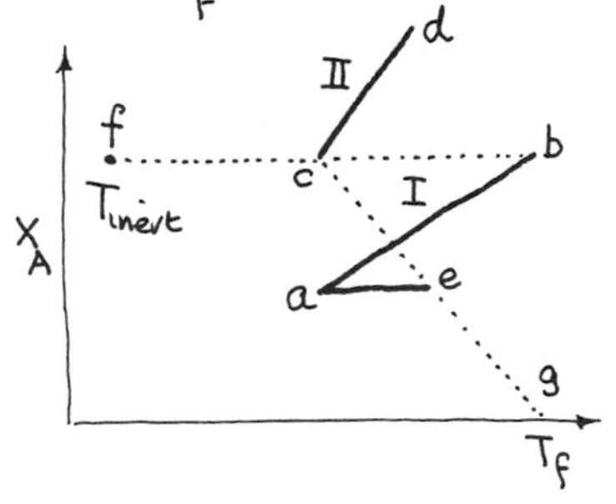

A8 . . .

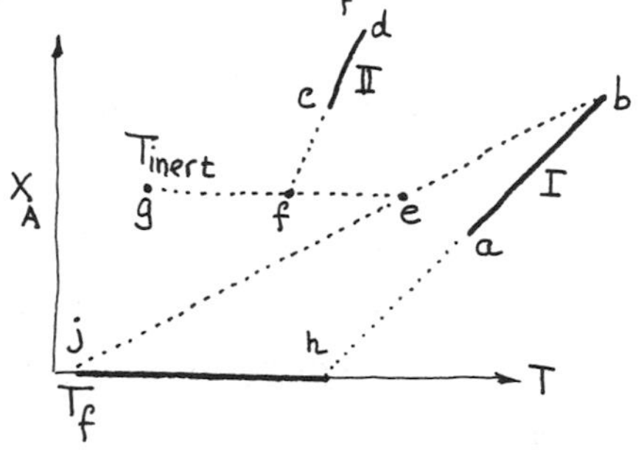

Chapter 24 Problems

Sketch the corresponding X_A vs T diagram for the two packed bed reactor system for an exothermic reaction where

- conversion: $X_{A1} = 0.6$, $X_{A2} = 0.9$
- recycle ratio: $\mathbf{R}_1 = 2$, $\mathbf{R}_2 = 1$
- heat exchangers all cool the reacting fluid

A9 . . .

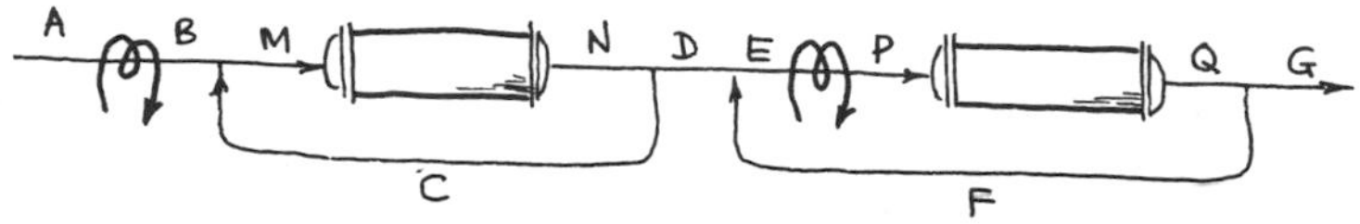

A10 . . .

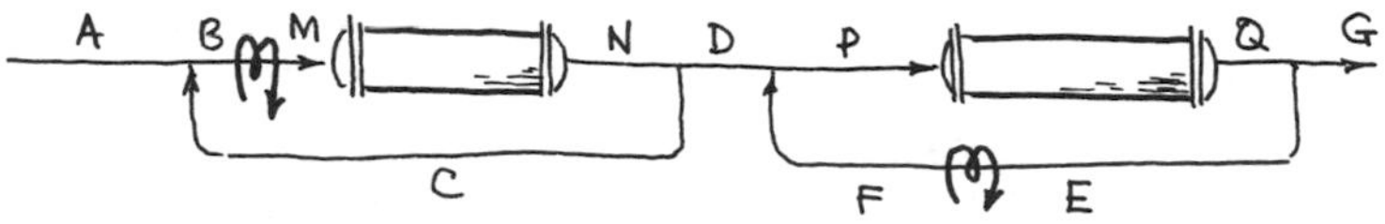

A11 . . .

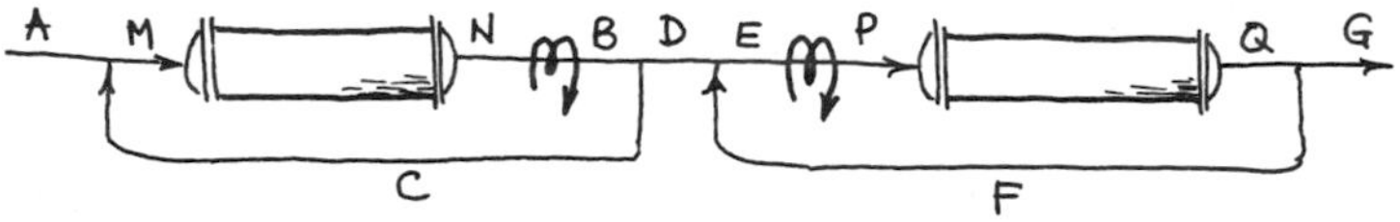

A12 . . .

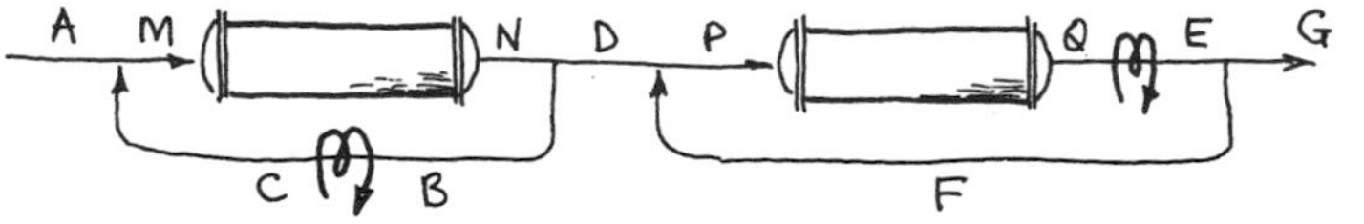

A single packed bed reactor is to treat 0.1 m^3/s of gaseous feed at 300 K and 2.49 MPa (or 24.6 atm) under various conditions. The maximum allowable temperature is 900 K unless otherwise noted; the kinetics and thermodynamics of the exothermic reactions are given to us on the accompanying chart. Prepare a sketch showing the details of the system you plan to use:

- type of reactor: plug, recycle, or mixed (∞ recycle)
- amount of catalyst used
- heat duty ahead of the reactor and at the reactor itself
- the temperature of all flowing streams

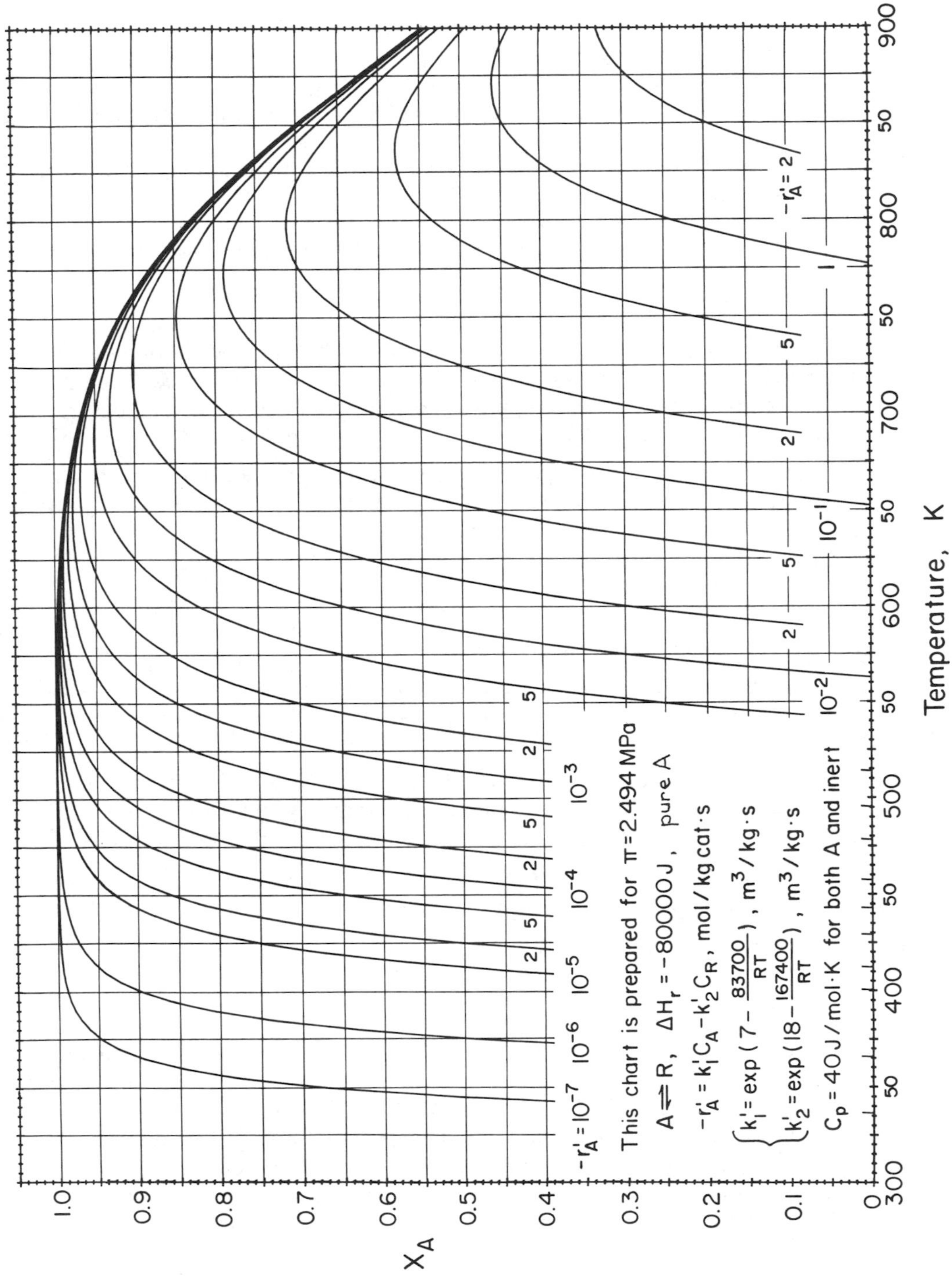
This chart is prepared for $\pi = 2.494$ MPa
$A \rightleftharpoons R$, $\Delta H_r = -80000$ J, pure A
$-r'_A = k'_1 C_A - k'_2 C_R$, mol/kg cat·s
$k'_1 = \exp\left(7 - \frac{83700}{RT}\right)$, m^3/kg·s
$k'_2 = \exp\left(18 - \frac{167400}{RT}\right)$, m^3/kg·s
$C_p = 40$ J/mol·K for both A and inert
$-r'_A = 10^{-7}$
10^{-6}
10^{-5}
10^{-4}
10^{-3}
10^{-2}
10^{-1}
1
$-r'_A = 2$
X_A
Temperature, K

Chapter 24 Problems

B13 . . . for a pure A feed, $X_A = 0.85$, in a reactor which follows the optimal temperature progression.

B14 . . . for a 50% A - 50% inert feed, $X_A = 0.70$, in an adiabatic reactor of your choice.

B15 . . . for a 20% A- 80% inert feed to an adiabatic reactor of your choice whose outlet is at $X_A = 0.75$ and T = 825 K.

B16 . . . for a 5% A - 95% inert feed, $X_A = 0.5$, in an adiabatic reactor of your choice.

We plan to use two adiabtic packed bed reactors (T_{max} = 900 K unless otherwise indicated) to treat 0.1 m^3/s of gaseous feed at 24.6 atm and 300 K. The reaction system is given in graph 1. Prepare a sketch of your recommended design and on it show

- the flow arrangement selected: plug, recycle (give **R** value), or mixed (whenever **R** > 5). Do not consider injection of cold fluid between stages unless the problem states that you are permitted to do so.
- weight of catalyst needed in each stage
- location and duty of heat exchangers
- temperature of the flowing streams

Also graph your operation on a T vs X_A diagram

C17 . . . for a pure A feed, $X_A = 0.85$

C18 . . . for a pure A feed, $X_A = 0.85$ and T_{max} = 550 K. In this problem, do not worry about the possibility of an unstable operating point. But before you build such a unit, you'd better check for this--otherwise you'll be in trouble.

C19 . . . for a 20% A - 80% inert feed, $X_A = 0.85$

C20 . . . for a 40% A - 60% inert feed, $X_A = 0.95$

C21 . . . for a 5% A - 95% inert feed, $X_A = 0.95$ (try cold feed injection)

C22 A gaseous feed (300 K, 24.6 atm, 0.1 m^3/s) is to react catalytically (exothermic system of graph 1) in two adiabatic packed beds with high recycle rate (assume mixed flow). After the first stage conversion is to be 70%, after the second stage, 85%. Instead of using a heat exchanger between the 2 stages we plan to inject cold inert gas ($C_{p,\,inert}$ = 40 J/mol·K). Sketch your recommended design, show temperatures, heat duty, catalyst requirement, and injection rate (m^3/s) of inert gas if the feed stream consists of 50% A -50% inerts and the inert gas is injected at 24.6 atm and 350 K.

D23 For the reaction system of graph 1, with gaseous feed of pure A (0.1 m^3/s at 24.6 atm and 300 K) determine the best distribution of catalyst (what fraction in each stage) and the heat exchanger duty for three adiabatic reactors in series, $X_A = 0.95$, $T_{max} =$ 900 K.

We are designing a plug flow reactor with internal heat exchange such that the fluid follows the optimal progression for minimum catalyst requirement. Gaseous feed at 0.1 m^3/s is available at 24.6 atm and 300 K, and the reaction system is shown in graph 1. We want to find how conditions change through the reactor. So find the total weight of catalyst needed, and then on a sketch, as shown below, give

- the temperature at 10% increments through the reactor
- the conversion of A at 10% increments through the reactor
- the heat duty ahead of the reactor and within each of the 10% increments

With such information we are ready for the heat transfer specialist. Make this calculation

E24 . . . for a pure A feed, $X_A = 0.85$, $T_{max} = 900$ K

E25 . . . for a 10% A - 90% inerts feed, $X_A = 0.95$, $T_{max} = 675$ K

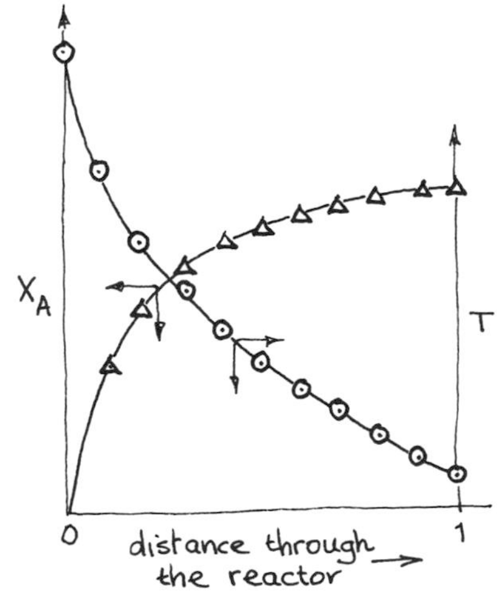

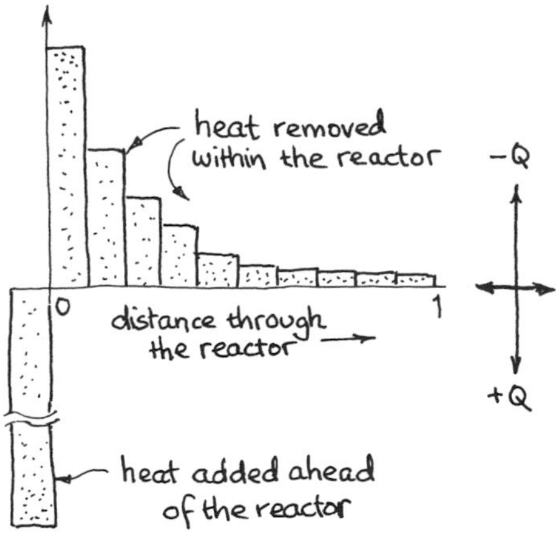

Chapter 24 Problems

We are designing a multistage adiabatic packed bed reactor system for treating the reaction of graph 1 at 24.6 atm, and one of the reactors in this series is to operate at the conditions listed below. Is this practical? Would the reactor be stable? If not, what temperature runaway point (± 25 K) can you expect?

The reactor in question is designed for

F26 . . . $X_A = 0.5$, $T = 725$ K, with a 5% A - 95% inert feed

F27 . . . $X_A = 0.75$, $T = 425$ K, with a 50% A - 50% inert feed

---

Chapter 25 FLUIDIZED REACTORS WITH FINE CATALYST PARTICLES.

As the decision tree on pg 21·7 shows, we turn to suspended solid reactors when very small catalyst particles are to be used. This is the situation with very active catalyst, and this is what we treat in this chapter.

Let us first sketch the contacting regimes encountered when a batch of solids is fluidized by gas at progressively higher and higher gas velocity.

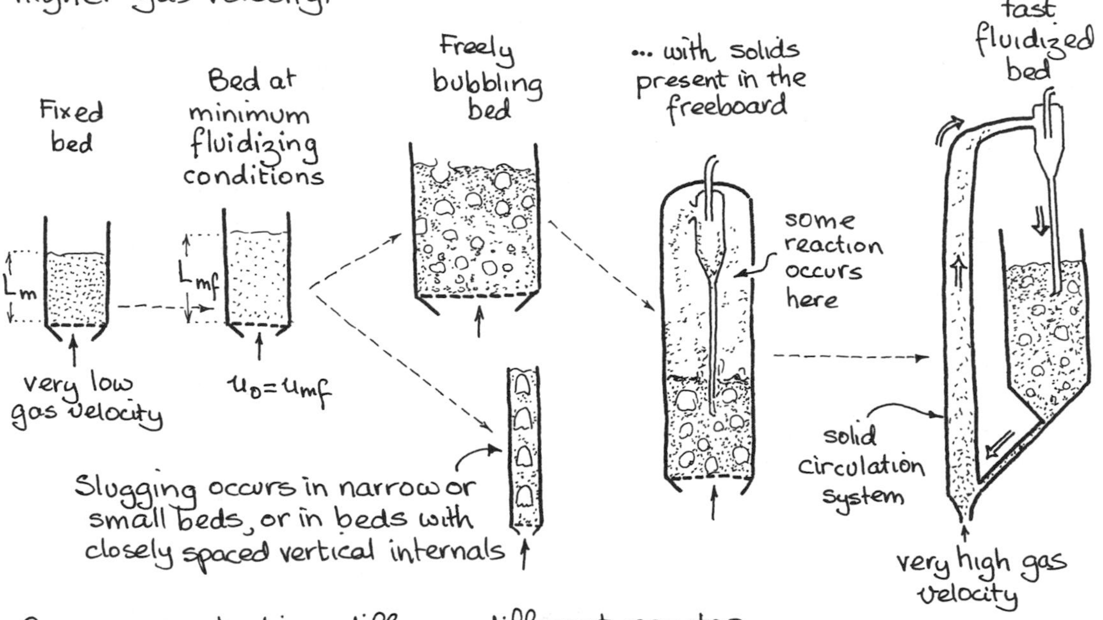

Because contacting differs, different reactor models must be used for these regimes. Kunii & Levenspiel (1991) present such models for

- the bubbling bed of fine particles
- the freeboard region above
- the fast fluidized regime

as well as reactor models for large particle beds. These are useful in other applications such as drying of grains, roasting of ores, incineration of wastes, coal combustion, etc.

In this chapter we only present the simplest of these reactor models, that for the bubbling bed of fine particles with negligible solids in the freeboard, hence negligible reaction above the bed.

The problem with design and scale up of suspended solids reactors is to properly characterize the flow pattern of gas and the contacting of gas with solid. The key to this is the nature of the bubbling action in the bed. For instance, at a given flow rate of reactant gas we may end up with a bed having a few large bubbles, or many small bubbles, or even a slugging bed, and this difference may lead to quite different conversion, product distribution, and so on. Thus a reasonable flow model should reflect the actual flow in the bed. This all boils down to using an **effective bubble size** as the key parameter in the model.

So now let us see what is known about bubbles in fluidized beds.

I. The Single Rising Bubble in a bed otherwise at Minimum Fluidizing Conditions

Here we have three pertinent findings:

1. The rise velocity of a single isolated bubble depends only on the bubble size, no matter what solids — large or small — are used [see Davidson & Harrison]

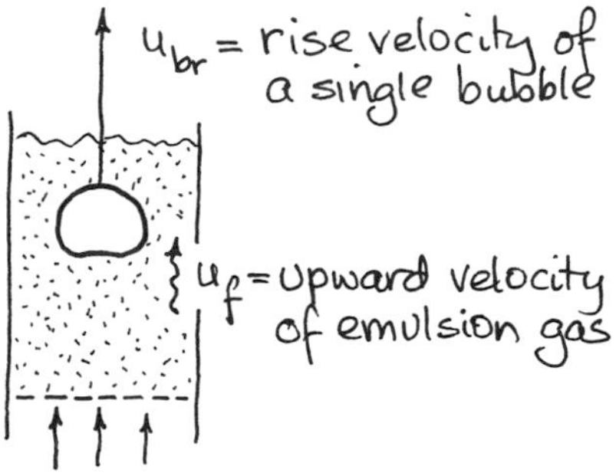

2. Rowe showed that every rising gas bubble drags behind it a wake of solids. We call

$$\alpha = \left(\frac{\text{volume of wake}}{\text{volume of bubble}}\right) \quad \cdots \begin{cases} \alpha \text{ varies between } 0.2 \,\&\, 2.0 \\ \text{depending on who does} \\ \text{the measuring \& reporting.} \end{cases}$$

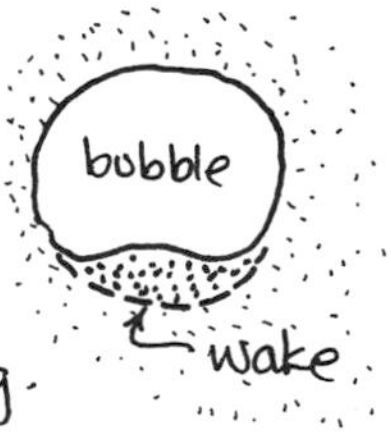

3. Davidson [again see Davidson & Harrison] also concluded from an elegant theory, and verified by experiment, that the gas behavior in the vicinity of a rising gas bubble depends only on the relative values of u_b and u_f. Close to the two extremes he found the following (u_b = bubble rise velocity in a bubbling bed).

In fine particle beds

$u_b \gg u_f$

FAST BUBBLE
CLOUDED BUBBLE
BUBBLE with HALO

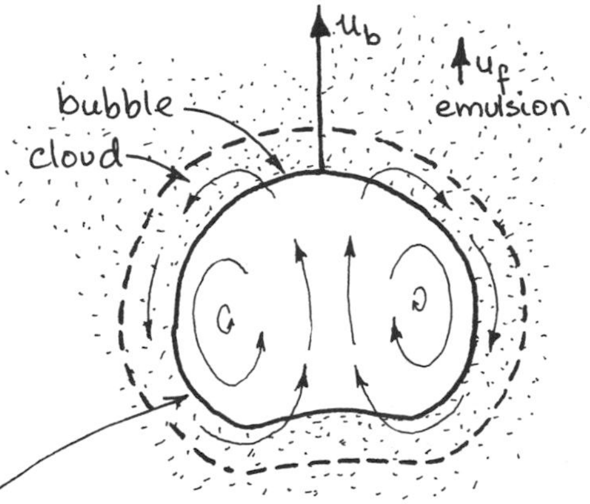

Here bubble gas does not flow through the rest of the bed, but circulates within the bubble and a thin cloud region surrounding the bubble. In fact the bubble gas forms a vortex ring and stays segregated from the rest of the gas passing through the bed. Theory says that:

$$\left(\frac{\text{thickness of cloud}}{\text{bubble diameter}}\right) \simeq \frac{u_f}{u_b}$$

In large particle beds

$u_b < u_f$

SLOW BUBBLE
CLOUDLESS BUBBLE

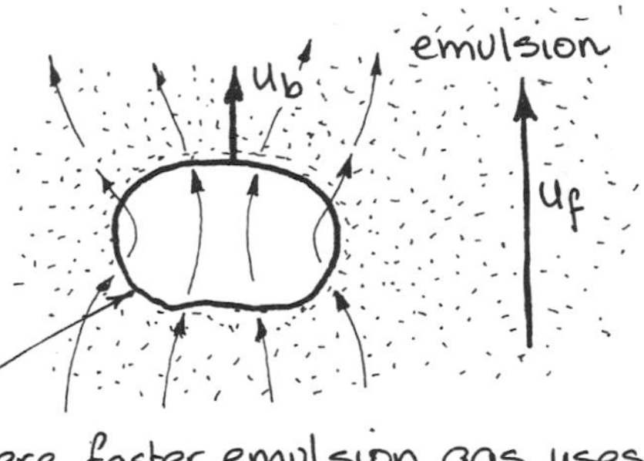

Here faster emulsion gas uses the bubble as a shortcut as it overtakes the bubble. This regime does not concern us with catalytic reactions.

As an example, if the bubble rises 25 times as fast as the emulsion gas (not at all uncommon) the cloud thickness will be just 2% of the bubble diameter. This is the regime that interests us.

We are now ready to develop the contacting & reactor model.

II. Contacting in a Fine Particle Bubbling Fluidized Bed.

Pass an excess of gas upward through a bed of fine particles. With a large enough bed diameter we get a freely bubbling bed of fast bubbles. The simplest flow model for such contacting which accounts for bubble, cloud and emulsion regions as well as gas interchange between regions is that of Kunii & Levenspiel (1991) Chapters 6 and 12 which assumes

- uniform bubble size in the bed
- gas flow near a bubble follows the Davidson model
- each bubble drags a wake of solids behind it. This generates a circulation of solids in the bed, upflow behind the bubbles and downflow everywhere else in the bed
- the emulsion stays at minimum fluidizing conditions, thus the relative velocity between gas and solids remains constant.

Let u_0 = superficial gas velocity in the bed, m/s
d = diameter, m
ε = fraction of voids in the bed, –
subscripts b, c, e refer to bubble, cloud and emulsion, respectively
subscripts m, mf, f refer to packed bed, minimum fluidization and bubbling fluidized bed conditions, respectively

In essence, given u_{mf}, ε_{mf}, u_0, α and the effective bubble size in the bed d_b, this model tells you all the other propertis of the bed – flows, region volumes, interchange rates, and consequently reactor behavior. By making the necessary material balances we find

$$u_{br} = 0.711\,(g d_b)^{1/2} \text{ m/s}$$ ... rise velocity of a single bubble in a bed otherwise at u_{mf}; from experiment

(g = acceleration of gravity $= 9.8\ \text{m/s}^2$)

$$u_b = u_0 - u_{mf} + u_{br},\ \text{m/s}$$ rise velocity of bubbles in a bubbling bed.

Note. For more accurate values of d_b and u_b see pgs 144–146 and top of pg 149 of Kunii and Levenspiel (1991).

$\delta = \frac{u_o - u_{mf}}{u_b} = 1 - \frac{u_{br}}{u_b}$, and for $u_b \gg u_{mf}$ we can use $\delta \cong \frac{u_o}{u_b}$

Useful relationships $\begin{cases} L_m(1-\varepsilon_m) = L_{mf}(1-\varepsilon_{mf}) = L_f(1-\varepsilon_f) \\ 1-\delta = \frac{L_{mf}}{L_f} = \frac{u_{br}}{u_b} = \frac{1-\varepsilon_f}{1-\varepsilon_{mf}} \end{cases}$

$\beta = \frac{3\delta\, u_{mf}/\varepsilon_{mf}}{u_{br} - u_{mf}/\varepsilon_{mf}}$ ... bed fraction in clouds

$\alpha\delta$ ... bed fraction in wakes

$1-\delta-\alpha\delta$ ... bed fraction in downflowing solids, this means emulsion and cloud, but not wake

$u_s = \frac{\alpha\delta u_b}{1-\delta-\alpha\delta}$, m/s ... downflow velocity of emulsion solids

$u_e = \frac{u_{mf}}{\varepsilon_{mf}} - u_s$, m/s ... rise velocity of emulsion gas

$$K_{bc} = 4.50\left(\frac{u_{mf}}{d_b}\right) + 5.85\left(\frac{\mathscr{D}^{1/2} g^{1/4}}{d_b^{5/4}}\right) = \frac{\text{interchange volume between b\&c, or c\&b/s}}{\text{volume of bubble}}, \ s^{-1}$$

... gas exchange coefficient between bubble and cloud-wake

$$K_{ce} = 6.77\left(\frac{\varepsilon_{mf}\mathscr{D} u_{br}}{d_b^3}\right)^{1/2} = \frac{\text{interchange volume/s}}{\text{volume of bubble}}, \ s^{-1}$$

... gas exchange coefficient between cloud-wake and emulsion

$\gamma_b = 0.001 \sim 0.01 = \frac{\text{volume of solids in bubble}}{\text{volume of bubble}}$ ... rough estimate from experiment

$$\gamma_c = (1-\varepsilon_{mf})\left[\frac{3u_{mf}/\varepsilon_{mf}}{u_{br} - u_{mf}/\varepsilon_{mf}} + \alpha\right] = \frac{\text{volume of solids in cloud and wake}}{\text{volume of bubble}}$$

$$\gamma_e = \frac{(1-\varepsilon_{mf})(1-\delta)}{\delta} - \gamma_c - \gamma_b = \frac{\text{volume of solids in the rest of the emulsion}}{\text{volume of bubbles}}$$

$m_b < 0.01$ ... fraction of bed solids in bubbles

$m_c = \frac{\gamma_c \delta}{(1-\delta)(1-\varepsilon_{mf})}$ ... fraction of bed solids in clouds

$m_e = 1 - m_c - m_b$ ... fraction of bed solids in the emulsion.

Note: the bubble wakes carry solids upward therefore the rest of the solids move downward. When this downflow is fast enough it can drag the upward percolating gas down with it. From the above expression for u_e this flow reversal (when emulsion gas begins to flow downward) occurs when

$$u_e < 0 \quad \ldots \text{or} \quad u_o > \underbrace{(3 \sim 11)}_{\text{this value is strongly dependent on } \alpha.} u_{mf}$$

So for a vigorously bubbling bed, $u_o/u_{mf} \gg 1$, we have downflow of emulsion gas. We picture such a bed as follows:

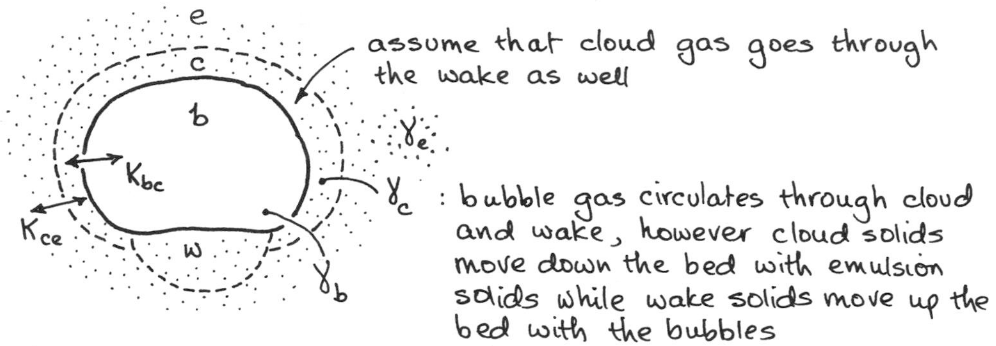

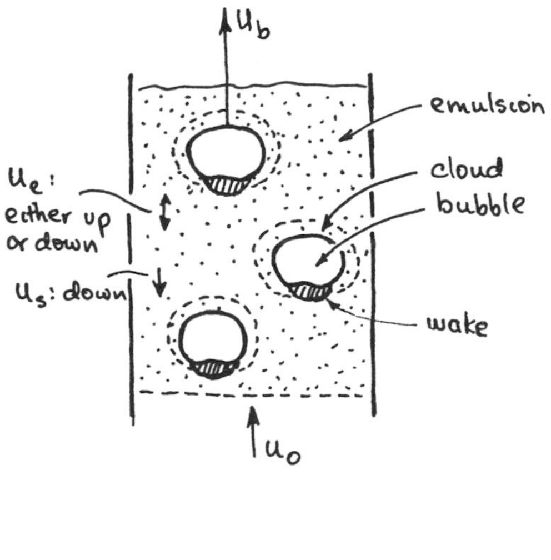

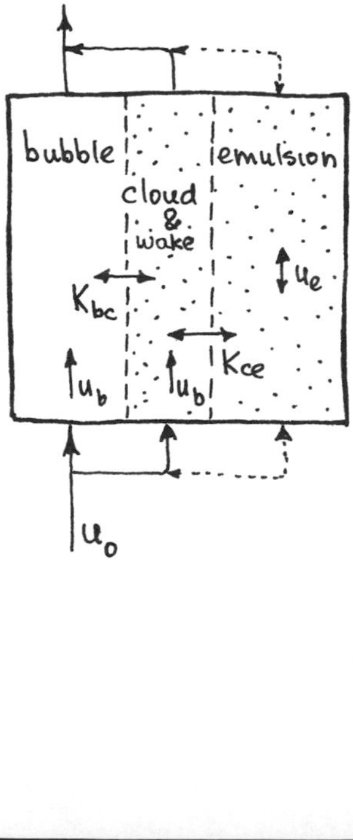

III. Application to Catalytic Reactions.

Here we make two additional assumptions:

- ignore the flow of gas through the cloud since the cloud volume is very small for fast bubbles, or $u_b \gg u_{mf}/\varepsilon_{mf}$.
- ignore the flow of gas, either up or down, through the emulsion since this flow is much smaller than the flow through the bubbles.

In effect, we consider the cloud and emulsion gas as stagnant. Of course more general expressions can be developed for beds where bubbles have thick clouds (not too fast bubbles), or where the emulsion throughflow is significant (u_0 close to u_{mf}, say $u_0 = 1 \sim 2\, u_{mf}$). However for vigorously bubbling beds of fine particles the above represent a reasonable simplification.

We next see how to calculate reactor performance in such a bed.

A. First order reaction.

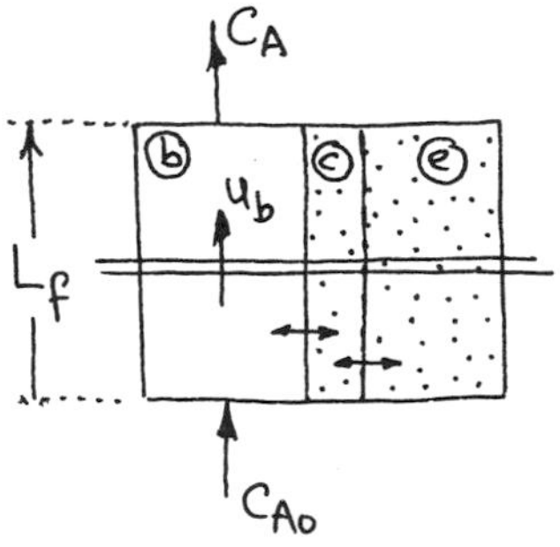

Let the reaction be

$$A \rightarrow R, \quad -r'_A = k' C_A, \quad \frac{mol}{kg \cdot s} \qquad \cdots (1)$$

(k': $m^3/kg \cdot s$)

Then for any slice of bed we have

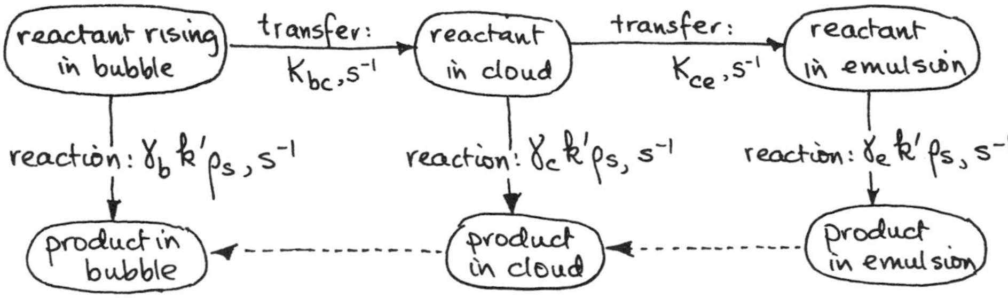

Accounting for these five resistances in series–parallel, eliminating cloud and emulsion concentrations, and integrating from the bottom to the top of the bed gives

$$\ln\frac{C_{A0}}{C_A}=\underbrace{\left[\underbrace{\gamma_b k'\rho_s+\cfrac{1}{\cfrac{1}{K_{bc}}+\cfrac{1}{\gamma_c k'\rho_s+\cfrac{1}{\cfrac{1}{K_{ce}}+\cfrac{1}{\gamma_e k'\rho_s}}}}}_{s^{-1}}\right]\overbrace{\underbrace{\frac{u_0}{(1-\varepsilon_f)u_b\rho_s}}_{L_f/u_b}}^{m^3\,\text{fluid}/kg}}_{\mathcal{K}'}\cdot\overbrace{\tau'}^{kg\cdot s/m^3\,\text{fluid}}\qquad\cdots(2)$$

$\tau' = W/v_0 = \dfrac{L_f(1-\varepsilon_f)\rho_s}{u_0}$

note these five resistance terms

$\mathcal{K}'$, effective rate constant for the fluidized bed, $m^3/kg\cdot s$

We also find that the average gas composition seen by the solids is approximately (from S. Kimura, personal communication)

$$\bar{C}_{A,\text{bathing the solids}}=\frac{C_{A0}-C_A}{\mathcal{K}'\tau'}=\frac{C_{A0}X_A v_0}{\mathcal{K}'W}\qquad\cdots(3)$$

This quantity is important for G/S reactions because it is this that the solids see and react with.

Let us now look at **packed bed reactors**. Assuming plug flow we have

for plug flow

$$\ln\frac{C_{A0}}{C_A}=k'\tau'\qquad\cdots(4)$$

$$\bar{C}_{Ap}=\frac{C_{A0}-C_{Ap}}{k'\tau'}\qquad\cdots(5)$$

Comparing eqs. 2 and 4, and 3 and 5 shows that a fluidized bed can be treated as a plug flow reactor as long as:

k' is replaced by $\mathcal{K}'$

k': true reaction rate constant, used for fixed beds

$\mathcal{K}'$: effective rate constant, used for fluidized beds.

Example 1 First order catalytic reaction in a fluidized bed.

Reactant gas ($u_0 = 0.3$ m/s, $v_0 = 0.3\pi$ m³/s passes upward through a 2 m diameter fluidized bed ($u_{mf} = 0.03$ m/s, $\varepsilon_{mf} = 0.5$, $\varepsilon_f = 0.60$) containing 7 tons of catalyst ($W = 7000$ kg, $\rho_s = 2000$ kg/m³). Reaction proceeds as follows

$$A \rightarrow R, \quad -r_A' = k' C_A \quad \ldots \text{ with } k' = 400 \times 10^{-6} \frac{\text{m}^3 \text{ fluid}}{\text{kg}\cdot\text{s}}$$

(a) Calculate the conversion of reactant.

(b) Find the proper mean concentration of A seen by the solids.

(c) If gas were made to flow downward through the solids we would have a packed bed. Assuming plug flow of gas find the conversion of reactant for this situation.

Additional data.

$C_{A0} = 100$ mol/m³, $\mathcal{D} = 20 \times 10^{-6}$ m²/s, $\alpha = 0.33$

Estimated bubble size in the bed: $d_b = 0.32$ m

Solution

Preliminary Determine the rise velocity of bubbles

$$u_{br} = 0.711\,(9.8 \times 0.32)^{1/2} = 1.26 \text{ m/s}$$

$$u_b = 0.30 - 0.03 + 1.26 = 1.53 \text{ m/s}$$

Now see whether the fast bubble model of this chapter applies.

- Check for slugging: The bubble size (32 cm) is small compared to the bed size (200 cm), hence no slugging.
- Check the fast bubble assumption: Take the velocity ratio

$$\frac{u_b}{u_f} = \frac{u_b}{u_{mf}/\varepsilon_{mf}} = \frac{1.53}{0.03/0.5} = 25.5$$

Since the bubble rises ~25 times as fast as the emulsion gas we have a fast bubble with thin cloud – less than 1 cm thick.

Thus we can safely use the **bubbling bed model** of this chapter.

25.10

(a) Calculate X_A Replacing numbers into the expressions for this model gives, in turn,

$$\delta = \frac{0.30}{1.53} = 0.196$$

$$K_{bc} = 4.50\left(\frac{0.03}{0.32}\right) + 5.85\left(\frac{(20\times10^{-6})^{1/2}(9.8)^{1/4}}{(0.32)^{5/4}}\right) = 0.614\ s^{-1}$$

$$K_{ce} = 6.77\left(\frac{0.5\ (20\times10^{-6})\ 1.26}{(0.32)^3}\right)^{1/2} = 0.133\ s^{-1}$$

$\gamma_b = 0.001 \sim 0.01$ Since no value is given take a mean value, say 0.003. We shall see that this term has no effect on X_A.

$$\gamma_c = (1-0.5)\left(\frac{3\times 0.03/0.5}{1.26 - 0.03/0.5} + 0.33\right) = 0.24$$

$$\gamma_e = \frac{(1-0.5)(1-0.196)}{0.196} - 0.24 - \underbrace{0.003}_{\text{negligible}} = 1.81$$

$$k'\rho_s = (400\times10^{-6})(2000) = 0.8\ \text{m}^3\ \text{fluid}/\text{m}^3\ \text{solid}\cdot\text{s}$$

$$\ln\frac{C_{A0}}{C_A} = \left[\underbrace{0.003(0.8)}_{\text{negligible}} + \cfrac{1}{\cfrac{1}{0.614} + \cfrac{1}{0.24(0.8) + \cfrac{1}{\cfrac{1}{0.133} + \cfrac{1}{1.81(0.8)}}}}\right]$$

$$\times \frac{0.3}{(1-0.60)(1.53)(2000)} \cdot \frac{7000}{0.3\pi} = [0.210] \times 1.82 = 0.38$$

Therefore

$$\frac{C_A}{C_{A0}} = 0.68 \quad \ldots \text{ or } \mathbf{X_A = 32\%} \quad \longleftarrow$$

(b) Find $\bar{C}_A$ seen by the solids Again, replacing values gives

$$\bar{C}_A = \frac{(C_{A0} - C_A)v_0}{k'\ W} = \frac{(100-68)\ 0.3\pi}{(400\times10^{-6})7000} = \mathbf{11\ mol/m^3} \quad \longleftarrow$$

(c) Calculate X_A for a fixed bed. From eq 4

$$\ln \frac{C_{A0}}{C_{Ap}} = k'\tau' = (400 \times 10^{-6}) \frac{7000}{0.3\pi} = 2.97$$

Therefore

$$\frac{C_{Ap}}{C_{A0}} = 0.05 \quad \ldots \text{ or } \quad X_A = 95\% \quad \longleftarrow$$

Comments

- The conversion in the fluidized bed is drastically lower than in the packed bed (32% vs 95%), and is even much below mixed flow (75%). This comes from the severe bypassing of reactant gas in the large gas bubbles. Reduce the size of bubbles in the bed and the conversion will rise spectacularly.

- Gas enters at $C_{A0} = 100$, leaves at $C_A = 68$, however the solids see a much lower concentration of A, or $C_A = 11$. Thus the solids, mostly in the emulsion, are starved for gaseous reactant. This sort of finding, quite general for fast bubble beds, is of great importance in G/S reactions. Thus in combustion and roasting of fine solids these solids may be starved for oxygen even the off gas from the bed may contain a significant amount of oxygen

B The Denbigh reaction and its special cases.

Consider the first order catalytic reaction scheme

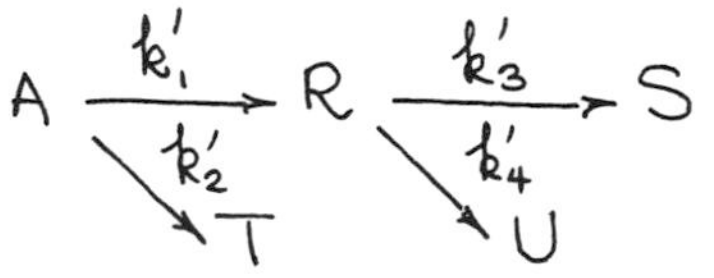

$$A \xrightarrow{k_1'} R \xrightarrow{k_3'} S, \quad A \xrightarrow{k_2'} T, \quad R \xrightarrow{k_4'} U \qquad \ldots \text{ and let } \begin{cases} k_{12}' = k_1' + k_2' \\ k_{34} = k_3' + k_4' \end{cases}$$

In treating this reaction scheme we also solve all its special cases

$$A \to R \to S, \quad A \begin{smallmatrix} \nearrow R \\ \searrow S \end{smallmatrix}, \quad A \to R \to S \text{ with } A \to S, \quad A \to R \to S \text{ with } A \to T, \quad R \begin{smallmatrix} \nearrow S \\ \searrow T \end{smallmatrix} \text{ from } A \to R.$$

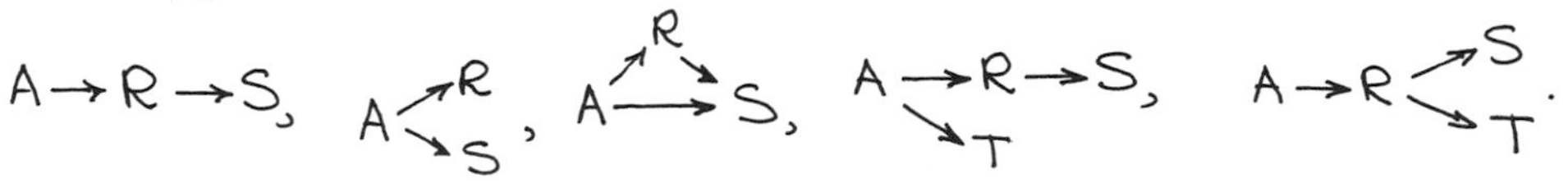

For isothermal **plug flow** a direct extension of the equations of chapter 8 gives

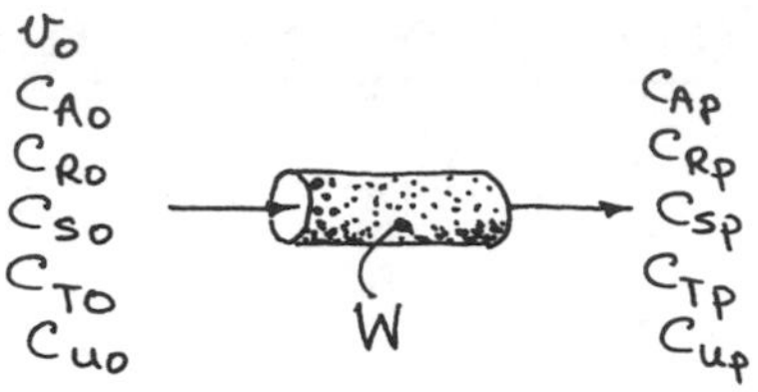

$$\frac{C_{Ap}}{C_{A0}} = \exp(-k'_{12}\tau') \qquad \cdots (7)$$

($\tau' = W/v_0$)

$$\frac{C_{Rp}}{C_{A0}} = \frac{k'_1}{k'_{34}-k'_{12}}\left[\exp(-k'_{12}\tau') - \exp(-k'_{34}\tau')\right] + \frac{C_{R0}}{C_{A0}}\exp(-k'_{34}\tau') \qquad \cdots (8)$$

$$\frac{C_{Sp}}{C_{A0}} = \frac{k'_3}{k'_{34}}\left\{\frac{k'_1 k'_3}{k'_{34}-k'_{12}}\left[\frac{\exp(-k'_{34}\tau')}{k'_{34}} - \frac{\exp(-k'_{12}\tau')}{k'_{12}}\right] + \frac{k'_1}{k'_{12}} + \frac{C_{R0}}{C_{A0}}\left[1-\exp(-k'_{34}\tau')\right]\right\} + \frac{C_{S0}}{C_{A0}} \qquad \cdots (9)$$

$$\frac{C_{Tp}}{C_{A0}} = \frac{k'_2}{k'_{12}}\left[1-\exp(-k'_{12}\tau')\right] + \frac{C_{T0}}{C_{A0}} \qquad \cdots (10)$$

$\frac{C_{Up}}{C_{A0}}$ = same as $\frac{C_{Sp}}{C_{A0}}$ but with $k'_3 \to k'_4$ and $C_{S0} \to C_{U0}$ (11)

The maximum for C_R for the special case where $C_{R0}=0$ is given by

$$\frac{C_{R\,max,\,p}}{C_{A0}} = \frac{k'_1}{k'_{12}}\left(\frac{k'_{12}}{k'_{34}}\right)^{k'_{34}/k'_{34}-k'_{12}} \qquad \cdots (12)$$

and

$$\tau'_{\text{at } C_{R\,max}} = \frac{\ln(k'_{34}/k'_{12})}{k'_{34}-k'_{12}} \qquad \cdots (13)$$

For the **fluidized bed** the effective rate constants, the k' values, must account for the mass transfer and reaction steps as reactant and the various intermediates and products move from bubble to cloud to emulsion. Solving we find that the concentrations at the exit of the fluidized bed are given by

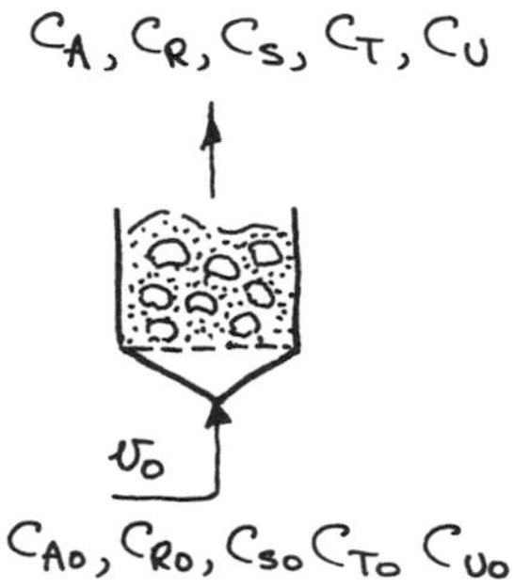

$$\frac{C_A}{C_{A0}} = \exp(-K'_{12}\tau') \quad \cdots (14)$$

$$\frac{C_R}{C_{A0}} = \frac{K'_{AR}}{K'_{34}-K'_{12}}\left[\exp(-K'_{12}\tau')-\exp(-K'_{34}\tau')\right] + \frac{C_{R0}}{C_{A0}}\exp(-K'_{34}\tau') \quad \cdots (15)$$

$$\frac{C_S}{C_{A0}} = \frac{k'_3}{k'_{34}}\left\{\frac{K'_{34}K'_{AR}}{K'_{34}-K'_{12}}\left[\frac{\exp(-K'_{34}\tau')}{K'_{34}} - \frac{\exp(-K'_{12}\tau')}{K'_{12}}\right] + \frac{k'_1}{k'_{12}} - \frac{K'_A}{K'_{12}}\exp(-K'_{12}\tau') + \frac{C_{R0}}{C_{A0}}\left[1-\exp(-K'_{34}\tau')\right]\right\} + \frac{C_{S0}}{C_{A0}} \quad \cdots (16)$$

$$\frac{C_T}{C_{A0}} = \frac{k'_2}{k'_{12}}\left[1-\exp(-K'_{12}\tau')\right] + \frac{C_{T0}}{C_{A0}} \quad \cdots (17)$$

$\frac{C_U}{C_{A0}}$ = same as $\frac{C_S}{C_{A0}}$ but with $k'_3 \longrightarrow k'_4$ and $C_{S0} \longrightarrow C_{U0}$ $\quad \cdots (18)$

The maximum of R for the special case where $C_{R0} = 0$ is given by

$$\frac{C_{R\max}}{C_{A0}} = \frac{K'_{AR}}{K'_{12}}\left(\frac{K'_{12}}{K'_{34}}\right)^{K'_{34}/K'_{34}-K'_{12}} \quad \cdots (19)$$

and

$$\tau_{\text{at } C_{R\max}} = \frac{\ln(K'_{34}/K'_{12})}{K'_{34}-K'_{12}} \quad \cdots (20)$$

In these expressions

$$K'_{12} = \underbrace{\left[\gamma_b k'_{12}\rho_s + \cfrac{1}{\cfrac{1}{K_{bc}} + \cfrac{1}{\gamma_c k'_{12}\rho_s + \cfrac{1}{\cfrac{1}{K_{ce}} + \cfrac{1}{\gamma_e k'_{12}\rho_s}}}}\right]}_{s^{-1}} \underbrace{\frac{u_0}{(1-\varepsilon_f)\,u_b\,\rho_s}}_{m^3\,\text{fluid/kg}} \quad \cdots (21)$$

K'_{34} = same as K'_{12} except that $k'_{12} \longrightarrow k'_{34}$ $\quad \cdots (22)$

$$K'_A = \frac{\left[\dfrac{K_{bc}K_{ce}}{\gamma_c^2} + \left(k'_{12}\rho_s + \dfrac{K_{ce}}{\gamma_c} + \dfrac{K_{ce}}{\gamma_e}\right)\left(k'_{34}\rho_s + \dfrac{K_{ce}}{\gamma_c} + \dfrac{K_{ce}}{\gamma_e}\right)\right]\left[\dfrac{K_{bc}\,u_o\,k'_1\,k'_{34}\rho_s}{(1-\varepsilon_{mf})\,u_{br}}\right]}{\left[\left(k'_{12}\rho_s + \dfrac{K_{bc}}{\gamma_c}\right)\left(k'_{12}\rho_s + \dfrac{K_{ce}}{\gamma_e}\right) + \dfrac{k'_{12}\rho_s K_{ce}}{\gamma_c}\right]\left[\left(k'_{34}\rho_s + \dfrac{K_{bc}}{\gamma_c}\right)\left(k'_{34}\rho_s + \dfrac{K_{ce}}{\gamma_e}\right) + \dfrac{k'_{34}\rho_s K_{ce}}{\gamma_c}\right]} \quad \cdots (23)$$

$$K'_{AR} = \frac{k'_1}{k'_{12}} K'_{12} - K'_A \quad \cdots (24)$$

[when $k'_{34} \ll k'_1$, say 1/100, then this term becomes very small and can be ignored]

In the above expressions the interchange coefficients K_{bc} and K_{ce} for reacting species A and R are assumed to be equal. This is equivalent to assuming that the diffusion coefficients of A and R are identical

Comments

(a) If $\mathcal{D}_A \neq \mathcal{D}_R$ then K_{bc} and K_{ce} for A differ from K_{bc} and K_{ce} for R. In such a situation we must keep track of the specific K_{bc} and K_{ce} values in eqs 21 ~ 24. This development is given by Levenspiel et al, IEC/PDD 17 478 (1978).

(b) **Fluidized vs fixed bed.** If we put $K_{bc} = K_{ce} = \infty$ in the above fluidized bed equations we find that

$$K'_{12} \rightarrow k'_{12}, \quad K'_{34} \rightarrow k'_{34}, \quad K'_A \rightarrow 0, \quad K_{AR} \rightarrow k'_1$$

and all the fluidized bed equations reduce to the corresponding plug flow equations.

(c) **Special cases.** The general expressions for the Denbigh reaction reduce directly to all the special cases. Thus

- for $A \xrightarrow{1} R \xrightarrow{3} S$ put $k'_2 = k'_4 = 0$ in the derived equations
- for $A \begin{smallmatrix} \xrightarrow{1} R \\ \xrightarrow{2} T \end{smallmatrix}$ put $k'_3 = k'_4 = 0$.

and so on.

(d) By putting numbers in the above expressions we can verify the following

- the fluidized bed always needs more catalyst than a fixed bed to achieve a given X_A, or to reach $C_{R\,max}$.

- For **reactions in series** the fluidized bed always gives a lower yield of intermediate compared to a fixed bed. Thus

for $A \xrightarrow{1} R \xrightarrow{3} S$ $$\left(\frac{C_{R\,max}}{C_{A0}}\right)_{fluidized} = \frac{K'_{AR}}{K'_1}\left(\frac{K'_1}{K'_3}\right)^{K'_3/(K'_3-K'_1)}$$

- For **reactions in parallel**, of same order the product distribution does not change with fluidized bed operations. Thus

for $A \overset{1\nearrow R}{\underset{2\searrow T}{}}$ $$\left(\frac{C_R}{C_R+C_S}\right) = \frac{k'_1}{k'_1+k'_2}$$

for both fluidized and fixed bed reactors.

Example 2. Catalytic series reactions in a fluidized bed.

Reactant A decomposes by first order catalytic reactions as follows:

$$A \xrightarrow{k'_1} R \xrightarrow{k'_3} S \qquad \text{where} \begin{cases} k'_1 = 400\times10^{-6}\ m^3/kg\cdot s \\ k'_3 = 25\times10^{-6}\ m^3/kg\cdot s \end{cases}$$

Using a 2 m diameter reactor and introducing an A-inert feed at $u_0 = 0.30$ m/s, find the amount of catalyst needed to achieve $C_{R,max}$, evaluate $C_{R,max}$ as well as X_A at $C_{R,max}$.

(a) for fixed bed operations (assume plug flow).

(b) for fluidized bed operations ($u_{mf} = 0.03$ m/s, $\varepsilon_{mf} = 0.5$) if the effective bubble size in the bed is estimated as $d_b = 0.32$ m, a rather large value.

Additional data.

$C_{A0} = 100\ mol/m^3$, $\rho_s = 2000\ kg/m^3$, $\mathscr{D} = 20\times10^{-6}\ m^2/s$ for both A and R

$\alpha = 0.33$ (rough estimate), $\varepsilon_f = 0.60$.

Solution

Preliminary. The arguments of example 1 apply directly to this problem. Thus we are dealing with a bubbling bed with fast bubbles (no slugging) and can safely use the **bubbling bed model** of this chapter.

25.16

(a) Fixed bed. From eqs 7, 12, 13 we find

$$W_p = \frac{v_0 \ln(k_3'/k_1')}{k_3'-k_1'} = \frac{0.3\pi \ln(25/400)}{(25-400)\,10^{-6}} = 7000 \text{ kg}$$

$$\left(\frac{C_{R\max}}{C_{A0}}\right)_p = \left(\frac{k_1'}{k_3'}\right)^{k_3'/k_3'-k_1'} = \left(\frac{400}{25}\right)^{25/25-400} = 0.83$$

$$\frac{C_{Ap}}{C_{A0}} = \exp\left(-\frac{k_1' W}{v_0}\right) = \exp\left(-\frac{(400\times10^{-6})7000}{0.3\pi}\right) = 0.05$$

or $X_A = 95\%$

(b) Fluidized bed. From the equations of the bubbling bed model

$$u_{br} = 0.711(9.8\times0.32)^{1/2} = 1.26 \text{ m/s}$$

$$u_b = 0.30-0.03+1.26 = 1.53 \text{ m/s}$$

$$\delta = \frac{0.30}{1.53} = 0.196$$

$$K_{bc} = 4.50\left(\frac{0.03}{0.32}\right) + 5.85\,\frac{(20\times10^{-6})^{1/2}(9.8)^{1/4}}{(0.32)^{5/4}} = 0.614 \text{ s}^{-1}$$

$$K_{ce} = 6.77\left(\frac{0.5(20\times10^{-6})\,1.26}{(0.32)^3}\right)^{1/2} = 0.133 \text{ s}^{-1}$$

$\gamma_b = 0.001 \sim 0.01$ ... take as 0.003

$$\gamma_c = 0.5\left(\frac{3(0.03)/0.5}{1.26-0.03/0.5} + 0.33\right) = 0.24$$

$$\gamma_e = \frac{(1-0.5)(1-0.196)}{0.196} - 0.24 - 0.003 = 1.81$$

Next calculate the needed K values. Since $k_2' = k_4' = 0$ we have

$$K_{12}' \rightarrow K_1' \quad \text{and} \quad K_{34}' \rightarrow K_3'$$

Thus eqs 21~24 give

$$K'_{12} = K'_1 = \left[0.003(0.8) + \cfrac{1}{\cfrac{1}{0.614} + \cfrac{1}{0.24(0.8) + \cfrac{1}{\cfrac{1}{0.133} + \cfrac{1}{1.81(0.8)}}}}\right] \frac{0.30}{(1-0.60)(1.53)(2000)}$$

$$= 51.2 \times 10^{-6} \text{ m}^3 \text{ fluid/kg·s}$$

Similarly

$$K'_{34} = K'_3 = 14.6 \times 10^{-6} \text{ m}^3 \text{ fluid/kg·s}$$

Replacing values into eq 23 gives

$$K'_A = 12.2 \times 10^{-6} \text{ m}^3 \text{ fluid/kg·s}$$

and eq 24 gives

$$K'_{AR} = (51.2 - 12.2)10^{-6} = 39.0 \times 10^{-6} \text{ m}^3 \text{ fluid/kg·s}$$

Finally eqs 19, 20 and 14 give

$$\frac{C_{R\,max}}{C_{A0}} = \frac{K'_{AR}}{K'_1}\left(\frac{K'_1}{K'_3}\right)^{K'_3/K'_3 - K'_1} = \frac{39.0}{51.2}\left(\frac{51.2}{14.6}\right)^{14.6/14.6-51.2} = \underline{0.46}$$

$$W_{fluidized} = \frac{v_0 \ln(K'_3/K'_1)}{K'_3 - K'_1} = \underline{32300 \text{ kg}}$$

$$\frac{C_A}{C_{A0}} = \exp(-K'_1\tau') = \exp\left[-\frac{(51.2\times10^{-6})(32300)}{0.3\pi}\right] = 0.17$$

$$\text{or } \underline{X_A = 83\%}$$

Note how much more catalyst is needed for the fluidized bed than for the packed bed (32 tons vs 7 tons) and how the maximum concentration of intermediate is depressed ($C_{R\,max}$ = 46 vs 83). All this is a consequence of gas bypassing in the large bubbles. Just cut down the bubble size, by baffles or what have you, and the performance of the bed will improve greatly.

IV Discussion.

This chapter has used the terms 'large and small' particles, 'high and low' velocity, and various forms of contacting. It would be helpful to know, even if only approximately, the range of conditions where these terms apply. The sketch below, prepared from Grace, Can. J. Chem. Eng. 64 353 (1986) is helpful in this regard.

$$u^* = u_0 \left[\frac{\rho_g^2}{\mu \, (\rho_s - \rho_g) g} \right]^{1/3}$$

$$d_p^* = d_p \left[\frac{\rho_g \, (\rho_s - \rho_g) g}{\mu^2} \right]^{1/3}$$

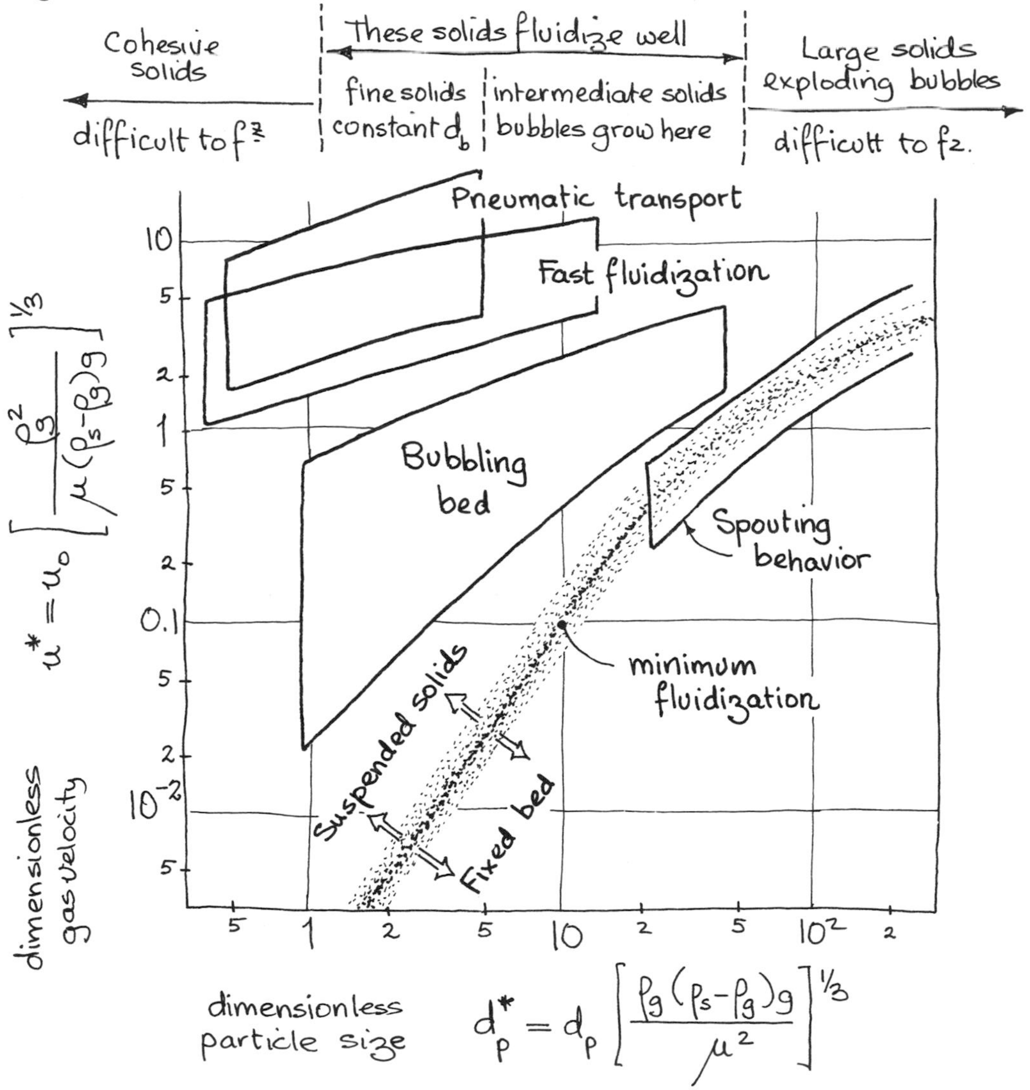

Chapter 25 Problems

In example 1 the conversion is very low and unsatisfactory. One suggestion for improvement is to insert baffles into the bed and thereby cut down the effective bubble size. Find X_A if

A1 . . . $d_b = 16$ cm

A2 . . . $d_b = 8$ cm

In example 1 another suggestion for improving performance is to use a shallower bed, keeping W unchanged, thereby decreasing the superficial gas velocity. Find X_A if we double the bed cross sectional area (thus make $u_o = 15$ cm/s) and

A3 . . . keep d_b unchanged at $d_b = 32$ cm

A4 . . . make $d_b = 8$ cm by suitable baffles

In example 1 still another suggestion is to use a narrower and taller bed, keeping W unchanged. Following this suggestion find X_A if we halve the bed cross sectional area (thus make $u_o = 60$ cm/s) and

A5 . . . keep $d_b = 32$ cm

A6 . . . make $d_b = 8$ cm by suitable baffles

And still another suggestion for raising the conversion in example 1 is to use more solids. So for the same bed diameter (2 m) and same mean bubble size (0.32 m) find X_A and the mean concentration of gas seen by the solids C_A if we use

A7 . . . 14 tons of catalyst

A8 . . . 21 tons of catalyst

A9 Mathis and Watson in AIChE J **2** 518 (1956) reported on the catalytic conversion of cumene in both fluidized and packed beds of catalyst

$$\underset{\text{cumene}}{C_9H_{12}} + O_2 \xrightarrow{\text{catalyst}} \underset{\text{phenol}}{C_6H_5OH} + \underset{\text{acetone}}{(CH_3)_2O} + C$$

In very dilute cumene-air mixtures the kinetics are essentially first order reversible with respect to cumene with an equilibrium conversion of 94%.

Chapter 25 Problems

In packed bed experiments (L_m = 76.2 mm) using downflow of gas (u_o = 64 mm/s) the conversion of cumene was found to be 60%. However, with upflow of gas at the same flow rate in the same bed, the solids fluidize (u_{mf} = 6.1 mm/s) and bubbles of gas were observed roughly 13.5 mm in diameter. What conversion do you expect to find under these conditions?

Estimated values: $\varepsilon_m = 0.4$, $\mathcal{D}_{\text{cumene-air}} = 2 \times 10^{-5}\ m^2/s$
$\varepsilon_{mf} = 0.5$, $a = 0.33$

B10* Example 2 showed that a bed with 32 cm bubbles needed 32 tons of catalyst fo give C_{Rmax} = 44. Suppose we diluted the bed 4:1 with inert solids, thus raising the height of bed but keeping all else unchanged. How would this affect C_{Rmax} and the weight of catalyst needed to achieve C_{Rmax}?

B11* In example 2 a fluidized bed with 32 cm bubbles required W = 31.7 tons of catalyst to give C_{Rmax}/C_{A0} = 0.44, instead of W = 7 tons and C_{Rmax}/C_{A0} = 0.83 for plug flow. Find C_{Rmax} and the corresponding W if the mean bubble size in the bed is reduced by suitable baffles to d_b = 8 cm.

B12 Find C_{Rmax}/C_{A0} and W at C_{Rmax} and then compare these with the corresponding plug flow values for the data of example 2 with the following changes

$$k_1' = 25 \times 10^{-6}\ m^3/kg{\cdot}s \quad \text{and} \quad k_3' = 400 \times 10^{-6}\ m^3/kg{\cdot}s$$

The parallel catalytic decompositions

$$A \nearrow R \qquad k_1' = 400 \times 10^{-6}\ m^3/kg{\cdot}s$$
$$A \searrow S \qquad k_2' = 25 \times 10^{-6}\ m^3/kg{\cdot}s$$

occur with the flows and bed conditions of Example 1. Find X_A and the fraction of R in the R-S product from the 7 ton fluidized bed and compare with plug flow for the same τ'.

B13 . . . In the fluidized bed d_b = 0.32 m

B14 . . . In the fluidized bed d_b = 0.08 m

Chapter 25 Problems

A15 Calculate the conversion in a fluidized bed reactor for the catalytic hydrogenation of nitrobenzene to analine

$$\underset{A}{C_6H_5NO_2\,(g)} + 3\,H_2\,(g) \xrightarrow[270^\circ C]{\text{catalyst}} \underset{R}{C_6H_5NH_2\,(g)} + 2\,H_2\,(g)$$

Data	$L_m = 1.4$ m	$\rho_c = 2.2$ g/cm^3	$d_b = 10$ cm
	$d_t = 3.55$ m	$\mathcal{D}_{eff} = 0.9$ cm^2/s	$f_w = 0.33$
	$T = 270°C$	$u_{mf} = 2$ cm/s	$\varepsilon_m = 0.4071$
		$u_o = 30$ cm/s	$\varepsilon_{mf} = 0.60$

We plan to use an excess of hydrogen in which case we can ignore expansion, and can assume simple first order kinetics

$$A \rightarrow R \qquad -r_A''' = k''' C_A \quad \text{with} \quad k''' = 1.2 \text{ cm}^3/\text{cm}^3 \text{ cat}\cdot\text{s}$$

Fast fluidized circulation system. We plan to run the reactions of the examples in this chapter in a fast fluidized bed system in which 20% of the solid will be in the transport line reactor and cyclone, reacting away, the rest in the fluidized bed storage unit. Smaller catalyst solids will be used, however, since the reactions are not diffusion influenced the rates will remain the same as in the examples.

C16 . . . For the reaction of Example 1 of this chapter find the total weight of catalyst needed to get the same output as the 7 ton fluidized bed.

C17 . . . For the reaction of Example 2 of this chapter find the total weight of solids needed to treat the feed of this example to its C_{Rmax}, and find C_{Rmax} for this operation.

Chapter 26. TUBE WALL, MONOLITH and PLATE CATALYTIC REACTORS

The previous chapters considered the catalyst to be in particle form. Here we deal with reactors in which the catalyst coats a surface, either in a porous layer or in an impervious layer. Low pressure drop is the main feature of these units.

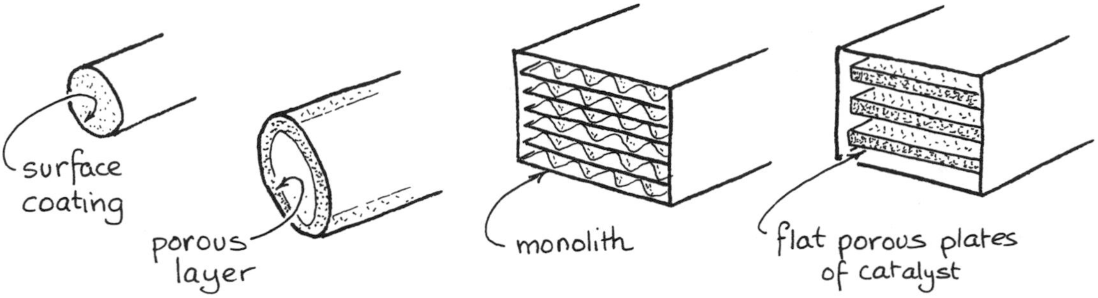

For isothermal steady state operations the treatment of these reactors is straightforward. However, for unsteady state operations, for example in catalytic converters for automobiles, things become more difficult. This short chapter deals with the simple steady state case.

I Isothermal Steady State Operations.

Consider reacting gas flowing past an element of catalyst surface

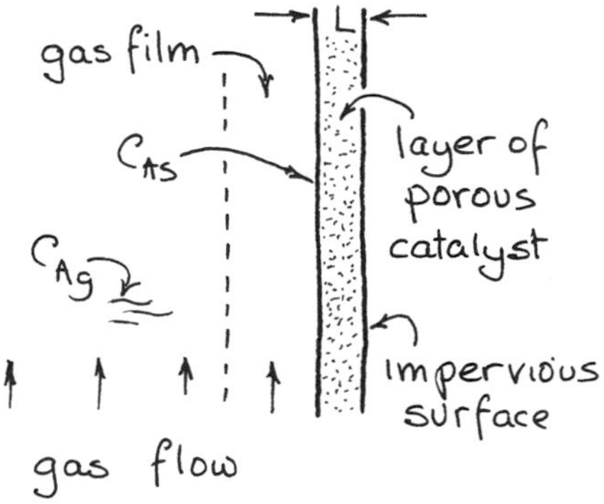

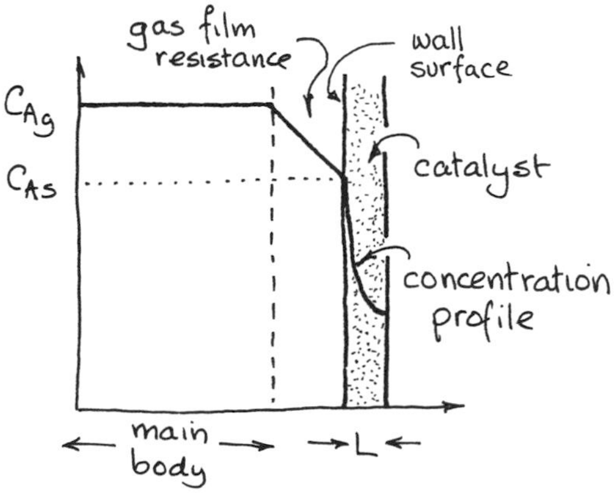

Accepting film theory we see that reactant A from the gas stream must first get to the surface (mass transfer resistance), then either react there (if nonporous) or else penetrate and diffuse into the catalyst layer to react. These are resistances in series, thus for unit surface of catalyst layer

$$r''_{A,\text{overall}} = r''_{A,\text{mass transfer}} = r''_{A,\text{reaction}} \quad \cdots \text{mol/m}^2\text{surf}\cdot\text{s} \cdots (1)$$

$r''_{A,\text{mass transfer}} = k_g (C_{Ag} - C_{As})$, with k_g in $\text{m}^3/\text{m}^2\,\text{surf}\cdot\text{s}$

$r''_{A,\text{reaction}} = k'' f(C_A)\mathcal{E} = \frac{V_s}{S} k''' f(C_A)\mathcal{E}$

the effectiveness factor $\mathcal{E}$ is always based on k'''

Mass transfer term. There are many empirical expressions for this. Let us use the following correlations here

For **turbulent flow in tubes**

$$Sh = \frac{k_g d_t}{\mathscr{D}} = 0.023\, Re^{0.8}\, Sc^{1/3} \quad \cdots (2)$$

For **laminar flow in straight tubes**

$$\overline{Sh} \begin{cases} = 3.66 + \dfrac{0.085\, Gz}{1 + 0.047\, Gz^{2/3}} & \cdots \text{when } Gz < 16 \\ = 1.86\, Gz^{1/3} & \cdots \text{when } Gz > 16 \end{cases} \quad \cdots (3)$$

($\overline{Sh}$: mean value)

where the Graetz number: $Gz = Re \cdot Sc \cdot (d_{tube}/L_{tube})$

For **laminar flow in coiled tubes**

$$\overline{Sh} \begin{cases} = Sh_{straight} + 10\, De & \cdots \text{when } De < 10 \\ = Sh_{straight}\left[1 + 1.4\, De\right] & \cdots \text{when } De > 10 \end{cases} \quad \cdots (4)$$

where the Dean number: $De = Re\left(d_{tube}/d_{coil}\right)$

For other channel shapes (flat plates, annular, irregular) use the above equations with the equivalent diameter

$$d_e = \frac{4\,(\text{cross section})}{(\text{wetted perimeter})}$$

Combining and eliminating the intermediate concentration C_{AS} from eq. 1 gives the desired final rate expression. Thus

For **1st order reaction**, $-r_A'' = k''C_A$

$$-r_A'' = \frac{1}{1/k_g + 1/k''\varepsilon}\, C_{Ag} \qquad (5)$$

$-r_A''$ based on surface of catalyst layer S, not the total surface of the porous structure

ε based on $k''' = k''(V_s/S)$

Special cases.

- for film diffusion control: $-r_A'' = k_g C_{Ag}$
- for reaction control: $-r_A'' = k'' C_{Ag} \varepsilon$

For **2nd order reaction**, $-r_A'' = k''C_A^2$ we get from Chap. 11

$$-r_A'' = \frac{k_g}{2k''\varepsilon}\left(2k''\varepsilon C_{Ag} + k_g - \sqrt{k_g^2 + 4k_g k''\varepsilon C_{Ag}}\right) \qquad (6)$$

This equation is not solvable directly for porous structures because ε is based on C_{As}, not C_{Ag}.

Special cases

- for film diffusion control: $-r_A'' = k_g C_{Ag}$
- for reaction control: $-r_A'' = k'' C_{Ag}^2\, \varepsilon$

  (ε based on C_{Ag})

For **the rate form** $-r_A'' = \dfrac{k_1 C_A}{k_2 + C_A}$

$$-r_A'' = \frac{1}{2}\left[k_1\mathcal{E} + k_2 k_g + k_g C_{Ag} \pm \sqrt{(k_1\mathcal{E} + k_2 k_g - k_g C_{Ag})^2 - 4k_g^2 k_2 C_{Ag}}\right] \quad \cdots (7)$$

This equation is not solvable directly for porous structures because $\mathcal{E}$ is based on C_{As}, not C_{Ag}

Special cases.

- for film diffusion control $\qquad \cdots -r_A'' = k_g C_{Ag}$
  $k_g \ll (k_1/k_2)$
- for reaction control, first order regime $\qquad \cdots -r_A'' = \dfrac{k_1}{k_2} C_{Ag}\mathcal{E}$
  $k_g \gg (k_1\mathcal{E}/k_2)$ and $k_2 \gg C_A$
- for reaction control, zero order regime $\qquad \cdots -r_A'' = k_1\mathcal{E}$
  $k_g \gg k_1$ and $C_A \gg k_2$

The **performance equation** for these reactors is

$$\tau'' = \frac{S}{v_0} = \frac{S C_{A0}}{F_{A0}} = C_{A0}\int \frac{dX_A}{-r_A''} \quad \cdots \text{m}^2\text{surf}\cdot\text{s/m}^3 \qquad \cdots (8)$$

$\dfrac{S}{v_0}$ ← based on surface of catalyst layer

References. C. Horvath and coworkers, C.E.S. 29 2259 (1974); 28, 375 (1973); in "Enzyme Engineering" (Pye and Wingard, eds.) vol. 2, p. 259, Plenum.

Example Determining the performance of a catalytic converter

Waste gas from an industrial operation contains trace quantities of an organic A, which must be removed or destroyed before the air can be vented to the atmosphere. One suggestion for doing this passes the gas through a monolith reactor which contains catalyst to oxidize the organic into harmless compounds. To test this scheme we plan to run the experiment sketched below. What fraction of organic do you expect will be destroyed?

Air with 1% organic A
$u_0 = 0.13$ m/s
300K and 3.85 atm
$\rho = 2.3$ kg/m^3
$\mu = 30 \times 10^{-6}$ kg/m·s
$\mathcal{D} = 10^{-5}$ m^2/s

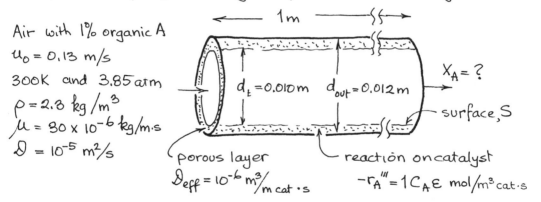

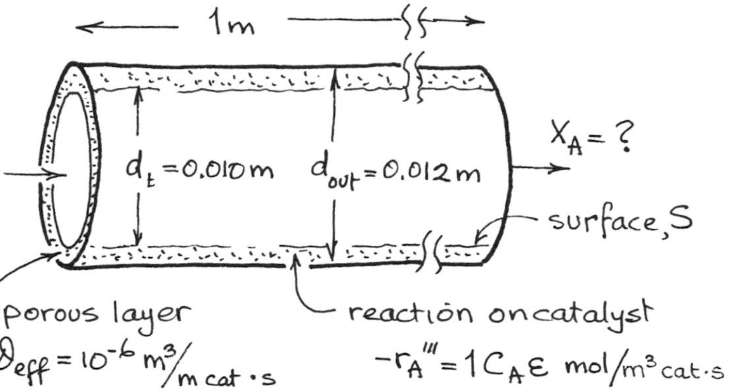

Solution

(a) Calculate k_g, the mass transfer coefficient

$$Re = \frac{d_t u_0 \rho}{\mu} = \frac{0.01(0.13)(2.3)}{30\times10^{-6}} = 99.67$$

$$Sc = \frac{\mu}{\mathcal{D}\rho} = \frac{30\times10^{-6}}{(10^{-5})(2.3)} = 1.3$$

$$Gz = Re \cdot Sc \cdot \frac{d}{L} = 99.67\,(1.3)\,\frac{0.01}{1} = 1.3$$

$$\overline{Sh} = \frac{\bar{k}_g d_t}{\mathcal{D}} = 3.66 + \frac{0.085\,(1.3)}{1 + 0.047\,(1.3)^{2/3}} = 3.76$$

$$\therefore k_g = 3.76\,\frac{\mathscr{D}}{d_t} = 3.76\,\frac{10^{-5}}{0.01} = 0.00376\ \text{m/s}$$

(b) Evaluate k''_{rx}, the rate based on the wall area of the catalyst layer

$$k''_{rx} = \frac{k'''_{rx}}{\left(\dfrac{\text{area of wall}}{\text{vol. of catalyst}}\right)} = \frac{1}{\left(\dfrac{4(0.01)}{(0.002)(0.022)}\right)} = 0.0011\ \text{m}^3/\text{m}^2\,\text{surface}\cdot\text{s}$$

(c) Evaluate $\mathcal{E}$, the effectiveness factor for the reaction in the porous catalyst

$$M_T = L\sqrt{\frac{k'''}{\mathscr{D}}} = 0.001\sqrt{\frac{1}{10^{-6}}} = 1$$

$$\therefore \mathcal{E} = 0.76$$

← pg. 22.4, for flat plates

(d) Evaluate $k''_{overall}$, which includes the effect of mass transfer resistance

$$k''_{overall} = \frac{1}{\dfrac{1}{k_g} + \dfrac{1}{k''_{rx}\mathcal{E}}} = \frac{1}{\dfrac{1}{0.00376} + \dfrac{1}{(0.0011)(0.76)}} = 6.84\times10^{-4}\ \frac{\text{m}^3}{\text{m}^2\,\text{surf}\cdot\text{s}}$$

(e) Conversion of organic

$$\frac{S}{v_0} = \frac{\text{wall surface}}{(\text{vel.})(\text{c.s. area})} \rightarrow \tau''$$

$$k''_{overall}\,\tau'' = -\ln(1-X_A) \quad \text{or} \quad X_A = 1 - e^{-k''_{overall}\tau''}$$

$$X_A = 1 - e^{-6.84\times10^{-4}\left(\frac{\pi d L}{u\cdot\frac{\pi d^2}{4}}\right)} = 1 - e^{-6.84\times10^{-4}\left(\frac{1}{0.13\left(\frac{0.01}{4}\right)}\right)} = 0.88$$

$\therefore$ Fraction of incoming organic which is oxidized $= \mathbf{0.88}$

Chapter 26 Problems

A1 Air containing A at C_{Ag} flows past a surface which catalyzes the reaction of A to product. Develop the overall rate expression for the reaction of A which accounts for film diffusion resistance at the catalyst surface. The kinetics of the surface reaction is given by $-r_A'' = k_1 C_A - k_2$.

A2 Reactant gas passes in plug flow through a tubular reactor 4 cm ID. Reaction occurs in the main body of the gas ($A \rightarrow R$, $-r_A = 10^4\, C_A$ mol/hr·m^3) and at the tube wall ($-r_A'' = 200\, C_A$ mol/hr·m^{2}surf). We suspect that film resistance at the wall may also influence the rate and we estimate that $k_g = 200$ m/hr for the flow conditions within the reactor.

(a) Develop an overall rate expression, based on unit surface, accounting for these three factors.

(b) What fraction of the reaction occurs at the tube wall.

(c) What overall rate would we find if we ignored the mass transfer effect.

Assume that the main core of fluid is well mixed laterally (this is actually implied when we use the concept of film resistance) and that film volume is small compared to the vessel volume.

B3 Methanation reactor. At high pressure and temperature, ≈ 50 atm and 500 °C, methane can be produced as follows

$$CO + 3H_2 \rightarrow CH_4 + H_2O, \quad r_{CH_4} = k_1\, C_{CO} C_{H_2}$$

This reaction is to be run in a 25.4 mm ID tubular reactor with catalyst-coated walls, where conversion to methane is practically instantaneous. For a flow rate of 0.4 m/s of a pure stoichiometric reactant mixture how long should the reactor be for 90% conversion to methane?

Data: At the conditions in the reactor

$$\bar{\rho} \approx 10\ \text{kg/m}^3, \quad \mu \approx 2 \times 10^{-5}\ \text{kg/m·s}, \quad \mathcal{D} \approx 2 \times 10^{-5}\ \text{m}^2/\text{s} \quad \text{and } Re \approx \frac{d_t u \rho}{\mu} \approx 9000$$

B4 Exhaust air from our process contains small amounts of impurity, about 1%. This concentration is too high and most of this impurity must be destroyed before the air can be vented. For this we pass the exhaust air (0.5 m/s, 20 °C, 2 atm) through a 50 mm ID tube coated inside with a catalyst which decomposes A into harmless products according to the following Langmuir-Hinshelwood kinetics

$$A \rightarrow R, \quad -r_A'' = \frac{2.63\, C_A}{0.47 + C_A} \quad \frac{\text{mol}}{\text{m}^2\cdot\text{s}}$$

(a) How long must the tube be to destroy 99% of the entering impurity A?

(b) Would it be preferable to first drop the pressure to 1 atm, then pass the exhaust air through the tube? How long would the tube be if this were done?

Chapter 26 Problems

Let us design a monolith reactor to oxidize the organics in the exhaust gases of the example problem in this chapter. The reactor is to consist of 1 m long parallel plates of porous catalyst separated by gaps for gas flow. The gas velocity approaching the plates is to be $u_o = 0.1$ m/s. Find the percent of organics oxidized in this unit. Consider the following combinations of plate thickness and gap width

B5 . . . both 2 mm

B6 . . . both 8 mm

B7 The exhaust air from our process contains a small amount of impurity A (less than 1%). This concentration is still too high and most of the A must be destroyed before this exhaust air can be vented. For this we pass the air (1m/s, 20°C, 1 atm) through a 10cm ID tube coated with a most effective catalyst which immediately destroys impurity A on contact. Thus at the tube surface $C_A = 0$. How long must the tube be to destroy 90% of the impurity entering the tube?

C8 A catalyst coated monolith reactor is used to decompose A which enters the reactor at $C_{A0} = 10$ mmol/m^3. The length of the reactor is such that A leaves the reactor at $C_{Af} = 1.0$ mmol/m^3. The kinetics of the decomposition on the catalyst surface is as follows

$$A(g) \rightarrow A(\text{surface}) \begin{cases} \nearrow \text{R (surface)} \rightarrow \text{R (g)} \ \ldots \ r_R'' = 40\, C_A, \ \text{mmol/m}^2\ \text{cat} \cdot \text{s} \\ \searrow \text{S (surface)} \rightarrow \text{S (g)} \ \ldots \ r_S'' = 10\, C_A, \ \text{mmol/m}^2\ \text{cat} \cdot \text{s} \end{cases}$$

In addition, the film mass transfer coefficient for reactant A is $k_g = 10$ m^3/m^2 cat · s.

Find the concentration of R in the exit stream from the reactor for high recycle flow of gas through the reactor (assume mixed flow).

(a) Ignore the film mass transfer resistance (assume that $k_g \rightarrow \infty$).

(b) Account for film resistance.

C9 Repeat the previous problem with one change: the gas is not recycled, but passes in plug flow through the reactor.

Chapter 31. DEACTIVATING POROUS CATALYST PELLETS: KINETICS AND PERFORMANCE EQUATIONS FOR A BATCH OF PELLETS.

I. Rate Forms.

The effectiveness of catalyst pellets may change with use. We measure this by the pellet activity

$$a = \frac{-r_A'}{-r_{A0}'} = \frac{\text{rate at which the pellet converts A to product}}{\text{rate of reaction with a fresh pellet}}$$

Usually "a" starts at 1 and decreases with time. In general, in terms of the fluid bathing the pellet we write

$$\begin{pmatrix}\text{reaction}\\ \text{rate}\end{pmatrix} = f_1\begin{pmatrix}\text{main stream}\\ \text{temperature}\end{pmatrix} \cdot f_2\begin{pmatrix}\text{main stream}\\ \text{composition}\end{pmatrix} \cdot \begin{pmatrix}\text{activity}\\ \text{of pellet}\end{pmatrix}$$

$$\begin{pmatrix}\text{deactivation}\\ \text{rate}\end{pmatrix} = f_3\begin{pmatrix}\text{main stream}\\ \text{temperature}\end{pmatrix} \cdot f_4\begin{pmatrix}\text{main stream}\\ \text{composition}\end{pmatrix} \cdot f_5\begin{pmatrix}\text{present state}\\ \text{of pellet}\end{pmatrix}$$

As an example of this formulation consider the reaction $A \rightarrow R$, n^{th} order kinetics and Arrhenius temperature dependency

For reaction: $$-r_A' = k' C_A^n a = k_0' e^{-E/RT} C_A^n a$$

For deactivation: $$-\frac{da}{dt} = k_d C_i^m a^d = k_{d0} e^{-E_d/RT} C_i^m a^d$$

(d = order of deactivation)

(C_i = concentration of material in the gas phase, either A, R or P which is responsible for deactivation)

There are four types of deactivation expressions:

Parallel deactivation: $A \rightarrow R + P\downarrow$
(carbon deposition in catalytic cracking of hydrocarbons: $C_{11}H_{24} \rightarrow 2C_5H_{12} + C\downarrow$)

$$-\frac{da}{dt} = k_d C_A^m a^d$$

Series deactivation: $A \rightarrow R$, $R \rightarrow P\downarrow$ $$-\frac{da}{dt} = k_d C_R^m a^d$$

Side by side deactivation: $A \rightarrow R$, $P \rightarrow P\downarrow$ $$-\frac{da}{dt} = k_d C_P^m a^d$$

Independent (of concentration) deactivation
(high temperature change in structure of the catalytic surface) $$-\frac{da}{dt} = k_d a^d$$

We may use m_A, m_R, m_P in the above expressions to designate the concentration dependency of the deactivation.

II. Experimental Devices and Strategy.

Here we a choice of three broad types of experimental devices

Batch S/batch G:
useful for fast deactivation but can only test some of the simpler rate forms

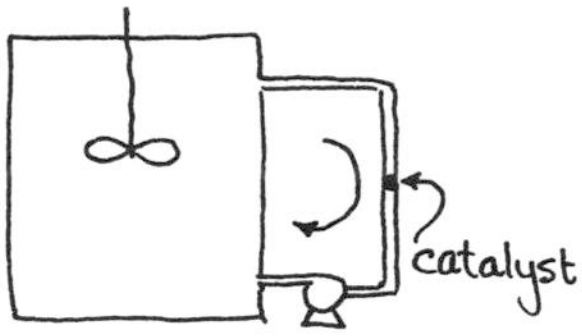

Batch S/flow G:
useful only for slow deactivation, but very good there, can test any rate form

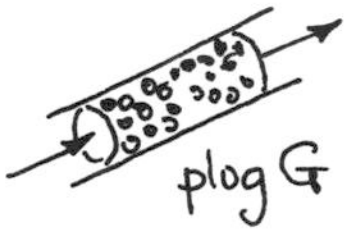

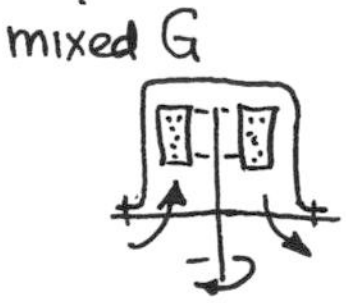

Flow S/flow G
not too helpful because the flow pattern of gas often is questionable

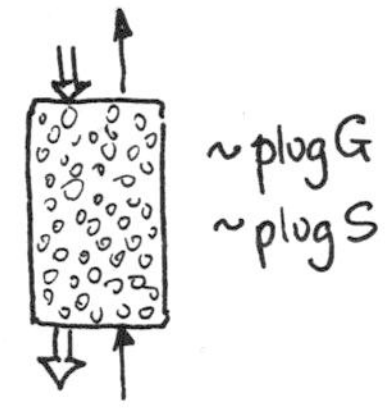

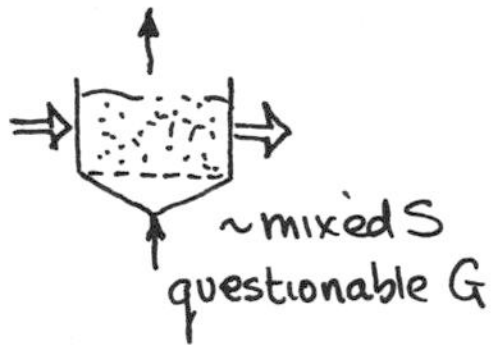

By fast deactivation we mean that $t_{deact} \cong t_{rx}$

The performance equations for batch solids are developed in this chapter. The flowing solids systems are treated in chapter 33.

In general we have five kinetic constants to evaluate: k', k_d, m, n, d. This can require much effort. To simplify try clues from chemistry and mass transfer to suggest values for some of these constants. For example theory suggests that:

m and n may correspond to the stoichiometric coefficients.

$d \cong 0$ for strong chemical bonding of the feed impurity with the catalyst surface, and with no pore diffusion resistance for P.

$d = 1$ for parallel deactivation with no pore diffusion resistance for reactant A

$d \to 3$ for parallel deactivation with strong pore diffusion resistance for reactant A.

$d \cong 1$ for series deactivation in any diffusion regime.

To evaluate more than two kinetic constants it is best to design experiments which uncouple reaction and deactivation effects. then each can be studied separately. The batch S/flow G reactor does this best as follows

- run a series of short time experiments (consider $a \cong$ constant during each run) to give k' and n.
- keep the composition of fluid constant during a long time run to evaluate the deactivation kinetics.

The mixed flow reactor with variable flow (so as to maintain a constant composition in the reactor) is just the type of reactor to meet these requirements.

The next section treats batch S/flow G reactors, useful for slowly deactivating systems. The section following that treats batch S/batch G, particularly useful for rapidly deactivating catalysts.

III. Finding the Rate Equation from batch S/flow G Experiments.

This contacting scheme can test the most general of rate forms, hence it is the most flexible and useful of experimental reactors. Unfortunately, however, this device can only be used for slow deactivation. By "slow" we mean that we can assume steady state within the reactor and unchanging catalyst activity while taking conversion data. Thus we can uncouple reaction and deactivation kinetics and study them separately. More concisely then, slow deactivation means that $t_{deactivation} \gg t_{rx}$.

When deactivation is relatively fast ($t_{deactivation} \approx t_{rx}$) then the batch S/flow G reactor is always in severe transient conditions and it is not possible to uncouple the reaction and deactivation effects. It becomes difficult to interpret the measured data and this type of contacting scheme is not useful.

Let us develop the conversion equations for a variety of contacting patterns. Cases Ⓐ to Ⓓ which follow illustrate the use of the different experimental devices by testing the simplest of meaningful rate forms, or

$$\left.\begin{aligned} -r'_A &= k'C_A a \\ -\frac{da}{dt} &= k_d a \end{aligned}\right\} \quad \text{... or } m=0,\ n=1,\ d=1$$

Cases Ⓔ and Ⓕ present the most general rate form that can be tested conveniently in mixed flow reactors. Case Ⓔ shows that the steady flow reactor can only be used to fit rate forms where deactivation is concentration independent, or

$$\left.\begin{aligned} -r'_A &= k'C_A^n a \\ -\frac{da}{dt} &= k_d a^d \end{aligned}\right\} \quad \text{... or } m=0.$$

Case (F) shows that the variable flow reactor which keeps C_{Af} constant, because it uncouples reaction and deactivation kinetics, can handle the most general of rate forms, or

$$\left.\begin{aligned} -r'_A &= k' C_A^n \, a \\ -\frac{da}{dt} &= k_d C_i^m a^d \end{aligned}\right\} \quad \text{--- no restriction.}$$

Throughout we take $\varepsilon_A = 0$. For $\varepsilon_A \neq 0$ the resulting expressions are messier.

A. Batch S/mixed constant flow G, m=0, n=1, d=1.

The performance equations are

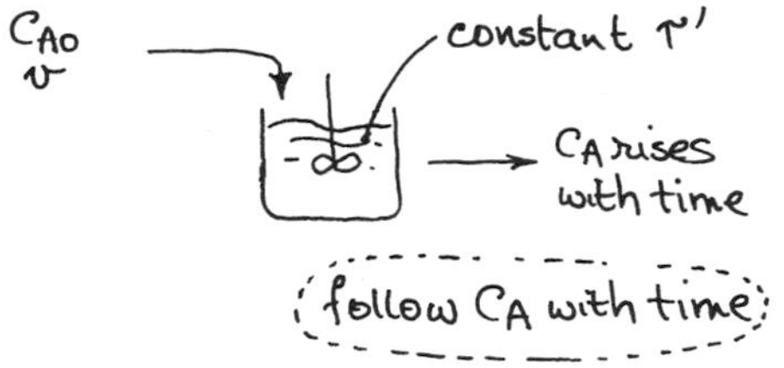

$$\tau' = \frac{W C_{A0}}{F_{A0}} = \frac{C_{A0} - C_A}{k' C_A a} \quad \cdots (1)$$

$$-\frac{da}{dt} = k_d \, a \quad \cdots (2)$$

Integrating eq. 2 and replacing in eq 1 gives

$$\boxed{\ln\left(\frac{C_{A0}}{C_A} - 1\right) = \ln(k'\tau') - k_d t} \quad \cdots (3)$$

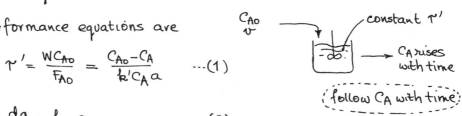

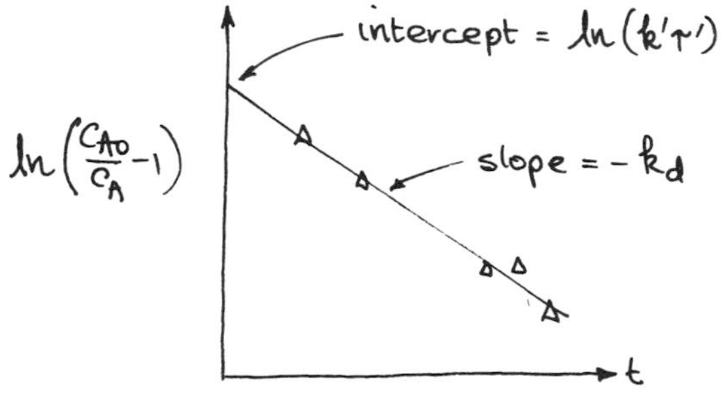

This plot of equation 3 gives the two unknowns k_d and k'

B. Batch S/plug constant flow G, m=0, n=1, d=1.

The performance equations for plug flow G are

$$\tau' = \int_{C_A}^{C_{A0}} \frac{dC_A}{k' C_A a} \quad \cdots (4)$$

$$-\frac{da}{dt} = k_d a \quad \cdots (5)$$

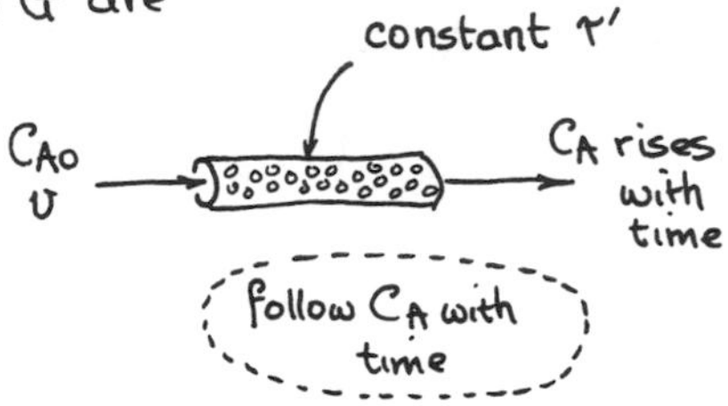

Integrating eq 5, replacing in eq 4, integrating again and rearranging gives

$$\ln \ln \frac{C_{A0}}{C_A} = \ln (k'\tau') - k_d t \quad \cdots (6)$$

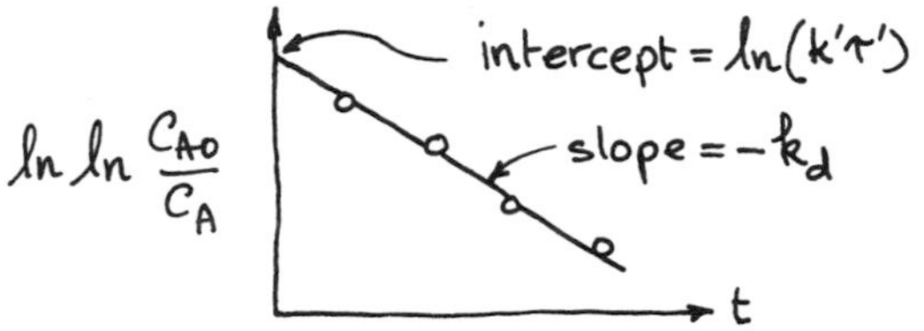

This plot of eq 6 gives k_d and k'

C. Batch S/mixed decreasing flow G to keep C_A constant m=0, n=1, d=1.

Integrating the performance equations of case (A) with τ' and t as variables gives

$$\ln\left(\frac{\tau'}{\tau'_0}\right) = k_d t$$

(τ'_0 at $t=0$)

where $$\tau'_0 = \frac{C_{A0} - C_A}{k' C_A} \quad \cdots (7)$$

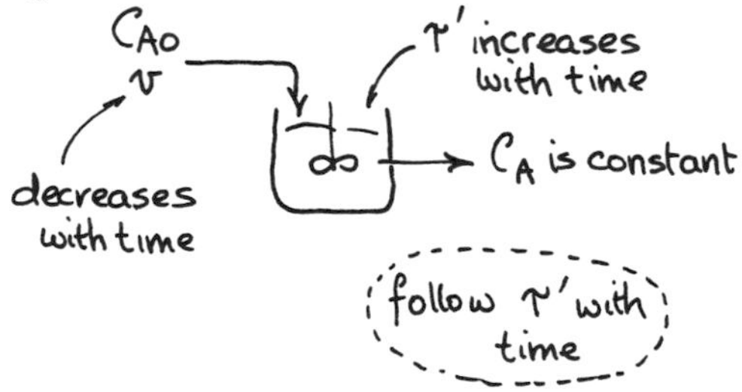

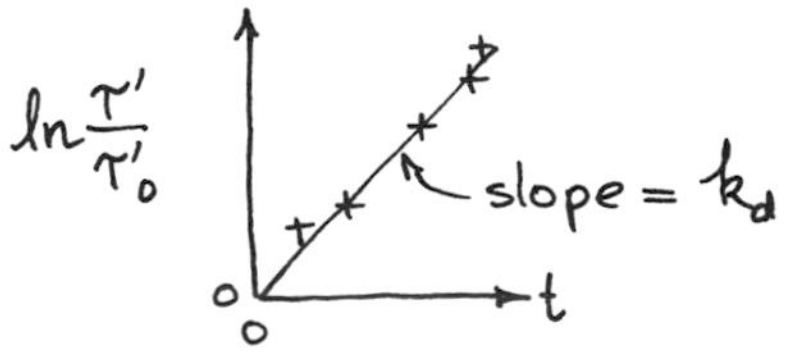

τ'_0 gives k', then the slope on this plot gives k_d

D. Batch S/plug decreasing flow G to keep C_A constant
$m=0,\ n=1,\ d=1.$

Integrating the performance equations of case (B) with τ' and t as variables gives

$$\ln\left(\frac{\tau'}{\tau'_0}\right) = k_d t \qquad \cdots (8)$$

where

$$\tau'_0 = \frac{1}{k'} \ln \frac{C_{A0}}{C_A}$$

at $t=0$

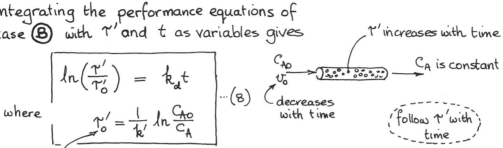

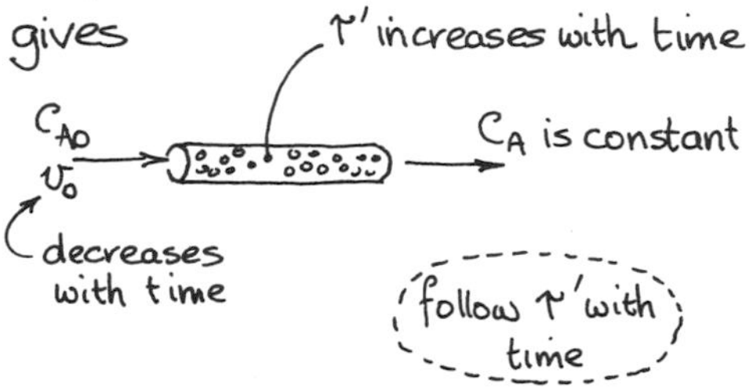

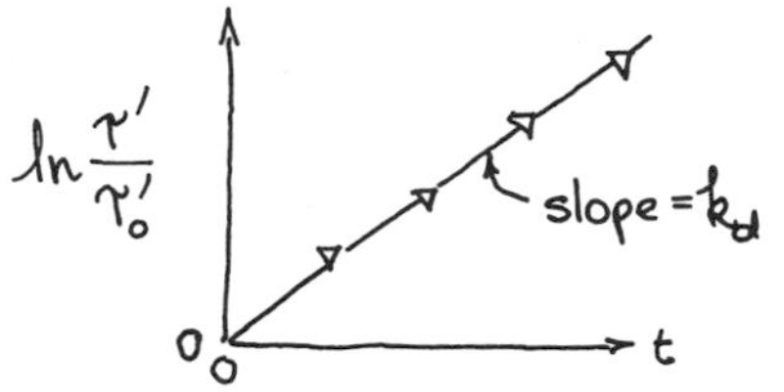

τ'_0 gives k', then the slope on this plot gives k_d

E. Batch S/mixed constant flow G, $m=0$, any n, any d.

Start by considering mixed flow G and n^{th} order reaction kinetics The performance equations then become

$$\tau' = \frac{W C_{A0}}{F_{A0}} = \frac{C_{A0}-C_A}{k' C_A^n a} \qquad \cdots (9)$$

$$-\frac{da}{dt} = k_d a^d \quad \cdots \text{ or } \cdots \quad a = \left[1+(d-1)k_d t\right]^{1/1-d} \qquad \cdots (10)$$

At $t=0$ eq 9 gives

$$\frac{C_{A0}-C_A}{C_A^n} = k'\tau'$$

So at any time eqs 9 and 10 give what looks like a complicated expression

$$\left[\frac{\left(\frac{C_{A0}-C_A}{C_A^n}\right)_{t=0}}{\left(\frac{C_{A0}-C_A}{C_A^n}\right)_t}\right]^{d-1} = \frac{1}{a^{d-1}} = 1+(d-1)k_d t \qquad d \neq 1 \quad \cdots (11)$$

Evaluate the kinetic constants as follows

step 1. Using data from a series of short time runs with fresh catalyst ($a \approx 1$), each run at different C_A, rearrange eq 9, take logs, and plot as shown

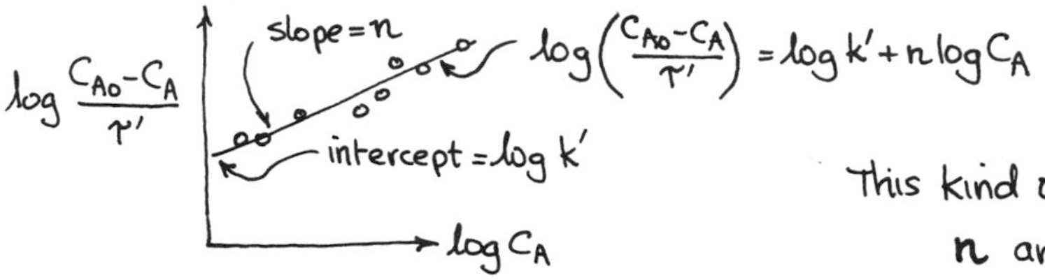

This kind of plot gives **n** and **k'**

step 2. Use the data from a long time run and guess values of d until the plot below gives a straight line

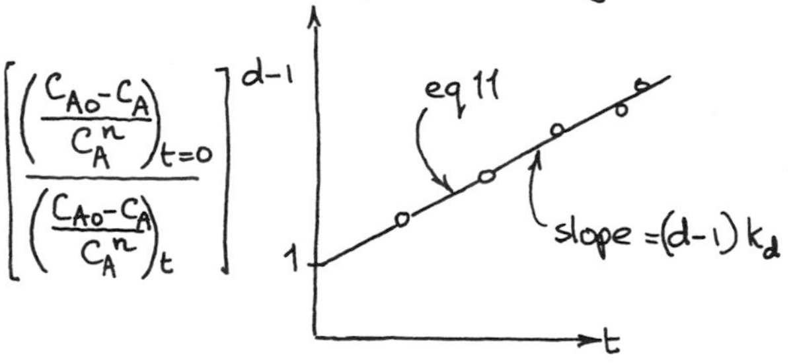

This plot gives **d** and $\mathbf{k_d}$

Thus we end up knowing k', k_d, n and d.

Comments and Extensions

(a) For the special case of **d=1** eq 10 becomes

$$a = e^{-k_d t} \quad \cdots (10')$$

and eq 11 becomes

$$\ln\left[\frac{\left(\frac{C_{A0}-C_A}{C_A^n}\right)_{t=0}}{\left(\frac{C_{A0}-C_A}{C_A^n}\right)_t}\right] = k_d t \qquad \cdots (11')$$

In evaluating the kinetic constants step 1 remains unchanged, however in step 2 plot as follows, without trial and error, to find k_d

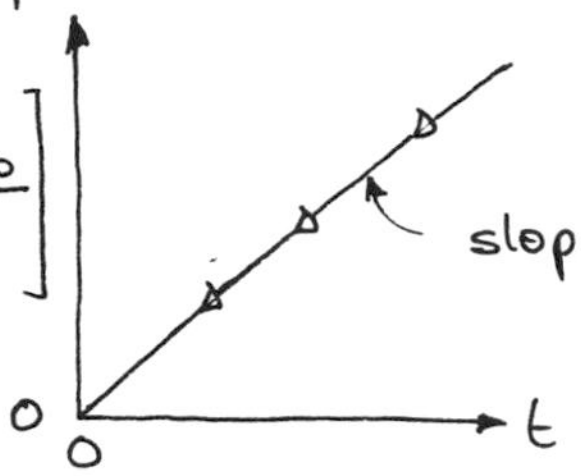

(b) Here we have treated n^{th} order kinetics, $-r_A' = k' C_A^n$. For more general kinetics, say

$$-r_A = k' f(C_A)$$

simply replace C_A^n by $f(C_A)$ in the above expressions. Other than this the analysis remains unchanged.

(c) For packed bed experiments, hence plug constant flow G and any kinetics

$$-r_A = k' f(C_A)$$

simply replace the term

$$\frac{C_{A0}-C_A}{C_A^n} \quad \text{by} \quad \int \frac{dC_A}{f(C_A)}$$

in the above expressions. Other than this the analysis remains unchanged.

(d) Unfortunately if deactivation is concentration dependent, thus $m \neq 0$, and if the concentration varies during a run or along the reactor, then the experimental strategy described in this section will not work. We must use the experimental strategy described in the next section.

F. Batch s/mixed changing flow G to keep C_A constant, any n, any m_A, any d.

Because it uncouples rate and deactivation effects this is the only device which can test the general deactivation equation and evaluate its five constants. The performance equation thus becomes

$$\tau' = \frac{C_{A0} - C_A}{k' C_A^n a} \quad \cdots (12)$$

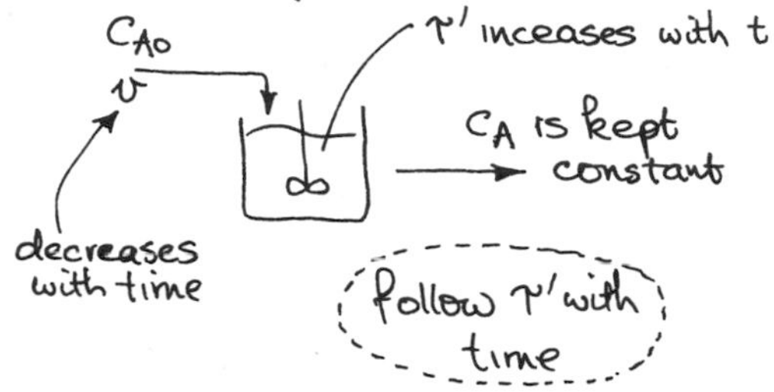

$$-\frac{da}{dt} = k_d C_A^m a^d \quad \cdots (13)$$

Here we must make a series of long time runs, each at a different C_A level

- the short time data at different C_A will give k' and n.
- one long time run will give d and $(k_d C_A^m)$.
- the series of long time runs will give k_d and m separately.

Let us outline the procedure

step 1 For short time runs at $a \cong 1$ eq 12 becomes

$$\frac{C_{A0} - C_A}{C_A^n} = k' \tau'$$

Now follow the procedure of step 1 case (E). This gives k' and n.

step 2 For a single long time run at fixed C_A eqs 12 and 13 combined give

$$\ln\left[\frac{(\tau')_t}{(\tau')_{t=0}}\right] = (k_d C_A^m)\,t \quad \cdots \text{ for } d=1 \qquad \cdots (14)$$

$$\left[\frac{(\tau')_t}{(\tau')_{t=0}}\right]^{d-1} = 1 + (d-1)(k_d C_A^m)\,t \quad \cdots \text{ for } d \neq 1 \qquad \cdots (15)$$

To test for $d=1$ plot $\ln(\tau'/\tau'_0)$ vs t. The slope gives $k_d C_A^m$.

To test for $d \neq 1$ plot as shown

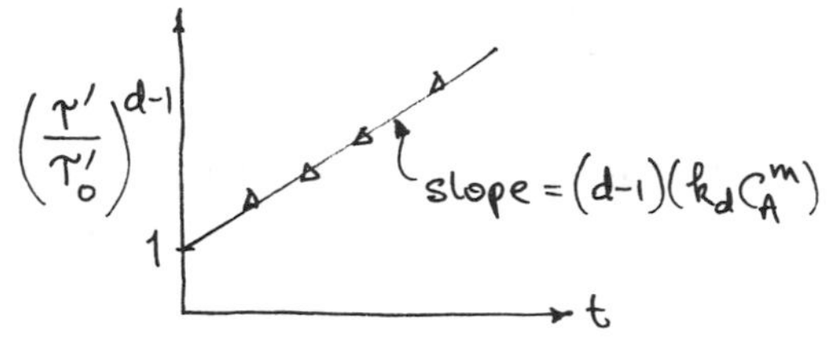

Guess d until the data fall on a straight line. This gives **d** and $k_d C_A^m$

step 3. Plot the data for two or more long time runs, each at a different C_A level.

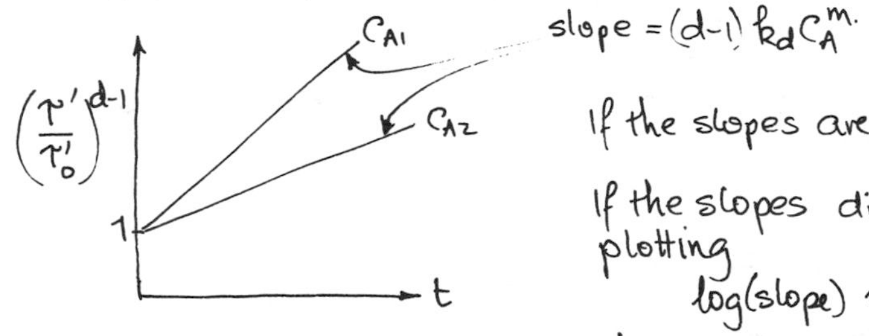

If the slopes are the same then **m=0**

If the slopes differ find m by plotting

$\log(\text{slope})$ vs $\log C_A$

This will give **m** and $\boldsymbol{k_d}$ separately.

With this 3 step procedure we can find k', n, k_d, m and d. Unfortunately a considerable amount of trial & error must be used, however this is the penalty we pay for trying to use a rate form which has 5 constants.

Comments and Extensions.

(a) Here we have treated n^{th} order reaction and $m_A \neq 0$ type deactivation

- for other reaction types, say

$$-r_A' = k'(C_A - C_{Ae}), \quad \text{or} \quad -r_A' = \frac{k'C_A}{M + C_A}, \quad \text{or} \quad -r_A' = k' f(C_A), \text{ etc.}$$

simply replace C_A^n by $f(C_A)$ in step 1. The rest remains the same

- for other deactivation forms, say

$$-\frac{da}{dt} = k_d C_P^m a^d, \quad \text{or} \quad -\frac{da}{dt} = k_d C_R^m a^d$$

keep the pertinent concentration fixed (C_A and C_P, or C_A and C_R) during a run and the analysis follows directly.

(b) In experiments, if simple kinetic models won't fit your data you will have to go to the mixed flow reactor of constant composition, so why not do all your experiments in that reactor right from the start. Only an unrepentent optimist would start with another reactor type and hope for the best. Of course with poor, inadequate or scattered data one need not go beyond the simplest of kinetic models.--- any model will fit poor data.

(c) Here we have treated the case where

$$t_{deactivation} \gg t_{reaction}.$$

When this is not so we will have difficulty uncoupling rate and deactivation effects. The batch S/ batch G reactor may have to be used, but its weakness is that it can only test some of the simpler kinetic forms (see next section). Another alternative is to use the flow S reactor. (see chapter 33). But this also has its problems, uncertain and difficult to define gas flow pattern.

IV. Finding the Rate Equation from batch S/batch G Experiments.

For fast deactivation we have difficulties with the batch S/flow G reactor. This leaves two choices, the batch S/batch G reactor or the flow S/flow G reactor. The batch S/batch G system is by far the simpler of the two, and a proper choice of V/w can give reliable data. So let us consider this system.

Here are some possible experimental set ups:

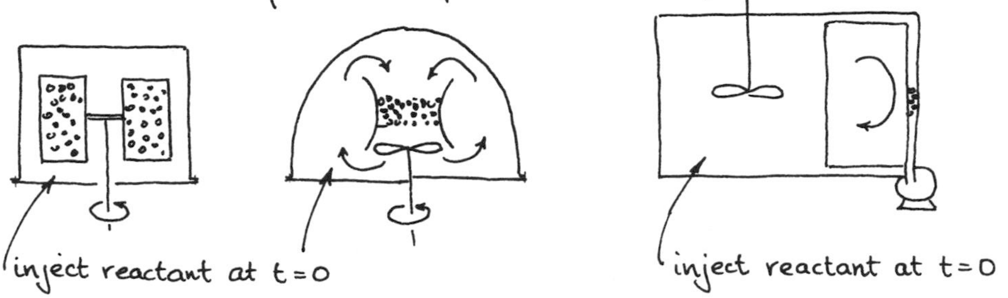

The strategy is to follow C_A vs t for at least two series of experiments, each starting at different C_{A0}. The initial rate information will give n, while the time run will give d.

A. Batch S/batch G, m=0, n=1, d=1.

Here time is the one independent variable so we can write

$$-\frac{dC_A}{dt} = -r_A = \frac{W}{V}(-r_A') = \frac{W}{V}(k'C_A a) = k C_A a \quad \text{where } k = k'W/V \qquad \cdots (16)$$

$$-\frac{da}{dt} = k_d a \qquad \cdots (17)$$

Integrating eq 17, replacing in eq 16, integrating again and manipulating gives eventually

$$\boxed{\ln \ln \frac{C_A}{C_{A\infty}} = \ln \frac{k}{k_d} - k_d t \quad \cdots \text{where } C_{A\infty} = C_{A0} e^{-k/k_d} \ (\neq 0)} \qquad \cdots (18)$$

Graphically

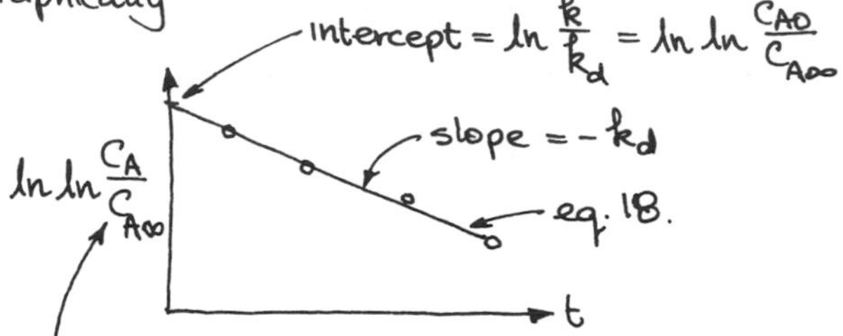

Make a run to $t=\infty$ to find $C_{A\infty}$. Then make this plot to find k and k_d

Even for an irreversible reaction $C_{A\infty}$ never drops to zero. However if it is too low it becomes hard to interpret results since a small error in $C_{A\infty}$ would really foul things up. To keep $C_{A\infty}$ not too small make k small, therefore use small W/V. This factor can be controlled by the experimenter.

B. Batch S/batch G, m=0, n=2, d=1.

Here we have

$$-\frac{dC_A}{dt} = kC_A^2 a \quad \cdots \text{ with } k = \frac{k'W}{V}$$

$$-\frac{da}{dt} = k_d a$$

Combining integrating and manipulating gives

$$\ln\left[\frac{C_A(C_{A0}-C_{A\infty})}{C_{A0}(C_A-C_{A\infty})}\right] = k_d t \quad \cdots \text{where } C_{A\infty} = \frac{C_{A0}}{1+\frac{C_{A0}k}{k_d}} \quad \cdots (19)$$

Graphically

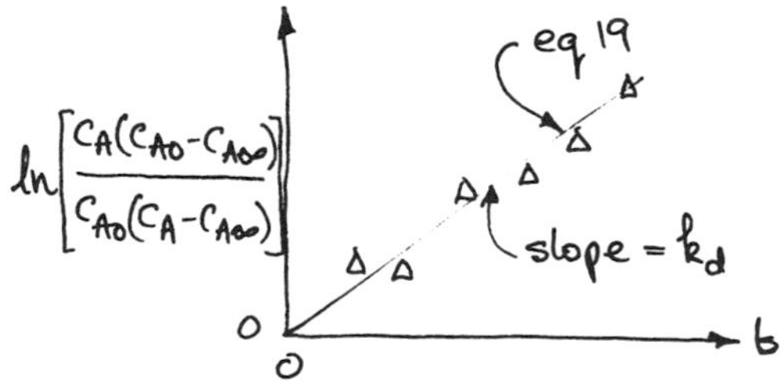

Make a run to $t=\infty$ to find $C_{A\infty}$.

Then make this plot to find k_d

Then replace in eq 19 to find k

C. Batch S / batch G, $m=0$, $n=1$, $d=2$.

Here we have

$$-\frac{dC_A}{dt} = kC_A a \quad \dots \text{ with } k = \frac{k'W}{V}$$

$$-\frac{da}{dt} = k_d a^2$$

Combining, integrating and manipulating gives

$$\boxed{\ln\frac{C_{A0}}{C_A} = \frac{k}{k_d}\ln(1+k_d t) \quad \text{and} \quad C_{A\infty}=0} \qquad \dots(20)$$

Graphically

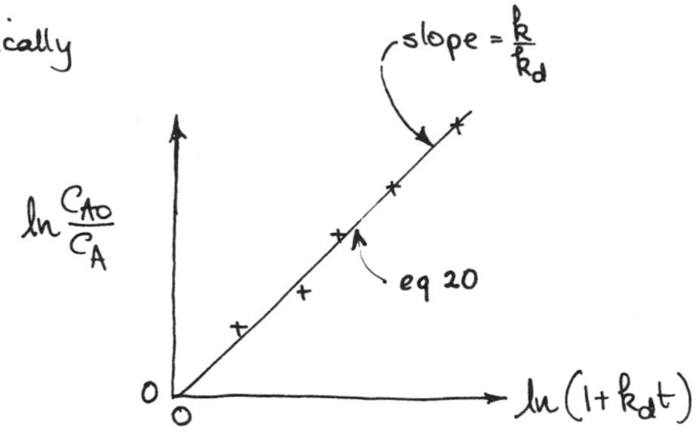

This equation requires a trial and error solution

- guess k_d until the graph above gives a straight line through the origin. This gives the correct value for k_d.
- from the slope of this correct graph we then find k.

All other rate forms which were tried ended up requiring a trial & error solution, as in this case.

V. How Pore Diffusion Resistance Distorts the Kinetics of Deactivating Catalyst Pellets.

Consider the rather simple kinetics: $n=1$, $m=0$, any d, and spherical pellets.

For no deactivation

$$\begin{cases} -r_A' = k' C_A \mathcal{E} \\ a = 1 \end{cases}$$

→ $\mathcal{E}=1$ for no pore diffusion resistance

→ $\mathcal{E}=\dfrac{1}{M_T}$, $M_T = L\sqrt{\dfrac{k'''}{\mathcal{D}_{eff}}}$, for strong diffusion resistance

With deactivation

$$\begin{cases} -r_A' = (k'a)\, C_A \mathcal{E} \\ -\dfrac{da}{dt} = k_d a^d \end{cases}$$

→ $\mathcal{E}=1$ for no pore diffusion resistance

→ $\mathcal{E}=\dfrac{1}{M_{Td}}$, $M_{Td} = L\sqrt{\dfrac{k'''a}{\mathcal{D}_{eff}}}$, for strong pore diffusion resistance

so all we have to do is replace k' by $(k'a)$ everywhere, both in the rate equation and in the Thiele modulus

As time passes 'a' decreases as follows

$$a = \exp(-k_d t) \quad \cdots \text{ for } d=1$$

$$a = [1+(d-1)k_d t]^{1/1-d} \quad \cdots \text{ for } d\neq 1$$

Thus M_{Td} and 'a' both decrease with time, $\mathcal{E}$ rises, and the net effect is that the reaction rate decreases with time (because 'a' decreases faster than $\mathcal{E}$ rises). Graphically then use the $\mathcal{E}$ vs M_T chart of Chapter 23 but with M_T replaced by M_{Td}

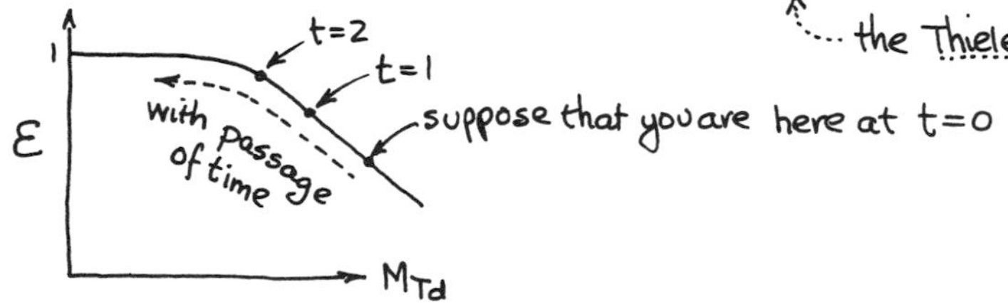

← the Thiele Modulus for deactivating catalysts

For other kinetics (1st order reversible, nth order, etc) use the appropriate chart from Chapter 23, but again replace M_T by the corresponding M_{Td}

A. Performance equations.

As an example consider first order reaction and first order deactivation. For batch uniform S/ plug flow G integration of the rate expression for the various diffusion and deactivation regimes gives

	no resistance to pore diffusion	strong resistance to pore diffusion
without deactivation	$\ln \frac{C_{A0}}{C_A} = k'\tau'$ ···(21) (chapter 3, 21)	$\ln \frac{C_{A0}}{C_A} = \frac{k'\tau'}{M_T}$ ···(22) (chapter 22, 23)
with deactivation	$\ln \frac{C_{A0}}{C_A} = (k'a)\tau'$ $= k'\tau' \exp(-k_d t)$ ···(23) (eq 6, this chapter)	$\ln \frac{C_{A0}}{C_A} = \frac{(k'a)\tau'}{M_{Td}}$ $= \frac{k'\tau'}{M_T} \cdot \exp\left(-\frac{k_d t}{2}\right)$ ···(24)

For given $k'\tau'$, in other words for given treatment rate the sketch below shows how C_A at the exit changes with time.

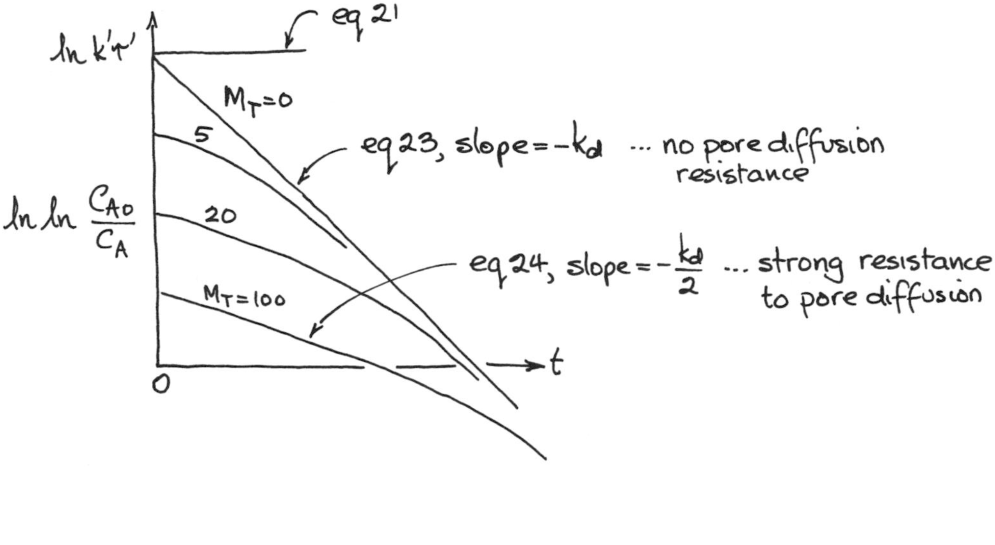

Comments and Extensions

(a) For mixed flow we get equations and charts identical to the above except for the following change

$$\ln\frac{C_{A0}}{C_A} \Longrightarrow \frac{C_{A0}-C_A}{C_A}$$

(b) For other reaction orders and deactivation orders similar equations can be developed for the above four kinetic regimes. For example, for 2nd order reaction batch S/mixed flow G we have, from Chapter 4 and Chapter 23,

$$\ln\frac{C_{A0}}{C_A} = k'\tau' \Longrightarrow \left(\frac{C_{A0}}{C_A}\right)^2 - \frac{C_{A0}}{C_A} = k' C_{A0}\tau' \quad \text{... and so on}$$

$$\text{with } M_T = L\sqrt{\frac{3}{2}\frac{k''' C_{A0}}{\mathscr{D}_{eff}}}$$

(c) The diagram on pg 31.17 for 1st order systems shows that the conversion decreases more slowly in the presence of strong pore diffusion resistance than in the diffusion-free regime. This result should apply generally to all reactor types and reaction kinetics.

(d) Concentration dependent deactivation, say

$$-\frac{da}{dt} = k_d C_A a,$$

has not yet been treated in the above simple manner. However we may expect the same sort of influence of pore resistance on deactivation. Thus the reaction rate should decrease more slowly in the regime of strong pore diffusion resistance. Experimentally, such systems should always be studied in mixed flow reactors, otherwise the analysis of the results becomes monstrously difficult.

(e) The treatment given here on concentration independent deactivation comes from Krishnaswamy and Kittrell, AIChE Journal, 27 120 (1981) and from A. Stephanakis (personal communication). Khang and Levenspiel IEC/F 12 185 (1973) make a stab at concentration dependent deactivation and end up with many special cases.

Example 1 Interpreting kinetic data in the presence of pore diffusion resistance and deactivation.

The catalytic decomposition of reactant ($A \rightarrow R$) is studied in a packed bed reactor filled with 2.4 mm pellets and using a very high recycle rate of product gases (assume mixed flow). The results of a long-time run and additional data are given below

t, hr	0	2	4	6
X_A	0.75	0.64	0.52	0.39

$\mathcal{D}_{eff} = 5 \times 10^{-10}\ m^3/m\ cat \cdot s$

$\rho_s = 1500\ kg/m^3 cat$

$\tau' = 4000\ kg \cdot s/m^3$

Find the kinetics of reaction and deactivation, both in the diffusion-free and in the strong pore diffusion resistance regime.

Solution.

First of all, note that deactivation occurs during the run, so guess or try to fit the data with the simplest rate form for such situations, or

$$\left.\begin{aligned} -r_A' &= k' C_A a \\ -\frac{da}{dt} &= k_d a \end{aligned}\right\}$$

The performance equations for this rate form and mixed flow are

IN DIFFUSION-FREE REGIME ... $\left(\frac{C_{A0}}{C_A} - 1\right) = k'\tau' a = k'\tau' e^{-k_d t}$

IN STRONG DIFFUSION REGIME ... $\left(\frac{C_{A0}}{C_A} - 1\right) = k'\tau' a \mathcal{E} = \frac{k'\tau'}{M_{Td}} a = \frac{k'\tau'}{M_T} \cdot \underbrace{e^{-k_d t/2}}_{a^{1/2}}$ (with $a = e^{-k_d t}$)

If this rate form is correct then in either case, for both strong or no diffusion resistance effects a plot of $\ln\left(\frac{C_{A0}}{C_A} - 1\right)$ vs t should give a straight line. Making this tabulation and plot, as shown on the next page gives ...

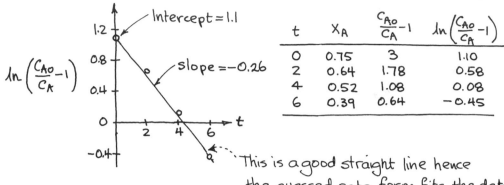

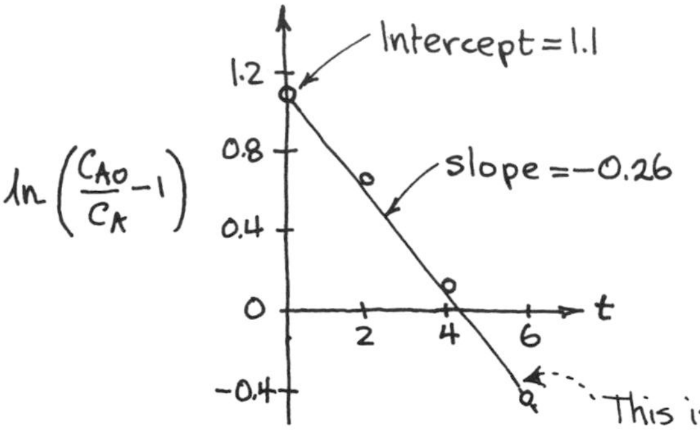

t	X_A	$\frac{C_{A0}}{C_A}-1$	$\ln\left(\frac{C_{A0}}{C_A}-1\right)$
0	0.75	3	1.10
2	0.64	1.78	0.58
4	0.52	1.08	0.08
6	0.39	0.64	−0.45

Next see about pore diffusion effects

Guess no intrusion of diffusional effects. Then the performance equation is

$$\ln\left(\frac{C_{A0}}{C_A}-1\right) = \underbrace{\ln(k'\tau')}_{\text{from figure} \ldots 1.1} - k_d t$$

k_d ... -0.26

... thus $k' = 7.5\times10^{-4}\ m^3/kg\cdot s$, $k_d = 0.26\ hr^{-1}$

Now check the Thiele modulus to verify that we really are in the diffusion resistance free regime. Thus at t=0

$$M_T = L\sqrt{\frac{k'''}{\mathcal{D}_{eff}}} = \frac{2.4\times10^{-3}}{6}\sqrt{\frac{(7.5\times10^{-4})(1500)}{5\times10^{-10}}} = 18.9 \ !!!$$

unfortunately this value indicates strong pore diffusion resistance, so our guess was wrong

Guess that the runs were made in the regime of strong resistance to pore diffusion. Then

$$\ln\left(\frac{C_{A0}}{C_A}-1\right) = \underbrace{\ln\left(\frac{k'\tau'}{M_T}\right)}_{\text{intercept}=1.1} - \frac{k_d}{2}\,t \qquad \ldots \text{thus } k_d = 0.52\ hr^{-1}$$

$\frac{k_d}{2}$: slope = −0.26

From the value for the intercept

$$\frac{k'\tau'}{M_T} = 3.0$$

$$\therefore \quad k' = 9\,\frac{L^2 \rho_s}{(\tau')^2 \mathscr{D}_{eff}} = (9)\cdot\frac{\left(2.4\times10^{-3}/6\right)^2 (1500)}{(4000)^2 (5\times10^{-10})} = 0.27\ \frac{m^3}{kg\cdot s}$$

Check the Thiele modulus at t=0

$$M_T = L\sqrt{\frac{k'\rho_s}{\mathscr{D}_{eff}}} = \frac{2.4\times10^{-3}}{6}\sqrt{\frac{(0.27)(1500)}{5\times10^{-10}}} = 360$$

O.K., our guess is verified

Hence the final rate equations:

(a) IN THE DIFFUSION-FREE REGIME (for very small d_p) WITH DEACTIVATION

$$-r_A' = 0.27\, C_A a,\ \frac{mol}{kg\cdot s} \quad \text{... with ...} \quad -\frac{da}{dt} = 0.52a,\ hr^{-1} \quad \longleftarrow$$

(b) IN THE STRONG PORE DIFFUSION RESISTANCE REGIME (for large d_p) WITH DEACTIVATION

$$-r_A' = 0.27 C_A a \mathcal{E} \quad \text{... with} \quad -\frac{da}{dt} = 0.52a$$

$$\mathcal{E} = \frac{1}{M_{Td}} = \frac{1}{L}\sqrt{\frac{5\times10^{-10}}{0.27(1500)a}} = \frac{1.11\times10^{-6}}{L\,a^{1/2}}$$

combining all gives

$$-r_A' = \frac{3\times10^{-7}}{L} C_A a^{1/2},\ \frac{mol}{kg\cdot s} \quad \text{... with ...} \quad -\frac{da}{dt} = 0.52a,\ hr^{-1} \quad \longleftarrow$$

(L in m)

Note: In the strong pore diffusion regime the rate is lower but the catalyst deactivates more slowly. Actually, for the catalyst used here if we could have been free of diffusional resistances reaction rates would have been 360 times as fast as those measured.

Chapter 31 Problems

Reactant A at 1 mol/m^3 and 0.005 mol/min enters a recirculating type mixed flow reactor containing deactivating catalyst (W = 0.005 kg) and there decomposes ($A \rightarrow R$). Preliminary experiments indicate that the deactivation is concentration independent. Develop kinetic equations to represent the reaction and the deactivation from the following data

	t, hr = 0	10	20	30	40	50	In a separate run with fresh catalyst	
A1 . . .	C_A = 0.10	-	0.27	0.40	-	0.69	C_A = 0.25	for F_{A0} = 0.015
A2 . . .	C_A = 0.10	0.16	-	-	0.53	0.70	= 0.167	= 0.015
A3 . . .	C_A = 0.20	0.43	-	0.64	-	0.73	= 0.50	= 0.02
A4 . . .	C_A = 0.20	0.38	0.43	-	-	0.50	= 0.50	= 0.05

The kinetics of a catalytic reaction $A \rightarrow R$ are studied at temperature T in a basket reactor (batch S/mixed flow G) in which the exit gas composition is kept unchanged by adjusting the feed rate of reactant gas. What can you say about the rates of reaction and deactivation from the following experimental results.

B5 . . .	Run 1	C_{A0} = 1 mol/lit	t, hr	0	1	2	3
		X_A = 0.5	τ', $\frac{\text{gm·min}}{\text{lit}}$	1	e	e^2	e^3
	Run 2	C_{A0} = 2 mol/lit	t, hr	0	1	2	3
		X_A = 0.667	τ', $\frac{\text{gm·min}}{\text{lit}}$	2	2e	$2e^2$	$2e^3$
B6 . . .	Run 1	C_{A0} = 2 mol/lit	t, hr	0	1	2	3
		X_A = 0.5	τ', $\frac{\text{gm·min}}{\text{lit}}$	1	e	e^2	e^3
	Run 2	C_{A0} = 20 mol/lit	t, hr	0	0.5	1	1.5
		X_A = 0.8	τ', $\frac{\text{gm·min}}{\text{lit}}$	1	e	e^2	e^3

C7 In an automobile's catalytic converter CO and hydrocarbons present in the exhaust gases are oxidized. Unfortunately the effectiveness of these units decreases with use. The phenomenon was studied by Summers and Hegedus in J. Catalysis **51** 185 (1978) by means of an accelerated aging test on a palladium impregnated porous pellet packed converter. From the reported data on hydrocarbon conversion shown below, develop an expression to represent the deactivation rate of this catalyst.

t, hr	5	10	15	20	25	30	35	40
$X_{hydrocarbon}$	0.57	0.53	0.52	0.50	0.48	0.45	0.43	0.41

Problem prepared by Dennis Timberlake

Chapter 31 Problems

C8 In catalytic dehydrogenation of hydrocarbons the catalyst activity decays with use because of carbon deposition on the active surfaces. Let us study this process in a specific system.

A gaseous feed (10% C_4H_{10} - 90% inerts, $\pi = 1$ atm, $T = 555$ °C) flows ($\tau' = 1.1$ kg·hr/m^3) through a packed bed of alumina-chromia catalyst. The butane decomposes by a first order reaction

$$C_4H_{10} \rightarrow C_4H_8 \rightarrow \text{carbon}$$
$$\searrow \text{ other gases}$$

and the behavior with time is as follows

t, hr	0	1	2	3	4	5
X_A	0.89	0.78	0.63	0.47	0.34	0.26

Examination of the 0.55 mm pellets shows the same extent of carbon deposition at the entrance and the exit of the reactor, suggesting concentration independent deactivation. Develop rate equations for reaction and deactivation.

This problem was devised from the information given by Kunugita *et al* J. Ch. E. Japan **2** 75 (1969).

C9 Polyvinylchloride (PVC) is one of the most widely used polymers today. Its monomer is produced by reacting HCl and C_2H_2 over carbon-supported $HgCl_2$ catalyst

$$\underset{(A)}{CH\equiv CH} + \underset{(B)}{HCl(g)} \xrightarrow[100\sim 240\,°C]{HgCl_2} \underset{\text{vinyl chloride}}{CH_2=CHCl}$$

The kinetics of this system are studied in a basket type mixed flow reactor ($T = 214$°C, $W = 0.02$ kg cat, $d_p = 250$ μm, spinning rate = 2500 rpm) with a steady flow of feed gas ($\pi = 1$ atm, $p_A = 0.12$ atm, $p_B = 0.88$ atm, $v = 0.02$ m^3/min). HCl is in large enough excess that we can take as a fair approximation

$$\varepsilon_A \approx 0 \quad \text{and} \quad -r_A = kC_A^{0.5}$$

From the following data find kinetic expressions for reaction and for deactivation

t, hr	0	3.7	7.2	10	15
p_A, atm	0.040	0.055	0.068	0.082	0.093

This problem was inspired by the PhD thesis of S. Shankar, Monash U., Australia, 1976.

Chapter 31 Problems

C10 Metallic catalysts promote the hydrogenation of ethylene

$$C_2H_4 + H_2 \xrightarrow{cat} C_2H_6 \quad \text{or} \quad A + B \longrightarrow R$$

however, the catalyst deactivates with use. To study this effect we pass a gaseous feed (27% C_2H_4, 73% H_2, $\pi = 1$ atm, T = 40.1 °C) through a packed bed of Ni impregnated alumina balls ($d_p = 1.2$ cm, $W/F_{A0} = 484$ kg·min/mol) and we carefully measure the outlet composition as follows

t, hr	0	9
$P_{C_2H_4}$, atm	0.245	0.250

Chemical studies also suggest that

$$-r'_A = k'C_B a \quad \text{and} \quad -\frac{da}{dt} = k_d C_A a^d$$

First find the rate of reaction at t = 0 and t = 9. Beware, just because X_A is very small in the reactor (this can well be treated as a differential reactor) does not mean that you can take $\varepsilon_A \approx 0$. Then find the rate equations for reaction and for deactivation assuming that d = 3.

This problem is developed from Koestenblatt and Ziegler, AIChE J **17** 891 (1971).

C11 In the presence of the enzyme called isomerase glucose converts directly to fructose

$$\underset{\text{glucose}}{C_6H_{12}O_6} \xrightarrow{\text{isomerase}} \underset{\text{fructose}}{C_6H_{12}O_6} \quad \text{or} \quad A \xrightarrow{E} R$$

Glucose is not very sweet, but fructose is, so this is a neat way of preparing very sweet syrups. Also, if the enzyme can be immobilized on some surface it can be used again and again. This would be most attractive commercially.

In the presence of immobilized enzymes the reaction can be well described by a reversible Michaelis-Menten mechanism

$$-r'_A, \frac{\text{mol conv}}{\text{hr}\cdot\text{gm enzyme}} = \frac{k'[C_A - \frac{C_R}{K}]}{K_M + C_A + \frac{K_M}{K_R}C_R}$$

where $K = \dfrac{C_{Re}}{C_{Ae}}$ = equilibrium constant and K_M and K_R are the M·M constants.

By more than luck it is reported that at 60 °C $K_M \approx K_R$ and K = 1. In this situation the rate reduces to first order reversible kinetics, which on integration for plug flow gives

$$\tau', \frac{\text{gm enzyme}\cdot\text{hr}}{\text{lit}} = \frac{W_E}{v_0} = \frac{W_E C_{A0}}{F_{A0}} = \frac{K_M + C_{A0}}{2k'} \ln\frac{1}{1 - 2X_A}$$

For 150 ml/hr of a 50 weight percent glucose feed containing 3.6 mol glucose/lit passing through a packed bed of pure glass beads coated with 10 gm of freshly prepared enzyme, conversion of glucose is 40%. Unfortunately, the activity of the enzyme decreases with time, and so does conversion, as follows

t, hr	0	400	800
X_A	0.40	0.27	0.16

For the particular feed of this experiment find expressions for the rates of reaction and deactivation.

This problem is taken in large part from Havewala and Pitcher, Jr. (see Pye and Wingard). Also it is interesting to note that this reaction probably is the most important large scale application of immobilized enzymes today.

C12 The following data on an irreversible reaction are obtained with decaying catalyst in a batch reactor (batch-solids, batch-fluid). What can you say about the kinetics

C_A	1.000	0.802	0.675	0.532	0.422	0.368
t, hr	0	0.25	0.5	1	2	∞

C13 The reversible catalytic reaction

$$A \leftrightarrow R, \quad X_{Ae} = 0.5$$

proceeds with decaying catalyst in a batch reactor which contains 5 m^3 of gas and 1.25 gm of catalyst. What can you say about the kinetics of reaction and the kinetics of deactivation from the following data obtained at 300 K and 2.5 MPa

t, hr	0	0.25	0.5	1	2	∞
C_A, mol/lit	1.000	0.901	0.830	0.766	0.711	0.684

Our reaction $A \rightarrow R$ proceeds in a packed bed of large slowly deactivating catalyst particles and is performing well in the strong pore diffusion regime. With fresh pellets conversion is 88%, however after 250 days conversion drops to 64%. How long can we run the reactor before conversion drops to

D14 . . . 50%

It has been suggested that we replace these large particles with very small particles so as to operate wholly in the diffusion-free regime and thus use less catalyst for the same conversions. How long a run time can we expect before the conversion drops from 88% to 64% if the catalyst is used in

D15 . . . a packed bed reactor

D16 . . . a fluidized solids reactor (assume mixed flow of fluid)

Chapter 31 Problems

The enzyme catalase effectively decomposes hydrogen peroxide

$$H_2O_2 \xrightarrow{\text{catalase}} H_2O + \frac{1}{2}O_2$$

and the kinetics of this reaction are to be evaluated from an experiment in which dilute H_2O_2 flows through a packed bed of kieselguhr particles impregnated with immobilized enzyme.

From the data below, reported by Krishnaswamy and Kittrell, AIChE J **28** 273 (1982), develop rate expressions to represent this decomposition, both in the diffusion free regime and in the strong pore diffusion regime, for the catalyst at hand. Note that the conversion decreases with time in all runs showing that the catalyst deactivates with use.

D17* ... run E (modified)

$\tau' = 4100$ kg cat·s/m^3

$\bar{d}_p = 360 \times 10^{-6}$ m

$\rho_s = 630$ kg/m^{3}cat

$\mathcal{D}_{eff} = 5 \times 10^{-10}$ m^3/m cat·s

elapsed time, hr	X_A
0	0.795
1.25	0.635
2.0	0.510
3.0	0.397
4.25	0.255
5.0	0.22
6.0	0.15
7.0	0.104

D18* ... run B

$\tau' = 4560$ kg cat·s/m^3

$\bar{d}_p = 1.45 \times 10^{-3}$ m

$\rho_s = 630$ kg/m^{3}cat

$\mathcal{D}_{eff} = 5 \times 10^{-10}$ m^3/m cat·s

elapsed time, hr	X_A
0.25	0.57
1.0	0.475
2.0	0.39
3.0	0.30
4.0	0.23
5.0	0.186
6.0	0.14
7.0	0.115

Chapter 32. Reactors Containing a Batch of Slowly Deactivating Catalyst Pellets.

A batch of slowly deactivating catalyst pellets exhibits three extremes in contacting

Extreme (X)
unmixed batch S / plug flow G

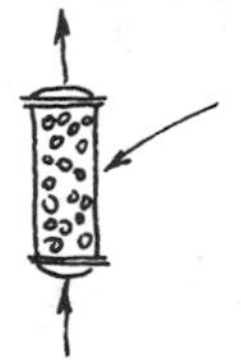

Extreme (Y)
mixed batch S / mixed flow G

Extreme (Z)
mixed batch S / plug flow G

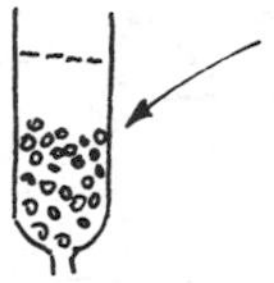

Extreme (Y) should be isothermal, (X) could be quite non isothermal, (Z) somewhere in between. The ordinary fluidized bed of fine particles has batch mixed S / intermediate gas flow as given by the model of chapter 25. It too should be close to isothermal.

Let us develop the conversion equations and find the performance of the above reactor types for the nth order kinetic forms of chapter 31, or

$$-r_A' = k' C_A^n a \quad \cdots \text{with} \quad -\frac{da}{dt} = k_d C_i^m a^d$$

We first take up the once through batch reactor and the various ways of running these units. We then take up the reactor system where unconverted reactant is separated from the product stream and then recycled. Finally, we take up the batch S / batch G system. We sketch these systems as follows:

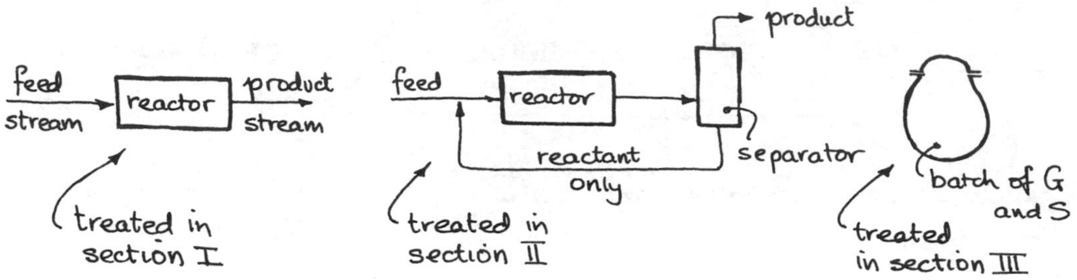
feed
stream
reactor
product
stream
treated in
section I
feed
reactor
product
reactant
only
separator
treated in
section II
batch of G
and S
treated
in section III

I. Batch S/Once Through G Reactors.

Consider the reaction $A \rightarrow R$ taking place on slowly deactivating catalyst. Here are some of the ways of running the reactor.

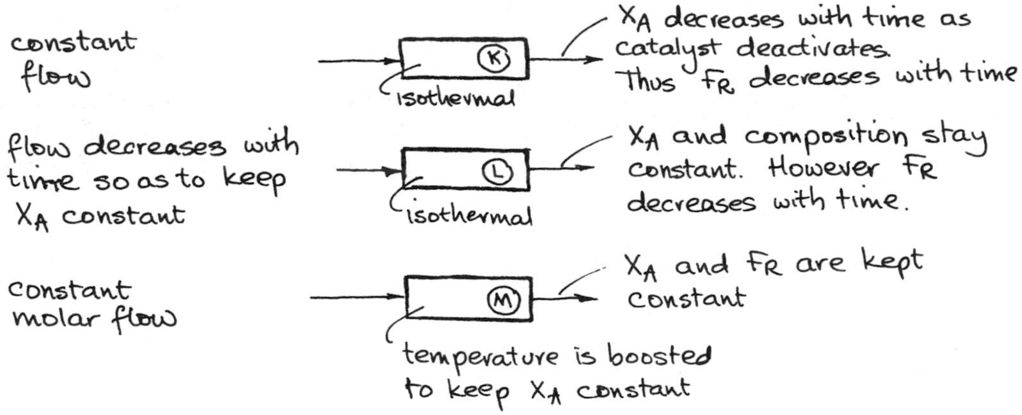
constant
flow
K
isothermal
X_A decreases with time as
catalyst deactivates.
Thus F_R decreases with time
flow decreases with
time so as to keep
X_A constant
L
isothermal
X_A and composition stay
constant. However F_R
decreases with time.
constant
molar flow
M
temperature is boosted
to keep X_A constant
X_A and F_R are kept
constant

Let us develop the performance equations for these different ways of running the reactor and let us compare the results to see which is best in this or in that situation

Policy (K). Isothermal batch S/once through constant G flow.

As catalyst activity drops with time so does reactor performance. When deactivation is of the type where the catalyst activity varies along the reactor then the performance can only be calculated by difficult 2 dimensional methods. This applies for reactors of type ⓧ with $m \neq 0$ deactivation. For all other cases the performance can be evaluated either analytically or by a straightforward numerical procedure. We treat these cases here.

As an illustration of what occurs suppose we have plug flow of gas. Then the performance equation is

$$\frac{W}{F_{A0}} = \int_0^{X_{Af}} \frac{dX_A}{k' a C_A^n}$$

constant (W, F_{A0}, k')

"a" decreases with time, therefore X_{Af} must also decrease with time to keep the integral unchanged.

Let us show how to evaluate the changing conditions with time.

A. General calculation procedure.

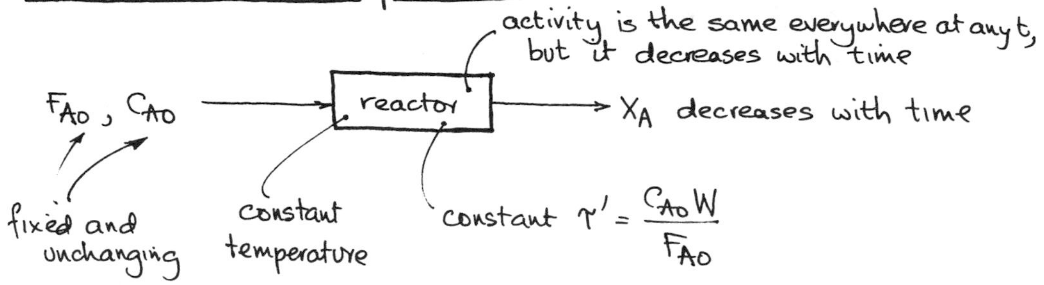

Suppose we want to find a_{final} and $\overline{X}_A$ (over the whole run) for a run time t_{run} in a reactor of given type and size which is processing a given feed.

First calculate k' k_d C_{A0} τ' and F_{A0} at the operating temperature

Second choose a series of "a" values and tabulate as follows

32.4

choose a	from which $-\Delta a$	and $\bar{a}$	from deactivation kinetics $\Delta t = -\Delta a / k_d \overline{C_i^m}\, \bar{a}^d$	from which t	then from the performance equation X_A
1				0	0.700
	0.04	0.98	say 1.8		
0.96				1.8	0.681
	0.04	0.94	2.1		
0.92				3.9	0.667

keep going till you reach t_{run}

$\overline{C_i^m}$ should be the proper average concentration of poisoning agent as seen by the solid.

- for (Y) it is the composition in the exit gas from the reactor.
- for (X) and (Z) you must average C_i^m through the reactor, thus

$$\overline{C_i^m} = \frac{1}{L}\int_0^L C_i^m\, dz$$

- For $C_i^m \Rightarrow C_A$ (or $m=1$, $i=A$) the proper average is $C_{A,lm.}$ between inlet and exit

for (X) and (Z) X_A is found from

$$\frac{\tau'}{C_{A0}} = \frac{W}{F_{A0}} = \int_0^{X_A} \frac{dX_A}{-r_A'} = \frac{1}{k'\bar{a}} \int_0^{X_A} \frac{dX_A}{C_A^n}$$

$\bar{a}$: 1, 0.96, 0.92, …

for (Y) X_A is found from

$$\frac{\tau'}{C_{A0}} = \frac{W}{F_{A0}} = \frac{X_A}{-r_{A,f}} = \frac{X_A}{k'\bar{a}C_A^n}$$

$\bar{a}$: 1, 0.96, 0.92, …

Third plot X_A vs t and evaluate $\overline{X_A} = \dfrac{\int_0^{t_{run}} X_A\, dt}{t_{run}}$

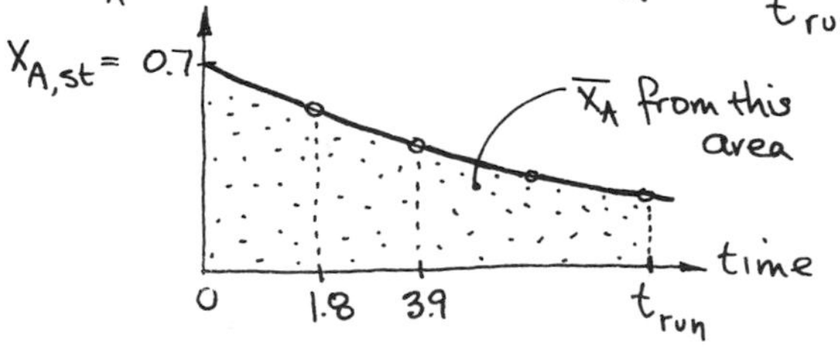

Conversely we can find t_{run} and a_{final} for a specified $\overline{X_A}$.

B. Integrated performance expressions: constant flow, constant T, falling X_A.

For a few simple kinetics we are able to obtain analytic expressions for the changing X_A vs t, and sometimes also for $\overline{X}_A$ vs t_{run}. This allows us to bypass the numerical procedure described above. So for

$A \rightarrow R$
isothermal
constant feed rate

... with
- $C_{A,st}$ and $X_{A,st}$ at $t=0$
- C_A and X_A at any t
- $\overline{C}_A$ and $\overline{X}_A$ over a run time t_{run}

... we have:

Batch S/mixed flow G : n=1, m=0, d=1.

$$k_d t = \ln\left(\frac{1-X_A}{X_A} \cdot \frac{X_{A,st}}{1-X_{A,st}}\right) \qquad \text{... where } k'\tau' = \frac{X_{A,st}}{1-X_{A,st}}$$

$$\overline{X}_A = 1 - \frac{1}{k_d t_{run}} \cdot \ln\left[X_{A,st} + e^{k_d t_{run}}(1-X_{A,st})\right]$$

Batch S/mixed flow G : n=1, m=0, any d except 1.

$$k_d t = \frac{1}{d-1}\left(\frac{1-X_A}{X_A} \cdot \frac{X_{A,st}}{1-X_{A,st}}\right)^{d-1} - \frac{1}{d-1} \qquad \text{... where } k'\tau' = \frac{X_{A,st}}{1-X_{A,st}}$$

$$\overline{X}_A = \frac{X_{A,st}}{k_d t_{run}(1-X_{A,st})} \ln\left[1 + k_d t_{run}(1-X_{A,st})\right] \qquad \text{... for } d=2$$

$$\overline{X}_A = \frac{1}{t_{run}} \int_0^{t_{run}} X_A \, dt \qquad \text{... for any } d$$

Batch S/mixed flow G : n=2, m=0, d=1.

$$k_d t = \ln\left[\frac{(1-X_A)^2}{X_A} \cdot \frac{X_{A,st}}{(1-X_{A,st})^2}\right] \qquad \text{... where } k'\tau' C_{A0} = \frac{X_{A,st}}{(1-X_{A,st})^2}$$

$$\overline{X}_A = \frac{1}{t_{run}} \int_0^{t_{run}} X_A \, dt$$

Batch S/mixed flow G : $n=2$, $m=0$, $d>1$

$$k_d t = \frac{1}{d-1}\left[\frac{(1-X_A)}{X_A}\cdot\frac{X_{A,st}}{(1-X_{A,st})}\right]^{d-1} - \frac{1}{d-1}$$

... where $k' C_{A0} \tau' = \dfrac{X_{A,st}}{(1-X_{A,st})}$

... and $\bar{X}_A = \dfrac{1}{t_{run}}\displaystyle\int_0^{t_{run}} X_A dt$

Batch S/plug flow G : $n=1$, $m=0$, $d=1$

$$k_d t = \ln\left[\frac{\ln(1-X_{A,st})}{\ln(1-X_A)}\right]$$

... where $k'\tau' = -\ln(1-X_{A,st})$

$$k_d t_{run}\frac{\bar{C}_A}{C_{A0}} = ei\left[k'\tau' \exp(-k_d t_{run})\right] - ei\left[k'\tau'\right]$$

(ei: one of the family of many exponential integrals)

Here are two useful exponential integrals

$$Ei(x) = \int_{-\infty}^{x} \frac{e^u}{u} du = 0.57721 + \ln x + x + \frac{x^2}{2\cdot 2!} + \frac{x^3}{3\cdot 3!} + \cdots$$

$$ei(x) = \int_{x}^{\infty} \frac{e^{-u}}{u} du = 0.57721 - \ln x + x - \frac{x^2}{2\cdot 2!} + \frac{x^3}{3\cdot 3!} - \cdots$$

x	Ei(x)	ei(x)
0	$-\infty$	$+\infty$
0.01	-4.0179	4.0379
0.02	-3.3147	3.3547
0.05	-2.3679	2.4679
0.1	-1.6228	1.8229

x	Ei(x)	ei(x)
0.2	-0.8218	1.2227
0.3	-0.3027	0.9057
0.5	0.4542	0.5598
1.0	1.8951	0.2194
1.4	3.0072	0.1162

x	Ei(x)	ei(x)
2.0	4.9542	0.04890
2.5	7.0738	0.02491
3.0	9.9338	0.01305
5.0	40.185	0.00115
7.0	191.50	0.00012

for $x \geq 10$

$$Ei(x) = e^{x}\left[\frac{1}{x} + \frac{1}{x^2} + \frac{2!}{x^3} + \frac{3}{x^4} + \cdots\right]$$

$$ei(x) = e^{-x}\left[\frac{1}{x} - \frac{1}{x^2} + \frac{2!}{x^3} - \frac{3}{x^4} + \cdots\right]$$

Reference: "Tables of Sines, Cosines and Exponential Integrals", Vol I & II, by WPA, for NBS (1940).

Batch S/plug flow G : $n=1$, $m=0$, $d>1$

$$k_d t = \frac{1}{d-1}\left[\frac{\ln(1-X_{A,st})}{\ln(1-X_A)}\right]^{d-1} - \frac{1}{d-1}$$

... where $k'\tau' = -\ln(1-X_{A,st})$

... and $\bar{X}_A = \dfrac{1}{t_{run}}\displaystyle\int_0^{t_{run}} X_A dt$

Batch S/ plug flow G: n=2, m=0, d=1.

$$k_d t = \ln\left(\frac{1-X_A}{X_A}\cdot\frac{X_{A,st}}{1-X_{A,st}}\right) \qquad \ldots \text{where } k'\tau' C_{A0} = \frac{X_{A,st}}{1-X_{A,st}}$$

$$\bar{X}_A = 1 - \frac{1}{k_d t_{run}} \ln\left[X_{A,st} + e^{k_d t_{run}}\cdot(1-X_{A,st})\right]$$

Batch S/ plug flow G: n=2, m=0, any d≠1.

$$k_d t = \frac{1}{d-1}\left(\frac{1-X_A}{X_A}\cdot\frac{X_{A,st}}{1-X_{A,st}}\right)^{d-1} - \frac{1}{d-1} \qquad \ldots \text{where } k'\tau' C_{A0} = \frac{X_{A,st}}{1-X_{A,st}}$$

$$\bar{X}_A = \frac{X_{A,st}}{(1-X_{A,st})\,k_d t_{run}} \ln\left[1 + k_d t_{run}(1-X_{A,st})\right] \qquad \ldots \text{for } d=2$$

$$\bar{X}_A = \frac{1}{t_{run}} \int_0^{t_{run}} X_A\, dt \qquad \ldots \text{for all } d>1$$

Policy Ⓛ. Isothermal batch S/ once through, decreasing G feed, keeping X_A constant.

To keep X_A constant we must adjust the flow rate of gas. To illustrate, suppose that we have plug flow of gas. Then

$$\frac{W}{F_{A0}} = \frac{1}{k'a} \int_0^{X_A} \frac{dX_A}{C_A^n}$$

- W: constant
- k': constant
- a: decreases with time
- $\int_0^{X_A} \frac{dX_A}{C_A^n}$: constant since X_A is to be kept unchanged with time

Since "a" decreases with time F_{A0} must be lowered accordingly such that

$$\frac{F_{A0}}{a} = F_{A0,st} = \text{constant}$$

A. General calculation procedure.

The procedure here is identical to the previous case except that the last column in the table of step 2 becomes

$$F_{A0} = (F_{A0,st})\,a$$

and the integration of step 3 becomes

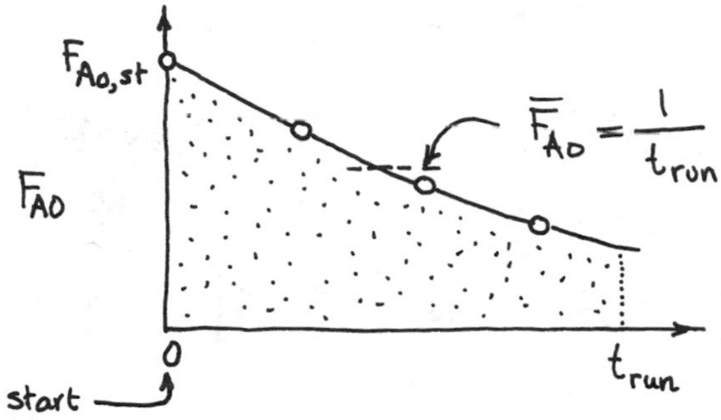

$$\bar{F}_{A0} = \frac{1}{t_{run}} \int_0^{t_{run}} F_{A0}\, dt$$

B. Integrated performance expressions: decreasing flow, constant T, constant X_A.

Batch S/plug flow G: $n=1$, $m=0$, $d=1$.

$$k'\bar{\tau}' k_d t_{run} = \left(\ln \frac{C_{A0}}{C_A}\right)\left(e^{k_d t_{run}} - 1\right)$$

Batch S/plug flow G: $n=1$, $m=0$, $d \neq 1$, $d \neq 0$.

$$k'\bar{\tau}' d\, k_d t_{run} = \left(\ln \frac{C_{A0}}{C_A}\right)\left\{\left[k_d (d-1) t_{run} + 1\right]^{d/d-1} - 1\right\}$$

Batch S/plug flow G: $n \neq 1$, $m=0$, $d=1$

$$(n-1) k' C_{A0}^{n-1} \bar{\tau}\, k_d t_{run} = \left[\left(\frac{C_A}{C_{A0}}\right)^{1-n} - 1\right]\left(e^{k_d t_{run}} - 1\right)$$

Policy (M). Rising T, batch S / once through, constant G feed, keeping X_A constant.

To keep X_A constant while the catalyst deactivates one should boost the temperature. As illustration, for plug flow of gas

$$\frac{W}{F_{A0}} = \frac{\tau'}{C_{A0}} = \frac{1}{k'a\,C_{A0}^{n}} \int_0^{X_A} \frac{dX_A}{(1-X_A)^n}$$

- $\frac{W}{F_{A0}}$: constant
- X_A is constant, hence this term (the integral) must stay constant
- $k'a\,C_{A0}^{n}$: since all else stays unchanging with time this term must be kept constant as catalyst deactivates

In the regime of no pore diffusion resistance we must change T with time such that

$$k'a = \text{constant} \quad \cdots \text{ for all liquid systems}$$

$$\frac{k'a}{T^n} = \text{constant} \quad \cdots \text{ for } \begin{cases}\text{ideal gases with} \\ n^{th} \text{ order reactions}\end{cases}$$

In the regime of strong resistance to pore diffusion we must change T with time such that

$$k'a\,\mathcal{D}_{eff} = \text{constant} \quad \cdots \text{ for liquids}$$

$$\frac{k'a\,\mathcal{D}_{eff}}{T^{n+1}} = \text{constant} \quad \cdots \text{ for } \begin{cases}\text{ideal gases and} \\ n^{th} \text{ order reactions}\end{cases}$$

or else

$$\frac{k'a}{T^{n-1/2}} = \text{constant} \quad \cdots \text{ for ordinary diffusion in pores } (\mathcal{D} \propto T^{3/2})$$

$$\frac{k'a}{T^{n+1/2}} = \text{constant} \quad \cdots \text{ for Knudsen diffusion in pores } (\mathcal{D} \propto T^{1/2})$$

A. General calculation procedure.

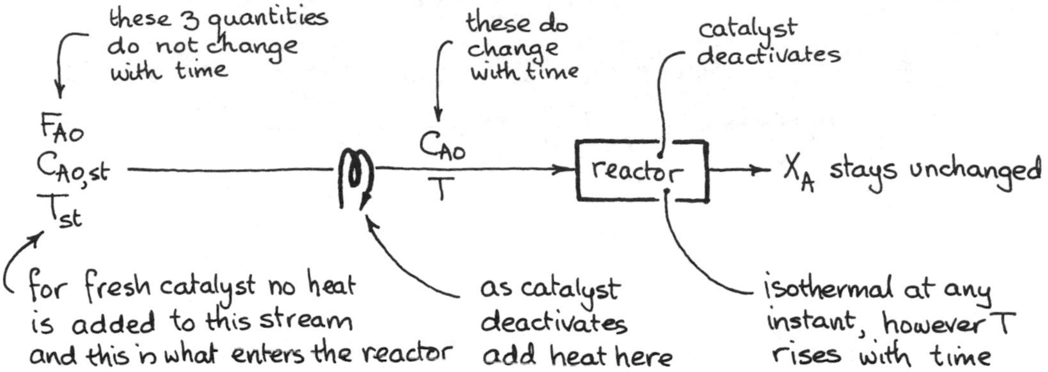
these 3 quantities do not change with time
these do change with time
catalyst deactivates
F_{A0}
$C_{A0,st}$
T_{st}
C_{A0}
T
reactor
X_A stays unchanged
for fresh catalyst no heat is added to this stream and this is what enters the reactor
as catalyst deactivates add heat here
isothermal at any instant, however T rises with time

Here we must raise T with time, hence k', k_d, C_{A0}, τ and T all change with time. We want to know how long we can run the reactor before the temperature rises to the maximum allowable T^*.

Step 1. At the start, with given $\tau'_{st} = \dfrac{C_{A0,st}W}{F_{A0}}$ and $a=1$ calculate X_A from the performance equation, thus

$$\frac{\tau'_{p,st}}{C_{A0,st}} = \frac{W_p}{F_{A0}} = \int_0^{X_A} \frac{dX_A}{k'C_A^n} \quad \text{... or ...} \quad \frac{\tau'_{m,st}}{C_{A0,st}} = \frac{W_m}{F_{A0}} = \frac{X_A}{k'C_A^n}$$

Step 2. At selected temperatures, say $T_1, T_2, \ldots$ calculate $a_1, a_2, \ldots$ so that X_A stays unchanged. In other words keep

$$\frac{k'a}{T^x} = \text{constant}$$

$k' = k'_0 e^{-E/RT}$

use the appropriate value for x. From the previous page this is either $x = 0, n,$ etc. depending on the system

Thus we find

$$a_1 = \left(\frac{T_1}{T_{st}}\right)^n e^{-\frac{E}{R}\left(\frac{1}{T_{st}} - \frac{1}{T_1}\right)}, \quad a_2 = \left(\frac{T_2}{T_{st}}\right)^n e^{-\frac{E}{R}\left(\frac{1}{T_{st}} - \frac{1}{T_2}\right)}, \quad \ldots$$

Step 3. Find how long it takes for the activity to drop to $a_1, a_2, a_3, \ldots$

To summarize we tabulate the calculation procedure:

select T	from step 2 a	$-\Delta a$	$\bar{a}$	$\bar{T}$	$\bar{k}_d$	$\Delta t = \frac{-\Delta a}{\bar{k}_d \bar{a}^d}$	t from start
500	1.00						0
		0.20	0.90	505	$k_{d,505}$	3.2 hr.	
510	0.80						3.2
		0.14	0.73	515	$k_{d,515}$	2.9 hr	
520	0.66						6.1

↑ stop when you reach T^*

↓ this gives the time of run, or time to reach T^*

B. Integrated performance expressions: constant F_{A0}, constant X_A, rising T

In certain cases we can bypass this 3 step procedure and can integrate directly

Batch S/plug flow L : $n=1$, $m=0$, $d=1$ -- liquids

$$k_{do}\, t_{run} = \frac{E}{E_d}\left[\exp\left(\frac{E_d}{RT_{st}}\right) - \exp\left(\frac{E_d}{RT^*}\right)\right]$$

Batch S/plug flow G : n=2, m=0, d=1 ... ideal gas

$$k_{do}t_{run} = 2\,\mathbf{Ei}\left(\frac{E_d}{RT^*}\right) - 2\,\mathbf{Ei}\left(\frac{E_d}{RT_{st}}\right) - \frac{E}{E_d}\left[\exp\left(\frac{E_d}{RT^*}\right) - \exp\left(\frac{E_d}{RT_{st}}\right)\right]$$

↑ exponential integral, see pg. 32.6

Batch S/plug flow L : n=1, m=0, d=2 ... liquids

$$k_{do}t_{run} = \frac{E}{E_d - E}\exp\left(\frac{E}{RT^*}\right)\left[\exp\left(\frac{E_d - E}{RT_{st}}\right) - \exp\left(\frac{E_d - E}{RT}\right)\right]$$

Note: In these expressions T_{st} and T^* give t_{run} independent of W or conversion level.

↖ T^*: final and highest T for the run

Discussion of once through systems.

(a) In general, with a batch of deactivating catalyst we run the reactor until the catalyst is tired or exhausted. We then regenerate or replace the catalyst and repeat the cycle

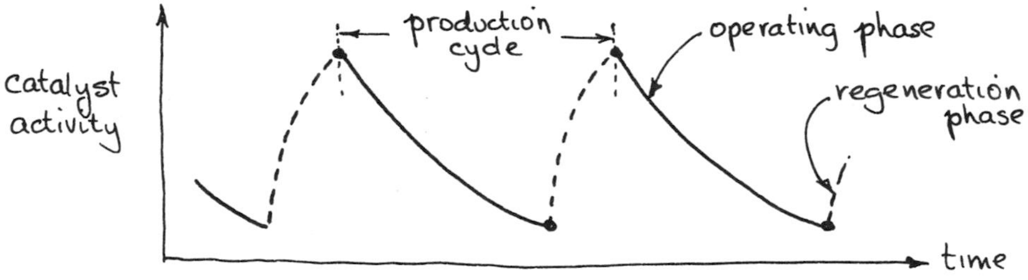

The overall economic problem requires searching for the best production cycle, thus finding

- which policy Ⓚ Ⓛ or Ⓜ, or which combination to use.
- how far to let the catalyst deactivate before regenerating it.
- how far to regenerate the catalyst (this also costs time and money).

This problem can only be treated by a trial and error search (see Park & Levenspiel IEC/PDD 15 534, 538 (1976)) and we do not consider it here. In this chapter we only consider the best way of running the reactor during the operating phase of the production cycle.

(b) **For the longest run time for given $\bar{X}_A$ and for fixed a_{final}.**

- if $E_d > E$: for liquids policy Ⓜ is best ; for gases policy Ⓜ is close to best, and it certainly is better than policy Ⓚ or Ⓛ.
- if $E_d < E$: policies Ⓚ and Ⓛ beat Ⓜ. In addition policy Ⓛ is better than policy Ⓚ, but usually only marginally so. This advantage is often offset by the extra complications in adapting the supporting equipment to the changing flow rates.

Thus for systems where deactivation is more temperature sensitive than reaction use a rising temperature policy and the gains can be very substantial. On the other hand, if deactivation is less temperature sensitive than reaction isothermal operations at T^* is best, often by much.

Deactivation is usually quite temperature insensitive if it is caused by a feed impurity or by a reaction product which is strongly and irreversibly attached to the active catalyst surface. On the other hand, deactivation is usually very temperature sensitive if it is a result of a structural change in the surface, or by a rate controlling surface reaction (adsorption, desorption, etc.).

(c) For policy Ⓜ be sure to start your run at the unique temperature such that the reactor reaches T^* **just at the end of the run.** Any other operating policy will be poorer.

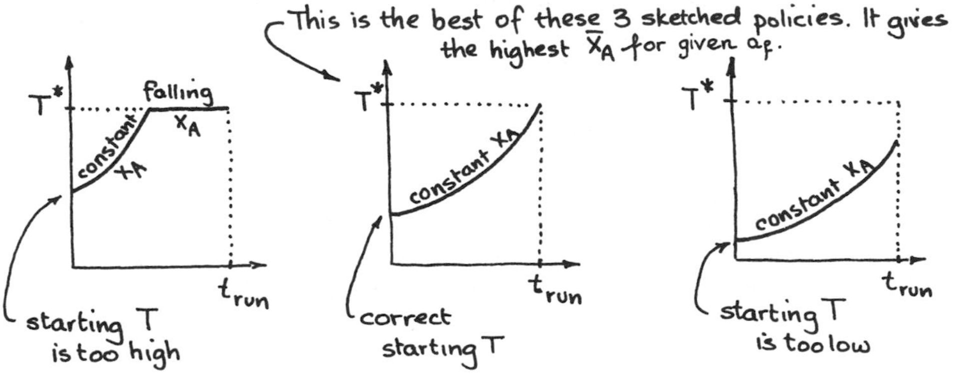

(d) For policy Ⓜ and fixed $\overline{X}_A$ and a_{final} if you want a longer run time you must use more catalyst. Thus for a given reaction there is a unique relationship between

$$W_{cat},\ t_{run},\ \overline{X}_A \text{ and } a_{final}.$$

(e) For the longest run time at given $\overline{X}_A$, regardless of a_{final} sometimes one of the two policies Ⓚ and Ⓜ is better, sometimes the other. For example, in problems 8 to 12 policy Ⓚ beats Ⓜ if $T^* < 512\,K$, but policy Ⓜ beats Ⓚ if $T^* > 512\,K$. In general, if the catalyst does not deactivate much during the run then Ⓚ beats Ⓜ, otherwise Ⓜ is better.

In fact the best policy of all is a combination of Ⓚ and Ⓜ, rising temperature to T^* followed by a constant temperature at T^*, as shown in the first sketch of the figures in the previous page. See Crowe Can J ChE <u>48</u> 576 (1970). We call this the (K·M) policy.

(f) The three policies ⓀⓁⓂ were developed only for $m=0$ kinetics. However they may be extended to $m \neq 0$ kinetics with no error

- for type Ⓨ reactors because here all the solids are bathed in exit gas, and so

$$k_d C_i^m = \text{constant}$$

(C_i^m measured at the exit)

- for type Ⓩ reactors because here every particle of solid samples all the gas in the reactor, and so

$$k_d \overline{C_i^m} = \text{constant}$$

($\overline{C_i^m}$ = mean value in the reactor), or

$$\overline{C_i^m} = \frac{\int_0^L C_i^m\, dz}{L}$$

Even for type Ⓧ reactors, the ordinary packed bed, the constant conversion policy can be best. However, here the optimum requires that the temperature be varied with position along the reactor as well as with time. How to do this is shown by Crowe CES <u>31</u> 959 (1976).

II. Reactors with Separation and Reuse of Unconverted Reactant.

Consider the nth order reaction $A \to R$ taking place on slowly deactivating catalyst, plus a separation system where unused reactant is completely separated from the product stream, concentrated to the initial feed concentration and reused. We then have the following attractive ways, policies Ⓤ Ⓥ Ⓦ of operating the system

Policy Ⓤ. Constant feed, production, temperature but increasing recycle

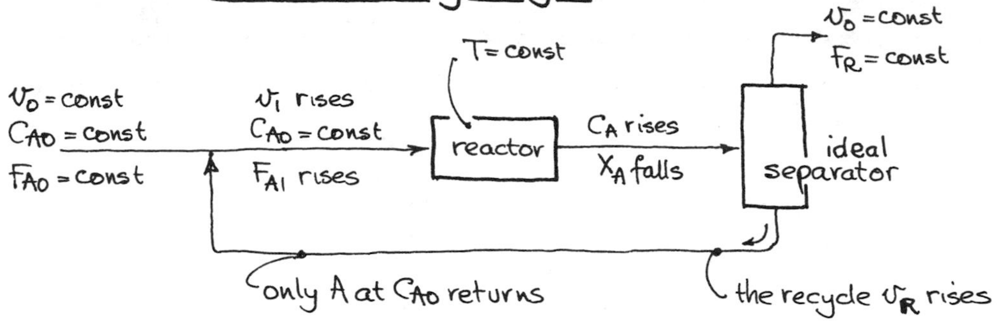

A material balance for recycle systems with complete return of unused reactant gives

$$\mathbf{R} = \frac{v_R}{v_0} = \frac{1-X_A}{X_A} \qquad \text{...and...} \qquad F_{A0} = F_{A1} X_A$$

Then for plug flow in the reactor

$$\frac{W}{F_{A1}} = \int_{in}^{out} \frac{dX_A}{-r_A} \qquad \text{...or...} \qquad \frac{W}{F_{A0}} = \frac{1}{a} \left[\frac{1}{X_A} \int_0^{X_A} \frac{dX_A}{k' C_A^n} \right]$$

- W/F_{A0}: constant
- a: decreases with time
- X_A (upper limit): must decrease with time
- bracketed term: because "a" decreases with time this term must also decrease. This means that X_A must fall.

Rearranging gives

$$a = \frac{F_{A0}}{W X_A k'} \int_0^{X_A} \frac{dX_A}{C_A^n} \quad \text{... and ...} \quad R = \frac{1-X_A}{X_A} \quad \cdots (1)$$

(R rises with time)

In a similar manner we get, for mixed flow,

$$a = \frac{F_{A0}}{W k' C_A^n} \quad \text{... and ...} \quad R = \frac{1-X_A}{X_A} \quad \cdots (2)$$

(R rises with time)

These equations tell what recycle rate has to be used so as to keep the feed and production rate constant

Now there comes a time when the activity falls so low that even with infinite recycle one cannot make the needed amount of product. This maximum time for operations is given by

$$a_{lowest} = \frac{F_{A0}}{W k' C_{A0}^n} \quad \text{... and} \quad \begin{cases} R \to \infty \\ X_A \to 0 \\ C_A \to C_{A0} \end{cases}$$

To find how things change in the system first calculate F_{A0}, W and $X_{A_{st}}$ for fresh catalyst. Then tabulate as follows

take increments of X_A	evaluate C_A from $C_A = C_{A0}\left(\frac{1-X_A}{1+\varepsilon_A X_A}\right)$	calculate a from eq 1	find $\bar{C}_A$ in the increment	$\bar{a}$	$\Delta t = \frac{\Delta a}{k' \bar{C}_i^m \bar{a}^d}$	t
suppose $X_{A,st} = 0.7$	suppose $= 30$	at start $= 1$				0
			32.5	0.95	3 days	3
0.65	35	0.9				
			37.5	0.85	5 days	8
0.6	40	0.8				
			⋮	⋮	7 days	15
⋮	⋮	⋮				⋮
$X_{A,\infty} = 0$	100	$\neq 0$				∞

With this policy recycle increases with time so the separator should be designed to handle the flows **at the end of the operating cycle.**

Policy (V). Decreasing feed and production, increasing recycle, constant flow through reactor, constant temperature.

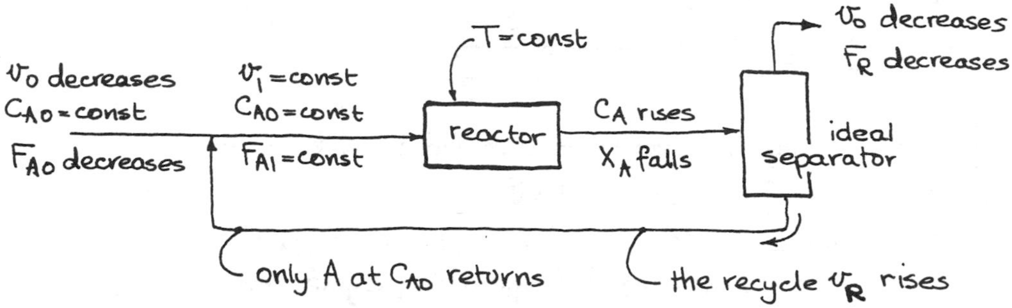

A material balance for this system gives

For plug flow: $$\frac{W}{F_{A1}} = \frac{1}{k'a}\int_0^{X_A} \frac{dX_A}{C_A^n} \quad \cdots \text{and} \quad F_{A0} = F_R = F_{A1}X_A \quad \cdots (3)$$

(W/F_{A1}: constant; a: falls; X_A ← must fall accordingly)

For mixed flow: $$\frac{W}{F_{A1}} = \frac{X_A}{k'aC_A^n} \quad \cdots \text{and} \quad F_{A0} = F_R = F_{A1}X_A \quad \cdots (4)$$

To find how things change with time first calculate F_{A0}, W and $X_{A,st}$. Then for plug flow as illustration tabulate as follows:

take increments of X_A	C_A	in eq 3 evaluate $\int_0^{X_A}\cdots$	$a = \dfrac{\int_0^{X_A}\cdots}{\int_0^{X_{A,st}}\cdots}$	Δa	$\bar{C}_A$	$\bar{a}$	Δt	t	$F_R = \dfrac{F_{A0,st}X_A}{X_{A,st}}$
$X_{A,st}$	$C_{A,st}$		1	⋮	⋮	⋮	⋮	0	⋮
⋮	⋮							⋮	

(for mixed flow use eq 4 here; Δt from deactivation kinetics)

Then integrate to find $\bar{F}_R$:

$$\bar{F}_R = \frac{1}{t_{run}} \int_0^t F_R \, dt$$

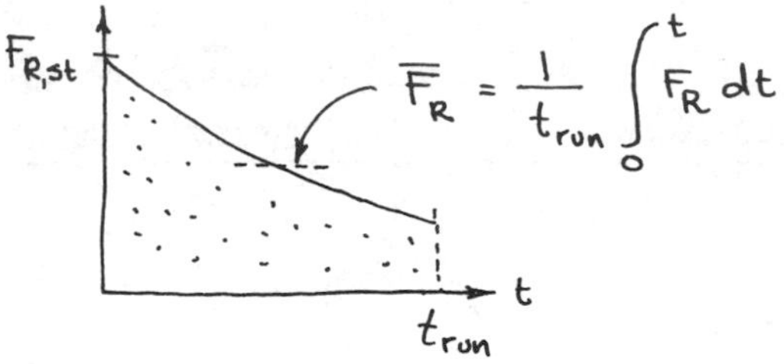

With this policy X_A decreases with time and so does the production of R. This can continue until $t \to \infty$. Also note that the capacity of the separation system is determined by the conditions at the **end of the operating cycle**. Here recycle is highest.

Policy Ⓦ. Constant flows and production, rising reactor temperature.

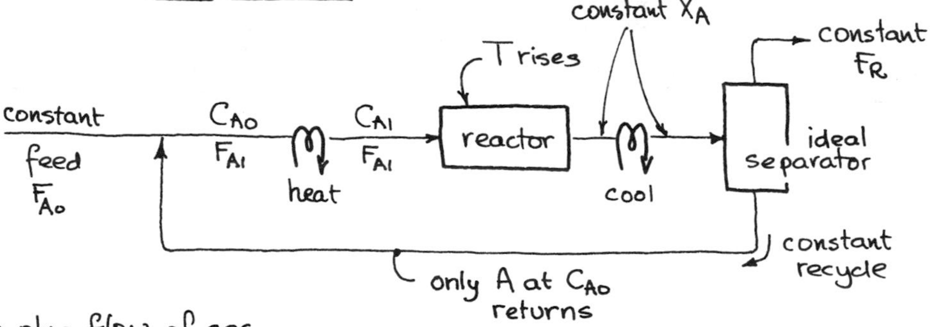

For plug flow of gas

$$\frac{W}{F_{A1}} = \frac{1}{k' a C_{A1}^n} \int_0^{X_A} \frac{dX_A}{(1-X_A)^n} \quad \cdots \text{and} \quad F_{A1} = F_{A0} X_A \qquad \cdots (5)$$

constant / falls / keep constant

Note that k' must rise and this is done by raising the T. As with policy Ⓜ we must keep

$$k'a = \text{constant} \quad \cdots \text{for liquids}$$

$$\frac{k'a}{T^x} = \text{constant} \quad \cdots \text{for ideal gases} \cdots \text{see pg 32.9 for } x.$$

The calculation procedure is the same as for policy (M). Also, the duty of the separator does not change with time however the heating and cooling duties change during the operating cycle.

Discussion of recycle systems.

(a) Comparison of policies

- Policies (U) and (W) maintain constant flows and composition of entering and leaving streams ... important if the reactor-separator is part of a larger processing system.
- Policy (W) also maintains a constant duty on the separator, hence it uses the separator most efficiently.
- From the standpoint of good catalyst utilization policy (W) is by far the best of the three policies if $E_d > E$, which usually is the case.

Overall we conclude that unless the cost of heat exchangers and the cost of heating and cooling is the dominating economic factor (W) usually represents the most attractive policy.

(b) For constant temperature operations we should run policies (U) and (V) at the maximum allowable temperature. For the rising temperature of policy (W) we should start at a temperature such that T^* is reached just at the end of the run.

(c) When other considerations enter the picture such as product distribution, more complex kinetics, partial separation in the separator the resulting equations will be quite different, however the general strategy treating these policies will be unchanged.

(d) Reactor shutdown for regeneration or replacement of catalyst can lead to all sorts of headaches. To avoid this, parallel or series reactors can be used. Thus if the run takes 30 days and regeneration takes 10 days then you can get smooth continuous operations with 4 reactors, 3 running at any time, the fourth being regenerated.

(e) Note the close similarity between policies (K)(L)(M) and (U)(V)(W).

III. Batch Mixed S / Batch Mixed G Reactors.

Here the same sort of rules apply for optimal operations as for the batch S/flow G reactor. Thus for the kinetics

$$\left.\begin{aligned} -r_A' &= k' C_A^n a \\ -\frac{da}{dt} &= k_d a^d \end{aligned}\right\} \text{ or } m=0$$

- we should use a rising temperature policy when $E_d > E$, otherwise run the reactor at the maximum allowable temperature.
- for the rising temperature policy adjust the reactor temperature so that at any time

$$k'a = k_0' e^{-E/RT} a = \text{constant} = (k')_{\text{at start of run.}}$$

Thus start at that temperature such that the reactor just reaches T^* at the end of the run.

When deactivation is concentration dependent, or $m \neq 0$, numerical methods must be used to find the optimal temperature progression.

Chapter 32 Problems

We plan to run an isomerization of A to R in a packed bed reactor (pure A, $F_{A0} = 5$ kmol/hr, W = 1 ton catalyst, $\pi = 3$ atm, T = 730 K). The catalyst deactivates so we plan to make 120 day runs, then regenerate the catalyst.

(a) Plot conversion and activity versus time for the run and

(b) find $\bar{X}_A$ for the 120 day run

The rate of reaction with C_A in mol/m³ is described by

$$-r'_A = 0.2\, C_A^2 a \quad \frac{\text{mol A}}{\text{kg cat·hr}}$$

and the rate of deactivation is given by

A1 . . . $-\dfrac{da}{dt} = 8.3125 \times 10^{-3}, \ \text{day}^{-1}$

This expression represents poisoning by a feed impurity.

A2 . . . $-\dfrac{da}{dt} = 10^{-3}\,(C_A + C_R)a, \ \text{day}^{-1}$

This represents poisoning by both reactant and by product, thus pore diffusion resistance does not influence the deactivation rate.

A3 . . . $-\dfrac{da}{dt} = 3.325\, a^2, \ \text{day}^{-1}$

This represents fairly strong pore diffusion resistance.

A4 . . . $-\dfrac{da}{dt} = 666.5\, a^3, \ \text{day}^{-1}$

This represents very strong pore diffusion resistance.

The reaction rate A → R proceeds at 700 °C on a slowly deactivating catalyst by a first order rate

$$-r'_A = 0.03\, C_A a \quad \frac{\text{mol}}{\text{kg·min}}, \quad C_A \text{ in } \frac{\text{mol}}{\text{m}^3}$$

We plan to feed a packed bed reactor (W = 100 kg) with 1 m³/min of fresh A at 8 atm and 700 °C and run the unit until the catalyst activity drops to 10% of the fresh catalyst, then regenerate the catalyst and repeat the cycle. Find

(a) the run time for this operation and

(b) the mean conversion of reactant over the run

The deactivation is well described by

Chapter 32 Problems

A5 . . . $-\frac{da}{dt} = 0.023\, a, \quad day^{-1}$

A6 . . . $-\frac{da}{dt} = 0.3\, a^2, \quad day^{-1}$

A7 . . . $-\frac{da}{dt} = 0.3\, a^3, \quad day^{-1}$

An isomerization takes place on deactivating catalyst with negligible heat effect ($\Delta H_r \approx 0$) as follows

$$A \rightarrow R \quad \begin{cases} -r'_A = 2.4 \times 10^4\, e^{-7000/T}\, C_A^2 a, & \frac{mol}{kg \cdot min} \\ -\frac{da}{dt} = 2.6 \times 10^{18}\, e^{-25000/T}\, a, & day^{-1} \end{cases}$$

First show that you will need 900 kg of fresh catalyst in a packed bed reactor operating at 500 K to give 90% conversion for a feed $F_{A0} = 5000$ mol/min, $C_{A0} = 50$ mol/m^3 at 500 K and $\pi \approx 2$ atm.

Then find the longest possible run time for operations at these conditions of W, F_{A0}, π and for $\bar{X}_A = 0.90$ if the reactor is operated *isothermally*

A8 . . . at 600 K, at which temperature $C_{A0} = 41.67$ mol/m^3

A9 . . . at 520 K, at which temperature $C_{A0} = 48.08$ mol/m^3

A10* . . . at the temperature which you guess will give the longest run time. This should represent the best isothermal temperature for this mean conversion and bed weight.

Finally find the longest possible run time for these conditions of W, F_{A0}, π and for $\bar{X}_A = 0.90$ if the reactor is operated optimally (that means a rising temperature policy) starting the run at 500 K and ending at 600 K.

B11 . . . Use 20 K increments of temperature to reduce the amount of calculation needed.

B12 . . . Solve more accurately, either using half degree temperature increments (with a computer) or by using the exact integrated expression for these kinetics.

Chapter 32 Problems

With fresh catalyst our packed bed reactor operates at 600 K. However, this catalyst deactivates with use, therefore to maintain optimum operations we have to continuously raise the temperature of the reactor. After four months our reactor reaches 800 K, the upper allowable temperature limit, so we shut down the unit to regenerate the catalyst. The kinetics of the reaction with fresh catalyst is given by

$$A \rightarrow R, \quad -r'_A = k'C_A^2, \quad k' = k'_0\, e^{-7200/T}$$

however the deactivation kinetics is unknown. Find the activity of the catalyst at the end of the run

B13 ... if the reacting fluid is liquid

B14 ... if the reacting fluid is an ideal gas. Consider both the diffusion free and the strong pore diffusion regimes.

We wish to treat a gaseous feed stream ($F_{A0} = 5000$ mol/min, $C_{A0} = 50$ mol/m^3, $T = 500$ K, $\pi \approx 2$ atm) in a catalyst packed reactor. At this temperature the kinetics of reaction and of deactivation are given by

$$A \rightarrow R, \quad -r'_A = 0.02\, C_A^2 a \quad \frac{\text{mol}}{\text{kg·min}}; \quad -\frac{da}{dt} = 0.005\, a, \quad \text{day}^{-1}$$

Since reactant A can be cleanly and completely separated from the product stream we plan to use a reactor/reactant recycle system with changing recycle, 50% conversion/pass for fresh catalyst, and complete conversion of reactant to product (policy U of this chapter).

First determine how much catalyst is needed in the packed bed reactor. Then determine how long we can use a batch of catalyst before it needs to be regenerated if the separator can handle

C15 ... any amount of fluid from the reactor.

C16 ... twice its initial load.

Chapter 33. Reactors with Flowing Deactivating Catalyst Particles

When the catalyst deactivates rapidly it must be replaced frequently, and this is often done by passing a stream of catalyst through the reactor. We also often use catalyst circulation between two units. In the first unit the catalyst decays while promoting the the gas reaction. It is then regenerated as it flows through the second unit. We call this the **reactor-regenerator** system.

We here develop the performance equations for single reactors and for reactor-regenerators. For the latter this will allow us to interrelate the behavior of the two units in terms of the kinetics, the contacting patterns, the solid circulation rate, and the size of the two units. This should help us optimize operations, to find solid circulation rate and what size ratio of units to use.

We illustrate the approach with the simplest of kinetics. We start with single reactors, then we treat the reactor-regenerator.

I. Performance Equations for the Simplest of Kinetics $n=1,\ m_1=m_2=0,\ d_1=d_2=1.$

Take the reaction $A \rightarrow R$. Then we have

for reaction : $-r_A' = k' C_A a$ ... and $R = k'\tau'$

for deactivation: $-\dfrac{da}{dt} = k_d a$ ... and $R_d = k_d \bar{t}_{s1}$

for regeneration : $\dfrac{da}{dt} = k_r(1-a)$ ... and $R_r = k_r \bar{t}_{s2}$

(dimensionless groups for reactor and regenerator)

The nomenclature used is as follows

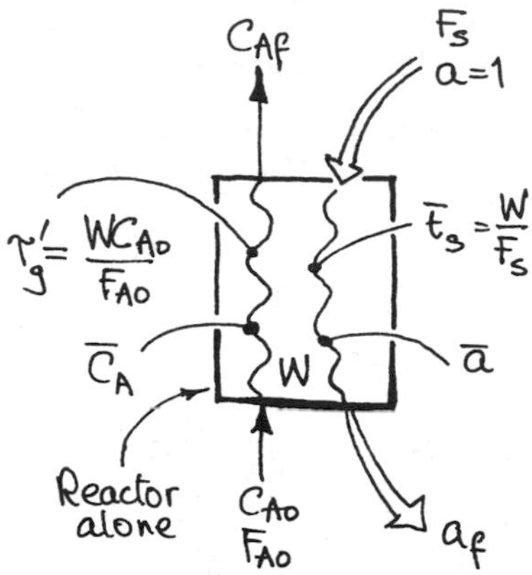

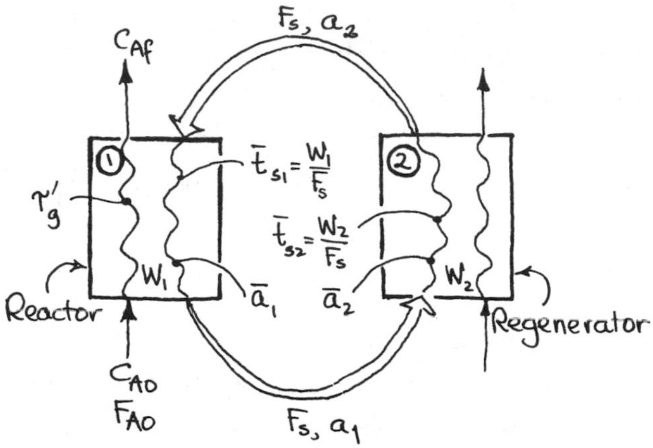

Since deactivation is first order with respect to the activity, and regeneration too, we can treat the flowing solids as a microfluid, if we wish, with "a" as the concentration of active species. Thus for the streams leaving the reactor and regenerator we may write a_f, a_1 and a_2 instead of $\bar{a}_f$, $\bar{a}_{1,leaving}$, $\bar{a}_{2,leaving}$.

A. Mixed flow S (reactor alone)

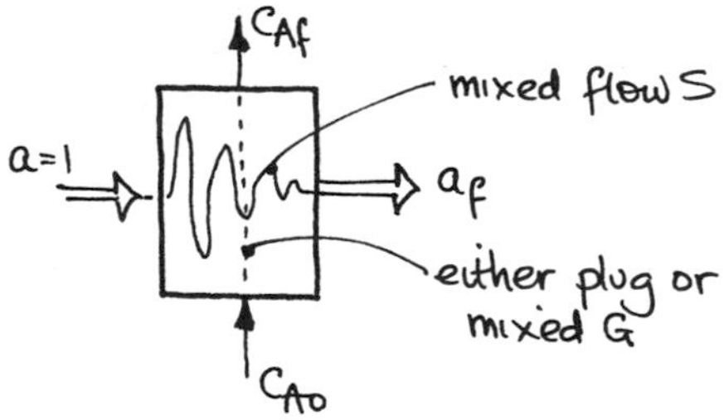

For solids: $\bar{t}_s = \frac{1-a_f}{k_d a_f}$

For mixed flow G: $\tau'_g = \frac{C_{A0}-C_{Af}}{k' C_{Af} a_f}$

For plug flow G: $\tau'_g = \int_{C_{Af}}^{C_{A0}} \frac{dC_A}{k' C_A a_f}$

$$a_f = \frac{1}{1+R_d} \quad \text{with } a_f = \bar{a}$$

$$\frac{C_{Af}}{C_{A0}} = \frac{1}{1+Ra_f} = \frac{1+R_d}{1+R_d+R}$$

$$\frac{C_{Af}}{C_{A0}} = e^{-Ra_f} = e^{-R/1+R_d}$$

B. Plug flow S (reactor alone)

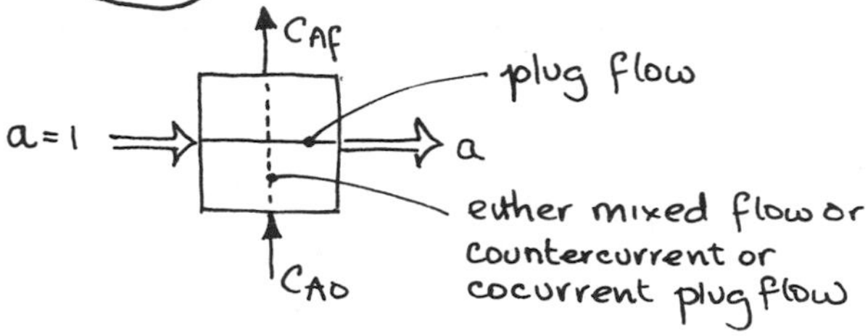

For solids :
$$\bar{t}_s = \int_a^1 \frac{da}{k_d a}$$

also
$$\bar{a} = \frac{a_{in} - a_{out}}{\ln(a_{in}/a_{out})}$$

For mixed flow G:
$$\tau'_g = \frac{C_{A0} - C_{Af}}{k' C_{Af} \bar{a}}$$

For plug flow G : (both co and countercurrent)
$$\tau'_g = \int_{C_{Af}}^{C_{A0}} \frac{dC_A}{k' C_A a}$$

"a" varies with position in the reactor, or
$$a = e^{-R_d(\ell/L)}$$

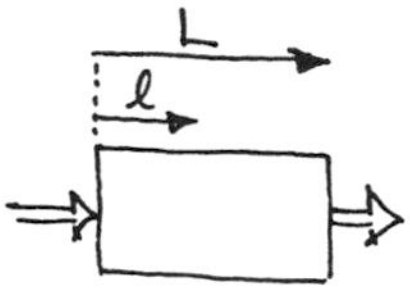

$$a = e^{-R_d}$$

$$\bar{a} = \frac{1-a}{\ln 1/a} = \frac{1 - e^{-R_d}}{R_d}$$

$$\frac{C_{Af}}{C_{A0}} = \frac{1}{1 + R\bar{a}} = \frac{R_d}{R_d + R - Re^{-R_d}}$$

$$\frac{C_{Af}}{C_{A0}} = e^{-R\bar{a}} = e^{-\frac{R}{R_d}(1 - e^{-R_d})}$$

Note: we get the same answer for co and countercurrent flow. So for the same processing rates countercurrent has no advantage

C Mixed flow S / mixed flow S. (reactor) (regenerator)

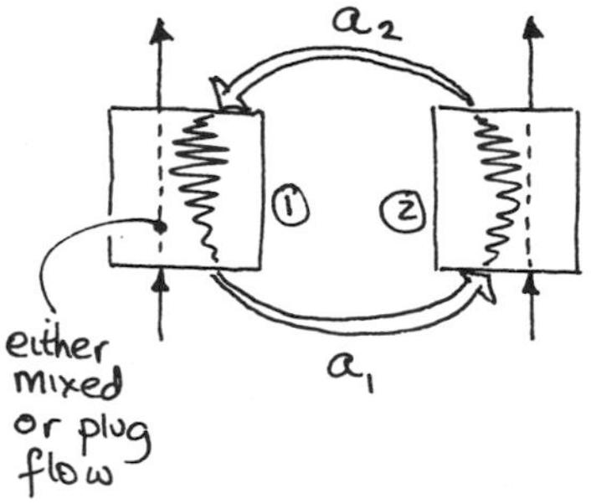

For solids in the reactor :
$$\bar{t}_{s1} = \frac{a_2 - a_1}{k_d a_1}$$

For solids in the regenerator :
$$\bar{t}_{s2} = \frac{a_2 - a_1}{k_r (1 - a_2)}$$

Combining and rearranging gives

For solids — in the reactor and at exit:

$$a_1 = \frac{R_r}{R_r + R_d + R_r R_d}$$

For solids — in the regenerator and at exit:

$$a_2 = a_1(1+R_d) = \frac{R_r(1+R_d)}{R_r + R_d + R_r R_d}$$

For reactor gas in mixed flow:

$$\frac{C_{Af}}{C_{A0}} = \frac{1}{1+Ra_1} = \frac{R_r + R_d + R_r R_d}{R_r + R_d + R_r R_d + RR_r}$$

For reactor gas in plug flow:

$$\frac{C_{Af}}{C_{A0}} = e^{-Ra_1} = e^{-\frac{RR_r}{R_r + R_d + R_r R_d}}$$

D. Mixed flow S (reactor) / plug flow S (regenerator)

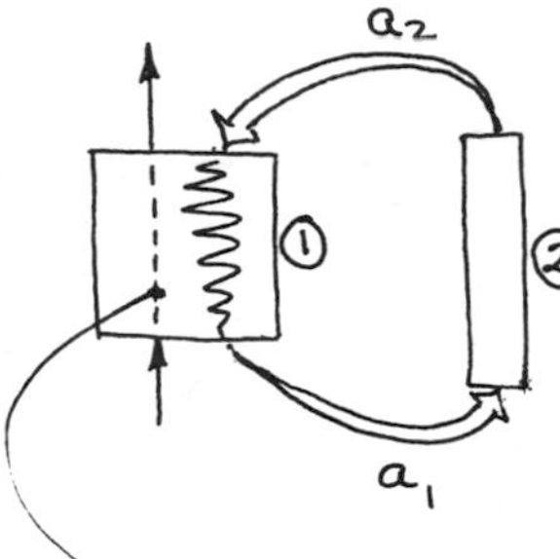

For solids in the reactor:

$$\bar{t}_{s1} = \frac{a_2 - a_1}{k_d a_1}$$

For solids in the regenerator:

$$\bar{t}_{s2} = \int_{a_1}^{a_2} \frac{da}{k_r(1-a)}$$

Combining gives

For solids — in the reactor and at exit:

$$a_1 = \frac{1 - e^{-R_r}}{1 + R_d - e^{-R_r}}$$

For solids — exit of regenerator:

$$a_2 = a_1(1+R_d) = \frac{(1-e^{-R_r})(1+R_d)}{1 + R_d - e^{-R_r}}$$

For reactor gas in mixed flow:

$$\frac{C_{Af}}{C_{A0}} = \frac{1}{1+Ra_1} = \frac{1 + R_d - e^{-R_r}}{1 + R_d + R - e^{-R_r} - Re^{-R_r}}$$

For reactor gas in plug flow:

$$\frac{C_{Af}}{C_{A0}} = e^{-Ra_1} = e^{-\frac{R + Re^{-R_r}}{1 + R_d - e^{-R_r}}}$$

E. Plug flow S / mixed flow S.
(reactor) (regenerator)

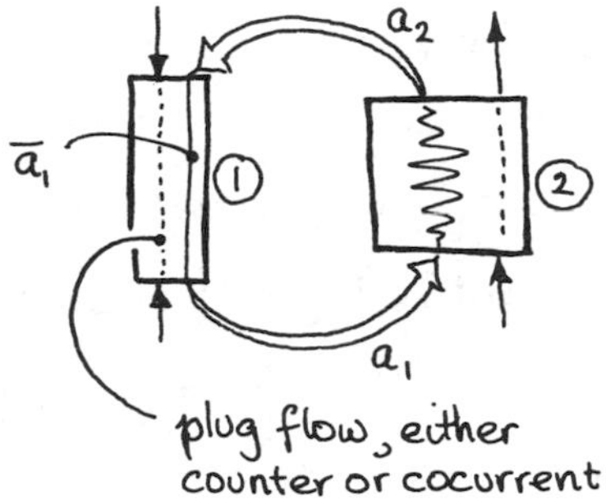

For solids in the reactor: $\bar{t}_{s1} = \int_{a_1}^{a_2} \frac{da}{k_d a}$

For solids in the regenerator: $\bar{t}_{s2} = \frac{a_2 - a_1}{k_r(1-a_2)}$

Combining and rearranging gives

For solids:

- at exit of the reactor: $$a_1 = \frac{R_r e^{-R_d}}{1+R_r-e^{-R_d}}$$
- within the reactor: $$\bar{a}_1 = \frac{a_{in}-a_{out}}{\ln a_{in}/a_{out}} = \frac{R_r(1-e^{-R_d})}{R_d(1+R_r-e^{-R_d})}$$
- in the regenerator: $$a_2 = a_1 e^{R_d} = \frac{R_r}{1+R_r-e^{-R_d}}$$

For reactor gas in mixed flow:

$$\frac{C_{Af}}{C_{A0}} = \frac{1}{1+R\bar{a}} = \frac{R_d(1+R_r-e^{-R_d})}{R_d+R_rR_d+RR_r-R_de^{-R_d}-RR_re^{-R_d}}$$

For reactor gas in either cocurrent or countercurrent plug flow:

$$\frac{C_{Af}}{C_{A0}} = e^{-\frac{RR_r(1-e^{-R_d})}{R_d(1+R_r-e^{-R_d})}}$$

II. Performance Equations for Concentration Dependent Deactivation: $n=1$, $m_1=1$, $m_2=0$, $d_1=1$, $d_2=1$.

Consider the reaction $A \rightarrow R$ with: $-r_A' = k' C_A a$

for deactivation: $-\frac{da}{dt} = k_d C_A a$

for regeneration: $\frac{da}{dt} = k_r(1-a)$

The performance equations for these kinetics are identical to those of section I whenever at least one phase is in mixed flow (cases A, B, C, D, but not E), with the following modifications:

- For **mixed flow of reactor gas** put

$$R_d = k_d C_{Af} \bar{t}_{s1}$$

and solve the resulting set of equations by trial and error, guessing either C_{Af} or a_1.

- For **plug flow of reactor gas** put

$$R_d = k_d \bar{C}_A \bar{t}_{s1} \qquad \text{where } \bar{C}_A = \frac{C_{A0} - C_{Af}}{\ln C_{A0}/C_{Af}} = \frac{C_{A0}(1 - e^{-Ra_1})}{Ra_1}$$

and solve the set of equations by guessing either $\bar{C}_A$ or a_1.

For cocurrent or countercurrent plug flow of gas and solid in the reactor (case E) this simple extension to the already-developed equations does not work.

III. Deactivation in Fluidized Beds – The Bubbling Bed Model: $n=1$, $m=0$ or 1, $d=1$, a Single Reactor.

If we feel dissatisfied (and we often should) with the plug or mixed flow assumptions for gas in a fluidized bed of fine particles and would like a better assumption we could use the bubbling bed model of chapter 25. Thus for a fluidized bed with through flow of solids a reasonable contacting pattern would be

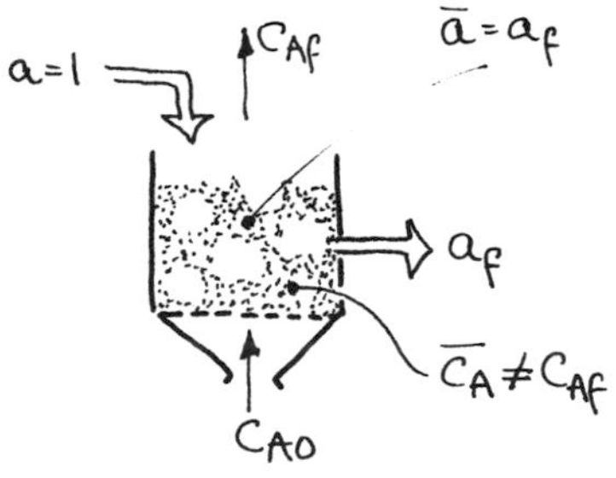

mixed flow S / bubbling bed G

The analysis then combines the treatment of this chapter with that of chapter 25 to evaluate the 3 unknowns, a_f, $\bar{C}_A$ and X_A

As an example, for the kinetics

$$-r_A' = k' C_A a \quad \cdots \text{and} \quad -\frac{da}{dt} = k_d a$$

in a fluidized bed with continual solid replacement we find

$$a_f = \bar{a} = \frac{1}{1+R_d} = \frac{1}{1+k_d \bar{t}_s}$$

$$X_A = 1 - e^{-\mathcal{K}'\tau'} = 1 - e^{-\frac{\mathcal{K}' W}{v_0}}$$

where

$$\mathcal{K}' = \left[\gamma_b k' \rho_s a_f + \frac{1}{\dfrac{1}{K_{bc}} + \dfrac{1}{\gamma_c k' \rho_s a_f + \dfrac{1}{\dfrac{1}{K_{ce}} + \dfrac{1}{\gamma_e k' \rho_s a_f}}}} \right] \frac{u_0}{(1-\varepsilon_{mf}) u_{br} \rho_s}$$

and

$$\bar{C}_{A,\ \text{bathing the solids}} = \frac{C_{A0} X_A v_0}{k' W \bar{a}}, \qquad \bar{a} = a_f$$

Again, for concentration dependent deactivation, or

$$-r_A = k' C_A a \quad \cdots \text{and} \quad -\frac{da}{dt} = k_d C_A a$$

use $R_d = k_d \bar{C}_A \bar{t}_s$ in the above expressions. Often trial and error methods have to be used to evaluate a_f, $\bar{C}_A$ and X_A

IV. Optimum Size Ratio for Reactor-Regenerator.

Various size combinations can give the same conversion of reactant. By the optimum size ratio we mean that pair which requires the smallest amount of catalyst for given feed, X_A and given solid circulation rate.

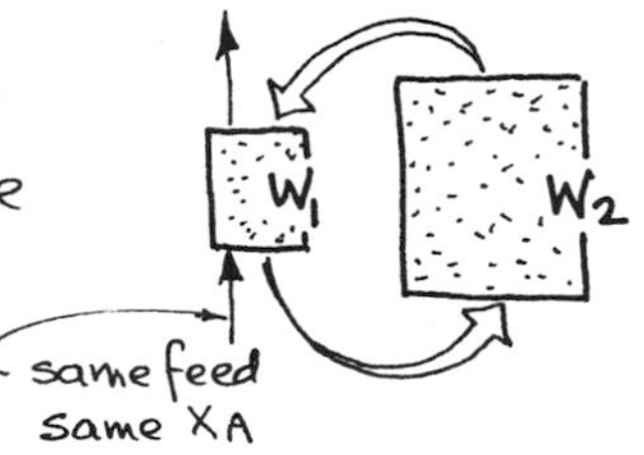

It should be easy to convince yourself from qualitative considerations alone that there should be an optimum ratio and that it would require a small regenerator if regeneration is very fast, but a large regenerator if regeneration is very slow.

Quantitatively the optimum size ratio $\frac{W_1}{W_2} = \frac{t_{s1}}{t_{s2}}$ is given as follows:

for mixed flow S (reactor) / mixed flow S (regenerator)

$$\frac{W_1}{W_2} = \left(\frac{k_r}{k_d}\right)^{1/2}$$

for mixed flow S (reactor) / plug flow S (regenerator)

$$\frac{W_1}{W_2} = \left(\frac{k_r}{k_d}\right)^{1/2} \cdot \frac{e^{R_r/2} - e^{-R_r/2}}{R_r} \quad \cdots \text{or} \quad W_1 = \frac{F_s\left(e^{R_r/2} - e^{-R_r/2}\right)}{(k_d k_r)^{1/2}}$$

for plug flow S (reactor) / mixed flow S (regenerator)

$$\frac{W_1}{W_2} = \left(\frac{k_r}{k_d}\right)^{1/2} \cdot \frac{R_d}{e^{R_d/2} - e^{-R_d/2}} \quad \cdots \text{or} \quad W_2 = \frac{F_s\left(e^{R_d/2} - e^{-R_d/2}\right)}{(k_d k_r)^{1/2}}$$

By replacing numbers into any of the above expressions we see that the slower step always requires the larger reactor, while the faster step requires the smaller reactor.

To find the actual sizes, W_1 and W_2, combine the performance equation with the size ratio equation for the particular flows at hand.

Chapter 33 Problems

Fine catalyst particles are fed and removed continuously at 5 kg/s from a pilot plant fluidized bed reactor about 0.36 m ID and about 0.4 m high containing 200 kg of catalyst. Feed gas consisting of pure A at 0.5 mol/s and 0.01 m^3/s reacts on contact with catalyst, and at the same time the incoming fresh catalyst deactivates. The reaction and deactivation kinetics are well represented by

$$A \rightarrow R, \quad -r_A' = k'C_A a \quad \text{and} \quad -\frac{da}{dt} = k_d a$$

The flow of solids can reasonably be represented by mixed flow however we are uncertain about the flow pattern of gas. Find the kinetic constants k' and k_d, if for the gas and solid streams leaving the reactor

A1 . . . $X_A = 0.99$ and $\bar{a} = 0.01$, assuming mixed flow of gas.

A2 . . . $X_A = 0.67$ and $\bar{a} = 0.2$, assuming plug flow of gas.

Problems 1 and 2 assumed concentration independent deactivation. This assumption is often made because of simplicity, even though the deactivation is likely to be concentration dependent. So here assume concentration dependent deactivation of the form

$$-\frac{da}{dt} = k_d C_A a$$

A3 . . . with this change redo problem 1.

A4 . . . with this change redo problem 2.

Suppose that conversion of reactant A is 50% and $\bar{a} = 0.2$ for the reactor of the previous problems. Also suppose that we wish to raise the conversion above 50% by changing the operating conditions. This can be done in a number of ways:

(a) by doubling the solids in the reactor

(b) by halving the gas flow rate

(c) by doubling the solids flow rate

Examine these alternatives and find which gives the largest increase in X_A

A5 . . . assuming mixed flow of gas.

A6 . . . assuming plug flow of gas.

Chapter 33 Problems

Reactant gas ($C_{A0} = 100\ mol/m^3$, $u_o = 0.3\ m/s$, $v_0 = 0.3\pi\ m^3/s$) passes upward through a 2 m diameter fluidized bed reactor ($u_{mf} = 0.03\ m/s$, $\varepsilon_{mf} = 0.5$) containing seven tons of catalyst ($W = 7000$ kg, $\rho_s = 2000\ kg/m^3$). Reaction and deactivation of catalyst proceed as follows

$$A \rightarrow R, \quad -r'_A = k'C_A a \quad \text{with} \quad k' = 0.01\ m^3/kg{\cdot}s$$

$$-\frac{da}{dt} = k_d a \quad \text{with} \quad k_d = 2.4 \times 10^{-3}\ s^{-1}$$

Since the catalyst deactivates we introduce continuously a small stream of fresh catalyst ($F_s = 0.7$ kg/s) and we remove an equal amount of spent catalyst from the bed.

A7 ... Calculate X_A assuming mixed flow of gas.

A8 ... Calculate X_A assuming plug flow of gas.

A9* ... Calculate X_A assuming that the flow of gas follows the bubbling bed model.

Additional data: $\mathcal{D} = 20 \times 10^{-6}\ m^2/s$, $\alpha = 0.33$, estimated bubble size = 0.32 m, and take $\gamma_b = 0.003$. Note that these conditions represent an extension of the conditions of example 1 of chapter 25 to deactivating catalysts.

With fresh catalyst gaseous A reacts as follows

$$A \rightarrow R, \quad -r'_A = k'C_A a \quad \text{with} \quad k' = 1\ m^3/kg{\cdot}s$$

We wish to develop a process for treating 1 m^3/s of 100 mol A/m^3 feed to 90% conversion, and since the catalyst decays very rapidly we are forced to turn to the solid circulation reactor-regenerator system. The kinetics of this deactivation and regeneration are given by

$$-\frac{da}{dt} = a,\ s^{-1} \qquad \frac{da}{dt} = 0.01\,(1-a),\ s^{-1}$$

(a) If the catalyst did not decay what weight of packed bed would be needed?

(b) In the circulation system and with the deactivating catalyst what size of reactor and of regenerator do we need to minimize the total weight of catalyst if the circulation rate of catalyst is $F_s = 10$ kg/s? Assume

B10 ... mixed flow of G and S in reactor, mixed flow of S in regenerator.

B11* ... mixed flow of G and S in reactor, plug flow of S in regenerator.

B12* ... plug flow of G and S in reactor, mixed flow of S in regenerator.

Chapter 33 Problems

Our present fluidized reactor-regenerator system which has $W_1 = W_2$ gives 50% conversion of gaseous reactant, with the mean activity of catalyst streams entering and leaving the reactor being

$$\bar{a}_2 = 0.25, \quad \bar{a}_1 = 0.01$$

The kinetics are reasonably represented by

$$A \rightarrow R, \quad -r'_A = k'C_A a, \quad \begin{cases} -\dfrac{da}{dt} = k_d a & \text{in reactor} \\ \dfrac{da}{dt} = k_r(1-a) & \text{in regeneration} \end{cases}$$

and both solid and gas are in mixed flow everywhere. How do the following single changes affect the conversion of gas? Comparing answers will tell which change is most effective.

B13 . . . Double the circulation rate of solids.

B14 . . . Halve the gas flow rate.

B15 . . . Double the size of either the reactor or regenerator. Which is preferable ?

B16 We plan to design and build a completely new reactor-regenerator system for the above reaction. For identical gas feed rate, total weight of catalyst, solid circulation rate and flow pattern of solids what size ratio of reactor-regenerator would you recommend, and what conversion of gas can you expect to get?

C17* The <u>raining solids reactor</u> is one way of effecting a catalytic reaction having very rapid catalyst deactivation. Here gas flows up a tube in plug flow and solids fall down the tube in plug flow. For the simplest of kinetics

$$-r'_A = k'C_A a$$

$$-\frac{da}{dt} = k_d a$$

develop the performance equation for such reactors and check it with the equation given in this chapter.

Chapter 33 Problems

The <u>transfer line reactor</u> is also useful for fast catalyst decay. Here gas flows up the tube carrying the solids with it, as in pneumatic conveying. For the simplest of kinetics

$$-r'_A = k'C_A a \quad \text{and} \quad -\frac{da}{dt} = k_d a$$

develop the performance equation for such reactors and compare your expression with that given in this chapter.

C18 . . . Assume mixed flow of solids.

C19 . . . Assume plug flow of solids.

Chapter 34. G/L REACTIONS ON SOLID CATALYST: TRICKLE BEDS, SLURRY REACTORS, THREE PHASE FLUIDIZED BEDS, etc.

These reactions are of the form

$$A(g \xrightarrow{\text{dissolve}} l) + B(l) \xrightarrow[\text{catalyst}]{\text{on solid}} \text{products.}$$

and they can be run in a number of ways:

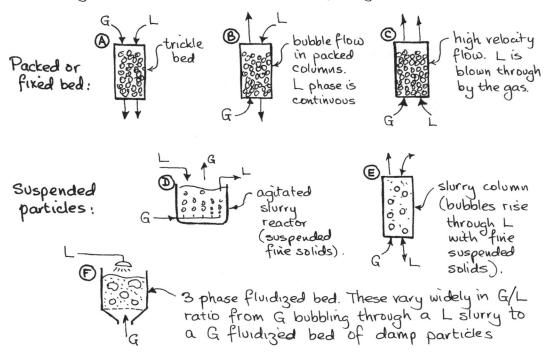

Packed or fixed bed:

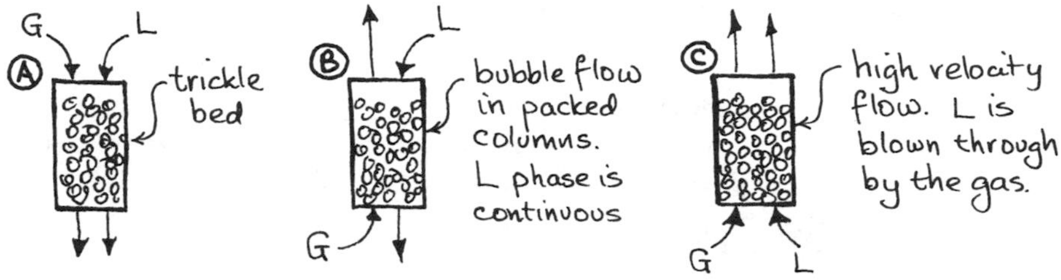

Suspended particles:

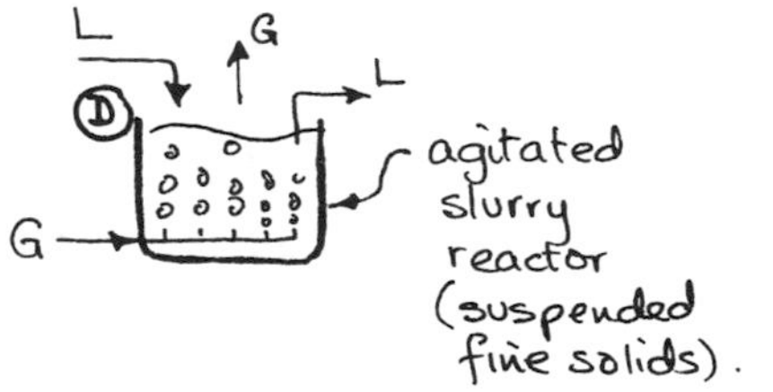

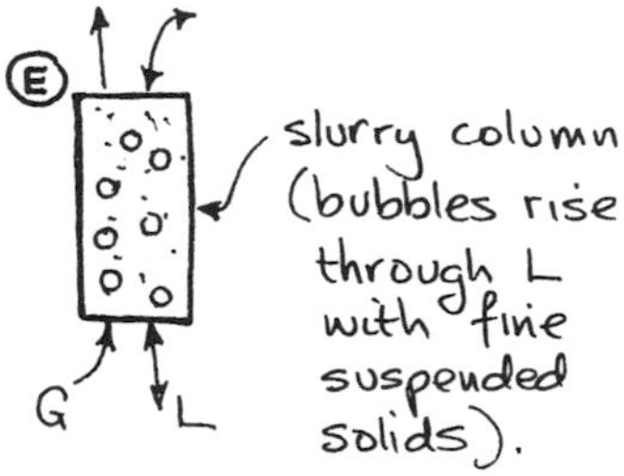

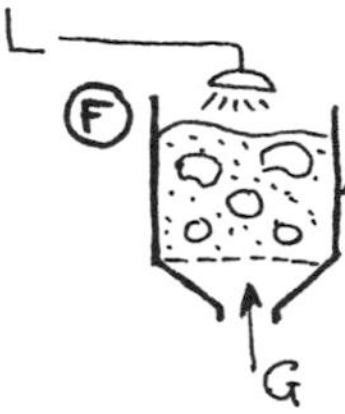

3 phase fluidized bed. These vary widely in G/L ratio from G bubbling through a L slurry to a G fluidized bed of damp particles

The packed bed contactors use large solid particles, the slurry reactors, very fine suspended solids, while the fluidized bed can use either depending on the flow rates.

Flow patterns: Overall, all other things equal (which they are not):

- countercurrent plug flow is the most desirable flow pattern
- cocurrent plug flow is next

- then plug/mixed flow
- and worst of all in terms of driving forces is mixed/mixed flow.

In the above 6 types of contactors flows approximate the ideals as follows

- scheme Ⓐ and Ⓒ: close to cocurrent plug flow
- scheme Ⓑ: between countercurrent plug and plug G/mixed L, depending on the extent of backmixing induced by the rising bubbles
- scheme Ⓓ: mixed G/mixed L
- scheme Ⓔ: between countercurrent plug and plug G/mixed L, depending on the L backmixing which can be quite large. Much depends on the vessel geometry, baffle design, bubble size, etc.
- scheme Ⓕ: plug G/mixed L

I. The General Rate Equation.

Consider the reaction and stoichiometry:

$$A(g \rightarrow \ell) + bB(\ell) \xrightarrow[\text{surface}]{\text{on catalyst}} \text{products} \qquad \cdots b = \left(\frac{\text{mol B}}{\text{mol A}}\right)$$

$$\left.\begin{aligned} -r_A''' &= k_A''' C_A C_B \\ -r_B''' &= k_B''' C_A C_B \end{aligned}\right\} \text{ where } \left.\begin{aligned} -r_A''' &= -r_B'''/b & \cdots\ &\text{mol/m}^3\ell\cdot\text{s} \\ k_A''' &= k_B'''/b & \cdots\ &\text{m}^3\ell/\text{mol}\cdot\text{s} \end{aligned}\right\}$$

Gas reactant must first dissolve in the L, then both reactants must diffuse or move to the catalyst surface for reaction to occur. Thus the resistance to transfer across the G/L interface and then to the surface of solid both enter the rate expression.

To develop the rate equation let us draw on the 2 film theory, and let us use the following nomenclature:

$H_A = \frac{p_A}{C_A}$, Henry's law constant $[\text{Pa}\cdot\text{m}^3 l/\text{mol}]$

$a_i = \frac{\text{gas-liquid interfacial area}}{\text{volume of reactor}}$

$a_c = \frac{\text{external surface of particles}}{\text{volume of reactor}}$ $\quad \frac{\text{for}}{\text{spheres}} \quad \frac{6 f_s}{d_p}$

$f_s = \frac{\text{volume of particles}}{\text{volume of reactor}}$, called solid loading

$f_l = \frac{\text{volume of liquid}}{\text{volume of reactor}}$, called liquid holdup

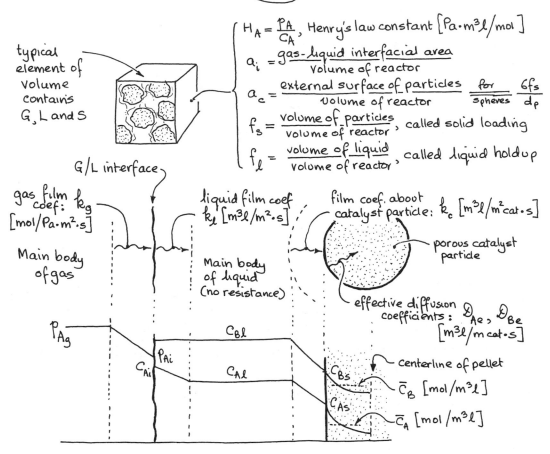

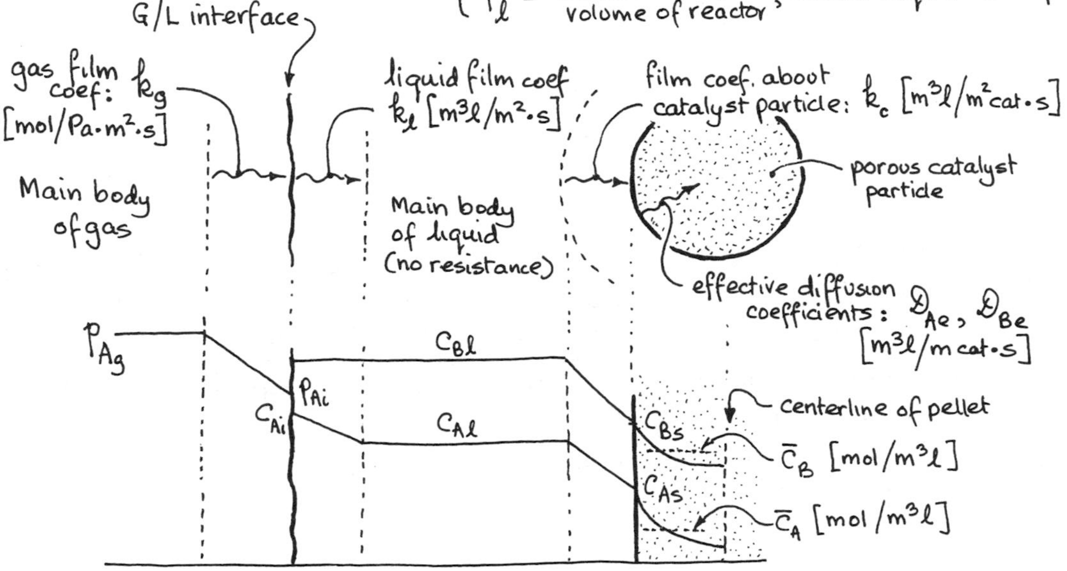

We can then write

for A:

$$-r_A'''' = \frac{1}{\dfrac{1}{k_{Ag} a_i} + \dfrac{H_A}{k_{Al} a_i} + \dfrac{H_A}{k_{Ac} a_c} + \dfrac{H_A}{(k_A''' \bar{C}_B)\,\mathcal{E}_A f_s}}\, p_{Ag} \qquad (1)$$

($\mathcal{E}_A$: effectiveness factor for the first order reaction of A with rate constant $(k_A''' \bar{C}_B)$)

these rates are related by $-r_A''' = \frac{-r_B'''}{b}$

for B:

$$-r_B'''' = \frac{1}{\dfrac{1}{k_{Bc} a_c} + \dfrac{1}{(k_B''' \bar{C}_A)\,\mathcal{E}_B f_s}}\, C_{Bl} \qquad (2)$$

($\mathcal{E}_B$: effectiveness factor for the first order reaction of B with rate constant $(k_B''' \bar{C}_A)$)

Now either eq 1 or eq 2 should give the rate of reaction. Unhappily even with all the system parameters known (k, a, f, etc) we still cannot solve these expressions because $\bar{C}_B$ is not known in eq 1 and $\bar{C}_A$ is not known in eq 2. However, if $\bar{C}_A \cong C_{As}$ and $\bar{C}_B \cong C_{Bs}$ (negligible pore resistance) then we can relate these unknown concentrations with known values as follows:

$$-r_A'''' = \frac{1}{\frac{1}{k_{Ag}a_i} + \frac{H_A}{k_{Al}a_i} + \frac{H_A}{k_{Ac}a_c}}\left(p_{Ag} - H_A C_{As}\right) \qquad (3)$$

and

$$-r_B'''' = k_{Bc}a_c\left(C_{Bl} - C_{Bs}\right) \qquad (4)$$

Either solve eqs 1 and 4 simultaneously or eqs 2 and 3 simultaneously to find the rate of reaction at any point in the reactor. This is best done by trial and error: either guess C_{Bs} and replace in eqs 1 and 4 until the rates match, or guess C_{As} and replace in eqs 2 and 3 until the rates match. Also, since $\mathcal{D}_A$ and $\mathcal{D}_B$ are usually not too different in liquids we can simplify by making

$$\mathcal{D}_{Ae} = \mathcal{D}_{Be} \quad \ldots\text{and}\ldots \quad k_{Ac} = k_{Bc}$$

II Simplification of the General Rate Equation.

Extreme 1: $C_{Bl} \gg C_{Al}$. In systems with pure liquid B and slightly soluble gas A we can take

$$C_{Bs} = \bar{C}_{B,\text{within pellet}} = C_{Bl} \quad \ldots \text{same value everywhere}$$

With C_B constant the reaction becomes first order overall and the above rate expressions with their required trial and error all reduce to one directly solvable expression

$$-r_A'''' = \frac{1}{\frac{1}{k_{Ag}a_i} + \frac{H_A}{k_{Al}a_i} + \frac{H_A}{k_{Ac}a_c} + \frac{H_A}{(k_A'''C_{Bl})\mathcal{E}_A f_s}}\, p_{Ag} \qquad (5)$$

where $(k_A'''C_{Bl})$ = first order rate constant for A

Extreme 2: $C_{B\ell} \ll C_{A\ell}$. In systems with dilute liquid reactant B, highly soluble A, and high pressure, we can take

$$C_{A\ell} = \frac{p_{Ag}}{H_A} \quad \text{... throughout}$$

The rate becomes first order with respect to B and reduces to

$$-r_B'''' = \cfrac{1}{\cfrac{1}{k_{Bc}a_c} + \cfrac{1}{\underbrace{\left(\cfrac{k_B'''p_{Ag}}{H_A}\right)}\mathcal{E}_B f_s}} C_{B\ell} \qquad (6)$$

(underbraced term: first order rate constant which is used to calculate $\mathcal{E}_B$)

How to test whether these extremes apply, and other comments.

(a) By the unequal signs $\gg$ or $\ll$ we mean 2 or 3 times as large.

(b) If $\frac{p_{Ag}}{H_A} \ll C_{B\ell}$ then for sure B is in excess and eq 5 applies.

(c) More generally compare the rates calculated from eqs 5 and 6 and use the smaller one. Thus

- thus if $r''''_{eq5} \ll r''''_{eq6}$ then $C_{B\ell}$ is in excess and extreme 1 applies.
- if $r''''_{eq5} \gg r''''_{eq6}$ then eq 6 gives the rate of reaction

(d) Nearly always does one or other of the extremes apply.

(e) **On wettability**: In slurry reactors the catalyst particle swims about the fluid and is completely wetted. However, in the trickle bed, especially with maldistribution of gas and liquid a significant fraction of the catalyst may be dry and thus have an effectiveness factor of zero.

If you happen to have a way of estimating the wetted fraction, say from black magic, then the overall effectiveness factor to be used in eqs 1 to 6 is

$$\mathcal{E}_{overall} = \left(\mathcal{E}_{\text{from pore diffusion theory}}\right)\left(\begin{array}{c}\text{fraction of solid}\\ \text{which is wetted}\end{array}\right)$$

III. Performance Equations for an Excess of B, or $C_B \gg C_A$

All types of contactors – trickle beds, slurry reactors and fluidized beds – can be treated at the same time. What is important is to recognize the flow patterns of the contacting phases.

A. Mixed flow G / any flow L.

A material balance about the whole reactor gives

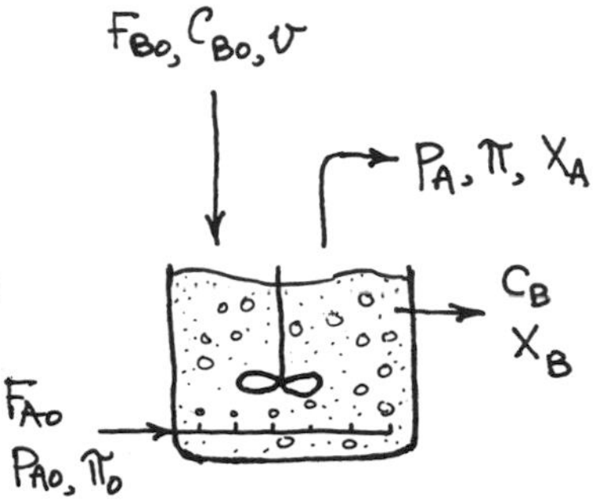

$$\underbrace{F_{A0} X_A}_{\text{I}} = \underbrace{\frac{1}{b} F_{B0} X_B}_{\text{II}} = \underbrace{(-r_A'''')\, V_r}_{\text{III}} \quad \cdots (7)$$

where $\frac{1}{b} F_{B0} X_B = \frac{1}{b} v (C_{B0} - C_B)$

I: rate of loss of A; II: rate of loss of B; III: rate of reaction

Solution is straightforward. Just combine I & III or II & III.

B. Plug flow G / any flow L.

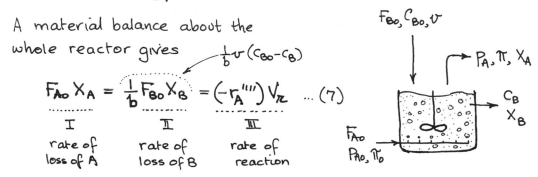

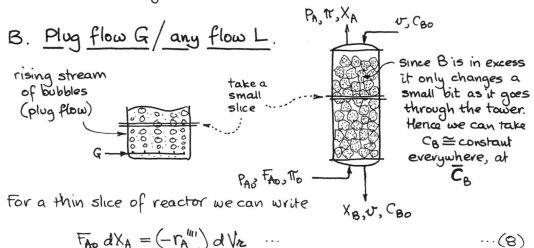

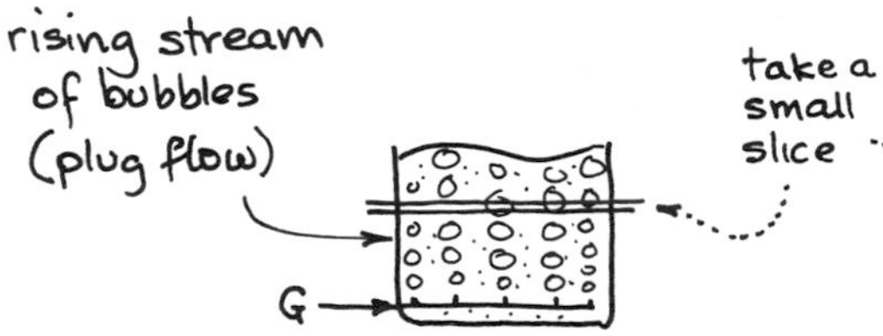

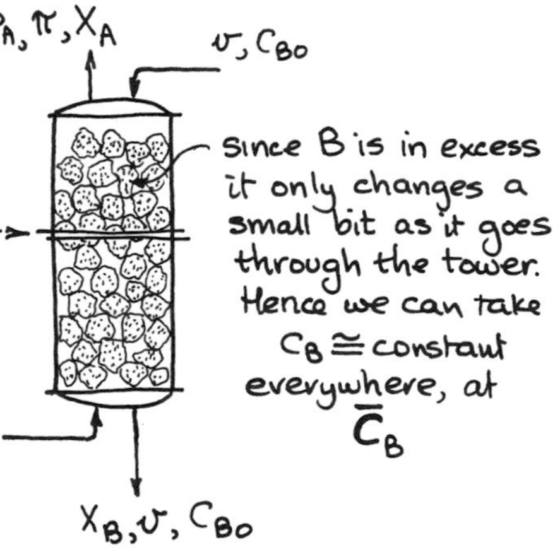

For a thin slice of reactor we can write

$$F_{A0}\, dX_A = (-r_A'''')\, dV_r \quad \cdots \quad \cdots (8)$$

where

$$1 - X_A = \frac{p_A(\pi_0 - p_{A0})}{p_{A0}(\pi - p_A)} \underset{\text{only}}{\overset{\text{dilute}}{=}} \frac{p_A \pi_0}{p_{A0} \pi} \underset{\pi = \text{const.}}{\overset{\text{dilute}}{=}} \frac{p_A}{p_{A0}}$$

and

$$-dX_A = \frac{\pi(\pi_0 - p_{A0})\, dp_A}{p_{A0}(\pi - p_A)^2} \overset{\text{dilute}}{=} \frac{\pi_0\, dp_A}{p_{A0}\, \pi} \underset{\pi = \text{const.}}{\overset{\text{dilute}}{=}} \frac{dp_A}{p_{A0}}$$

Overall around the whole reactor

$$\frac{V_r}{F_{Ao}} = \int_0^{X_A} \frac{dX_A}{(-r_A'''')} \quad \cdots \text{with} \cdots \quad F_{Ao}X_A = \underbrace{\frac{F_{Bo}}{b}X_B}_{\frac{v}{b}(C_{Bo}-C_B)} \qquad \cdots (9)$$

(use $\bar{C}_B$ here, in $(-r_A'''')$)

C. Mixed flow G / batch L.

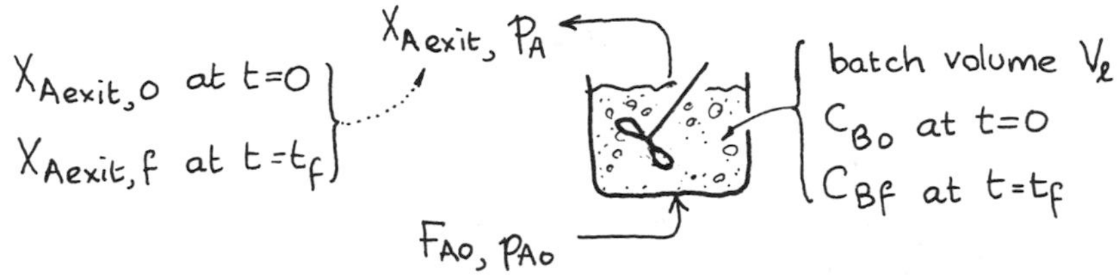

Here the material balance becomes

$$\underbrace{F_{Ao}X_{Aexit}}_{\text{I}} = \underbrace{\frac{V_l}{b}\left(-\frac{dC_B}{dt}\right)}_{\text{II}} = \underbrace{(-r_A'''')V_r}_{\text{III}} \qquad \cdots (10)$$

The general procedure for finding the processing time is:

Pick a number of C_B values	From I and III calculate	
C_{Bo}	$X_{Aexit,o}$	$(-r_A'''')_o$
⋮	⋮	⋮
C_{Bf}	$X_{Aexit,f}$	$(-r_A'''')_f$

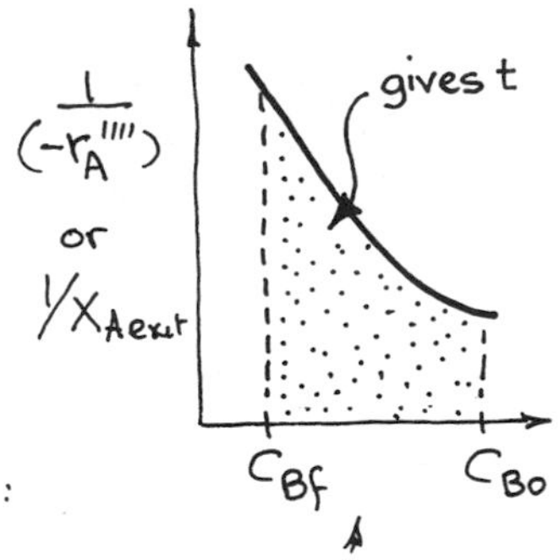

Then from II & III, or I & III solve for t:

$$t = \frac{V_l}{bV_r}\int_{C_{Bf}}^{C_{Bo}} \frac{dC_B}{(-r_A'''')} = \frac{V_l}{bF_{Ao}}\int_{C_{Bf}}^{C_{Bo}} \frac{dC_B}{X_{Aexit}} \qquad \cdots (11)$$

D. Plug flow G / batch uniform L.

Now C_B changes with time, but assume that it changes slowly enough so that an element of gas sees the same C_B as it flows through the unit.

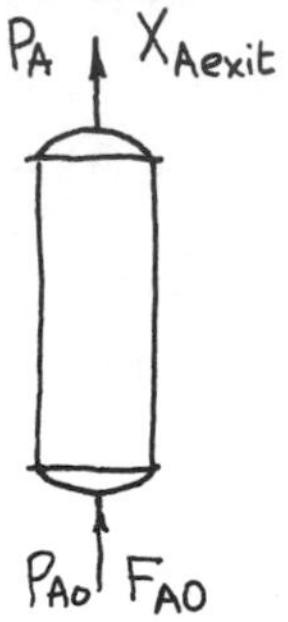

Since C_B is in excess it could be recirculated. In any case, take the same C_B value throughout the unit.

For a tiny slice of contactor in a short time interval in which C_B is practically unchanged we may write. $F_{Ao}\, dX_A = (-r_A'''')\, dV_r$.
So for the whole reactor

$$\frac{V_r}{F_{Ao}} = \int_0^{X_{Aexit}} \frac{dX_A}{(-r_A'''')} \qquad \cdots (12)$$

← because C_B changes with time $X_{A,exit}$ and $(-r_A'''')$ do so too.

Considering B we may now write

$$F_{Ao} X_{Aexit} = \frac{V_l}{b}\left(-\frac{dC_B}{dt}\right)$$

and on integrating we find the processing time to be

$$t = \frac{V_l}{b F_{Ao}} \int_{C_{Bf}}^{C_{Bo}} \frac{dC_B}{X_{Aexit}} \qquad \cdots (13)$$

The procedure is then as follows:

Choose C_B	Solve eq 12 to give X_{Aexit}
C_{Bo}	$X_{Aexit,o}$
⋮	⋮
C_{Bf}	$X_{Aexit,f}$

⟹ then solve eq 13 graphically

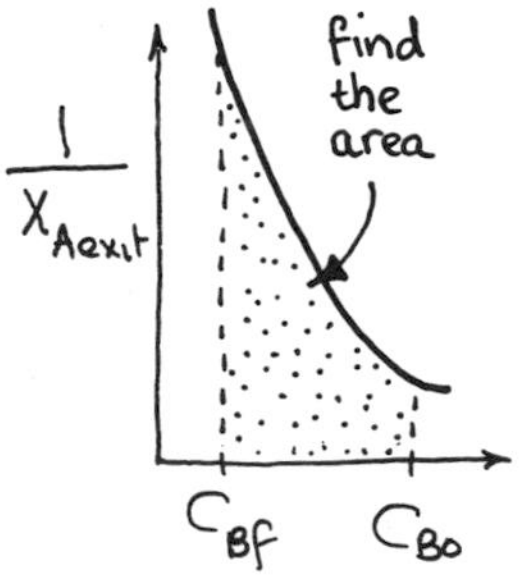

E. Special case of pure gaseous A.

One often encounters this situation, especially in hydrogenations. Here one usually recycles the gas, in which case p_A and C_A stay unchanged; hence the above equations for both batch and flow systems simplify enormously.

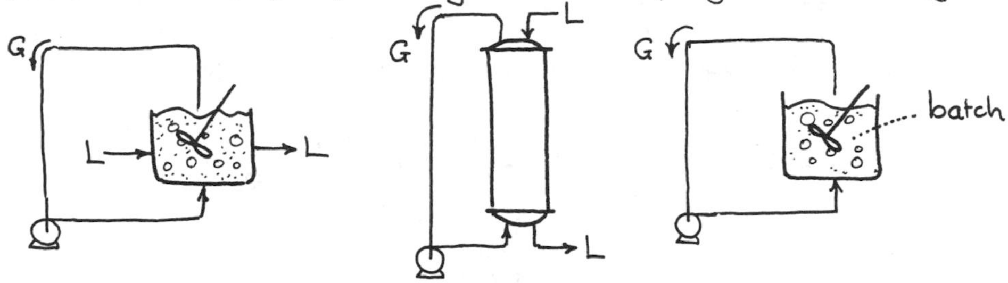

In solving problems it is suggested that one write down the basic material balances and then carefully see what simplifications apply ... is p_A constant? is $m=0$? ... and so on.

F. Comments.

(a) This treatment assumes that

- In plug flow the dissolved but unreacted A which flows down the column in the liquid is negligible
- In mixed flow the liquid leaving the reactor contains a negligible amount of dissolved A.

If this is not so then you must include this term in the development of the performance equation. Fortunately, since B is in excess in the liquid C_A is often not too large.

(b) In bubble slurry reactors reactant A, in plug flow, contacts liquid, in mixed flow. The performance equation for this situation is awkward. I don't know how to develop it. However the result lies somewhere between eqs 7 and 9

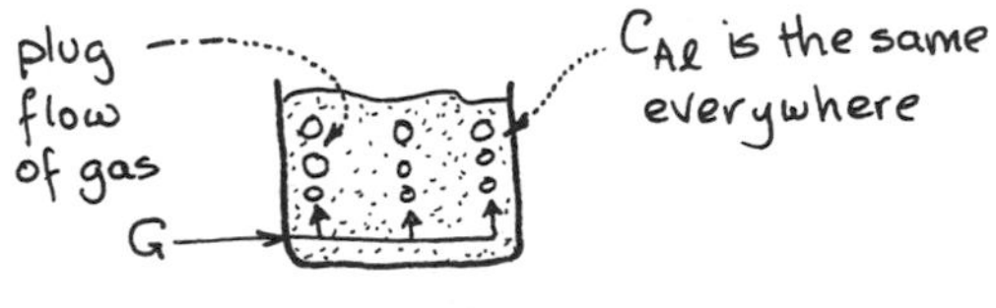

(c) The rate expressions used so far have been first order with respect to A and first order with respect to B. But how do we deal with more general rate forms, for example:

$$A(g) + bB(\ell) \xrightarrow[\text{catalyst}]{\text{on solid}} \cdots, \quad -r_A''' = \frac{-r_B'''}{b} = k_A''' C_A^n C_B^m$$

To be able to combine the chemical step with the mass transfer steps in simple fashion, as shown in chapter 11, we must linearize this non linear rate form, thus

$$-r_A''' = k_A''' C_A^n C_B^m \Longrightarrow -r_A''' = \left[\left(k_A''' \bar{C}_B^{\,m}\right) \bar{C}_A^{\,n-1}\right] C_A \qquad \cdots (14)$$

mean values at locations where reaction occurs

This approach is not completely satisfactory but is our most reasonable. Thus, instead of eq 5, the rate form to be used in all the performance expressions will be

$$-r_A'''' = \frac{1}{\dfrac{1}{H_A k_{Ag} a_i} + \dfrac{1}{k_{A\ell} a_i} + \dfrac{1}{k_{Ac} a_c} + \dfrac{1}{\left(k_A''' \bar{C}_B^{\,m} \bar{C}_A^{\,n-1}\right) \varepsilon_A f_s}} \cdot \frac{p_A}{H_A} \qquad \cdots (15)$$

IV Performance Equation for Excess of A. ($C_A \gg C_B$)

Here again we treat the contactors according to the flow pattern of G and L therein.

Plug flow L/any flow G (tower and packed bed operations)

Here we have simply

$$\frac{V_r}{F_{B0}} = \int_0^{X_B} \frac{dX_B}{-r_B''''} \quad \text{where} \quad 1 - X_B \cong \frac{C_B}{C_{B0}} \qquad \cdots (16)$$

($-r_B''''$ given by eq 6)

Mixed flow L / any flow G (tank operations of all types)

Here the performance equation is simply

$$\frac{V_r}{F_{B0}} = \frac{X_B}{-r_B''''} \qquad \cdots (17)$$

where $X_B = 1 - \frac{C_B}{C_{B0}}$, and $-r_B''''$ is given by eq 6

Batch L / any flow G Noting that $C_A \cong$ constant throughout time (because it is in excess) the performance equation for B becomes

$$-\frac{dC_B}{dt} = -r_B = \frac{V_r}{V_l} r_B'''' \quad \cdots \text{or} \cdots \quad t = \int_0^t \frac{dC_B}{-r_B} \qquad \cdots (18)$$

V Which Kind of Contactor to use.

This depends on

- where the controlling resistance lies in the rate expression
- the advantages of one contacting pattern over another
- the difference in auxiliary equipment needed.

The overall economics which accounts for these three factors will determine which set up and reactor type is best.

Let us briefly look at these factors in turn

1. **The rate**: We should favor the contactor which favors the weakest step in the rate. Thus

- if the main resistance lies in the G/L film use a contactor with large interfacial surface area.
- if the resistance lies at the L/S boundary use a large exterior surface of solid, or large f_s
- if the resistance to pore diffusion intrudes use tiny particles.

and so on.

From prediction we can find the weakest step by inserting all transfer coefficients (k_g, k_ℓ, ...) and system parameters (a_i, a_s, ...) into the rate equation and then see which resistance term dominates. Unfortunately the values of these quantities usually are not well known.

From experiment we can change one or other factor in the rate expression, for example

- solid loading (this changes f_s alone, hence only changes the last resistance term in the rate expression)
- size of catalyst particle (affects both $\mathcal{E}$ and a_s)
- intensity of agitation of the liquid (affects the mass transfer terms terms in the rate)
- π, C_B, p_A, and so on.

This should tell which factor strongly affects the rate and which does not.

Boosting the weakest step in the rate by a proper choice of particle size, solid loading and reactor type can strongly affect the overall economics of the process.

2. Contacting: Plug flow of the limiting component, the one which is not in excess, is certainly better than mixed flow. However, except for very high conversions this factor is of minor importance.

3. Supporting equipment: Slurry reactors can use very fine catalyst particles and this can lead to problems of separating catalyst from liquid. Trickle beds don't have this problem, and this is the big advantage of trickle beds. Unfortunately these large particles in trickle beds mean much lower reaction rates. With regard to rate the trickle bed can only hold its own

- for very slow reactions on porous solids where pore diffusion limitations do not appear, even for large particles
- for very fast reactions on non porous catalyst-coated particles.

Overall, the trickle bed is simpler, the slurry reactor usually has a higher rate, the fluidized bed is somewhere in between.

VI Applications

Here is a short list of applications of these reactors.

- The catalytic hydrogenation of petroleum fractions to remove sulfur impurities: Hydrogen is very soluble in the liquid, high pressure is used while the impurity is present in the liquid in low concentration. All these factors tend to lead to extreme 2 (excess of A).

- The catalytic oxidation of liquid hydrocarbons with air or oxygen. Since oxygen is not very soluble in the liquid, while the hydrocarbon could well be present in high concentration we could end up in extreme 1 (excess of B).

- The removal of dissolved organics from industrial waste water by catalytic oxidation as an alternative to biooxidation. Here oxygen is not very soluble in water, but the organic waste is also present in low concentration. It is therefore not clear in what regime the kinetics lie. The catalytic oxidation of phenol is an example of such an operation.

- The removal of airborne pollutants by adsorption and/or reaction. These operations usually lead to extreme 1.

- The illustrative examples and many of the problems which follow are adapted from or are extensions of problems prepared by Ramachandran & Choudhary, Chem. Eng. pg. 74, Dec. 1 1980.

Example 1. Hydrogenation of acetone in a packed bubble column.

Aqueous acetone ($C_{B0}=1000\ mol/m^3 l$, $v_l=10^{-4}\ m^3 l/s$) and hydrogen (1 atm, $v_g=0.04\ m^3 g/s$, $H_A=36845\ Pa\cdot m^3 l/mol$) are fed to the bottom of a long narrow column (5 m high, 0.1 m² cross section) packed with Raney nickel catalyst ($d_p=5\times10^{-3}\ m\ cat$, $\rho_s=4500\ kg/m^3 cat$, $f_s=0.6$, $\mathcal{D}=8\times10^{-10}\ m^3 l/m\ cat\cdot s$) and kept at 14°C. At these conditions acetone is hydrogenated to propanol according to the reaction

$$\underset{A}{H_2(g\to l)} + \underset{B}{CH_3\text{-}CO\text{-}CH_3(l)} \xrightarrow[\text{catalyst}]{\text{on}} CH_3\text{-}CHOH\text{-}CH_3$$

with rate given by

$$-r_A' = -r_B' = k' C_A^{1/2} C_B^0 \qquad \text{and}\ldots \quad k' = 2.35\times10^{-3}\ \frac{m^3 l}{kg\cdot s}\left(\frac{mol}{m^3 l}\right)^{1/2}$$

What will be the conversion of acetone in this unit?

Additional data. The mass transfer rate constants are estimated to be:

$$(k_{Ai}a_i)_{g+l} = 0.02\ \frac{m^3 l}{m^3 r\cdot s} \qquad k_{Ac}a_c = 0.05\ \frac{m^3 l}{m^3 r\cdot s}$$

↳ the sum of gas + liquid film conductances.

Solution.

Before rushing to our equations to do the appropriate integrations needed for plug flow let us consider the situation

- $C_{B0}=1000$ while C_A is given by Henry's law as

$$C_A = \frac{p_A}{H_A} = \frac{101325}{36845} = 2.75\ mol/m^3 l$$

  Comparing values shows that $C_B \gg C_A$ and we are in extreme 1 of pg. 34.4.

- Next, we are dealing with pure hydrogen, thus p_A is

constant throughout the packed column. And since the rate is only dependent on C_A, and not on C_B, this means that the rate of reaction is constant throughout the column.

Let us next look at the rate. From pg 23.4

$$M_T = L\sqrt{\frac{n+1}{2}\cdot\frac{k' C_A^{\,n-1}}{\mathscr{D}_{eff}}\rho_s}$$

$$= \frac{5\times10^{-3}}{6}\sqrt{\frac{1.5}{2}\cdot\frac{(2.35\times10^{-3})(2.75)^{-1/2}(4500)}{8\times10^{-10}}} = 64.4$$

$$\therefore\ \mathcal{E} = \frac{1}{64.4} = 0.0155$$

Replacing all known values into eq 15 gives

$$-r_A'''' = \frac{1}{\underbrace{\frac{1}{0.02}}_{58\%} + \underbrace{\frac{1}{0.05}}_{23\%} + \underbrace{\frac{1}{(2.35\times10^{-3})(1)(2.75)^{-1/2}(0.0155)(0.6)(4500)}}_{19\%}}\cdot\frac{101325}{36845}$$

$$= 0.0317\ \text{mol/m}^3\text{r}\cdot\text{s}$$

Next, to the material balance. With constant rate this becomes

$$F_{Ao}X_A = \frac{F_{Bo}X_B}{b} = (-r_A'''')V_r$$

- $F_{Ao}X_A$: not particularly useful
- $\frac{F_{Bo}X_B}{b}$: use this term in which $F_{Bo} = v_\ell C_{Bo} = 10^{-4}(1000) = 0.1$ mol/s

Thus on rearranging

$$X_B = \frac{b(-r_A'''')V_r}{F_{Bo}} = \frac{(1)(0.0317)(5\times0.1)}{0.1}$$

$$= 0.158, \quad \text{or}\quad \underline{16\%\ \text{conversion}} \leftarrow$$

Example 2. Hydrogenation of a batch of butynediol in a slurry reactor

Hydrogen gas is bubbled into an agitated tank ($V_r = 2\,m^3r$) containing liquid butynediol ($C_{B0} = 2500\ mol/m^3\ell$) plus a dilute suspension of palladium-impregnated porous catalyst pellets ($d_p = 5\times10^{-5}\ m\,cat$, $\rho_s = 1450\ kg/m^3cat$, $\mathcal{D}_{eff} = 5\times10^{-10}\ m^3\ell/m\,cat\cdot s$, $f_s = 0.0055$). Hydrogen dissolves in the liquid ($H_A = 148000\ Pa\cdot m^3\ell/mol$) and reacts with the butynediol on the catalyst surface, as follows:

$$\underset{A}{H_2(g\rightarrow\ell)} + \underset{B}{\text{butynediol}(\ell)} \xrightarrow[\text{catalyst}]{\text{on}} \text{butenediol}$$

and at 35°C

$$-r_A' = k' C_A C_B \qquad \text{and}\cdots \qquad k' = 5\times10^{-5}\ m^6\ell/kg\cdot mol\,cat\cdot s$$

Unused hydrogen is recompressed and recirculated, and the whole operation takes place at 14.6 atm and 35°C.

Find how long it will take for 90% conversion of reactant.

Additional data. The mass transfer rates are given as:

$$(k_{Ai}a_i)_{g+\ell} = 0.277\ \frac{m^3\ell}{m^3r\cdot s} \qquad k_{Ac} = 4.4\times10^{-4}\ \frac{m^3\ell}{m^3r\cdot s}$$

($g+\ell$: the sum of the gas and liquid films)

Solution

First compare C_A and C_B

$$C_A = \frac{p_A}{H_A} = \frac{14.6\,(101325)}{148000} = 10\ mol/m^3\ell$$

$$C_{B0} = 2500\ \&\ C_{Bf} = 250\ mol/m^3\ell$$

Both at the beginning and at the end of the batch run $C_B \gg C_A$

Although C_A stays constant throughout the batch run C_B does not, so we will have a changing rate with time and with C_B. So let us evaluate the rate at any particular value of C_B.

(34.17)

$$a_c = \frac{6 f_s}{d_p} = \frac{6(0.0055)}{5\times10^{-5}} = 660 \; m^2/m^3 \qquad \therefore \; k_{Ac} a_c = 4.4\times10^{-4}(660) = 0.29 \; \frac{m^3 l}{m^3 r \cdot s}$$

$$M_T = L\sqrt{\frac{k' C_B \rho_s}{\mathcal{D}_{eff}}} = \frac{5\times10^{-5}}{6}\sqrt{\frac{(5\times10^{-5})\, C_B\, (1450)}{5\times10^{-10}}} = 0.1\, C_B^{1/2} \qquad \cdots (i)$$

Replacing in the rate expression of eq 15 gives

$$-r_A'''' = \frac{1}{\frac{1}{0.277} + \frac{1}{0.29} + \frac{1}{(5\times10^{-5}) C_B (1450)(\mathcal{E}_A)(0.0055)}} \cdot \frac{14.6(101325)}{148000}$$

$\mathcal{E}_A$ evaluated at $M_T = 0.1 C_B^{1/2}$

$$= \frac{1}{0.70584 + \frac{250.8}{C_B \cdot (\mathcal{E}_A \text{ at } M_T = 0.1 C_B^{1/2})}} \qquad \cdots (ii)$$

Choose a number of C_B values	M_T from eq (i)	$\mathcal{E}_A$ from pg 23.1	$-r_A''''$ from eq (ii)	$1/(-r_A'''')$
2500	5	0.19	0.8105	1.23
1000	3.16	0.29	0.6367	1.57
250	1.58	0.5	0.3687	2.71

Now from eq 11 the reaction time is given by

$$t = \frac{V_l}{b V_r} \int_{C_{Bf}}^{C_{B0}} \frac{dC_B}{(-r_A'''')}$$

With $b = 1$ & $V_l \cong V_r$ this time becomes

$t = \underline{3460 \text{ s}}$ ←

(or 57 min 40 s)

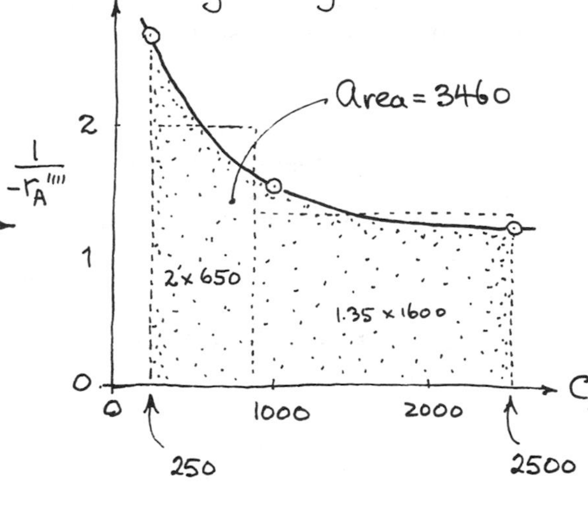

Chapter 34 Problems

A1 Trickle bed oxidation. Dilute aqueous ethanol (about 2 - 3%) is oxidized to acetic acid by the action of pure oxygen at 10 atm in a trickle bed reactor packed with palladium-alumina catalyst pellets and kept at 30 °C. According to Sato *et al*, Proc. First Pacific Chem. Eng. Congress, Kyoto, pg 187, 1972, the reaction proceeds as follows

$$\underset{(A)}{O_2\,(g \rightarrow \ell)} + \underset{(B)}{CH_3CH_2OH(\ell)} \xrightarrow[\text{catalyst}]{\text{on}} CH_3COOH\,(\ell) + H_2O$$

with rate

$$-r_A' = k'C_A, \quad k' = 1.77 \times 10^{-5}\ m^3/kg{\cdot}s$$

Find the fractional conversion of ethanol to actetic acid if gas and liquid are fed to the top of a reactor in the following system

Gas stream:	$v_g = 0.01\ m^3/s$, $H_A = 86000\ Pa{\cdot}m^3/mol$
Liquid stream:	$v_\ell = 2 \times 10^{-4}\ m^3/s$, $C_{B0} = 400\ mol/m^3$
Reactor:	5 m high, $0.1\ m^2$ cross section, $f_s = 0.58$
Catalyst:	$d_p = 5\ mm$, $\rho_s = 1800\ kg/m^3$, $\mathcal{D}_{eff} = 4.16 \times 10^{-10}\ m^3/m\ cat{\cdot}s$
Kinetics:	$k_{Ag}a_i = 3 \times 10^{-4}\ mol/m^3{\cdot}Pa{\cdot}s$, $k_{A\ell}a_i = 0.02\ s^{-1}$, $k_{Ac} = 3.86 \times 10^{-5}\ m/s$

A2 Slurry column oxidation. Instead of using a trickle bed reactor of ethanol oxidation (see previous problem) let us consider using a slurry reactor. For this type of unit

$$(k_{Ai}a_i)_{g+\ell} = 0.052\ s^{-1}, \quad k_{Ac} = 4 \times 10^{-4}\ m/s$$
$$d_p = 10^{-4}\ m, \quad f_g = 0.05, \quad f_\ell = 0.75, \quad f_s = 0.2$$

Take all flows and other values from the previous problem, and then find the expected fractional conversion of ethanol in this reactor.

A3 Slurry tank hydrogenation. Predict the conversion of glucose to sorbitol in a stirred slurry reactor using pure hydrogen gas at 200 atm and 150 °C. The catalyst used is porous Raney nickel, and under these conditions Brahme and Doraiswamy IEC/PDD, **15**, 130 (1976) report that the reaction proceeds as follows

$$\underset{(A)}{H_2(g \rightarrow \ell)} + \underset{(B)}{\text{glucose, } C_6H_{12}O_6(\ell)} \xrightarrow[\text{catalyst}]{\text{solid}} \text{sorbitol, } C_6H_{14}O_6(\ell)$$

with

$$-r_A' = -r_B' = k'C_A^{0.6}C_B, \quad k' = 5.96 \times 10^{-6} \frac{mol}{kg{\cdot}s} \left(\frac{m^3}{mol}\right)^{1.6}$$

Data:

Gas stream:	$v_g = 0.2\ m^3/s$, $H_A = 277600\ Pa{\cdot}m^3/mol$
Liquid stream:	$v_\ell = 0.01\ m^3/s$, $C_{B0} = 2000\ mol/m^3$
Reactor:	$V_r = 2\ m^3$, $f_s = 0.056$
Catalyst:	$d_p = 10\ \mu m$, $\rho_s = 8900\ kg/m^3$, $\mathcal{D}_{eff} = 2 \times 10^{-9}\ m^3/m\ cat{\cdot}s$
Kinetics:	$(k_{Ai}a_i)_{g+\ell} = 0.05\ s^{-1}$, $k_{Ac} = 10^{-3}\ m/s$

A4 Multistage bubble column hydrogenation. In the previous problem conversion to sorbitol is not as high as desired so let us consider an alternative design, one which uses an upflow of gas and liquid through a long narrow multistage column 0.25 m^2 in cross section and 8 m high containing semisuspended solids ($d_p = 10^{-3}$ m, $f_s = 0.4$). What will be the conversion with this arrangement?

Data:

$(k_{Ai}a_i)_{g+\ell} = 0.025\ s^{-1}$, $k_{Ac} = 10^{-5}\ m/s$

All other values are unchanged from the previous problem.

A5 Three phase fluidized bed hydrogenation. Aniline is to be hydrogenated in a three-phase fluidized bed of porous clay particles impregnated with nickel catalyst. The well agitated batch of liquid is kept at 130 °C by heat exchanger tubes passing through the fluidized bed, and by bubbling hydrogen vigorously and at a high rate through the bed at 1 atm. According to Govindarao and Murthy, J. Appl. Chem. Biotechnol. **25**, 169 (1975), at these conditions reaction proceeds as follows

$$\underset{(A)}{3H_2(g \rightarrow \ell)} + \underset{(B)}{2\,C_6H_5NH_2(\ell)} \xrightarrow[\text{catalyst}]{\text{Ni}} \underset{\text{cyclohexyl-aniline}}{C_6H_{11}NHC_6H_5} + NH_3$$

with rate

$$-r'_A = k'C_A, \quad k' = 0.05\ m^3/kg\ cat{\cdot}s$$

Find the time needed for 90% conversion of this batch of aniline.

Data:

Gas stream:	pure H_2 at 1 atm, $H_A = 28500\ Pa{\cdot}m^3/mol$
Batch of liquid:	$C_{B0} = 1097\ mol/m^3$
Reactor:	$f_g = 0.10$, $f_\ell = 0.65$, $f_s = 0.25$
Catalyst:	$d_p = 300\ \mu m$, $\rho_s = 750\ kg/m^3$, $\mathcal{D}_{eff} = 8.35 \times 10^{-10}\ m^3/m\ cat{\cdot}s$
Kinetics:	$(k_{Ai}a_i)_{g+\ell} = 0.04\ s^{-1}$, $k_{Ac} = 10^{-5}\ m/s$

Assume that the fraction of NH_3 in the gas stream is very small at any time.

Chapter **34** Problems

A6 Bubble column hydrogenation. Consider a different design to effect the hydrogenation of the previous problem, one which uses a long narrow bubble column of semisuspended 3 mm catalyst particles ($f_s = 0.4$, $f_\ell = 0.5$, $f_g = 0.1$). The batch of liquid aniline is circulated through an external heat exchanger (volume of liquid in the loop outside the reactor equals the total volume of the reactor) and hydrogen is bubbled through the column. Find the time needed for 90% conversion of aniline in this unit.

Data: Here $((k_{Ai}a_i)_{g+\ell} = 0.02\ s^{-1}$, $k_{Ac} = 7 \times 10^{-5}\ m/s$

All other values not mentioned here remain unchanged from the previous problem.

A7 Trickle bed gas absorber-reactor. Sulfur dioxide is to be removed from a gas by passing the gas and water through a bed of highly porous activated carbon kept at 25 °C. In this system sulfur dioxide and oxygen dissolve in water and react on the solid to give sulfur trioxide, as follows

$$SO_2\,(g \rightarrow \ell) + \frac{1}{2} O_2\,(g \rightarrow \ell) \xrightarrow[\text{solid}]{\text{on}} SO_3(\ell)$$

where

$$-r_{SO_2} = k' C_{oxygen}, \quad k' = 0.01553\ m^3/kg{\cdot}s$$

Find the fraction of sulfur dioxide removed from a gas stream under the following conditions

Gas stream:	$v_g = 0.01\ m^3/s$, $\pi = 101325$ Pa entering $SO_2 = 0.2\%$, $H = 380000\ Pa{\cdot}m^3/mol$ entering $O_2 = 21\%$, $H = 87000\ Pa{\cdot}m^3/mol$
Liquid stream:	$v_\ell = 2 \times 10^{-4}\ m^3/s$
Reactor:	2 m high, $0.1\ m^2$ cross section, $f_s = 0.6$
Catalyst:	$d_p = 5$ mm, $\rho_s = 850\ kg/m^3$, $\mathcal{D}_{eff} = 5.35 \times 10^{-10}\ m^3/m\ cat{\cdot}s$
Kinetics:	$(k_i a_i)_{g+\ell} = 0.01\ s^{-1}$, $k_c = 4 \times 10^{-5}\ m/s$

A8 Hydrogenation in a slurry reactor. The batch hydrogenation of Example 2 takes just about an hour to run. Let us suppose that in practical operations we can run 8 batches of fluid per day in this unit. Thus, in the long run a batch of fluid is processed every three hours.

Another way of running this reaction is to feed the agitated reactor continuously at such a rate that we get 90% conversion of butynediol. How do these two processing rates compare in the long term? Give your answer as $F_{B0,\ continuous}/F_{B0,\ batch}$. Assume that the liquid feed composition, gas composition and pressure, mass transfer and chemical rates are the same in both batch and continuous operations.

Chapter 41. Kinetics of 2-Fluid Reactions, Both G/L and L/L.

For convenience in notation let us talk of G/L reactions, even though what we say holds equally for L/L reactions. This chapter concerns kinetics of these reaction, the next deals with design.

Consider the second order reaction

$$A(g \rightarrow l) + bB(l) \longrightarrow R(s \text{ or } l \text{ or } g) \qquad -r_A = kC_AC_B$$

- A: present in gas, but soluble in liquid with solubility given by $p_{Ai} = H_AC_{Ai}$
- B: present in liquid and unable to enter the gas phase
- reaction occurs in liquid only, maybe close to the interface (in the liquid film), maybe in the main body of liquid

In this and the next chapter we only treat this reaction.

I. The Rate Equation.

For unit volume of contactor V_r with its gas, liquid, and solid

$$f_l = \frac{V_l}{V_r}, \quad f_g = \frac{V_g}{V_r}, \quad \epsilon = f_l + f_g,$$

$$a_l = \frac{S}{V_l}, \quad a = \frac{S}{V_r}$$

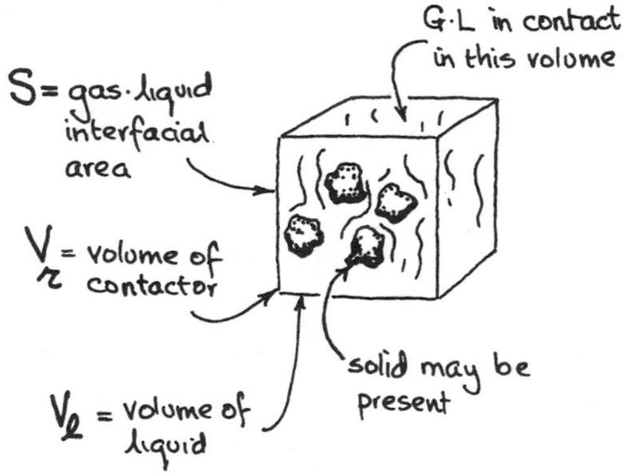

$$-r_A'''' = -\frac{1}{V_r}\frac{dN_A}{dt}$$

$$-r_{Al} = -\frac{1}{V_l}\frac{dN_A}{dt}$$

$$-r_A'' = -\frac{1}{S}\frac{dN_A}{dt}$$

These rates are related by

$$r''''V_r = r_lV_l = r''S$$

or

$$r'''' = f_lr_l = ar''$$

Now reactant A must move from gas to liquid for reaction to occur, hence diffusional resistances enter the rate. Here we will develop everything in terms of two film theory. Other theories can be used and they give essentially the same result, but with more impressive mathematics.

1. <u>For straight mass transfer (absorption) of A</u> we have two resistances in series ... of the gas film and of the liquid film. Thus

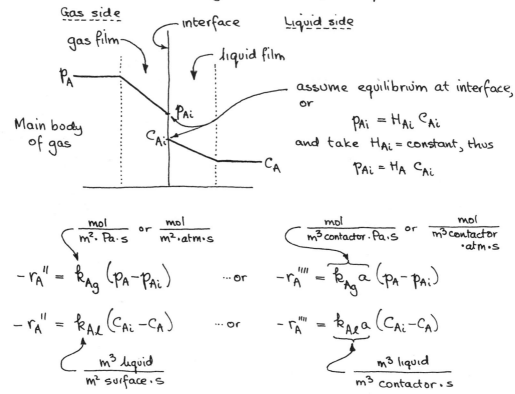

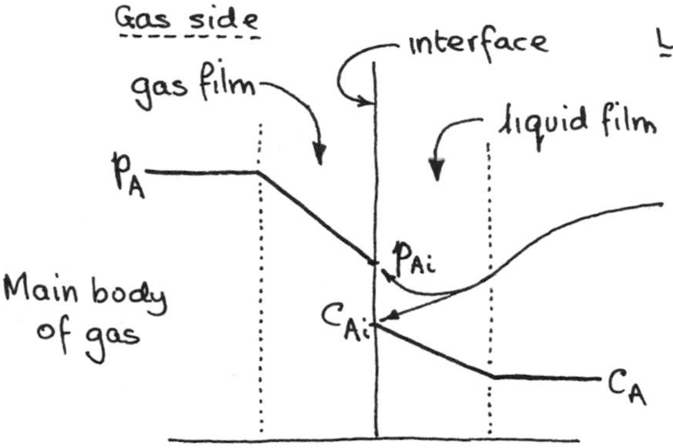

assume equilibrium at interface, or

$$p_{Ai} = H_{Ai}\, C_{Ai}$$

and take H_{Ai} = constant, thus

$$p_{Ai} = H_A\, C_{Ai}$$

k_{Ag}: $\dfrac{\text{mol}}{\text{m}^2\cdot\text{Pa}\cdot\text{s}}$ or $\dfrac{\text{mol}}{\text{m}^2\cdot\text{atm}\cdot\text{s}}$ $\qquad$ $k_{Ag}a$: $\dfrac{\text{mol}}{\text{m}^3\,\text{contactor}\cdot\text{Pa}\cdot\text{s}}$ or $\dfrac{\text{mol}}{\text{m}^3\,\text{contactor}\cdot\text{atm}\cdot\text{s}}$

$$-r_A'' = k_{Ag}(p_A - p_{Ai}) \quad \text{...or} \quad -r_A'''' = k_{Ag}a\,(p_A - p_{Ai})$$

$$-r_A'' = k_{Al}(C_{Ai} - C_A) \quad \text{...or} \quad -r_A'''' = k_{Al}a\,(C_{Ai} - C_A)$$

k_{Al}: $\dfrac{\text{m}^3\,\text{liquid}}{\text{m}^2\,\text{surface}\cdot\text{s}}$ $\qquad$ $k_{Al}a$: $\dfrac{\text{m}^3\,\text{liquid}}{\text{m}^3\,\text{contactor}\cdot\text{s}}$

Combining gives

$$\boxed{-r_A'''' = \frac{1}{\dfrac{1}{k_{Ag}a} + \dfrac{H_A}{k_{Al}a}}\,(p_A - H_A C_A)}$$

$-r_A''''$: mass transfer rate, $\dfrac{\text{mol A}}{\text{m}^3\,\text{contactor}\cdot\text{s}}$ $\qquad$ H_A: $\dfrac{\text{Pa}\cdot\text{m}^3\,\text{liquid}}{\text{mol}}$

2. **For transfer of A followed by reaction with B** we have three resistances in series ... of the gas film, of the liquid film, and of the main body of liquid.

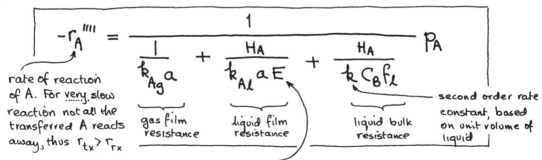

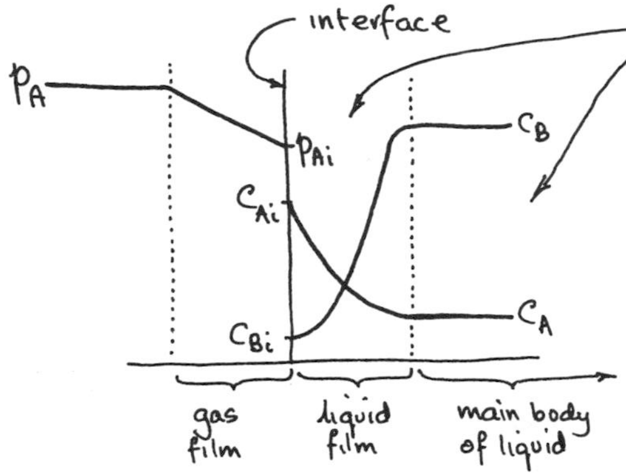

Reaction can take place in both the liquid film and in the main body of liquid. Fast reactions occur in a narrow zone within the film, slow reactions spread through the film and main body of liquid.

For second order reaction in the liquid

$$-r_A'''' = k\,C_A C_B \cdot f_\ell$$

(k: $\frac{m^3\ liquid}{mol \cdot s}$)

All sorts of special forms of the rate equation can result depending on the relative values of the rate constants k_{Ag}, $k_{A\ell}$ and k, the concentration ratio of reactants p_A/C_B, and Henry's constant. Happily, an overall rate expression can be written which accounts for all these factors, as follows

$$-r_A'''' = \frac{1}{\dfrac{1}{k_{Ag}\,a} + \dfrac{H_A}{k_{A\ell}\,a\,E} + \dfrac{H_A}{k\,C_B f_\ell}}\; p_A$$

- $-r_A''''$: rate of reaction of A. For very slow reaction not all the transferred A reacts away, thus $r_{tx} > r_{rx}$
- $\frac{1}{k_{Ag}a}$: gas film resistance
- $\frac{H_A}{k_{A\ell}aE}$: liquid film resistance
- $\frac{H_A}{kC_Bf_\ell}$: liquid bulk resistance
- k: second order rate constant, based on unit volume of liquid

The absorption of A from gas is larger when reaction occurs within the liquid film than for straight mass transfer. Thus for the same concentrations at two film boundaries we have

$$\begin{pmatrix}\text{Liquid film}\\ \text{enhancement}\\ \text{factor}\end{pmatrix},\ E = \left(\frac{\text{rate of take up of A from gas with reaction occurring}}{\text{rate of take up of A for straight mass transfer}}\right)$$

same C_{Ai}, C_A, C_{Bi}, C_B in the two cases

The only problem now is to evaluate E. This quantity depends on three extremes for the film Ⓧ, Ⓨ and Ⓩ. Assuming fixed values at the film boundaries for C_{Ai} and C_B these extremes are as follows

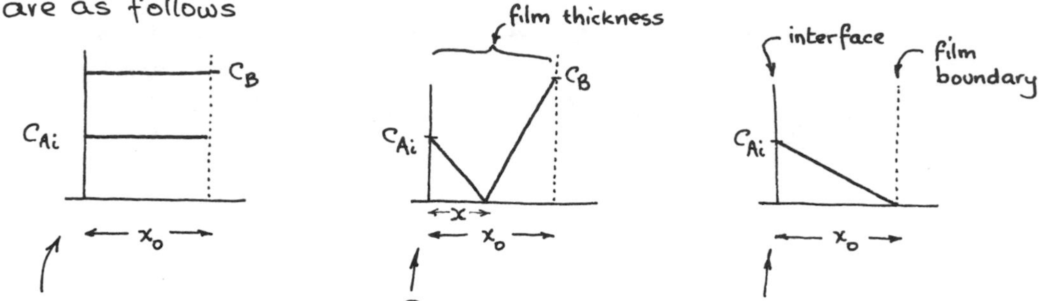

Ⓧ Maximum conversion possible in film for the reaction with rate constant k

$k_{Al} C_{Ai} C_B x_o$

Ⓨ Maximum conversion in film with an infinitely fast reaction

$k_{Al}\left(C_{Ai} + \frac{\mathcal{D}_B}{\mathcal{D}_A}\frac{C_B}{b}\right)$

Ⓩ Maximum transfer of A through the film by straight mass transfer

$k_{Al} C_{Ai}$

The two parameters needed to find E are defined in terms of various ratios of Ⓧ, Ⓨ and Ⓩ. Thus

$$E_i = \begin{pmatrix}\text{enhancement factor for}\\ \text{infinitely fast reaction}\end{pmatrix} = \frac{Ⓨ}{Ⓩ} = 1 + \frac{\mathcal{D}_B C_B}{b\,\mathcal{D}_A C_{Ai}}$$

$$M_H^2 = \begin{pmatrix}\text{film conversion}\\ \text{parameter}\end{pmatrix} = \begin{pmatrix}\text{maximum possible}\\ \text{conversion in the film}\\ \text{compared with maximum}\\ \text{transport through film}\end{pmatrix} = \frac{Ⓧ}{Ⓩ} = \frac{\mathcal{D}_A k C_B}{k_{Al}^2}$$

this stands for the **Hatta modulus**

Approximate expressions for E in terms of E_i and M_H are

$$E = M_H\sqrt{\frac{E_i - E}{E_i - 1}} \Bigg/ \tanh M_H\sqrt{\frac{E_i - E}{E_i - 1}}$$

... from van Krevelen & Hoftijzer Rec. Trav. Chim. 67 563 (1948)

$$E = 1 + (E_i - 1)\left[1 - \exp\left\{\frac{1 - \sqrt{1 + M_H^2}}{E_i - 1}\right\}\right]$$

... from Baldi and Sicardi CES 30 617 (1975)

In graphical form, with all special cases and distinctive zones shown, we have

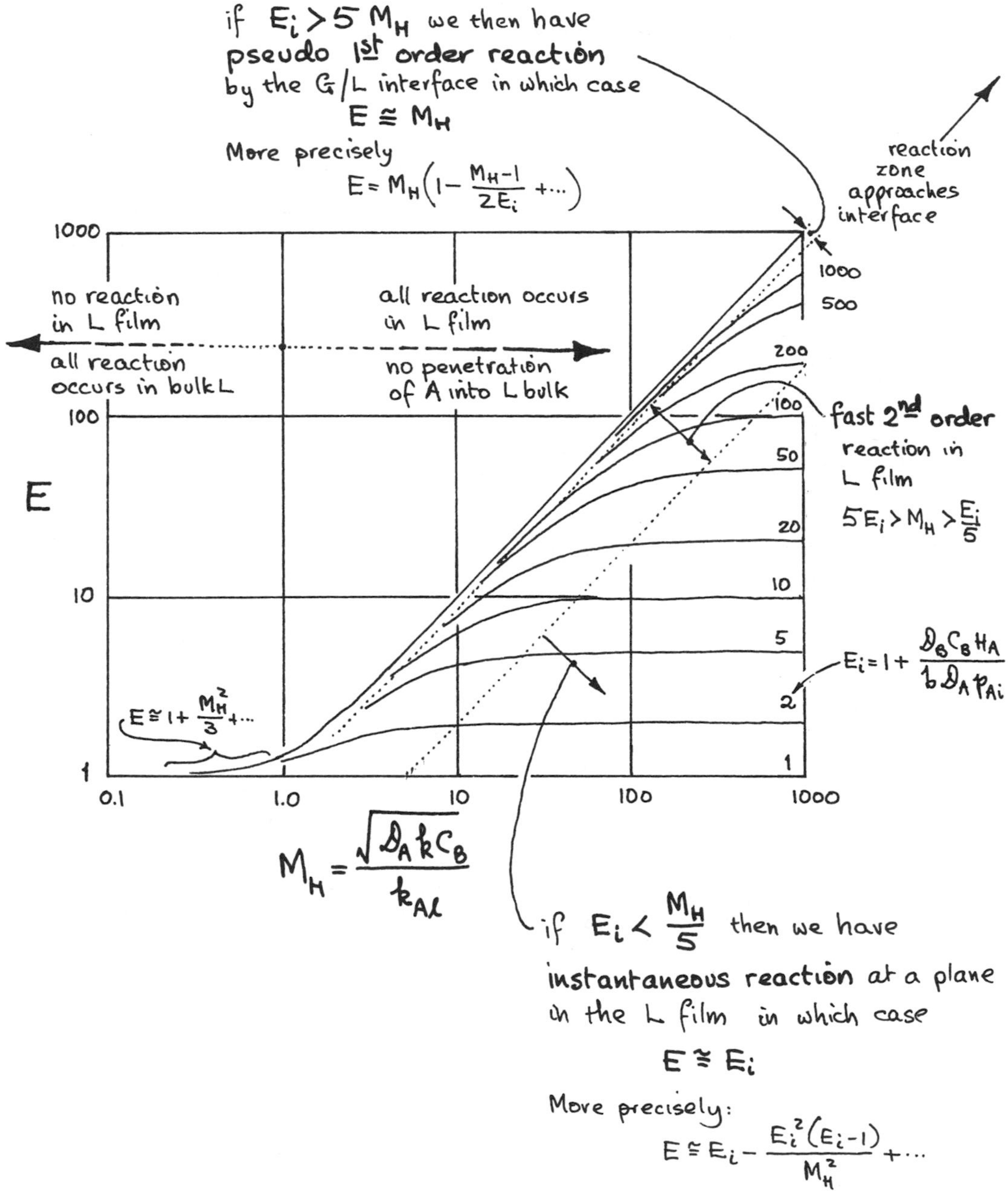
if $E_i > 5\,M_H$ we then have
pseudo 1st order reaction
by the G/L interface in which case
$E \cong M_H$
More precisely
$E = M_H\left(1 - \frac{M_H - 1}{2E_i} + \cdots\right)$
reaction zone approaches interface
1000
no reaction in L film
all reaction occurs in bulk L
all reaction occurs in L film
no penetration of A into L bulk
100
E
10
1
0.1
1.0
10
100
1000
1000
500
200
100
50
20
10
5
2
1
fast 2nd order reaction in L film
$5E_i > M_H > \frac{E_i}{5}$
$E_i = 1 + \frac{\mathcal{D}_B C_B H_A}{b\,\mathcal{D}_A p_{Ai}}$
$E \cong 1 + \frac{M_H^2}{3} + \cdots$
$M_H = \frac{\sqrt{\mathcal{D}_A k C_B}}{k_{Al}}$
if $E_i < \frac{M_H}{5}$ then we have
instantaneous reaction at a plane in the L film in which case
$E \cong E_i$
More precisely:
$E \cong E_i - \frac{E_i^2(E_i - 1)}{M_H^2} + \cdots$

3. **Special cases.** Let us look at some of the special forms and extremes of the general rate expression of pg 3.

(a) **Gas film control.** If this resistance owervhelms the others then the general rate expression reduces to

$$-r_A'''' = k_{Ag}\, a\, p_A$$

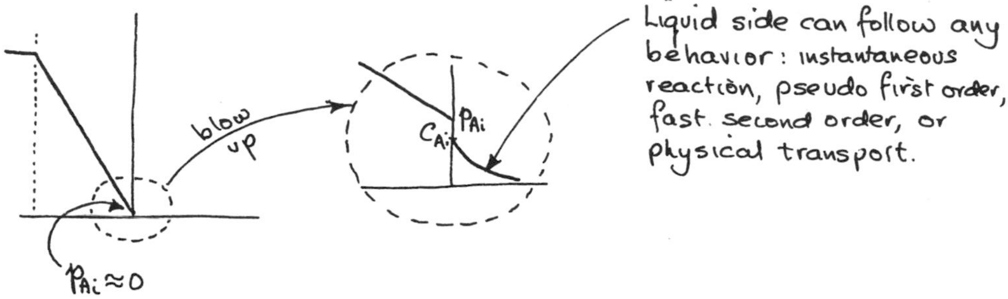

(b) **Liquid film.** Here we have a number of behavior patterns possible

- **Instantaneous reaction within film** $(k \to \infty)$
  This is an idealization for very fast reactions. Here

$$-r_A'''' = \frac{\dfrac{\mathcal{D}_B C_B H_A}{b\,\mathcal{D}_A} + p_A}{\dfrac{1}{k_{Ag}a} + \dfrac{H_A}{k_{Al}a}} \quad \cdots \text{when } E_i < \frac{M_H}{5}$$

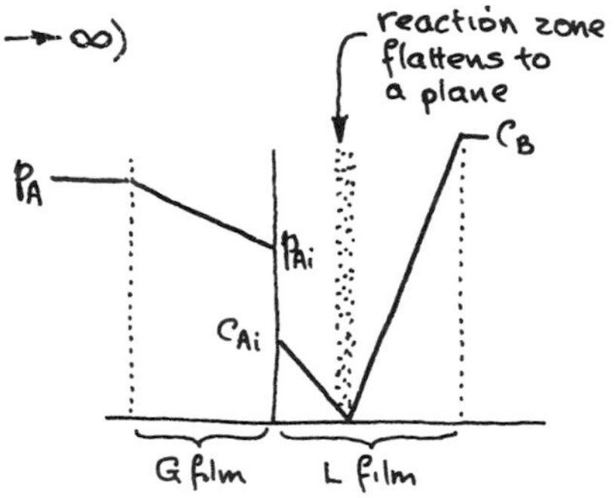

- **Instantaneous reaction at interface.** $(k \to \infty)$
  For high C_B and low p_A the reaction zone shifts to the interface and we end up with gas film control, or

$$-r_A'''' = k_{Ag}\, a\, p_A \quad \cdots \text{when} \begin{cases} E_i > 5 M_H \text{ and} \\ k_{Ag}a p_A < \dfrac{k_{Al} a C_B \mathcal{D}_B}{b\,\mathcal{D}_A} \end{cases}$$

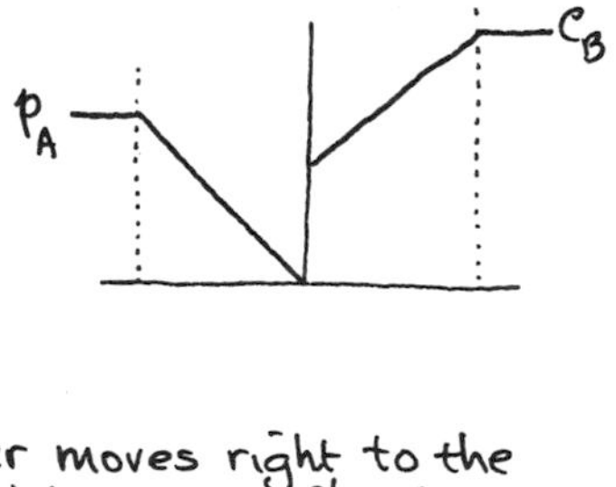

Since k is never ∞ the reaction zone never moves right to the interface. In the real world we always find pseudo 1st order behavior (see below). Nevertheless this ideal is a useful simplification.

- **Pseudo 1st order reaction with respect to A** occurs when $C_B \cong$ constant, thus for high C_B in the reaction zone. Here

$$E = M_H = \frac{\sqrt{\mathcal{D}_A k C_B}}{k_{Al}} \quad \cdots \text{when } E_i > 5 M_H$$

- **Second order reaction within the film**
This case is difficult to solve and requires a computer

- **Physical transport** occurs when reaction is very slow.

(c) **Note**: We can have most of the reaction in one location but the resistance elsewhere

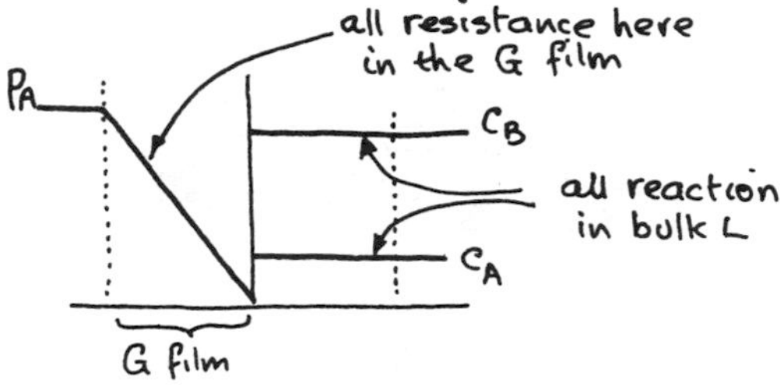

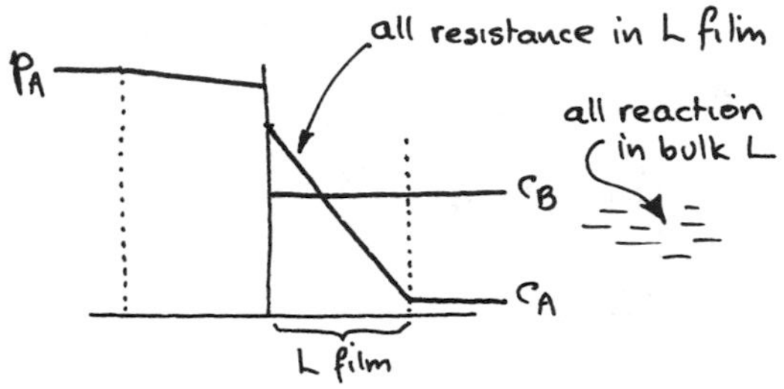

(d) Summary of rate regimes and special equation forms from very fast to very slow reaction

Instantaneous reaction. (at a plane in the L)

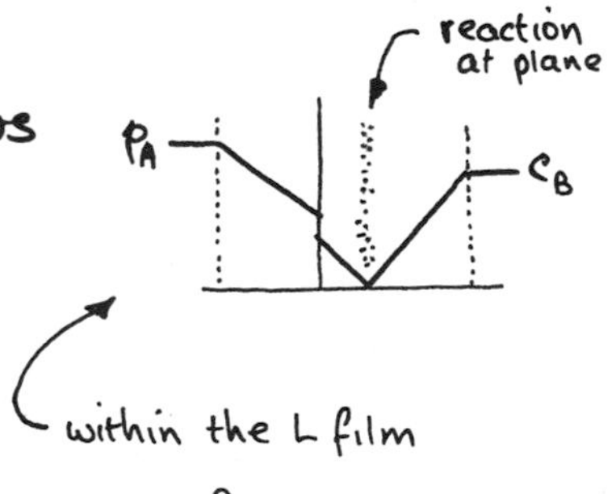

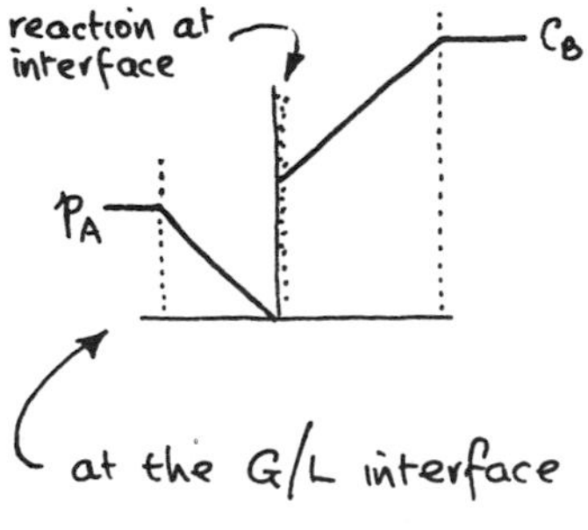

$$-r_A'''' = \frac{\dfrac{\mathcal{D}_{Bl}}{\mathcal{D}_{Al}} \dfrac{C_B H_A}{b} + p_A}{\dfrac{1}{k_{Ag} a} + \dfrac{H_A}{k_{Al} a}}$$

$$-r_A'''' = k_{Ag}\, a\, p_A$$

This situation occurs when

$$k_{Ag}\, p_A \leq \frac{k_{Bl}}{b} C_B$$

Fast reaction (all within L film)

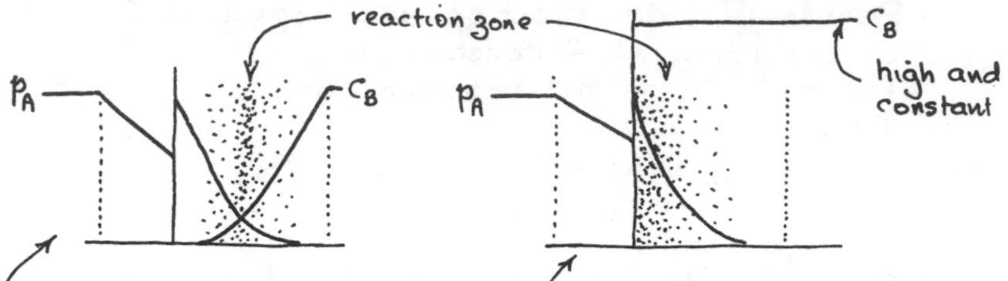

fast 2nd order reaction

$$-r_A'''' = \frac{1}{\dfrac{1}{k_{Ag}a} + \dfrac{H_A}{k_{Al}aE}}\, p_A$$

pseudo 1st order reaction

$$-r_A'''' = \frac{1}{\dfrac{1}{k_{Ag}a} + \dfrac{H_A}{a\sqrt{\mathcal{D}_A k C_B}}}\, p_A$$

Intermediate reaction rate (reacts in L film and in body of L).

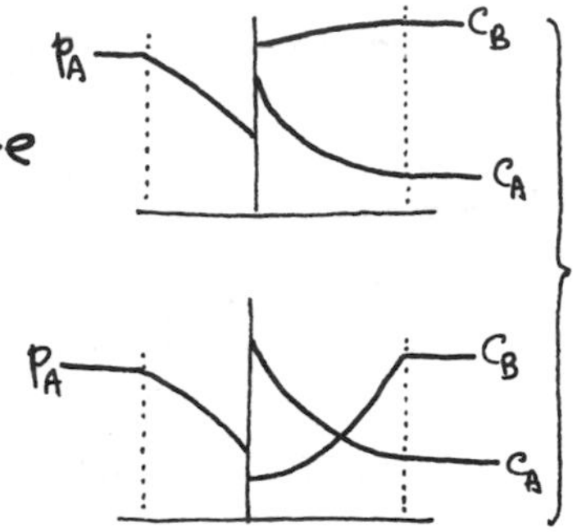

general equation

$$-r_A'''' = \frac{1}{\dfrac{1}{k_{Ag}a} + \dfrac{H_A}{k_{Al}aE} + \dfrac{H_A}{kC_Bf_l}}\, p_A$$

E from chart

Slow reaction (negligible reaction in film, but film does provide a resistance)

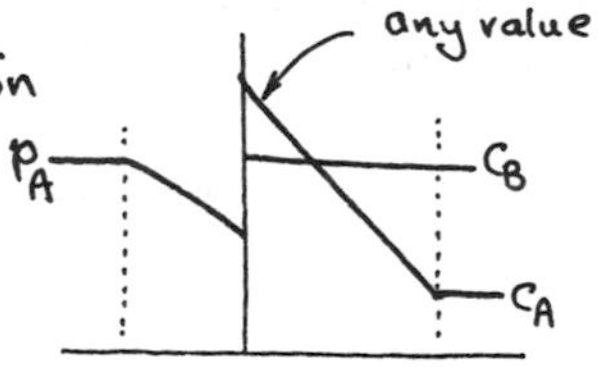

$$-r_A'''' = \frac{1}{\dfrac{1}{k_{Ag}a} + \dfrac{H_A}{k_{Al}a} + \dfrac{H_A}{kC_Bf_l}}\, p_A$$

Very slow reaction (no diffusional resistance of any kind)

same rate of reaction everywhere in the L, in film and main body

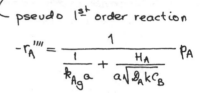

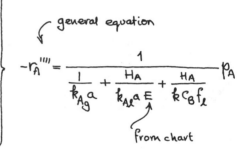

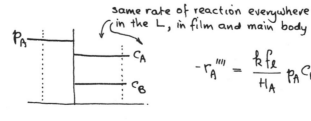

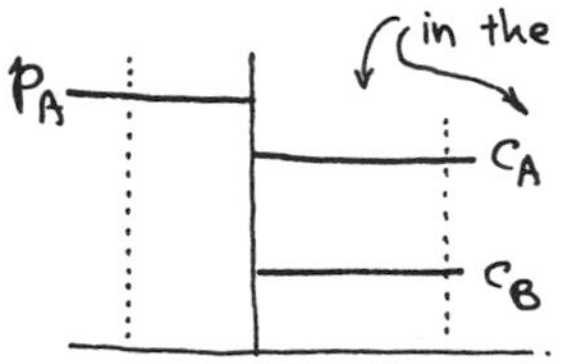

$$-r_A'''' = \frac{kf_l}{H_A}\, p_A C_B$$

II How to use the General Rate Equation.

Given estimates for k_ℓ k_g k H_A p_A and C_B the only problem in evaluating the rate comes from finding E. Proceed as follows

Step 1. Calculate $M_H = \dfrac{\sqrt{\mathcal{D}_A k C_B}}{k_{A\ell}}$ and $E_i = 1 + \dfrac{\mathcal{D}_B C_B H_A}{b \mathcal{D}_A p_{Ai}}$

Since p_{Ai} is unknown start by guessing that the gas phase resistance is negligible. Thus guess that $p_{Ai} = p_A$. If we later find that the gas phase resistance is important we will correct this initial guess by guessing a lower value.

Step 2 Evaluate E from E_i and M_H.

(a) When $M_H > 2$ all reaction takes place in the liquid film. In this regime proceed as follows:

- if $E_i > 5 M_H$ then $E = M_H$. Check the figure if you doubt it.
- if E_i and M_H do not differ by more than a factor of 5 then find E from the figure.
- if $M_H > 5E_i$ then you may have to resort to trial and error. Start by guessing that $E = E_i$. Put this value for E and all other values into the general rate expression and compare the magnitude of the G film and L film resistance terms. If the G film resistance term is not negligible then the original guess (that $p_{Ai} = p_A$) is wrong, so guess a new lower value for p_{Ai}. For example, if you think that the gas film resistance is 80% of the total then guess $p_{Ai} = 0.2\, p_A$. With this new guess determine the corresponding E_i, then E, and then insert into the general rate expression. Keep adjusting p_{Ai} until

$$\left(\begin{array}{c}\text{the guessed fraction}\\ \text{of resistance contributed}\\ \text{by the gas film,}\end{array}\ \frac{p_A - p_{Ai}}{p_A}\right) = \left(\begin{array}{c}\text{fraction of resistance}\\ \text{contributed by the gas film}\\ \text{in the general rate equation}\end{array}\right)$$

when the right p_{Ai} is found then the corresponding E is the correct one to use. If the guessed $p_{Ai} \rightarrow 0$ we end up with gas film control.

(b) **When $M_H < 0.02$** all reaction takes place in the main body of L and $E = 1$. Remember however that the main resistance is not necessarily in the L bulk. It can be in the G film, or L film. It all depends on the relative size of the three resistance terms in the general rate equation.

(c) **When $0.02 < M_H < 2$** then we are in the intermediate regime where reaction occurs in significant proportions in both L film and L bulk. From the figure we find that $E = 1 + M_H^2/3$.

Step 3. Evaluate $-r_A''''$. With E now known we can find $-r_A''''$, where reaction is taking place, where the resistance to reaction lies, and what is happening within the L film. All this is important in helping us select the proper type of contactor. As a rule

- film resistance dominates and controls all the way down to very slow reactions
- L bulk resistance only controls for very very slow reactions
- G film controls for very soluble gases ($H_A \cong 1$ Pa·m³/mol) such as NH_3, and also for very fast reaction of gases of any solubility
- L film controls for very sparingly soluble gases ($H_A \cong 10^5$ Pa·m³/mol) such as oxygen in water, and also when the reaction rate is not very fast.

Chapter 41 Problems

Gaseous A absorbs and reacts with B in liquid according to

$$A(g \rightarrow \ell) + B(\ell) \rightarrow R(\ell), \quad -r_A = kC_AC_B$$

in a packed bed under conditions where

$k_{Ag}a = 0.1$ mol/hr·m³ of reactor·Pa $\qquad f_\ell = 0.1$ m³ liquid/m³ reactor

$k_{A\ell}a = 100$ m³ liquid/m³ reactor·hr $\qquad \mathcal{D}_{A\ell} = \mathcal{D}_{B\ell} = 10^{-6}$ m²/hr

$a = 100$ m²/m³ reactor

At a point in the reactor where $p_A = 100$ Pa and $C_B = 100$ mol/m³ liquid

(a) calculate the rate of reaction in mol/hr·m³ of reactor.

(b) Describe the following characteristics of the kinetics

- location of major resistance (gas film, liquid film, main body of liquid)
- location of reaction zone
- behavior in liquid film (pseudo first order reaction, instantaneous, second order reaction, physical transport)

for the following values of reaction rate and Henry's law constant

		k, m³ liquid/mol·hr	H_A, Pa·m³ liquid/mol
A1	...	10	10^5
A2	...	10^8	10^5
A3	...	10^6	10^4
A4	...	10	10^3
A5	...	10^6	10^2
A6	...	10^{-4}	1
A7	...	10^{-2}	1
A8	...	10^8	1

Air with gaseous A bubbles through a tank containing aqueous B. Reaction occurs as follows

$$A(g \rightarrow \ell) + 2B(\ell) \rightarrow R(\ell), \quad -r_A = kC_AC_B^2$$

For this system

$k_{Ag}a = 0.01$ mol/hr·m³·Pa $\qquad f_\ell = 0.98$

$k_{A\ell}a = 20$ hr⁻¹ $\qquad H_A = 10^5$ Pa·m³/mol, very low solubility

$D_{A\ell} = D_{B\ell} = 10^{-6}$ m²/hr $\qquad a = 20$ m²/m³

Chapter 41 Problems

For the reactor conditions listed below

(a) locate the resistance to reaction (what % in gas film, in liquid film, in main body of liquid)

(b) locate the reaction zone

(c) determine the behavior in the liquid film (whether pseudo first order, instantaneous, physical transport, etc.)

(d) calculate the rate of reaction ($mol/m^3 \cdot hr$)

	p_A, Pa	C_B, mol/m^3	k, $m^6/mol^2 \cdot hr$	
A9 ...	5×10^3	100	10^6	
A10 ...	5×10^3	1	10^6	
A11 ...	5×10^5	10	1	... $\pi = 10$ atm
A12 ...	5×10^5	100	10^6	... $\pi = 10$ atm

A13 At high pressure CO_2 is absorbed into a solution of NaOH in a packed column. The reaction is as follows

$$\underset{(A)}{CO_2} + \underset{(B)}{2NaOH} \rightarrow Na_2CO_3 + H_2O \quad \text{with} \quad -r_{A\ell} = kC_AC_B$$

Find rate of absorption, the controlling resistance, and what is happening in the liquid film, at a point in the column where $p_A = 10^5$ Pa and $C_B = 500\ mol/m^3$.

<u>Data</u>: $k_{Ag} = 10^{-4}\ mol/m^2 \cdot s \cdot Pa$ $\quad H_A = 25{,}000\ Pa \cdot m^3/mol$
$k_{A\ell} = 1 \times 10^{-4}\ m/s$ $\quad \mathcal{D}_A = 1.8 \times 10^{-9}\ m^2/s$
$a = 100\ m^{-1}$ $\quad \mathcal{D}_B = 3.06 \times 10^{-9}\ m^2/s$
$k = 10\ m^3/mol \cdot s$ $\quad f_\ell = 0.1$

Adapted from Danckwerts (1970)

A14 For the column of the previous problem, and CO_2 partial pressure of 1 atm find the concentration of NaOH in the liquid which should be used to insure that no unreacted CO_2 enters the main body of the liquid. Find the rate of reaction under these conditions.

A15 Gaseous A is to be absorbed by liquid containing B in an experimental packed column. The reaction is elementary second order, A + B →R + S, and the system conditions are estimated to be as follows

$k_{Ag} = 10^{-3}$ mol/m^2·hr·Pa $k = 10^5$ m^3/mol·hr $H_A = 10^4$ Pa·m^3/mol
$k_{A\ell} = 1$ m/hr, $\mathcal{D}_A = \mathcal{D}_B = 10^{-6}$ m^2/hr $f = 0.1$
$a = 100$ m^{-1} $C_B = 1000$ mol/m^3 $= 1$ MPa

We intend to run our experiments where the liquid film is in the pseudo first order regime. To insure this, the pressure of A must lie in some range of values. Find this range and the corresponding absorption rate $-r_A'''$.

A16 For the experiment of the above reaction suppose we plan to use pure gaseous A. What range of total pressure p would insure staying in the pseudo first order regime, and find the corresponding rate of reaction.

A17 Hydrogen sulfide is absorbed by a solution of methanolamine (MEA) in a packed column. At the top of the column gas is at 20 atm and it contains 0.1% of H_2S, while the absorbent contains 250 mol/m^3 of free MEA. The diffusivity of MEA in solution is 0.64 times that of H_2S. The reaction is normally regarded as irreversible and instantaneous

$$\underset{(A)}{H_2S} + \underset{(B)}{RNH_2} \rightarrow HS^- + RNH_3^+$$

For the flow rates and packing used

$k_{A\ell}\, a = 0.03$ s^{-1}
$k_{Ag}\, a = 60$ mol/m^3·s·atm
$H_A = 1 \times 10^{-4}$ m^3·atm/mol, Henry's law constant for H_2S in water.

(a) Find the rate of absorption of H_2S in MEA solution

(b) To find out whether it is worthwhile using MEA absorbent determine how much faster is absorption with MEA compared to absorption in pure water.

Adapted from Danckwerts (1970)

---

van Krevelens and van Hooren in Rec. Trav. Chim. **67** 587 (1948) studied the reaction of CO_2 with alkaline hydroxide solutions in a small column 3 cm ID, 15 to 30 cm high, packed with 0.5 cm ceramic Raschig rings. The mechanism of reaction with an excess of OH^- ion is viewed to be

$$CO_2 + OH^- \rightarrow HCO_3^- \quad \text{(moderately rapid)}$$
$$HCO_3^- + OH^- \rightarrow CO_3^{=} + H_2O \quad \text{(very rapid)}$$

or, overall,

$$CO_2 + 2OH^- \rightarrow CO_3^{=} + H_2O$$

Here are the data for two of their reported 17 runs.

Chapter 41 Problems

Data:	Run 5, for KOH	Run 2, for NaOH Solution
k_g	1.85×10^{-2}	2.6×10^{-2} mol/s·m²·atm
k_ℓ	4.3×10^{-6}	1.15×10^{-6} m²/s
k	4.6	5.0 m³/mol·s
$\mathcal{D}_{CO_2} = \mathcal{D}_{OH^-} = D$	2.0×10^{-9}	2.0×10^{-9} m²/s
$p_{A,\,in}$	0.216	0.076 atm
$C_{OH^-,in}$	290	410 mol/m³
H_A	0.03125	0.03125 atm·m³/mol
a, estimated from Perry	220	220 m²/m³
f_ℓ, estimated from Perry	0.5	0.5
$-r_A''$, measured	7.8×10^{-4}	2.6×10^{-4} mol/s·m²
$-r_A''$, calculated by authors	7.7×10^{-4}	2.6×10^{-4} mol/s·m²

(a) Calculate the rate of reaction

(b) Locate the main resistance to absorption and reaction

(c) Compare your calculated rates to the above reported rates. If they differ try to explain why they do.

Do these three tasks

A18 . . . for the KOH solution of run 5

A19 . . . for the NaOH solution of run 2

Note: The numbers reported in the authors' M_2 column on pg 589 are all too big by a factor of 10. The authors could not have gotten their reported rates using the tabulated values, so most likely this is a typographical or transcribing error in the article.

These problems were prepared by duWayne Zuelhsdorff.

A20 Most of the organs of the human body are designed with a large safey factor. For example one can get by with one kidney, half an intestine, very little brain, etc. In particular the lungs have a lot of spare capacity, which often gets crudded with tar and stuff. Let us estimate this spare capacity of a healthy lung, both at rest and at maximum exertion.

First, the transport of O_2 across the lung membrane is enhanced by its reaction with haemoglobin (Hm). Simplified we have

$$O_2 + Hm \underset{2}{\overset{1}{\rightleftharpoons}} (Hm{\cdot}O_2) \qquad \begin{array}{l} r_1 = k_1 C_{O_2} C_{Hm} \\ r_2 = k_2 (Hm{\cdot}O_2) \end{array}$$

In the lung the forward reaction dominates, in the body tissues the reverse dominates. Assume the membrane to be a liquid film and ignore the reverse reaction.

Chapter 41 Problems

Additional data:

$H_{O_2} = 0.937$ atm·m^3/mol . . . for O_2 in water, Perry 3/98

$\mathcal{D}_{O_2,\ell} = 7.1 \times 10^{-10}$ m^2/s . . . Sherwood *et al* pg 333

$\mathcal{D}_{Hm,\ell} = 8.3 \times 10^{-12}$ m^2/s . . . Sherwood *et al* pg 333

$k_1 = 1.8 \times 10^3$ m^3/mol·s . . . Sherwood *et al* pg 333

$x_0 \approx 0.5 \times 10^{-6}$ m . . . total membrane thickness; Comroe, pg 4

$C_{Hm} = 2.25$ mol/m^3 . . . in blood: Comroe, pg 185

$k_{Ag} = 0.03$ mol/s·m^2·atm . . . a guess

In the lung

$V_{blood} = 1.07 \times 10^{-4}$ m^3 . . . Sherwood *et al* pg 333

$V_{expanded\ lung} = V_r = 6.5 \times 10^{-3}$ m^3 . . . Grey, pg 1130

$S_{membrane} \approx 70$ m^2 . . . Comroe, pg 9

$p_{O_2} = 0.137$ atm . . . Comroe, pg 9

Oxygen consumption of a human

at rest: 1.5×10^{-4} mol/s . . . from problem 1.8

running from a lion: 36×10^{-4} mol/s . . . Comroe, pg 4

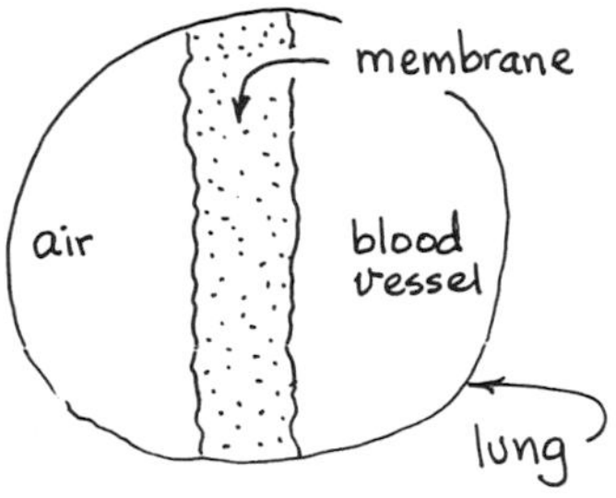

Problem devised by Greg Golike

Chapter 42. DESIGN OF G/L AND L/L REACTORS.

We must first choose the right kind of contactor, then find the size needed. There are two kinds of contactor – towers and tanks. Here are some examples

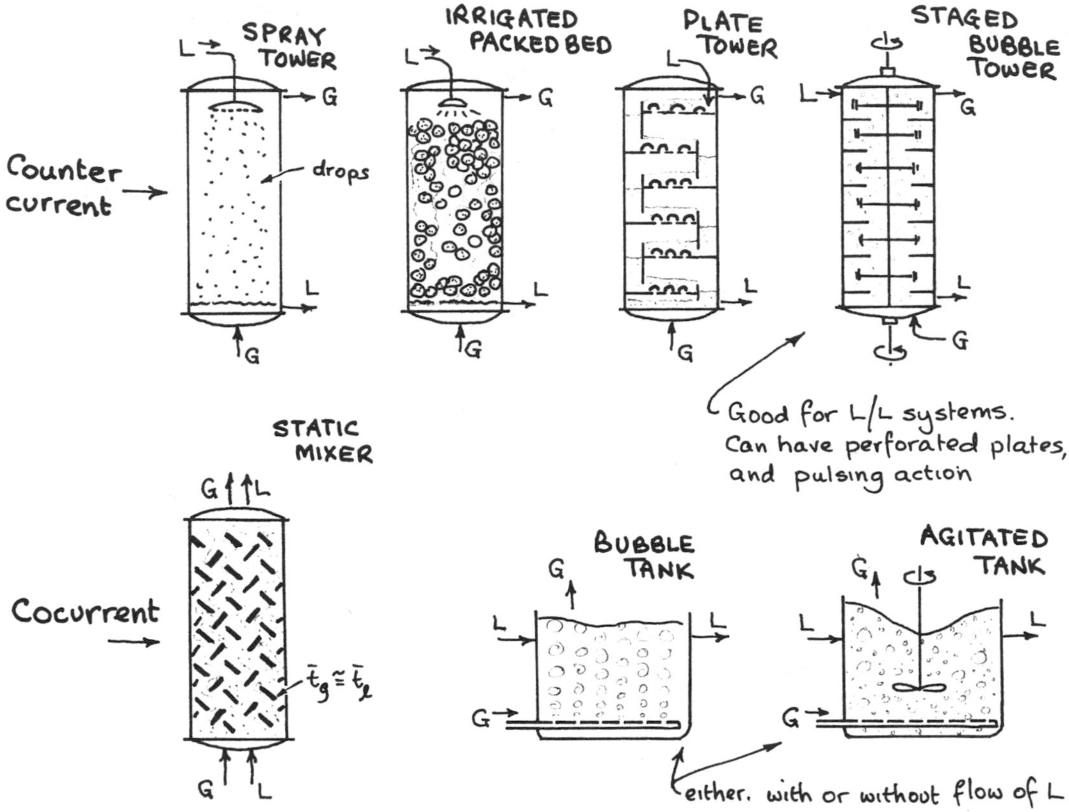

As may be expected these contactors have widely different G/L volume ratios, interfacial areas, k_g and k_ℓ, and concentration driving forces. The particular properties of the system you are dealing with, the solubility of gaseous reactant, the concentration of reactants, etc. — in effect the location of the main resistance in the rate equation — will suggest that you use one class of reactor and not another.

Here are some of the characteristics of these contactors

Flow pattern	Contactor	a (m^2/m^3)	$f_\ell = \frac{V_\ell}{V}$ $(-)$	Capacity	Comments
Counter current flow	Spray tower	60	0.05	low	Good for very soluble gases high k_g/k_ℓ
	Packed bed	100	0.08	high	Good all rounder, but must have $F_\ell/F_g \cong 10$
	Plate tower	150	0.15	medium-high	
	Staged bubble column	200	0.9	low	Needs mechanical mixer or pulsing device. Good for slightly soluble gases and L/L. Has low k_g/k_ℓ.
Cocurrent flow	Static mixer	200	0.2~0.8	very high	Very flexible, little reported data $\bar{t}_g \cong \bar{t}_\ell$.
Mixed flow of L	Bubble tank	20	0.98	medium	Cheap to build
	Agitated tank	200	0.9	medium	Cheap to build but needs a mechanical agitator.

1. Factors to consider in selecting a contactor.

(a) **Contacting pattern.** We idealize these as follows

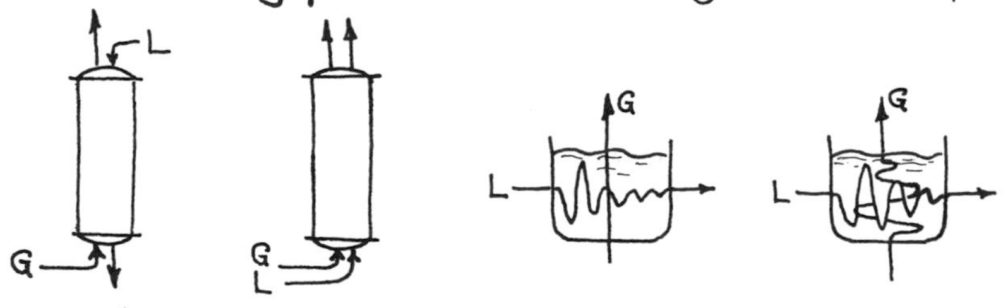

steady state operations

plug G/plug L   plug G/plug L   plug G/mixed L   mixed G/mixed L

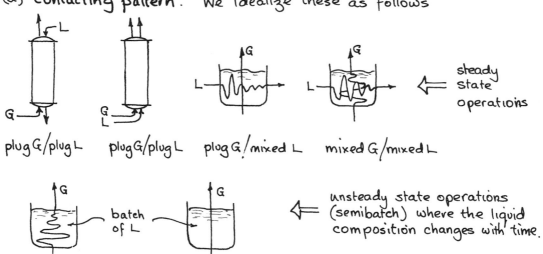

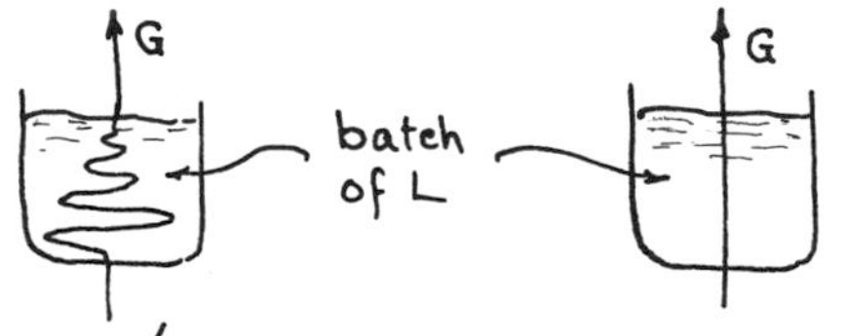

unsteady state operations (semibatch) where the liquid composition changes with time.

mixed G/batch uniform L   plug G/batch uniform L

- Towers approximate plug G/plug L.
- Bubble tanks approximate plug G/mixed L.
- Agitated tanks approximate mixed G/mixed L.

As we shall see, towers have the largest driving force and in this respect have an advantage over tanks. Agitated tanks have the smallest driving force.

(b) **k_g and k_ℓ**. For liquid droplets in gas k_g is high, k_ℓ is low. For gas bubbles rising in liquid k_g is low, k_ℓ is high.

(c) **Flow rates.** Packed beds work best with $F_\ell/F_g \cong 10$ at 1 atm. Other contactors are more flexible in that they work well in a wider range of F_ℓ/F_g values.

(d) **If the resistance is in the films** you want a large interfacial area "a", thus most agitated contactors and most columns. If L film dominates stay away from spray contactors. If G film dominates stay away from bubble contactors

(e) **If the resistance is in the main body of L** you want large $f_\ell = V_\ell/V_r$. Stay away from towers. Use tank contactors.

(f) **Solubility**. For very soluble gases, those with a small value of Henry's law constant H (NH_3 for example), gas film controls thus avoid bubble contactors. For gases of low solubility in the liquid, thus high H value (O_2, N_2 as examples) liquid film controls, so avoid spray towers.

(g) Reaction lowers the resistance of the liquid film so

- For absorption of **highly soluble** gases chemical reaction **is not helpful.**
- For absorption of **slightly soluble** gases chemical reaction **is helpful** and does speed up the rate.

2. **General plan.** In this chapter we will take up the design for

- straight mass transfer
- mass transfer plus reaction for all but very slow reactions

We will not take up

- mass transfer plus reaction for very slow reactions.

The term "not very slow reaction" means that A reacts away fast enough in the liquid so that only a negligible amount is able to accumulate in the bulk of the liquid. Thus $M_H \geqslant 1$ and

$$\begin{pmatrix}\text{the rate of loss}\\ \text{of A by the gas}\end{pmatrix} = \begin{pmatrix}\text{rate of reaction}\\ \text{of A in the liquid}\end{pmatrix}$$

By "very slow reaction" we mean that a significant fraction of absorbed A does not react away, and either accumulates in the liquid or is carried out of the reactor by the liquid. Thus $M_H \ll 1$ and

$$\begin{pmatrix}\text{the rate of loss}\\ \text{of A by the gas}\end{pmatrix} > \begin{pmatrix}\text{rate of reaction}\\ \text{of A in the liquid}\end{pmatrix}$$

We must treat the "very slow reaction" case separately because the flow of A in two separate streams — upward in the G, downward in the L — leads to complications in the material balance and in expressing rates. Luckily, this situation is not too important in industrial practice.

In this chapter we develop the performance expressions for the reaction

$$A(g \rightarrow \ell) + bB(\ell) \rightarrow \text{products}(\ell)$$

a gas phase reactant which has to first enter the liquid, then react

this equation as written indicates that reaction takes place in the liquid only

There are many many other types of reactions. These are treated in later chapters, as extensions of this simple first case.

3. **Nomenclature.** We use the following symbols in our development.

a = interfacial contact area per unit volume of reactor (m^2/m^3).
f_ℓ = volume fraction of the phase in which reaction occurs (–).
i = any participant, reactant or product, in the reaction.
A, B, R, S = participants in the reaction.
U = carrier or inert component in a phase, hence neither reactant, product nor diffusing component.
T = total moles in the reacting (or liquid) phase.
$Y_A = p_A/p_U$, moles A/mole inert in the gas (–).
$X_A = C_A/C_U$, moles A/mole inert in the liquid (–).
F_g', F_ℓ' = molar flow rate of all the gas and all the liquid (mol/s).
$F_g = F_g' \, p_U/\pi$, upward molar flow rate of inerts in the gas (mol/s).
$F_\ell = F_\ell' \, C_U/C_T$, downward molar flow rate of inerts in the liquid phase (mol/s).

With this nomenclature we have the following relationships among the various concentration measures.

$$\pi = p_A + p_B + \cdots + p_U$$

$$C_T = C_A + C_B + \cdots + C_U$$

$$dY_A = d\left(\frac{p_A}{p_U}\right) = \frac{p_U\,dp_A - p_A\,dp_U}{p_U^2} \cong \frac{dp_A}{p_U}$$

$$dX_A = d\left(\frac{C_A}{C_U}\right) = \frac{C_U\,dC_A - C_A\,dC_U}{C_U^2} \cong \frac{dC_A}{C_U}$$

these approximations only hold for dilute systems.

Note how similar this language is to that used in mass transfer operations.

I. Straight Mass Transfer.

A. Plug flow G/plug flow L — countercurrent flow in a tower.

To develop the performance equation we combine the rate equation with the material balance. Thus for steady state countercurrent operations we have for a differential element of volume

$$\begin{pmatrix}\text{A lost}\\ \text{by gas}\end{pmatrix} = \begin{pmatrix}\text{A gained}\\ \text{by liquid}\end{pmatrix} = (-r_A'''')\,dV_r$$

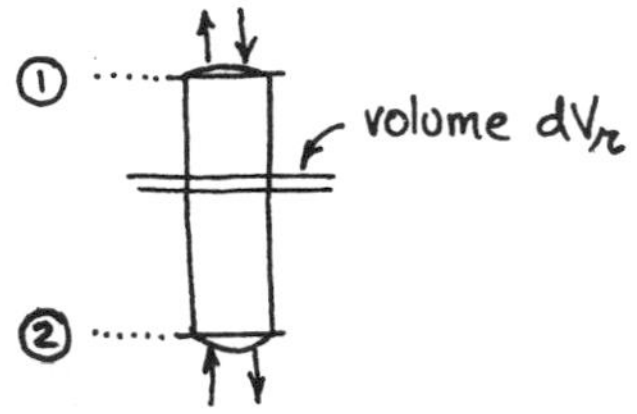

or

$$F_g\,dY_A = F_l\,dX_A = (-r_A'''')\,dV_r$$

$$\frac{F_g \pi\, dp_A}{(\pi-p_A)^2} = d\left(\frac{F_g' p_A}{\pi}\right) = \frac{F_g'\,dp_A}{\pi-p_A}$$

$$\frac{F_l C_T\, dC_A}{(C_T-C_A)^2} = d\left(\frac{F_l' C_A}{C_T}\right) = \frac{F_l'\,dC_A}{C_T-C_A}$$

$$(-r_A'')a = k_{Ag}a(p_A-p_{Ai}) = k_{Al}a(C_{Ai}-C_A)$$

Integrating for the whole tower gives

$$V_r = \frac{F_g}{a}\int_{Y_{A1}}^{Y_{A2}} \frac{dY_A}{-r_A''} = \frac{F_l}{a}\int_{X_{A1}}^{X_{A2}} \frac{dX_A}{-r_A''}$$

$$= F_g \pi \int_{p_{A1}}^{p_{A2}} \frac{dp_A}{k_{Ag}a(\pi-p_A)^2(p_A-p_{Ai})} = \int_{p_{A1}}^{p_{A2}} \frac{F_g'\,dp_A}{k_{Ag}a(\pi-p_A)(p_A-p_{Ai})} \quad \cdots(1)$$

$$= F_l C_T \int_{C_{A1}}^{C_{A2}} \frac{dC_A}{k_{Al}a(C_T-C_A)^2(C_{Ai}-C_A)} = \int_{C_{A1}}^{C_{A2}} \frac{F_l'\,dC_A}{k_{Al}a(C_T-C_A)(C_{Ai}-C_A)}$$

In brief the design procedure is as follows

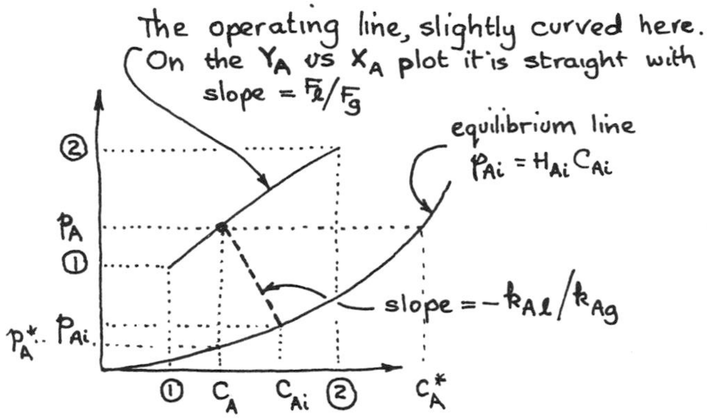

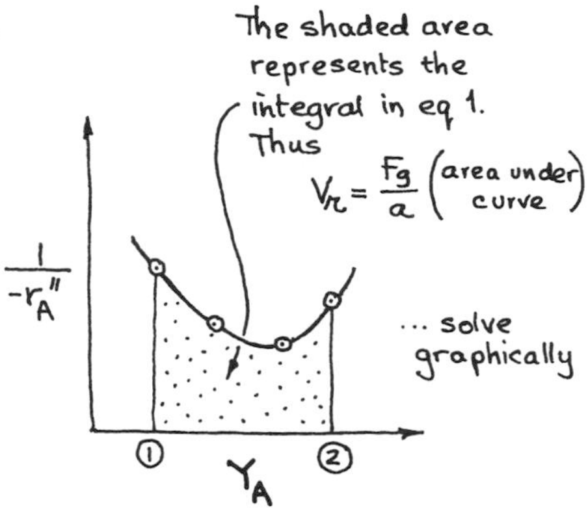

For **dilute systems** $C_A \ll C_T$ and $p_A \ll \pi$, so $F_g' \cong F_g$, $F_l' \cong F_l$ so the differential material balance becomes

$$\frac{F_g}{\pi} dp_A = \frac{F_l}{C_T} dC_A = (-r_A'')\, a\, dV_r$$

The integrated expression, eq 1, then simplifies to

$$V_r = \frac{F_g}{\pi k_{Ag} a} \int_{p_{A1}}^{p_{A2}} \frac{dp_A}{p_A - p_{Ai}} = \frac{F_l}{C_T k_{Al} a} \int_{C_{A1}}^{C_{A2}} \frac{dC_A}{C_{Ai} - C_A}$$

$$= \frac{F_g}{\pi K_{Ag} a} \int_{p_{A1}}^{p_{A2}} \frac{dp_A}{p_A - p_A^*} = \frac{F_l}{C_T K_{Al} a} \int_{C_{A1}}^{C_{A2}} \frac{dC_A}{C_A^* - C_A} \quad \cdots (2)$$

liquid in equilibrium with gas p_A, or $C_A^* = p_A/H_A$

Overall mass transfer coefficient on gas basis

$$\frac{1}{K_{Ag}} = \frac{1}{k_{Ag}} + \frac{H_A}{k_{Al}}$$

gas in equilibrium with liquid C_A, or $p_A^* = H_A C_A$

overall mass transfer coefficient on liquid basis

$$\frac{1}{K_{Al}} = \frac{1}{H_A k_{Ag}} + \frac{1}{k_{Al}}$$

B. Plug flow G/plug flow L — mass transfer for cocurrent flow in a tower.

The equations for this case are identical to those for countercurrent flow, shown above, except that F_ℓ is replaced by $-F_\ell$.

operating line, slightly curved.

$$\text{slope} = \frac{-F_\ell\, C_T (\pi - p_A)^2}{F_g\, \pi\, (C_T - C_A)^2}$$

tie line, which represents a typical point in the tower

equilibrium curve

$F_g, p_{Ain} \qquad F_\ell, C_{Ain}$

$F_g, p_{Aout} \qquad F_\ell, C_{Aout}$

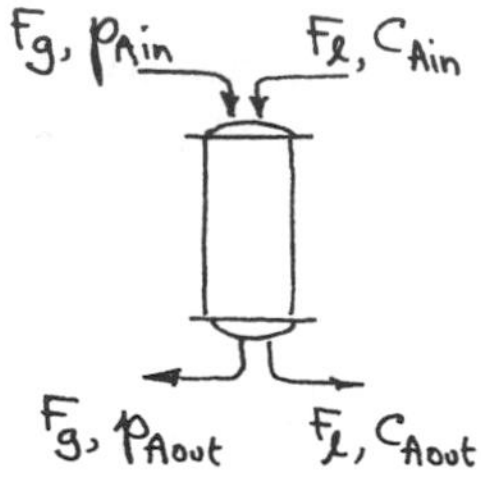

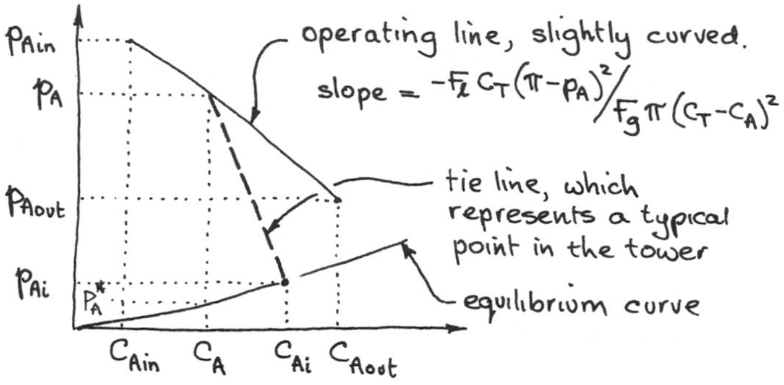

The integration differs from the countercurrent case because the p_A vs C_A progression is not the same

C. Mixed flow G/mixed flow L — mass transfer in an agitated tank.

Since the composition is uniform everywhere in the vessel make the material balance about the vessel as a whole. Then

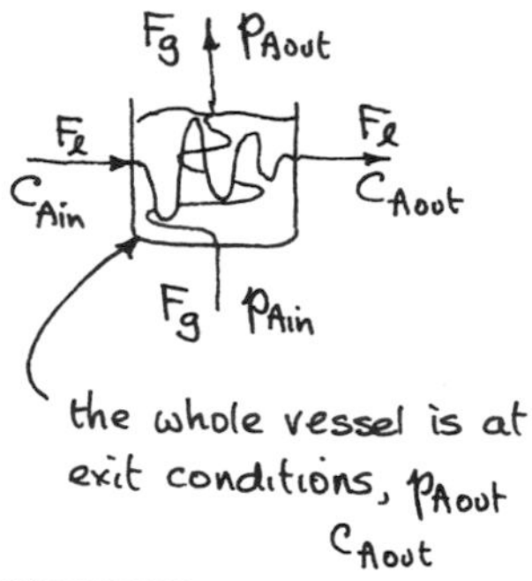

$$\begin{pmatrix} \text{A lost} \\ \text{by gas} \end{pmatrix} = \begin{pmatrix} \text{A gained} \\ \text{by liquid} \end{pmatrix} = \begin{pmatrix} \text{A} \\ \text{transferred} \end{pmatrix}$$

$F_g \uparrow p_{Aout}$

$F_\ell \quad C_{Ain}$ · · · $F_\ell \quad C_{Aout}$

$F_g \uparrow p_{Ain}$

the whole vessel is at exit conditions, p_{Aout}, C_{Aout}

In symbols

$$\underbrace{F_g \left(Y_{Ain} - Y_{Aout} \right)}_{\text{I}} = \underbrace{F_\ell \left(X_{Aout} - X_{Ain} \right)}_{\text{II}} = \underbrace{\left(-r'''''_{Aout} \right) V_r}_{\text{III}}$$

or for dilute systems

· · · (3)

$$\underbrace{\frac{F_g}{\pi} \left(p_{Ain} - p_{Aout} \right)}_{\text{I}} = \underbrace{\frac{F_\ell}{C_T} \left(C_{Aout} - C_{Ain} \right)}_{\text{II}} = \underbrace{\left(-r'''''_{Aout} \right) V_r}_{\text{III}} \qquad -r'''''_A = (-r''_A)\, a$$

To find V_r given the feed streams and one outlet

- find C_{Aout} from I and II

- evaluate $-r''''_{Aout} = \left[\dfrac{1}{\dfrac{1}{k_{Ag}a} + \dfrac{H_A}{k_{Al}a}}\right](p_{Aout} - H_A C_{Aout})$

- from I and III find V_r

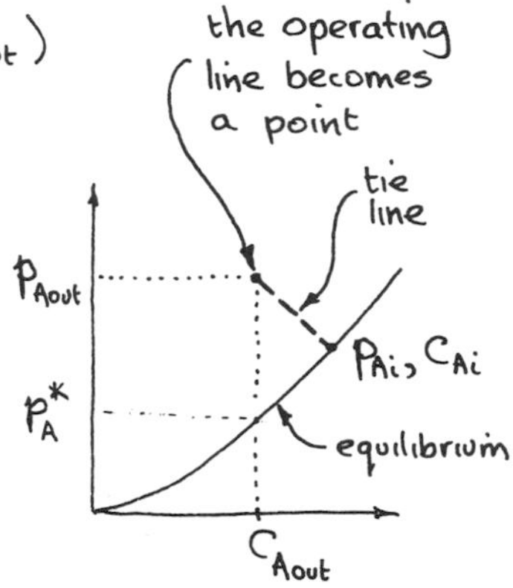

To find C_{Aout} and p_{Aout} in a given vessel V_r

- guess p_{Aout}
- I and II then give C_{Aout}
- evaluate $-r''''_{Aout}$ with these p_{Aout} and C_{Aout} values
- I and III then give V_r based on the initial guessed p_{Aout} value.
- See if this V_r agrees with the given V_r. If not guess another p_{Aout} and repeat the procedure.

D. Plug flow G/mixed flow L – mass transfer in a bubble tank.

Here gas contacts liquid at exit conditions. So for a "slice" of rising gas

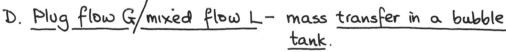

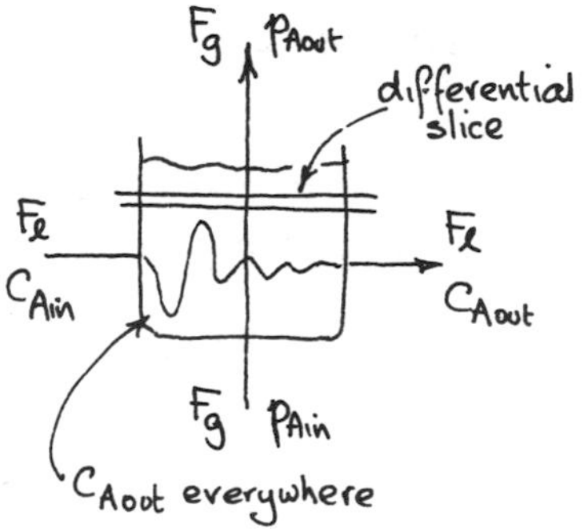

$$F_g\, dY_A = (-r_A'''')\Big|_{\text{liquid at exit conditions}} dV_r \quad \cdots (i)$$

a material balance about the whole vessel also gives

$$F_g(Y_{Ain} - Y_{Aout}) = F_l(X_{Aout} - X_{Ain}) \quad \cdots (ii)$$

Integrating (i) and joining in with (ii) then gives

$$V_r = F_g \int \frac{dY_A}{(-r_A'')a} \quad \cdots \text{with} \quad F_g(Y_{Ain} - Y_{Aout}) = F_l(X_{Aout} - X_{Ain})$$

(I) … (II)

and for dilute systems … (4)

$$V_r = \frac{F_g}{\pi} \int \frac{dp_A}{(-r_A'')a} \quad \cdots \text{with} \quad \frac{F_g}{\pi}(p_{Ain} - p_{Aout}) = \frac{F_l}{C_T}(C_{Aout} - C_{Ain})$$

(I) … (II)

also $= F_g'$

p_A changes as we integrate but C_A remains constant at C_{Aout} throughout

To find V_r given the feed and one outlet

- find the other outlet from II
- evaluate $$-r_A'''' = \left[\frac{1}{\frac{1}{k_{Ag}a} + \frac{H_A}{k_{Al}a}}\right](p_A - H_A C_A)$$
- integrate I to find V_r

To find the outlet composition given the feed composition and reactor volume V_r

- guess C_{Aout}, and from II find p_{Aout}
- take p_{Ain}, p_{Aout} and an intermediate p_A, and for each calculate $-r_A''''$.
- insert in the integral of I and find V_r
- compare with the given V_r. If different guess another C_{Aout} and repeat the procedure.

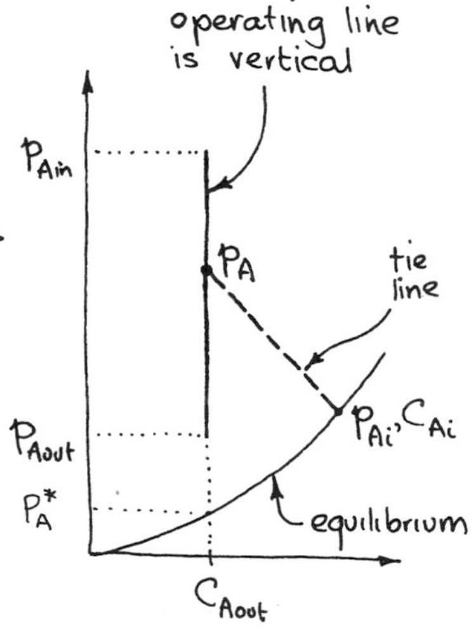

E. Mixed flow G / batch uniform L — mass transfer to a stirred batch of liquid.

Here compositions and rates change with time, so at any instant equate

$$\begin{pmatrix}\text{loss of A}\\ \text{from G}\end{pmatrix} = \begin{pmatrix}\text{accumulation}\\ \text{of A in liquid}\end{pmatrix} = \begin{pmatrix}\text{rate of tranfer}\\ \text{of A from G to L}\end{pmatrix}$$

In symbols this becomes

$$\underbrace{F_g(Y_{Ain}-Y_{Aout})}_{\text{I}} = \underbrace{V_\ell \frac{dC_A}{dt}}_{\text{II}} = \underbrace{(-r_A'''')V_r}_{\text{III}}$$

or for dilute systems (also $= F_g'$) $\quad\cdots(5)$

$$\underbrace{\frac{F_g}{\pi}(p_{Ain}-p_{Aout})}_{\text{I}} = \underbrace{V_\ell \frac{dC_A}{dt}}_{\text{II}} = \underbrace{(-r_A'''')V_r}_{\text{III}}$$

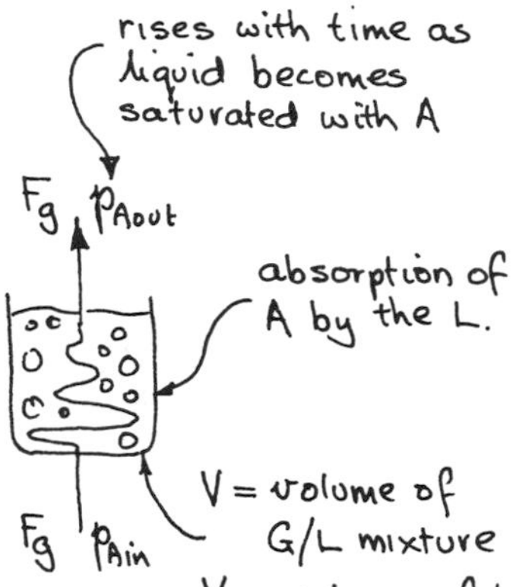

V_ℓ = volume of L
C_{Ao} = initial C_A
C_{Af} = final C_A

To find the time t needed for a given extent of absorption, in other words to find t need to go from C_{Ao} to C_{Af}.

- choose a number of C_A values. Usually C_{Ao}, C_{Af} and one $C_{A,intermediate}$ are sufficient.
- for each C_A determine the corresponding p_{Aout} at that time. This is given by I and III. On rearranging we find

$$p_{Aout} = \frac{\dfrac{F_g}{\pi}p_{Ain} + H_A C_A\left[\dfrac{1}{1/k_{Ag}a + H_A/k_{A\ell}a}\right]V_r}{\dfrac{F_g}{\pi} + \left[\dfrac{1}{1/k_{Ag}a + H_A/k_{A\ell}a}\right]V_r}$$

this expression only good for dilute systems. For non dilute systems the expression is messier.

- now for each point evaluate the rate

$$-r_A'''' = \left[\frac{1}{1/k_{Ag}a + H_A/k_{A\ell}a}\right](p_{Aout} - H_A C_A)$$

- From II and III we can find the time. Rearranging and integrating gives

$$t = f_l \int_{C_{A0}}^{C_{Af}} \frac{dC_A}{-r_A''''} \quad \cdots (6)$$

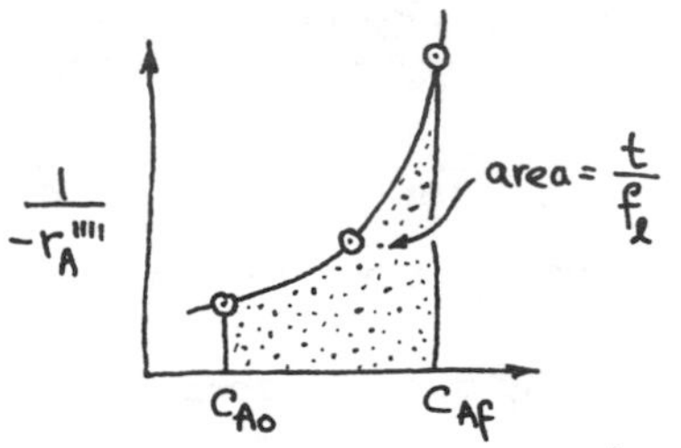

To find the absorption efficiency (fraction of entering A absorbed) start by assuming that all entering A is absorbed, or that $p_{Aout} = 0$. Then I and II give

$$t_{min} = \frac{V_l (C_{Af} - C_{A0})}{F_g Y_{Ain}}$$

and thus

$$\begin{pmatrix}\text{absorption} \\ \text{efficiency}\end{pmatrix} = \frac{t_{min}}{t} = \frac{V_r (C_{Af} - C_{A0})}{F_g Y_{Ain} \int_{C_{A0}}^{C_{Af}} \frac{dC_A}{-r_A''''}} \quad \cdots (7)$$

F. Comments.

(a) The p_A vs C_A diagrams for the same inlet and outlet conditions give

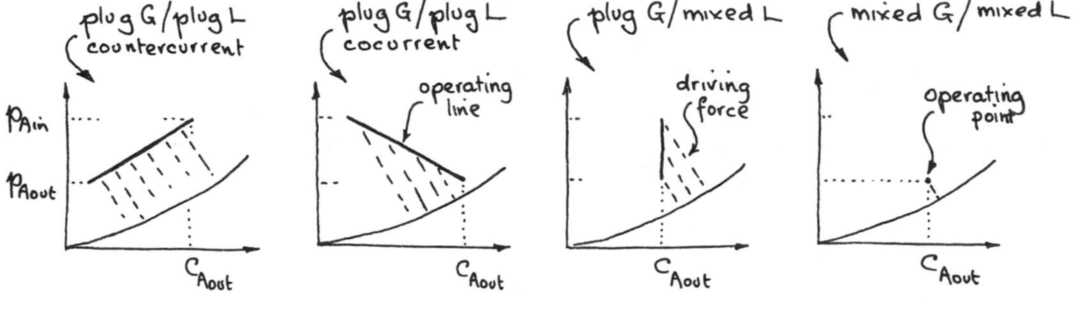

From the left to the right we have the largest to the smallest driving force; countercurrent best, agitated tanks poorest. This ordering does not extend automatically to reacting systems.

(b) If the operating line crosses the equilibrium then the proposed operation won't work, one cannot absorb that much gas.

II. Mass Transfer plus Not Very Slow Reaction.

Here we only treat the reaction $A(g\to l) + bB(l) \to$ products (l). We assume that the rate is fast enough so that no unreacted A enters the main body of the liquid. This assumes that the Hatta modulus is not very much smaller than unity.

A. Plug flow G/plug flow L – mass transfer + reaction in a countercurrent tower.

The performance equation is obtained by combining the material balance with the rate equation. Thus for a differential element of volume we write

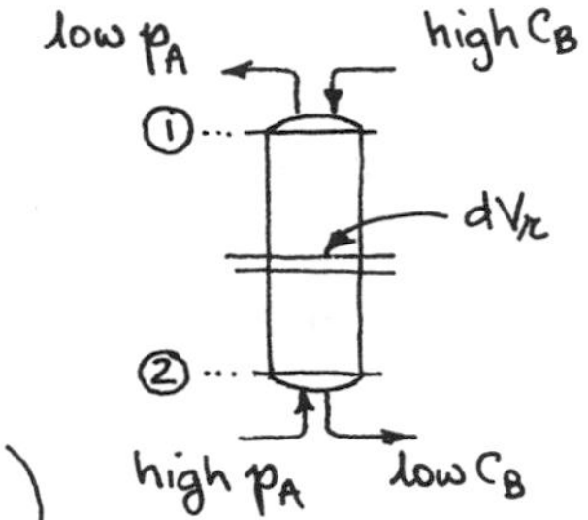

$$\underbrace{\begin{pmatrix}\text{A lost}\\ \text{by gas}\end{pmatrix}}_{I} = \underbrace{\frac{1}{b}\begin{pmatrix}\text{B lost}\\ \text{by liquid}\end{pmatrix}}_{II} = \underbrace{\begin{pmatrix}\text{disappearance}\\ \text{of A by reaction}\end{pmatrix}}_{III}$$

or

$$F_g\, dY_A = -\frac{F_l\, dX_B}{b} = (-r_A'''')\, dV_r$$

where $F_g\, dY_A = F_g\, d\left(\frac{p_A}{p_u}\right)$, $\quad -\frac{F_l\, dX_B}{b} = -\frac{F_l}{b}\, d\left(\frac{C_B}{C_u}\right) = -\frac{1}{b}\, d\left(\frac{F_l' C_B}{C_T}\right)$

$(-r_A'''') = (-r_A'')a$ where $(-r_A'')$ is the general rate expression developed in chapter 41.

For dilute systems $p_u \cong \pi$ and $C_u \cong C_T$ in which case the above expressions simplify to

$$\frac{F_g}{\pi}\, dp_A = -\frac{F_l}{bC_T}\, dC_B = (-r_A'')a\, dV_r$$

Rearranging and integrating I and II, II and III, I and III gives

In general

$$V_r = F_g \int_{Y_{A1}}^{Y_{A2}} \frac{dY_A}{(-r_A'')a} = \frac{F_l}{b} \int_{X_{B2}}^{X_{B1}} \frac{dX_B}{(-r_B'')a} \quad \cdots \text{with} \quad F_g(Y_{A2}-Y_{A1}) = \frac{F_l}{b}(X_{B1}-X_{B2})$$

also good from point 1 to any point i in the tower ...(8)

For dilute systems

$$V_r = \frac{F_g}{\pi} \int_{p_{A1}}^{p_{A2}} \frac{dp_A}{(-r_A'')a} = \frac{F_l}{bC_T} \int_{C_{B2}}^{C_{B1}} \frac{dC_B}{(-r_A'')a} \quad \cdots \text{with} \quad \frac{F_g}{\pi}(p_{A2}-p_{A1}) = \frac{F_l}{bC_T}(C_{B1}-C_{B2})$$

To solve for V_r

- pick a few p_A values, usually p_{A1}, p_{A2} and one intermediate value are enough, and for each p_A find the corresponding C_B.
- evaluate the rate for each point from

$$(-r_A'')a = \left[\frac{1}{\frac{1}{k_{Ag}a} + \frac{H_A}{k_{Al}aE} + \frac{H_A}{kC_B f_l}} \right] p_A$$

- integrate the performance equation graphically

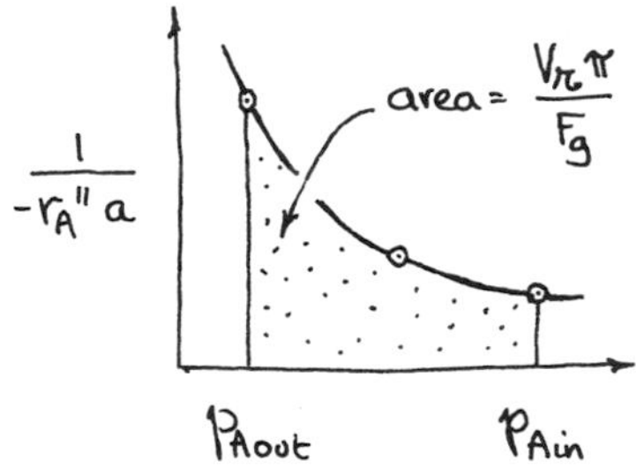

B. Plug flow G/plug flow L — mass transfer + reaction in a cocurrent tower.

Here simply change F_l to $-F_l$ (for upflow of both streams) or F_g to $-F_g$ (for downflow of both streams) in the equations for countercurrent flow. Be sure to find the proper C_B value for each p_A. The rest of the procedure remains the same.

C. Mixed flow G/mixed flow L – mass transfer + reaction in an agitated tank contactor.

Since the composition is the same everywhere in the vessel make an accounting about the vessel as a whole. Thus

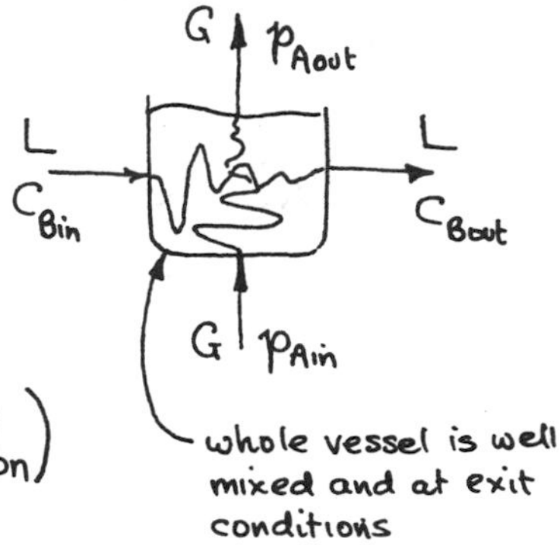

$$\begin{pmatrix}\text{A lost}\\ \text{by gas}\end{pmatrix} = \frac{1}{b}\begin{pmatrix}\text{B lost by}\\ \text{liquid}\end{pmatrix} = \begin{pmatrix}\text{disappearance}\\ \text{of A by reaction}\end{pmatrix}$$

In symbols these equalities become

$$F_g(Y_{Ain}-Y_{Aout}) = \frac{F_l}{b}(X_{Bin}-X_{Bout}) = (-r_A'''')\Big|_{\text{at exit conditions for both G and L}} V_r$$

and for dilute systems ... (9)

$$\frac{F_g}{\pi}(p_{Ain}-p_{Aout}) = \frac{F_l}{bC_T}(C_{Bin}-C_{Bout}) = (-r_A'''')\Big|_{\text{at exit}} V_r$$

To find V_r : the solution is direct; evaluate $-r_A''''$ from known stream compositions and solve eq 9.

To find C_{Bout} and p_{Aout} given V_r : guess p_{Aout}, evaluate C_{Bout}, then $-r_A''''$, then V_r. Compare the calculated V_r value with the true value. If different guess another p_{Aout}.

D. Plug flow G/mixed flow L — mass transfer + reaction in bubble tank contactors.

Here we must make two accountings, a differential balance for the loss of A from the gas because G is in plug flow, and an overall balance for B because L is in mixed flow.

Focusing on a bit of rising gas we have

$$\begin{pmatrix}\text{A lost}\\ \text{by gas}\end{pmatrix} = \begin{pmatrix}\text{disappearance}\\ \text{of A by reaction}\end{pmatrix}$$

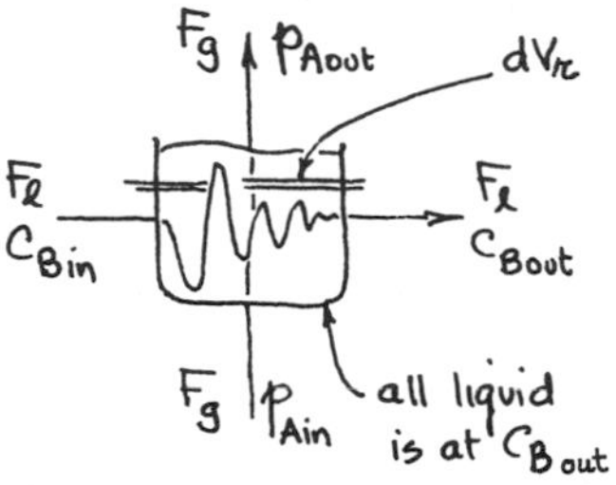

or

$$F_g\, dY_A = (-r_A'''')\Big|_{\text{L at exit conditions}} dV_r \qquad \cdots \text{(i)}$$

For the liquid as a whole and for the gas as a whole, thus a balance about the whole reactor

$$\begin{pmatrix}\text{all A lost}\\ \text{by gas}\end{pmatrix} = \frac{1}{b}\begin{pmatrix}\text{all B lost}\\ \text{by liquid}\end{pmatrix} \quad \cdots \text{or} \cdots \quad F_g\,\Delta Y_A = \frac{F_l}{b}\,\Delta X_B \qquad \cdots \text{(ii)}$$

Integrating eq (i) along the path of the bubble and also using eq (ii) gives

In general

$$V_r = F_g \int_{Y_{Aout}}^{Y_{Ain}} \frac{dY_A}{(-r_A'')\,a} \quad \cdots \text{with} \cdots \quad F_g\,(Y_{Ain} - Y_{Aout}) = \frac{F_l}{b}\,(X_{Bin} - X_{Bout})$$

for liquid at $C_{B,out}$

For dilute systems $\cdots$ (10)

$$V_r = \frac{F_g}{\pi} \int_{p_{Aout}}^{p_{Ain}} \frac{dp_A}{(-r_A'')\,a} \quad \cdots \text{with} \cdots \quad \frac{F_g}{\pi}\,(p_{Ain} - p_{Aout}) = \frac{F_l}{bC_T}\,(C_{Bin} - C_{Bout})$$

If V_r is to be found and the exit conditions are known then the procedure is direct. Pick a number of p_A values and integrate graphically.

If $p_{A\,out}$ and $C_{B\,out}$ are to be found in a reactor of known volume V_r then we require a trial and error solution. Simply guess $C_{B\,out}$ and then see if $V_{calculated} = V_{given}$.

E. Mixed flow G/batch uniform L – absorption + reaction in a batch agitated tank contactor.

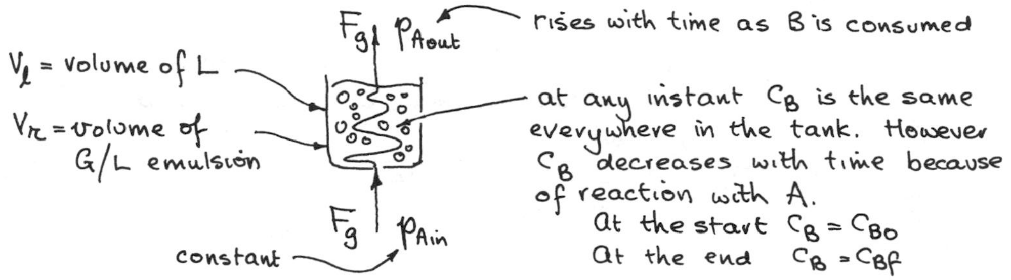

F_g $p_{A\,out}$
rises with time as B is consumed
V_l = volume of L
V_r = volume of G/L emulsion
at any instant C_B is the same everywhere in the tank. However C_B decreases with time because of reaction with A.
At the start $C_B = C_{B0}$
At the end $C_B = C_{Bf}$
F_g $p_{A\,in}$
constant

Since this is not a steady state operation composition and rates all change with time.

At any instant the material balance equates three quantities, and thus in general

$$\underbrace{F_g\left(Y_{A\,in} - Y_{A\,out}\right)}_{\text{I}} = \underbrace{-\frac{V_l}{b}\frac{dC_B}{dt}}_{\text{II}} = \underbrace{(-r_A'''')\,V_r}_{\text{III}} \qquad \cdots (11a)$$

I: loss of A from gas

II: decrease of B with time in L

III: disappearance of A or B by reaction. In the rate expression use $p_{A\,out}$ since G is in mixed flow.

For dilute systems

$$\frac{F_g}{\pi}\left(p_{A\,in} - p_{A\,out}\right) = -\frac{V_l}{b}\frac{dC_B}{dt} = (-r_A'''')\,V_r \qquad \cdots (11b)$$

To find the time needed for a given operation

- choose a number of C_B values, say C_{Bo}, C_{Bf} and an intermediate C_B value. For each C_B value guess p_{Aout}.
- Next calculate M_H, E_i, and then E and $-r_A''''$. This may require trial and error, but not often.
- See if terms I and III are equal to each other

$$(-r_A'''')\,V_r \overset{?}{=} F_g\left(\frac{p_{Ain}}{\pi-p_{Ain}} - \frac{p_{Aout}}{\pi-p_{Aout}}\right)$$

and keep adjusting p_{Aout} until they do.

As a shortcut: if $p_A \ll \pi$ and if $E = M_H$ then E is independent of p_A in which case I and III combine to give

$$p_{Aout} = p_{Ain}\Bigg/ 1 + \frac{\pi V_r}{F_g}\left(\frac{1}{\dfrac{1}{k_{Ag}a} + \dfrac{H_A}{k_{Al}aE} + \dfrac{H_A}{kC_B f_l}}\right)$$

and

$$-r_A'''' = p_{Ain}\Bigg/\left(\frac{\pi V_r}{F_g} + \frac{1}{k_{Ag}a} + \frac{H_A}{k_{Al}aE} + \frac{H_A}{kC_B f_l}\right)$$

- Next combine terms II and III to find the processing time

$$t = \frac{f_l}{b}\int_{C_{Bf}}^{C_{Bo}} \frac{dC_B}{-r_A''''} \quad \cdots \text{solve graphically} \cdots$$

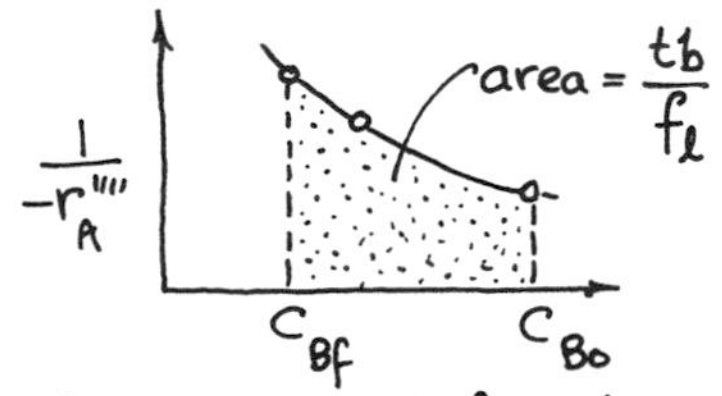

- This time can be compared with the minimum needed if all A reacts and none escapes the vessel. Thus $p_{Aout} = 0$ at all times

$$t_{min} = \frac{\frac{1}{b}V_l(C_B - C_{Bf})}{F_g\left(p_{Ain}/\pi - p_{Ain}\right)} = \frac{\frac{1}{b}\left(\text{amount of B reacted away in the vessel}\right)}{\left(\text{amount of A entering the vessel in unit time}\right)}$$

- Combining t and t_{min} gives the efficiency of utilization of A. Thus

$$\left(\begin{matrix}\text{\% of entering A}\\ \text{which reacts with B}\end{matrix}\right) = \frac{t_{min}}{t}$$

Chapter 42 Problems

We plan to remove about 90% of the A present in a gas stream by absorption in water which contains reactant B. Chemicals A and B react in the liquid as follows

$$A(g \rightarrow \ell) + B(\ell) \rightarrow R(\ell), \quad -r_A = kC_AC_B$$

B has a negligible vapor pressure, hence does not go into the gas phase. We plan to do this absorption in either a packed bed column, or an agitated tank contractor or a bubble contactor.

(a) What volume of contactor is needed and

(b) where does the resistance of absorption-reaction lie?

Data:

For the gas stream:

$F_g = 90000$ mol/hr at $\pi = 10^5$ Pa.
$p_{A,in} = 1000$ Pa
$p_{A,out} = 100$ Pa

Physical data:

$\mathcal{D} = 3.6 \times 10^{-6}$ m^2/hr
$C_U = 55{,}556$ mol H_2O/m^3 liquid, at all C_B

For the packed bed (concurrent and countercurrent):

$F_\ell = 900{,}000$ mol/hr	$k_{A\ell}a = 72$ hr^{-1}
$C_{B,in} = 55.56$ mol/m^3	$a = 100$ m^2/m^3
$k_{Ag}a = 0.36$ mol/hr·m^3·Pa	$f_\ell = V_\ell/V = 0.08$

For the agitated tank:

$F_\ell = 9000$ mol/hr	$k_{A\ell}a = 144$ hr^{-1}
$C_{B,in} = 5556$ mol/m^3 (about 10% B)	$a = 200$ m^2/m^3
$k_{Ag}a = 0.72$ mol/hr·m^3·Pa	$f_\ell = V_\ell/V = 0.9$

For the bubble tank:

$F_\ell = 9000$ mol/hr	$k_{A\ell}a = 14.4$ hr^{-1}
$C_{B,in} = 5556$ mol/m^3 (about 10% B)	$a = 20$ m^2/m^3
$k_{Ag}a = 0.072$ mol/hr·m^3·Pa	$f_\ell = V_\ell/V = 0.98$

Note that F_ℓ and $C_{B,in}$ are very different in packed beds and tank contactors. Here is the reason why. Packed columns need $F_\ell/F_g \approx 10$ for satisfactory operations. This means large F_ℓ, and so as not to waste reactant B, it is introduced in low concentration. On the other hand, tank contactors do not have this flow restriction. Thus we can use low F_ℓ and high $C_{B,in}$, as long as we introduce sufficient B to react with A.

Chapter 42 Problems

	Henry's law constant: H_A, $Pa \cdot m^3/mol$	For reaction: k, $m^3/mol \cdot hr$		Type of contactor T = tower, countercurrent CT = tower, cocurrent A = agitated tank B = bubble tank
A1 . . .	0.01	0	In these problems of straight mass transfer assume that no B is present in the system.	A
A2 . . .	10^{-4}	0		B
A3 . . .	18	0		T
A4 . . .	18	0		CT
A5 . . .	1.8	0		T
A6 . . .	1.8	0		CT
A7 . . .	10^5	∞		T
A8 . . .	10^5	∞		B
A9 . . .	10^5	2.6×10^9		B
A10 . . .	10^5	2.6×10^7		A
A11 . . .	10^5	2.6×10^5		A
A12 . . .	10^3	2.6×10^5		B
A13 . . .	10^3	2.6×10^3		T
A14 . . .	10^3	2.6×10^3		CT
A15* . . .	10^5	2.6×10^9		CT
A16* . . .	10^5	2.6×10^7		T
A17* . . .	10^5	2.6×10^5		CT
A18* . . .	10^3	2.6×10^5		T

A19 Danckwerts and Gillham in Trans. I. Chem.E. **44** 42 March 1966 studied the rate of CO_2 absorption into an alkaline buffer solution of K_2CO_3 and $KHCO_3$. The resulting reaction can be represented as

$$\underset{(A)}{CO_2\,(g \rightarrow \ell)} + \underset{(B)}{OH^-(\ell)} \rightarrow HCO_3^- \quad \text{with} \quad -r_A = kC_AC_B$$

In the experiment pure CO_2 at 1 atm was bubbled into a packed column irrigated by rapidly recirculating buffer solution kept at 20 °C and close to constant C_B. Find the fraction of entering CO_2 absorbed.

Data:			
Column:	$V_r = 0.6041\ m^3$	$f_\ell = 0.08$ $\quad a = 120\ m^2/m^3$	
Gas:	$\pi = 101325\ Pa$	$H_A = 3500\ Pa \cdot m^3/mol$	$v_0 = 0.0252\ m^3/s$
Liquid:	$\overline{C}_B = 300\ mol/m^3$	$\mathcal{D}_{A\ell} = \mathcal{D}_{B\ell} = 1.4 \times 10^{-9}\ m^2/s$	
Rates:	$k = 0.433\ m^3/mol \cdot s$	$k_{A\ell}a = 0.025\ s^{-1}$	

Problem by Barry Kelly.

Chapter 42 Problems

B20 A column packed with 5 cm polypropylene saddles ($a = 55 m^2/m^3$) is being designed for the removal of chlorine from a gas stream ($G = 100$ mol/s·m², 2.36% Cl_2) by countercurrent contact with an NaOH solution ($L = 250$ mol/s·m², 10% NaOH, $C_B = 2736$ mol/m³) at about 40 ~ 45 °C at 1 atm.

How high should the tower be for 99% removal of chlorine? Double the calculated height to take care of deviations from plug flow.

Data: The reaction $Cl_2 + 2NaOH \rightarrow$ products is very very fast and irreversible.

For these very high flow rates (close to the limits allowed) an extrapolation of the correlations in Perry 5/18 gives

$k_g a = 133$ mol/hr·m³·atm $\qquad H_A = 125 \times 10^{-6}$ atm·m³/mol

$k_\ell a = 45$ hr⁻¹ $\qquad \mathcal{D} = 1.5 \times 10^{-9}$ m²/s

---

We wish to lower the concentration of B in the liquid ($V_\ell = 1.62$ m³, $C_U = 55555.6$ mol/m³) of an agitated tank reactor by bubbling gas ($F_g = 9000$ mol/hr, $\pi = 10^5$ Pa) containing A ($p_{A,in} = 1000$ Pa) through it. A and B react as follows

$$A(g \rightarrow \ell) + B(\ell) \rightarrow \text{product}(\ell), \quad -r_A'''' = kC_AC_B$$

a) How long must we bubble gas through the vessel to lower the concentration from $C_{B0} = 555.6$ to $C_{Bf} = 55.6$ mol/m³?

(b) What percent of entering A passes through the vessel unreacted?

Additional data:

$k_{Ag}a = 0.72$ mol/hr·m³·Pa $\qquad f_\ell = 0.9$ m³ liquid/m³ total

$k_{A\ell}a = 144$ hr⁻¹ $\qquad \mathcal{D}_A = \mathcal{D}_B = 3.6 \times 10^{-6}$ m²/hr, $\quad a = 100$ m²/m³

	Henry's law constant H_A, Pa·m³/mol	Reaction rate constant k, m³/mol·hr
C21 ...	10^5	∞
C22 ...	10^3	2.6×10^{11}
C23 ...	10^5	2.6×10^9
C24 ...	10^3	2.6×10^5
C25* ...	10^5	2.6×10^5
C26* ...	10^5	2.6×10^3

51

Chapter 51. KINETICS OF G/S REACTIONS. THE SHRINKING CORE MODEL (SCM) FOR PARTICLES OF UNCHANGING SIZE.

Here we take up the simplest model, the SCM, for the reaction of gas with particles of unchanging size. Later chapters treat shrinking and growing solids and other sorts of particle kinetics.

I The Shrinking Core Model (SCM). See Yagi & Kunii, pg 231

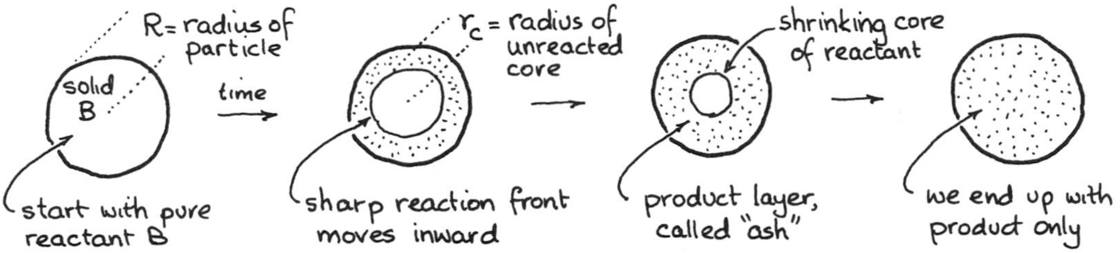

We start with this model because it often reasonably represents the behavior of real particles, and because it gives simple easy to handle conversion expressions.

For a reaction such as $A(g) + bB(s) \longrightarrow R(g) + S(s)$ we have the following three resistances in series

(1) Diffusion of A through the gas film surrounding the particle

$$-\frac{1}{S_{ex}}\frac{dN_A}{dt} = k_g(C_{Ag}-C_{As}) \quad \cdots \; k_g = \frac{m}{s}$$

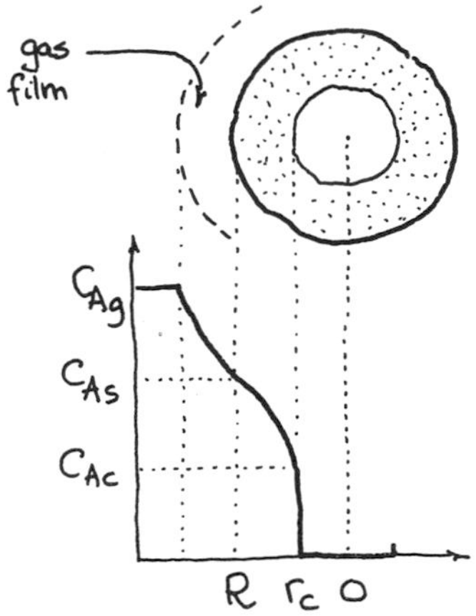

(2) Diffusion of A through the ash layer

$$-\frac{1}{S_{\text{at any } r}}\frac{dN_A}{dt} = \mathcal{D}_e\frac{dC_A}{dr} \quad \cdots \; \mathcal{D}_e = \frac{m^2}{s}$$

(3) Reaction at the unreacted core

$$-\frac{1}{S_{\text{at core}}}\frac{dN_A}{dt} = k_s C_{Ac} \quad \cdots \; k_s = \frac{m}{s}$$

With G/S reactions we represent the rate very differently from other systems. Thus we use as kinetic parameter

τ = time for complete conversion of the particle

It can well happen that one or other of the resistances controls. In this situation integration of the rate expression gives, see CRE[2] chapter 12:

Film diffusion controls

$$\frac{t}{\tau} = X_B = 1-\left(\frac{r_c}{R}\right)^3 \quad \text{... where} \quad \tau = \frac{\rho_B R}{3 b k_g C_{Ag}}$$

- t: time to reach conversion X_B
- τ: time for complete conversion
- ρ_B: molar density of B in the particle.
- k_g: gas film coefficient for mass transfer. As an example for a single particle we have

$$\frac{k_g d_p}{\mathscr{D}} = 2 + 0.6\,(Re)^{1/2}(Sc)^{1/3}$$

Ash diffusion controls

$$\frac{t}{\tau} = 1-3(1-X_B)^{2/3}+2(1-X_B) = 1-3\left(\frac{r_c}{R}\right)^2+2\left(\frac{r_c}{R}\right)^3 \quad \text{... where} \quad \tau = \frac{\rho_B R^2}{6 b \mathscr{D}_e C_{Ag}}$$

- $\mathscr{D}_e$: effective diffusion coefficient of A through the ash layer

Reaction controls

$$\frac{t}{\tau} = 1-(1-X_B)^{1/3} = 1-\left(\frac{r_c}{R}\right) \quad \text{... where} \quad \tau = \frac{\rho_B R}{b k_s C_{Ag}}$$

- k_s, C_{Ag}: for first order reaction with respect to gaseous A

Graphically these conversion-time expressions are as follows

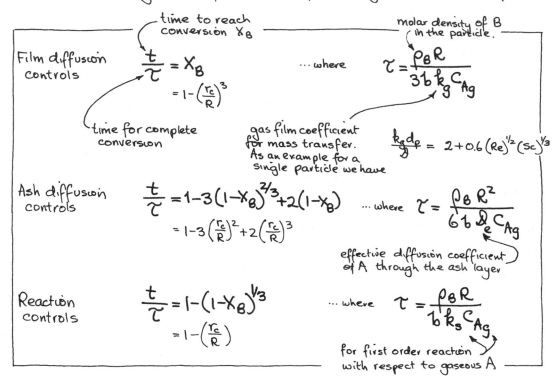

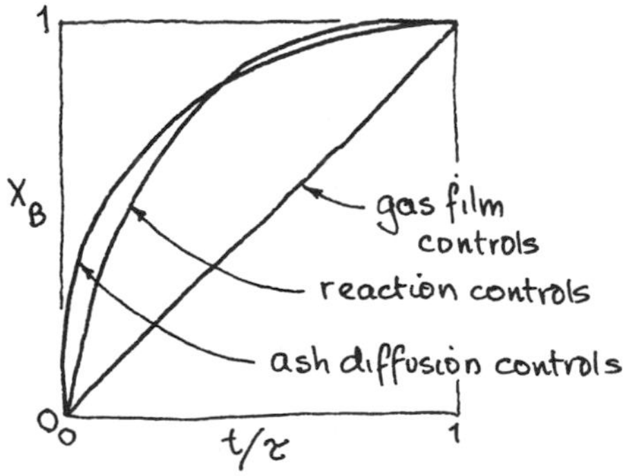

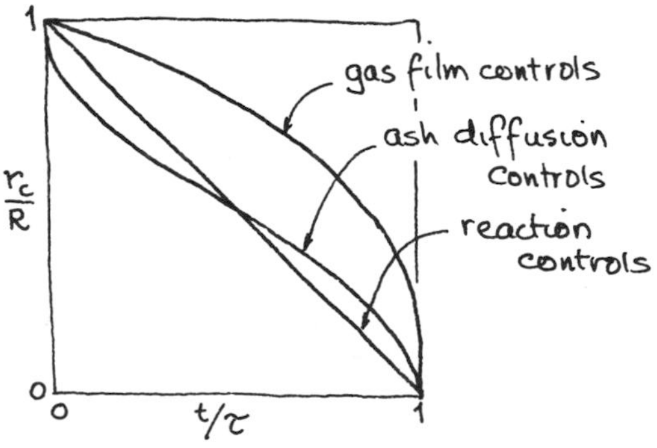

In general more than one resistance influences the conversion of the particle. So combining the three individual rate expressions for film, ash and reaction mechanisms and eliminating the concentration at intermediate locations C_{As} and C_{Ac} gives the **instantaneous rate of reaction** while the particle is being converted.

$$-\frac{1}{S_{ex}}\frac{dN_A}{dt} = \left[\frac{b}{\frac{1}{k_g} + \frac{R(R-r_c)}{r_c \mathcal{D}} + \frac{R^2}{r_c^2 k_s}}\right] C_{Ag} \quad \text{... with } X_B = 1-\left(\frac{r_c}{R}\right)^3$$

The time needed to reach any particular conversion is given as

$$t_{\substack{\text{accounting for}\\ \text{all resistances}}} = t_{\substack{\text{film}\\ \text{alone}}} + t_{\substack{\text{ash}\\ \text{alone}}} + t_{\substack{\text{reaction}\\ \text{alone}}} \quad \text{... at given } X_B$$

(film alone: this is the time needed to reach X_B if film resistance was controlling)

and the time for complete conversion of the particle is

$$\tau_{\substack{\text{accounting for}\\ \text{all resistances}}} = \tau_{\substack{\text{film}\\ \text{alone}}} + \tau_{\substack{\text{ash}\\ \text{alone}}} + \tau_{\substack{\text{reaction}\\ \text{alone}}} \quad \text{... to reach } X_B = 1$$

Replacing the individual t values with their conversion expressions shows how the conversion changes with time when all resistances are significant. Thus

$$\frac{t_{total}}{\tau_{total}} = \frac{t_{film} + t_{ash} + t_{reaction}}{\tau_{total}}$$

$$= X_B \frac{\tau_{film}}{\tau_{total}} + \left[1 - 3(1-X_B)^{2/3} + 2(1-X_B)\right]\frac{\tau_{ash}}{\tau_{total}} + \left[1-(1-X_B)^{1/3}\right]\frac{\tau_{reaction}}{\tau_{total}}$$

(accounting for all resistances)

II Clues for Finding the Controlling Mechanism.

1. **Film vs ash diffusion.** Resistance to diffusion through the ash layer is usually greater than through the gas film, so whenever an ash layer is present we can safely ignore the resistance to diffusion through the gas film.

2. **Conversion-time data; ash diffusion vs reaction.** To see which of these mechanisms controls plot

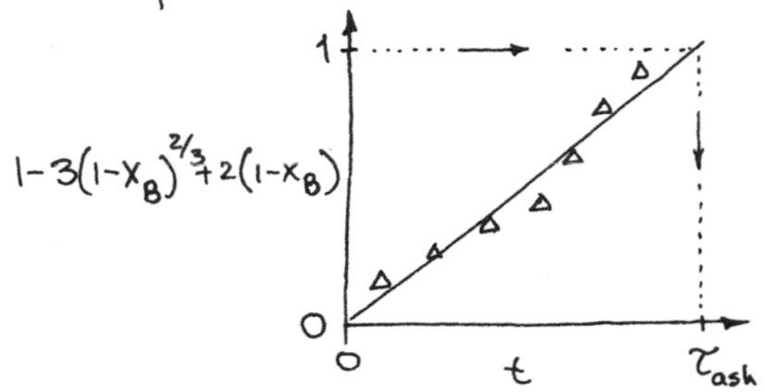

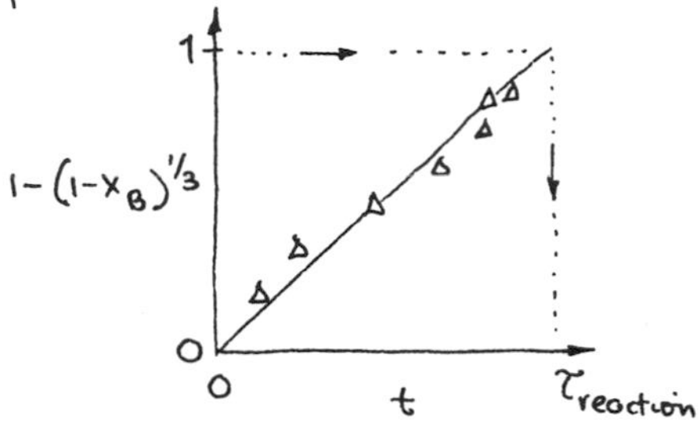

evaluate τ and test the straight line fit. Unfortunately the close similarity in shape of the two X_B vs t curves usually makes this an unreliable way of distinguishing between these mechanisms.

3. **Temperature; ash diffusion vs reaction.** The reaction step is usually much more temperature sensitive than either of the diffusion steps. Of course, if the solid experiences structural changes with temperature, for example sintering, then the resistance to diffusion can change dramatically.

4. **Particle size and conversion** The above equations show that to reach any conversion level X_B

$t \propto R^{1.5\text{ to }2.0}$ ... for film diffusion control. Exponent drops as R rises

$t \propto R^2$ ... for ash diffusion control

$t \propto R$ ... for reaction control

... taking data with different sizes of solids is a sharp way of telling which of these mechanisms controls.

These relationships show that for an increase in particle size R the rate slows more sharply if ash diffusion controls than if reaction controls. Thus if reaction controls at given R then you may find a switch to ash diffusion control with larger particles. Summarizing

- It is unsafe to extrapolate reaction control to larger particles, but it is safe to extrapolate reaction control to smaller particles.
- conversely, it is safe to extrapolate ash diffusion control to larger particles, but not to smaller particles.

III The SCM for non Spherical Particles of Unchanging Size.

The conversion-time expressions for various shapes of solids are as follows:

	Film diffusion control	Ash layer diffusion control	Reaction control
Flat plate $X_B = 1 - \frac{l}{L}$	$\frac{t}{\tau} = X_B$ $\tau = \frac{\rho_B L}{b k_g C_{Ag}}$	$\frac{t}{\tau} = X_B^2$ $\tau = \frac{\rho_B L^2}{2 b \mathscr{D}_e C_{Ag}}$	$\frac{t}{\tau} = X_B$ $\tau = \frac{\rho_B L}{b k_s C_{Ag}}$
Cylinder $X_B = 1 - \left(\frac{r_c}{R}\right)^2$	$\frac{t}{\tau} = X_B$ $\tau = \frac{\rho_B R}{2 b k_g C_{Ag}}$	$\frac{t}{\tau} = X_B + (1-X_B)\ln(1-X_B)$ $\tau = \frac{\rho_B R^2}{4 b \mathscr{D}_e C_{Ag}}$	$\frac{t}{\tau} = 1-(1-X_B)^{1/2}$ $\tau = \frac{\rho_B R}{b k_s C_{Ag}}$
Sphere $X_B = 1 - \left(\frac{r_c}{R}\right)^3$	$\frac{t}{\tau} = X_B$ $\tau = \frac{\rho_B R}{3 b k_g C_{Ag}}$	$\frac{t}{\tau} = 1 - 3(1-X_B)^{2/3} + 2(1-X_B)$ $\tau = \frac{\rho_B R^2}{6 b \mathscr{D}_e C_{Ag}}$	$\frac{t}{\tau} = 1-(1-X_B)^{1/3}$ $\tau = \frac{\rho_B R}{b k_s C_{Ag}}$

The size dependency of τ, the form of the combined expressions, and the clues for finding the mechanism are all the same as for spherical particles.

IV Final Comments.

(a) The SCM is the simplest realistic model for the conversion of solid particles. Often it fits the data, but with Murphy's law skulking about waiting to catch you off guard, it probably will not in your case. In such situations you will have to go to more complicated models. For this see chapter 55.

(b) For second order reactions with respect to gas phase reactant A simply put

$$\tau_{reaction} = \frac{\rho_B R}{b k_s C_{Ag}^2} \quad \ldots \text{with } k_s = \frac{m^4}{mol \cdot s}$$

For other reaction orders use a similar modification.

Chapter 51 Problems

Spherical solid particles containing B are roasted isothermally in an oven with gas of constant composition. Solids are converted to a firm non-flaking product according to the SCM as follows

$$A(g) + B(s) \rightarrow R(g) + S(s), \quad C_A = 0.01 \text{ kmol/m}^3, \quad \rho_B = 20 \text{ kmol/m}^3$$

From the following conversion data (by chemical analysis) or core size data (by slicing and measuring) determine the rate controlling mechanism for the transformation of solid.

A1 . . .

d_p, mm	X_B	t, min
1	1	4
1.5	1	6

A2 . . .

d_p	X_B	t, sec
1	0.3	2
1	0.75	5

A3 . . .

d_p, mm	X_B	t, sec
1	1	200
1.5	1	450

A4 . . .

d_p	X_B	t, sec
2	0.875	1
1	1	1

Assuming that chemical reaction is first order with respect to A, develop a rate expression to represent the conversion of spherical particles of radius R (cm) in a gas environment C_A (kmol/m^3) for the data of

B5 . . . problem 1.

B6 . . . problem 2 (only for particles 1 cm in diameter).

B7 . . . problem 3.

B8 Uranium dioxide is attacked by hydrofluoric acid to give uranium tetra fluoride

$$UO_2(s) + 4HF(g) \rightarrow UF_4(s) + 2H_2O(g)$$

The following data are obtained on this reaction using spherical particles of UO_2 in a uniform environment

t, min	4	12	25	35	42
X_B	0.32	0.64	0.875	0.96	0.99

Visual examination of partly reacted solids suggests that reaction follows the SCM. Find the mechanism and rate equation of represent this reaction.

Chapter 51 Problems

B9 Uniform sized spherical particles of UO_3 are reduced to UO_2 in a uniform environment with the following results

t, hr	0.180	0.347	0.453	0.567	0.733
X_B	0.45	0.68	0.80	0.95	0.98

If reaction follows the SCM find the controlling mechanism and a rate equation to represent this reduction.

B10* Gaseous A at 0.05 $kmol/m^3$ and solid B at 200 $kmol/m^3$ react according to the SCM yielding solid product. From the following data develop a rate equation to account for the conversion of solid of size R (m) at temperature T (K).

d_p, cm	T, °C	X_B	t, hr
1	327	1	5
2	353	1	5
2	327	1	10

$$A(g) + B(s) \rightarrow R(g) + S(s)$$

B11* Calcium carbide reacts with nitrogen by the SCM to give cyanamide and carbon as follows

$$CaC_2 + N_2 \rightarrow [CaCN_2 + C]_{solid}$$

With pure nitrogen at 1 atm Yagi and Kunii in CES **16** 364 (1961) report the following conversion data

d_p, cm	T, °C	τ, hr
0.2	1060	10
0.2	1100	3
0.4	1100	6

Develop a rate equation to represent the nitrogenation of particles of radius R (mm) in a nitrogen atmosphere of pressure π atm and in the temperature range of 1060 - 1100 °C.

On doubling the particle size from R to 2R the time for complete conversion triples. What is the contribution of ash diffusion to the overall resistance for particles of size

C12 . . . R?

C13 . . . 2R?

Chapter 51 Problems

A spherical solid particle of size d_p reacts with gas according to the SCM. The particle is completely converted to product solid in $\tau = 200$ min, and in the process the ash diffusion and reaction steps contribute 50% each to the overall resistance. How long will it take to achieve the conditions outlined below, and what will be the relative resistance of the ash diffusion step in these processes?

C14 . . . Complete conversion of particles of size $4d_p$.

C15 . . . 27.1% conversion of particles of size d_p.

For the reaction $2A(g) + 3B(s) \rightarrow 2R(g) + 2S(s)$, and with conversion by the SCM with $\mathcal{D}_{eff} = 10^{-5}$ m^3/m cat·s and $k_s = 0.01$ m/s, find the percent contribution of ash diffusion to the overall resistance

C16 . . . for complete conversion of particles 1 cm in radius.

C17 . . . for 48.8% conversion of particles 1 cm in radius.

Chapter 52. G/S Reactors, Solids of Unchanging Size, Known Uniform Gas Environment, the SCM.

Yagi & Kunii CES 16 364, 372 (1961)
also see Yagi & Kunii pg 231

I. The Discrete Size Distribution.

In processing solids we usually deal with a more or less wide spread of particle sizes. And since our primary measurement of particle size is made in discrete size intervals (the screen analysis) we describe the size spread accordingly, in terms of a discrete size distribution. Thus

F, kg/s (or m³/s)

$F(R_1) = \frac{kg}{s}$ (or $\frac{m^3}{s}$) of particles of size 1

$F(R_2) = \cdots$

$\vdots$

$F(R_i) = \frac{kg}{s}$ of particles of size i

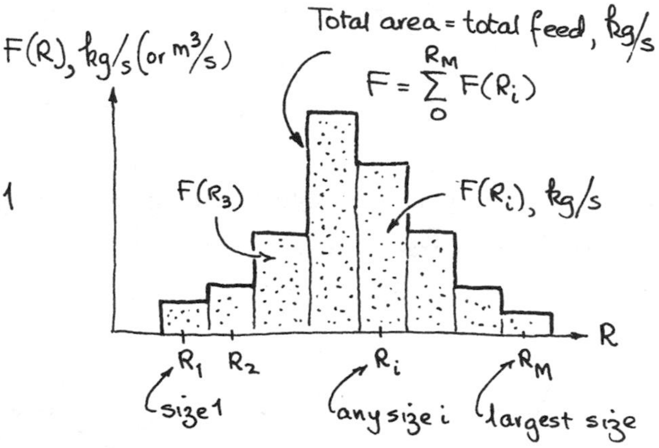

Only with shrinking and growing solids (chapter 54) do we have to introduce and use a continuous size distribution of solids

II. Design of Single Reactors.

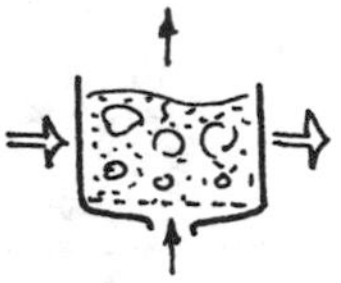

Fluidized bed
Solids : mixed
Gas : ?

Moving bed
cross, counter or cocurrent
plug/plug

Shaft kiln
plug/plug

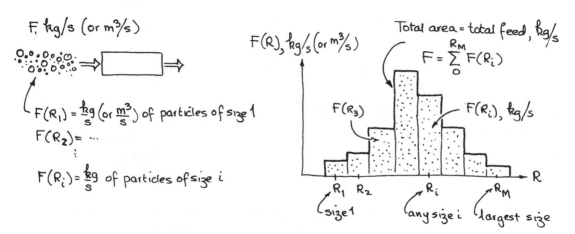

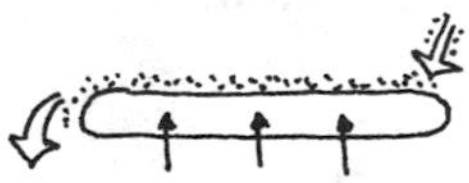

Moving bed
Solids : plug

In this chapter we assume that the reacting solids are in the same gas environment everywhere. Thus only solids change composition and we can use a one phase analysis. Also note that in a fluidized bed $\bar{t}_s$ is so large that each particle wanders all over the bed, samples all the gas in the reactor hence sees $\bar{C}_A$ of the reactor. Thus the one phase analysis can also be used here if $\bar{C}_A$ is known.

Since a stream of solid particles can be treated as a macrofluid we can develop the performance equation for any and all kinds of reactors from the residence time distribution theory of chapter 61. Thus

$$1-\bar{X}_B = \int_0^{\tau} (1-X_B)_{\substack{\text{individual}\\ \text{particle}}} \, E_t \, dt \qquad \cdots (1)$$

$(1-X_B)$ from chapter 51; E_t from chapter 61

In this chapter we solve this general performance equation for macrofluids for various particle kinetics, size distributions, and flow patterns, including elutriation and attrition of solids.

A. Plug flow of solids.

Feed consists of different sizes

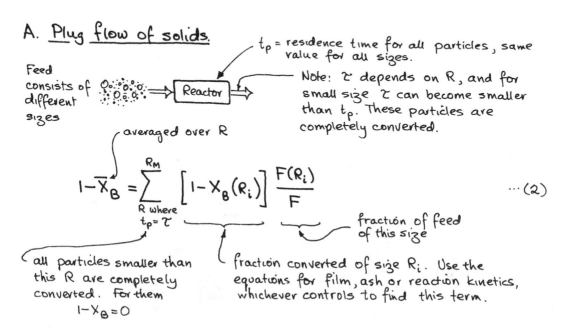

t_p = residence time for all particles, same value for all sizes.

Note: τ depends on R, and for small size τ can become smaller than t_p. These particles are completely converted.

$$1-\bar{X}_B = \sum_{\substack{R \text{ where}\\ t_p=\tau}}^{R_M} \left[1-X_B(R_i)\right] \frac{F(R_i)}{F} \qquad \cdots (2)$$

$\bar{X}_B$: averaged over R

$\frac{F(R_i)}{F}$: fraction of feed of this size

$t_p=\tau$: all particles smaller than this R are completely converted. For them $1-X_B=0$

$[1-X_B(R_i)]$: fraction converted of size R_i. Use the equations for film, ash or reaction kinetics, whichever controls to find this term.

B. Mixed flow, one size of spherical particles.

For mixed flow the general conversion expression, eq 1, becomes:

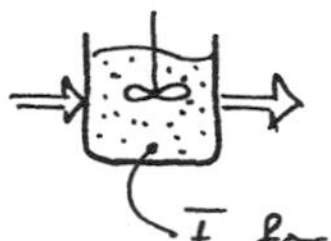
leaving solids are of different ages, hence different X_B.
$\bar{t}$ for solids

$$1-\overline{X}_B = \int_0^{\tau} (1-X_B)_{\text{individual particle}} \cdot \frac{1}{\bar{t}} e^{-t/\bar{t}}\, dt \qquad \cdots (3)$$

($\overline{X}_B$: averaged over time)

Using the proper X_B vs t expression from chapter 51 gives

Film diffusion control:

$$\overline{X}_B = \frac{\bar{t}}{\tau}\left(1-e^{-\tau/\bar{t}}\right) \qquad \cdots (4)$$

Ash diffusion control:

$$1-\overline{X}_B = \frac{1}{5}\left(\frac{\tau}{\bar{t}}\right) - \frac{19}{420}\left(\frac{\tau}{\bar{t}}\right)^2 + \frac{41}{4620}\left(\frac{\tau}{\bar{t}}\right)^3 - 0.00149\left(\frac{\tau}{\bar{t}}\right)^4 + \cdots \qquad \cdots (5)$$

Reaction control:

$$\overline{X}_B = 3\frac{\bar{t}}{\tau} - 6\left(\frac{\bar{t}}{\tau}\right)^2 + 6\left(\frac{\bar{t}}{\tau}\right)^3\left(1-e^{-\tau/\bar{t}}\right)$$

$$1-\overline{X}_B = \frac{1}{4}\left(\frac{\tau}{\bar{t}}\right) - \frac{1}{20}\left(\frac{\tau}{\bar{t}}\right)^2 + \frac{1}{120}\left(\frac{\tau}{\bar{t}}\right)^3 - \cdots \qquad \cdots (6)$$

(this form is sometimes useful for large $\bar{t}/\tau$)

C. Mixed flow of a size mixture of spherical particles.

With a size mixture for sure each size has its own τ, thus $\tau(R_i)$. Next, as the solids flow through the reactor all the sizes can have the same mean residence time ... or they can have different values, or $\bar{t}(R_i)$. Here is an example of when this could occur.

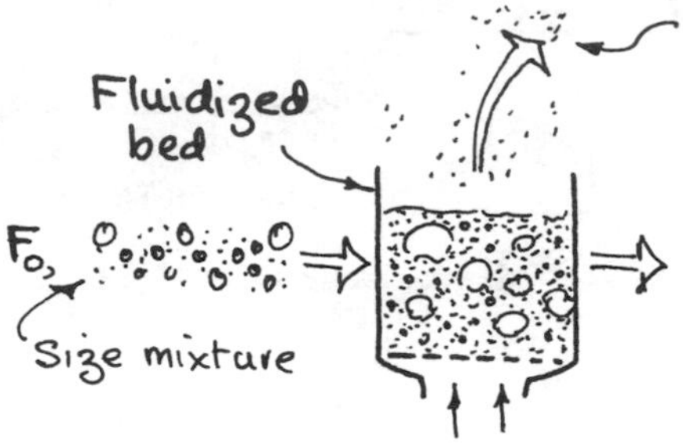

At high gas velocity the small particles are rapidly blown out of the bed, thus $\bar{t}_{fines}$ is small, $\bar{t}_{coarse}$ is large

Of course if the gas velocity is lowered or if an efficient cyclone is used to return the carryover then $\bar{t}$ will be the same for all sizes of solid.

When $\bar{t}$ and τ are different for each size of solid the conversion equations are direct extensions of the one-size solids equations. Thus

Film diffusion control:

$$\bar{\bar{X}}_B = \sum^{R_M} \left[\frac{\bar{t}(R_i)}{\tau(R_i)} \left(1 - e^{-\tau(R_i)/\bar{t}(R_i)}\right) \right] \frac{F_0(R_i)}{F_0} \quad \cdots (7)$$

Ash diffusion control:

$$1 - \bar{\bar{X}}_B = \sum^{R_M} \left[\frac{1}{5} \left(\frac{\tau(R_i)}{\bar{t}(R_i)} \right) - \frac{19}{420} \left(\cdots \right)^2 + \cdots \right] \frac{F_0(R_i)}{F_0} \quad \cdots (8)$$

Reaction control

$$\bar{\bar{X}}_B = \sum^{R_M} \left[3 \left(\frac{\bar{t}(R_i)}{\tau(R_i)} \right) - 6 \left(\cdots \right)^2 + 6 \left(\cdots \right)^3 \left(1 - e^{-\tau(R_i)/\bar{t}(R_i)}\right) \right] \frac{F_0(R_i)}{F_0} \quad \cdots (9)$$

averaged over size and residence time

fraction of feed solids which are of size R_i

In these expressions $\tau(R_i)$ is given by the kinetics of the G/S reaction (see chapter 51) and $\bar{t}(R_i)$ is determined by the hydrodynamics of the flow system. The next section shows how to find $\bar{t}(R_i)$ for the different sizes of solid in a mixture in the presence of elutriation, sedimentation and attrition.

III. Reactors with Elutriation and/or Sedimentation and maybe a bit of Attrition.

Ideally in mixed flow of solids the size distribution of entering and leaving streams and of the vessel's contents are identical. Also $\bar{t}$ is the same for all sizes of solid

same size distribution,
same $\bar{t}(R_i)$

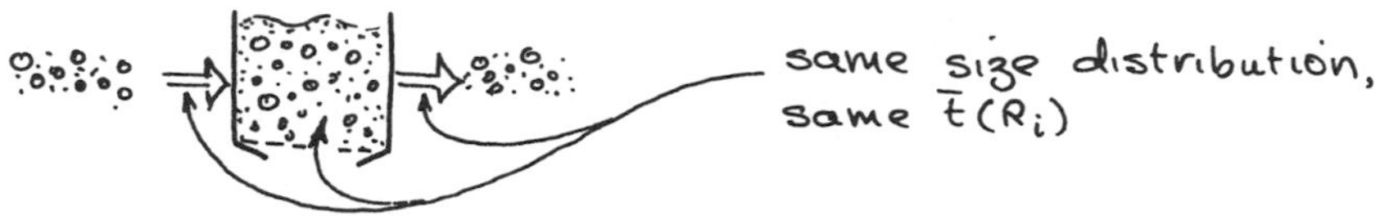

However it is possible to have mixed flow for each size of solid but with different $\bar{t}$ for each size. This can occur

- in reactors **with one exit stream** (pure sedimentation or pure elutriation)

At steady state the inlet and outlet streams have the same size distribution. However the reactor has a different size distribution.

... here $\begin{cases} \bar{t}_{fines} \text{ is short} \\ \bar{t}_{coarse} \text{ is long} \end{cases}$

... here $\begin{cases} \bar{t}_{fines} \text{ is long} \\ \bar{t}_{coarse} \text{ is short} \end{cases}$

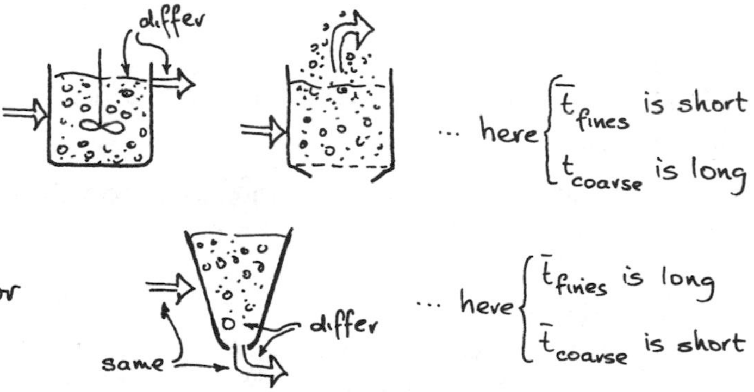

- in reactors **with two exit streams** (fluidized beds with elutriation).

All three flow streams have different size distribution

mainly fines
mainly large solids

... here $\begin{cases} \bar{t}_{fines} \text{ is short} \\ \bar{t}_{coarse} \text{ is long} \end{cases}$

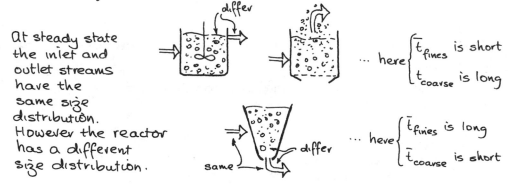

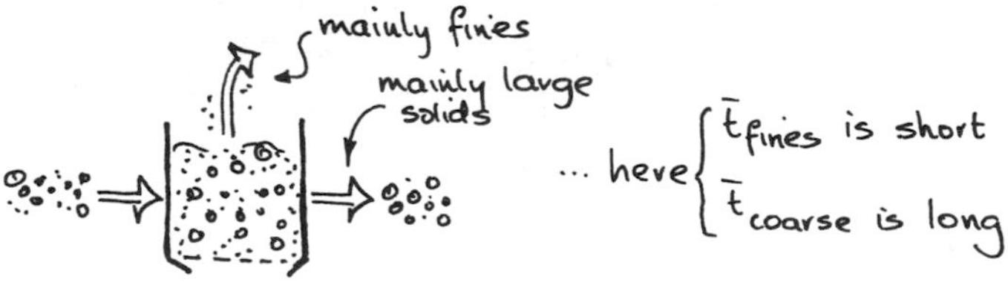

This section shows how to find $\bar{t}$ for the different sizes of solid, or $\bar{t}(R_i)$. This information is needed in the conversion equations of the previous section.

A. Elutriation and its measure.

Let us use the following nomenclature

For a **batch solids** system:

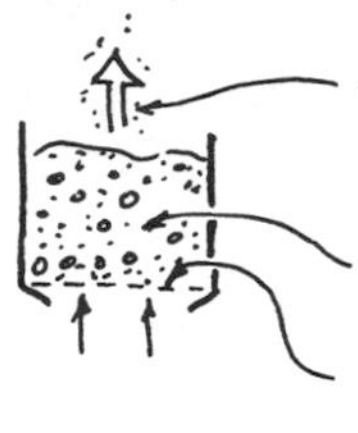

$\left\{ \begin{array}{l} F_2, \text{ total solids removed/s} \\ F_2(R_i), \text{ kg of } R_i \text{ solids removed/s} \end{array} \right.$

$\left\{ \begin{array}{l} W, \text{ total weight of bed, kg} \\ W(R_i), \text{ weight of } R_i \text{ solids in the bed.} \end{array} \right.$

A_t, cross sectional area of bed

For a **flowing solids** system:

F_0, $F_0(R_i)$

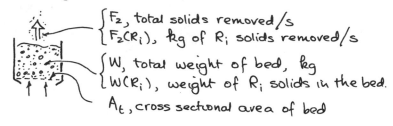

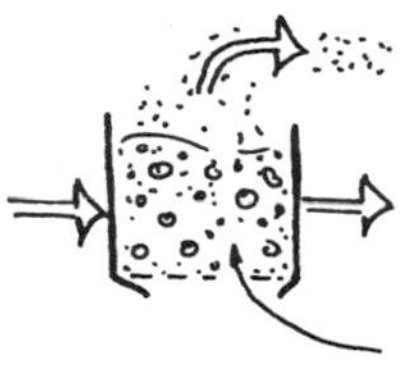

F_2, $F_2(R_i)$ } ... carryover stream

F_1, $F_1(R_i)$ } ... outflow or exit stream.

W, $W(R_i)$ } ... the bed

Elutriation refers to the selective washing away or removal of fines from a bed consisting of a mixture of particle sizes. We characterize it by the **elutriation constant**, defined for particles of size R_i in either of two ways:

$$\begin{pmatrix} \text{rate of removal} \\ \text{of } R_i \text{ solids} \\ \text{per area of bed,} \\ \text{kg/m}^2\cdot\text{s} \end{pmatrix} = \underset{\uparrow\ \text{kg/m}^2\cdot\text{s}}{K_i^*} \begin{pmatrix} \text{fraction of bed weight} \\ \text{consisting of } R_i \text{ solids} \end{pmatrix}$$

and in symbols

$$\boxed{-\frac{1}{A_t}\frac{dW(R_i)}{dt} = K_i^* \frac{W(R_i)}{W}} \qquad \cdots (10)$$

Alternatively we may define the elutriation constant as

$$\begin{pmatrix} \text{rate of removal} \\ \text{of solids of size } R_i, \\ \text{kg/s} \end{pmatrix} = K_i \begin{pmatrix} \text{weight of that size of} \\ \text{solid in the bed, kg} \end{pmatrix}$$

and in symbols

$$\boxed{-\frac{dW(R_i)}{dt} = \overset{\overset{s^{-1}}{\downarrow}}{K_i}\, W(R_i)} \qquad \cdots (11)$$

Comparing definitions shows that

$$K_i = K_i^* \frac{A_t}{W} \qquad \cdots (12)$$

For beds of different geometry and weight K^* should be constant or close to constant, while K should vary with A_t and W. Thus a value for K only applies to a bed of given geometry. Change the total bed weight and you must change K.

We can evaluate these elutriation constants for each size of solid in a mixture either by batch or by steady flow experiments.

B. Experimental devices to find the elutriation constant.

1. **The ordinary batch experiment.** Start with solids of size $R_1, R_2, \cdots, R_n$ which elutriate and sizes R_I which are too large to be blown out of the bed. Then at any time write

$$-\frac{dW_1}{dt} = K_1 W_1 = \frac{K_1^* A_t}{W} \cdot W_1 \qquad \cdots \text{where } W_1 = W_{10} \text{ at } t=0 \qquad (13)$$

Similarly for $R_2, R_3, \cdots, R_n$. We now proceed in one of two ways depending on how much the total bed weight changes.

Case 1 $W \cong$ constant. Here the bed weight only changes slightly during the run. So, on integrating eq 13 for a time run t we obtain

$$\ln \frac{W_{1,0}}{W_1} = K_1 t = \frac{K_1^* A_t}{W} t \qquad \cdots (14)$$

from which we can find K_1. Similarly, by measuring the carryover of particles of size 2, 3 ⋯ we find $K_2, K_3, \cdots$.

The rate of carryover of solids at any time is then found to be

$$-\frac{dW_{total}}{dt} = K_1 W_1 + K_2 W_2 + \cdots \qquad [kg/s] \qquad \cdots (15)$$

Case 2 **$W \neq$ constant.** Here a significant fraction of the bed solids is blown out of the bed during the experimental run. On integrating eq 13 we find, after rearrangement

$$\frac{W_1}{W_{10}} = \left(\frac{W_2}{W_{20}}\right)^{K_1/K_2} = \left(\frac{W_3}{W_{30}}\right)^{K_1/K_3} = \cdots \qquad \cdots (16)$$

and

$$K_1^* A_t t = \underset{\uparrow \text{inert}}{W_I} \ln\left(\frac{W_{10}}{W_1}\right) + \sum_{i=1}^{n} W_{i0}\left(\frac{K_1}{K_i}\right)\left[1 - \left(\frac{W_1}{W_{10}}\right)^{K_i/K_1}\right] \qquad \cdots (17)$$

Equation 16 with bed weights measured before and after a run gives the K ratios. Inserting these values into eq 17 then gives K_1^*, from which all other K^* values can be found.

This treatment comes from Kumar, M.S. thesis, Oregon State U. 1977.

2. Steady state recirculating batch experiment.

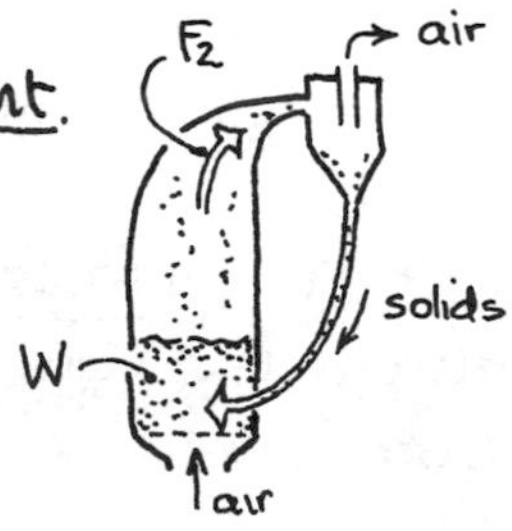

Here you measure $F_2(R_i)$ and $W(R_i)$. Then a material balance for any size R_i gives

$$K(R_i) = \frac{F_2(R_i)}{W(R_i)} \qquad \cdots (18)$$

Comments

(a) This treatment assumes that each size of solid acts independent of the other solids in the bed, whether these others are large or small, whether they elutriate or not. Recent experiments by Geldart (AIChE annual meeting, Miami 1978) challenge this assumption and suggest that elutriating fines increase the elutriation of the larger particles.

(b) Correlations for κ^* are available in the literature, however since κ^* is quite sensitive to gas velocity and other system variables it is best to measure κ^* for your own solid mixture in your own equipment.

C. Finding $\bar{t}(R_i)$ in ordinary flow reactors with elutriation.

Assuming that the size distribution of exit stream F_1 and of the bed are identical a material balance for each size of solid gives

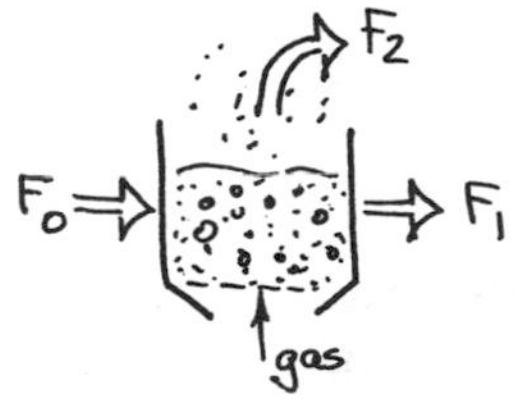

$$F_1 = F_1(R_1) + F_1(R_2) + \cdots = \sum_i F_1(R_i) = \sum_i \frac{F_0(R_i)}{1 + \frac{W}{F_1}\kappa(R_i)} \qquad \cdots (19)$$

$$\bar{t}(R_i) = 1 \Big/ \left(\frac{F_1}{W} + \kappa(R_i)\right) \qquad \cdots (20)$$

$$F_2(R_i) = \kappa(R_i) \cdot \frac{F_1(R_i)}{F_1} \cdot W = \kappa(R_i) \cdot W(R_i) \qquad \cdots (21)$$

This is the information needed to evaluate the size distribution of exit streams and $\bar{t}(R_i)$. The procedure is as follows: with known elutriation constants for all sizes of solid guess F_1 until eq 19 is satisfied. This gives the size distribution of stream F_1. Then eq 20 gives $\bar{t}(R_i)$ and eq 21 gives stream F_2.

D. Finding $\bar{t}(R_i)$ in pure elutriation or sedimentation reactors.

We may look at these operations as a special case of ordinary elutriating reactors, but with no outflow F_1

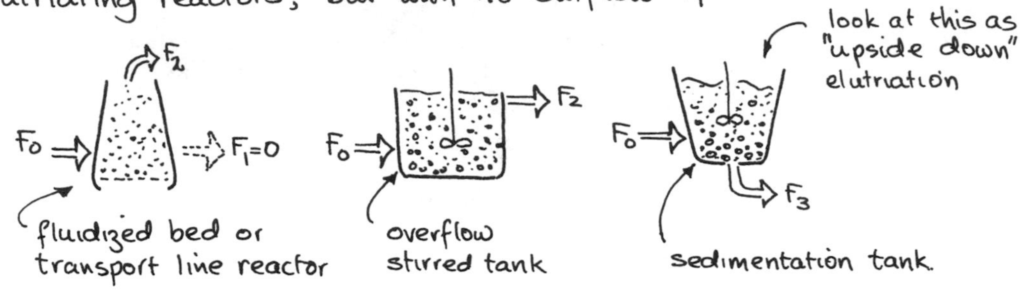

Here eq 19 disappears and eq 20 combined with eq 11 becomes

$$\bar{t}(R_i) = \frac{1}{\kappa(R_i)} = \frac{W(R_i)}{F_2(R_i)} \quad \text{or } F_3(R_i) \qquad \cdots (22)$$

Thus measuring the size distribution within the bed and of the entering or leaving stream (these should be identical) gives κ values for all sizes of solid (from eq 18). Equation 22 then gives $\bar{t}$ for all sizes of solid.

Comments

(a) For preferential removal of fines κ is large for small R. For preferential removal of the larger solids (sedimentation) κ is large for large R. In all cases, with one exit stream κ cannot be zero for any of the sizes of solid.

(b) Since larger particles need a longer time to react we may find it advantageous to use a reactor with preferential removal of fines. Preferential removal of coarse solids is not of use in reactors with unchanging particle size, but is extremely useful for reactors with growing solids (chapter 54).

E. Finding $\bar{t}(R_i)$ in reactors with both elutriation and sedimentation.

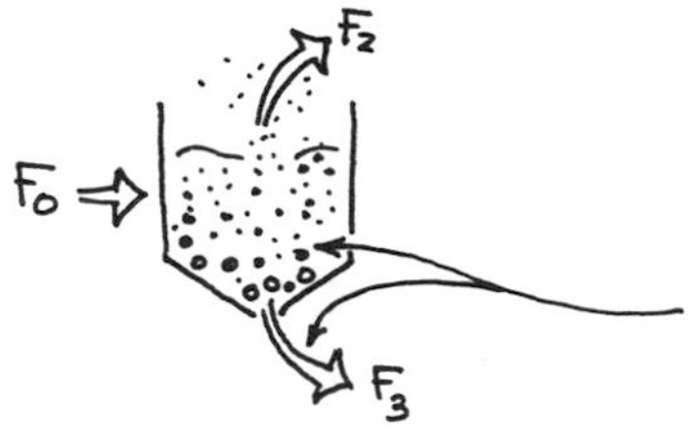

Here all the size distributions, of F_0, F_1, F_2 and W differ.

What differs from case D is that here the size distribution of W and F_3 are not the same

For each size of solid we can write

$$F_0(R_i) = F_2(R_i) + F_3(R_i)$$

From elutriation and sedimentation data we have

$$K_2(R_i) = \frac{F_2(R_i)}{W(R_i)} \quad \text{... and ...} \quad K_3(R_i) = \frac{F_3(R_i)}{W(R_i)}$$

(K_2 for elutriation; K_3 for sedimentation)

Combining the above expressions relates the flow rate of size R_i to its weight in the bed by

$$F_0(R_i) = W(R_i)\left[K_2(R_i) + K_3(R_i)\right] \qquad \cdots (23)$$

The mean residence time of size R_i in the bed is then simply

$$\bar{t}(R_i) = \frac{W(R_i)}{F_0(R_i)} = \left[\frac{1}{K_2(R_i) + K_3(R_i)}\right] \qquad \cdots (24)$$

Given the K values for all sizes of solids and the flow rate into the reactor first find $W(R_i)$ from eq 23, then find $\bar{t}(R_i)$ from eq 24. Note that since we have two leaving streams of solids the K values of some of the sizes could well be zero.

G. Crude treatment of elutriation and attrition in a batch of solids

On fluidizing a batch of solids fines are elutriated, but they are also generated within the bed by attrition. How to evaluate the attrition and elutriation constants in this situation? The treatment is straightforward if we assume that

- attrition takes place by grinding small chips off large particles, and not by particle shattering

- attrition is slow enough so that the size distribution and weight of the bed solids — all except the fines — changes negligibly during the run.

- attrition generates fines of one size and at a constant rate.

Let us look at the generated fines as an input stream of fine solids. Our nomenclature is then

F_2 (fines)

... and $W \begin{pmatrix} \text{fines in} \\ \text{carryover} \end{pmatrix} = \begin{pmatrix} \text{total fines carried} \\ \text{out of the bed} \\ \text{since } t=0 \end{pmatrix}$

Fictitious feed stream of fines

F_0 (fines)

$K \text{ (fines)} = \dfrac{F_2 \text{(fines)}}{W \text{(fines)}}$

$\left. \begin{array}{l} W_0 \text{ (fines) at } t=0 \\ W \text{ (fines) at time } t \end{array} \right\}$ weight of fines in the bed

batch of solids whose weight W changes very little during the run. Thus the fines are a small part of the total weight of the bed.

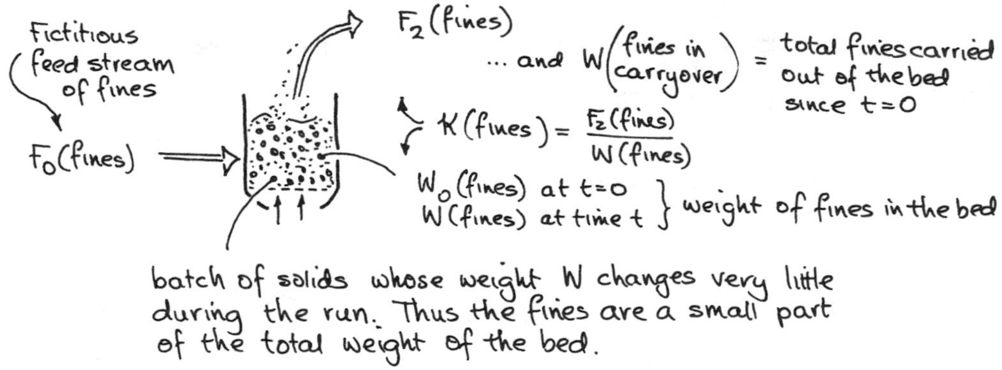

At any time t after the start of the run a material balance for the fines gives

$$\begin{pmatrix} \text{Fictitious input,} \\ \text{actually generation} \end{pmatrix} = \text{Output} + \text{Accumulation}$$

or

$$F_0 \text{ (fines)} = F_2 \text{ (fines)} + \frac{d \, W \text{(fines)}}{dt}$$

Solving gives the weight of **fines in the bed** as a function of time

$$W(fines) = \underbrace{\frac{F_0(fines)}{K(fines)}\left[1 - e^{-K(fines)t}\right] + \underbrace{W_0(fines)\, e^{-K(fines)t}}_{\text{originally in the bed}}}_{\text{at time } t} \quad \cdots (25)$$

In terms of the total carryover of fines we have

$$\begin{pmatrix} \text{total} \\ \text{carryover} \end{pmatrix} = \begin{pmatrix} \text{initially} \\ \text{in bed} \end{pmatrix} + \begin{pmatrix} \text{flow in} \\ \text{from } t=0 \end{pmatrix} - \begin{pmatrix} \text{in bed} \\ \text{at time } t \end{pmatrix}$$

$$W\begin{pmatrix} \text{fines in} \\ \text{carryover} \end{pmatrix} \qquad W_0(fines) \qquad F_0(fines)\cdot t \qquad W(fines)$$

Rearranging gives the **fines in the carryover stream**

$$W\begin{pmatrix} \text{fines in} \\ \text{carryover} \end{pmatrix} = \left[W_0(fines) - \frac{F_0(fines)}{K(fines)} \right]\left[1 - e^{-K(fines)t}\right] + F_0(fines)\cdot t \quad \cdots (26)$$

The unknowns of the system $K(fines)$, $W_0(fines)$ and $F_0(fines)$ can be found by using eq 26 with the slopes and intercept of typical experiments, as shown

Initial slope= $W_0(fines)\, K(fines)$

$W\begin{pmatrix} \text{fines in} \\ \text{carryover} \end{pmatrix}$

final slope = $F_0(fines)$
If the slope is close to zero then attrition is negligible and can be ignored.

Intercept = $W_0(fines) - \dfrac{F_0(fines)}{K(fines)} \cong W_0(fines)$

run time
for slow attrition

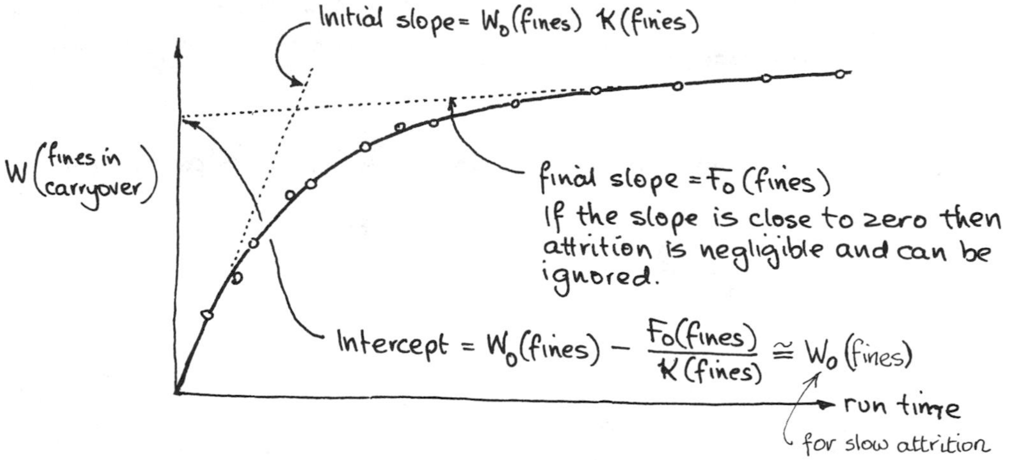

Comments.

(a) The above graph gives F_0 (fines). This allows us to estimate the load on cyclones, etc. Simply add this fictitious feed to the regular feed to the reactor.

(b) If you are dissatisfied with the assumptions of this simple treatment and prefer something more rigorous try—.

(c) We can always find $\kappa(R_i)$ in any set up by taking, at any instant, a sample of the size distribution of bed and of carryover solids. However this measurement doesn't tell anything about the attrition rate of solids. A time run is needed to find this.

IV Multistage Reactors for Spherical Particles.

For the same gas composition in each of the N equal size stages (assume mixed flow in all stages) the performance expression becomes

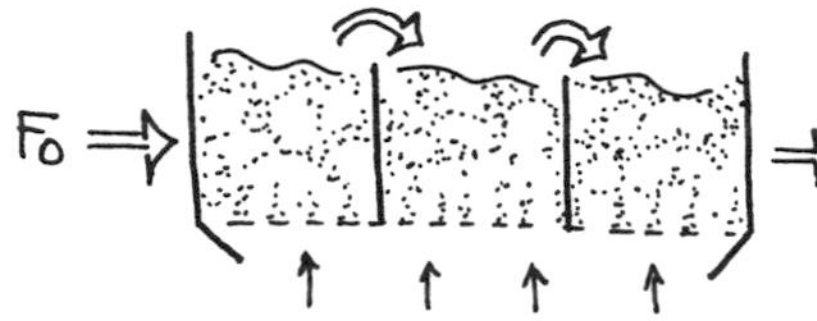

$$1-\bar{X}_B = \int_0^{\tau} (1-X_B)_{\text{particle}} \cdot \frac{1}{(N-1)!\,\bar{t}_i}\left(\frac{t}{\bar{t}_i}\right)^{N-1} e^{-t/\bar{t}_i}\,dt \qquad \cdots (27)$$

- $(1-X_B)_{\text{particle}}$: from chapter 51
- per stage: $\bar{t}_i = \dfrac{W_{\text{per stage}}}{F_0}$
- RTD in N equal sized mixed flow vessels in series, from chapter 66

For **reaction control** integration for any number of stages gives

$$1-\bar{X}_B = \sum_{m=0}^{m=N-1} \frac{(N-m+2)!}{(N-m-1)!\,m!}\left(\frac{\bar{t}_i}{\tau}\right)^{3-m} e^{-\tau/\bar{t}_i} + \sum_{m=0}^{m=3} \frac{(N+m-1)!\,3!}{(N-1)!\,m!\,(3-m)!}\left(-\frac{\bar{t}_i}{\tau}\right)^{m} \qquad \cdots (28)$$

This expression becomes, with $y = \tau/\bar{t}_i$,

$$N=2 \qquad \bar{X}_B = \frac{6}{y} - \frac{6}{y^2}\left(3+e^{-y}\right) + \frac{24}{y}\left(1-e^{-y}\right) \qquad \ldots (29)$$

$$N=3 \qquad \bar{X}_B = \frac{3}{y}\left(3-e^{-y}\right) + \frac{12}{y^2}\left(3+2e^{-y}\right) + \frac{60}{y}\left(1-e^{-y}\right) \qquad \ldots (30)$$

For high conversion, hence small y, these expressions become

$$N=2 \qquad 1-\bar{X}_B = \frac{y^2}{20} - \frac{y^3}{60} + \frac{y^4}{280} - \frac{y^5}{1680} + \cdots \qquad y<1 \qquad \ldots (31)$$

$$N=3 \qquad 1-\bar{X}_B = \frac{y^3}{120} - \frac{y^4}{280} + \cdots \qquad y<1 \qquad \ldots (32)$$

For **film diffusion control** integration of eq 27 gives

$$N=2 \qquad \bar{X}_B = \frac{2}{y} - \left(\frac{2}{y}+1\right)e^{-y} \qquad \text{with } y = \tau/\bar{t}_i \qquad \ldots (33)$$

$$N=3 \qquad \bar{X}_B = \frac{3}{y} - \left(\frac{3}{y}+2+\frac{y}{2}\right)e^{-y} \qquad \ldots (34)$$

$$N=4 \qquad \bar{X}_B = \frac{4}{y} - \left(\frac{4}{y}+3+y+\frac{y^2}{6}\right)e^{-y} \qquad \ldots (35)$$

For **ash diffusion control** tedious numerical integration of eq 27 must be used. However comparing the calculated conversion with that for reaction control shows that the latter will give a conservative estimate for $\bar{X}_{B,ash}$ in multistage operations.

Comments

(a) Comparison with single stage operations will tell whether it pays to multistage. For high conversion the gain can be substantial. For example for 99% conversion of solids and reaction control 2 stage operations reduces the total size of the reactor down to 20% of that for 1 stage operations.

(b) Often the multistaging of fluidized beds only requires the placing of a baffle or two in the right place.

(c) For a wide size distribution of solids, both rectangular and symmetric triangular, the conversion-time behavior for mixed flow (fluidized beds) and for SCM/reaction control kinetics is well approximated by a stream of solids of mean particle size of these distributions.

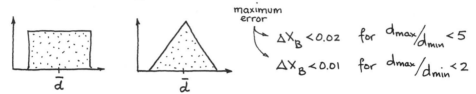

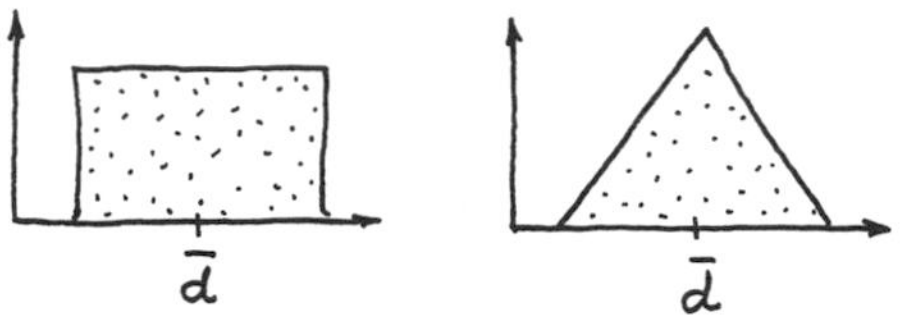

maximum error

$\Delta X_B < 0.02$ for $d_{max}/d_{min} < 5$

$\Delta X_B < 0.01$ for $d_{max}/d_{min} < 2$

We may expect similar error limits with this approximation for SCM/ash diffusion kinetics controlling.

For more on conversions in systems with wide size distributions see Murhammer et al, Chem. Eng. J. 32 87 (1986).

(d) The general performance expression for the reaction of solids is

$$1-\bar{X}_B = \int_0^{\tau} \left[1-X_{B,\text{single particle}}\right] E_t \, dt \qquad \cdots (36)$$

so if the contacting of solids does not follow plug flow or mixed flow use the actual RTD curve for solids, see chapter 61

(e) If the particle is not spherical nor close to spherical (see chapter 51 for the expressions for cylindrical or flat plate particles), or if a kinetic model other than the SCM applies then insert the corresponding X_B vs t expression into eq 36 and solve. Sometimes this can be done analytically. However it can always be done numerically.

The following X_B vs t graphs present a few solutions for single stage and multistage operations for various shapes of particles and various controlling kinetics.

Single stage and multistage operations with cylindrical, needle like or fibrous particles.

Particles react by the shrinking core model.

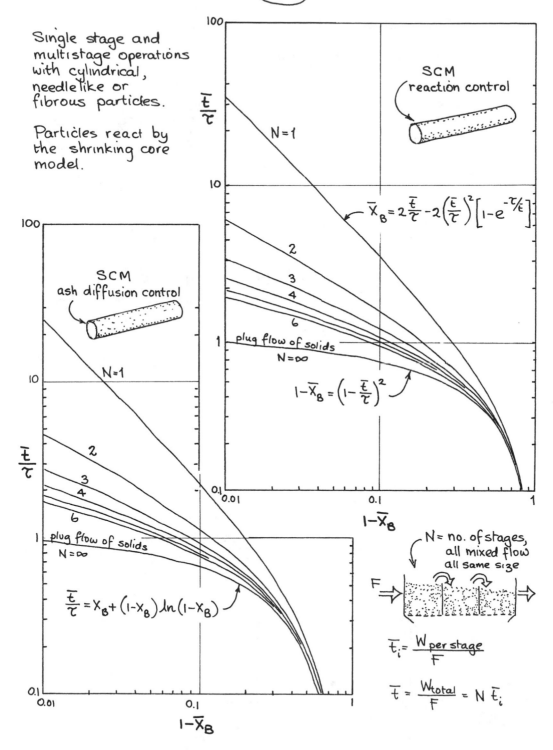

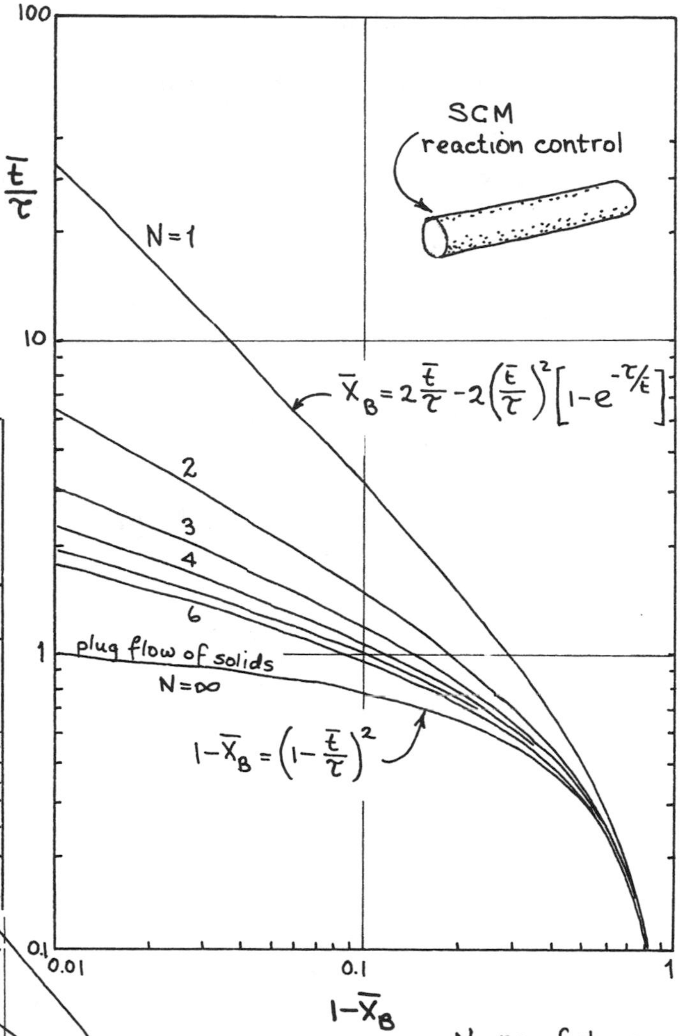

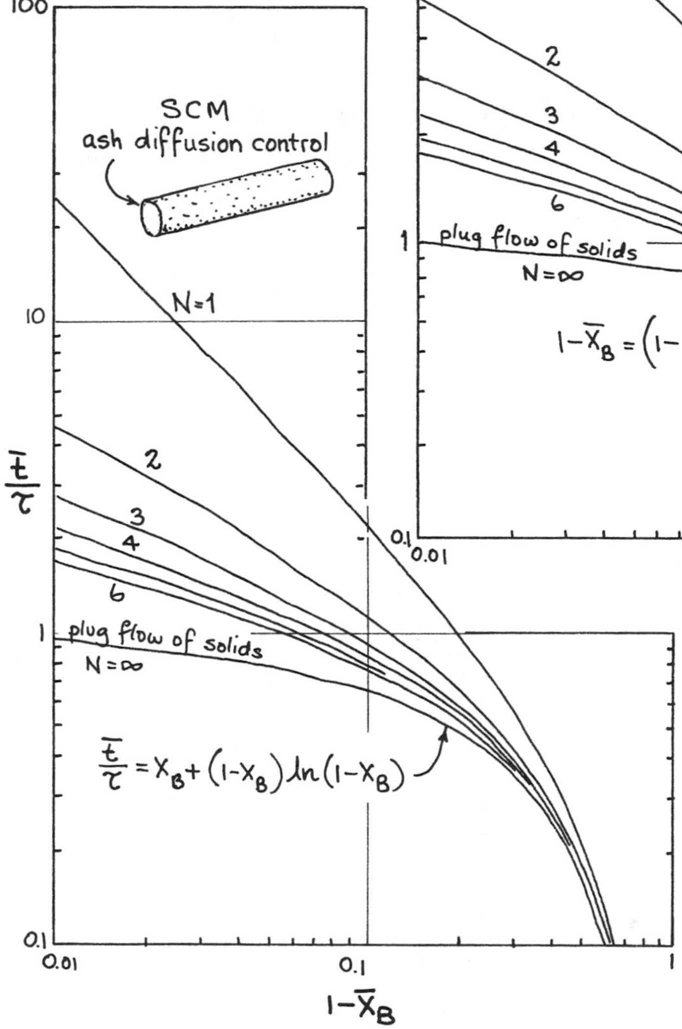

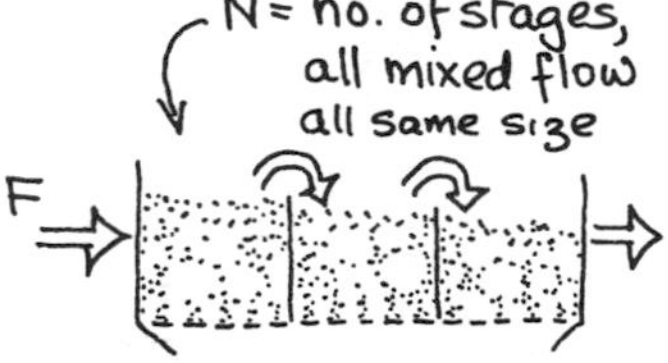

SCM reaction control

$$\bar{X}_B = 2\frac{\bar{t}}{\tau} - 2\left(\frac{\bar{t}}{\tau}\right)^2\left[1 - e^{-\tau/\bar{t}}\right]$$

plug flow of solids
N = ∞

$$1 - \bar{X}_B = \left(1 - \frac{\bar{t}}{\tau}\right)^2$$

N = 1

2
3
4
6

SCM ash diffusion control

N = 1

2
3
4
6

plug flow of solids
N = ∞

$$\frac{\bar{t}}{\tau} = X_B + (1 - X_B)\ln(1 - X_B)$$

N = no. of stages, all mixed flow all same size

$$\bar{t}_i = \frac{W_{per\,stage}}{F}$$

$$\bar{t} = \frac{W_{total}}{F} = N\,\bar{t}_i$$

Single stage and multistage operations of particles of various shapes which react by the shrinking core model.

SCM
reaction control

flat plate

SCM
film diffusion control
with constant k_g

flat plate

sphere

cylinder

$$\overline{X}_B = \frac{\overline{t}}{\tau}\left(1 - e^{-\tau/\overline{t}}\right)$$

N=1

$\dfrac{W_{total}}{F}$

$$\frac{\overline{t}}{\tau} = \frac{N\overline{t_i}}{\tau}$$

time for complete conversion of a particle

2

3

4

6

plug flow of solids
N=∞

$$\overline{X}_B = \frac{\overline{t}}{\tau}$$

100

10

1

0.1

0.01

0.1

1

$1 - \overline{X}_B$

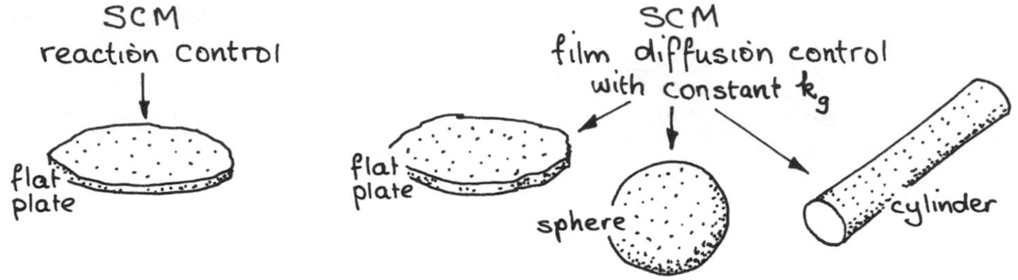

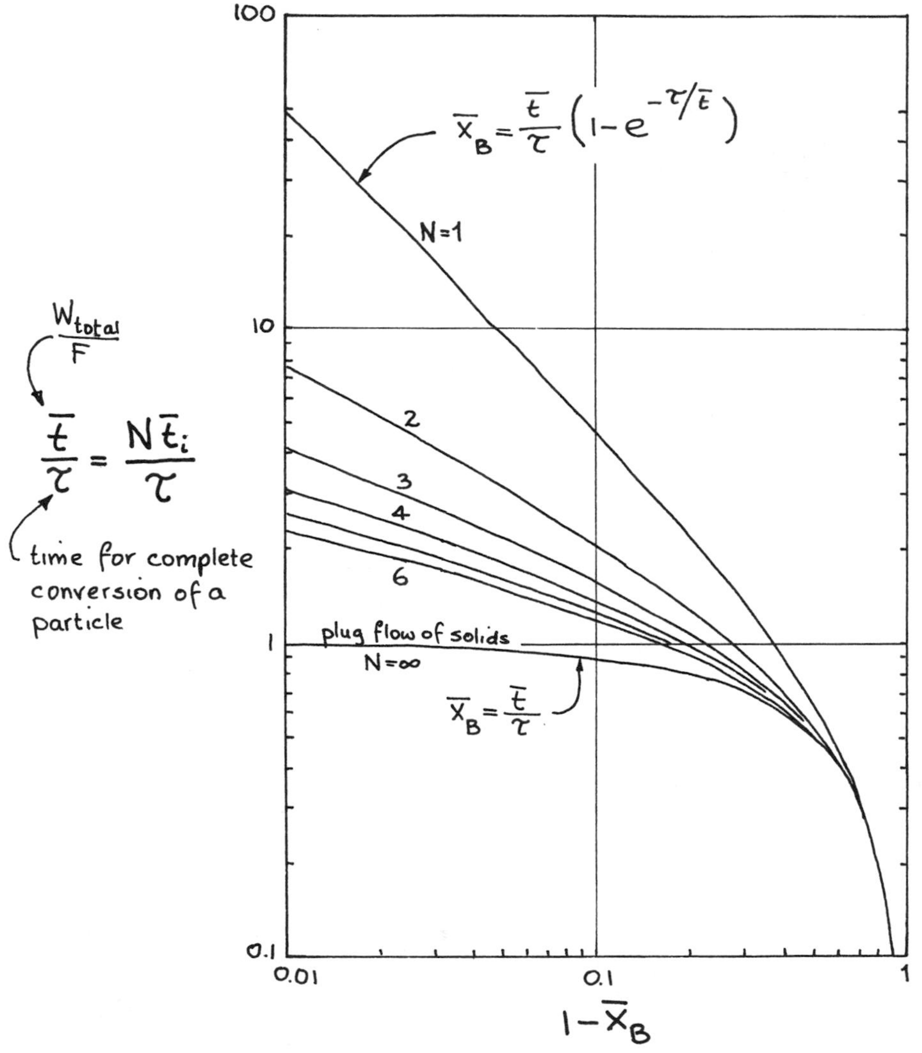

V What Kind of Reactor to Use on the Commercial Scale

This depends on various factors, primarily

- the size of particles being processed
- the heat duty
- the required uniformity of composition of product solids

The decision tree is as follows:

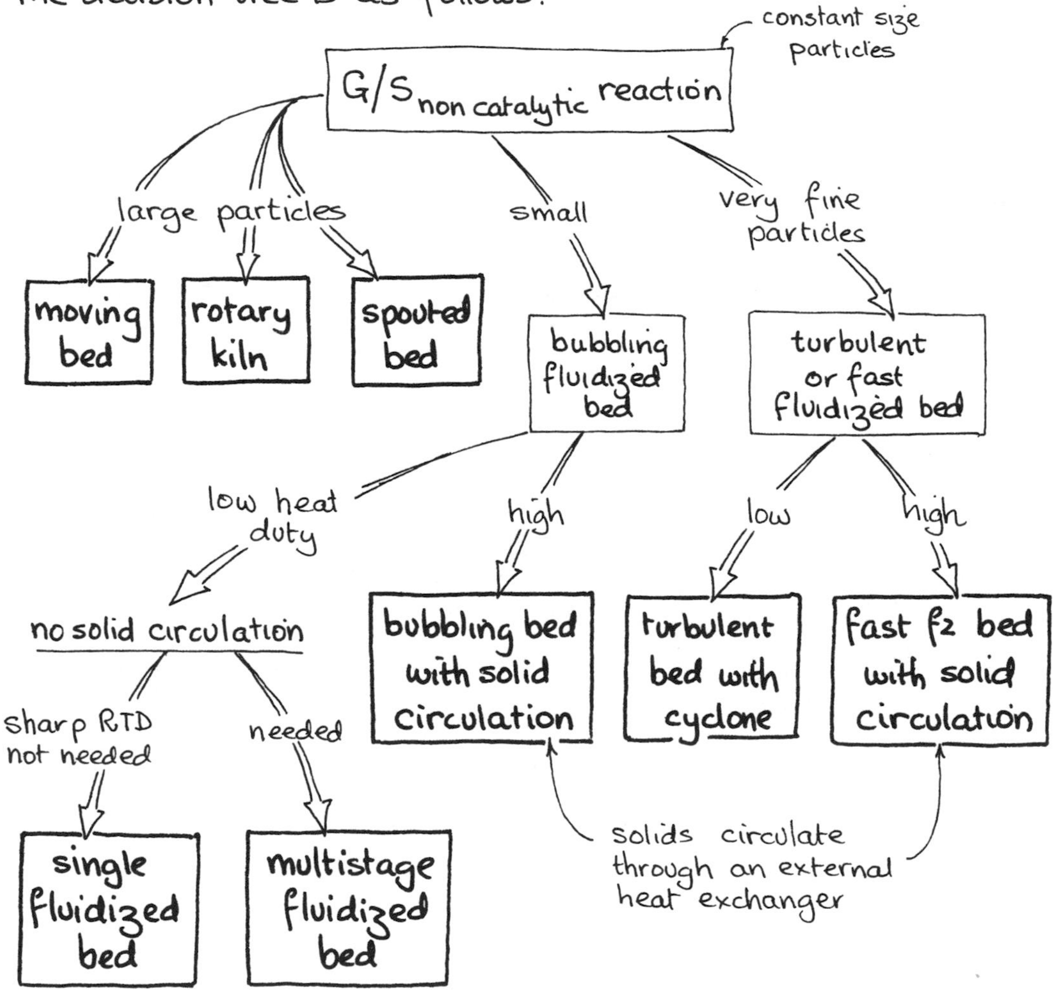

Chapter 52 Problems

A stream of particles of one size are 80% converted (SCM/ash diffusion control, uniform gas environment) on passing through a reactor. If the reactor is made twice the size but with the same gas environment, same feed rate and same flow pattern of solids what would be the conversion of solids? The solids are in

A1 ... plug flow.

A2 ... mixed flow.

A stream of solid particles, R = 1 mm, passes through a bench scale fluidized bed (mixed flow) reactor. The solids react with gas to give a solid product according to the SCM/reaction control as follows

$F_0 = 100$ gm/min, $W = 1000$ gm, $\bar{X}_B = 0.65$

Assuming that the solids find themselves in the same gas environment in all cases

A3 ... calculate the expected conversion in a commercial sized fluidized reactor of 4 tons treating 40 kg/min of R = 1 mm solid.

A4 ... Repeat problem 3 for a feed or R = 2.5 mm solids, all other values unchanged.

A5 ... Find the size of single fluidized reactor needed to treat 4 tons/hr of R = 1 mm particles to 99% conversion.

B6 ... Repeat problem 5 for a 2 stage fluidized bed reactor.

At present, with a given feed rate of one size of solids, we get 99.75% conversion in a single fluidized reactor, and reaction proceeds according to the SCM/reaction control. How much can the feed rate of solids be raised

B7 ... if we add baffles to the existing fluidized bed so that it now acts as two identical fluidized beds?

B8 ... if we add a second identical fluidized bed in series with the first?

In all cases the gas composition is assumed to be unchanged.

In a uniform environment 4 mm solid particles are 87.5% converted to product solid in 8 min according the the SCM. With this information we wish to design a fluidized reactor to treat a steady stream of equal weights of 1 mm and 2 mm particles.

Chapter 52 Problems

C9 . . . Find the conversion of solids for $\bar{t}$ = 40 min with reaction control.

C10 . . . Repeat for ash diffusion control.

A solid feed consisting of

20 wt% of 1 mm particles and smaller
30 wt% of 2 mm particles
50 wt% of 4 mm particles

passes through a rotating tubular reactor somewhat like a cement kiln where it reacts with gas to give a hard non friable solid product (SCM/reaction control, τ = 4 hours for 4 mm particles).

C11 . . . Find the residence time needed for 100% conversion of solids.

C12 . . . Find the mean conversion of solids for a residence time of 15 min.

A continuous feed of solids consisting

30% of 50 μm particles
40% of 100 μm particles
30% of 200 μm particles

reacts with fluidizing gas according to the SCM to form solid product. The reactor is constructed from a 1 m length of 10 cm pipe and contains 10 kg solids.

C13 . . . Find $\bar{\bar{X}}_B$ for a feed rate of 2 kg solids/min if the rate is reaction controlled with τ (100 μm) = 10 min.

C14 . . . Find $\bar{\bar{X}}_B$ for a feed rate of 0.5 kg solids/min if the rate is ash diffusion controlled with τ (100 μm) = 10 min.

C15 . . . Find $\bar{\bar{X}}_B$ for a feed rate of 1 kg solids/min if the rate is reaction controlled with τ (100 μm) = 10 min and where carryover of fines is so large that the mean residence time of the different sizes is quite different, as follows

$\bar{t}$ = 4 min for 50 μm particles
$\bar{t}$ = 10 min for 100 μm particles
$\bar{t}$ = 16 min for 200 μm particles

Chapter 52 Problems

C16 A metallurgical ash contains the oxides of chromium which are extremely toxic. These oxides can be made harmless by reacting them with reducing gases (H_2 + CO). The reaction is rather complex but can be approximated by

$$0.6\,(H_2 + CO) + (\text{toxic oxides}) \rightarrow (\text{harmless solids}) + H_2O + CO_2$$

In an experiment wherein a batch of ash is bathed by a 3% (H_2 + CO) gas we find that

55% of the toxicity is removed in 2.8 min
87.5% of the toxicity is removed in 6.0 min

In a second experiment with 6% (H_2 + CO) everything happens twice as fast.

With this information we want to design a continuous solids flow detoxifier to treat 12 kg/min of toxic ash so as to remove 99% of the toxicity. How much solid must the detoxifier hold

(a) if the unit is a fluidized bed reactor where the solids contact a 9% (H_2 + CO) gas?

(b) if the unit is a rotating tube reactor through which the particles tumble in close to plug flow while contacting a 6% (H_2 + CO) gas, on the average?

D17 Consider the following steady-state operations of a fluidized bed. A mixture of solids A and B (40 kg A/hr and 60 kg B/hr) is fed continuously to a bed which contains 100 kg solids. Because of the high gas velocity used 20 kg solids/hr, all A, are blown out of the bed; the rest of the solids leave through the overflow pipe.

(a) Find the mean residence time in the vessel of solids A, of solids B, and of the total solid stream.

(b) Find κ_A and κ_B.

D18 With a uniform feed rate of a single size of particle to a fluidized bed and fixed gas flow rate, 50% of the solids are blown out as carryover. With unchanged flow rates of solids and gas but with a doubling of the height of the fluidized bed find how the following change

(a) mean residence time of solids in the bed,

(b) elutriation constants κ and κ^*,

(c) fraction of product which leaves as carryover.

Assume unchanged bed density.

D19 A closed loop recirculating system consisting of fluidized bed and return cyclone is used to evaluate the elutriation constants of solids. In a typical experiment the bed is charged with

8 kg of coarse solid
1 kg of R = 50 μm solid
1 kg of R = 100 μm solid

At a given gas velocity carryover is 0.3 kg/s and 1 kg of solids is present in the recycle loop at any time. A sample of the circulating steam shows that it consists of 2 parts of 50 μm material to 1 part of 100 μm material.

(a) Find κ for the 50 μm and the 100 μm solids.

(b) Develop a power law expression for k as a function of particle size in the range of 50 to 100 μm solids. Indicate all units in this equation.

A batch of solids is fluidized at high air velocity in a bed 0.1 m^2 in cross section, and after a 10 minute run the entrained solids are collected and analyzed. From the following results

(a) calculate the elutriation constants for A and B.

(b) If the entrained solids were collected and immediately returned to the bed what would be the entrainment rate of solids under these conditions?

	Initial bed composition, kg	Entrained solids after a 10 min run, kg
D20 . . .	A = 20, B = 20, I = 60	A = 4, B = 2, I = 0
D21 . . .	A = 60, B = 20, I = 20	A = 45, B = 10, I = 0

Note: For problem 20 it is reasonable to assume that the bed weight changes only slightly during the elutriation experiment.

D22 We plan to feed a fluidized reactor (W = 1.2 ton) with 1.2 ton/hr or reactant solids of various sizes A, B, ... Unfortunately at the gas velocities used we expect some elutriation to occur.

(a) Find the composition of the bed and of the two leaving streams of solid.

(b) Find the flow rates of carryover and outflow streams.

(c) Find the mean residence time of solids $\bar{t}_A$, $\bar{t}_B$ and $\bar{t}_{overall}$ in the bed.

Show your answers in a sketch.

The size distribution of the feed and the estimated elutriation constants for these solids are given as

	solid A = 30%	$\kappa_A = 2\ hr^{-1}$
Feed	solid B = 40%	$\kappa_B = 0.5\ hr^{-1}$
	solid C = 30%	$\kappa_C = 0.125\ hr^{-1}$

Chapter 52 Problems

D23 A mixture of 60 kg A and 40 kg I are to be fluidized at high air velocity in a large experimental bed (c. s. area = 0.4 m^2). Estimate the amount and composition of entrained solids in a 500 sec run if $\kappa_A^* = 0.5$ kg/m^2·s and $\kappa_I^* = 0$.

D24 A batch of solids (900 kg A, 600 kg B) is to be fluidized in a bed (c. s. area = 1 m^2) containing many horizontal tubes. At the planned air velocity literature correlations give $\kappa_A^* = 0.5$ kg/m^2·s and $\kappa_B^* = 0.25$ kg/m^2·s. Estimate the amount and composition of entrained solids after a 30 minute run.

D25 A batch of 60 kg A and 40 kg B is fluidized. The air velocity used is rather high and the solids blown from the bed are trapped in a cyclone and are immediately returned to the bed. At steady state 36 kg A/hr and 8 kg B/hr are blown out and returned to the bed.

We plan to run this unit continuously where this A - B mixture (100 kg/hr) is fed continuously to a bed containing 100 kg solids, the air velocity is kept identical to the batch run, and the entrained solids are not returned to the bed. Find the mean residence time of solids A and B in the continuous flow fluidized bed.

D26 In processes where particles are grown in a fluidized bed it is advantageous to have a bed geometry where the large particles are selectively removed leaving the small particles behind to grow. This preferential removal is most simply studied with non growing particles. Here is a typical experiment of this kind.

Equal weights of 200, 300, and 400 μm solids are fed at 1.8 kg/min to a fluidized bed with an udder-shaped section from which solids are milked and removed. After steady state is achieved flow is stopped and the bed solids are screened. Results show that the bed composition is

30 kg of 200 μm particles
20 kg of 300 μm particles
15 kg of 400 μm particles

Find an expression for the upside down elutriation constant. (Should we call this the milking constant?)

D27 A batch of solids (60 kg) is fluidized at a constant gas velocity, and the carryover is cyclone-separated and weighed at regular time intervals. From the data below find the attrition constant (kg fines generated/kg bed solid·s) and the elutriation constant for this system.

t, sec	Solids collected, gm	t	Solids collected
0-40	640	240-280	50
40-80	400	280-320	30
80-120	250	320-360	20
120-160	160	360-400	10
160-200	100	400-440	10
200-240	60	440-600	40

D28 We are presently designing a steady flow pilot plant shale burner (W = 500 kg). Our planned feed is

$F_A = 1$ kg/s of $R_A = 50$ μm particles
$F_B = 1$ kg/s of $R_B = 100$ μm particles
$F_C = 1$ kg/s of $R_C = 200$ μm particles

Shale burns without changing size, leaves as a hard nonfriable ash, and reacts according to the SCM/ash diffusion control with $\tau = 10$ s for the R = 50 μm solids. Also, at the gas velocities chosen the elutriation is rather severe and is characterized by

$$\kappa = (40\ \mu m^2/s)R^{-2},\quad s^{-1}$$

Estimate the carbon utilization in this burner.

Hydrogen sulfide is removed from coal gas by passing the gas through a moving bed of iron oxide particles. In the coal gas environment (consider uniform) the solids are converted from Fe_2O_3 to FeS by the SCM/reaction control, $\tau = 1$ hr. Find the fractional conversion of oxide to iron sulfide if the RTD of solids in the reactor is approximated by

E29 . . .

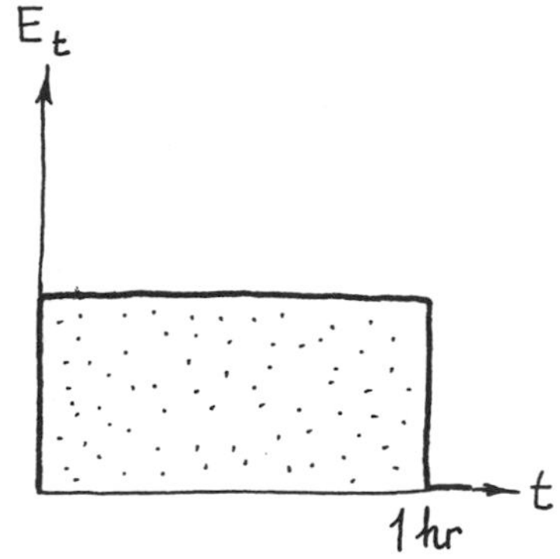

E30 . . .

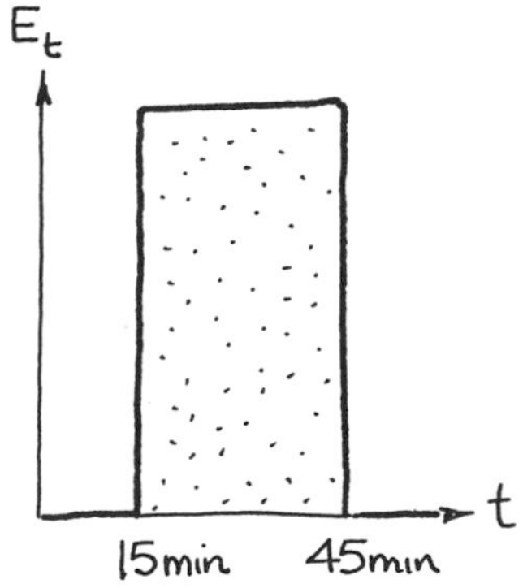

Chapter 53. G/S REACTORS, SOLIDS OF UNCHANGING SIZE CHANGING GAS ENVIRONMENT, THE SCM.

When the gas environment is known and close to constant everywhere in the reactor then the one phase analysis of chapter 52 can be used. For example

Fluidized bed with a large excess of gas and large particles. This gives a slow bubble bed, see chapter 25.

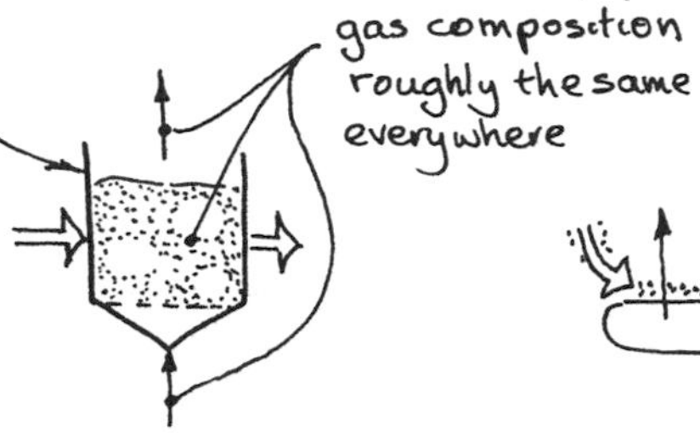

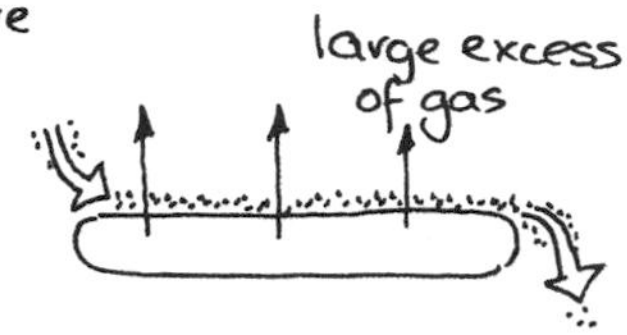

But often the gas composition changes as it passes through the reactor. As examples we have the fluidized bed,

Vigorously fluidized bed of fine particles. This gives a fast-bubble bed.

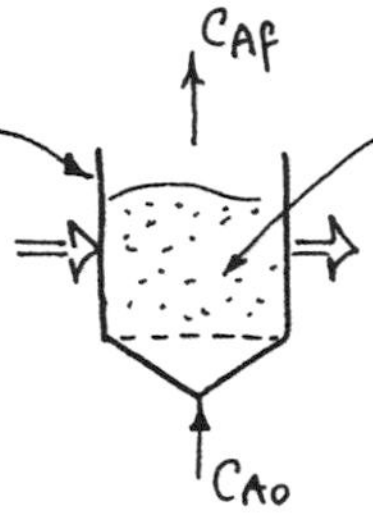

The composition of gas seen by the solids may be quite different from C_{Ao} and C_{Af}, as in Example 1 chapter 25 where

$$C_{Ao} = 100$$
$$C_{Af} = 68$$

but $C_{A\,\text{seen by solids}} = 11$!!

also coal gasifiers (21% O_2 enters, no O_2 leaves, what gas do the solids see), iron ore reducers, blast furnaces, etc.

We may also have a stagewise changing environment, such as in a succession of reactors, each "seeing" a different gas composition, or...

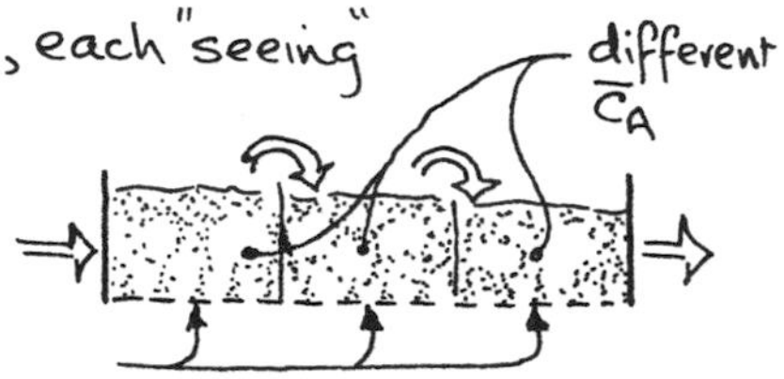

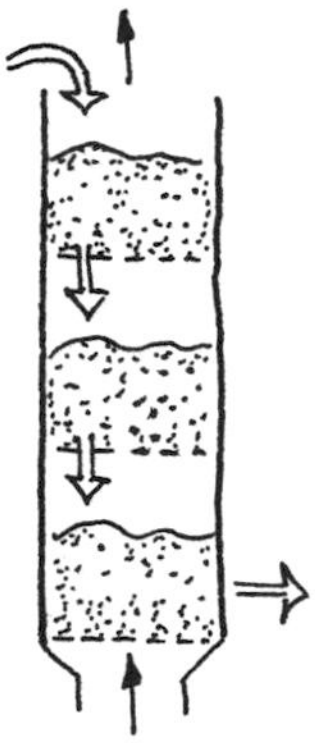

we may have completely different operations in two environments, as in reactor – regenerator systems. An example of this is the removal of H_2S from hot coal gas

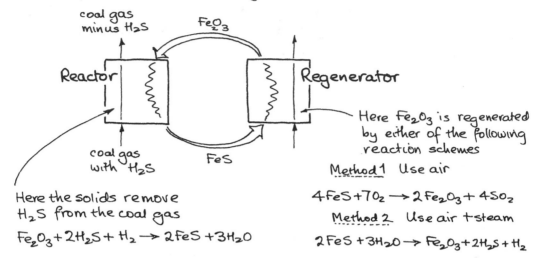

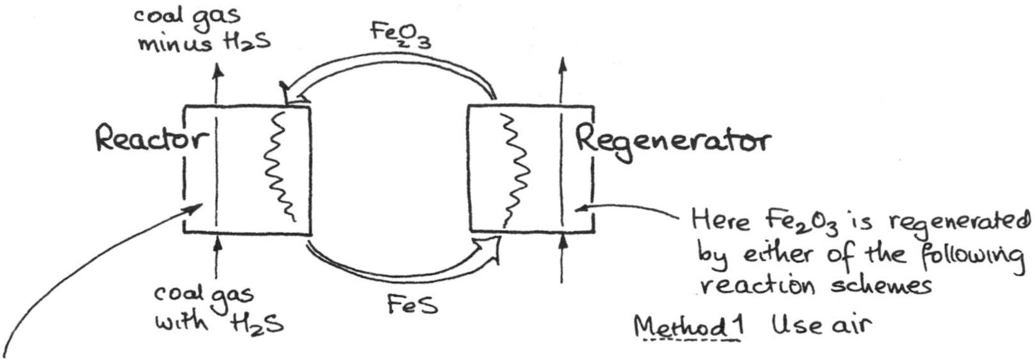

Here the solids remove H_2S from the coal gas

$$Fe_2O_3 + 2H_2S + H_2 \rightarrow 2FeS + 3H_2O$$

Method 1 Use air

$$4FeS + 7O_2 \rightarrow 2Fe_2O_3 + 4SO_2$$

Method 2 Use air + steam

$$2FeS + 3H_2O \rightarrow Fe_2O_3 + 2H_2S + H_2$$

The strategy for the two phase analysis is to write the equations for the conversion of solids, for the conversion of gas, the material balance relating the consumption of gas and solid, and then solve for the various contacting patterns.

The reaction stoichiometry is taken as

$$A(g) + bB(s) \longrightarrow \text{products}$$

the surface reaction is either first or second order with respect to A,

$$-\frac{1}{S_e}\frac{dN_A}{dt} = k_s C_A \quad \text{(m/s)} \quad \cdots \text{or} \quad -\frac{1}{S_e}\frac{dN_A}{dt} = k_s C_A^2 \quad \text{(m}^4\text{/mol·s)}$$

and when we talk of reaction order it is always with respect to A, the gas phase reactant. We do not talk of reaction order with respect to the solids.

We use the following nomenclature,

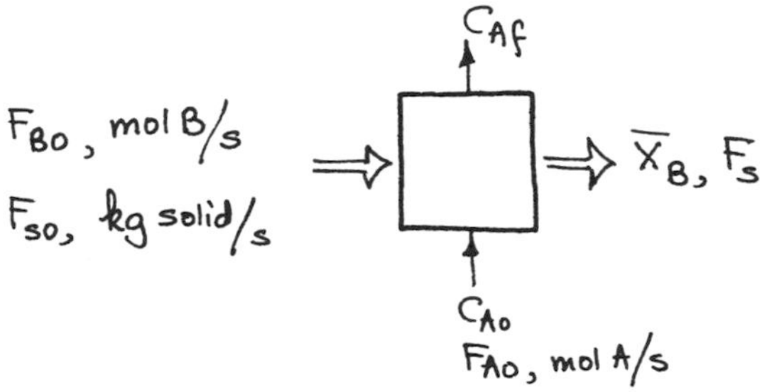

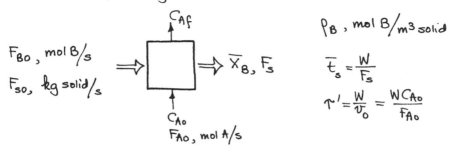

ρ_B, mol B/m³ solid

$$\bar{t}_s = \frac{W}{F_s}$$

$$\tau' = \frac{W}{v_0} = \frac{W C_{A0}}{F_{A0}}$$

and we treat in turn

- single reactors with two changing phases
- reactor–regenerator systems

I. Single Reactors

A. Mixed flow S/ mixed, plug or bubbling bed G.

(Mixed flow: good assumption for fluidized beds)

Material balance. Over the whole reactor we have

$$(\text{loss of A}) = \frac{1}{b}(\text{loss of B}) \quad \cdots \text{ or } \quad F_{A0}\left(1 - \frac{C_{Af}}{C_{A0}}\right) = \frac{1}{b} F_{B0} \overline{X}_B$$

Therefore

$$\frac{C_{Af}}{C_{A0}} = 1 - \frac{F_{B0}\overline{X}_B}{b F_{A0}}$$

or

$$\overline{X}_B = \frac{b F_{A0}}{F_{B0}}\left(1 - \frac{C_{Af}}{C_{A0}}\right) \quad \cdots (1)$$

[if expansion is important then this term becomes $\left(\dfrac{1 - C_{Af}/C_{A0}}{1 + \varepsilon_A C_{Af}/C_{A0}}\right)$]

For the solids. Since the solids move about the whole bed they react in a gas environment $\overline{C}_A$. Thus

Film control: $\bar{X}_B = \frac{\bar{t}}{\tau}\left(1-e^{-\tau/\bar{t}}\right)$ ... where $\tau = \frac{\rho_B R}{3b k_g \bar{C}_A}$ ... (2a)

Ash control: $1-\bar{X}_B = \frac{1}{5}\left(\frac{\tau}{\bar{t}}\right) - \frac{19}{420}\left(\frac{\tau}{\bar{t}}\right)^2 + \cdots, \quad \frac{\tau}{\bar{t}} \leq 1$ ... where $\tau = \frac{\rho_B R^2}{6b \mathscr{D}_e \bar{C}_A}$ ... (2b)

Reaction control: $\bar{X}_B = 3\left(\frac{\bar{t}}{\tau}\right) - 6\left(\frac{\bar{t}}{\tau}\right)^2 + 6\left(\frac{\bar{t}}{\tau}\right)^3\left[1-e^{-\tau/\bar{t}}\right]$ ... where $\tau = \frac{\rho_B R}{b k_s \bar{C}_A}$ ... (2c)

Note: we must use the proper $\bar{C}_A$ in the bed.

Note also that

$$\tau = \tau_0\left(\frac{C_{A0}}{\bar{C}_A}\right) \quad \text{... and} \quad \bar{t} = \frac{W}{F_s} \qquad \text{... (3)}$$

(τ: in a $\bar{C}_A$ environment; τ_0: in a C_{A0} environment)

<u>For the gas.</u> Here the gas sees an average solid mixture $\bar{X}_B$ everywhere. Thus

Mixed flow G.

First order for A ... $\bar{C}_A = C_{Af}$, $\quad \frac{C_{Af}}{C_{A0}} = \frac{1}{1+\tilde{k}'\tau'}$ ... (4a)

Second order for A ... $\bar{C}_A = C_{Af}$, $\quad \tilde{k}'\tau' = \frac{C_{A0}-C_{Af}}{C_{Af}^2}$ ... (4b)

Plug flow G.

First order for A ... $\bar{C}_A = \frac{C_{A0}-C_{Af}}{\ln(C_{A0}/C_{Af})}$, $\quad \frac{C_{Af}}{C_{A0}} = e^{-\tilde{k}'\tau'}$ ... (5a)

Second order for A ... $\bar{C}_A = \frac{C_{A0}C_{Af}}{C_{A0}-C_{Af}}\ln\frac{C_{A0}}{C_{Af}}$, $\quad \frac{C_{Af}}{C_{A0}} = \frac{1}{1+\tilde{k}'\tau' C_{A0}}$ ... (5b)

Bubbling bed model for fluidized beds of fine particles. From chapter 25 we find

$$\ln\frac{C_{A0}}{C_{Af}} = \underbrace{K'}_{\frac{m^3}{kg\cdot s}}\cdot\underbrace{\frac{W}{v_0}}_{\tau'} = \underbrace{\left[\overbrace{\gamma_b}^{\frac{m^3\,solid}{m^3}}\tilde{k}'\rho_s + \cfrac{1}{\cfrac{1}{K_{bc}} + \cfrac{1}{\gamma_c\tilde{k}'\rho_s + \cfrac{1}{\cfrac{1}{K_{ce}} + \cfrac{1}{\gamma_e\tilde{k}'\rho_s}}}}\right]}_{s^{-1}} \underbrace{\frac{\overbrace{u_0}^{\delta}}{u_b}}_{\frac{m^3}{m^3\,bed}}\cdot\overbrace{\frac{1}{(1-\varepsilon_f)\rho_s}}^{\frac{m^3\,bed}{kg}}\cdot\underbrace{\frac{W}{v_0}}_{\frac{kg\cdot s}{m^3}} \quad \cdots (6a)$$

and

$$\bar{C}_A = \frac{C_{A0}\left(1-e^{-K'\tau'}\right)}{\tilde{k}'\tau'} = \frac{X_{Af}}{\tilde{k}'\tau'} = \frac{X_{Af}\,v_0}{\tilde{k}'W} \quad \cdots (6b)$$

In the above expressions $\tilde{k}'$ is not a true unchanging rate constant for the gas. It is a quantity which depends on the solid environment met by the gas. Thus

$$\tilde{k}' = f(X_B) \quad \cdots \text{ and } \tilde{k}' \to 0 \text{ as } X_B \to 1$$

Equations 1,2,3,4 or 1,2,3,5 or 1,2,3,6 represent the performance expressions for various flow patterns of gas. Solving simultaneously gives the values for $\tilde{k}'$, C_{Af}, $\bar{C}_A$ and $\bar{X}_B$. Examples 1 and 2, at the end of this chapter illustrate this procedure.

II Reactor - Regenerator Systems.

For easy visualization consider that particles are blackened in the reactor, whitened in the regenerator. We may then call these units the **blackener** and **whitener** respectively

Since reaction proceeds by the SCM an originally white particle which circulates between reactor and regenerator will have a varying number of concentric black and white rings. This is then represented by the sketch at the top of the next page. Note, a long stay in a reactor, say the blackener, leaves an all black particle, while a short stay leaves rings.

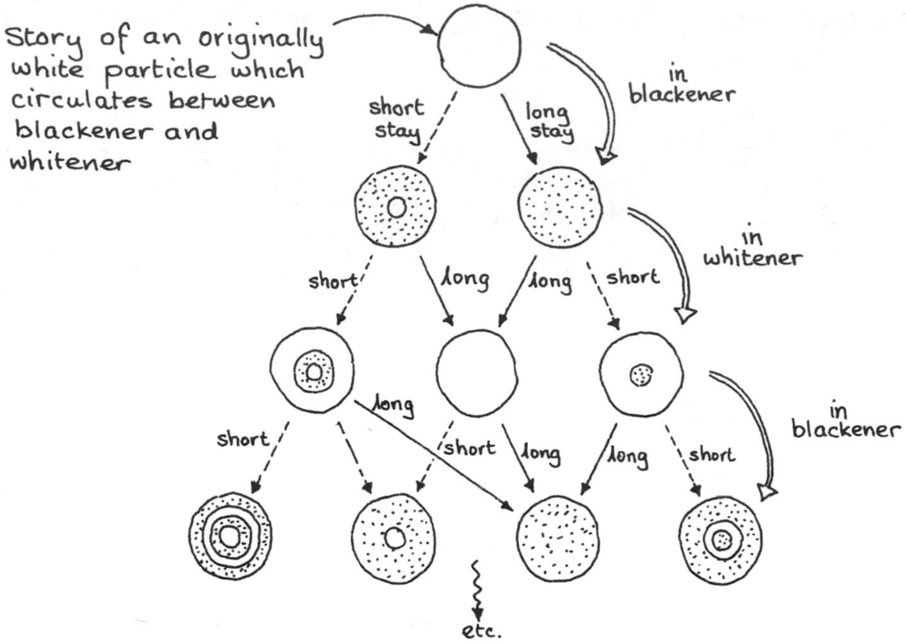
Story of an originally white particle which circulates between blackener and whitener
short stay
long stay
in blackener
short
long
long
short
in whitener
long
short
short
long
long
short
in blackener
etc.

The circulation system can then be represented as follows

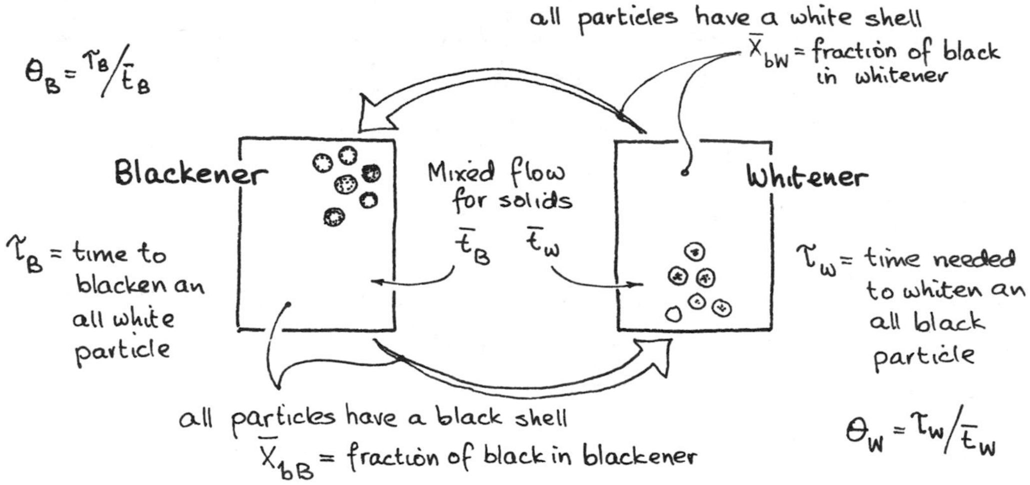
all particles have a white shell
$\bar{X}_{bW}$ = fraction of black in whitener
$\theta_B = \tau_B / \bar{t}_B$
Blackener
Mixed flow for solids
$\bar{t}_B$
$\bar{t}_W$
Whitener
τ_B = time to blacken an all white particle
τ_W = time needed to whiten an all black particle
all particles have a black shell
$\bar{X}_{bB}$ = fraction of black in blackener
$\theta_W = \tau_W / \bar{t}_W$

With mixed flow of solids in both units, SCM/reaction control kinetics, one size of solid, we can relate analytically the parameters of the system. The results are shown on the next page.

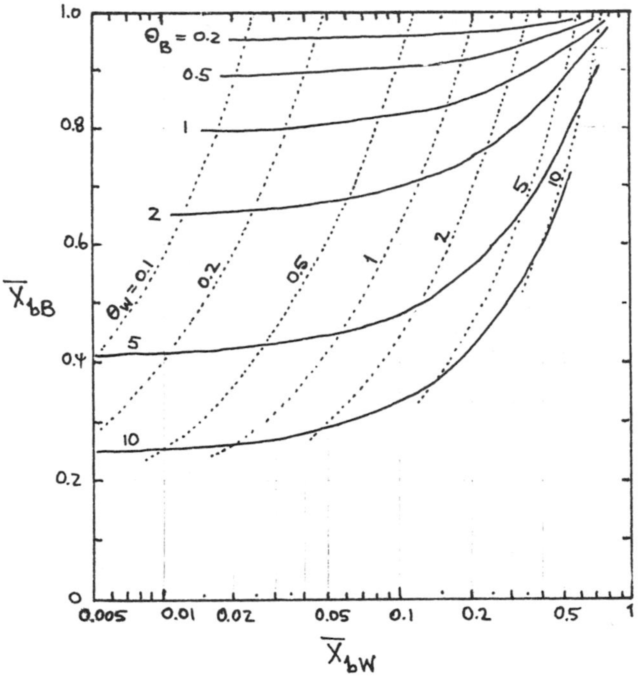

The relationship between $\bar{t}$, $\bar{X}$ and τ in the two units is shown here. Note that

$$\Theta_B = \frac{\tau_B}{\bar{t}_B}, \quad \Theta_W = \frac{\tau_W}{\bar{t}_W}$$

The **best size ratio** to use is that which minimizes the catalyst weight in the whole system for a given circulation rate of solids, F_s, and given blackening rate, $\Delta X_b \cdot F_s$. The figure below gives the optimum size ratio

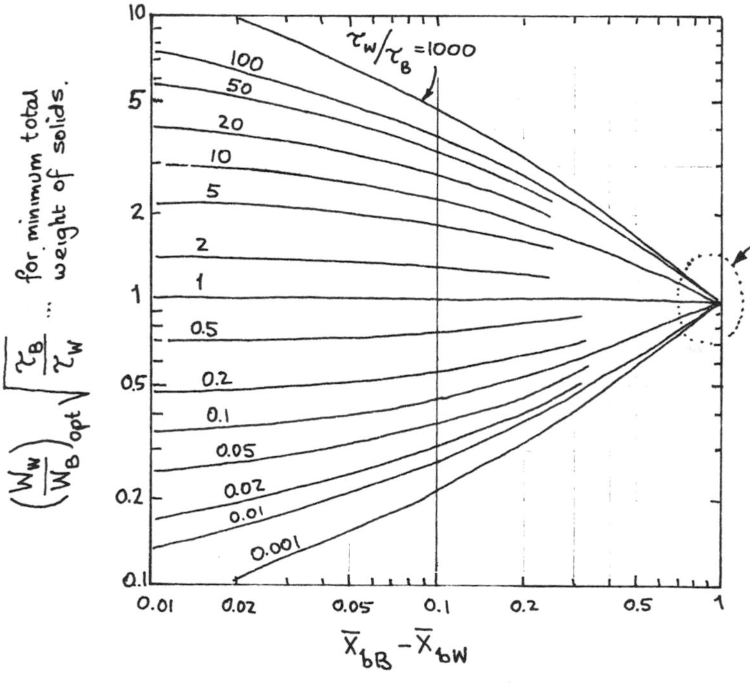

Note, for very large conversion/pass the optimum size ratio approaches

$$\frac{W_W}{W_B} = \sqrt{\frac{\tau_W}{\tau_B}}$$

which is identical to circulating catalyst which deactivates in one unit, regenerates in the other, see chapter 33.

These charts reasonably represent ash diffusion or any intermediate kinetics as long as $\bar{t} > \tau$ in both units.

For a wide size distribution of particle sizes, for other than mixed flow in both units, for ash diffusion kinetics where $\bar{t} < \tau$, or for kinetics other than the SCM we may find it simplest to use the Monte Carlo procedure to evaluate the behavior of the blackener – whitener system.

This treatment of solid circulation systems comes from Kimura et al, CES 34 1195 (1979), J. Chem Eng Japan 12 224 (1979).

Example 1. Detoxifying an ash in a fluidized bed.

Oxides of chromium which are present in a particular ash are water-soluble and extremely toxic; however, when they are reduced they become insoluble and hence harmless. So let us consider developing a process for detoxifying this ash by reacting it with CO and H_2 in a fluidized bed reactor. The various reactions involved

$$CrO_3 \;\&\; (CrO_4)^{=} \xrightarrow[CO]{H_2} Cr_2O_3 \;\&\; (Cr_2O_4)^{=}$$

can be represented by

$$A(g) + 0.6\,B(s) \longrightarrow \cdots \qquad \text{where } \overline{mw}_B = 0.152 \text{ kg/mol}$$

Determine the height of fluidized bed needed to convert 98% of the oxides present in a continuous feed of 700 kg/hr of ash containing 5% oxides, by reaction with a fluidizing gas containing 4 mol % of reducing agents CO and H_2.

Data Operating conditions = 600°C, close to 1 atm

Bed diameter = 1.22 m

ρ_{solids} = 1450 kg/m³

Measured at 600°C, 1atm … $\begin{cases} u_{mf} = 0.01 \text{ m/s} \\ u_0 = 0.20 \text{ m/s} \end{cases}$

Estimated bubble size: d_b = 0.15 m

$\varepsilon_{mf} = 0.5$

$\varepsilon_f = 0.6$

$\mathscr{D}_{in\ gas} = 8\times10^{-5}$ m²/s

$\alpha_{estimated} = 0.33$

Kinetics To evaluate the kinetics of this reaction experiments are made with a batch of solids in a small reactor and a large throughflow of gas such that C_A stays at its feed value during the run. The conversion of B is followed with time and the results are plotted as follows

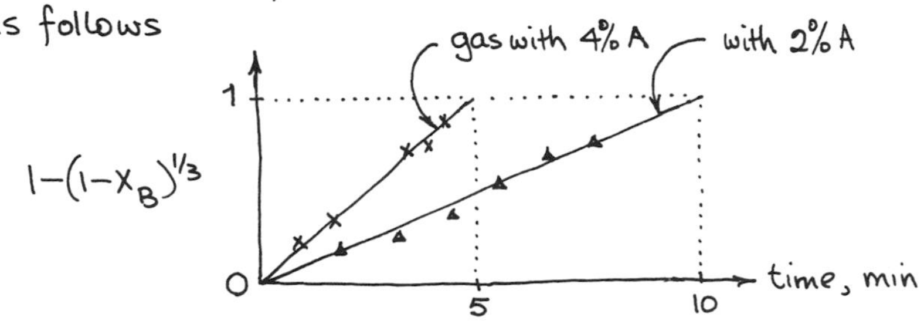

The good straight line fit and the fact that the time for reaction is proportional to C_A means that one can represent the conversion of solids by

- first order kinetics with respect to gaseous A
- SCM/reaction control with respect to solid reactant B, and with $\tau_o = 5\text{min}$ in the gas feed atmosphere

Sketch of what is known

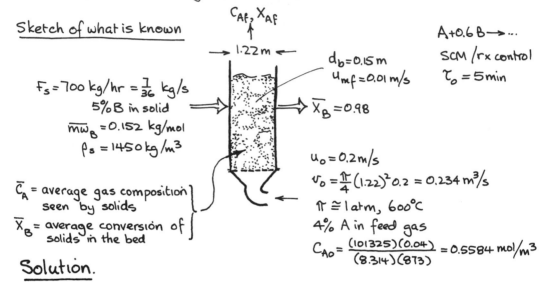

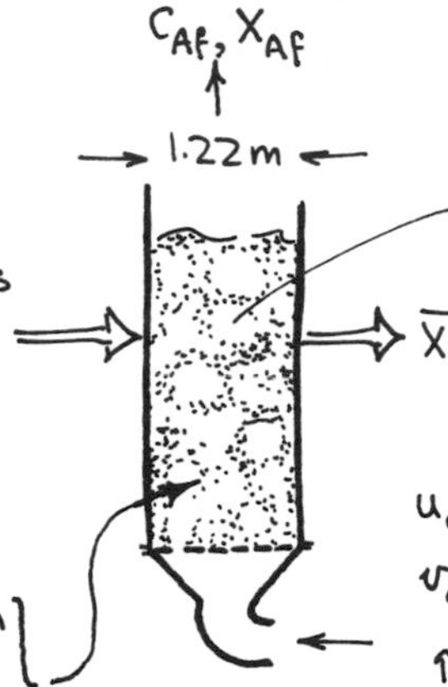

$A + 0.6B \rightarrow \ldots$

SCM/rx control

$\tau_o = 5\text{min}$

$d_b = 0.15\text{m}$

$u_{mf} = 0.01\text{ m/s}$

$F_s = 700\text{ kg/hr} = \frac{7}{36}\text{ kg/s}$

5% B in solid

$\overline{mw}_B = 0.152\text{ kg/mol}$

$\rho_s = 1450\text{ kg/m}^3$

$\bar{X}_B = 0.98$

$u_o = 0.2\text{m/s}$

$v_o = \frac{\pi}{4}(1.22)^2 0.2 = 0.234\text{ m}^3/\text{s}$

$\pi \cong 1\text{atm}, 600°\text{C}$

4% A in feed gas

$C_{Ao} = \frac{(101325)(0.04)}{(8.314)(873)} = 0.5584\text{ mol/m}^3$

$\bar{C}_A$ = average gas composition seen by solids

$\bar{X}_B$ = average conversion of solids in the bed

Solution.

(a) Material balance to find C_{Af}.

Equation 1 of this chapter, $F_{Ao}\left(1 - \frac{C_{Af}}{C_{Ao}}\right) = \frac{F_{Bo}}{b}\bar{X}_B$ relates C_{Af} to $\bar{X}_B$. Let us evaluate terms

$$F_{Ao} = (0.234)\left(\frac{273}{873}\right)\left(\frac{1}{0.0224}\right)(0.04) = 0.131\text{ mol A/s}$$

$$F_{Bo} = (700)\left(\frac{1}{3600}\right)(0.05)\left(\frac{1}{0.152}\right) = 0.0640\text{ mol B/s}$$

Replacing these values into the material balance for $\bar{X}_B = 0.98$ gives

$$0.131\left(1 - \frac{C_{Af}}{C_{Ao}}\right) = \frac{0.064}{0.6}(0.98)$$

$$\therefore \frac{C_{Af}}{C_{Ao}} = 0.200$$

(b) Conversion of solids by the SCM/rx control.

For mixed flow of solids eq 52.6 gives

$$\bar{X}_B = 3\left(\frac{\bar{t}_s}{\tau}\right) - 6\left(\frac{\bar{t}_s}{\tau}\right)^2 + 6\left(\frac{\bar{t}_s}{\tau}\right)^3 \left[1 - e^{-\tau/\bar{t}_s}\right]$$

and for $\bar{X}_B = 0.98$ trial and error gives $\frac{\bar{t}_s}{\tau} = 12.3$. So for solids we have

(τ ← in actual bed environment)

$$\left.\begin{aligned} \frac{\bar{t}_s}{\tau} &= 12.3 \\ \frac{\tau}{\tau_0} &= \frac{C_{A0}}{\bar{C}_A} \quad \text{... with } C_{A0} = 0.5584 \\ \bar{t}_s &= \frac{W}{F_s} = \frac{W}{7/36} \end{aligned}\right\} \quad \text{combining gives} \quad \left.\begin{aligned} &W\left(\frac{\bar{C}_A}{C_{A0}}\right) = 717.5 \\ \text{or} \quad &W\bar{C}_A = 401 \end{aligned}\right\} \cdots \quad \cdots \text{(i)}$$

(c) For conversion of gas use the K·L model of chapter 25.

$$u_{br} = 0.711\,(g d_b)^{1/2} = 0.711\,(9.81 \times 0.15)^{1/2} = 0.862 \text{ m/s}$$

$$u_b = 0.2 - 0.01 + 0.862 = 1.052 \text{ m/s}$$

$$\delta = \frac{0.2}{1.052} = 0.190$$

$$K_{bc} = 4.5\left(\frac{0.01}{0.15}\right) + 5.85\left[\frac{(8\times10^{-5})^{1/2}(9.81)^{1/4}}{(0.15)^{5/4}}\right] = 1.29 \text{ s}^{-1}$$

$$K_{ce} = 6.77\left[\frac{0.5\,(8\times10^{-5})\,0.862}{(0.15)^3}\right]^{1/2} = 0.684 \text{ s}^{-1}$$

$$\gamma_b \cong 0$$

$$\gamma_c = (1-0.5)\left[\frac{3(0.01)/0.5}{0.862 - 0.01/0.5} + 0.33\right] = 0.201$$

$$\gamma_e \; \frac{(1-0.5)(1-0.190)}{0.190} - 0.201 - 0 = 1.93$$

$$\ln \frac{C_{A0}}{C_{Af}} = \left[\gamma_b \rho_s \tilde{k}' + \cfrac{1}{\cfrac{1}{K_{bc}} + \cfrac{1}{\gamma_c \rho_s \tilde{k}' + \cfrac{1}{\cfrac{1}{K_{ce}} + \cfrac{1}{\gamma_e \rho_s \tilde{k}'}}}} \right] \frac{u_o W}{v_0 (1-\varepsilon_f) u_b \rho_s}$$

($\gamma_b \rho_s \tilde{k}' \approx 0$)

Solving for W and replacing values gives

$$W = \frac{v_0 (1-\varepsilon_f) u_b \rho_s}{u_0} \ln \frac{C_{A0}}{C_{Af}} \left[\frac{1}{K_{bc}} + \cfrac{1}{\gamma_c \rho_s \tilde{k}' + \cfrac{1}{\cfrac{1}{K_{ce}} + \cfrac{1}{\gamma_e \rho_s \tilde{k}'}}} \right]$$

or

$$W = \left[910 + \cfrac{1176}{291\tilde{k}' + \cfrac{1}{1.461 + \cfrac{1}{2800\tilde{k}'}}} \right] \quad \cdots \quad \cdots \text{(ii)}$$

Finally from eq 25.3

$$\frac{C_A}{C_{A0}} = \frac{X_{Af} v_0}{\tilde{k}' W} = \frac{0.8(0.234)}{\tilde{k}' W} = \frac{0.187}{\tilde{k}' W} \quad \cdots \quad \cdots \text{(iii)}$$

Equations (i), (ii) and (iii) have 3 unknowns $\tilde{k}'$, $\frac{\bar{C}_A}{C_{A0}}$ and W. Solve. For this combine (i) and (iii)

$$\frac{\bar{C}_A}{C_{A0}} = \frac{0.187}{\tilde{k}'(717.5)} \cdot \frac{\bar{C}_A}{C_{A0}} \quad \cdots \text{or} \cdots \quad \tilde{k}' = 261 \times 10^{-6}$$

Replacing in (ii) gives the bed weight as: **W = 3650 kg** ←

The settled bed height is: $h_{mf} = \frac{3650}{\frac{\pi}{4}(1.22)^2(0.5)(1450)} = \mathbf{4.31\ m}$ ←

The fluidized bed height is: $h_f = 4.31 \left(\frac{1-0.5}{1-0.6} \right) = \mathbf{5.25\ m}$ ←

Note: This is a poor geometry, too tall and narrow. In the problems at the end of this chapter we will try some alternative geometries.

Example 2. G/S reaction with n^{th} order kinetics for solids.

Repeat Example 1 with one change, as follows. Instead of using the SCM/rx control model to represent the batch conversion of solids let us instead try to fit the data with first order kinetics, in which case we find the following graph

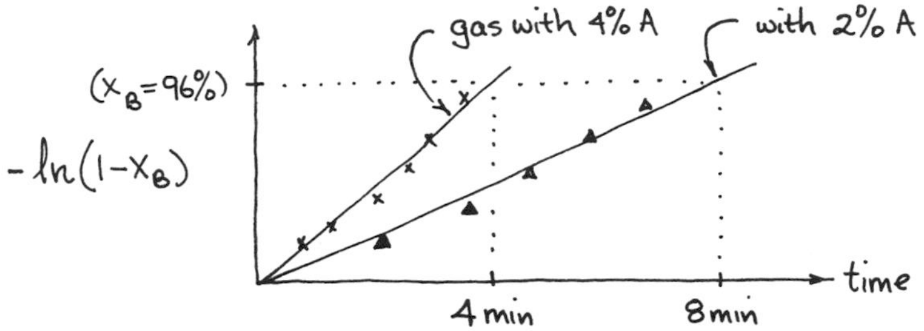

The reasonable fit shows that the conversion of B follows

- first order kinetics with respect to gaseous A
- first order kinetics with respect to solid B

or

$$-\frac{d(1-X_B)}{dt} = k_B \bar{C}_A (1-X_B) \qquad \cdots \text{(iv)}$$

($\bar{C}_A$: average seen by solids)

Solution.

(a) Material balance. This is identical to Example 1.

(b) Conversion of solids using first order kinetics.

First find the value of the rate constant k_B from the batch experiment. So integrating eq 4 gives

$$-\ln(1-X_B) = k_B C_A t$$

and replacing values for the 4% A run ($C_A = 0.5584\ \text{mol/m}^3$) gives

$$-\ln(1-0.96) = k_B(0.5584)(240)$$

$$\therefore k_B = 0.0240\ \text{m}^3/\text{mol}\cdot\text{s}$$

In the fluidized bed which is to be designed the solids will be in mixed flow, they see A at $\bar{C}_A$, and they follow first order kinetics with respect to B. Hence the performance equation for the solids is

$$1 - X_B = \frac{1}{1 + (k_B \bar{C}_A)\bar{t}_s} = \frac{1}{1 + k_B \bar{C}_A (W/F_s)}$$

Replacing values gives

$$1 - 0.98 = \frac{1}{1 + 0.024\,\bar{C}_A (W/F_s)}$$

or

$$\bar{C}_A W = 397 \quad \cdots \qquad \cdots \quad (v)$$

This value is close to that found in example 1, see eq (i) there. So from here on the solution follows part (c) of example 1, and we get the same final answer.

Example 3. Simplifying the flow model for gas in example 1.

In example 1 we assumed that the Kunii-Levenspiel model best represented the flow of gas through the fluidized bed. Let us see what happens if we assume a simpler flow model. So calculate the weight of bed solids needed if we assume

(a) Mixed flow of gas through the incinerator

(b) Plug flow of gas through the incinerator.

Compare your results with those given on pg. 53·12, for the more accurate K·L model.

Solution.

The sketch of what is known is shown on pg. 53·10. Also, parts (a) and (b) of pgs 53·10 & 53·11 are unchanged and apply here.

(a) Assume mixed flow of gas. Then

$$\bar{C}_A = C_{Af} = 0.2\,C_{A0} = 0.2(0.5584) = 0.1117 \text{ mol/m}^3$$

and from eq (1) of pg 53.11

$$W = \frac{401}{0.1117} = \underline{3591 \text{ kg}}$$

(b) Assume plug flow of gas. Then

$$\bar{C}_A = \frac{C_{A0} - C_{Af}}{\ln \frac{C_{A0}}{C_{Af}}} = \frac{0.5584\,(1-0.2)}{\ln \frac{1}{0.2}} = 0.2776 \text{ mol/m}^3$$

and from eq (i) of pg 53.11

$$W = \frac{401}{0.2776} = \underline{1445 \text{ kg}}$$

Note how much simpler are the solutions here. However, example 1 which uses the K·L model for gas flow through the fluidized bed gives a more accurate answer, or **W = 3650 kg**, and also predicts poorer behavior than either of the ideal flow patterns do.

Chapter 53 Problems

Gas A and solid B ($d_p = 0.3$ mm, $F_s = 1$ ton/hr, mol wt of B = 0.1 kg/mol) are fed continuously to a fluidized bed, react there and leave. The reaction is

$$A(g) + B(s) \rightarrow R(g) + S(s), \quad d_p \text{ unchanged}$$

Reaction is first order with respect to A, and in the feed gas environment the particles are converted to product with a shrinking core, reaction control mechanism in $\tau_0 = 1$ hr. Find the size of bed needed to give 90% conversion of solid in the exit stream

A1 ... using an equimolar feed of A and B, and assuming mixed flow of gas.

A2 ... using 2 mol A/mol B, assuming plug flow of gas.

A3* In the previous problems we assumed plug or mixed flow of gas. Plug flow is probably the best limiting assumptions we have today for slow-bubble fluidized beds (large d_p, high u_o). However, if d_p is very small then we get a fast-bubble bed (bubbles with thin clouds and much gas bypassing). Let us consider the latter situation here. Assuming flows and bed properties of example 1 chapter 25 and the bubbling bed model for the flow pattern of gas, find the size of bed needed for 90% conversion of solids using an equimolar feed of A and B, $F_s = 1$ ton/hr.

It is interesting to compare the results of problems 1 and 3.

Consider ash diffusion control for solids instead of reaction control, and second order reaction with respect to gas A instead of first order, and then redo

A4 ... problem 1

A5 ... problem 2

Product gas from coal gasification plants contains small amounts of H_2S, most of which must be removed before the gas can be used. One method for doing this is to pass the hot gas through a fluidized bed of Fe_2O_3 particles. Reaction occurs, H_2S is captured and FeS is produced

$$Fe_2O_3 \xrightarrow{+2H_2S} 2FeS$$

Fe_2O_3 is then regenerated in another reactor, as follows

$$2FeS \xrightarrow{+\frac{3}{2}O_2} Fe_2O_3$$

What weight of fluidized bed is needed to remove 99% of the H_2S from 800 m^3/s of 1000 K and 1 atm coal gas which contains 2% H_2S if we use Fe_2O_3 50% in excess of stoichiometric, if reaction is first order with respect to H_2S and follows the SCM/reaction control with $\tau_0 = 60$ sec in the entering coal gas environment.

Chapter 53 Problems

A6 . . . Assume mixed flow of gas.

A7 . . . Assume plug flow of gas.

A8* . . . Assume the bubbling bed model for the flow of gas. Take the bed properties to be that of example 1 chapter 25 ($u_o = 0.3$ m/s, $u_{mf} = 0.03$ m/s, $\varepsilon_{mf} = 0.5$, $d_b = 0.32$ m, etc.). But of course the bed diameter will be greater than 2 m.

Note: These feed figures represent the scale operations for a 1000 $MW_{electrical}$ gasification plant using high sulfur coal.

When high sulfur coal is burned in a central power station it produces significant amounts of SO_2, say 0.5%, in the flue gas. This SO_2 can be removed by contacting the flue gas with limestone before discharge to the atmosphere. Limestone reacts with SO_2 as follows

$$CaCO_3(s) + SO_2 + 0.5O_2 \rightarrow CaSO_4(s) + CO_2$$

The reaction is first order with respect to SO_2 and the particles of $CaCO_3$ are converted to $CaSO_4$ by the shrinking core model, reaction control, $\tau_0 = 10$ min in the feed environment.

If we wish to treat the gases from a 1000 $MW_{electrical}$ power station (2400 m^3 flue gas/s at 1000 K and 1 atm) in a fluidized contactor how large must the bed be (W) and at what rate (F_s) must fresh limestone be fed to the unit for 99% removal of SO_2 if the spent solids are

A9 . . . 25% converted to product and if gas follows mixed flow.

A10 . . . 25% conversion to product and if gas follows plug flow.

Comment: For the large volume of gas to be treated (2400 m^3/s) we would want very high velocities, hence large d_p and a slow bubble bed. Unfortunately, however, large d_p means large τ_0 hence a large bed. Maybe we should go to the transport line reactor with recirculation of fine solids, or maybe we should go to high pressure operations.

As an added headache the conversion of limestone to calcium sulfate is rarely over 25% in large particles, hence the amount of limestone needed for a large central power station comes to about 5000 tons/day. What would we do with this waste solid?

Our fluidized coal burner feeds high sulfur coal particles to a hot bed of limestone and coal ash. SO_2 is generated, and is removed by reaction with the limestone in the bed

$$CaCO_3(s) + SO_2 + 0.5O_2 \rightarrow CaSO_4(s) + CO_2$$

Chapter 53 Problems

At present with a steady feed of coal and fresh limestone we obtain 80% removal of the SO_2 while the limestone is 25% converted to sulfate. In other words we have 25% utilization of limestone. This fraction of SO_2 captured by limestone is too small for our purposes.

A11 . . . What bed size and limestone feed rate do we need (find W_2/W_1) for 96% capture of SO_2 if we keep an unchanged flow rate of coal and the same limestone utilization of 25%?

A12 . . . What feed rate of limestone (find F_{s2}/F_{s1}) will give 96% capture of SO_2 in a bed of same size and unchanged feed rate of coal?

Assume the SCM/reaction control, and mixed flow of gas as a crude first approximation.

A13 For the reactor of examples 1 and 2 what bed height would we find if we assumed mixed flow and then plug flow of gas in the fluidized bed?

A14* It seems that the reactor of example 1 is too long and narrow. So for the same volumetric flow rates of gas and solid let us try a 2 m diameter bed. Find the weight of catalyst needed with this change. Do you think that this change represents an improvement?

B15 Consider an iron oxide-sulfide system for removing of H_2S from coal gas, as described at the beginning of this chapter. In the reactor environment the time for complete sulfidation of a pure iron oxide particle is 12 min; in the regenerator the time for complete oxidation of a pure sulfide particle is 1 min. For the amount of coal gas to be treated the circulation rate of solids is to be 1000 kg/min if fresh solids are completely converted to sulfide in each pass.

Assuming the SCM/reaction control for the reaction of solid determine the required size of the reactor and of the regenerator if the mean conversion to sulfide in reactor and regenerator is to be 70% and 10%, respectively.

B16 An experimental iron oxide-iron sulfide recirculating system as described at the beginning of this chapter is being run to obtain kinetic data and to verify theory. In a given run the Fe_2O_3-FeS solids are circulated at a rate of $F_s = 1$ kg/min between the fluidized reactor (W = 60 kg) and fluidized regenerator (W = 30 kg). Coal gas containing 1% H_2S enters the reactor and 99% of the entering H_2S is absorbed by the solids in the reactor. The regenerator uses a large excess of air. The mean conversion of solids to sulfide in reactor and regenerator is 80% and 30%.

Chapter 53 Problems

Assuming the SCM/reaction control, find $\tau_{\text{to sulfide}}$ in the reactor environment and in the entering coal gas environment. Assume mixed flow and then plug flow of coal gas in the reactor.

B17 We are presently designing a large circulating Fe_2O_3-FeS system to remove 95% of the H_2S present in freshly prepared coal gas (800 m^3/s, 1000K, 1 atm, 2% H_2S); see the text of this chapter for details. Pilot plant data and design calculations give the following system parameters.

For the fluid bed which removes H_2S:	SCM, reaction control $\tau = 10$ min $\bar{X}_{Fe_2O_3 \text{ to } FeS} = 45\%$
For the fluid bed which regenerates Fe_2O_3:	SCM, reaction control $\tau = 1.5$ min $\bar{X}_{FeS \text{ to } Fe_2O_3} = 94.3\%$

What size of reactor and regenerator will be needed for this operation?

A18 Silicon nitride is formed by reacting silicon with nitrogen at high temperature

$$3\,Si(s) + 2N_2(g) \xrightarrow{\sim 1250°C} Si_3N_4(s)$$

In an experiment wherein a batch of very fine micron sized powder is bathed by gas consisting of 20% nitrogen in hydrogen carrier gas we find

55% of the silicon is converted in 2.8 hr
87.5% of the silicon is converted in 6.0 hr

In a second experiment using a gas with 40% nitrogen everything happens twice as fast.

With this information how much solid must a continuous solids flow reactor hold to treat 12kg/hr of silicon powder to 99% conversion

(a) if the unit is a fluidized bed in which the solids are bathed by a 60% nitrogen gas?

(b) if the unit is a rotating kiln through which the particles tumble in close to plug flow while contacting a 40% nitrogen gas?

Chapter 53 Problems

A19 A metallurgical ash contains oxides of chromium which are extremely toxic. These oxides can be made harmless by reacting them with reducing gases such as CO and H_2. The reaction is rather complex but can be approximated by

$$[CrO_3 + CrO_4^{=}] + 0.6\,[CO + H_2] \rightarrow [Cr_2O_3 + Cr_2O_4^{=}] + \ldots$$

In experiments wherein a batch of ash is bathed by a 3% $[CO + H_2]$ gas we find

55% of the toxicity is removed in 2.8 min.

87.5% of the toxicity is removed in 6.0 min.

When 6% $[CO + H_2]$ is used everything happens twice as fast.

(a) What do these experiments tell about the kinetics of the reaction?

With this information we want to design a detoxifier to continuously treat 12 kg/min of flowing ash so as to remove 99% of the toxicity.

(b) One scheme is to use a fluidized bed reactor in which ash is bathed by 9% $[CO + H_2]$ gas. How much solid should the reactor hold?

(c) Another scheme is to use a rotating tubular reactor through which the particles tumble in close to plug flow while contacting a 6% $[CO + H_2]$ gas, on the average. How much solid should this reactor hold?

Chapter 54. REACTION OF PARTICLES OF CHANGING SIZE.

I Kinetics of Particle Growth and Shrinkage.

Represent the kinetics by the change in radius of particle

$$\mathcal{R}(R) = \frac{dR}{dt}$$

The linear model is the simplest of rate forms. Thus

for linear growth: $\mathcal{R}(R) = \frac{dR}{dt} = k \qquad [k = \frac{m}{s}]$ ... (1)

for linear shrinkage: $\mathcal{R}(R) = \frac{dR}{dt} = -k \qquad [k = \frac{m}{s}]$ ... (2)

Linear growth often well represents deposition and condensation processes, while linear shrinkage often well represents dissolution, sublimation or G/S reaction processes.

Since the rate constant for linear shrinkage and for the SCM/reaction control both represent the disappearance of unreacted solid, they are related. For example, for the reaction

$$A(g) + bB(s) \rightarrow \text{product} \qquad -\frac{1}{S_{ex}}\frac{dN_A}{dt} = k_s C_{As}$$

(k_s: $\frac{m}{s}$, from chapter 51)

the relationship between rate constants is

$$k = \frac{b k_s C_{As}}{\rho_B}$$

(k: for shrinking particles; k_s: for SCM/reaction control; ρ_B: mol B/m³)

Because of the simplicity of this model and its good fit in so many situations it is the first model we turn to in this chapter. Nevertheless there are situations where other models are better.

One important case is that of extremely fast reactions such as the high temperature condensation or combustion of fine particles. Here the rate controlling step is the mass transfer of active component through the gas film surrounding the particle. The model which represents such situations is that of

reciprocal shrinkage: $$\mathcal{R}(R) = \frac{dR}{dt} = -\frac{k'}{R} \qquad \left[k' = \frac{m^2}{s}\right] \qquad \cdots (3)$$

or

reciprocal growth: $$\mathcal{R}(R) = \frac{dR}{dt} = \frac{k'}{R} \qquad \left[k' = \frac{m^2}{s}\right] \qquad \cdots (4)$$

These expressions show that the smaller the particle becomes the faster does it shrink (or grow).

Further discussion on these and other rate forms is found at the end of this chapter.

II. Measurement of Size Distribution of Solids and the Meaning of the term "Mean Particle Size".

Since the size of all the particles vary continuously with time the basic equations are formulated in terms of the **continuous size distribution**. Thus

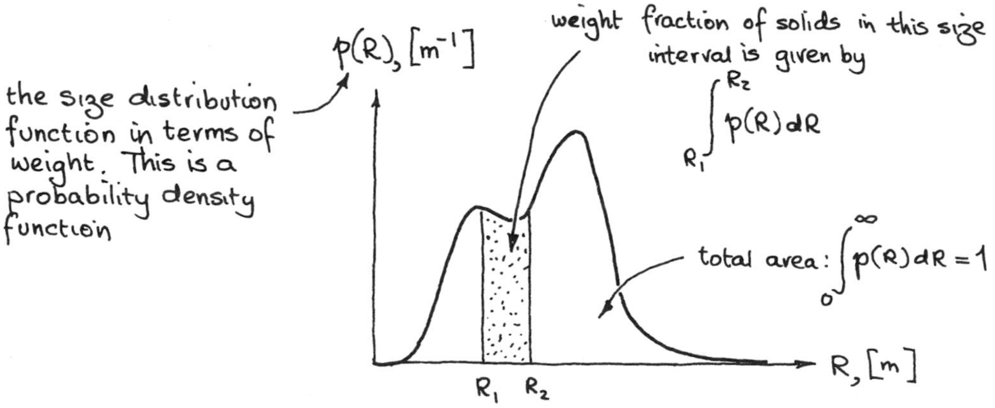

the size distribution function in terms of weight. This is a probability density function
p(R), [m⁻¹]
weight fraction of solids in this size interval is given by
$\int_{R_1}^{R_2} p(R)\,dR$
total area: $\int_0^\infty p(R)\,dR = 1$
R_1
R_2
R, [m]

For numerical calculations we still use the **discrete size distribution**, defined in the beginning of chapter 52, and used throughout that chapter.

The mean particle size can be defined in many different ways. For our purposes we find the following two definitions particularly useful. First we have

$$\bar{R}_w = \begin{pmatrix}\text{weight average}\\ \text{particle radius}\end{pmatrix} = \sqrt[3]{1\Big/\sum_i\left(\frac{F(R_i)/F}{R^3}\right)} = \sqrt[3]{1\Big/\int \frac{p(R)}{R^3}\,dR} \qquad \cdots (5a)$$

which represents that size of spherical particle whose weight is the mean of all the N particles in the mixture.

We also use

$$\bar{R}_s = \begin{pmatrix}\text{surface}\\ \text{mean size}\end{pmatrix} = 1\Big/\sum_i\left(\frac{F(R_i)/F}{R}\right) = 1\Big/\int\frac{p(R)}{R}\,dR \qquad \cdots (5b)$$

which is the size of particle whose surface to volume ratio equals that of all the solids in the mixture. This mean is useful for calculating the frictional pressure drop of flowing fluids.

III <u>Performance Equations for Single Reactors.</u>

Consider various contacting patterns, particle shapes and size distributions.

A. <u>Single particle, linear growth.</u>

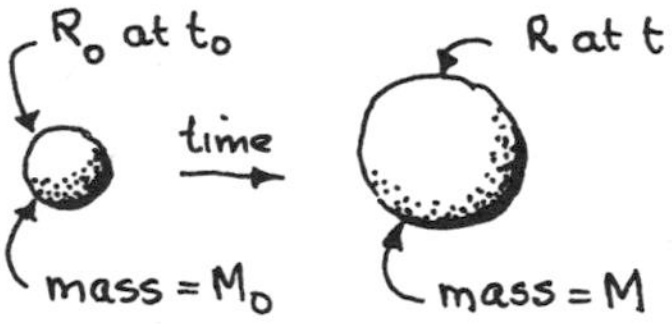

From eq 1 we find

1/3 for spheres
1/2 for cylinders
1 for flat plates

$$\frac{R}{R_o} = \left(\frac{M}{M_o}\right)^{1/3} = 1 + \frac{kt}{R_o} \qquad \cdots (6)$$

B. Single particle, linear shrinkage.

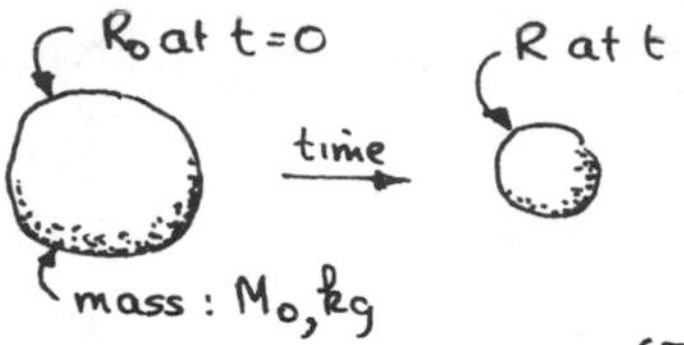

From eq 2 we find

$$\frac{R}{R_0} = \left(\frac{M}{M_0}\right)^{1/3} = (1-X_B)^{1/3} = 1 - \frac{kt}{R_0} \quad \cdots (7)$$

... where $\frac{R_0}{k} = \tau$ = time for complete reaction and disappearance of a particle.

C. Plug flow, one size feed, linear growth.

F, F_0, W and t are related by

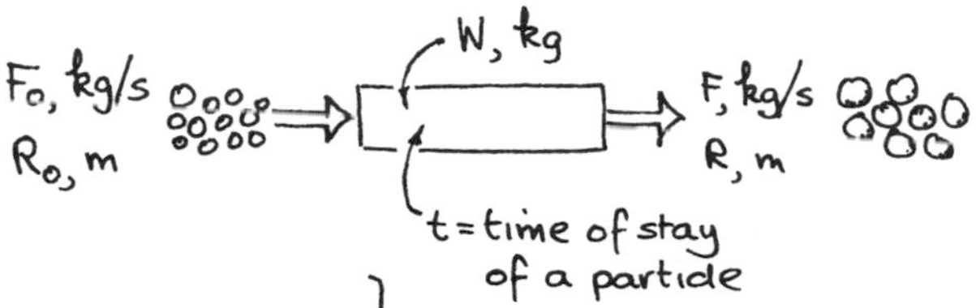

$$\left.\begin{aligned} \frac{Wk}{F_0R_0} &= \frac{1}{4}\left[\left(1+\frac{kt}{R_0}\right)^4 - 1\right] \\ \text{or} \quad \frac{W}{tF_0} &= 1 + \frac{3}{2}\left(\frac{kt}{R_0}\right) + \left(\frac{kt}{R_0}\right)^2 + \frac{1}{4}\left(\frac{kt}{R_0}\right)^3 \end{aligned}\right\} \quad \cdots (8)$$

D. Plug flow, one size feed, linear shrinkage.

The variables in the system are related by

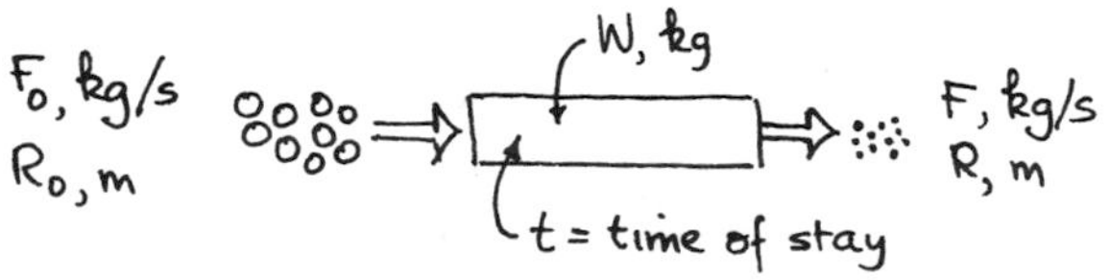

$$\left.\begin{aligned} \frac{Wk}{F_0R_0} &= \frac{1}{4}\left[1-\left(1-\frac{kt}{R_0}\right)^4\right] \\ \text{or} \quad \frac{W}{F_0t} &= 1 - \frac{3}{2}\left(\frac{kt}{R_0}\right) + \left(\frac{kt}{R_0}\right)^2 - \frac{1}{4}\left(\frac{kt}{R_0}\right)^3 \end{aligned}\right\} \text{ for } t < \frac{R_0}{k} \quad \cdots (9)$$

In the extreme where the particles shrink to zero, and nothing leaves

$$\frac{Wk}{F_0R_0} = \frac{1}{4} \quad \cdots (10)$$

E. Basic equations for mixed flow of solids.

Let us first present the general material balance, then see about solving it. For this consider a feed of wide size distribution entering a mixed flow reactor. Let elutriation occur and let the particle size change by some general kinetics $\mathcal{R}(R)$. We then have

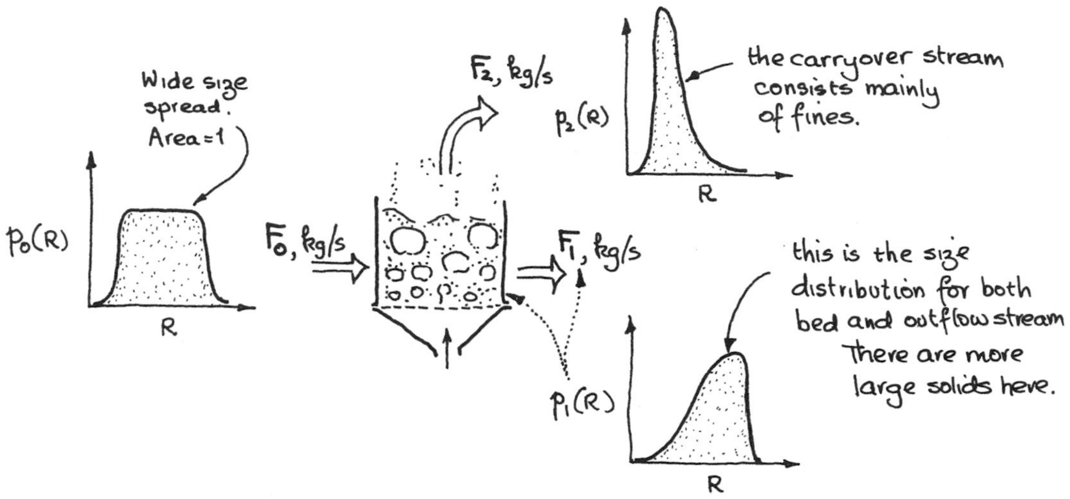
Wide size spread. Area = 1
$p_0(R)$
R
F_0, kg/s
F_2, kg/s
F_1, kg/s
$p_2(R)$
the carryover stream consists mainly of fines.
R
this is the size distribution for both bed and outflow stream
There are more large solids here.
$p_1(R)$
R

The material balance for solids of size between R and R+dR gives

$$F_0 \cdot p_0(R)\,dR - F_1 \cdot p_1(R)\,dR - W\cdot \kappa(R)\, p_1(R)\,dR - W\frac{d}{dR}\Big[\mathcal{R}(R)\cdot p_1(R)\Big]dR + \frac{3W}{R}\,\mathcal{R}(R)\cdot p_1(R)\,dR = 0 \quad \cdots (11)$$

- $F_0 \cdot p_0(R)\,dR$: in the feed, kg/s
- $F_1 \cdot p_1(R)\,dR$: outflow, kg/s
- $W\cdot \kappa(R)\, p_1(R)\,dR$: elutriation, kg/s
- $W\frac{d}{dR}[\mathcal{R}(R)\cdot p_1(R)]dR$: growth into and out of the interval, kg/s
- $\frac{3W}{R}\mathcal{R}(R)\cdot p_1(R)\,dR$: mass increase within the interval, kg/s
- the "3" is for spheres, use "2" for cylinders and "1" for flat plates

An overall balance over all sizes gives

$$F_2 + F_1 - F_0 = 3W \int_{\text{all } R} \frac{p_1(R)\cdot \mathcal{R}(R)\, dR}{R} \quad \cdots \begin{cases} >0 \text{ for growth} \\ <0 \text{ for shrinkage} \end{cases} \quad \cdots (12)$$

"3" for spheres
"2" for cylinders
"1" for flat plates

and finally the elutriation constant, from chapter 52, relates the composition of the two exit streams. Thus for each size slice $\bar{R}$ we can write

$$\kappa(\bar{R}) = \frac{F_2 \cdot p_2(R)\, dR}{W \cdot p_1(R)\, dR} \qquad \cdots (13)$$

A proper manipulation of these equations with formal integration will relate input to output streams. This gives

For a single size of spherical feed particles R_o

$$\left.\begin{aligned} \frac{W}{F_o} &= \int_{R_o}^{R\ \text{at}\ t=\infty} \frac{R^3}{\mathcal{R}(R)\cdot R_o^3} \cdot I \cdot dR \\ p_1(R) &= \frac{F_o}{W\cdot|\mathcal{R}(R)|} \cdot \frac{R^3}{R_o^3} \cdot I \end{aligned}\right\} \cdots \text{where } I = e^{-\int_{R_o}^{R} \frac{F_1/W + \kappa(R)}{\mathcal{R}(R)} dR} \qquad \cdots (14)$$

For a feed of a wide size spread of spherical particles

$$\left.\begin{aligned} \frac{W}{F_o} &= \int_{R^*}^{R\ \text{at}\ t=\infty} \frac{R^3}{\mathcal{R}(R)} \cdot I \left[\int_{R^*}^{R} \frac{p_o(R)\, dR}{R^3 I}\right] dR \\ p_1(R) &= \frac{F_o R^3}{W\cdot \mathcal{R}(R)} \cdot I \left[\int_{R^*}^{R} \frac{p_o(R)\, dR}{R^3 I}\right] \end{aligned}\right\} \cdots \text{where } I = e^{\int_{R^*}^{R} \frac{F_1/W + \kappa(R)}{\mathcal{R}(R)} dR} \qquad \cdots (15)$$

and

$$R^* = \begin{cases} \text{smallest feed size for growing solids} \\ \text{largest feed size for shrinking solids.} \end{cases}$$

For growth from seed of size $R_0 = 0$

$$W = \frac{4\pi \rho_s n_s}{3\,\mathcal{R}(R)} \int_0^\infty R^3 I \, dR \quad \ldots \text{ where } I = e^{-\int_0^R \frac{F_1/W + \kappa(R)}{\mathcal{R}(R)} dR}$$

$$p_1(R) = \frac{4\pi \rho_s n_s}{W \cdot \mathcal{R}(R)} R^3 I \qquad \text{and } n_s = \text{number of seed particles added}/\text{s} \qquad \ldots (16)$$

In a few special cases these equations can be solved analytically; in most cases a numerical procedure must be used. Let us first present some of these analytical solutions, then the general numerical procedure.

F. Mixed flow, one size feed, linear shrinkage, no elutriation.

1. Spherical particles.

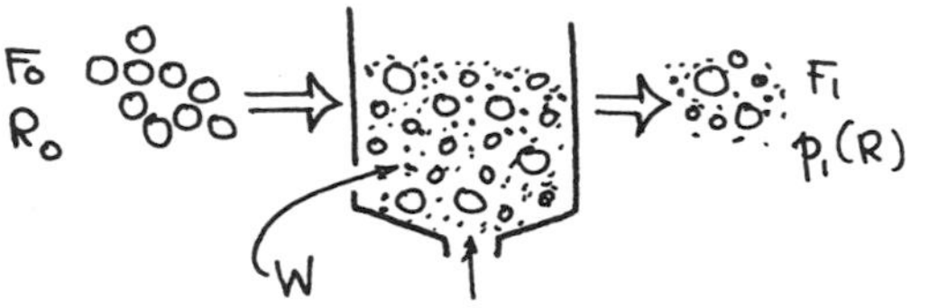

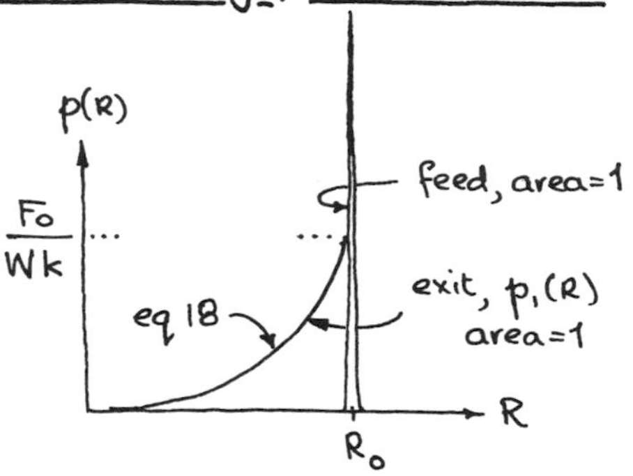

The material balance expressions of eq 14 reduce to

$$\frac{F_1}{F_0} = 1 - 3y + 6y^2 - 6y^3\left(1 - e^{-1/y}\right)$$
$$= \frac{1}{4y} - \frac{1}{20y^2} + \frac{1}{120y^3} - \frac{1}{480y^4} + \cdots \qquad \ldots (17)$$

$$y = \frac{\bar{t}}{\tau} = \left(\frac{W/F_1}{\text{time for complete disappearance of a particle}}\right) = \frac{Wk}{F_1 R_0}$$

$$p_1(R) = \frac{F_0}{Wk}\,\frac{R^3}{R_0^3}\, e^{-\frac{F_1(R_0-R)}{Wk}} \qquad \cdots (18)$$

and

$$\frac{\bar{R}_s}{R_0} = \frac{3y}{F_0/F_1 - 1} = \frac{3Wk}{R_0(F_0-F_1)} \qquad \cdots (19)$$

In the extreme where the particles all shrink to zero and no solids leave the reactor

$$\frac{F_0 R_0}{Wk} = 4 \quad \cdots \text{and} \quad \frac{\bar{R}_s}{R_0} = \frac{3}{4} \qquad \cdots (20)$$

2. Cylindrical particles (fibers).

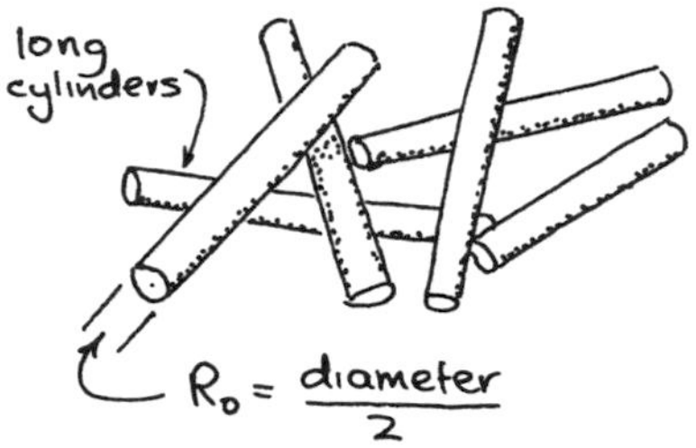

Equation 14 was developed for spherical particles. From the analogous expressions for cylindrical particles we find

$$\left.\begin{aligned}\frac{F_1}{F_0} &= 1 - 2y + 2y^2\left(1 - e^{-1/y}\right)\\ &= \frac{1}{3y} - \frac{1}{12y^2} + \frac{1}{60y^3} - \end{aligned}\right\} \qquad \cdots (21)$$

$$y = \frac{\bar{t}}{\tau} = \frac{Wk}{F_1 R_0}$$

$$p_1(R) = \frac{F_0}{Wk}\cdot\frac{R^2}{R_0^2}\, e^{-\frac{F_1(R_0-R)}{Wk}} \qquad \cdots (22)$$

In the extreme where all particles shrink to zero and no solids leave the reactor

$$\frac{F_0 R_0}{Wk} = 3 \qquad \cdots (23)$$

3. Flat plate particles.

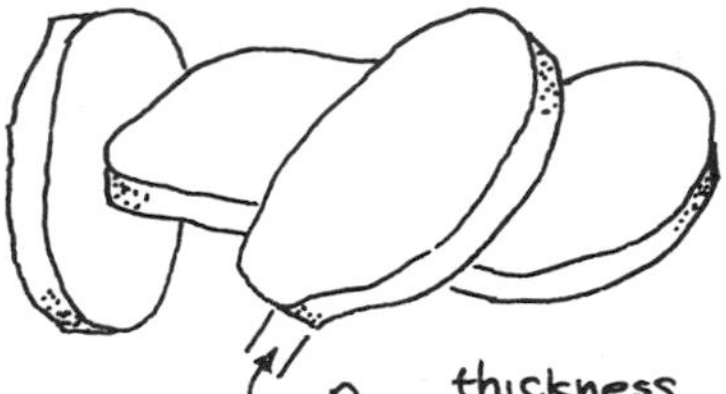

The general expression analogous to eq 14 reduces for this case to the following

$$\left.\begin{aligned} \frac{F_1}{F_0} &= 1 - y\left(1 - e^{-1/y}\right) \\ &= \frac{1}{2y} - \frac{1}{6y^2} + \frac{1}{24y^3} - \end{aligned}\right\} \quad \cdots (24)$$

$$y = \frac{Wk}{F_1 R_o}$$

$$p_1(R) = \frac{F_o}{Wk} \cdot \frac{R}{R_o} e^{-\frac{F_1(R_o - R)}{Wk}} \quad \cdots (25)$$

In the extreme where the particles all react to completion, and all disappear

$$\frac{F_o R_o}{Wk} = 2 \quad \cdots (26)$$

G. Mixed flow, one size feed, reciprocal shrinkage, no elutriation, spherical particles.

For high temperature combustion of small particles we have reciprocal shrinkage, the smaller the particle the faster it shrinks. For this situation we show

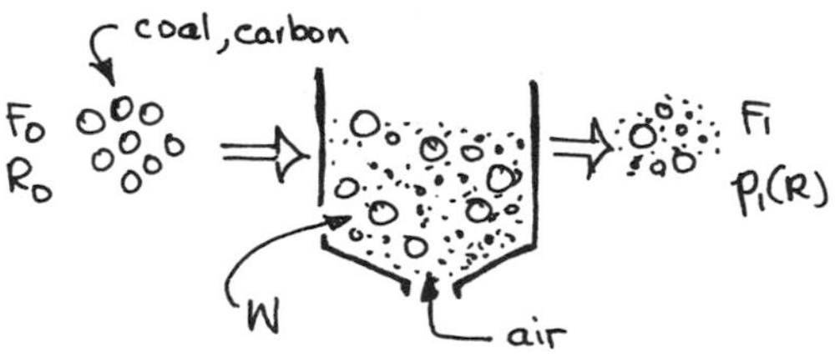

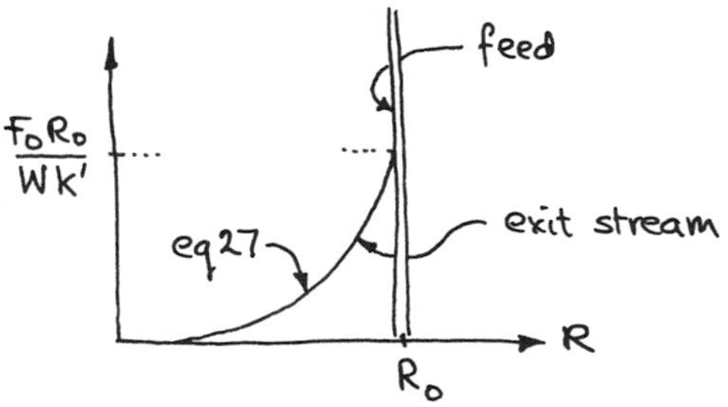

Solving the general shrinkage expression, eq 14, with the kinetics of reciprocal shrinkage, eq 3, and putting $K(R)=0$ gives

$$p_1(R) = \frac{F_0}{Wk'} \cdot \frac{R^4}{R_0^3} e^{-\frac{F_1(R_0^2-R^2)}{2Wk'}} \qquad \cdots \quad (27a)$$

with

$$\int_0^{R_0} p_1(R)\, dR = 1 \qquad \cdots \quad (27b)$$

Evaluating numerically the relationship between variables in eq (27a) so as to satisfy the condition of eq (27b) gives the following pairs of values

$y' = \frac{Wk'}{F_1 R_0^2}$	0.01	0.02	0.05	0.1	0.2	0.5	1	2	5	10
F_1/F_0	0.97	0.94	0.86	0.73	0.55	0.31	0.17	0.093	0.039	0.020

In addition

$$\frac{R_0}{\bar{R}_s} = \frac{F_1}{F_0}\left(1 - 2y' + 2y' e^{-1/2y'}\right) \qquad \cdots \quad (28)$$

In the extreme where no solids leave the system (complete carbon burn-up) these expressions reduce to

$$p_1(R) = \frac{F_0}{Wk'} \cdot \frac{R^4}{R_0^3} \qquad \cdots \quad (29)$$

$$\frac{F_0 R_0^2}{Wk'} = 5 \qquad \cdots \quad (30)$$

and the two mean measures of mean size of solids in the bed are found to be

$$\frac{\bar{R}_s}{R_0} = \frac{4}{5} \quad \cdots \text{and} \cdots \quad \frac{\bar{R}_w}{R_0} = \left(\frac{2}{5}\right)^{1/3} = 0.74 \qquad \cdots \quad (31)$$

H. General shrinkage process for particles in mixed flow, any feed (one size or a size spread), any shrinkage kinetics, with elutriation

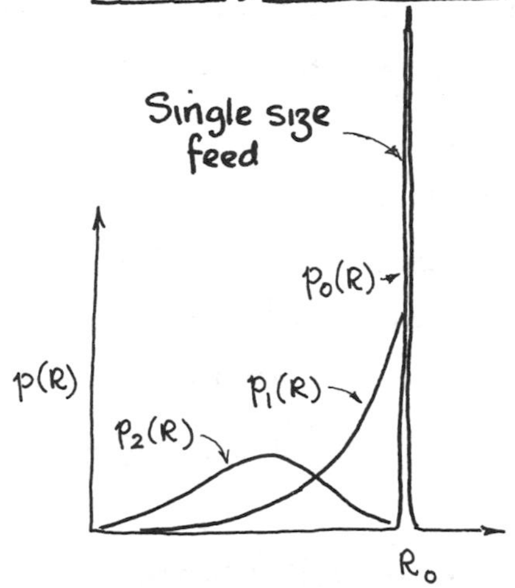

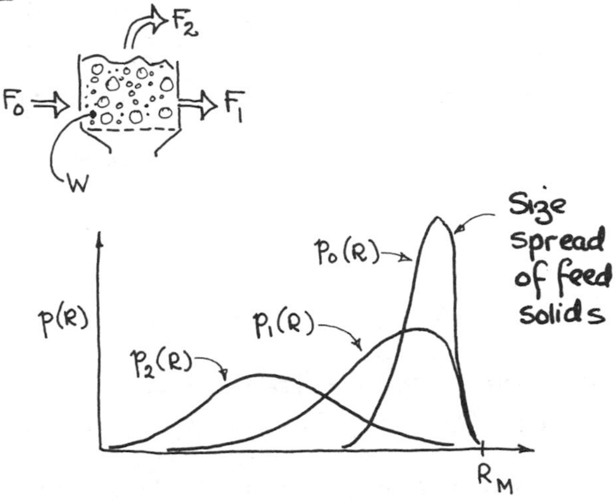

The more general cases pictured above cannot be solved analytically as were cases **F** and **G** so we must use a numerical procedure. The working equations are the rearrangement of the discrete analogs of eqs 11~13 written in the language of the discrete size distribution defined on pg 1 of chapter 52. Thus we have

negative (refers to $\mathcal{R}(R_{i+1})$)

$$\frac{F_1(R_i)}{F_1} = \frac{W(R_i)}{W} = \frac{F_o(R_i)\Delta R_i - \frac{W}{F_1} F_1(R_{i+1})\,\mathcal{R}(R_{i+1})}{-W\mathcal{R}(R_i) + F_1\Delta R_i + W\cdot\mathcal{K}(R_i)\Delta R_i - \frac{3W}{R_i}\mathcal{R}(R_i)\Delta R_i} \quad \cdots (32)$$

$$\sum \frac{F_1(R_i)}{F_1} = \sum \frac{W(R_i)}{W} = 1 \quad \cdots (33)$$

"3" for spheres
"2" for cylinders
"1" for flat plate particles

$$F_1 + F_2 - F_o = 3W \sum_i \frac{F_1(R_i)\,\mathcal{R}(R_i)}{F_1 \cdot R_i} \quad \cdots (34)$$

$$F_2(R_i) = W \cdot \frac{F_1(R_i)}{F_1}\,\mathcal{K}(R_i) \quad \cdots (35)$$

The **recommended calculation procedure** is as follows:

1. Choose reasonable size intervals ΔR_i, either all equal or based on the screen sizes being used. Then find the mean radius in each interval: $R_1, R_2, R_3, \cdots, R_i, \cdots, R_n$, where R_n is that interval which contains the **largest** size of feed solid.

2. Guess F_0, F_1 or W, whichever is unknown.

3. Evaluate the composition of the outflow stream $F_1(R_i)/F_1$ from eq 32. Be sure to put $F_1(R_{n+1})=0$, and start with size interval R_n working downward to R_{n-1}, R_{n-2}, and so on.

4. See if eq 33 is satisfied. If it is continue to step 5. If not go back to step 2 and guess again.

5. Evaluate the flow rate, kg/s, of total elutriated stream F_2 from eq 34.

6. Evaluate the composition of the carryover stream $F_2(R_i)$ from eq 35.

All is now known: F_0, F_1, F_2, and the three size distributions.

Overturf and Kayihan (Pow. Tech <u>23</u> 143 (1979)) recommend using the above procedure and warn of the dangers of what looks like a reasonable alternative – that of taking and using the discrete analog of the exact **integrated** expression, eq 14. Following that route may lead to very large errors unless very many size slices are taken, in some cases up to 3000. On the other hand, the procedure presented here is simpler, more direct, and gives reasonable answers with not too many size slices, say 10 or 20.

This procedure can be used with any shrinkage kinetics and any particle shape, and it can be extended to particles of changing density without difficulty.

I. Mixed flow, linear growth from seed of $R_o=0$, no elutriation.

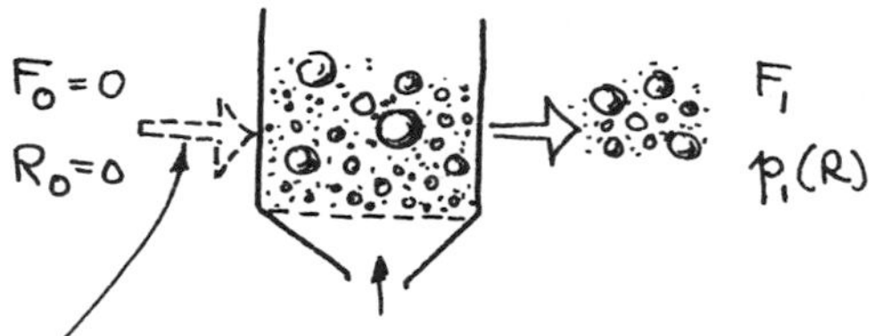

introduce n_s seed particles of size zero/s

$$n_s = \frac{F_o}{\frac{4}{3}\pi R_o^3 \rho_s} \qquad \text{or} \qquad \frac{F_o}{R_o^3} = \frac{4}{3}\pi \rho_s n_s$$

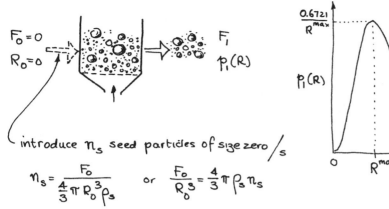

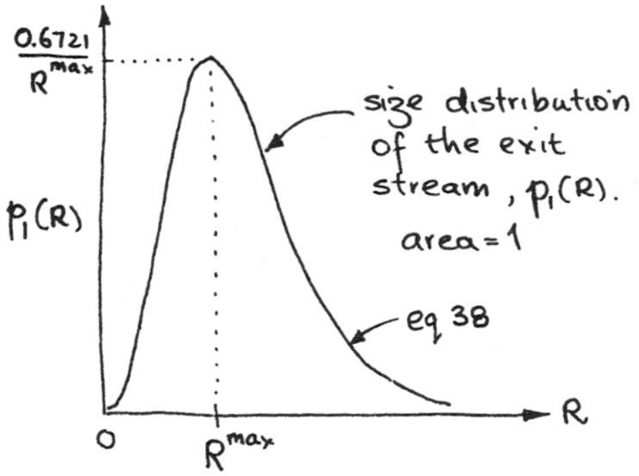

For this situation the material balance of eq 16 reduces to

$$F_1^4 = 8\pi n_s \rho_s W^3 k^3 \qquad \cdots (36)$$

$$R^{max} = \bar{R} = \frac{3Wk}{F_1} \qquad \cdots (37)$$

$$\left.\begin{aligned} p_1(R) &= \frac{1}{2R^{max}}\left(\frac{3R}{R^{max}}\right)^3 e^{-3R/R^{max}} \quad , m^{-1} \\ &= \frac{4\pi n_s \rho_s}{3Wk} R^3 e^{-F_1 R/Wk} \end{aligned}\right\} \qquad \cdots (38)$$

$$\left.\begin{aligned} W &= \frac{4\pi \rho_s n_s}{3k}\int_0^\infty R^3 e^{-F_1 R/Wk}\, dR \\ &= \frac{F_1 R^{max}}{6k}\int_0^\infty \left(\frac{3R}{R^{max}}\right)^3 e^{-3R/R^{max}}\, d\left(\frac{R}{R^{max}}\right) \end{aligned}\right\} \qquad \cdots (39)$$

J. Mixed flow, one size of spherical feed, linear growth, no elutriation.

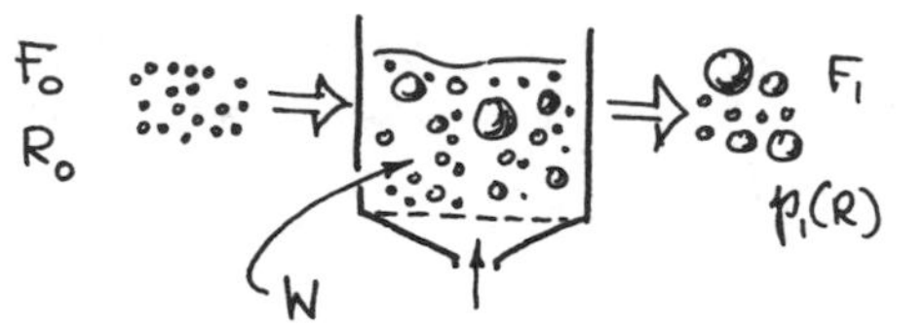

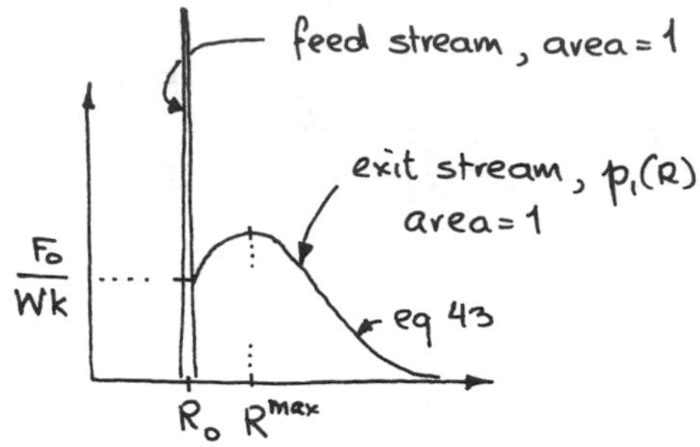

With $\kappa(R)=0$, $\mathcal{R}(R)>0$ and only one entering feed size eq 15 simplifies greatly and can be integrated explicitly. Thus

$$\frac{F_1}{F_0} = 1+3y+6y^2+6y^3 \quad \ldots \text{where } y = \frac{Wk}{F_1 R_0} \qquad \ldots (40)$$

$$\frac{R^{max}}{R_0} = 3y \qquad \ldots (41)$$

$$\frac{\overline{R}_s}{R_0} = \frac{3y}{1-F_0/F_1} = \frac{3Wk}{R_0(F_1-F_0)} \qquad \ldots (42)$$

$$p_1(R) = \frac{F_0}{Wk} \cdot \frac{R^3}{R_0^3} e^{-\frac{F_1(R-R_0)}{Wk}} \quad \ldots \text{and } R > R_0 \qquad \ldots (43)$$

K. Mixed flow, one size of spherical feed, linear growth, preferential removal of larger particles, no elutriation.

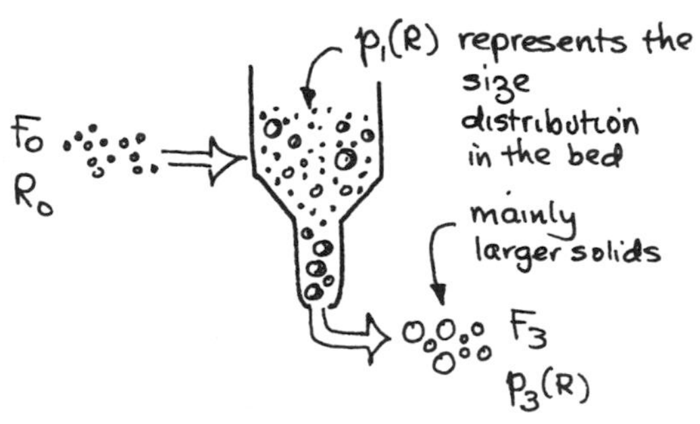

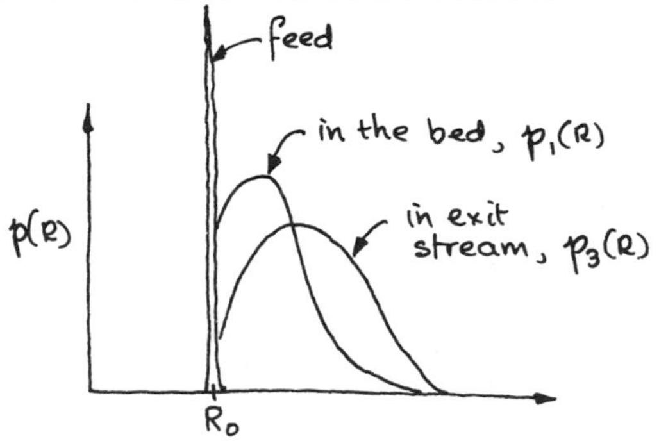

Look at the preferential removal of the larger solids as an "upside down" elutriation, thus

$F_1 = 0$, and $\kappa(R)$ increases with particle size

At present I know of no experimentally based expression for $\kappa(R)$, but some simple forms may well be

$$\kappa(R) = AR, \qquad \kappa(R) = AR^B, \qquad \kappa(R) = A + BR$$

Some of these cases can be solved analytically. Here is one:

For $R_0 = 0$ (or zero seed size), linear growth and $\kappa(R) = AR$ we find, on insertion into eq 16:

$$W = \frac{8\pi}{3} \cdot \frac{\rho_s n_s k}{A^2} \qquad \cdots (44)$$

$$F_3 = \rho_s n_s \left(\frac{2\pi k}{A}\right)^{3/2} \qquad \cdots (45)$$

$$p_1(R) = \frac{A^2}{2k^2} \cdot R^3 \cdot e^{-AR^2/2k} \qquad \cdots (46)$$

$$p_3(R) = \left(\frac{2}{9\pi}\right)^2 \left(\frac{A}{k}\right)^{5/2} \cdot R^4 e^{-AR^2/2k} \qquad \cdots (47)$$

$$\left(\text{Number of particles in the bed}\right) = n_s \left(\frac{\pi}{2kA}\right)^{1/2} \qquad \cdots (48)$$

$$\left.\begin{aligned} \bar{R}_w \text{ (in the bed)} &= \left(\frac{8}{\pi}\right)^{1/6} \left(\frac{k}{A}\right)^{1/2} \\ \bar{R}_w \text{ (in the exit)} &= \left(\frac{9\pi}{2}\right)^{1/6} \left(\frac{k}{A}\right)^{1/2} \end{aligned}\right\} \cdots \frac{\bar{R}_w \text{ (bed)}}{\bar{R}_w \text{ (exit)}} \cong \frac{3}{4} \qquad \cdots (49)$$

$$\bar{R}_s \text{ (in the bed)} = \left(\frac{8k}{\pi A}\right)^{1/2} \qquad \cdots (50)$$

K. General growth process for particles in mixed flow, any feed (seed, one size or spread of sizes), any growth kinetics, with elutriation or preferential removal of larger solids.

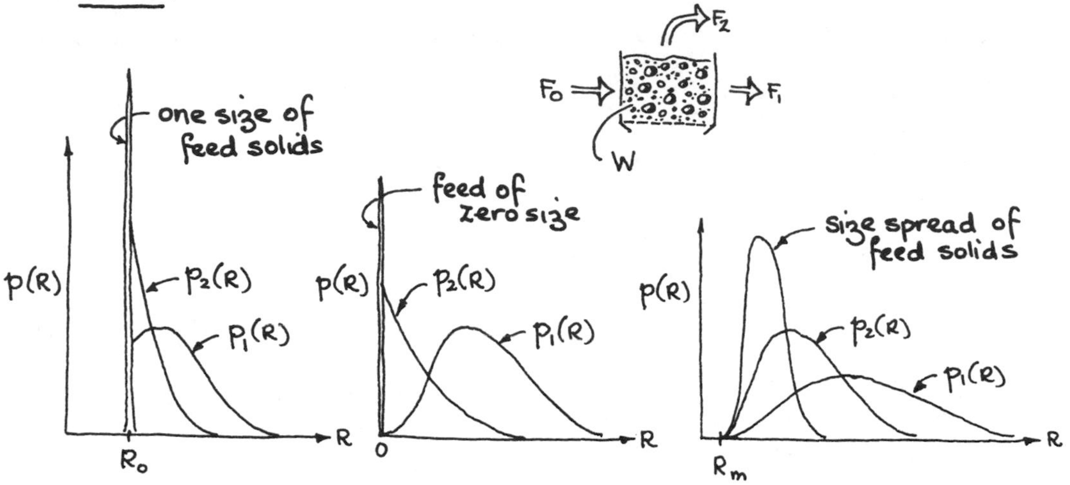

The more general cases pictured above require a numerical procedure to find the flows and size distributions. The working equations come from the discrete analogs of eq 11~13 and are

(ℛ: positive)

$$\frac{F_1(R_i)}{F_1} = \frac{F_0(R_i)\Delta R_i + \frac{W}{F_1} F_1(R_{i-1})\, \mathcal{R}(R_{i-1})}{W\mathcal{R}(R_i) + F_1\Delta R_i + W\kappa(R_i)\Delta R_i + \frac{3W}{R_i}\mathcal{R}(R_i)\Delta R_i} \quad \cdots (51)$$

$$\sum_i \frac{F_1(R_i)}{F_1} = 1 \quad \cdots (52)$$

"3" is for spheres
"2" for cylinders (fibers)
"1" for flat plates

$$F_1 + F_2 - F_0 = 3W \sum_i \frac{F_1(R_i)\,\mathcal{R}(R_i)}{F_1 \cdot R_i} \quad \cdots (53)$$

$$F_2(R_i) = \frac{W}{F_1} F_1(R_i) \cdot \kappa(R_i) \quad \cdots (54)$$

Since $F_1(R_i)/F_1 = W(R_i)/W$ for mixed flow of solids the above expressions can be written in terms of W instead of F_1 when needed, for example when $F_1 = 0$.

The **recommended calculation procedure** is as follows:

1. Choose reasonable size intervals ΔR_i, either all equal or based on the screen sizes being used. Then find the mean radius in each interval: $R_1, R_2, R_3, \cdots, R_i, \cdots$, where R_1 is the interval which contains the **smallest** size of feed solid.

2. Guess F_0, F_1 or W, whichever is unknown.

3. Evaluate the composition of the outflow stream $F_1(R_i)/F_1$ from eq 51. Start with size interval R_1 working upward to $R_2, R_3, \cdots$. Note that $F_1(R_0) = 0$, and continue calculating $F(R_i)$ values until the $F(R_i)$ value drops to zero.

4. See if eq 52 is satisfied. If it is continue to step 5. If not go back to step 2 and guess again.

5. Evaluate the flow rate of carryover stream, F_2 kg/s, from eq 53.

6. Evaluate the composition of carryover stream $F_2(R)$ from eq 54.

All is now known; the flows, bed weight, and size distributions.

As with shrinking solids, Overturf and Kayihan find this procedure simpler and more accurate than the others which have been proposed (see Kunii and Levenspiel chapter 14). See section H on shrinking solids for more discussion on this matter.

IV. General Procedure for Shrinking Particles.

So far we have focused exclusively on the changing solid and have ignored the gas composition. In G/S reactions which lead to particle shrinkage we may have, for example,

$$A(g) + bB(s) \longrightarrow \text{gaseous products, with } -\frac{1}{S_{ex}}\frac{dN_A}{dt} = k_s C_A$$

(k_s: rate constant for the SCM, reaction control, m/s.)

Thus

$$k = \frac{b k_s \bar{C}_A}{\rho_B}$$

(k: rate constant for linear shrinkage, m/s; ρ_B: mol B/m^3)

So when we have to account for the changing gas environment (since C_A influences k) we must use a two phase analysis. For this the material balance is given by

$$\underbrace{F_{A0}\left(1-\frac{C_{Af}}{C_{A0}}\right)}_{\text{disappearance of A, mol/s}} = \frac{1}{b} F_{B0} X_B = \underbrace{\frac{F_0}{b(mw)_B}\left(1-\frac{F_1}{F_0}\right)}_{\text{disappearance of B, mol/s}} \quad \ldots (55)$$

(F_{A0}: mol A/s; F_{B0}: mol B/s)

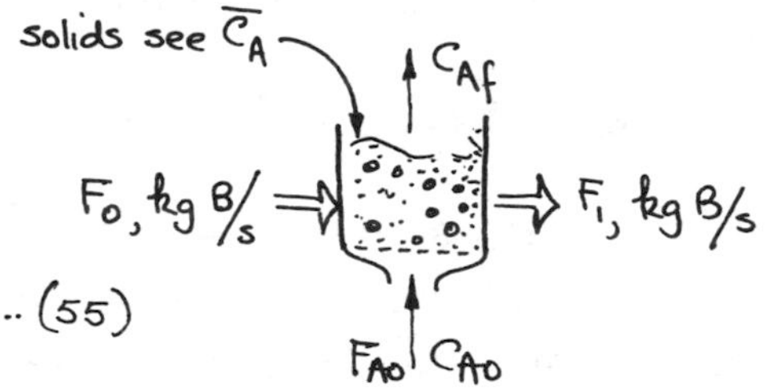

The overall G/S material balance is solved by using the equations of sections F to H with the methods of chapter 53. for the particular flow pattern of gas in the bed. In essense guess $\bar{C}_A$, treat the solid, treat the gas, and then see whether the material balance is satisfied.

V. General Design Procedure for Growing Particles.

For deposition of solid on the particles, say by reaction,

$$A(g) \xrightarrow{\text{on the surface}} b'B(s) \quad \text{...... kg or mols deposited} / \text{unit surface}$$

The rate constant k depends on the gas environment, for example

$$k = k' \overline{C}_A$$

Again a two phase analysis relates the disappearance of A in the gas to the generation of solid, thus

$$kg/s \longrightarrow \underbrace{F_{Ao}\left(1 - \frac{C_{Af}}{C_{Ao}}\right)}_{\text{disap. of } A} = \underbrace{\frac{F_o}{b'}\left(\frac{F_i}{F_o} - 1\right)}_{\text{generation of } B,} \quad kg/s \qquad \cdots (56)$$

Solve by combining the equations for section I through K, with the methods of chapter 53.

In some cases k is independent of the gas composition, and is only dependent on the temperature. Here the two phase analysis is unnecessary; just treat the solids alone

VI. Circulation System with Growing and Shrinking Particles.

Suppose that solids circulate between two mixed flow reactors, growing in one unit, shrinking in the other, with linear kinetics in both units, or equations (1) and (2). Graphically we represent this sort of operation as follows.

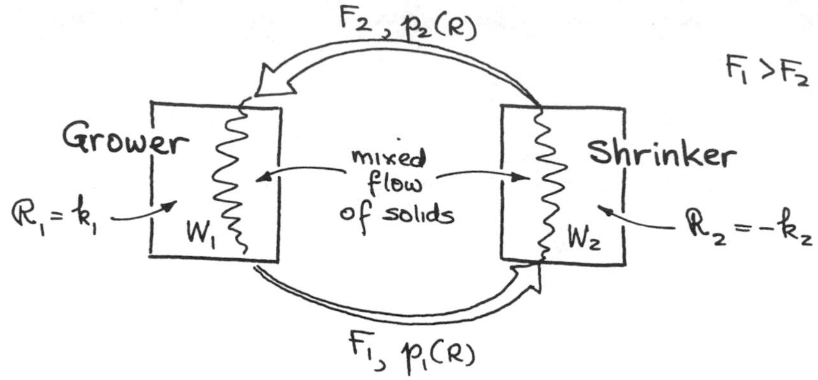

Analytic solution of the material balance equations shows that the following conditions must be met to achieve steady state operations

1. $W_1 k_1 = W_2 k_2$. The size ratio of reactors is inversely proportional to the kinetics in these units. Thus the slower process needs the larger reactor.

2. Seed must be added to the grower to offset the disappearance of particles in the shrinker. We define the seed rate as

$$n'_s = \left(\frac{\text{number of seed particles added to the grower}}{\text{volume of solids entering the grower}}\right)$$

3. The flows, bed weights and seed rate are related by

$$\left(\frac{F_1 - F_2}{F_2}\right)^4 = 6 n'_s \left(\frac{W_2 k_2}{F_2}\right)^3 \quad \cdots (57)$$

4. The size distribution is the same everywhere (in grower, shrinker, and transport lines) and is given by

$$p_1(R) = p_2(R) = \frac{1}{2 R^{max}} \left(\frac{3R}{R^{max}}\right)^3 e^{-3R/R^{max}} \quad \cdots (58)$$

where $R^{max} = \bar{R} = \dfrac{3 W_1 k_1}{F_1 - F_2}$

This may surprise you because on first thought you may expect smaller particles in the shrinker and larger particles in the grower. But think about it awhile and you may convince yourself.

The size distribution at steady state is shown at the right.

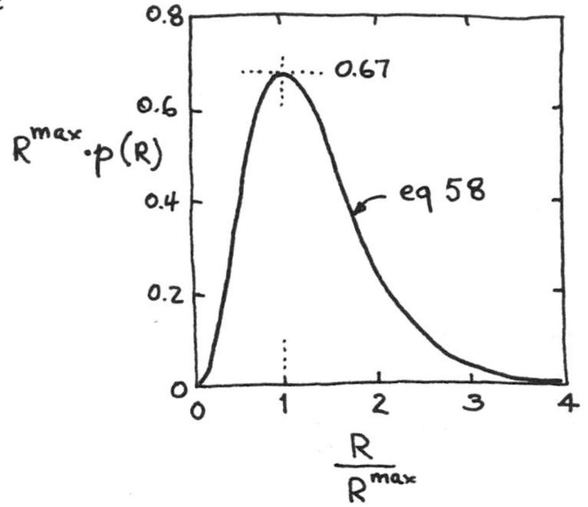

Comments.

(a) All the variables of the circulation system are interrelated. Change one and you affect all the others.

(b) Preliminary analysis suggests that this circulation system is inherently unstable, and must be continuously controlled. This can be done by adjusting the seed rate, by shifting part of the solids from unit to unit, changing the rate constants, and so on.

(c) This type of operation has interesting commercial possibilities. For example, in the cracking of crude oil, instead of using expensive catalyst, having carbon deposit on it, and then burning off the carbon, why not circulate carbon particles, letting them grow in the cracker, shrink in the regenerator? The K-K process presently under development by Japan Gasoline is just such a process.

VII. Discussion of Growth and Shrinkage Kinetics.

A. Mechanism of particle growth from seed.

Suppose a gas is introduced into an environment where it decomposes to produce solid, for example

$$SiH_4 \binom{\text{cool}}{\text{gas}} \xrightarrow[\text{environment}]{\text{in hot}} Si(s)\downarrow + 2H_2$$

At first the individual molecules of solid are dispersed throughout the reactor. How do they grow? Theory suggests that different mechanisms dominate and take over as the particles grow. Very briefly, since this is a major subject of study in itself,

1. **Coagulation**. Initially the molecules come together and fuse by the joint action of Brownian motion and van der Waals forces. In this regime the growth rate of particles is found to be

$$\frac{dR}{dt} = \frac{2kTf_s}{3\pi\mu R^2} \quad \cdots \text{ or } \quad \frac{dR}{dt} \propto R^{-2} \qquad \cdots (59)$$

(k = Boltzman constant; μ = viscosity; f_s = volume fraction of solids in G·S mixture)

By the time the particles grow to 0.1 μm they are so few and far apart (from the standpoint of Brownian motion) that the growth rate drops by a factor of 10^8 and the next mechanism becomes important.

2. **Coalescence** Here the distortion and kneading of the fluid eddies brings the particles together. In this regime the growth rate of particles is represented by

$$\frac{dR}{dt} = \frac{2f_s}{\pi} \cdot \frac{u\,Re^{1/2}\,R}{d_t} \quad \cdots \text{ or } \quad \frac{dR}{dt} \propto R \qquad \cdots (60)$$

(Re = Reynolds number; d_t = vessel diameter)

The following sketch shows this shift in mechanisms

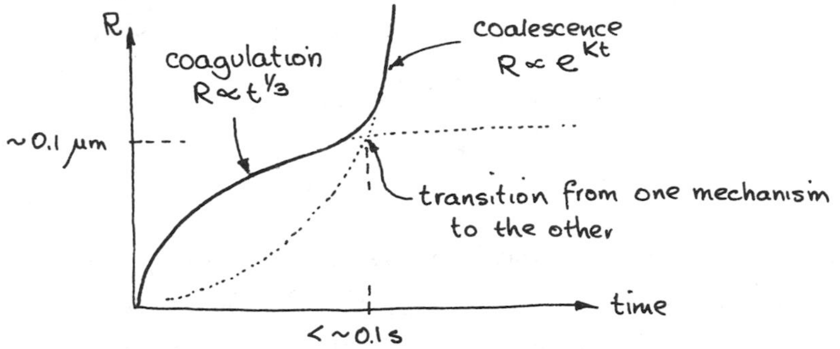

3. <u>Growth of larger particles</u>. When the particles reach ~10 μm they begin to grow primarily by either of the following mechanisms

(a) **Condensation**. Here individual molecules condense on the surface of the larger particles, often by dendritic growth. Molecular diffusion through the film around the particle controls here and the rate of growth is

$$\frac{dR}{dt} = \frac{\mathcal{D} C_B}{R \rho_s} \quad \cdots \text{ or } \quad \frac{dR}{dt} \propto \frac{1}{R} \qquad \cdots (61)$$

density of solid (ρ_s); diffusion coefficient and concentration of individual condensing molecules in the gas ($\mathcal{D}$, C_B)

(b) **Impaction**. Here the large particles sweep up and collect the finer particles, those smaller than ~10 μm. This is a vacuum cleaner effect and it represents the movement and action of large particles as they move through hazy smoky or foggy gas. For one size of smaller to be collected particles the growth rate of the larger particles is represented by

$$\frac{dR}{dt} = \frac{\Delta u \, f_s}{4} \quad \cdots \text{ or } \quad \frac{dR}{dt} = k \qquad \cdots (62)$$

$\frac{dR}{dt}$: growth rate of larger particles; Δu: relative velocity between larger particles and fines; f_s: volume fraction of fine solids in the hazy gas

4. <u>Summary</u>. The above discussion suggests that the growing particle passes through the following kinetic regimes

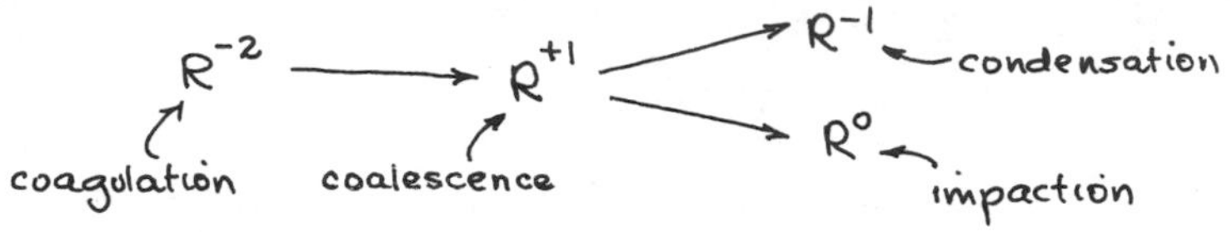
R^-2
R^+1
R^-1
R^0
condensation
coagulation
coalescence
impaction

The first two processes, coagulation and coalescence, are over very quickly (less than a second in most cases) thus the mechanism which dominates through most of the life of a particle is either condensation or impaction.

Theory thus suggests that **growing particles** are likely to follow **linear or reciprocal growth kinetics**, as expressed by

$$\mathcal{R}(R) = k \quad \cdots \text{ or } \quad \mathcal{R}(R) = \frac{k'}{R} \qquad \cdots (63)$$

For more on the mechanisms of particle growth see Levich chapters 1 and 5.

B. <u>Mechanism of particle shrinkage</u>.

The particle shrinks either because solid material vaporizes or because the solid reacts with a gaseous component which diffuses to the surface, for example

$$\text{C (particle)} + O_2 \left(\begin{matrix}\text{in surrounding} \\ \text{air}\end{matrix}\right) \longrightarrow CO_2 \text{ (gas)}$$

Thus the slow step of the process is either reaction at the surface or diffusion of gaseous reactant to the surface of the particle.

1. <u>Reaction control</u>. Here the rate of shrinkage is given by

$$-\frac{d\left(\begin{matrix}\text{volume of} \\ \text{particle}\end{matrix}\right)}{dt} = k_s \left(\begin{matrix}\text{surface of} \\ \text{particle}\end{matrix}\right)$$

or

$$\frac{dR}{dt} = -k \; ; \qquad \frac{t}{\tau} = 1-(1-X_B)^{1/3} \; ; \qquad \tau = \frac{\rho_B R_o}{b\, k_s\, C_{Ag}} \qquad (64)$$

Even when a thin layer of ash forms on a shrinking particle and continually flakes off the particle behavior follows reaction control kinetics, despite the fact that the main resistance may lie in the thin ash layer.

2. Film diffusion control. For high temperature processes such as combustion surface reaction is so fast that film diffusion becomes the slow and controlling step.

The rate coefficient for film diffusion depends on particle size, and typically for particles in free fall the well known correlation of Froessling, Gerland Beitr. Geophys. 52 170 (1938).

$$\frac{k_g d_p y}{\mathscr{D}} = 2 + 0.6\left(\frac{d_p u \rho}{\mu}\right)^{1/2}\left(\frac{\mu}{\rho \mathscr{D}}\right)^{1/3}$$

- k_g: mass transfer coefficient, see beginning of chapter 51.
- "2": for large particles drop this term
- $0.6(\ldots)^{1/2}(\ldots)^{1/3}$: for small particles drop this term
- $y = 1$ for diffusion through inert
- y = log mean mole fraction across the film of the inert in equimolar counter diffusion

The rate and conversion-time behavior of shrinking particles then shows the following extremes:

Small particles, film diffusion control.

$$-\frac{dR}{dt} = \frac{k'}{R} \; ; \qquad \frac{t}{\tau} = 1-(1-X_B)^{2/3} \; ; \qquad \tau = \frac{\rho_B R_o^2}{2b\mathscr{D} C_{Ag}} \qquad \cdots (65)$$

Large particles, film diffusion control

$$-\frac{dR}{dt} = \frac{k'}{R^{1/2}} \; ; \qquad \frac{t}{\tau} = 1-(1-X_B)^{1/2} \; ; \qquad \tau = (\text{const.})\frac{R_o^{3/2}}{C_{Ag}} \qquad \cdots (66)$$

3. Intermediate regime. Where both film and reaction resistances influence the rate we have

$$\frac{1}{S_{ex}}\frac{dN_A}{dt} = \frac{1}{\frac{1}{k_g}+\frac{1}{k_s}}\,C_{Ag}$$

thus

$$\frac{t}{\tau_{total}} = \left[1-(1-X_B)^{2/3}\right]\frac{\tau_{film}}{\tau_{total}} + \left[1-(1-X_B)^{1/3}\right]\frac{\tau_{reaction}}{\tau_{total}} \qquad \cdots (67)$$

this coefficient is for small particles. Use 1/2 for large

$\tau_{total} = \tau_{film} + \tau_{reaction}$

C. Other empirical rate expressions.

When linear or reciprocal kinetics do not reasonably represent the changing particle size other equation forms must be tried. Some of the simpler ones for shrinking particles are

First order shrinkage to a minimum size: $\mathcal{R}(R) = -k'(R-R_{min})$ ··· (68)

First order shrinkage: $\mathcal{R}(R) = -k'R$ ··· (69)

For growing particles

First order growth to a maximum size: $\mathcal{R}(R) = k'(R_{max}-R)$ ··· (70)

For some simple situations (single feed size, no elutriation) the material balance expressions for some of these rate expressions can be integrated analytically. However, the numerical procedures of eqs 32~35 and 51~54 can always be used.

Chapter 54 Problems

A1 Sugar is very expensive nowadays so I intend to buy Cuban sugar balls (crude brown sugar, very cheap), add them continuously with water to a large stirred tank, remove the thick syrup continuously, then crystallize and purify elsewhere to obtain refined sugar. The imported sugar balls are 1 cm in size, take 1 hour to dissolve in the tank, and I estimate that my small backyard unit can hold about 0.4 tons of dissolving sugar balls at any time.

(a) How many tons of sugar balls will I be able to treat per day?

(b) I just received word that the next batch of sugar balls will be 2 cm in size. What does this do to my treatment rate?

A2 One sad day the highly effective, but highly toxic fire retardant PBB (polybrominated biphenyl) was accidentally mixed with a batch of animal feed which was used on Michigan farms. This resulted in about 30,000 sick cows which had to be destroyed because of the contaminated meat. But what to do with the carcasses since no Michigan community wanted them buried nearby and no neighboring states would allow them in?

Here is a thought: why not cremate them in a fluidized sand bed incinerator since the high temperature in such a unit would break down the PBB to harmless chemicals. Now there happens to be a large fluidized sand incinerator handy into which the cows could be coaxed one by one to be nicely roasted to completion. How long would it take to dispose of the contaminated cows in this manner?

Data: Cows average 400 kg and under good fluidizing conditions would take up 30% of the 12 m^3 bed volume and would incinerate to completion in 12 hours, with linear shrinkage.

A3 Solid waste from a large lumber mill is burned to produce process steam. The solid waste from this operation consisting of cinders and ash (0.1 m^3/min, 80% cinders) goes to a final cleanup fluidized burner. There the cinders burn to completion by the reaction $C + O_2 \rightarrow CO_2$, while the ash which is much denser (8 to 1) falls through the air distributor (spaced bricks) and is removed.

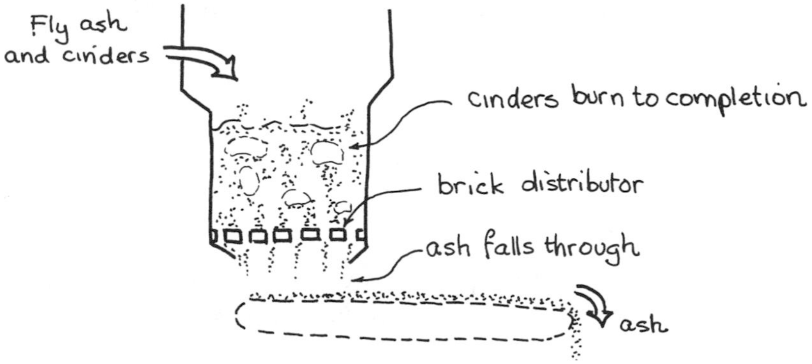

If the fluidized burner contains 10 m^3 of cinder-ash mixture (84% ash, bed voidage = 50%) find the time needed for a typical cinder particle to burn to completion.

A4 Kabel tells us in Chem. Eng. Educ. **13** 70 (1979) that the Saudi Arabians are considering lassoing wild roaming icebergs in Antarctica, taming them and then towing them to their main port, Jidda, as a source of fresh water. Naturally, some of the ice will melt during the trip home, but how much? If a captured iceberg has a mass of 10^8 tons and if it is towed at a speed of 0.5 m/s throughout its 9000 km trip to captivity estimate what fraction of the original iceberg will arrive at Jidda.

(a) Assume a spherical iceberg.

(b) Assume a flattish iceberg roughly 100 m thick.

Additional information:

$\rho_{ice} = 900$ kg/m^3 $\lambda_{melting} = 333000$ J/kg $T_{water} = 15$ °C
$h = 70$ W/m^2·K, for all iceberg surfaces

In principle Motorola's process for preparing ultra pure silicon is very simple. Just combine silicon with SiF_4 in one reactor, and then change the conditions in a second reactor so as to reverse the reaction

$$Si(s) + SiF_4(g) \underset{\text{reactor II}}{\overset{\text{reactor I}}{\rightleftharpoons}} 2SiF_2(g)$$

The plan is to produce 140 kg/hr of pure silicon in a 2 fluidized reactor process as sketched.

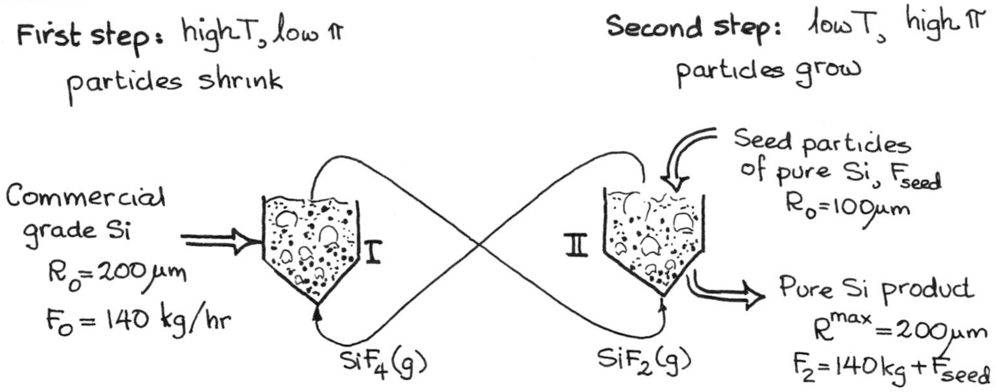

Commercial grade silicon (R = 200 μm) is fed to reactor **I** while seed particles of pure silicon (R_{seed} = 100 μm) are fed to reactor **II**.

A5 . . . In reactor **I** the particle radius shrinks by 20 μm/hr. If the particles stay in the reactor until they are all consumed find the size of reactor **I** needed.

A6 . . . In reactor **II** the particle radius grows by 100 μm/hr. From this information find the size of reactor **II** and the seed introduction rate needed if the most common size of exiting solids, R^{max}, is to be 200 μm.

J.C. Schumacher and Co. proposes to produce highly pure silicon from crude starting material by the following shift reactions

$$Si(s) + 2H_2(g) + 3SiBr_4(g) \underset{\text{reactor II, } 750\sim800\,°C}{\overset{\text{reactor I, } 550\sim650\,°C}{\rightleftharpoons}} 4SiHBr_3(g)$$

Suppose their process involves the two fluidized bed system as shown on the next page.

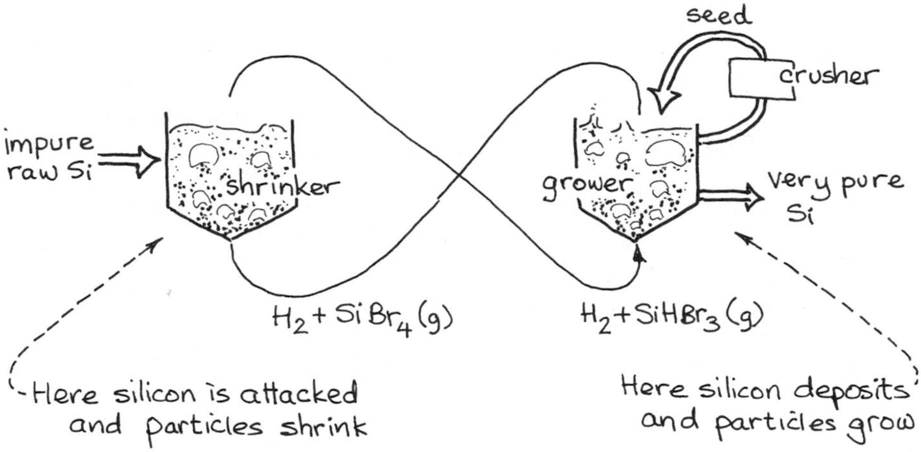

A7* . . . How much solid must the shrinker hold for a feed rate of 200 kg/hr of d_p = 1000 μm silicon particles if the shrinkage rate of silicon in the reactor environment is 500 μm diameter/hr? Solve by the numerical procedure outlined in this chapter taking 5 size slices, and then check your answer with the exact expression given in this chapter.

A8 . . . Suppose the fluidized bed grower had an efficient device which removed particles as soon as they reached 1000 μm diameter in size. Some of this product stream is then broken down to d_p = 200 μm particles and returned to the reactor as seed. The remainder, 200 kg/hr, then leaves as product. If the particle diameter grows at 400 μm/hr how much solid must the reactor hold?

Chapter 54 Problems

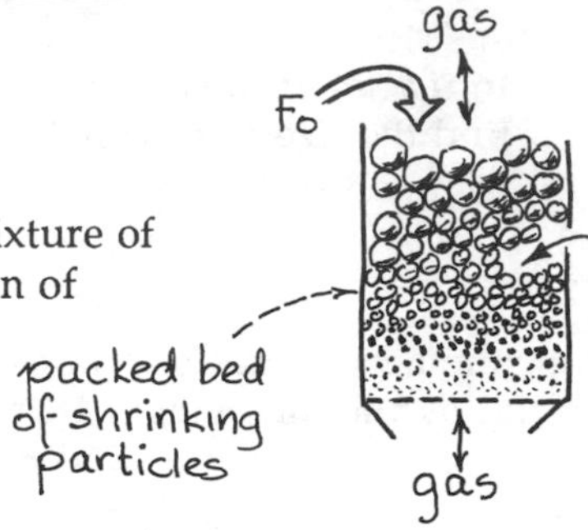

A9 A solid is attacked by gas as follows

$$A(g) + B(s) \rightarrow \text{gaseous product}$$

We wish to treat F_0 = 10 tons/hr of a size mixture of solids in a filter reactor. The size distribution of feed solids is

20% of d_p = 2 mm
30% of d_p = 1 mm
50% of d_p = 0.5 mm

The time for complete conversion of a d_p = 1 mm particle is 24 min, and the composition of the gas changes very little in passing through the bed. What will be the weight of the packed bed of shrinking and disappearing solids?

A10 Nonporous particles (d_p = 0.2 mm, ρ_s = 2 gm/cm³) are introduced at the bottom of a vertical transport line reactor (F_s = 8 kg/s), and are carried upward while reacting away with the carrier gas

$$A(g) + B(s) \rightarrow \left(\begin{matrix}\text{gaseous}\\ \text{products}\end{matrix}\right), \qquad \begin{matrix}\text{time for complete reaction of}\\ \text{a feed particle} = 10 \text{ s}\end{matrix}$$

A 400 cm² filter screen is placed at the exit of the reactor to trap any unreacted solids and allow them to react to completion. At steady state, assuming plug flow of solids, and a 5 second flight time of solids from entry to the filter,

(a) find the mass of solids in flight

(b) find the thickness of solid deposited on the filter (voidage of filter cake ε = 0.5).

A11 Battelle is developing a continuous process for making ultra pure silicon for solar cell applications based on the reaction

$$2Zn(g) + SiCl_4(g) \rightarrow 2ZnCl_2(g) + Si(s)$$

Gaseous reactants in separate streams enter a fluidized bed of silicon particles, combine and deposit silicon on the surface of the particles which then grow. Fresh seed particles are added continuously to the bed and product solids are removed continuously.

At 1200 K, just above the boiling point of zinc, the reaction is fast enough so that the deposition rate of solid depends primarily on the feed rate of gaseous reactants. For this special situation find the size distribution and mean sizes $\bar{R}$ and R^{max} of solids produced in a 100 kg bed and find the growth rate constant k for a seed stream of 1 kg/hr of 100 μm particles, and a silicon production rate of 78 kg/hr, thus F_1 = 79 kg/hr.

Chapter 54 Problems

B12 In a fluidized coal burner lumps of coal burn, ash flakes off, and the particles shrink down to nothing. However, because of the high fluidizing velocities used in these burners part of the coal could blow out of the bed before it has burned up, thereby affecting carbon utilization.

Find the carbon utilization of a 1 mm feed stream if a particle takes 50 s to burn away, and does so by linear shrinkage, if the elutriation constant is given by

$$\kappa(R) = (20\ \mu m/s)R^{-n} \quad \text{where } n = 1,$$

and if no unburned coal leaves with the ash stream.

Comment: Normally n = 2 ~ 3 however we choose n = 1 here to simplify the problem.

B13 The Nerva nuclear rocket of the 1960's was to be powered by a bundle of cylindrical fuel rods. This bundle would be made to go critical, hydrogen would be pumped along the rods, would get extremely hot, and would discharge at very high velocity giving enormous thrust. These rockets were to be man's long distance space explorers, going to Jupiter, Saturn, and beyond, maybe even to α-Centauri. But the project was scrapped and the fuel rods for these rockets, all 30,000 of them, are at Jackass Flats, Nevada, awaiting final disposal.

The fuel rods are graphite cylinders about 20 mm in diameter, 1.32 m long sprinkled with enriched uranium, worth over $100,000,000. At this price it is well worth recovering the uranium. The simplest scheme is to burn the rods and recover the uranium from the ash. For this the Idaho National Engineering Laboratory has constructed a fluidized bed 400 mm ID 3.3 m high containing 60 mesh alumina particles.

How long would it take to dispose of these 30,000 rods if they were dropped into the reactor one by one and allowed to burn to completion, if they did not break up but just became thinner and thinner, if only 2% of the reactor volume is allowed to consist of rods, and if each rod takes 4 hours to burn to completion with reaction controlled kinetics?

Chapter 55 KINETIC MODELS FOR THE REACTION OF SOLIDS.

The shrinking core model (SCM) is the most widely used and the most important of models. However it can only fit some of the many types of solid reactions. In searching for an appropriate model we should use all relevant information, from reaction chemistry to a physical examination of the pellet. Here are some of the clues to look for

- Is the particle porous or not?
- Does the porosity change during reaction?
- On slicing a pellet do you see a core of reactant surrounded by a shell of product?
- Does reaction produce a flaky product?
- Is reaction a straight thermal decomposition and not a G/S reaction, for example $CaCO_3 \xrightarrow{heat} CaO(s) + CO_2(g)$
- Is reaction a straight chemical action between constituents of the solid, for example solid rocket propellents which contain their own bound oxygen?
- Is it a reaction between two solids?
- Is it a reaction between two solids and a gas, for example

$$\underset{\text{particles}}{C(s)} + \underset{\text{particles}}{ZrO_2(s)} + Cl_2(g) \longrightarrow ZrCl_4(g) + CO_2(g)$$

and so on ...

What we need are simple models which can adequately describe and follow the behavior of reacting particles, and by 'simple models' we mean those whose predictions can be obtained by relatively simple mathematics, and whose parameters can be fitted directly by experiment

Let us outline some of the proposed models, starting with the shrinking core model.

A. SCM – the shrinking core model

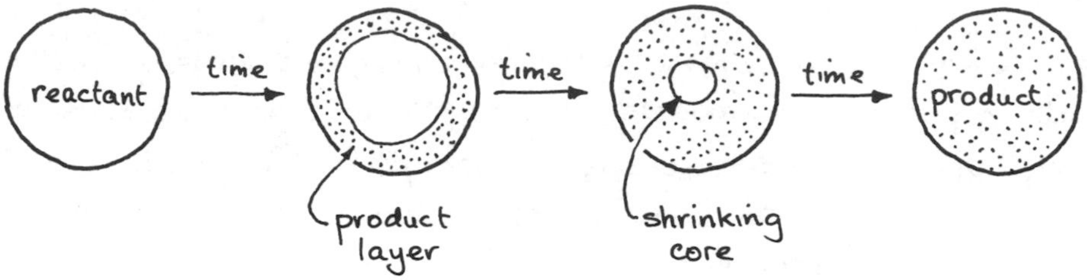

(a) For either extreme of reaction control or ash diffusion control the SCM is a one parameter model with either τ_{rx} or τ_{ash} as the characteristic time. From chapter 51 we find

$$SCM_{\text{reaction control}} \quad \text{gives} \quad \tau_{obs} = \tau_{rx} \propto R$$

$$SCM_{\text{ash diffusion control}} \quad \text{gives} \quad \tau_{obs} = \tau_{ash} \propto R^2$$

Graphically, we have for these extremes

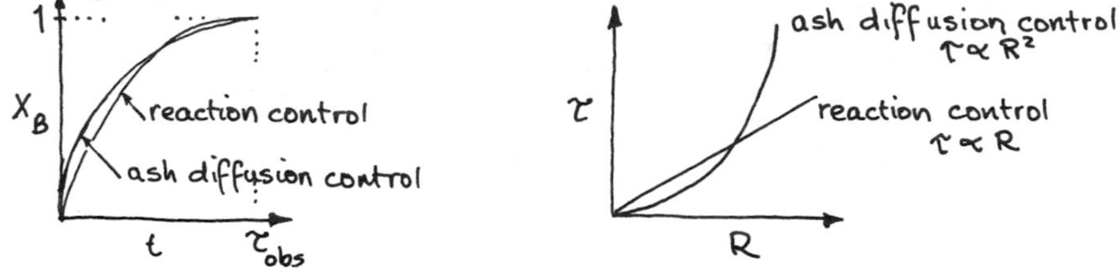

(b) **Shift in controlling mechanism**: as a pellet is being converted the controlling mechanism could shift to ash diffusion. The opposite does not occur. The reason for this is that the pellet starts with no ash layer, hence no resistance to ash diffusion. So overall, if ash diffusion control is observed it means that at low conversion of that pellet some other resistance must have controlled, but that the shift occured at such low X_B that we did not notice it. Graphically

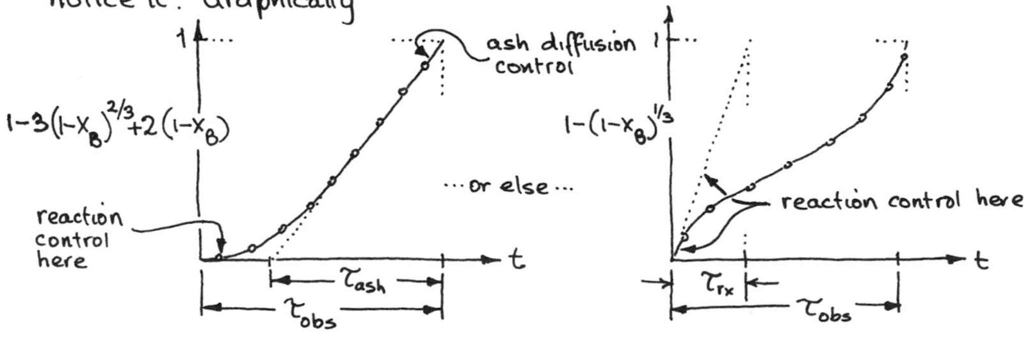

(c) Different controlling mechanisms for different particle sizes:

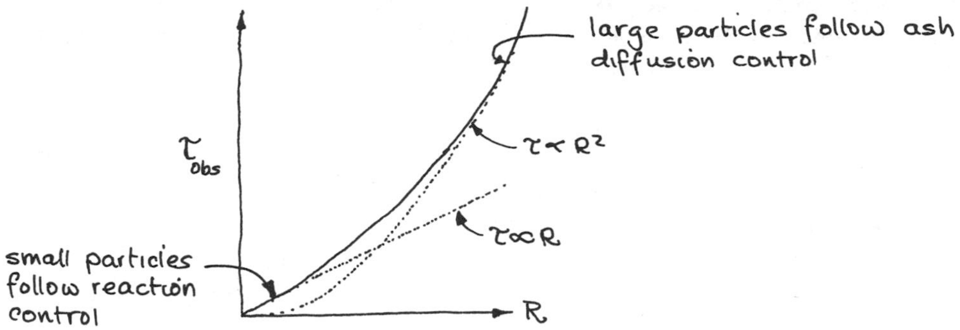

(d) The SCM is a phenomenological model, consequently many possible mechanisms of action and types of solid can give this observed behavior, for example both porous and non porous solids, reactions of solid with or without gas, etc.

(e) The SCM cannot account for S-shaped conversion-time behavior

(f) The SCM predicts that 100% conversion of solid will be achieved in a reasonable time, or twice the time it takes to get to 87% conversion. It cannot account for situations where the conversion seems to level off at a value below 100%.

For the first English language presentation of this model see Yagi & Kunii, pg 231.

B. UCM – the uniform conversion model.

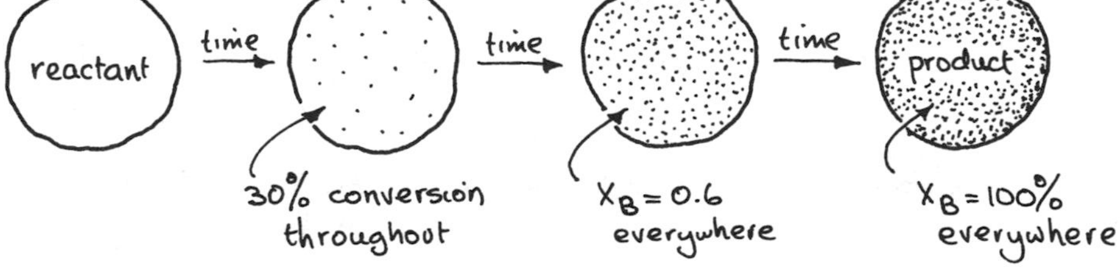

(a) The UCM is a one parameter model and many different mechanisms can give this observed behavior. Thus all sorts of conversion-time progressions and all sorts of R vs τ relationships can give rise to the UCM.

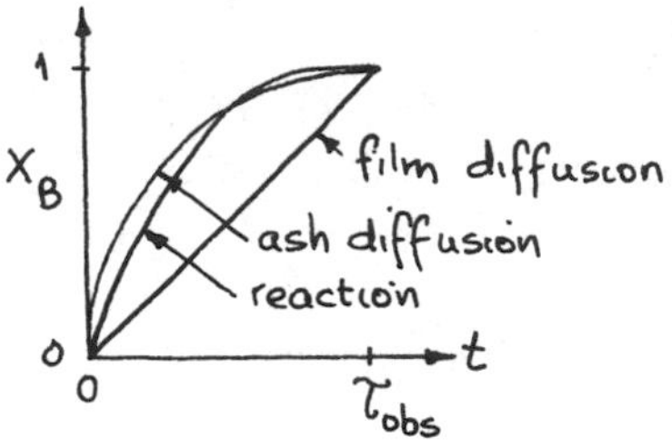

the UCM can give all these variations

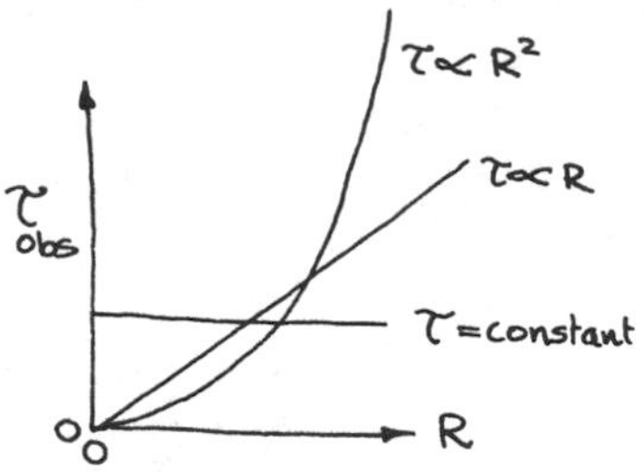

We will meet all these forms of the UCM as extremes of other models which we treat below.

C. GPM the grainy pellet model.

This is a simple representation of the reaction of porous solids

Assume that each pellet consists of spherical grains of solid, all of the same size. Assume no size change with reaction, thus no change in pellet voidage.

Assume that each grain reacts away according to the SCM with either ash diffusion or reaction control.

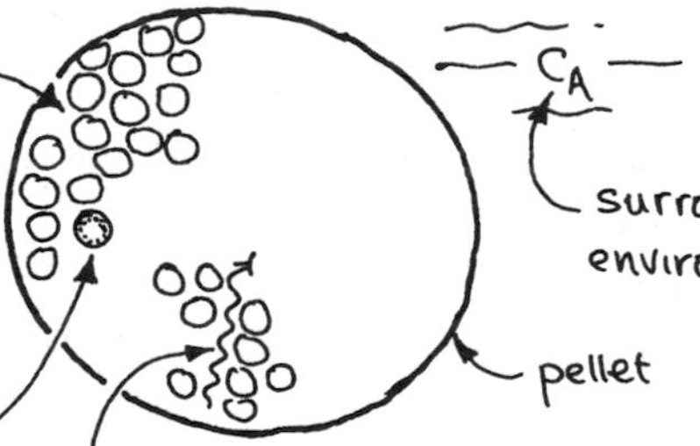

The movement of gaseous reactant between the grains into the pellet is subject to diffusional resistance

(a) The GPM is a two parameter model whose characteristic times are

τ_{grain} = time for complete conversion of a grain in a C_A environment.

τ_{diff} = time for complete conversion of a particle by diffusion if $\tau_{grain} = 0$

this assumes that the only resistance to the conversion of the pellet is that of diffusion of gaseous reactant between the grains

(b) At the extreme where $\tau_{diff} \ll \tau_{grain}$, thus negligible diffusion resistance, all the grains react away at the same time and in the same way. Here

- you observe the UCM
- X_B vs t follows the SCM with reaction or ash diffusion control.
- $\tau_{obs} = \tau_{grain}$ and this is independent of R.

This extreme is characteristic of small pellets.

(c) At the extreme where $\tau_{diff} \gg \tau_{grain}$

- you observe the SCM, with ash diffusion control
- $\tau_{obs} = \tau_{diff} \propto R^2$.

(d) In the intermediate regime, and this is the general case, both diffusion between grains and the conversion of grains influence the rate and you end up with behavior as shown in the sketches below.

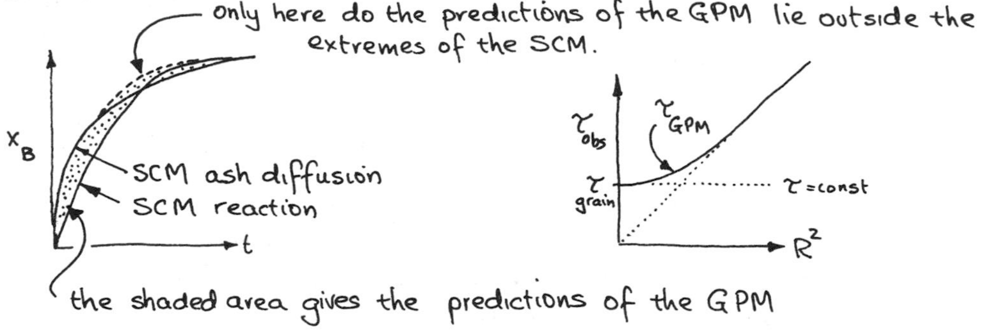
only here do the predictions of the GPM lie outside the extremes of the SCM.
X_B
SCM ash diffusion
SCM reaction
t
the shaded area gives the predictions of the GPM
τ_{obs}
τ_{GPM}
τ_{grain}
τ = const
R^2

(e) In most part the X_B vs t behavior of the GPM is sandwiched by the SCM curves, the R vs τ predictions are somewhat different, but then only for small R. In the intermediate regime the GPM requires a computer to generate the X_B vs t curves.

(f) The GPM can account for observations between the SCM and the UCM, it cannot account for S-shaped conversion-time behavior, and it cannot represent systems where the conversion levels off below 100%.

For more on models of porous reacting solids see

Sohn and Szekely CES 27 763 (1972); 29 630 (1974).
Ishida and Wen AIChE J 14 311 (1968).
Tien and Turkdogen Met. Trans. 3 2039 (1972).
Pigford and Sliger IEC/PDD 12 85 (1973).

D. CCM – the crackling core model.

This model represents particles which start as non-porous but become porous on reaction.

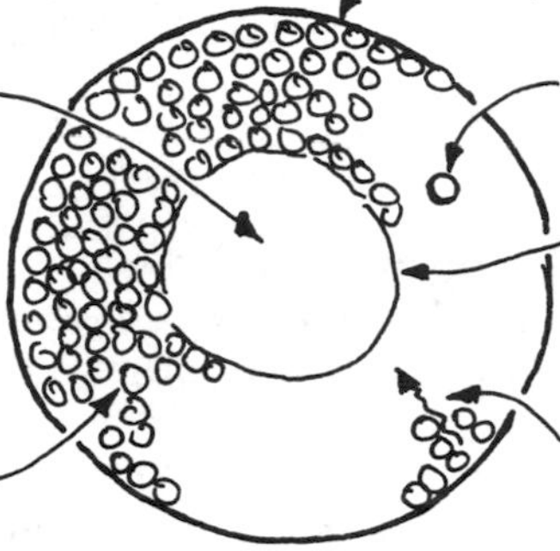

the pellet
Original non porous reactant material
The original solid crackles, crazes and fractures to form a porous structure which is looked upon as a grainy material
each grain reacts further by the SCM
the core shrinks as the crackling front advances inward
assume no diffusional resistance between the grains

(a) The CCM is a two parameter model whose parameters are the characteristic times:

τ_{core} = time for the crackling front to reach the center of the pellet, or time for the non porous material to be completely converted to grainy porous solid

τ_{grain} = time for complete conversion of a grain.

Sometimes the crackling represents a physical step alone, sometimes it is the first step of a two step reaction.

(b) At the extreme where $\tau_{core} \ll \tau_{grain}$, or fast crackling and slow grain conversion

- you observe the UCM
- X_B vs t follows the SCM with reaction or ash diffusion controlling.

- $\tau_{obs} = \tau_{grain}$, and this is independent of R.

This extreme is characteristic of small particles.

(c) At the extreme where $\tau_{core} \gg \tau_{grain}$, or slow crackling

- you observe the SCM
- X_B vs t follows the SCM with reaction control.
- $\tau_{obs} = \tau_{core} \propto R$

This extreme is characteristic of large particles.

(d) At the extreme where $\tau_{grain} \rightarrow \infty$ so that the particle only experiences the crackling step to some intermediate conversion in the time span of the experiment or of the observation

- you observe the SCM
- X_B vs t follows the SCM, reaction control, to a final conversion less than 100%
- $\tau_{obs} = \tau_{core} \propto R$

(e) In the intermediate regime the CCM gives the following behavior

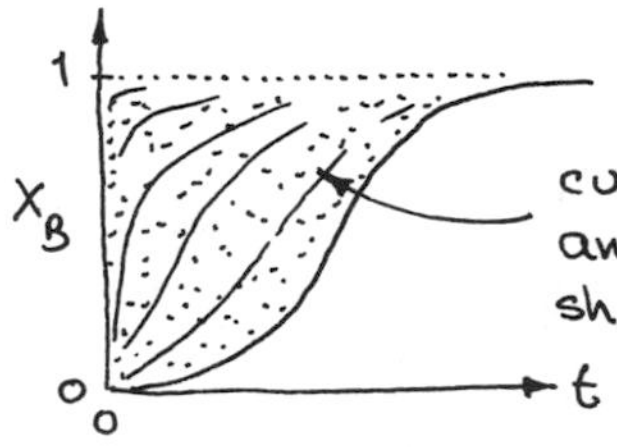

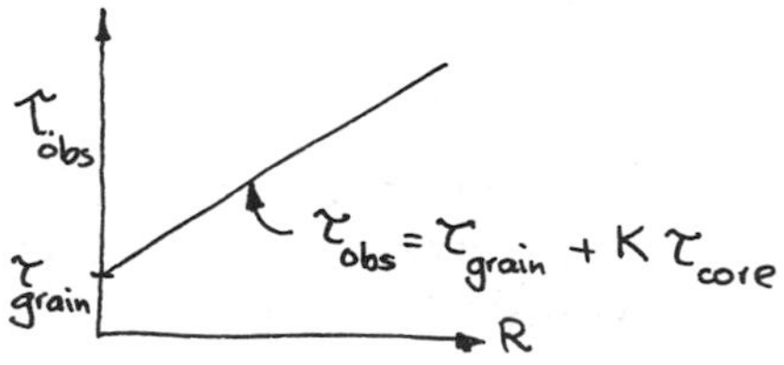

(f) The CCM can account for a one step reaction if the crackling step is a physical change, or a two step reaction.

(g) The general conversion-time expressions for this model are algebraic and need no computer solutions.

(h) The CCM can account for S-shaped conversion-time data which none of the earlier model can account for.

(i) The CCM can account for conversion curves which level off at less than 100% conversion. For example where $\tau_{grain} > \tau_{core}$ and $\tau_{grain} \to \infty$ you can view the two steps as occurring successively in time, the second step being so slow that it is not observed at all. Thus,

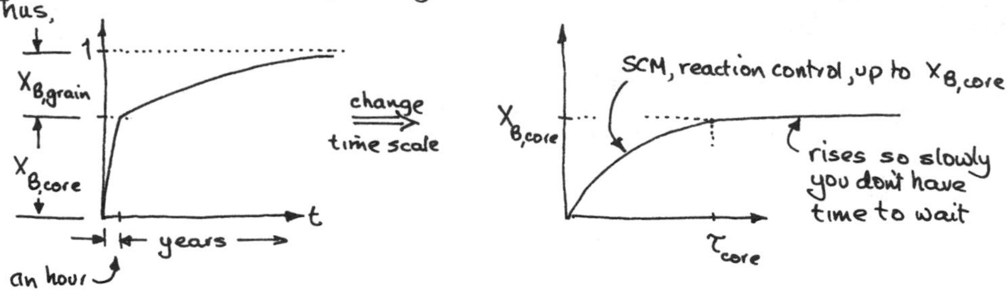

This sort of behavior is observed when the reaction of grains gives a product which becomes impervious to gas before the whole grain can react away, leaving islets of unreacted solid scattered throughout the pellet.

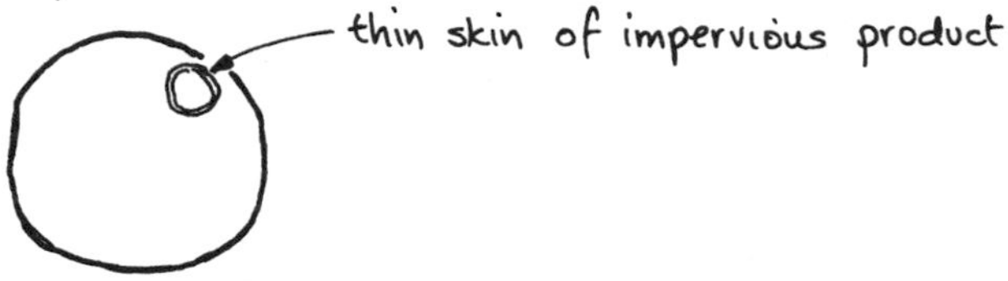

(j) The CCM can account for observations between the SCM and the UCM.

(k) The CCM is a special case of the CVM where you start with a non porous pellet and where the diffusional resistance in the grainy structure is negligible, except very close to the reaction front.

For more on this type of model see
Park and Levenspiel CES <u>30</u> 1207 (1975).

E. CVM – the changing voidage model.

Consider a grainy porous solid whose molar volume changes with reaction. The grains of the particle either swell or shrink as conversion advances. This changes the pellet voidage as well as the diffusional resistance between grains.

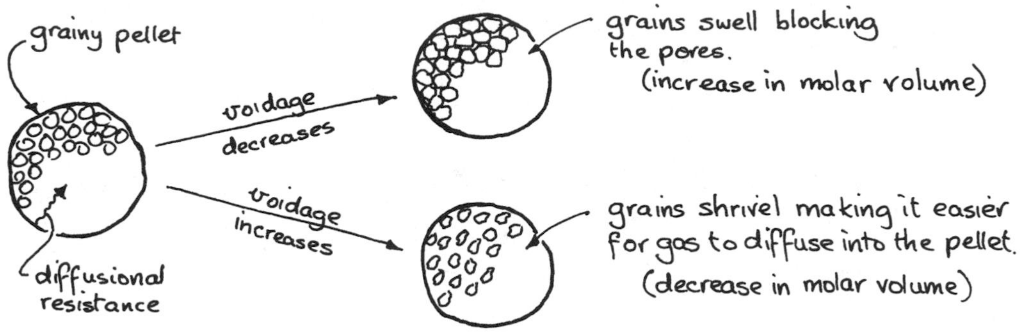
grainy pellet
diffusional resistance
voidage decreases
voidage increases
grains swell blocking the pores.
(increase in molar volume)
grains shrivel making it easier for gas to diffuse into the pellet.
(decrease in molar volume)

The CVM extends the GPM to situations where the diffusional resistance changes with extent of reaction.

Let us first relate the voidage ϵ, diffusivity between grains $\mathscr{D}$, and conversion of solid X_B. For this start with a solid of voidage or porosity ϵ_0 which consists of reactant B and inert I, let the reaction be

$$B(s) \longrightarrow sS(s),$$

and let the molar volumes of materials be V_B, V_S, V_I (where V_B = m³ B/mol B, V_S = m³S/mol S, V_I = m³ of inert present with each mole of B).
We now have two cases to treat.

Case 1 **Particle becomes more porous with reaction but stays of constant size.** Here the relationship between voidage and conversion is

$$X_B = \frac{\epsilon - \epsilon_0}{1-\epsilon_0}\left[\frac{V_B + V_I}{V_B - sV_S}\right] \quad \cdots \text{or} \quad \epsilon = \epsilon_0 + (1-\epsilon_0)X_B\left[\frac{V_B - sV_S}{V_B + V_I}\right]$$

Various relationships between $\mathscr{D}$ and ϵ can be suggested. Let us take the simplest which says that if the voidage doubles so does the diffusion coefficient, or

$$\frac{\mathscr{D}}{\mathscr{D}_0} = \frac{\epsilon}{\epsilon_0}$$

(a) The CVM is a two parameter model whose characteristic times are

τ_{grain} = time for complete conversion of a grain in a C_A environment.

τ_{diff} = time for complete conversion of a particle if $\tau_{grain} = 0$.

The initial voidage ϵ_o and the molar volumes are properties of the system.

(b) At the extreme where ϵ does not change this model reduces to the GPM.

(c) If you start with a practically non porous particle then $\mathscr{D}$ starts very small and reaction is very slow. As the pores open up the process speeds up enormously. Since the resistance to the opening of the pores dominates the process the reaction front moves slowly into the pellet, and so the conversion-time behavior approximates the SCM or CCM.

(d) Overall then the X_B vs t behavior for this model lies between the GPM (little change in ϵ) and the SCM or CCM (if $\epsilon_o \cong 0$). If the precise curves are wanted ... then back to the computer.

<u>Case 2</u>. **<u>Particle becomes less porous with reaction but stays of constant size.</u>** If the particle size remains unchanged the voidage decreases, the diffusivity between grains drops, and eventually reaction can stop. In terms of the molar volumes we then have

$$X_B = \frac{\epsilon_o - \epsilon}{1-\epsilon_o}\left[\frac{V_B + V_I}{sV_S - V_B}\right] \quad \longleftarrow \text{the relationship between voidage and conversion}$$

and reaction stops when the voidage decreases to zero, thus when the conversion reaches

$$X_{B,max} = \frac{\epsilon_o}{1-\epsilon_o}\left[\frac{V_B + V_I}{sV_S - V_B}\right]$$

Note that these expressions refer to the conversion at any point in the particle. If reaction is fast compared to diffusion then $X_{B,max}$ will be reached in a thin shell at the outside if the particle, pore blocking will occur there and the mean conversion of the whole pellet will be considerably below $X_{B,max}$. If reaction is slow then the whole pellet will reach $X_{B,max}$.

In real systems the reaction may slow down enormously, but may not stop completely. Also the voidage may decrease close to zero but never become zero. In light of this consider the following picture.

Regime 1. Voidage decreases to ϵ_{min} while the particle size stays unchanged, or

$$\left.\begin{array}{l}\epsilon \longrightarrow \epsilon_{min} \\ \mathcal{D} \longrightarrow \mathcal{D}_{min}\end{array}\right\} \text{ some voids always remain in the particle.}$$

Regime 2. Beyond the point where the particle voidage reaches ϵ_{min} the particle as a whole swells while the voidage stays at ϵ_{min} and the conversion slowly rises.

In regime 1 assume linear behavior. This gives

$$X_B = \frac{\epsilon_0 - \epsilon}{1-\epsilon_0}\left[\frac{V_B + V_I}{sV_S - V_B}\right] \quad \cdots \text{ and } \quad \frac{\mathcal{D}}{\mathcal{D}_0} = \frac{\epsilon}{\epsilon_0}$$

Transition between regimes occurs at

$$X_{B,transition} = \frac{\epsilon_0 - \epsilon_{min}}{1-\epsilon_0}\left[\frac{V_B + V_I}{sV_S - V_B}\right]$$

Finally, in regime 2 we have

$$\epsilon = \epsilon_{min} \quad \text{and} \quad \mathcal{D} = \mathcal{D}_{min}.$$

(a) Again, as with case 1, this is a two parameter model with V_i, $\mathcal{D}_o$, $\mathcal{D}_{min}$, ϵ_o and ϵ_{min} as measurables.

(b) The X_B vs t curve will look as follows

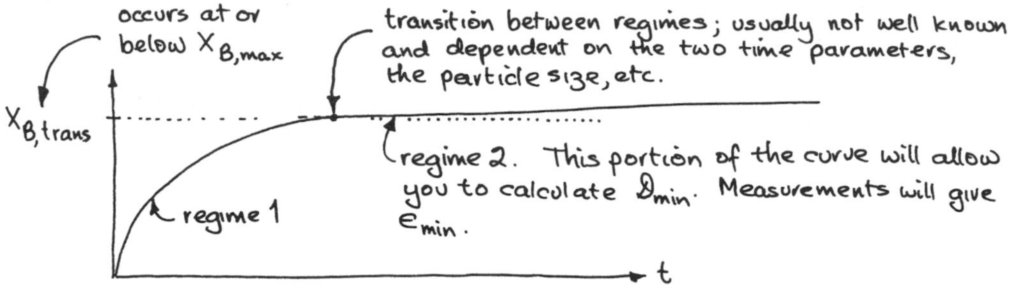
occurs at or below $X_{B,max}$
transition between regimes; usually not well known and dependent on the two time parameters, the particle size, etc.
$X_{B,trans}$
regime 2. This portion of the curve will allow you to calculate $\mathcal{D}_{min}$. Measurements will give ϵ_{min}.
regime 1
t

(c) If the particle as a whole expands while in regime 1 then the transition will not occur at the expected X_B. Since such expansion is difficult to measure it is probably best to find $X_{B,trans}$ from experiment and then adjust the term in the [···] brackets accordingly.

(d) Many variations of the assumptions of this type of model can be attempted. We stayed with the simplest, using linear relationships wherever possible. Unfortunately, even for these the conversion–time curves can only be obtained by computer. For more on this type of model see
Hartman and Coughlin AIChE J **22** 490 (1976)
IEC/PDD **13** 248 (1974).

Another type of CVM – the single pore model.

This model characterizes the porous particle by a typical cylindrical or flat plate pore. It views that the mouth of the pore either opens up or progressively plugs up as a result of the voidage change. The single pore model is quite a bit easier to deal with than the model described above. For more on this see:

Chu CES **27** 367 (1972)
Ramachandran and Smith AIChE J **23** 353 (1977)
Lee IEC/PDD **19** 242 (1980)

F. TDM – thermal decomposition models.

Case 1. Solid/solid reactions not involving any gaseous component.

Consider the endothermic reaction

$$B(s) \longrightarrow S(s) \qquad \cdots \Delta H_r > 0$$

Phase rule then requires that

$$P + V + R_x = C + 2 \quad \cdots \text{or} \quad 2 + V + 1 = 2 + 2 \quad \cdots \text{or} \quad V = 1$$

(one degree of freedom)

This means that we cannot arbitrarily set the pressure and temperature and expect to find B and S in equilibrium. If we operate at some set pressure, say 1 atm, then equilibrium will occur at some specific temperature T^* determined by thermodynamics. At T^* B and S will coexist, below T^* pure B will be the stable component, above T^* pure S will be the stable component.

So when a particle of cool B is introduced into a hot environment its surface heats up to T^*, decomposition occurs, a product layer forms, and the reaction front moves into the particle. From then on the driving force for reaction is the conduction of heat through the product layer to the moving reaction front. This heat flow supplies the heat needed for reaction and keeps the reaction front at close to constant temperature. Graphically

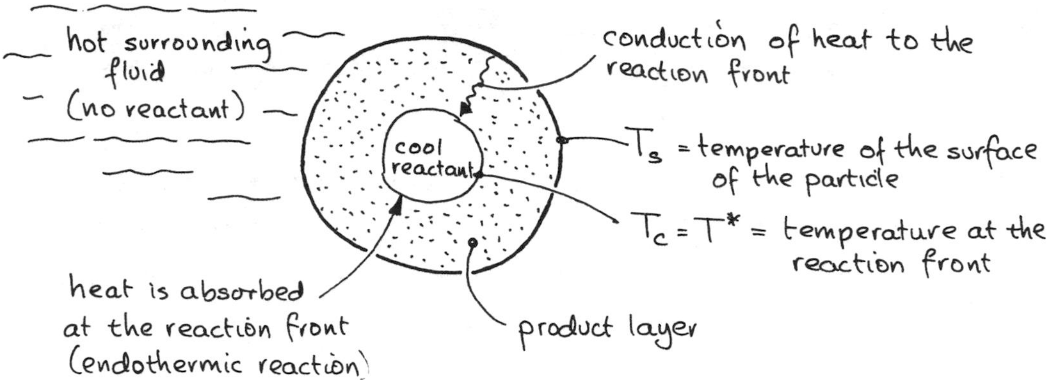

The behavior of the particle follows the SCM, ash diffusion control with $\tau_{obs} \propto R^2$. More precisely we find

$$\frac{t}{\tau_{obs}} = 1 - 3(1-X_B)^{2/3} + 2(1-X_B)$$

$$\tau_{obs} = \frac{\rho_B \Delta H_r R^2}{6 k_s (T_s - T_c)}$$

ρ_B — molar density of B in the solid, mol/m³

k_s — thermal conductivity through the ash layer.

(a) This model should apply when the particles are heated by hot gases. It should not be good for reactors which use induction heating.

(b) Exothermic solid to solid reactions do not fit this model. With large heat release such reactions are unstable.

Case 2. Solid/solid reactions which evolve gases. Consider the endothermic reaction

$$B(s) \longrightarrow R(g) + S(s) \qquad \cdots \Delta H_r > 0$$

Phase rule tells that

$$P + V + Rx = C + 2 \qquad \cdots \text{or} \quad 3 + V + 1 = 3 + 2 \qquad \cdots \text{or} \quad V = 1$$

($V = 1$: one degree of freedom)

Thus each temperature has its corresponding equilibrium partial pressure of R. Raise T above T^* or lower p_R below p_R^* and the reaction goes to completion.

Now suppose a cool particle of B is introduced into a hot environment. When the surface heats to T^*, p_R^* decomposition begins and product gas is evolved. The reaction front then moves into the particle, gas R is released at the front and diffuses out through the ash layer. Graphically

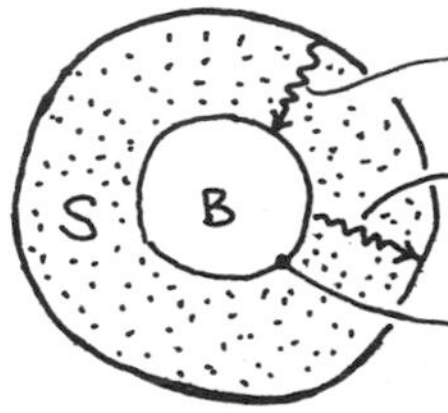

Here two processes influence the advance of the reaction front, the conduction of heat to the front and the diffusion of R through the ash layer away from the front. Both processes lead to ash diffusion control kinetics.

When the heat flow controls the decomposition front stays close to isothermal and we get precisely the same equations as for case 1. This is what is normally observed with real decomposing solids such as calcium carbonate

$$CaCO_3(s) \longrightarrow CaO(s) + CO_2(g)$$

(a) If the product gas cannot diffuse away fast enough from the reaction front it's partial pressure could rise causing cracking and fissuring of the product layer. This then would lead to the CCM with ash diffusion control. In extreme cases the product may flake off leading to shrinking particles.

(b) For reactions such as $B(s) \longrightarrow R(g) + T(g) + S(s)$ phase rule tells that $V=2$ (or 2 degrees of freedom). However, if the decomposition occurs in a gas initially free of R and T then the ratio of R to T remains constant during decomposition, $V=1$, and decomposition still occurs at some fixed temperature T^* as in case 2. The decomposition of sodium bicarbonate in dry air free of CO_2 is an example

$$2NaHCO_3(s) \longrightarrow Na_2CO_3(s) + CO_2(g) + H_2O(g)$$

Many variations of such systems can be found, for example the decomposition of uranylnitrate

$$UO_2(NO_3)_2(s) \longrightarrow UO_3(s) + NO_2(g) + NO(g) + O_2(g)$$

$$\ldots \Delta H_r = +322 \text{ kJ}$$

G. PCM — phase change models.

Here the reactant particle first comes to its new temperature where it is unstable. It then slowly and isothermally transforms to product by chemical change but without the action of a gaseous reactant. Uniform conversion of the particle and S-shaped conversion time curves are typical of these transformations. Here are two mechanistic models which represent this behavior.

1. Prout–Tompkins model: Product grows along planes from initially present nucleii.

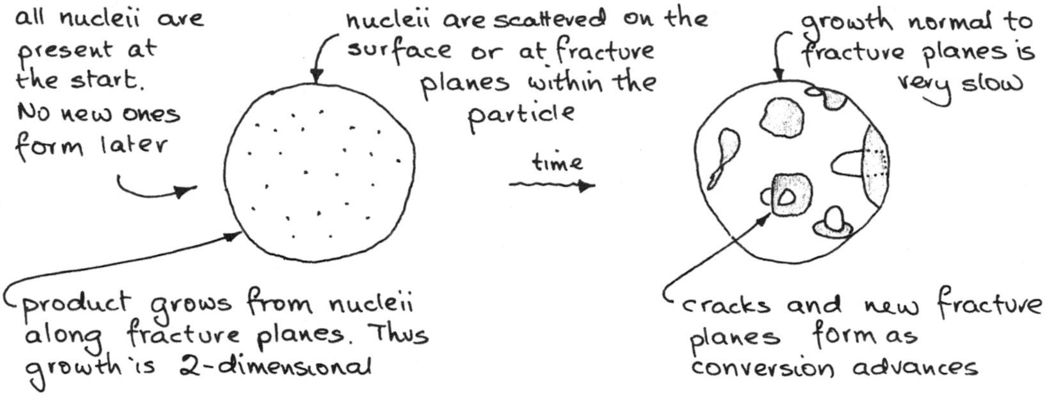

all nucleii are present at the start. No new ones form later
nucleii are scattered on the surface or at fracture planes within the particle
growth normal to fracture planes is very slow
time
product grows from nucleii along fracture planes. Thus growth is 2-dimensional
cracks and new fracture planes form as conversion advances

At first conversion is very slow because the boundaries between reactant and product are very small. Growth then speeds up and eventually slows down as advancing product fronts meet. The conversion – time expression representing this picture turn out to be autocatalytic in form and were derived by Prout and Tompkins, Trans. Faraday Soc. 40 488 (1944), as

$$\ln\left(\frac{X_B}{1-X_B}\right) = Mt - N$$

Graphically

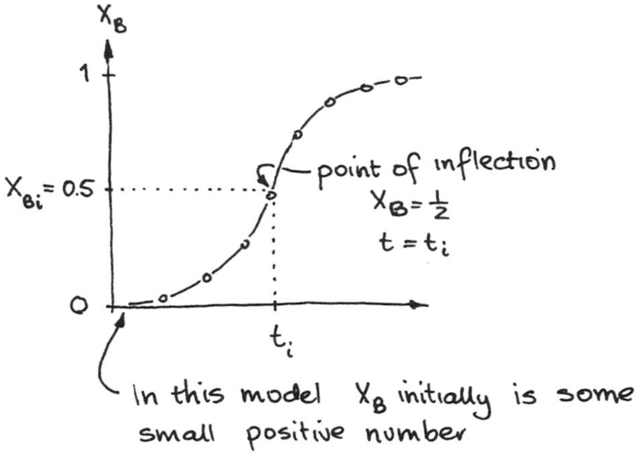

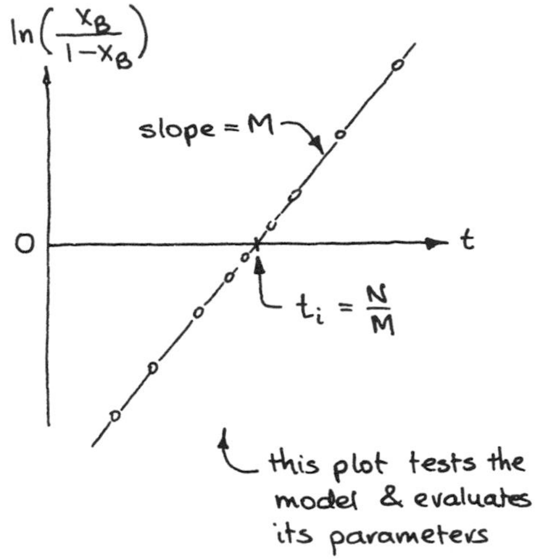

If the rates in the accelerating and decelerating arms of the curve differ and if the point of inflection occurs at $X_B \neq 0.5$ we get two different equations, one for each arm of the curve.

Below t_i and X_{Bi} :
$$\ln\left(\frac{X_B}{2X_{Bi}-X_B}\right) = M_1 t - N_1$$

Above t_i and X_{Bi} :
$$\ln\left(\frac{X_{Bmax}-X_B}{X_B+X_{Bmax}-2X_{Bi}}\right) = M_2 t - N_2$$

Graphically

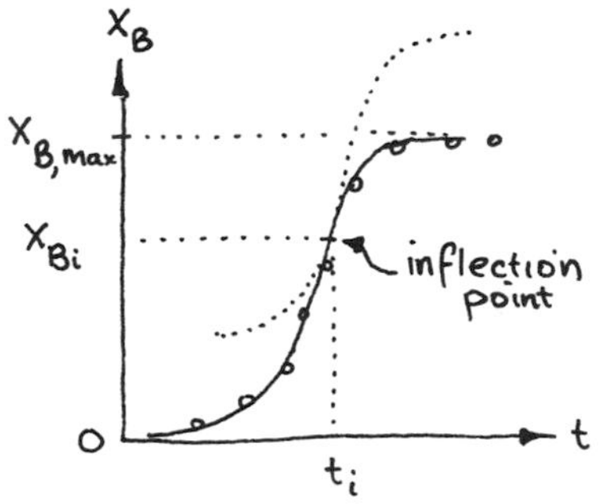

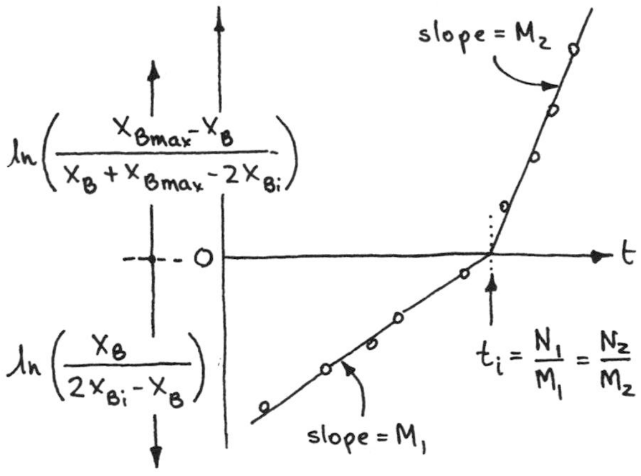

2. Avrami model : Linear, 2-d or 3-d growth of product from nucleii which are either all present at the start or are created continuously.

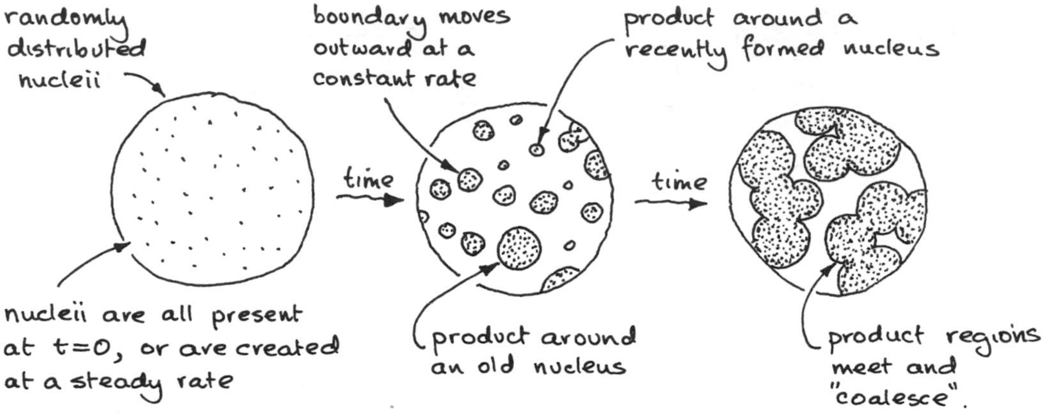
randomly distributed nucleii
boundary moves outward at a constant rate
product around a recently formed nucleus
time
time
nucleii are all present at t=0, or are created at a steady rate
product around an old nucleus
product regions meet and "coalesce".

Avrami's analysis in J. Chem. Phys. 8 212 (1940) gives the following conversion - time expression

$$X_B = 1 - e^{-Mt^N} \qquad \text{or} \qquad \ln\left(\frac{1}{1-X_B}\right) = Mt^N$$

where N depends on how the nucleii grow and when they are formed. N is determined as follows:

	One dimensional growth of product from nucleii (needle like)	2-dimensional growth (flat plate)	3-dimensional growth (spherical)
All nucleii are present at start	N = 1	N = 2	N = 3
Nucleii are formed at a steady rate	N = 2	N = 3	N = 4

This equation can be represented graphically in a number of ways.

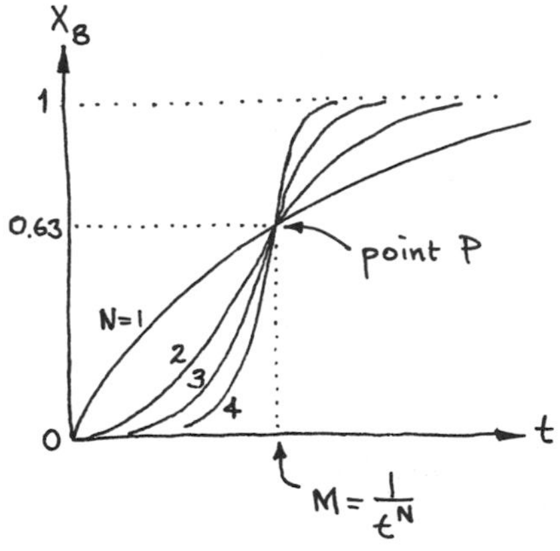

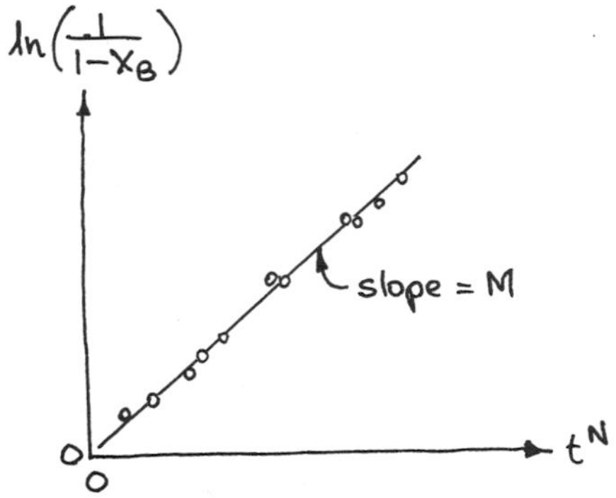

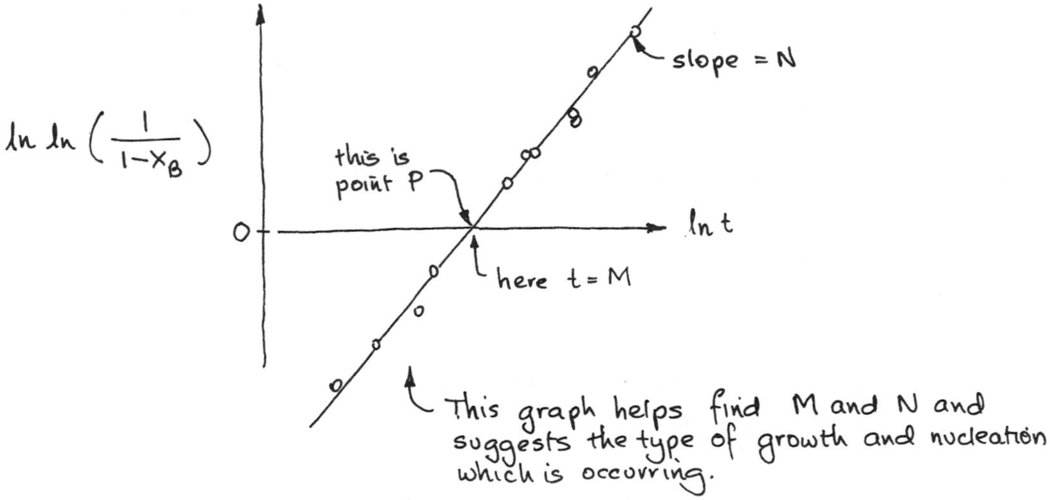

3. **Comments**. From the physical standpoint the Avrami and the Prout-Tompkins models are rather similar. They both can represent S-shaped conversion-time curves and so when one model reasonably represents the data then usually so does the other.

H. The SCM for multistep reactions.

Consider the following successive reaction of a solid

$$B(s) \xrightarrow{1} S(s) \xrightarrow{2} T(s) \xrightarrow{3} U(s) \xrightarrow{4} V(s) \xrightarrow{5} W(s)$$

(step 1: suppose very fast; step 3: suppose that this is the slowest step)

If step 3 is **very much slower** than the other steps we then observe the following progression of changes

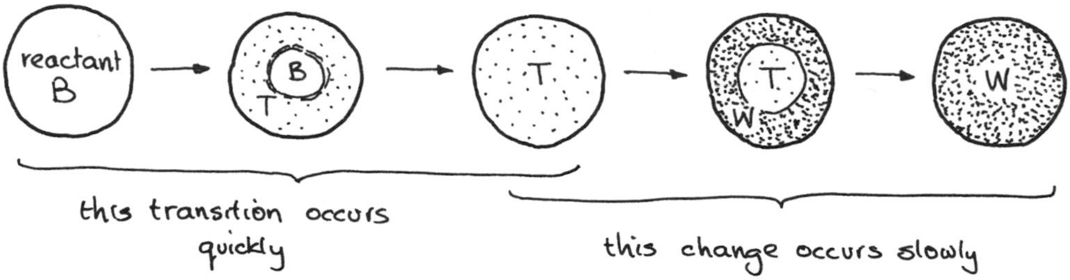

The reaction to T will be just about complete before the reaction to W starts. Thus we have

$$B(s) \xrightarrow[\text{by SCM}]{\text{fast}} T(s) \quad \cdots \text{followed by} \cdots \quad T(s) \xrightarrow[\text{by SCM}]{\text{slow}} W(s)$$

If the slowest step is **not much slower** than the other steps then you have an overlap in these successive reactions, or

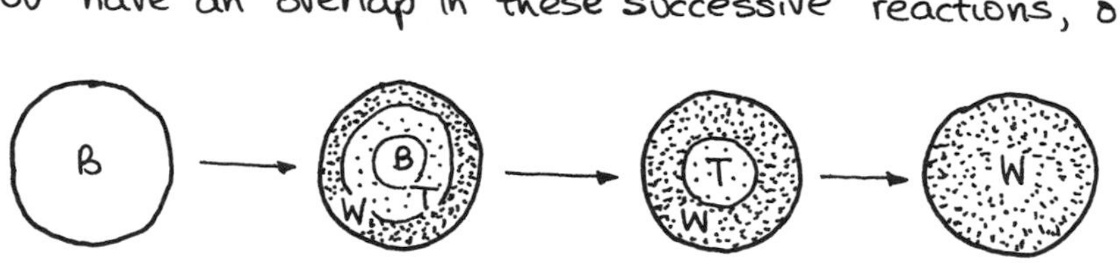

As a rule multistep reactions nearly always reduce to two-step behavior. In all cases the successive layers move inward according to the SCM with $X_B \propto R$ or $X_B \propto R^2$ depending on whether reaction or ash diffusion controls.

Tsay et al AIChE J 22 1064 (1976) look at a three step reaction this way.

I. Multistep reaction of porous particles: application of the GPM.

Consider the two step reaction: $B(s) \xrightarrow{1} S(s) \xrightarrow{2} T(s)$

- if diffusion is fast, reaction 1 intermediate, reaction 2 slow } ... the particle follows the UCM, both products S and T are present throughout reaction, each forming by the SCM. Here $\tau_{particle}$ is independent of R

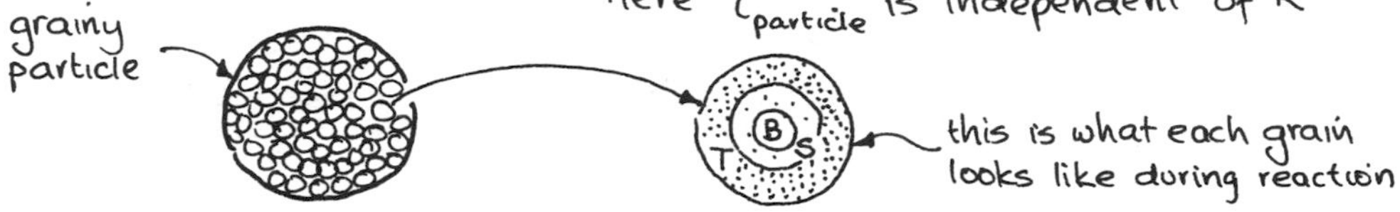

- if diffusion is fast, reaction 1 slow, reaction 2 fast } ... the particle follows the UCM of the reaction $B(s) \xrightarrow{1} T(s)$. Conversion-time behavior follows the SCM with $\tau_{particle}$ independent of R.

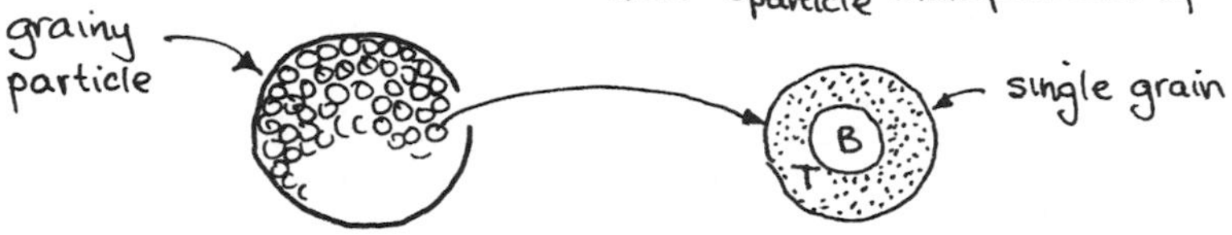

- if diffusion is slow, reaction 1 intermediate, reaction 2 fast } ... the particle follows the SCM for the reaction $B(s) \longrightarrow T(s)$ with ash diffusion control and $\tau \propto R^2$

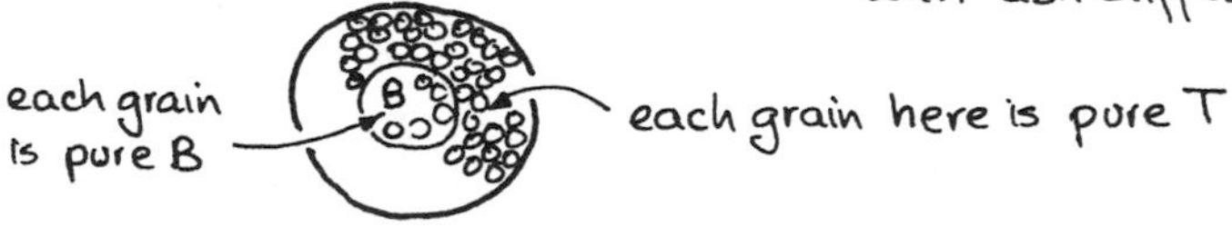

- if diffusion is slow, reaction 1 fast, reaction 2 not so fast } ... the core shrinks according to the SCM/ash diffusion control, all the concentric rings move inward according to this model, and $\tau_{particle} \propto R^2$

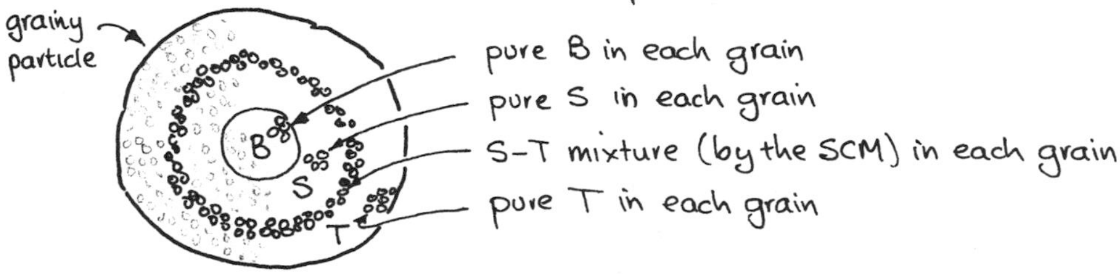

(a) From these extremes we conclude that

- if diffusion is faster than the next step you observe the UCM.
- if diffusion is slower than the next step you then observe the SCM.

(b) Reactions of 3 or more steps use the same kind of reasoning as the two-step reaction.

(c) The mathematics of the intermediate cases where the order of magnitude of the diffusion step is roughly that of the reaction step is probably pretty horrendous.

J. Multistep reaction of particles which become porous on reaction: application of the CCM.

Consider the two extremes for the multistep reactions

$$B(s) \xrightarrow{1} S(s) \xrightarrow{2} T(s) \xrightarrow{3} U(s) \xrightarrow{4} V(s) \xrightarrow{5} W(s)$$

B(s) non porous; S(s) porous; T(s) porous; U(s) porous; V(s) porous; W(s) porous

↑ the first step, the crackling step involves either a physical or a chemical change

- if **step 1 is slow** or $\tau_1 \gg \tau_2, \tau_3, \tau_4, \tau_5$ you then have

traces of S, T, U and V are present in the grains which are close to the reaction front

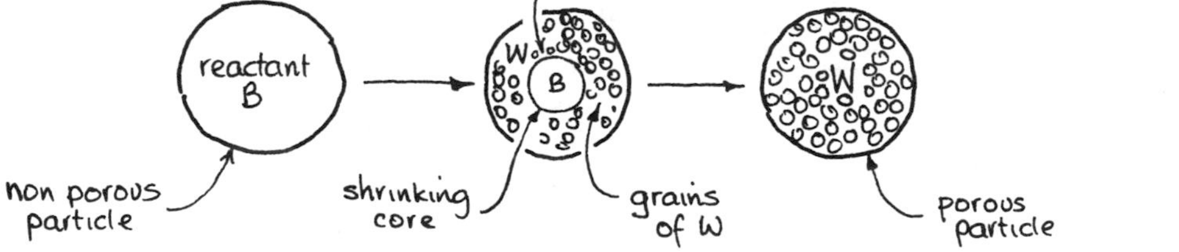

Here all the action piles up on the slowly receding boundary and you observe the SCM, reaction control, $\tau \propto R$ for the one step reaction $B(s) \longrightarrow W(s)$.

• if any other step, say step 3, is the slow step you then have

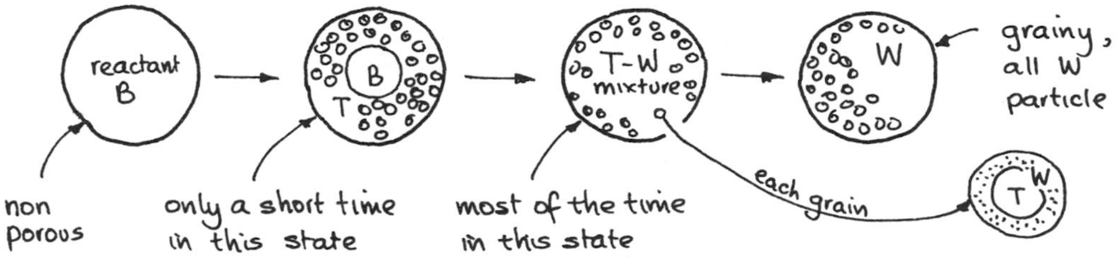

After a short period during which B disappears you will observe the reaction

$$T \xrightarrow{3} W,$$

UCM for the particle, but conversion-time by the SCM (reaction or ash diffusion kinetics), with $\tau_{particle}$ independent of R. Overall then we observe the two step reaction

$$B \xrightarrow[\text{crackling}]{\text{fast}} T \xrightarrow[\text{uniform}]{\text{slow}} W.$$

There are many intermediate situations depending on the relative values of $\tau_1, \tau_2, \ldots$. In most cases the multistep reactions reduce to either one or two step reactions with anywhere between SCM and UCM behavior

The most common and the most important reaction of this type is the reduction of iron oxide, or

$$Fe_2O_3 \longrightarrow Fe_3O_4 \longrightarrow FeO \longrightarrow Fe$$

K. Comments on multistep reactions.

This study of extremes should be helpful in suggesting what is going on in a real system when you slice a particle and examine it, and also follow X_B vs t and τ vs R.

There are many possible extensions of G/S reactions to more complicated stoichiometry and more complicated reaction chemistry.

L. An unusual mechanism involving the movement of loose atoms.

Le Page and Fane in J. inorg nucl. Chem. 36 87 (1974) suggest that the reaction

$$UO_3(s) \xrightarrow{+H_2} U_3O_8(s)$$

takes place by the migration of oxygen atoms through the crystal lattice to the crystal surface where they react with adsorbed hydrogen. This mechanism can give a linear increase of conversion with time, just like film diffusion, but unlike film diffusion it should have a high activation energy. Also, for porous solids and high diffusivity of hydrogen the rate should be insensitive to particle size.

Thus in the two step reduction

$$UO_3(s) \longrightarrow U_3O_8(s) \longrightarrow UO_2(s)$$

the first step involves oxygen migration with no change in phase. Only after all the loose oxygen is used up does the second step occur with its phase change and SCM, or GPM, or what have you.

This mechanism views two independent successive reactions, the second only starting after the first one is complete.

M. On the use of reaction order with respect to the unreacted solid.

The reaction order with respect to the unreacted solid may be defined by

$$\left.\begin{array}{l} A(g) + B(s) \longrightarrow \cdots \\ \text{at constant } C_A \end{array}\right\} \qquad -r_B = -\frac{d(1-x_B)}{dt} = k(1-x_B)^m$$

(m: order of reaction)

- For the SCM, reaction control, $m = 2/3$
- For the SCM, ash diffusion control m varies smoothly from $m = \infty$ at $X_B = 0$ down to $m = 1/3$ at $X_B = 1$.
- For the SCM, film diffusion control $m = 0$
- For most other kinetic models **m is not constant** but changes with X_B and the parameters of the system

In homogeneous reactions the reaction order is tied to the mechanism of action of the molecules and it has theoretical meaning. For catalyst decay the order of deactivation is a convenient tool which leads to generalizations, simple mathematics and simple design. However for the conversion of solids the reaction order does not seem to be a simplifying concept, and it does not particularly clarify. Thus it is best to avoid using it.

Chapter 55 Problems

A1 Calculate the time needed for the complete calcination of a limestone particle (d_p = 4 mm, ρ_s = 2900 kg/m^3, k_{eff} = 2 W/m·K) if the surface of the particle is kept 10 °C above the decomposition temperature of the solid. The calcination reaction proceeds as follows

$$CaCO_3(s) \rightarrow CaO(s) + CO_2, \quad \Delta Hr = 179500 \text{ J}$$

(mw = 100) (=56) (=44)

A2 We plan to calcine continuously 100 ton/hr of $CaCO_3$ particles (d_p = 4 mm) to 99% conversion in a fluidized bed. How large must the unit be if heat duty and film coefficient calculations suggest that the particle surface will be 34.7 °C above the decomposition temperature of the solid? For additional data see the previous problem.

A3 Aluminum trifluoride is formed by the thermal decomposition of its hydrate

$$AlF_3 \cdot \tfrac{1}{2}H_2O(s) \xrightarrow{600\,°C} AlF_3(s) + \tfrac{1}{2}H_2O \quad \Delta H_r = 71 \text{ kJ}$$

(mw = 98) (=89) (=9)

We plan to treat a pure hydrate feed in a one ton fluidized bed dehydrator under conditions (T = 623 °C) where a single particle is converted to product in 12 min. If the flow rate of solids from the reactor is 5 ton/hr determine

(a) the conversion of solids leaving the reactor and

(b) the flow rate of solids into the reactor.

A particle of solid B (d_p = 1 mm, ρ_s = 3250 kg/m^3) is immersed in gas (580 °C, 1 atm, containing 21% A) and they react as follows

$$A(g) + B(s) \rightarrow R(g) + S(s)$$

to give a particle of product S (ρ_s = 3000 kg/m^3). The conversion-time behavior is as follows

X_B	0.189	0.302	0.463	0.627	0.774	0.850	0.921
t, min	5	10	20	30	45	60	75

Suggest a mechanism of action and its kinetic constants, either ash diffusivity and/or reaction rate constant, etc.

A4 . . . if the X_B vs t curve is strongly size-dependent, say $t = kR \sim kR^2$.

A5 . . . if the X_B vs t curve is size-independent.

Chapter 55 Problems

The reduction of hematite proceeds as follows

Fe_2O_3	$\xrightarrow{1}$	Fe_3O_4	$\xrightarrow{2}$	FeO	$\xrightarrow{3}$	Fe
hematite		magnetite		wustite		iron
medium grey		dark grey		black		light grey
$X_B = 0$		$X_B = 0.11$		$X_B = 0.35$		$X_B = 1$
(B)		(S)		(T)		(U)

Starting with a dense non porous pellet of hematite compare the orders of magnitude of the characteristic reaction times τ_1, τ_2, τ_3 for the three reaction steps if on slicing a partly converted pellet you find the following

B6 . . .

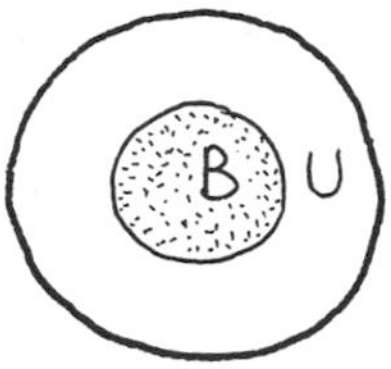

B7 . . .

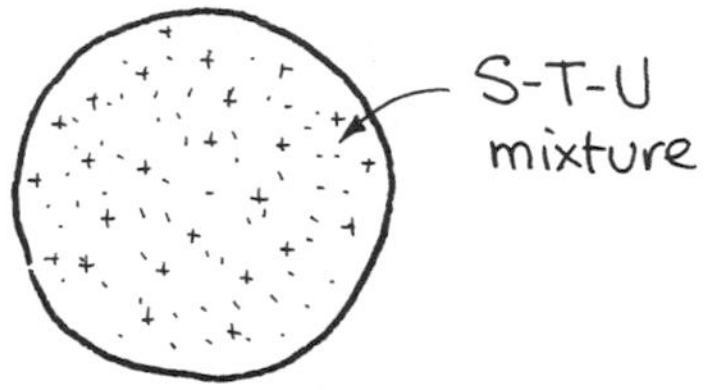

B8 . . .

B9 . . .

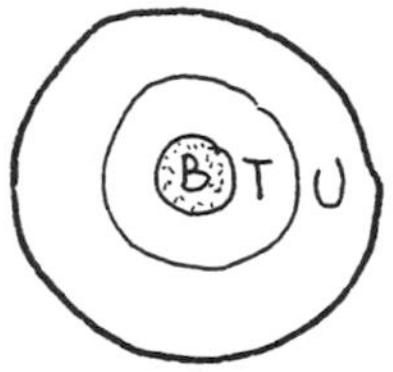

Refer to the iron ore reduction reaction above. Starting with a porous hematite pellet compare the orders of magnitude of the characteristic times of the diffusion step and the three reaction steps if on slicing a partly reacted pellet you find the following

B10 . . .

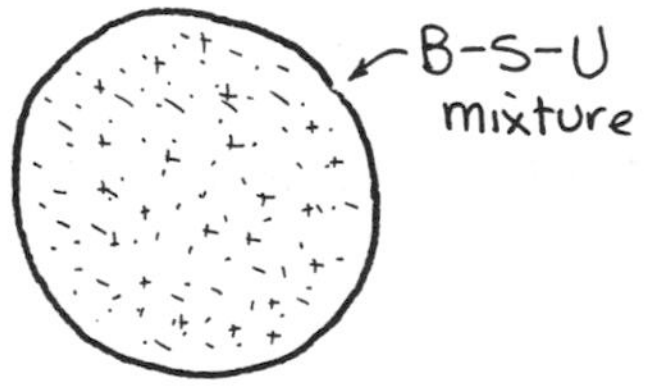

B11 . . .

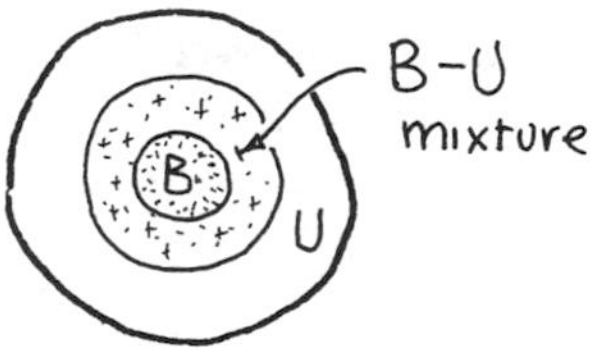

B12 . . .

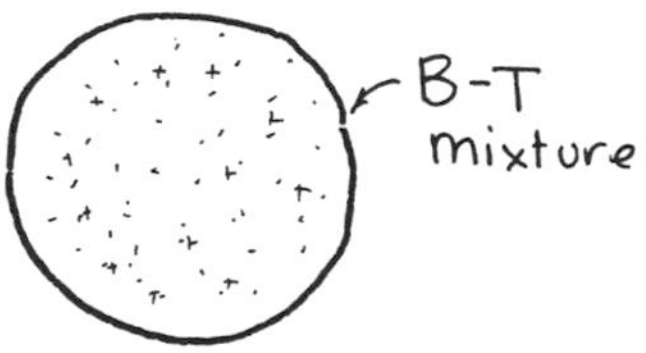

B13 . . .

Chapter 55 Problems

C14 In a hydrogen-nitrogen atmosphere (32% H_2, 552 °C) particles of UO_3 (d_p = 500 ~ 1000 μm) consisting of compressed fine crystals are reduced to UO_2 by a two step reaction

$$UO_3 \rightarrow U_3O_8 \rightarrow UO_2$$

The weight loss is carefully monitored to give the following conversion-time data

X_B (from UO_3 to UO_2)	0.167	0.333	0.500	0.667	0.833	0.917
t, sec	50	100	125	155	200	230

It is also reported that the size of particles has no effect on conversion rate. Find a rate expression and suggest a model to account for this behavior.

Data from LePage and Fane, J. Inorg. Nucl. Chem. **36** 87 (1974).

One way of removing SO_2 from hot combustion gases is to pass the SO_2-rich gas through a fluidized bed of limestone. The following reactions take place

$$CaCO_3(s) \xrightarrow{\text{heat}} CaO(s) + CO_2$$

$$CaO(s) + SO_2 + 0.5\,O_2 \rightarrow CaSO_4(s)$$

The first step is fairly rapid, the second step is slow.

First find the voidage of the particles when the $CaCO_3$ in the limestone is completely converted to CaO. Then find the maximum expected utilization of $CaCO_3$ for SO_2 removal

C15 . . . if the final solid is non porous

C16 . . . if the final solid has a residual dead-end voidage of 10%.

Data: Commercial limestone has the following properties:
Porosity = 5%, density = 2.71 gm/cm^3
Composition of solid by volume: 90% $CaCO_3$ - 10% inert

From the literature we also have

$CaCO_3$:	mw = 100,	V = 36.9 cm^3/mol
CaO:	mw = 56,	V =16.9 cm^3/mol
$CaSO_4$:	mw = 136,	V = 52.2 cm^3/mol

Chapter 55 Problems

D17 . . . A vertical reactor is packed to a height L with solid B, pure gaseous A is introduced above the solid and is kept at 1 atm there. A and B react by the shrinking core model, as follows:

$$A(g) + B(s) \rightarrow R(s)$$

Reaction is very fast and the pressure at the bottom of the reactor is found to be close to zero.

(a) What happens to the average reaction rate, $\overline{r'_A}$ if $L \rightarrow 2L$?

(b) What happens to the reaction rate if at the top of the reactor $p_A = 1 \rightarrow p_A = 2$ atm?

61

Chapter 61 FLOW PATTERN AND CONTACTING.

I. Overall Picture of Non Ideal Flow.

So far we have treated two flow patterns, **plug flow** and **mixed flow**. These can give very different behavior (size of reactor, distribution of products). We like these flow patterns and try to design equipment to approach one or the other because

- one or other often is optimum no matter what we are designing for.
- these two patterns are simple to treat.

But real equipment always deviates from these ideals. How to account for this? That is what this and the following chapters are about.

Overall three somewhat interrelated factors make up the contacting or flow pattern

- the **RTD** or residence time distribution of material which is flowing through the vessel.
- the **state of aggregation** of the flowing material, its tendancy to clump and for a group of molecules to move about together.
- the **earliness and lateness of mixing** of material in the vessel.

Let us discuss these three factors in a qualitative way at first, then see what we can do with them in a quantitative way.

A. The RTD, or exit age distribution function E_t.

We represent the time spent in the vessel by the flowing material by the E_t function, shown below:

Note that individual molecules or particles spend different lengths of time in the vessel

vessel

$\left\{\begin{array}{l}\text{constant}\\\text{flow rate}\end{array}\right.$

$\left\{\begin{array}{l}\text{fluid enters and leaves the}\\\text{vessel one time only.}\\\text{No multiple ins and outs.}\end{array}\right.$

$=$ plot this way $\Rightarrow$

E_t, s^{-1}

shaded area:
$E_t \cdot \Delta t = 0.2$

plot in such a way that area $= 1$

time, s

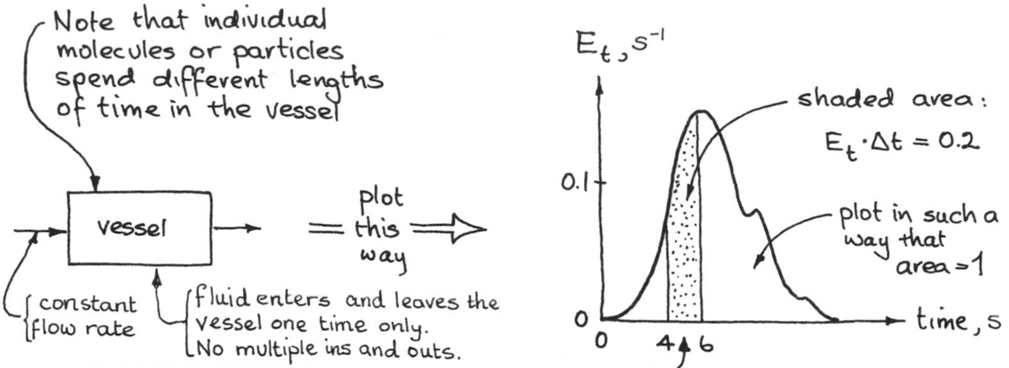

On this plot the area under the curve between any two times gives the fraction of flowing stream spending that much time in the vessel. Thus 20% of the flowing fluid spends between 4 and 6 mins in the vessel.

Later we will show how this E_t curve is found by experiment, and how it can be used for analysis of reactor behavior.

B. State of aggregation of the flowing stream.

Flowing material is in some particular state of aggregation, depending on its nature. In the extremes these states can be called **microfluids** and **macrofluids**

Macrofluid

Examples:
- non coalescing dispersed droplets
- solid particles
- very viscous liquids

molecules move about in clumps, and each clump is uniform in composition.

Microfluid

Examples:
- gases and
- ordinary not very viscous liquids

individual molecules have no attachment to or for their neighbors, each moves about independently.

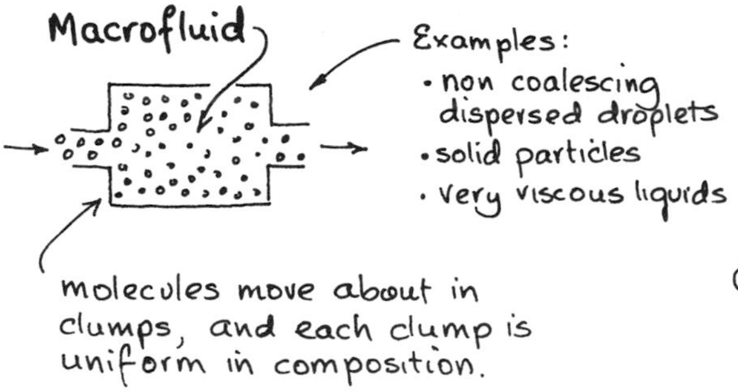

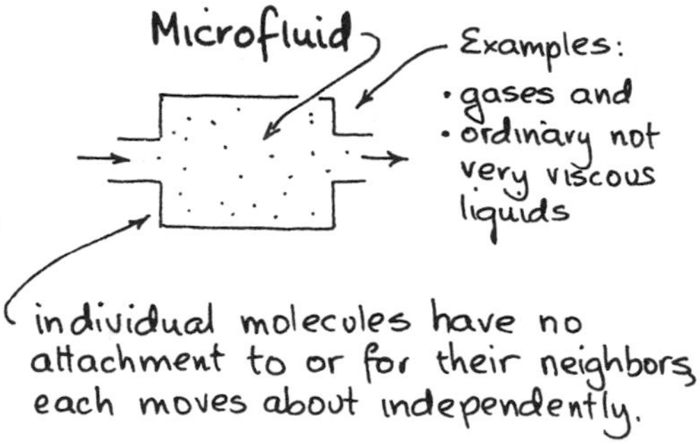

Two phase systems: A stream of solids always behaves as a macrofluid, but for gas reacting with liquid either phase can be a macro- or microfluid depending on the contacting scheme being used. The sketches below show completely opposite behavior. We treat these two phase reactors elsewhere in these notes.

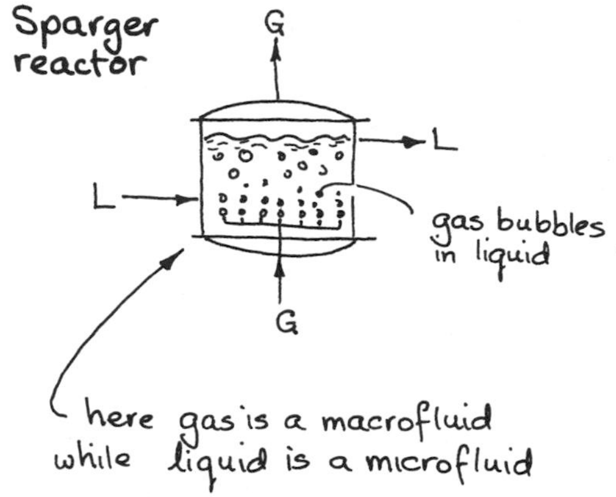

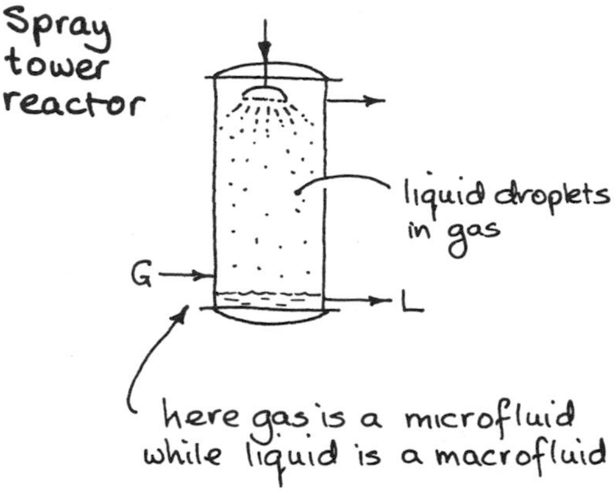

Single phase systems: these lie somewhere between the extremes of macro- and microfluids, where depending on the ratio of

- characteristic time for reaction $\bar{t}_{rx}$
- characteristic time for mixing of neighboring elements of the flowing fluid $\bar{t}_{mix}$.

Where $\bar{t}_{rx} \gtrapprox \bar{t}_{mix}$, or not very fast reaction, the microfluid extreme is a good approximation. This condition is typical of many industrial reactions and is what we assumed in all the early chapters on plug flow, mixed flow, etc.

Where $\bar{t}_{rx} \ll \bar{t}_{mix}$, or extremely fast reaction, we are in the intermediate regime between these extremes. Such systems include combustion, acid-base neutralization, high temperature reactions, free radical polymerizations, reactions (which need not be fast) of very viscous fluids in laminar flow, etc.

C. Earliness of mixing.

The fluid elements of a single flowing stream can mix with each other either early or late in their flow through the vessel. For example:

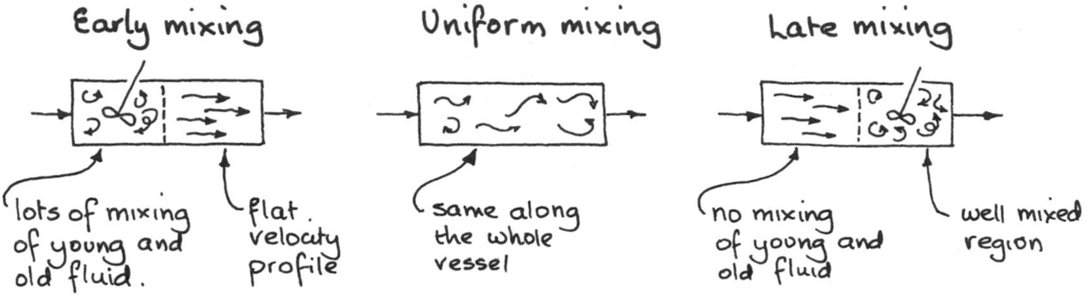
Early mixing
Uniform mixing
Late mixing
lots of mixing of young and old fluid.
flat velocity profile
same along the whole vessel
no mixing of young and old fluid
well mixed region

Usually this factor has little effect on overall behavior for a single flowing fluid. However for a system with two entering reactant streams it can be very important, for example

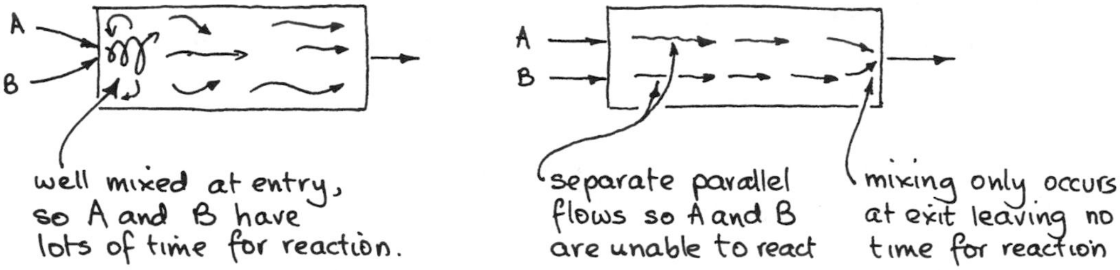
A
B
well mixed at entry, so A and B have lots of time for reaction.
A
B
separate parallel flows so A and B are unable to react
mixing only occurs at exit leaving no time for reaction

D. Role of RTD, state of aggregation and earliness of mixing in determining reactor behavior.

In some situations one of these three factors can be ignored, in others it can become crucial. Often, much depends on the time for reaction $\bar{t}_{rx}$, the time for mixing $\bar{t}_{mix}$, and the time for stay in the vessel $\bar{t}_{stay}$. In many cases $\bar{t}_{stay}$ has a meaning somewhat like $\bar{t}_{mix}$, but somewhat broader.

For a single flowing stream

- if $\bar{t}_{rx} \gg \bar{t}_{stay}$ then little reaction takes place so plug flow and mixed flow will give the same conversion
- if $\bar{t}_{rx} \approx \bar{t}_{stay}$ then only RTD need be known, whether plug flow, mixed flow, or where in between as determined by the RTD curve.
- if $\bar{t}_{rx} \ll (\bar{t}_{stay}$ or $\bar{t}_{mix})$ all three factors enter the picture to influence reactor behavior
- as a special case if reaction is first order then only RTD need be known no matter what the $\bar{t}$ values may be.

For separate reactant streams entering a reactor

- for any $\bar{t}_{rx}$ all three factors may be important, and any one may be crucial and control reactor behavior
- for $\bar{t}_{rx} \ll \bar{t}_{mix}$ these three physical factors which we are considering here will completely control reactor behavior, and chemical kinetics becomes unimportant. Fuel gas combustion is an example.

In this and the next few chapters we will treat single stream reactors with moderate or slower reaction rates, or $\bar{t}_{rx} \not\ll \bar{t}_{mix}$. This will include a large class of reactions encountered in practice. We will focus on the RTD and will see how it can tell where we are between the extremes of plug flow and mixed flow.

Later chapters may take up extremely fast reactions (where the state of aggregation and early or late mixing become dominant), and reactors with separate feeds. These systems are much harder to treat.

Finally, throughout the 60's chapters we will take $\varepsilon_A = 0$, thus we will not consider systems of changing density, caused either by changing temperatures or by reaction.

II. Conversion for a Single Phase Single Feed Reactor.

1. For a macrofluid, any RTD, any kinetics

$$\left(\frac{\bar{C}_A}{C_{A0}}\right)_{\text{at exit}} = \int_0^\infty \left(\frac{C_A}{C_{A0}}\right)_{\substack{\text{for an element or little}\\ \text{batch of fluid of age } t}} \cdot E_t \, dt$$

or in terms of conversions

$$\bar{X}_A = \int_0^\infty (X_A)_{\text{element}} \cdot E_t \, dt \qquad \ldots (1)$$

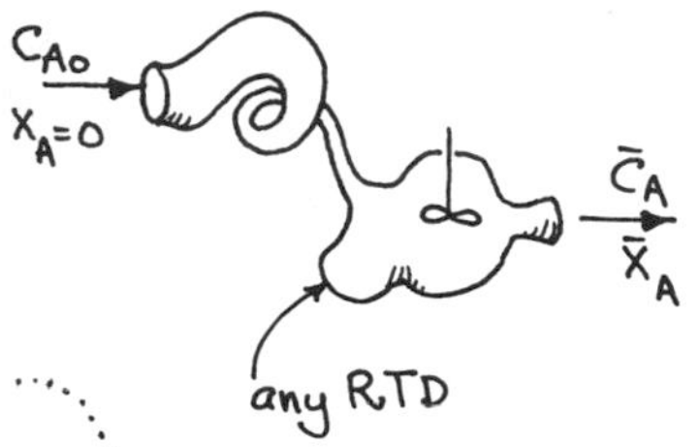

or in a form suitable for numerical integration

$$\frac{\bar{C}_A}{C_{A0}} = \sum_{\substack{\text{all age}\\ \text{intervals}}} \left(\frac{C_A}{C_{A0}}\right)_{\text{element}} \cdot E_t \, \Delta t$$

for the element or clump of material or particle of macrofluid conversion proceeds as follows

- for first order reaction : $\frac{C_A}{C_{A0}} = e^{-kt}$
- for second order reaction : $\frac{C_A}{C_{A0}} = \frac{1}{1+kC_{A0}t}$
- for any other kinetics, for reaction of solids, etc use the expression which represents that particular system.

2. For a microfluid, plug or mixed flow only, any kinetics.

$$\tau_{plug} = \int_{C_A}^{C_{A0}} \frac{dC_A}{-r_A} \; ; \quad \tau_{mixed} = \frac{C_{A0}-C_A}{-r_A}$$

... from earlier chapters and for $\varepsilon_A = 0$ only

3. **For a microfluid, any RTD but for first order kinetics only.**

↖ this includes first order reversible reactions

$$\frac{\bar{C}}{C_0} = \int_0^\infty \frac{C}{C_0} \cdot E_t \, dt$$

… For first order kinetics we see that macro- and microfluids behave alike.

↖ Note: from here on, throughout the 60's, we will drop the subscript A.

4. **For all other cases** exact prediction is not known today. It is thus best to take the closest approximating extreme. This is usually reasonable unless reaction is extremely fast, or $\bar{t}_{rx} \ll \bar{t}_{mix}$.

5. **Conversion of micro- and macrofluids in ideal reactors.**

The table below summarizes the performance equations for these ideals

	Plug flow macro and micro	Mixed flow microfluid	Mixed flow macrofluid
General kinetics:	$\tau = \int_C^{C_0} \frac{dC}{-r}$	$\tau = \frac{C_0 - C}{-r}$	$\frac{\bar{C}}{C_0} = \frac{1}{\tau}\int_0^\infty \left(\frac{C}{C_0}\right)_{batch} e^{-t/\tau} dt$
n^{th} order reaction $(R = C_0^{n-1} k\tau)$	$\frac{C}{C_0} = [1+(n-1)R]^{1/1-n}$ $R = \frac{1}{n-1}\left[\left(\frac{C}{C_0}\right)^{1-n} - 1\right]$	$\left(\frac{C}{C_0}\right)^n R + \frac{C}{C_0} - 1 = 0$ $R = \left(1-\frac{C}{C_0}\right)\left(\frac{C_0}{C}\right)^n$	$\frac{\bar{C}}{C_0} = \frac{1}{\tau}\int_0^\infty \left[1+(n-1)C_0^{n-1}kt\right]^{1/1-n} e^{-t/\tau} dt$
Zero order reaction $(R = k\tau/C_0)$	$\frac{C}{C_0} = 1-R, \quad R \le 1$ $C = 0, \quad R \ge 1$	$\frac{C}{C_0} = 1-R, \quad R \le 1$ $C = 0, \quad R \ge 1$	$\frac{\bar{C}}{C_0} = 1 - R + Re^{-1/R}$
First order reaction $(R = k\tau)$	$\frac{C}{C_0} = e^{-R}$ $R = \ln \frac{C_0}{C}$	$\frac{C}{C_0} = \frac{1}{1+R}$ $R = \frac{C_0}{C} - 1$	$\frac{\bar{C}}{C_0} = \frac{1}{1+R}$ $R = \frac{C_0}{C} - 1$
Second order reaction $(R = C_0 k\tau)$	$\frac{C}{C_0} = \frac{1}{1+R}$ $R = \frac{C_0}{C} - 1$	$\frac{C}{C_0} = \frac{-1+\sqrt{1+4R}}{2R}$ $R = \left(\frac{C_0}{C} - 1\right)\frac{C_0}{C}$	$\frac{\bar{C}}{C_0} = \frac{e^{1/R}}{R} \, ei\left(\frac{1}{R}\right)$ ← exponential integral, see pg. 32·6

6. Comparison of performance.

Comparing volumes required for a given duty will give an idea of the role played by segregation. The above equations show

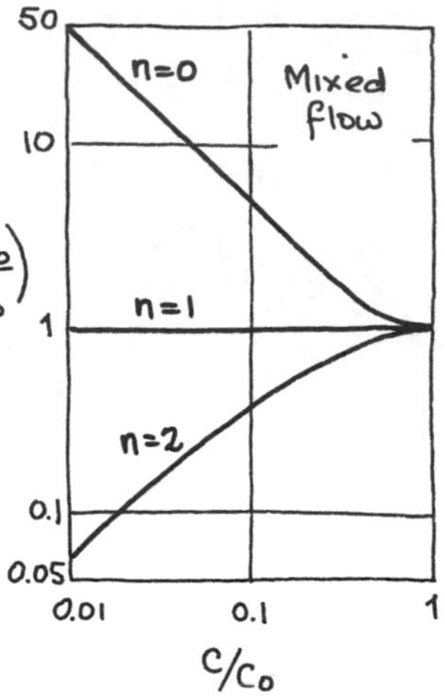

- For **mixed flow** microfluids react more efficiently when $n<1$, vice versa when $n>1$; and when $n=1$ the state of aggregation has no effect on conversion
- For **plug flow and a single feed** both macrofluids and microfluids give the same behavior.
- For **two feed streams** all sorts of additional factors intrude. We do not consider this here.

III Experimental Methods (non Chemical) for finding E_t:

The simplest and most direct way of finding the RTD uses a physical or non reactive tracer. For special purposes, however, we may want to use a reactive tracer. This chapter deals in detail with the non reactive tracer, and only briefly touches on the reactive tracer.

For the **non reactive tracer** all sorts of experiments can be used. Here are some.

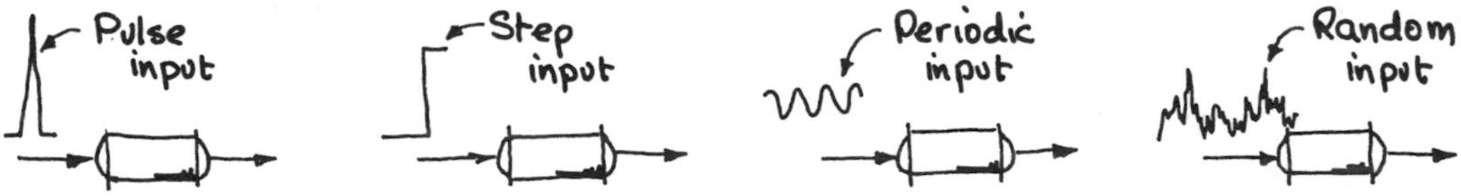

Of these, the pulse and step are easier to interpret, the periodic and random harder. Thus in this chapter we only consider the **pulse experiment** and the **step experiment**.

A. The pulse experiment.

Instantaneously introduce M units of tracer (moles or kg) into the fluid entering the vessel

υ lit/s

volume which contains flowing fluid

V = vessel volume, lit

Record the concentration of tracer in the fluid leaving the vessel.

Evaluate the area under the curve
$$\text{Area} = \int_0^\infty C\,dt = \sum C_i \Delta t_i$$

Evaluate the mean of the curve.
$$\bar{t} = \frac{\int t C\,dt}{\int C\,dt} = \frac{\sum C_i t_i \Delta t_i}{\sum C_i \Delta t_i}$$

see chapter 63

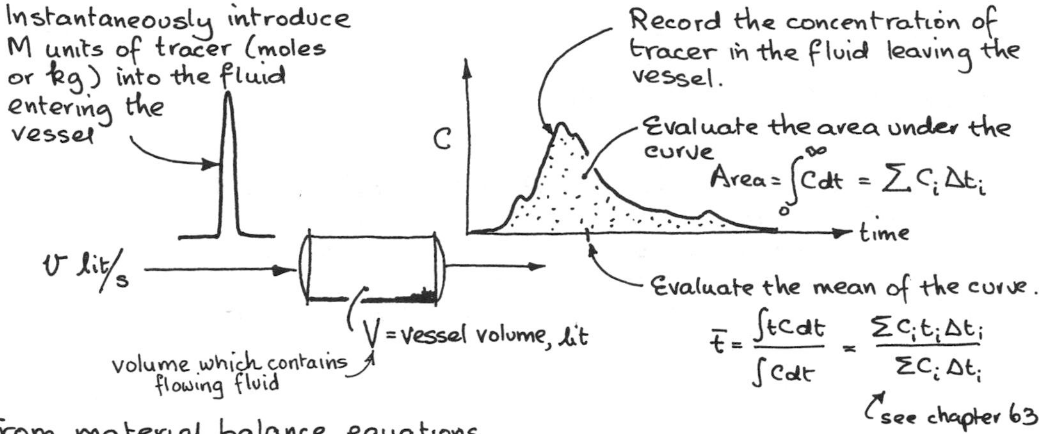

From material balance equations

$$\text{Area} = \frac{M}{\upsilon} \qquad \text{where } M = \begin{bmatrix} \text{kg or moles} \\ \text{added} \end{bmatrix} \qquad \cdots (2)$$

$\frac{kg \cdot s}{lit}$

$$\text{Mean:} \quad \bar{t} = \frac{V}{\upsilon} \qquad \cdots (3)$$

sec

(a) **Overall strategy.** First make a pulse injection and measure the response curve, C vs t. Then

- see if all is consistent with this C vs t curve, that the experiment is properly done and all is OK.

- change the scale on the C vs t curve to get the E_t curve or its dimensionless version E_θ.

- use the E curve to devise a flow model or to find the reactor behavior directly.

(b) **In testing for consistency** we have two equations, (2) and (3) and three quantities to deal with M, υ, V. Thus

- if we are given any one of the three quantities M, υ, or V, we can find the other two.

- if we are given two quantities we can find the third and also make a consistency test for the tracer experiment.
- if we know all three quantities M, v and V, then eqs 2 and 3 provide two tests of consistency to see that the experiment is run properly.

(c) Limitation. The analysis of this chapter only applies to situations where $v_{in} = v_{out}$ and where tracer is not lost from its flowing phase. Thus the analysis cannot be used if a phase vaporizes or if tracer disappears from its flowing phase either by some form of adsorption onto solid, or by transfer to another phase.

(d) If one tracer is confined to and can only flow within one region, while a second is able to move about in both regions of the vessel then experiments with the two tracers will give the volumes of the two regions. Just use eqs 2 and 3 with each tracer

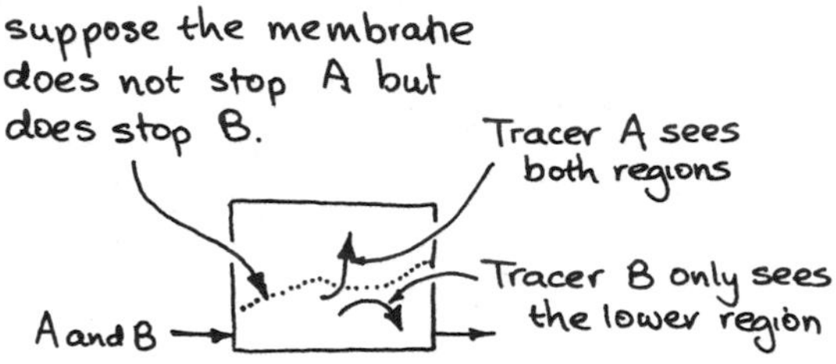
suppose the membrane
does not stop A but
does stop B.
Tracer A sees
both regions
Tracer B only sees
the lower region
A and B

- Physiological and pharmacological applications
- Molecular seives and porous solids
- Reversibly adsorbing solids

(e) Sometimes we don't have two distinct volumes, however it could be that part of a vessel is relatively stagnant so that tracer enters and leaves it very slowly. For such systems the tracer curve has a long tail.

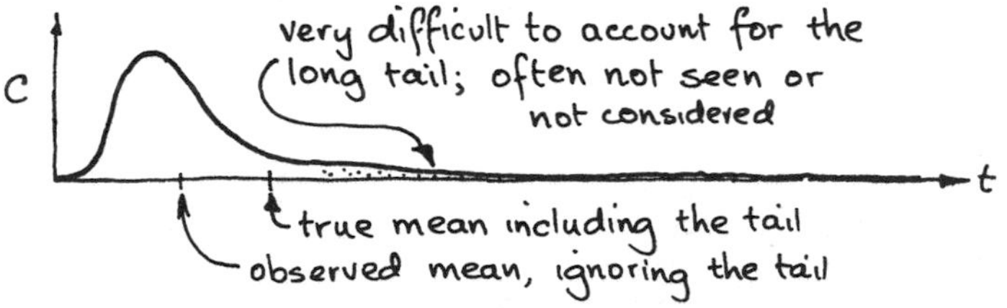
very difficult to account for the
long tail; often not seen or
not considered
C
t
true mean including the tail
observed mean, ignoring the tail

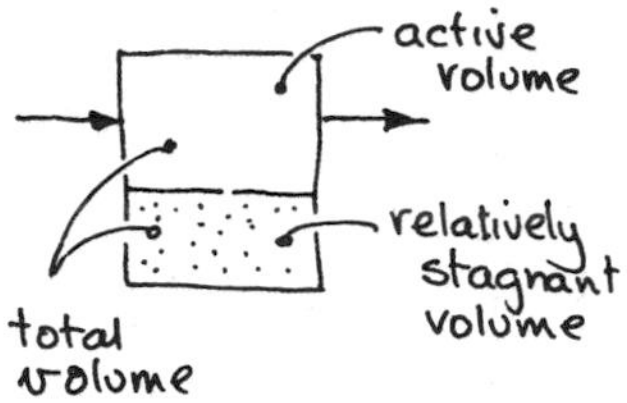
active
volume
relatively
stagnant
volume
total
volume

Ignoring the tail gives the **active vessel volume**. The difference between this and the **true volume** gives the **relatively stagnant vessel volume**.

(f) **Decaying tracer.** Suppose the tracer is radioactive or reacts away by some sort of first order process, say slow adsorption or slow chemical breakdown. Then simply correct the observed concentration upward to what it should be without decay or loss

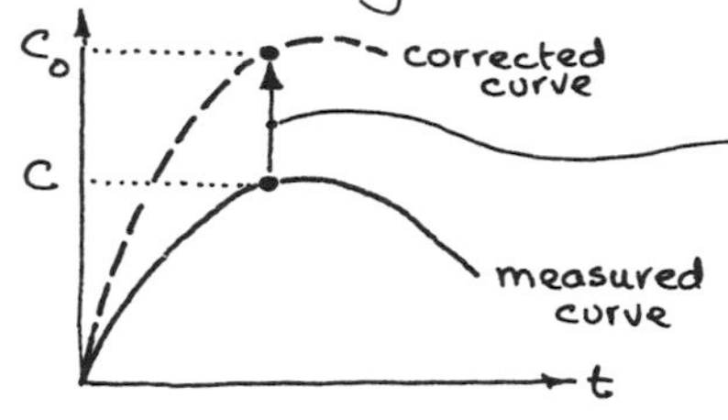

C_0
C
corrected curve
upward correction
measured curve
t

$$\therefore \frac{C}{C_0} = e^{-kt}, \quad \text{or}$$

$$C_0 = Ce^{kt} = Ce^{+0.693t/t_{1/2}}$$

(C_0: without decay; C: with decay)

(g) **Warnings** on choice of tracer and on experimental method.

- Use a proper tracer : same density as fluid, not adsorbed, etc.
- Inject properly : if the velocity profile at vessel inlet is flat introduce tracer uniformly across the cross section. If it is not flat introduce tracer proportional to the flow rate.
- Measure properly : average over all flow rates. This is called a mixing cup measurement.

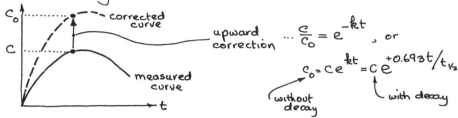

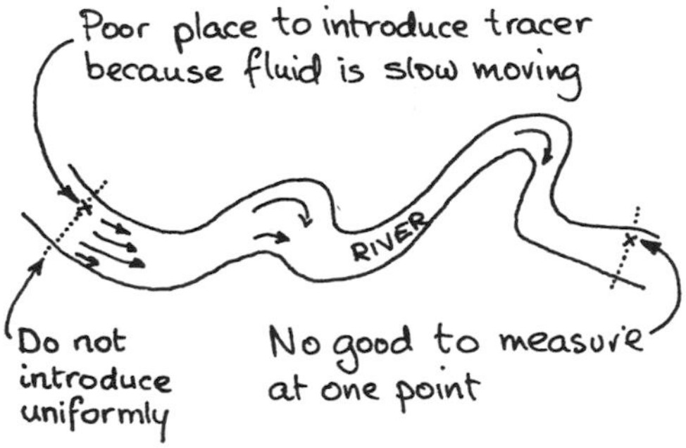

Poor place to introduce tracer because fluid is slow moving
RIVER
Do not introduce uniformly
No good to measure at one point

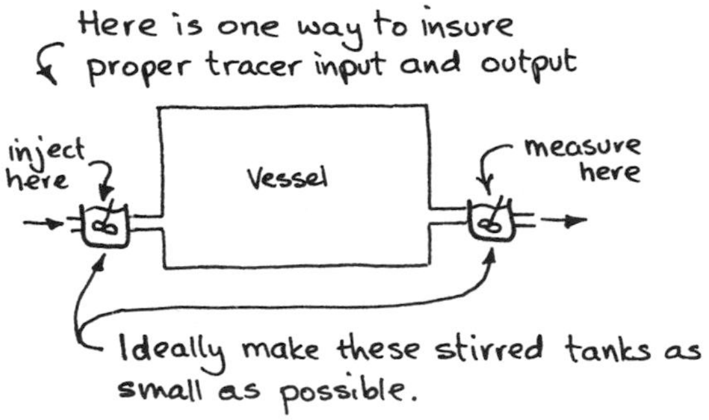

Here is one way to insure proper tracer input and output
inject here
Vessel
measure here
Ideally make these stirred tanks as small as possible.

If you do not introduce tracer properly or if you do not measure the concentration properly you get a response curve which is not the E curve but which with a proper flow model and the right mathematical manipulation may give the proper E curve.

Chapters 64 and 68 (especially 68) deals with this problem in detail.

(h) **The E curve.** To find the E_t curve (the RTD) from the experimental C vs t curve simply change the concentration scale so that the area under the response curve is unity. Thus simply divide the concentration readings by M/v.

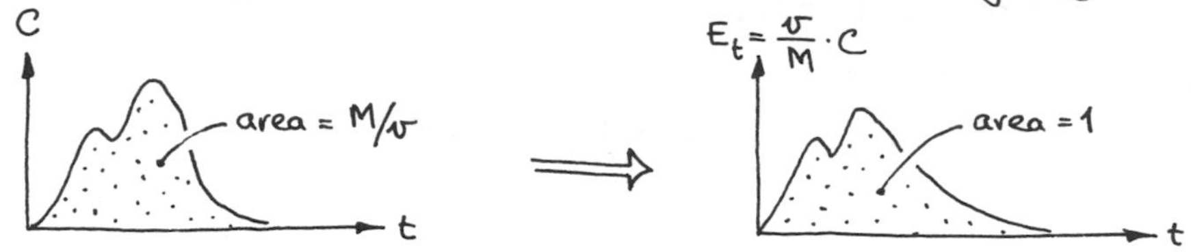

In terms of the dimensionless time scale

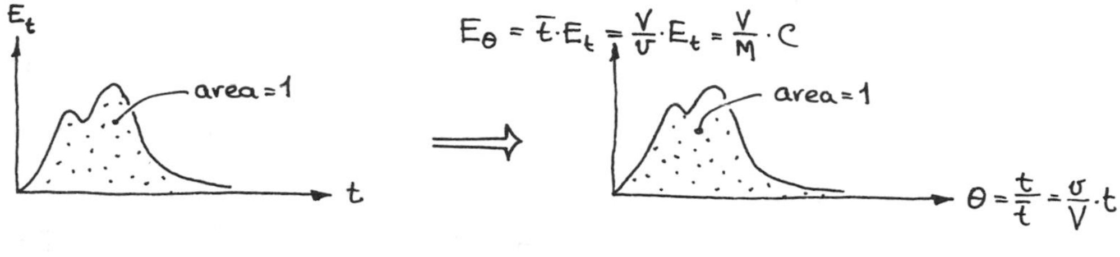

(i) **The delta function.** One E_t curve which may puzzle us is the queer one for plug flow. We call this the **Dirac δ function** and in symbols we show it as

$$\delta(t - t_0)$$

↑ this says that the pulse occurs at time t_0.

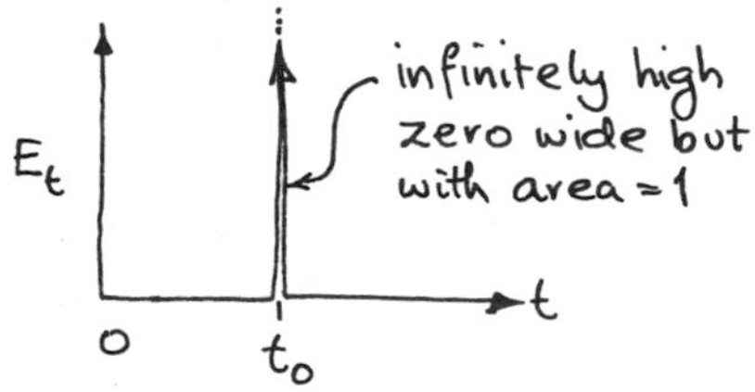

The two properties of this function which we need to know are

Area under the curve: $\displaystyle\int_0^\infty \delta(t-t_0)\,dt = 1$

Integration with a δ-function: $\displaystyle\int_0^\infty \delta(t-t_0)\,f(t)\,dt = f(t_0)$

Once we understand what this means we see that it is easier to integrate with a δ function than with any other. For example:

$$\int_0^\infty \delta(t-5)\,t^6\,dt = 5^6; \quad \int_0^\infty \delta(t-2)\,e^{-t}\,dt = e^{-2}; \quad \int_0^\infty \delta(t-3)\,4^t e^{2t}\,dt = 4^3 e^6$$

(j) **Example of the use of δ functions.** Suppose a first order reaction ($A \rightarrow R$, $-r_A = 0.003 C_A$ mol/m³·s) takes place in a plug flow reactor ($V = 2$ m³, $v = 0.05$ m³/s). Then $\bar{t} = 2/0.05 = 40$s, and the exit conversion, from eq. 1, is given by

$$\frac{C}{C_0} = \int_0^{\infty} \left(\frac{C}{C_0}\right)_{batch} \delta(t - t_0)\,dt = \int_0^{\infty} e^{-0.003t}\,\delta(t-40)\,dt$$

$$= e^{-0.003(40)} = 0.89 \qquad \ldots \text{ or } \quad X_A = 11\%$$

B. The step experiment.

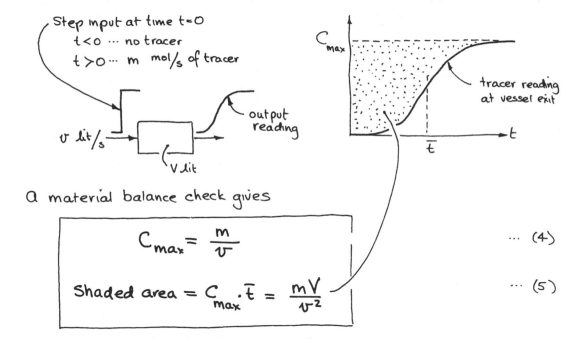

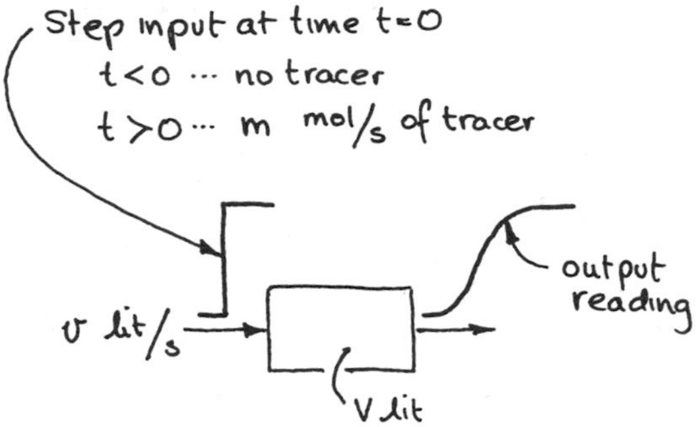

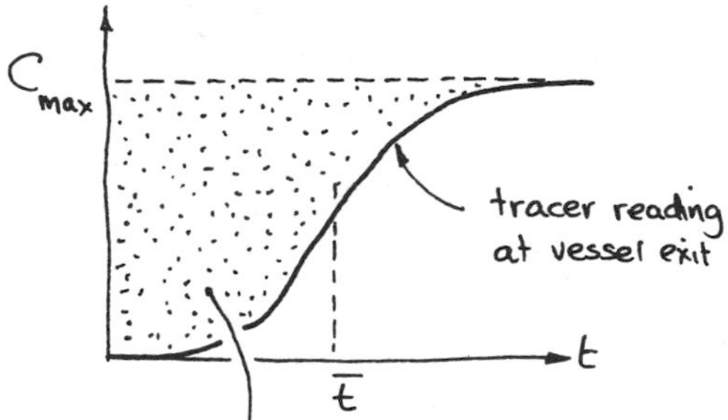

a material balance check gives

$$C_{max} = \frac{m}{v} \qquad \ldots (4)$$

$$\text{Shaded area} = C_{max} \cdot \bar{t} = \frac{mV}{v^2} \qquad \ldots (5)$$

(a) **Overall strategy.** First make a step concentration change at the inlet, measure the response curve and see if all is consistent. Then you have two choices:

- either go to the dimensionless step response curves F_t or F_θ and use these for flow modeling or for finding reactor output,
- or go directly to the pulse response curves E_t or E_θ and use these.

(b) **In testing for consistency** we again deal with three quantities m, v and V, and we have two equations, 4 and 5 to satisfy. Thus we can find any two unknowns, or with less than two unknowns we can make material balance checks to see if the data are consistent and properly taken.

(c) **Step-downs.** If we have a step-down instead of a step-up, or if the step-up does not start at $C=0$ it is no problem to flip the concentration scale or to shift it down so that at the start $C=0$.

(d) **The F curve.** To obtain the normalized step function, called the F curve simply change the concentration scale so that the curve rises from 0 to 1.

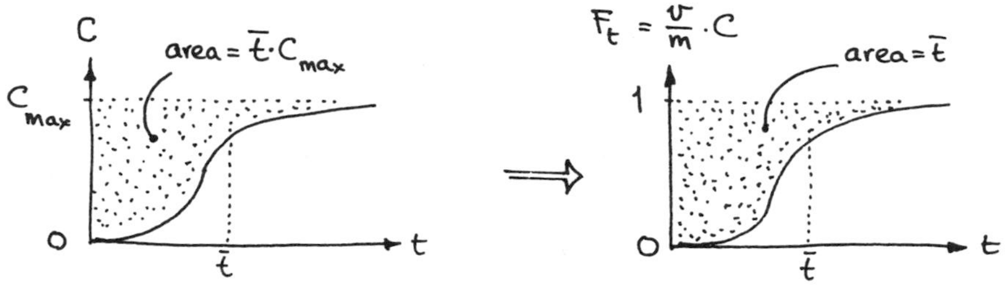

and in terms of the dimensionless time scale $\theta = t/\bar{t}$

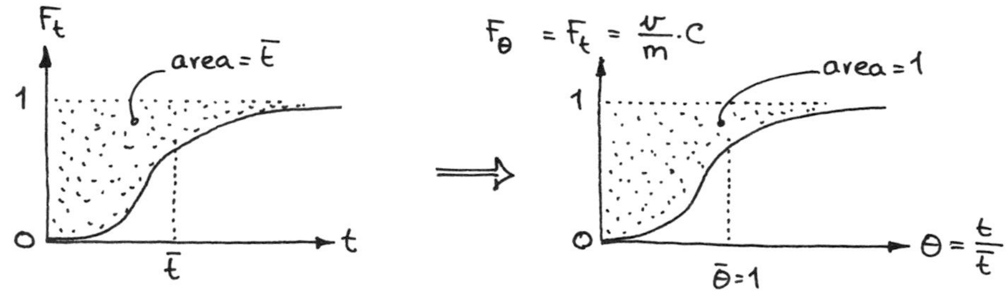

From these step response curves the mean residence time in the vessel may be found as follows:

$$\bar{t} = \frac{\int_0^{C_{max}} t\,dC}{\int_0^{C_{max}} dC} = \frac{1}{C_{max}} \int_0^{C_{max}} t\,dC = \int_0^1 t\,dF_t$$

... for more on this see chapter 63

(e) **The E and F curves.** The F curve is the integral of the E curve, while the E curve is the differentiated F curve. Thus

at given t: $E_t = \dfrac{dF_t}{dt}$ ... and ... $F_t = \int E_t\,dt$

In graphical form this relationship is

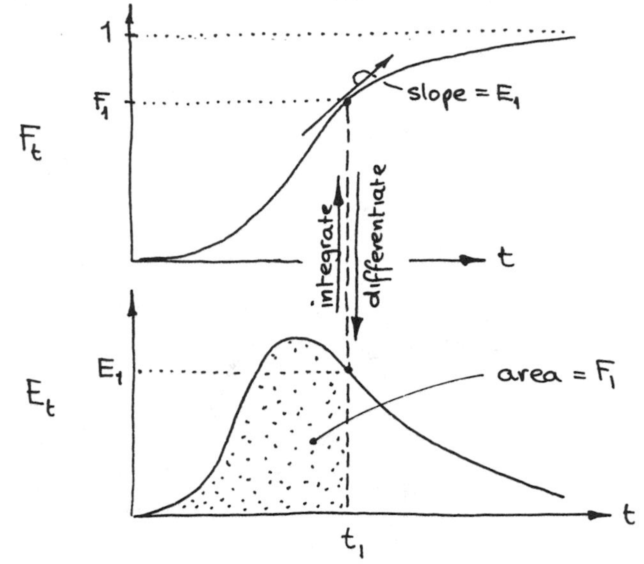

C. Summary of relationships between tracer curves.

$E_t = \dfrac{v}{M}\cdot C_{pulse}$, $F_t = \dfrac{v}{m}\cdot C_{step}$, $E_t = \dfrac{dF_t}{dt}$, $E_\theta = \dfrac{dF_\theta}{d\theta}$

at a given point on the curve

$\bar{t} = \dfrac{V}{v}$, $\theta = \dfrac{t}{\bar{t}}$, $\bar{\theta}_E = 1$, $E_\theta = \bar{t}\,E_t$, $F_t = F_\theta$

θ, E_θ, F_θ, F_t ... all dimensionless, $E_t = [\text{time}^{-1}]$

Let us show the relationship between these curves with a specific example of plug flow, and one of mixed flow.

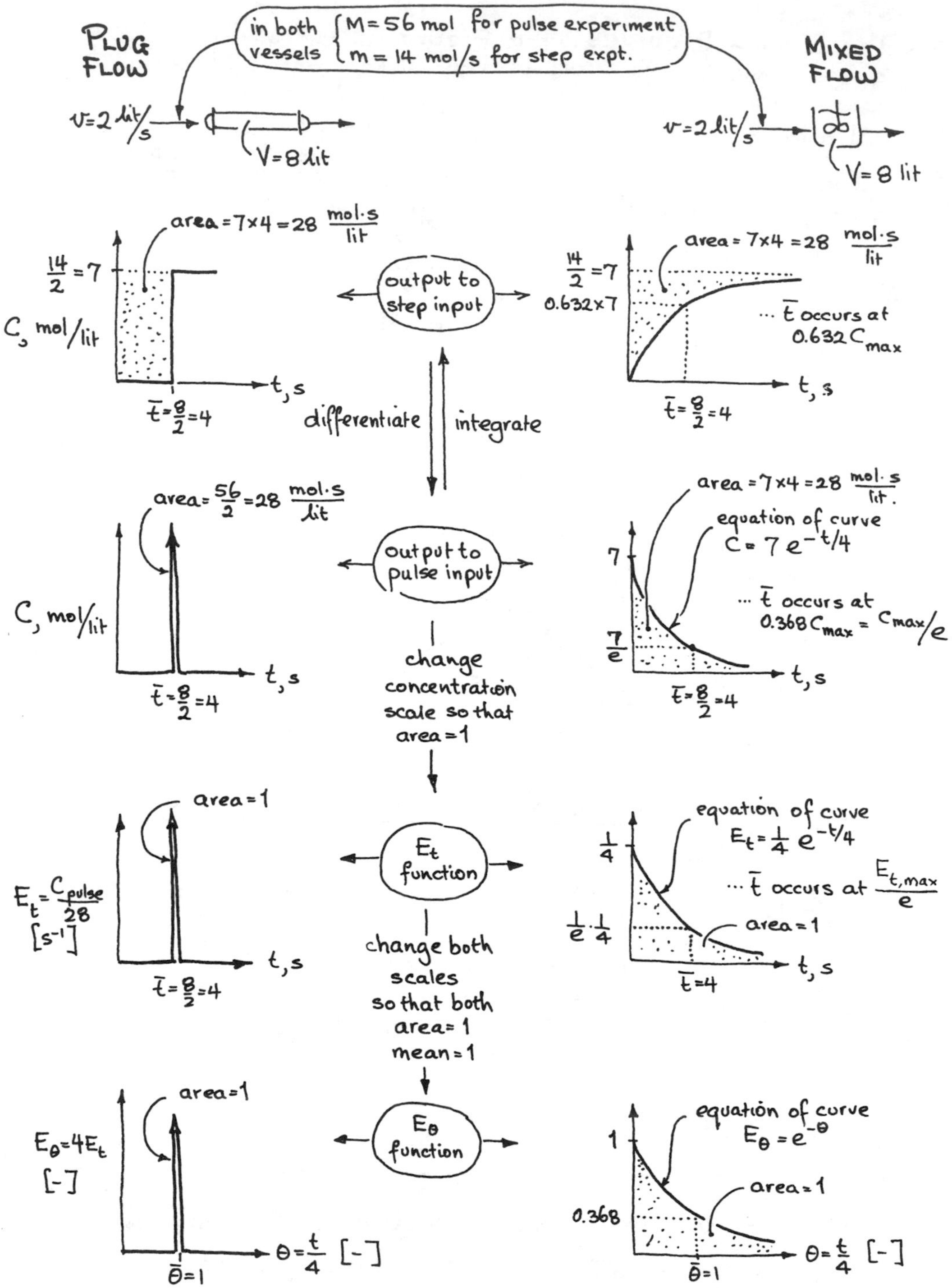
PLUG FLOW
in both vessels
M = 56 mol for pulse experiment
m = 14 mol/s for step expt.
MIXED FLOW
v = 2 lit/s
V = 8 lit
v = 2 lit/s
V = 8 lit
area = 7×4 = 28 mol·s/lit
14/2 = 7
C, mol/lit
t, s
t̄ = 8/2 = 4
output to step input
differentiate
integrate
area = 7×4 = 28 mol·s/lit
14/2 = 7
0.632×7
... t̄ occurs at 0.632 C max
t, s
t̄ = 8/2 = 4
area = 56/2 = 28 mol·s/lit
C, mol/lit
t, s
t̄ = 8/2 = 4
output to pulse input
change concentration scale so that area = 1
area = 7×4 = 28 mol·s/lit.
equation of curve
C = 7 e^(−t/4)
7
7/e
... t̄ occurs at 0.368 C max = C max/e
t, s
t̄ = 8/2 = 4
area = 1
E t = C pulse / 28
[s⁻¹]
t, s
t̄ = 8/2 = 4
E t function
change both scales so that both area = 1 mean = 1
equation of curve
E t = 1/4 e^(−t/4)
1/4
... t̄ occurs at E t,max / e
1/e · 1/4
area = 1
t, s
t̄ = 4
area = 1
E θ = 4E t
[−]
θ = t/4 [−]
θ̄ = 1
E θ function
equation of curve
E θ = e^(−θ)
1
0.368
area = 1
θ = t/4 [−]
θ̄ = 1

IV Experimental Methods (chemical) for finding E_t.

If tracer reacts away in the reactor with first order kinetics then for a continuous and constant tracer input (no pulse, no step,...) we have

$$\left(\frac{\bar{C}_A}{C_{A0}}\right)_{\text{at exit}} = \int_0^\infty \left(\frac{C_A}{C_{A0}}\right)_{\text{element}} \cdot E_t\,dt = \int_0^\infty e^{-kt} \cdot E_t\,dt$$

Given k and the measured $(\bar{C}_A/C_{A0})_{exit}$ the only unknown in the above equation is E_t. So we can use a series of k values, and for each measure $(\bar{C}_A/C_{A0})_{exit}$, and from this we should be able to construct the E_t curve.

Note that this equation is of the form of the **Laplace transform** of the E_t fuction

$$\bar{C} = \int_0^\infty e^{-st}\, E_t\,dt$$

so finding E_t is equivalent to evaluating the inverse of the Laplace transform for a series of s values. This can be done either

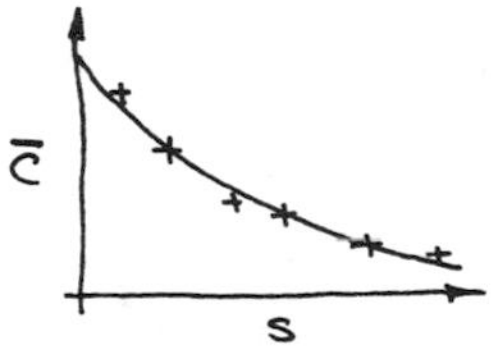

- analytically (first find an equation between s and $\bar{C}$, then invert this equation)
- numerically (this requires that you know the family of curves to which E_t belongs).

How to run such a reaction in practice?

- Run one known first order reaction at various temperatures, hence various k values.
- Run a number of independent reactions $\begin{cases} A \rightarrow R \\ B \rightarrow S \\ C \rightarrow T \\ \vdots \end{cases}$ at the same time, for example radioactive decay.
- Run a second order homogeneously catalysed reaction using several catalyst concentrations

$$A \xrightarrow{\text{catalyst } C} R \qquad \cdots \quad -r_A = (kC_c)C_A = k_{obs}C_A$$

V Summary:

In general the RTD, state of aggregation and earliness of mixing determine the behavior of the reactor. However, for a single flowing stream with not extremely fast reaction the RTD for the extremes of micro- and macrofluid behavior are a close approximation to the real system.

RTD curves can be obtained by either physical or chemical methods of experimentation and reactor behavior can be approximated directly from these curves.

Chapter 61 Problems

The following graphs show the tracer output from a vessel for a particular tracer input. For each case

(a) Show, if possible, whether the material balance is satisfied.

(b) Find the quantities asked for.

(c) Sketch the exit age distribution functions E_t and E_θ.

To make the mathematics bearable only simple idealized curves are shown.

A1 . . .

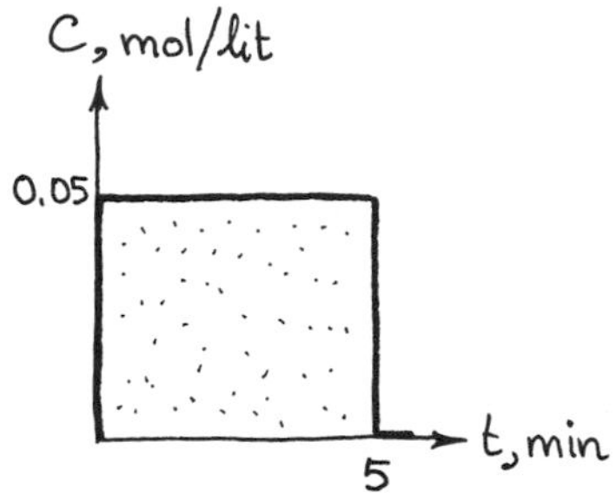

Given	Required
Pulse input	Consistent?
M = 1 mol at t = 0	V, E_t, E_θ
v = 4 lit/min	

A2 . . .

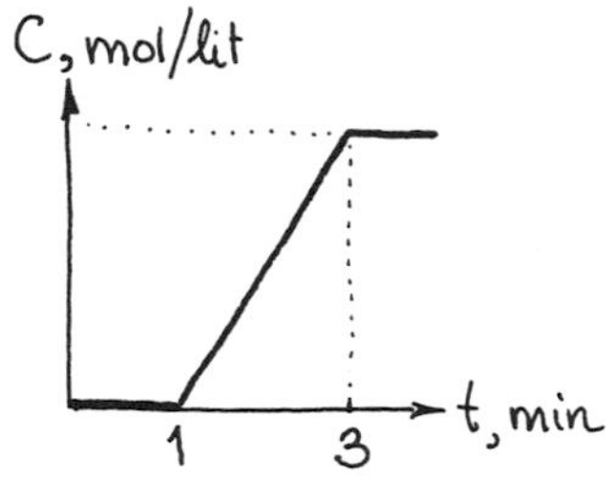

Given	Required
Step input	Consistent?
$t < 0$: no tracer	V, E_t, E_θ
$t > 0$: m = 0.5 mol/min	
v = 4 lit/min	

A3 . . .

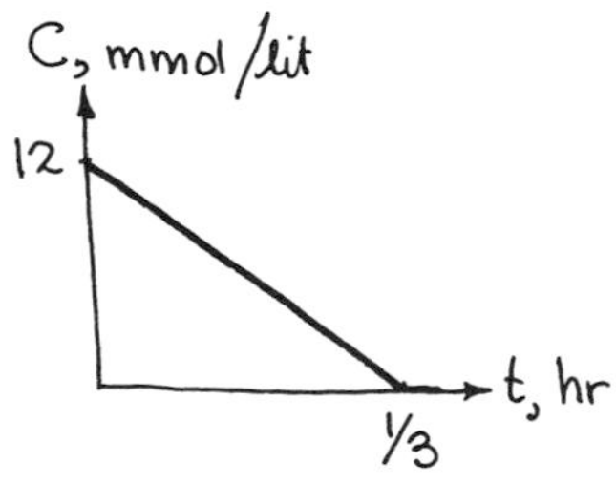

Given	Required
Step input	Consistent?
$t < 0$: C_{in} = 12 mmol/lit	m, v, E_t, E_θ
$t > 0$: $C_{in} = 0$	
V = 500 lit	

A4 . . .

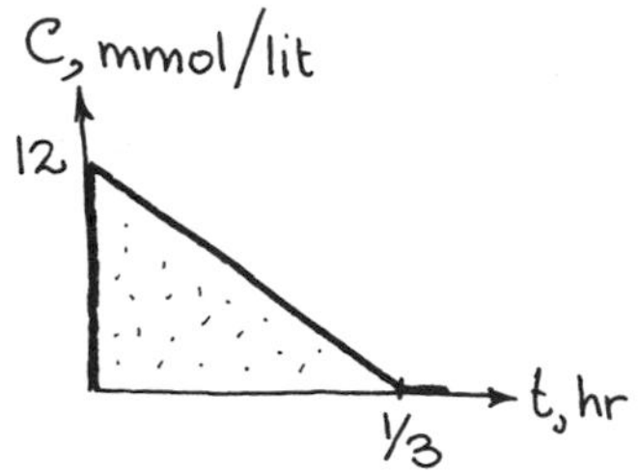

Given	Required
Pulse input	Consistent?
M unknown	M, v, E_t, E_θ
V = 500 lit	

Chapter **61** Problems

A5 . . .

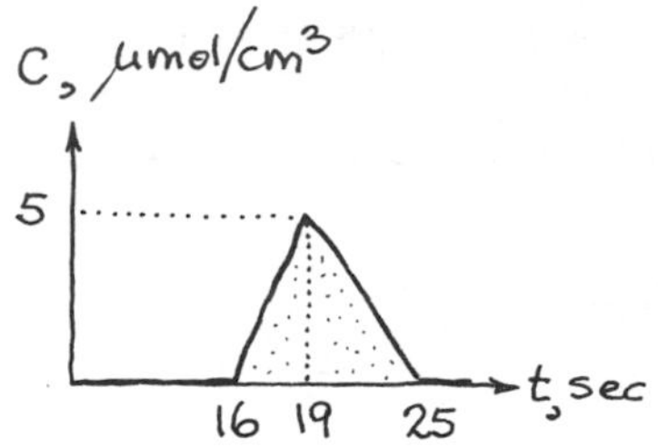

Given
Pulse input
$v = 4\ cm^3/sec$
$V = 60\ cm^3$

Required
Consistent?
M, E_t, E_θ

A6 . . .

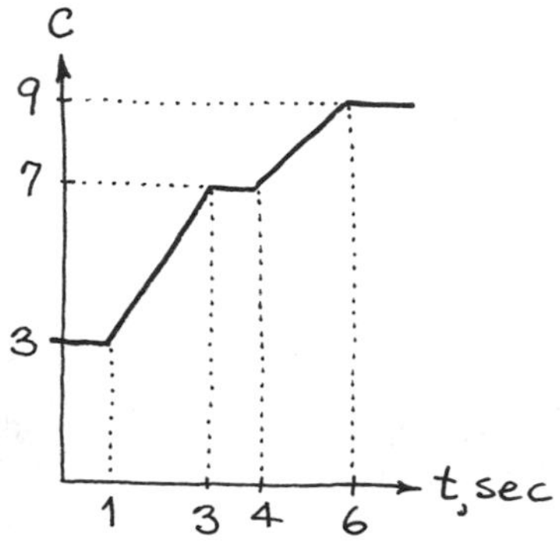

Given
Step input
$t < 0$: $C_{in} = 3$
$t > 0$: $C_{in} = 9$
V = 2 lit

Required
Consistent?
m, v, E_t, E_θ

A7 . . .

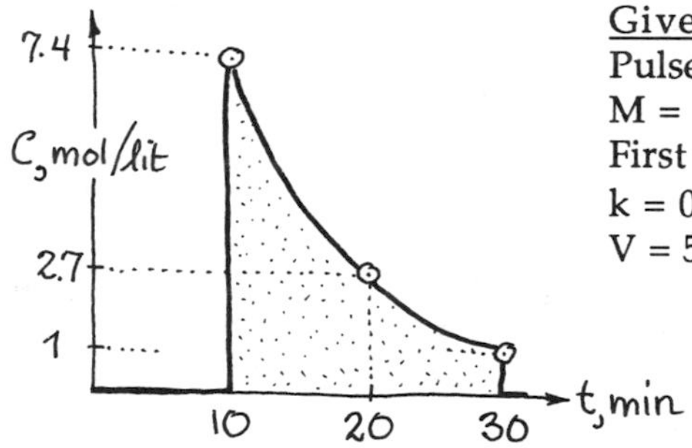

Given
Pulse of reactant A
M = 1 mol
First order reaction
$k = 0.1\ min^{-1}$
V = 50 lit

Required
Consistent?
v, E_t, E_θ

A8 . . .

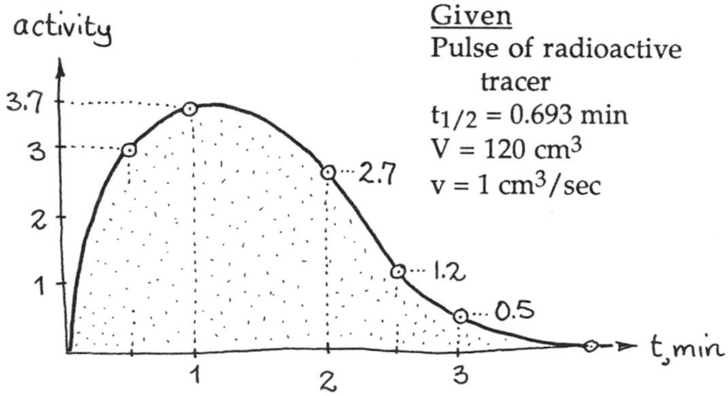

Given
Pulse of radioactive tracer
$t_{1/2} = 0.693$ min
$V = 120\ cm^3$
$v = 1\ cm^3/sec$

Required
Consistent?
E_t, E_θ

Chapter 61 Problems

A9 A batch of radioactive material is dumped into the Columbia River. At Bonneville Dam, about 240 miles downstream the flowing waters (6000 m^3/sec) are monitored for a particular radioisotope ($t_{1/2}$ > 10 yrs) and the following data are obtained.

(a) How many units of this tracer were introduced into the river?

(b) What is the volume of Columbia River waters between Bonneville dam and the point of introduction of tracer?

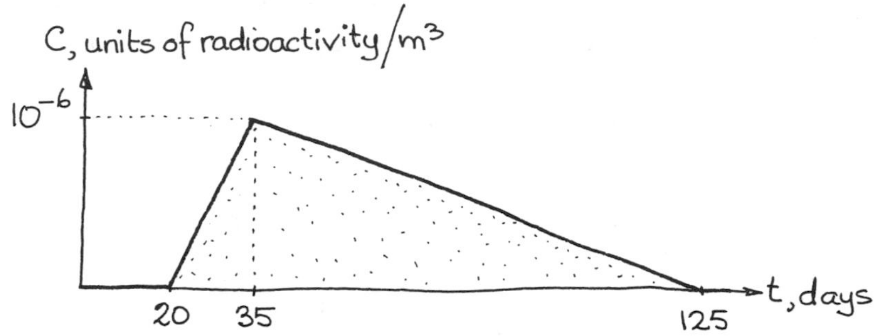

A10 A pipeline (10 cm I. D. , 19.1 m long) simultaneously transports gas and liquid from here to there. The volumetric flow rate of gas and liquid are 60000 cm^3/sec and 300 cm^3/sec respectively. Pulse tracer tests on the fluids flowing through the pipe give results as shown below. What fraction of the pipe is occupied by gas and what fraction by liquid?

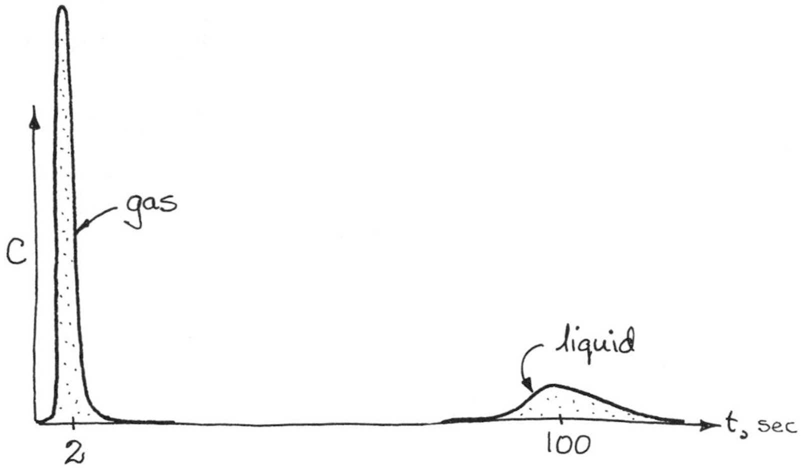

Chapter 61 Problems

A gas-liquid contactor consists of a column 20 m high, 1 m^2 cross section filled with packing ($\varepsilon = 0.5$). Gas flows at 0.5 m^3/sec through the unit, liquid at 0.1 m^3/sec. We wish to find the volume fraction occupied by flowing gas, flowing liquid, and stagnant liquid. For this, tracer is introduced into both the entering gas and the entering liquid stream and tracer output are measured. From the data below

(a) find the three required volumes. If the results are faulty, give a possible explanation.

(b) Sketch the E_t and E_θ curve for the gas in the vessel.

A11 . . .

Gas
pulse input

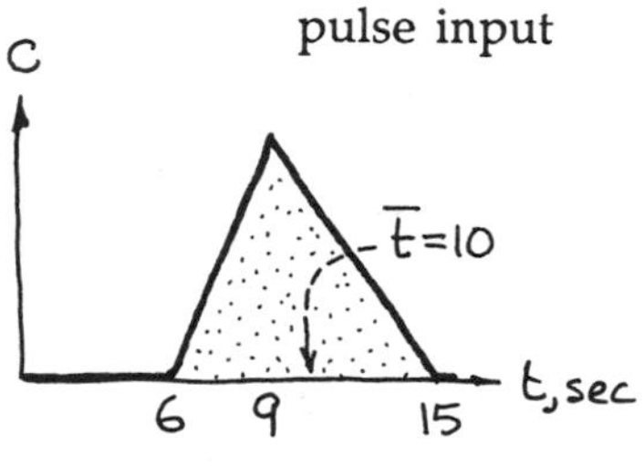

Liquid
pulse input

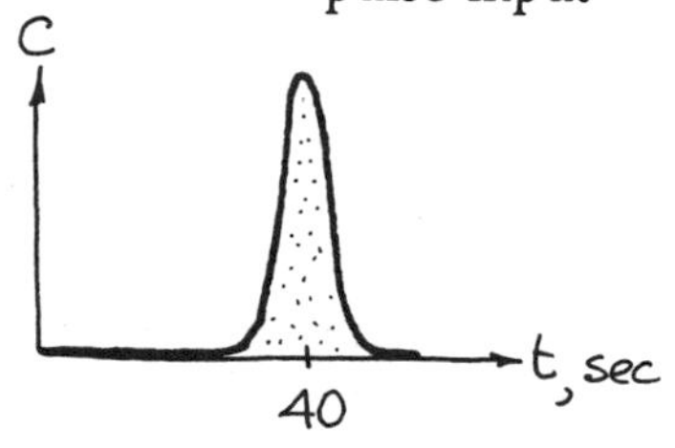

A12 . . .

Gas
step input

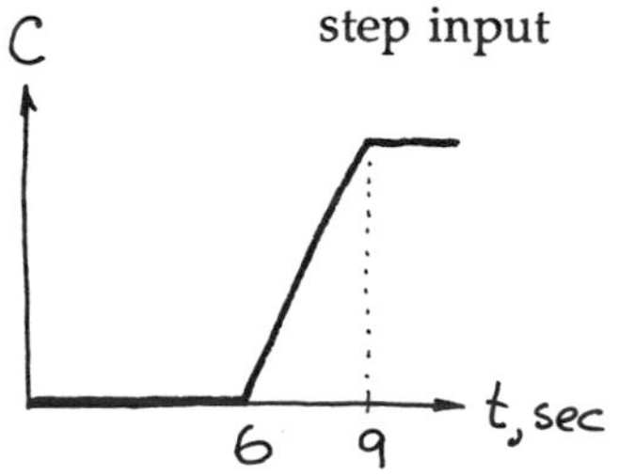

Liquid
pulse input

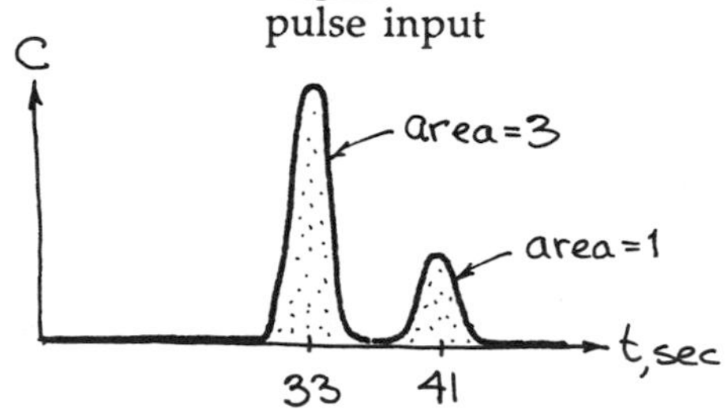

A13 . . .

Gas
step input

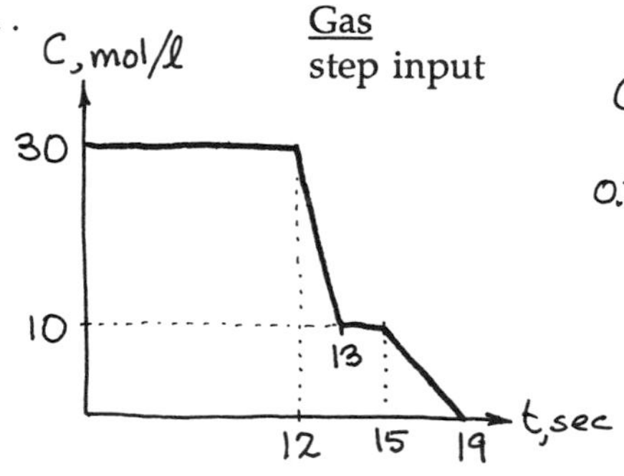

Liquid
step input

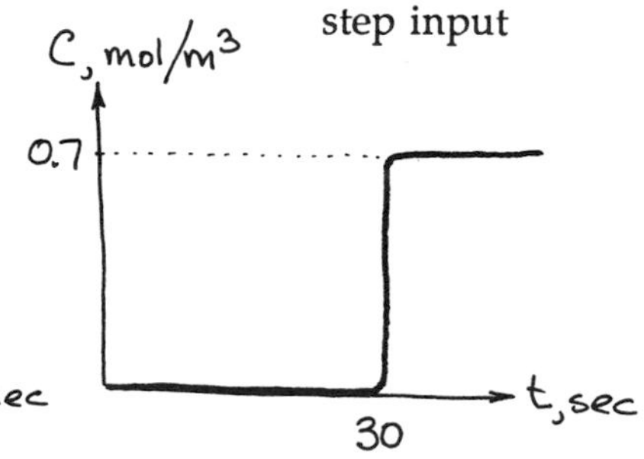

Chapter **61** Problems

A14 The Dow model 5 artificial kidney is a plastic single pass membrane exchanger, easily slipped in a coat pocket, and containing about 20000 reconstructed cellulose hollow fibers.

For tracer tests fluid flows at 500 cm^3/min through the shell side, the tube side is kept stagnant. Pulses of two different kinds of tracer are introduced into the entering shell side fluid. Tracer A cannot penetrate the membrane and therefore remains of the shell side. Tracer B passes freely through the membrane material into the tube side fluid. Find the volumes of shell side and of tube side fluid from the idealized data shown below.

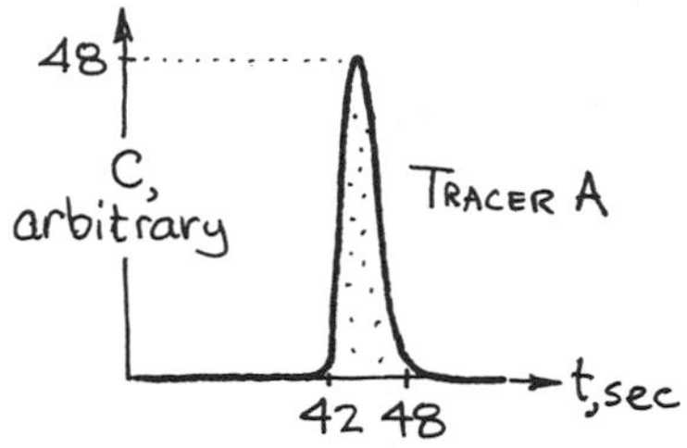

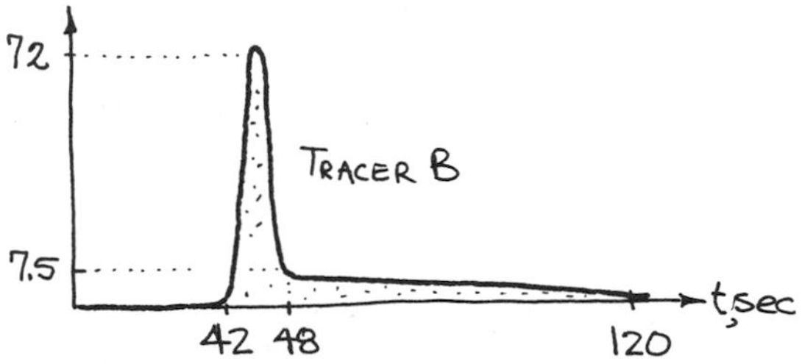

A15 A large tank (860 lit) is used as a gas-liquid contactor. Gas bubbles up through the vessel and out the top, liquid flows in at one port and out the other at 5 lit/sec. To get an idea of the flow pattern of liquid in this tank a pulse of tracer (M = 150 gm) is injected at the liquid inlet and measured at the outlet, as follows.

(a) Is this a properly done experiment? If so, find the E_θ curve.

(b) Qualitatively what do you think is happening in the vessel?

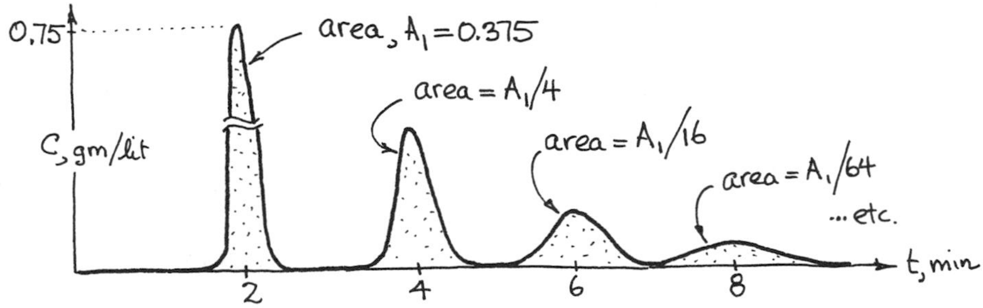

A16 The flow pattern of gas in a fluidized bed of porous particles (bed voidage = 0.5, particle porosity = 0.5) is studied using step tracer methods and two different tracers, helium and Freon-12. Helium is known to not adsorb on the porous surface of the solid, Freon-12 is suspected to adsorb. The output curves are shown as follows.

(a) Is Freon-12 adsorbed?

(b) If so, find the adsorption equilibrium constant **m**, defined as

$$\mathbf{m} = \frac{\text{volume adsorbed}}{\text{volume of porous solid}}$$

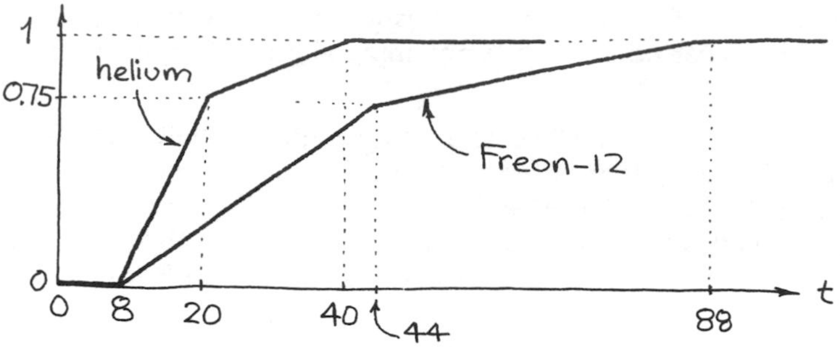

These curves approximate the reported data of Yoshida and Kunii, J. Chem. Eng. Japan **1** 11 (1968).

A liquid macrofluid reacts as it flows through a vessel. Find the conversion of A for the following flow patterns and reaction kinetics.

B17 . . .

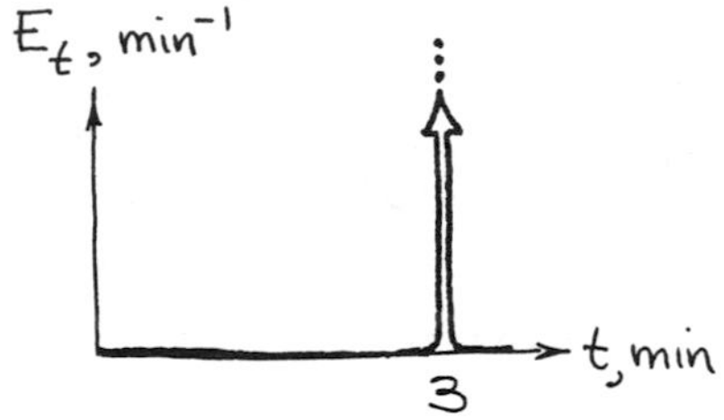

Determine $X_{A,\ macro}$

$A \rightarrow R + S + T$
$C_{A0} = 1$ mol/lit
$-r_A = kC_A$
$k = 1\ min^{-1}$
Also find $X_{A,\ micro}$ and compare.

B18 . . .

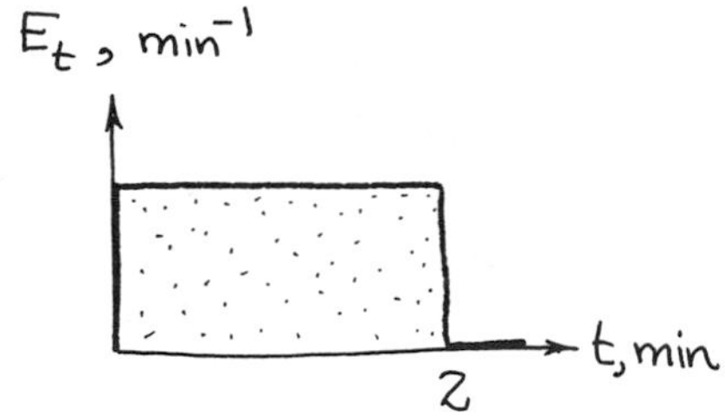

Determine $X_{A,\ macro}$

$A \rightarrow R$
$C_{A0} = 1$ mol/lit
$-r_A = kC_A^{0.5}$
$k = 2\ mol^{0.5}/lit^{0.5}{\cdot}min$

B19 . . .

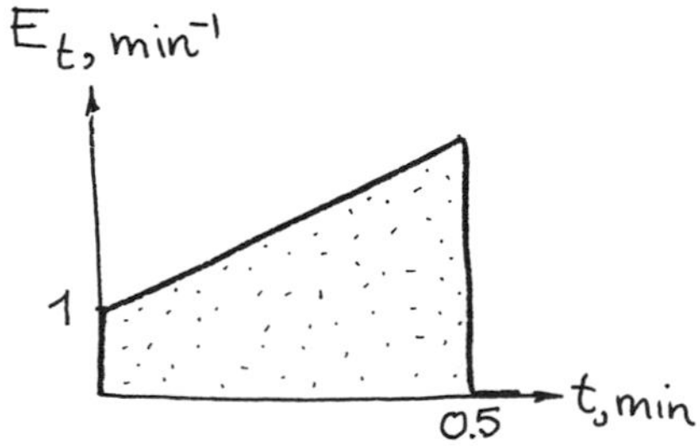

Determine $X_{A,\ macro}$

$A \rightarrow R$
$C_{A0} = 2$ mol/lit
$-r_A = kC_A^2$
$k = 2$ lit/mol·min

Chapter 61 Problems

B20 . . .

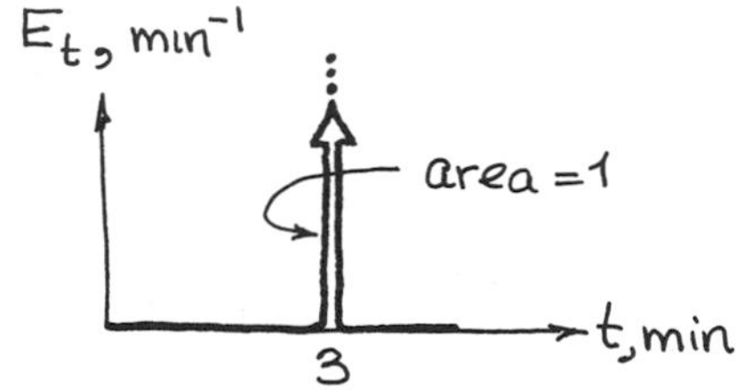

Determine $X_{A,\ macro}$

$A \rightarrow R$
$C_{A0} = 4$ mol/lit
$-r_A = k$
$k = 1$ mol/lit·min
Also find $X_{A,\ micro}$ and compare.

B21 . . .

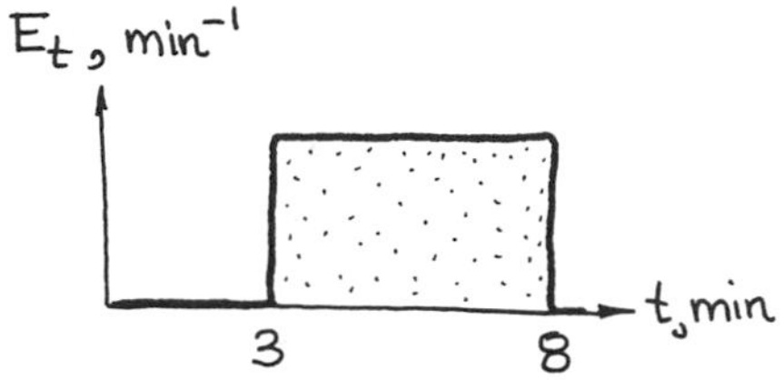

Determine $X_{A,\ macro}$

$A \rightarrow R$
$C_{A0} = 0.5$ mol/lit
$-r_A = kC_A^3$
$k = 2$ lit^2/mol^2·min

B22 . . .

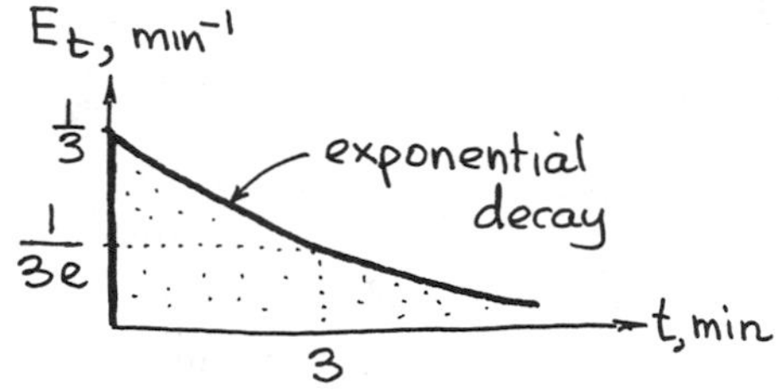

Determine $X_{A,\ macro}$

$A \rightarrow R$
$C_{A0} = 0.01$ mol/lit
$-r_A = kC_A$
$k = 0.667$ hr^{-1}
Also find $X_{A,\ micro}$ and compare.

B23 . . .

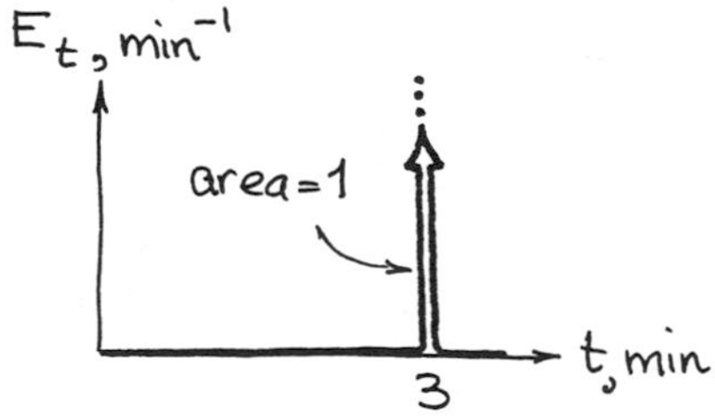

Determine $X_{A,\ macro}$

$A \rightarrow R$
$C_{A0} = 0.1$ mol/lit
$-r_A = kC_A^2$
$k = 1$ lit/mol·min
Also find $X_{A,\ micro}$ and compare.

B24 . . .

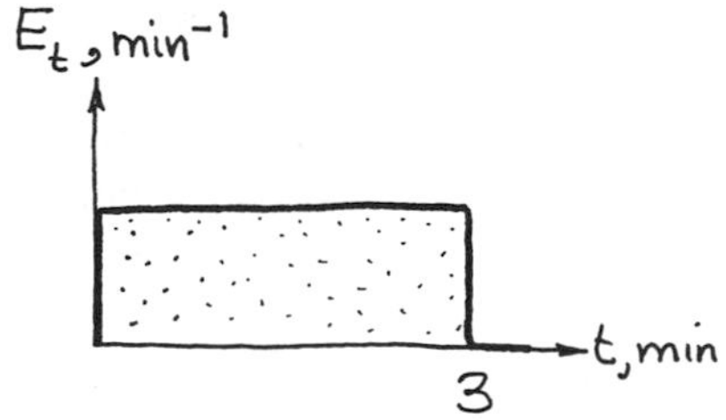

Determine $X_{A,\ macro}$

$A \rightarrow R$
$C_{A0} = 6$ mol/lit
$-r_A = k$
$k = 3$ mol/lit·min

Chapter 61 Problems

B25 . . .

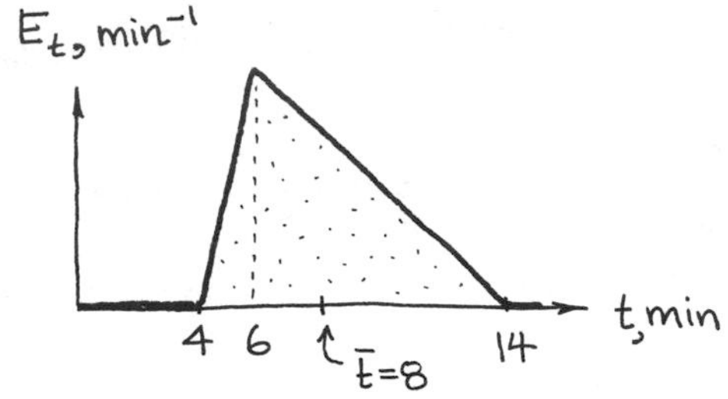

Determine $X_{A,\ \text{macro}}$

$A \rightarrow R$
$C_{A0} = 0.1$ mol/lit
$-r_A = k$
$k = 0.03$ mol/lit·min

B26 . . .

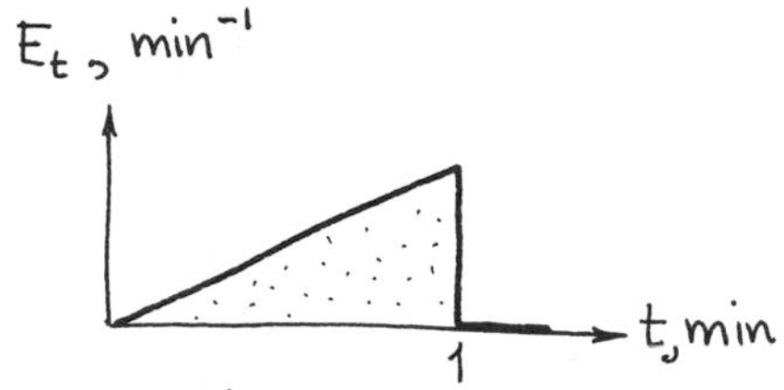

Determine $X_{A,\ \text{macro}}$

$A \rightarrow R$
$C_{A0} = 1$ mol/lit
$-r_A = kC_A^2$
$k = 1$ lit/mol·min

B27 . . .

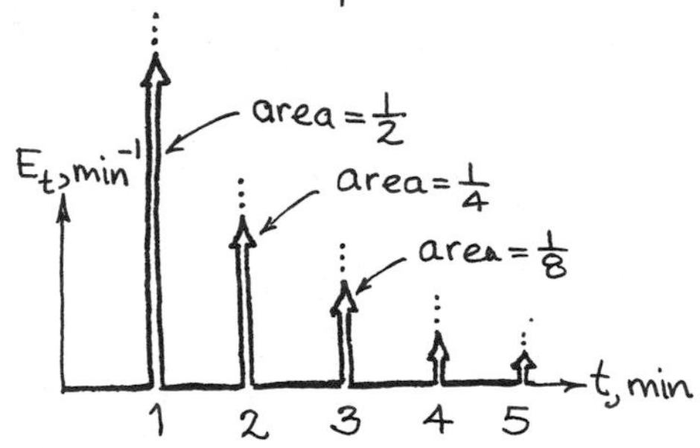

Determine $X_{A,\ \text{macro}}$

$A \rightarrow R$
$C_{A0} = 1$ mol/lit
$-r_A = kC_A$
$k = 1\ \text{min}^{-1}$

B28 . . .

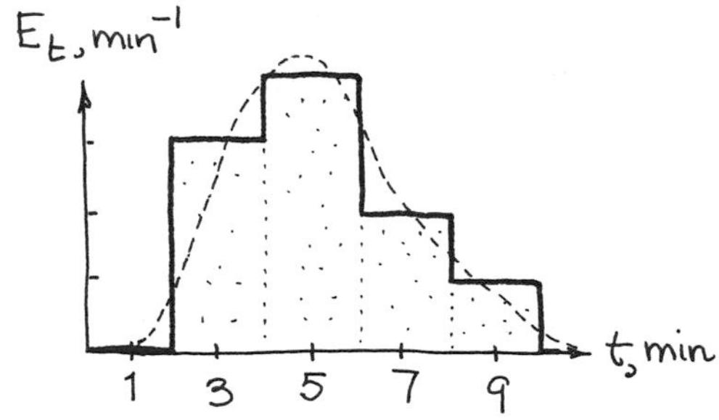

Determine $X_{A,\ \text{macro}}$

$A \rightarrow R$
$C_{A0} = 3.33$ mol/lit
$-r_A = kC_A^2$
$k = 0.3$ lit/mol·min

B29 . . .

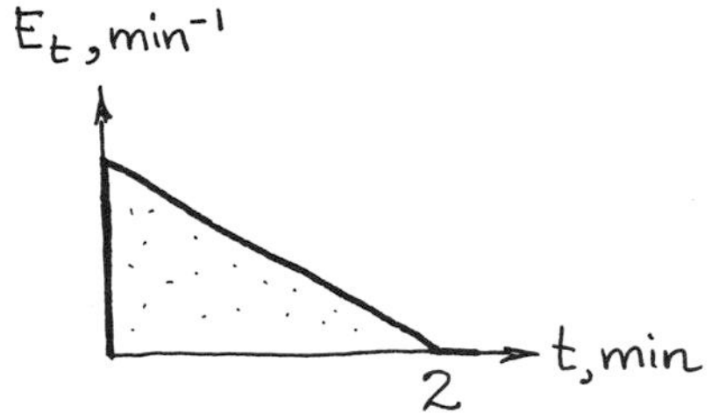

Determine $X_{A,\ \text{macro}}$

$A \rightarrow R + S$
$C_{A0} = 1$ mol/lit
$-r_A = kC_A$
$k = 1\ \text{min}^{-1}$

Chapter **61** Problems

Hydrogen sulfide is removed from coal gas by contact with a moving bed of iron oxide particles which convert to the sulfide as follows

$$Fe_2O_3 \rightarrow FeS$$

In our reactor the fraction of oxide unconverted in any particle is determined by its residence time t and the time needed for complete conversion of the particle τ, and this is given by

$$1 - X = \left(1 - \frac{t}{\tau}\right)^3 \quad \text{when } t < 1, \text{ and with } \tau = 1 \text{ hr.}$$

Find the conversion of iron oxide to sulfide if the RTD of solids in the contactor is approximated by the curve below

B30 . . .

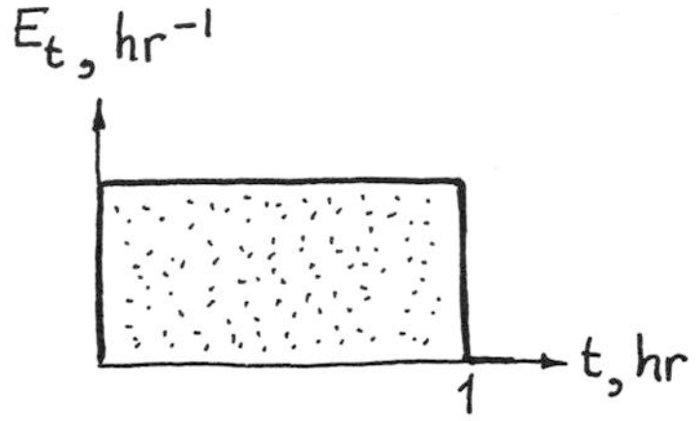

B31 . . .

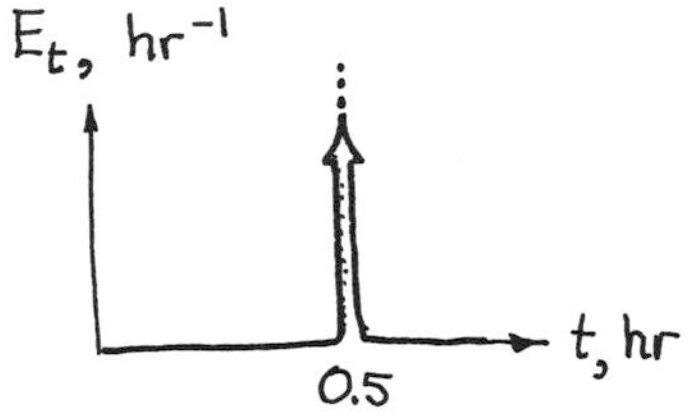

B32 . . .

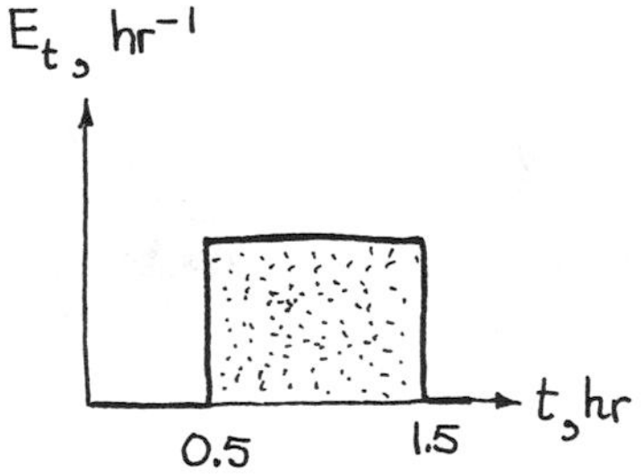

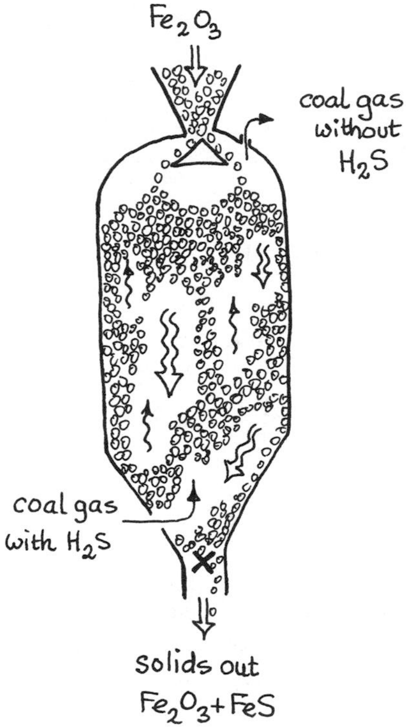

Dispersed noncoalescing droplets (C_{A0} = 2 mol/lit) react ($A \rightarrow R$, $-r_A = kC_A^2$, k = 0.5 lit/mol·min) as they pass through a contactor. Find the average concentration of A remaining in the droplets leaving the contactor if their RTD is given by the following curve

Chapter 61 Problems

B33 . . .

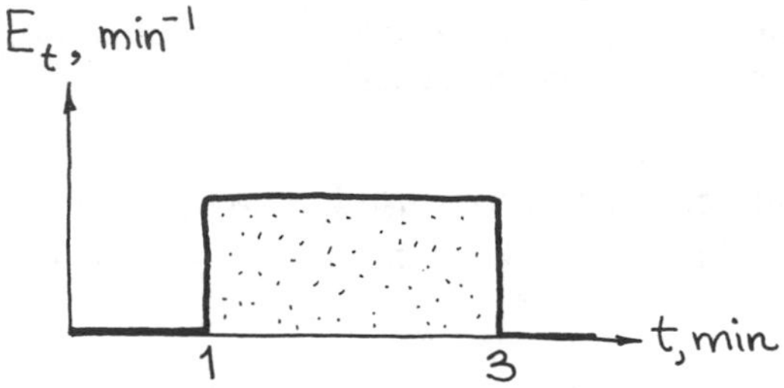

B34 . . .

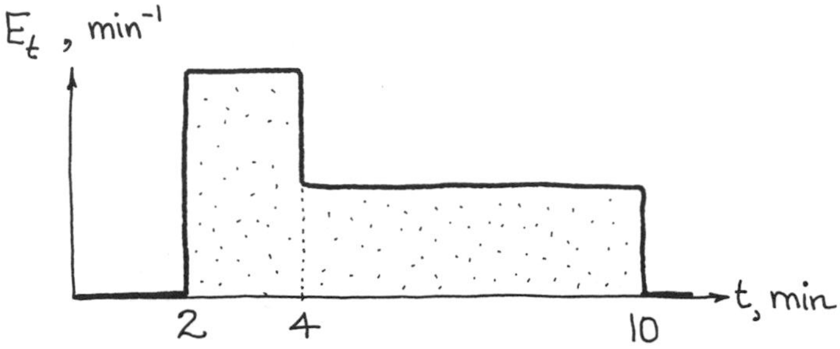

B35 . . .

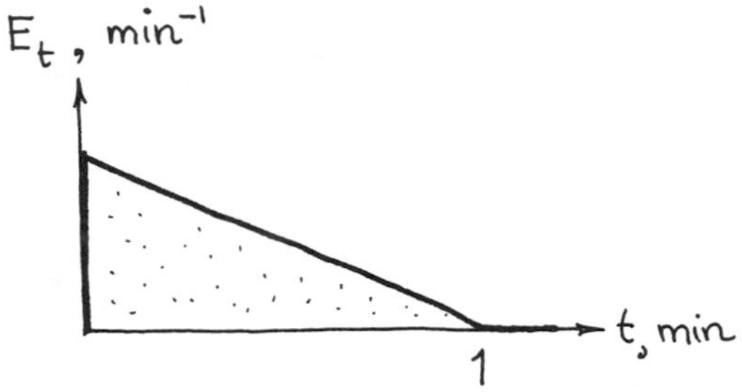

C36 Cold solids flow continuously into a fluidized bed where they disperse rapidly enough so that they can be taken as well mixed. They then heat up, they devolatilize slowly, and they leave. Devolatilization releases gaseous A which then decomposes by first order kinetics as it passes through the bed. When the gas leaves the bed decomposition of gaseous A stops. From the following information determine the fraction of gaseous A which has decomposed.

<u>Data:</u> Since this is a large-particle fluidized bed containing cloudless bubbles assume plug flow of gas through the unit. Also assume that the volume of gases released by the solids is small compared to the volume of carrier gas passing through the bed.

Mean residence time in the bed: $\bar{t}_s = 15$ min, $\bar{t}_g = 2$ s for carrier gas

For the reaction: $A \rightarrow$ products, $-r_A = kC_A$, $k = 1\ s^{-1}$

Chapter 61 Problems

C37* A large fluidized drier for wood chips operates today as follows: F_0 = 200 kg/min of wet wood chips (1 part moisture, 1 part wood) are fed continuously to the drier which contains W = 12000 kg of drying wood chips, while F_1 = 120 kg/min of partly dried wood chips leave the drier continuously. We wish to determine how a change in feed rate or bed weight will affect the moisture content of the product solids. So

(a) develop an expression for the moisture content of the leaving chips, expressed as y = kg H_2O/kg dry wood, as a function of F_0 and W.

(b) Find the moisture content of the product stream if the flow rate of feed is doubled while the bed weight remains unchanged.

Additional information: Assume that the drying rate of a chip, measured by -dy/dt, is proportional to its moisture content and that this proportionality constant does not change with changing operating conditions. Also accept that the moisture content of incoming chips stays fixed, and that the solids are well mixed in the drier.

A38 The EKAF chemical complex discharges harmless liquid waste through a long pipe (0.2 m^2 cross section, 10 km long, steady flow, pipe full of liquid) into Calapooya Creek. PCB (polychlorinated biophenyl) is used in the plant, is extremely dangerous to living creatures, and is not to be discharged into the stream. So a PCB monitor is installed at the pipe outlet.

Last week, due to an accident, a slug of PCB was lost down the drain and flushed into the river. From the following recording of the PCB monitor can you tell how much PCB entered the river?

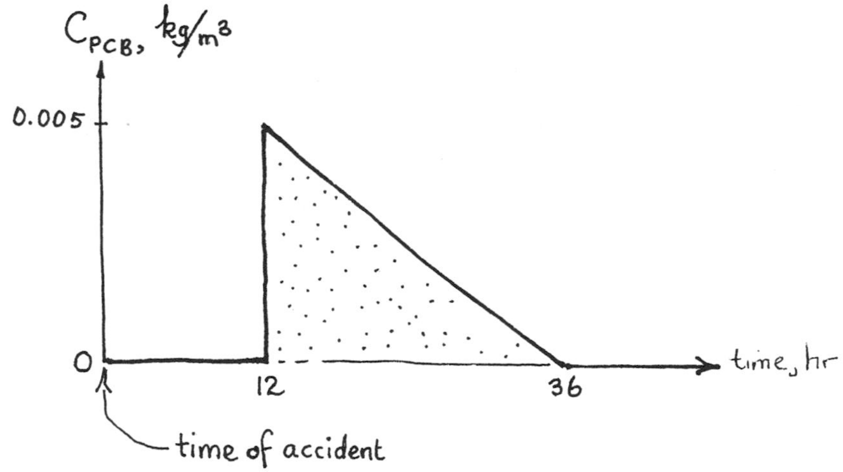

Chapter 62. COMPARTMENT MODELS.

Flow models can be of different levels of sophistication, and the compartment models of this chapter are the next stage beyond the very simplest, those that assume the extremes of plug flow and mixed flow. In the compartment models we consider the vessel and the flow through it as follows:

Total volume ... V

- V_p - plug flow region } V_a - active volume
- V_m - mixed flow region }
- V_d - dead or stagnant region within the vessel

Total throughflow ... v

- v_a - active flow, that through the plug and mixed flow regions
- v_b - bypass flow
- v_r - recycle flow

I Physical Tracer Method.

By comparing the E_t curve for the real vessel with the theoretical curves for various combinations of compartments and throughflow we can find which model fits the real vessel best. Of course the fit will not be perfect, however models of this kind are often a reasonable approximation to the real vessel.

The next few pages show what the E_t curves look like for various combinations of the above elements — certainly not all combinations.

Hints, suggestions and possible applications

(a) If we know M (kg of tracer introduced in the pulse) we can make a material balance check. Remember that $M = v$(area of curve). However, if we only measure the output C on an arbitrary scale we cannot find M or make this material balance check.

62.2

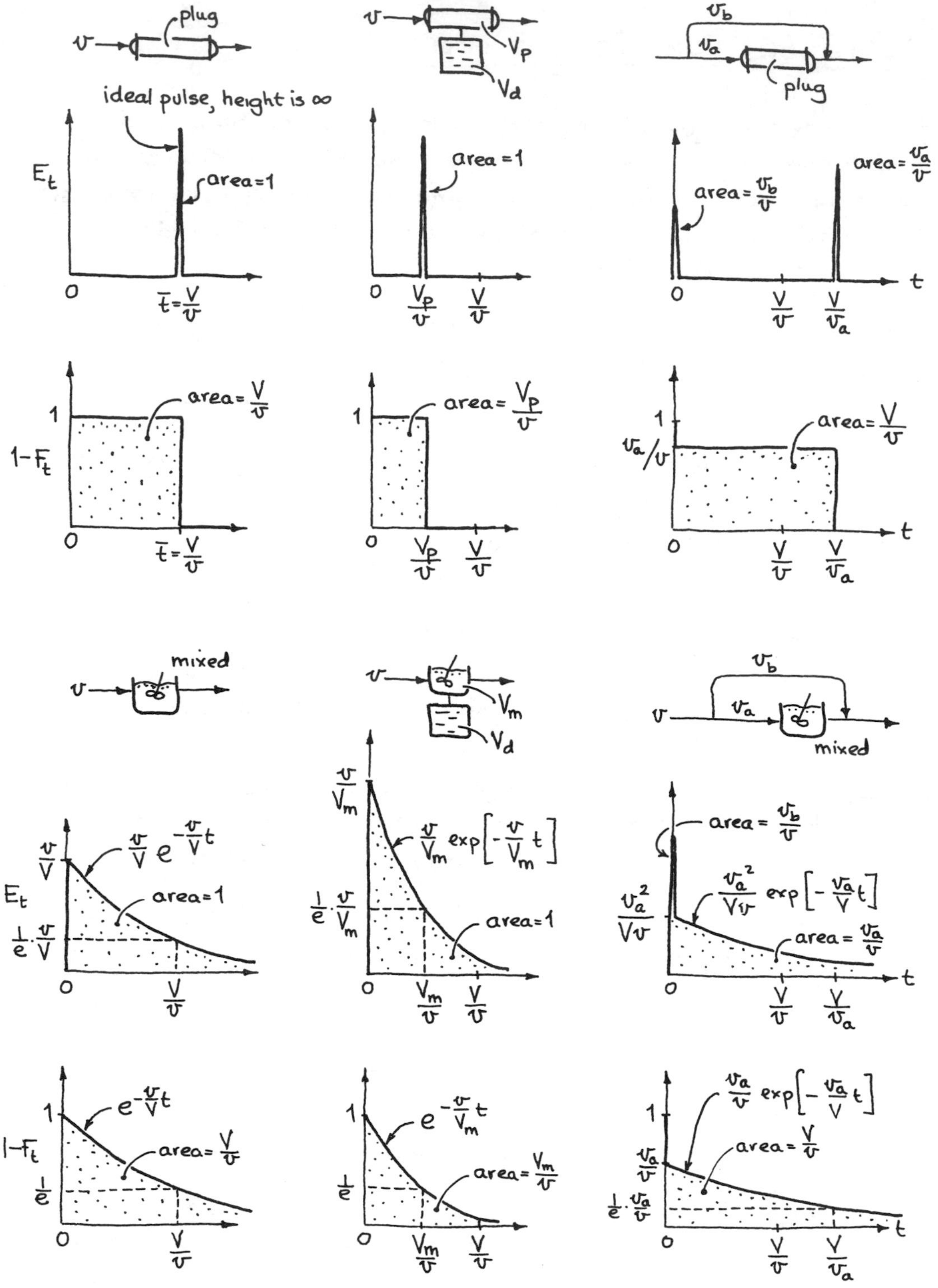
plug
v
V_p
V_d
v_b
v_a
ideal pulse, height is ∞
E_t
area=1
area = v_b/v
area = v_a/v
t
0
t̄ = V/v
V_p/v
V/v
V/v_a
1
1−F_t
area = V/v
area = V_p/v
v_a/v
mixed
V_m
v/V e^{−(v/V)t}
v/V
(1/e)·v/V
v/V_m exp[−(v/V_m) t]
(1/e)·v/V_m
V_m/v
v_a^2/(Vv) exp[−(v_a/V)t]
v_a^2/(Vv)
e^{−(v/V)t}
1/e
e^{−(v/V_m)t}
area = V_m/v
v_a/v exp[−(v_a/V) t]
(1/e)·v_a/v

area $= \dfrac{v_1}{v}$

area $= \dfrac{v_2}{v}$

E_t

$\dfrac{V_{p1}}{v_1}$ $\dfrac{V_{p2}}{v_2}$

overall mean $\bar{t} = \dfrac{V}{v} = \dfrac{V_{p1}+V_{p2}}{v_1+v_2}$

$1-F_t$

$\dfrac{v_2}{v}$

area $= \dfrac{V}{v}$

$\dfrac{V_{p1}}{v_1}$ $\dfrac{V_{p2}}{v_2}$

V_{p1}

R

V_{p2}

V_d

E_t

A_1

$A_1\left(\dfrac{R}{R+1}\right)$

$A_1\left(\dfrac{R}{R+1}\right)^2$

$A_1\left(\dfrac{R}{R+1}\right)^3$

$\cdots A_1 = \dfrac{1}{R+1}$

$\dfrac{V_{p1}}{(R+1)v}$ $\Delta t = \dfrac{V_{p1}}{(R+1)v} + \dfrac{V_{p2}}{Rv}$

V_1

v_1

v

v_2

V_2

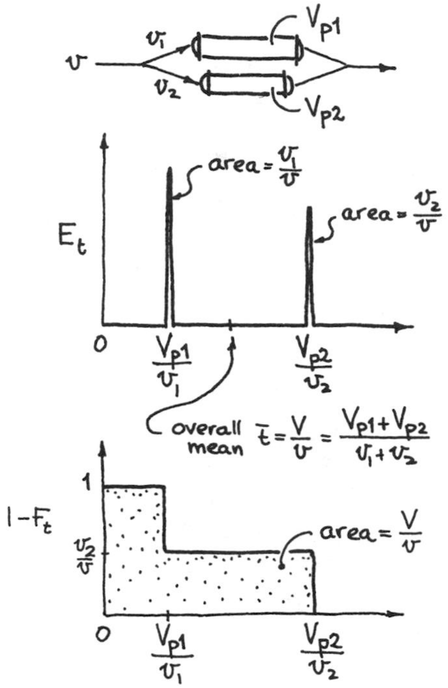

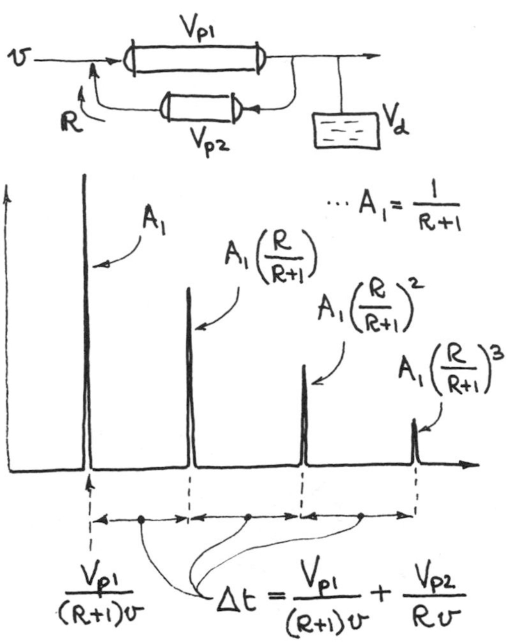

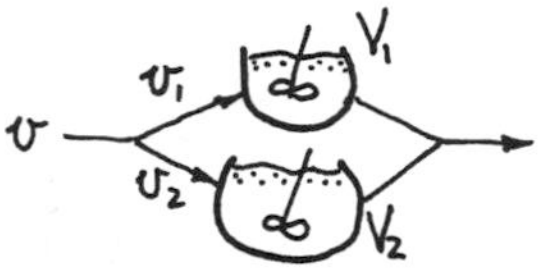

equation is the sum of two exponentials:

$$\dfrac{v_1^2}{vV_1} e^{-\frac{v_1}{V_1}t} + \dfrac{v_2^2}{vV_2} e^{-\frac{v_2}{V_2}t}$$

intercept:
$$\dfrac{v_1^2}{vV_1} + \dfrac{v_2^2}{vV_2}$$

E_t

area $= 1$

$\bar{t}$

$\bar{t} = \dfrac{V}{v} = \dfrac{V_1+V_2}{v_1+v_2}$

put on semi-log scale

$\log E_t$

$\log\left(\dfrac{v_1^2}{vV_1}\right)$

$\log\left(\dfrac{v_2^2}{vV_2}\right)$

slope $= 2.303 \dfrac{v_2}{V_2}$

slope $= 2.303 \dfrac{v_1}{V_1}$

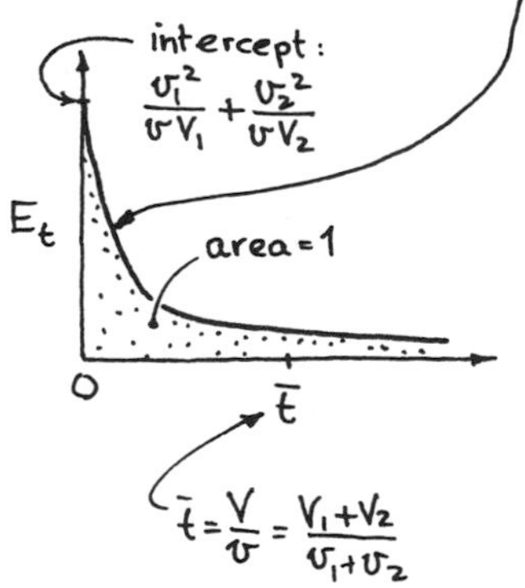

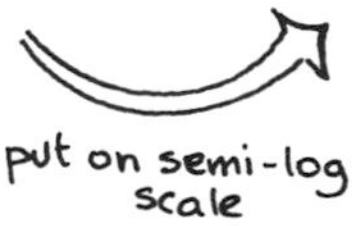

This method of plotting and fitting exponentials is only useful when $\bar{t}_1$ and $\bar{t}_2$ are very different.

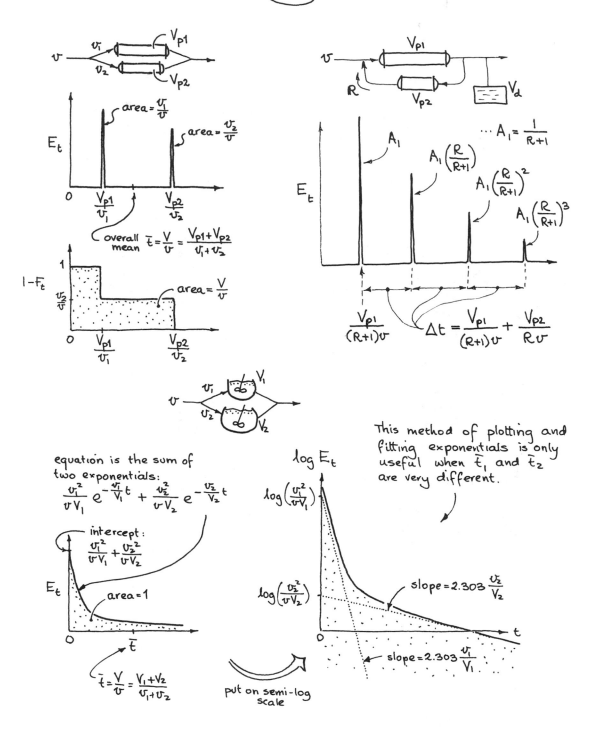

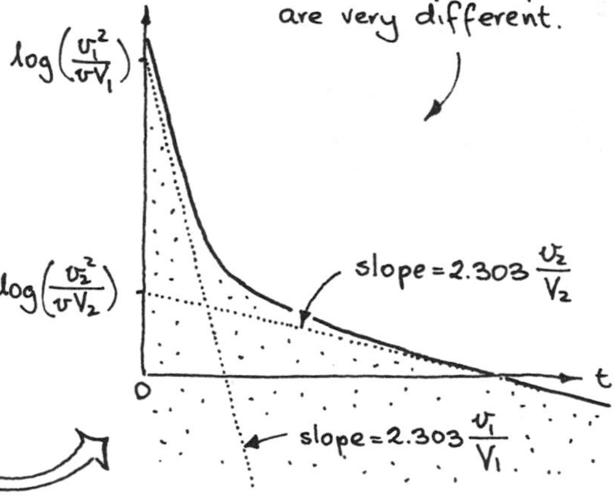

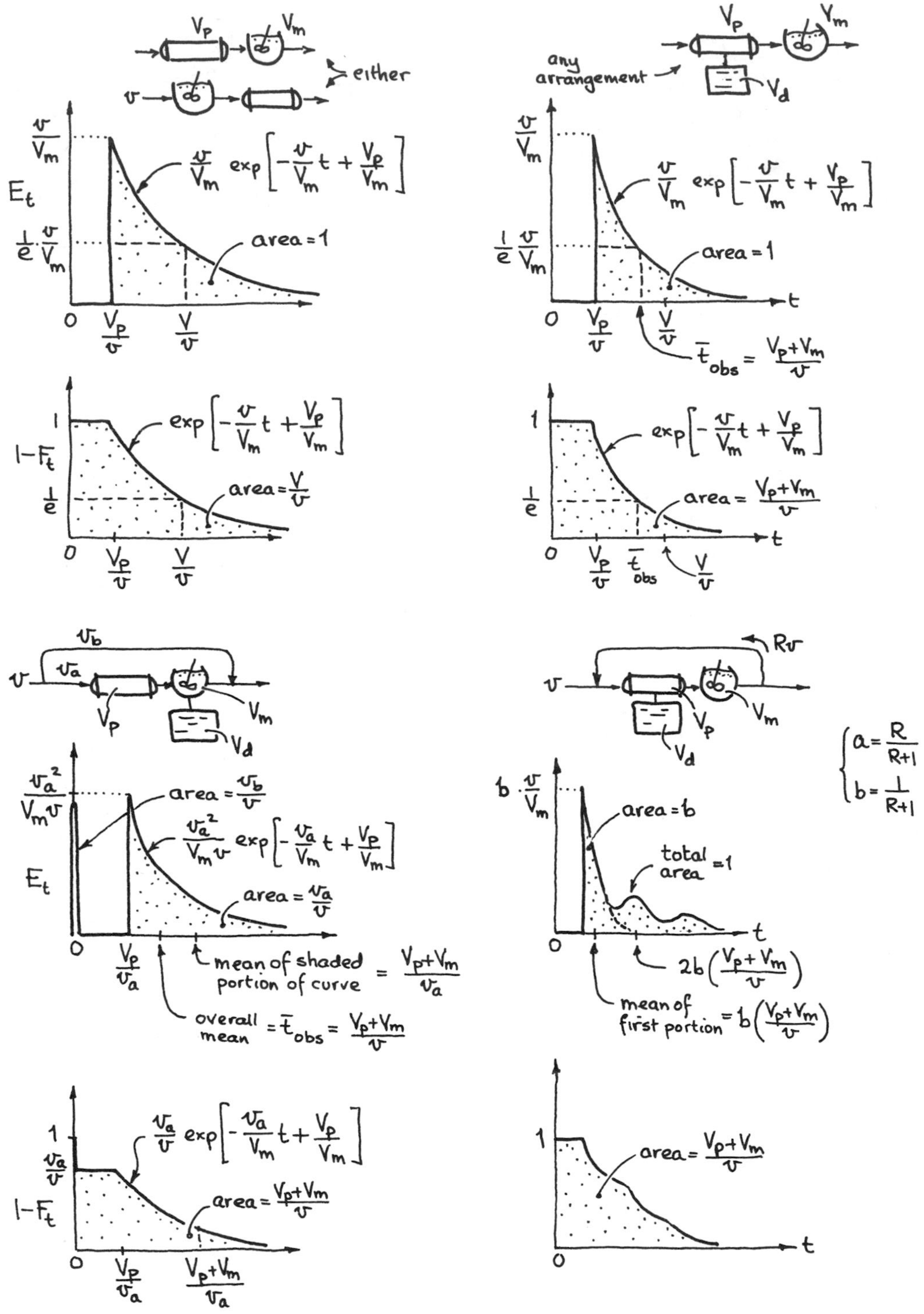
either
any arrangement
E_t
$\frac{v}{V_m}$
$\frac{1}{e}\cdot\frac{v}{V_m}$
$\frac{v}{V_m}\exp\left[-\frac{v}{V_m}t+\frac{V_p}{V_m}\right]$
area = 1
$\frac{V_p}{v}$
$\frac{V}{v}$
$\bar{t}_{obs}=\frac{V_p+V_m}{v}$
$1-F_t$
$\exp\left[-\frac{v}{V_m}t+\frac{V_p}{V_m}\right]$
area = $\frac{V}{v}$
area = $\frac{V_p+V_m}{v}$
$\bar{t}_{obs}$
v_b
v_a
V_p
V_m
V_d
Rv
$a=\frac{R}{R+1}$
$b=\frac{1}{R+1}$
$\frac{v_a^2}{V_m v}$
area = $\frac{v_b}{v}$
$\frac{v_a^2}{V_m v}\exp\left[-\frac{v_a}{V_m}t+\frac{V_p}{V_m}\right]$
area = $\frac{v_a}{v}$
$\frac{V_p}{v_a}$
mean of shaded portion of curve = $\frac{V_p+V_m}{v_a}$
overall mean = $\bar{t}_{obs}=\frac{V_p+V_m}{v}$
$b\cdot\frac{v}{V_m}$
area = b
total area = 1
$2b\left(\frac{V_p+V_m}{v}\right)$
mean of first portion = $b\left(\frac{V_p+V_m}{v}\right)$
$\frac{v_a}{v}\exp\left[-\frac{v_a}{V_m}t+\frac{V_p}{V_m}\right]$
area = $\frac{V_p+V_m}{v}$
$\frac{V_p+V_m}{v_a}$
t
0
1

(b) We must know $\bar{t}$, thus both V and v, if we want to properly evaluate all the elements of this model, including dead spaces. If we only measure $\bar{t}_{obs}$ we cannot find the size of these stagnant regions and must ignore them in our model building. Thus

If the real vessel has dead spaces: $\bar{t}_{obs} < \bar{t}$

If the real vessel has no dead spaces: $\bar{t}_{obs} = \bar{t}$

... where $\begin{cases} \bar{t} = \dfrac{V}{v} \\ \bar{t}_{obs} = \dfrac{V_{active}}{v} \end{cases}$

(c) The semi-log plot is a convenient tool for evaluating the flow parameters of a mixed flow compartment. Just draw the tracer response curve on this plot, find the slope and intercept and this gives the quantities A, B and C, as shown below

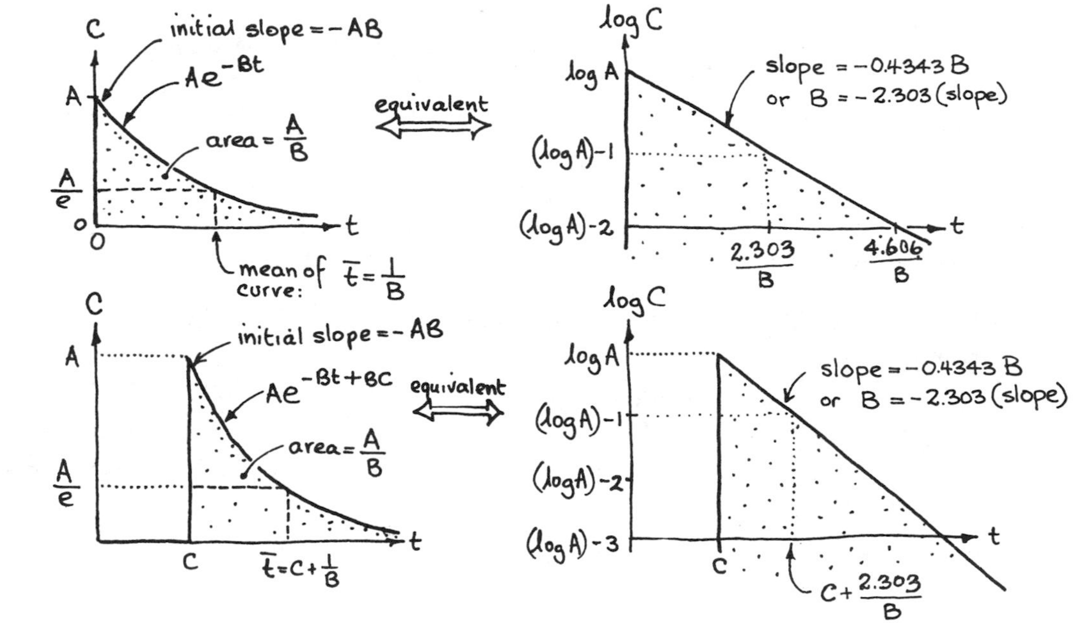

(d) Remember, we go from C to E_t and F_t as follows

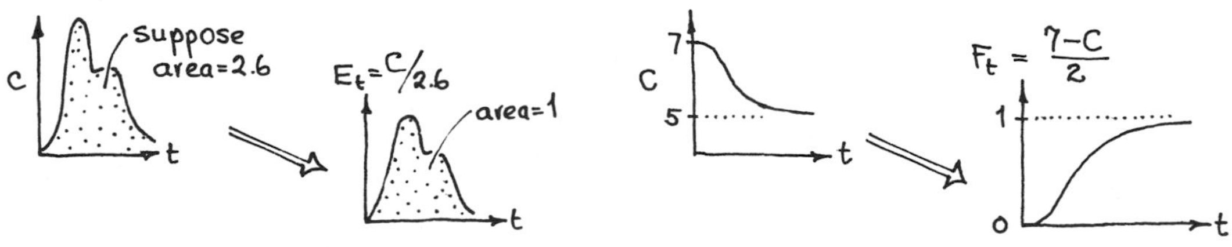

(e) This type of model is useful for diagnostic purposes, to pinpoint faulty flow and to suggest causes. For example if you expect **plug flow** and you know $\bar{t} = V/v$, here is what you could find

Slim trim curve means **reasonably good flow**

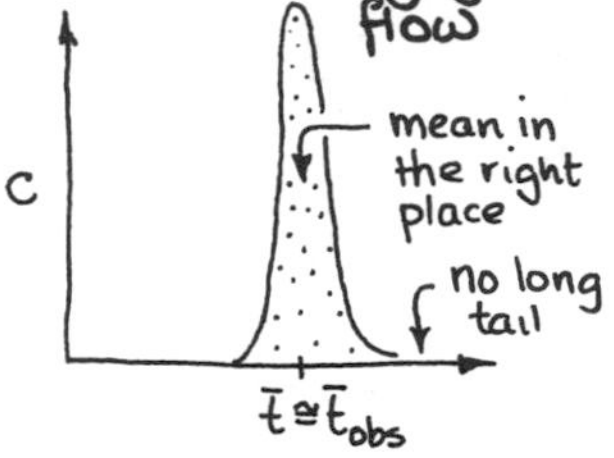

Early curve is a sure sign of **stagnant backwaters**

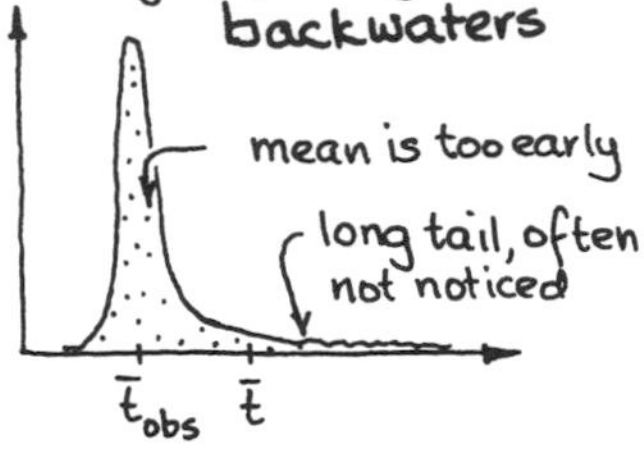

Multiple decaying peaks at regular intervals indicate **strong internal recirculation**

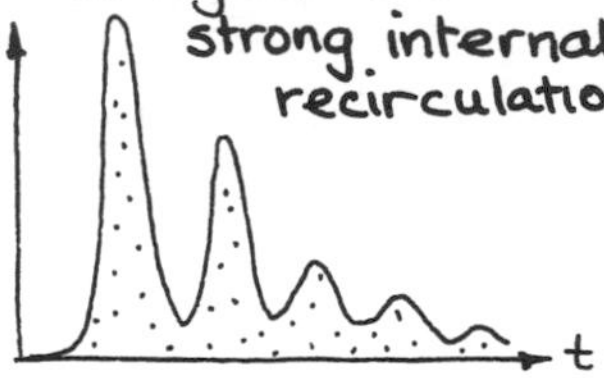

Double peaks come from flow in **parallel paths, channeling**

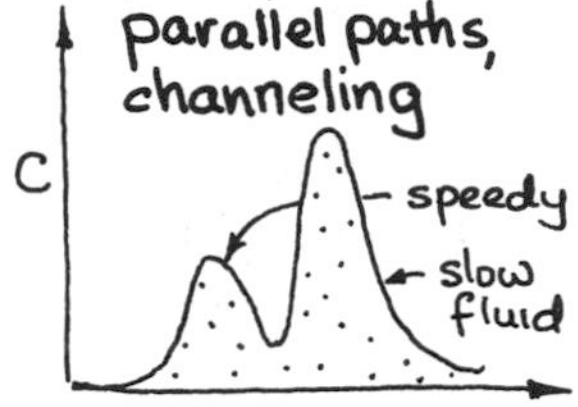

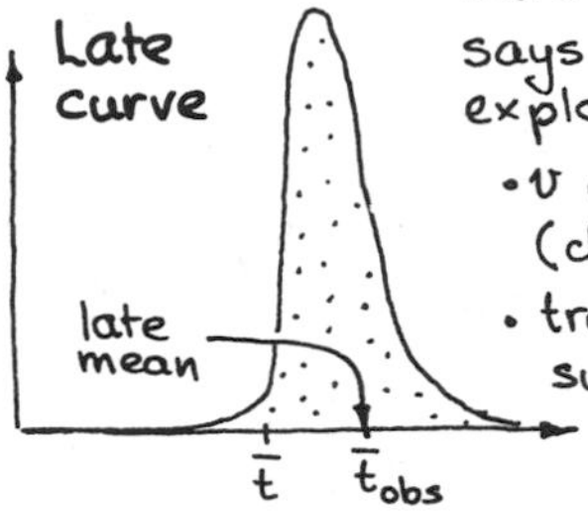

Late tracer is puzzling. Material balance says it can't happen so the only explanations are:

- v or V are incorrectly measured (check flow meters, etc)
- tracer is not inert (adsorbs on surface? Try a different one)

If you expect **mixed flow** here is the sort of thing that could happen.

Reasonably good flow

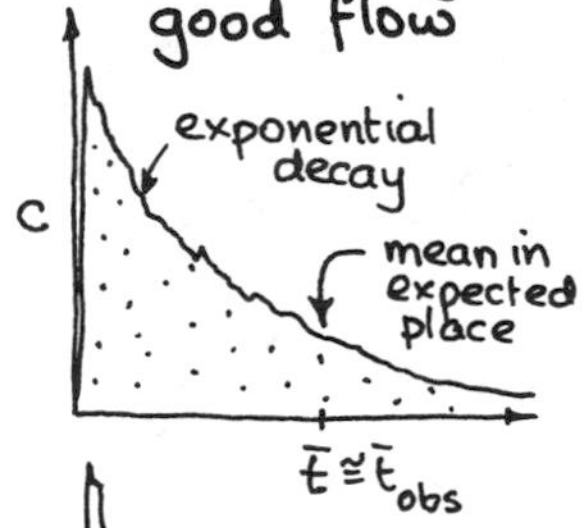

Time lag means plug flow in series with mixed flow (long inlet pipe? long lines to the recorder?)

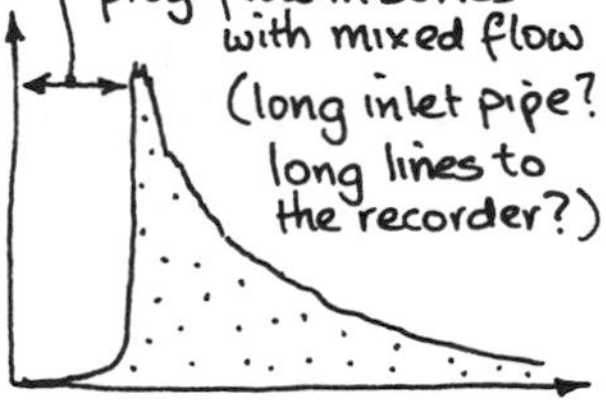

Slow internal circulation suggests
- sluggish slow turnover of fluid
- inadequate mixing
- draft tube effect.

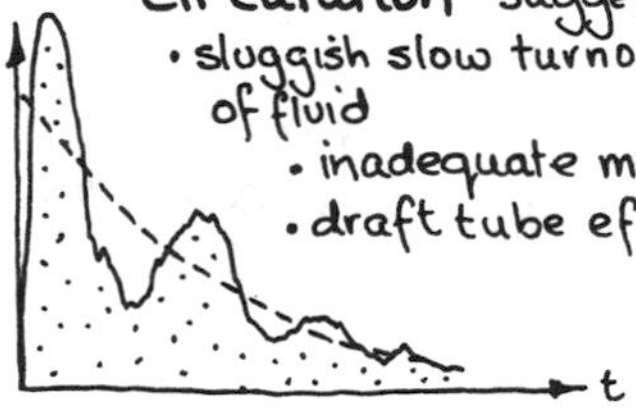

Early curve means **stagnant fluid**

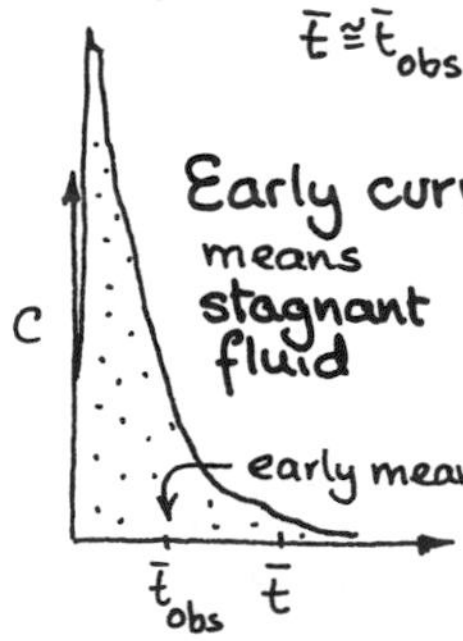

Late curve means either incorrect v or V or non inert tracer

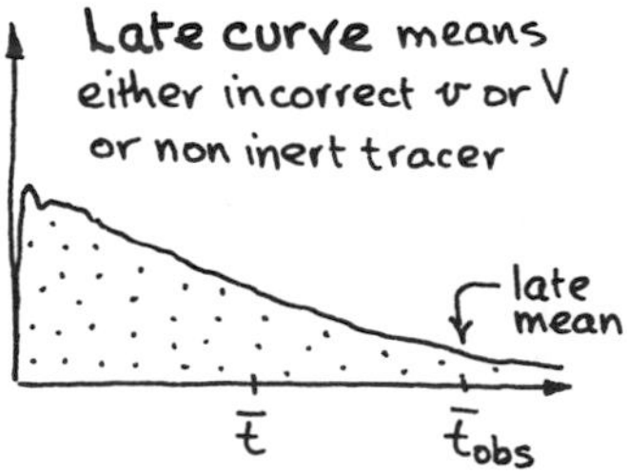

Sharp early peak indicates **shortcircuiting** from inlet to outlet

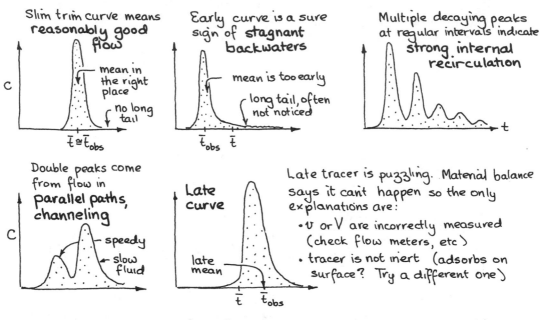

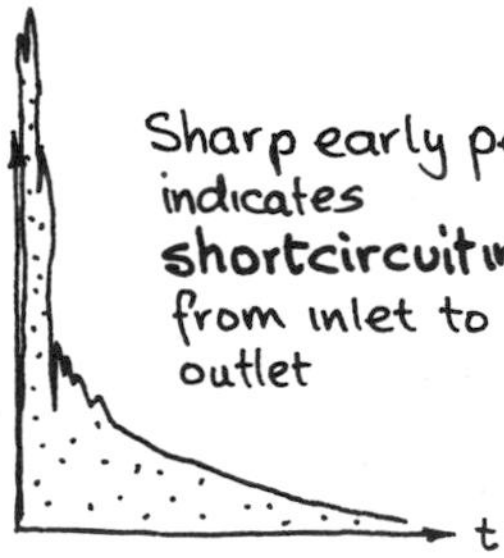

II Chemical Tracer Method.

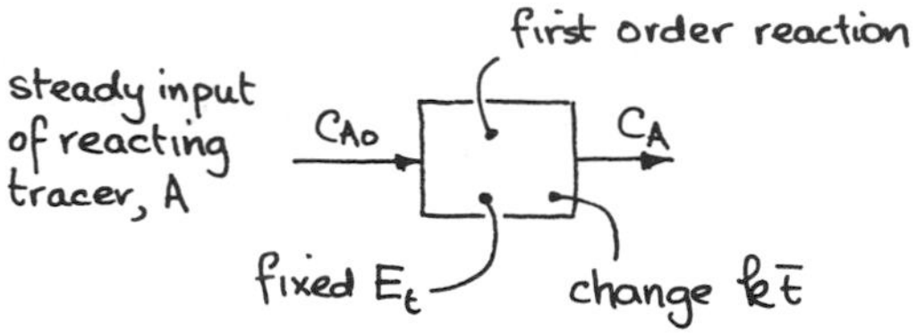

Chemical methods (see end of chapter 61) can be used very nicely with this type of model.
Simply change $k\bar{t}$ and measure C_A. A plot of $k\bar{t}$ vs $\frac{C_A}{C_{A0}}$ will give the flow parameters. For example

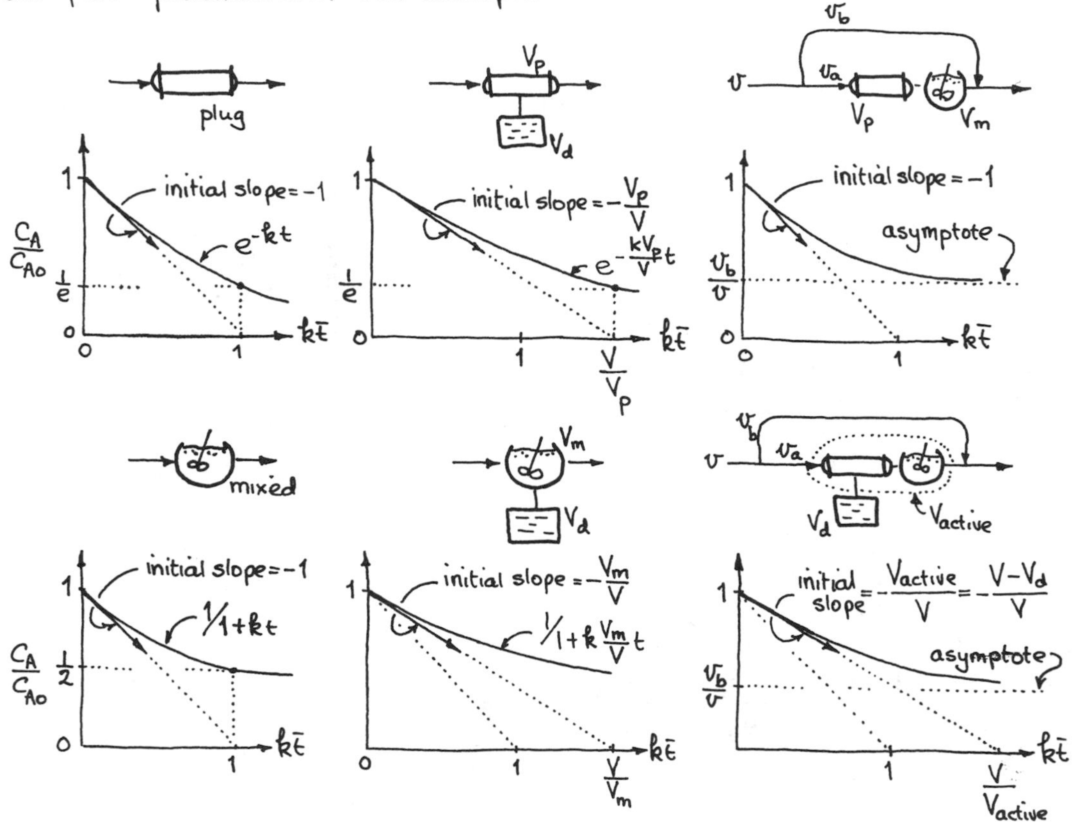

Dead regions and bypassing are easy to find by this method if k can be made to vary widely. Just find the initial slope and the asymptote.

In principle the shape of the C_A/C_{A0} vs $k\bar{t}$ curve can tell what kind of flow occurs in the active region. Unfortunately the shapes of the curves are quite similar with no distinguishing features. So this is not a sensitive way for studying models for flow intermediate between plug flow and mixed flow.

Chapter 62 Problems

A pulse of concentrated NaCl solution is introduced as tracer into the fluid entering a vessel ($V = 1\ m^3$, $v = 1\ m^3/min$) and the concentration of tracer is measured in the fluid leaving the vessel. Develop a flow model to represent the vessel from the tracer output data sketched below.

A1 . . .

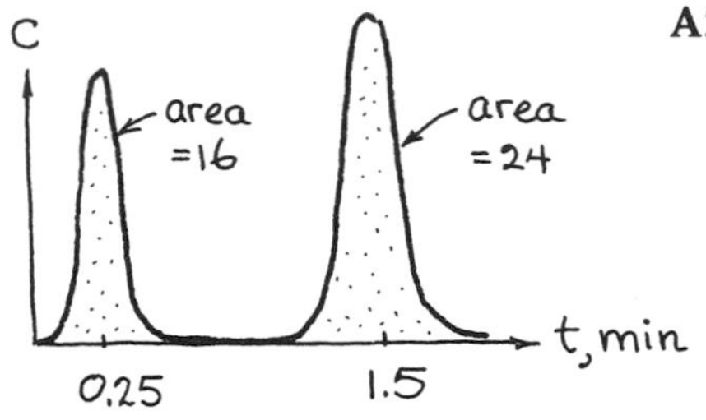

A2 . . .

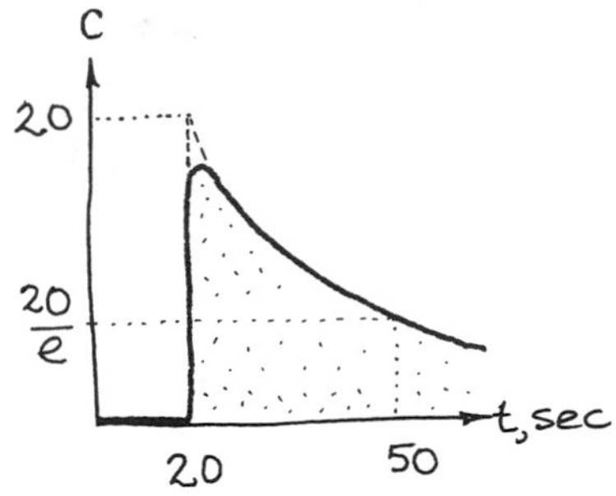

A3 . . .

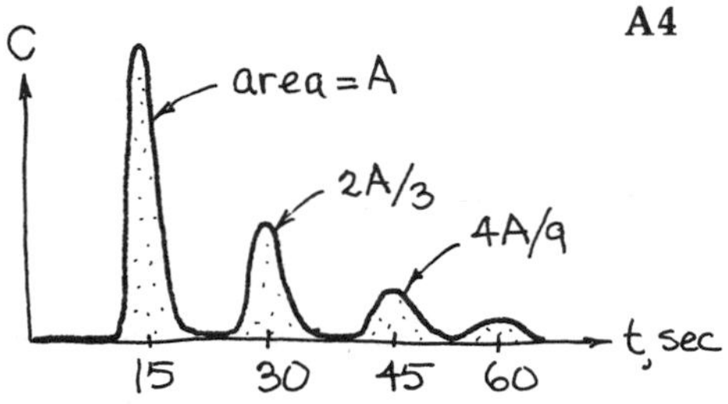

A4 . . .

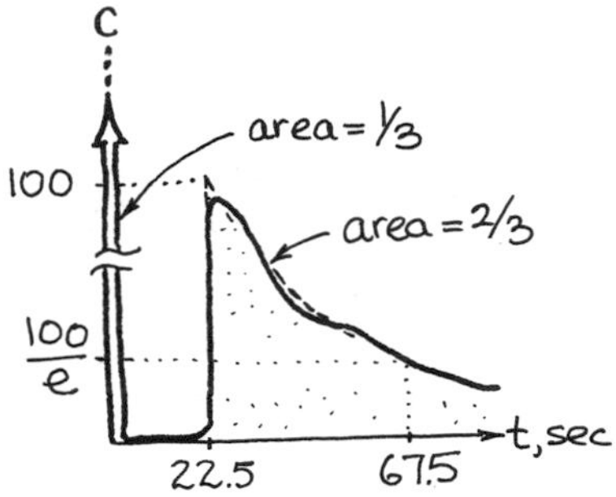

A5 . . .

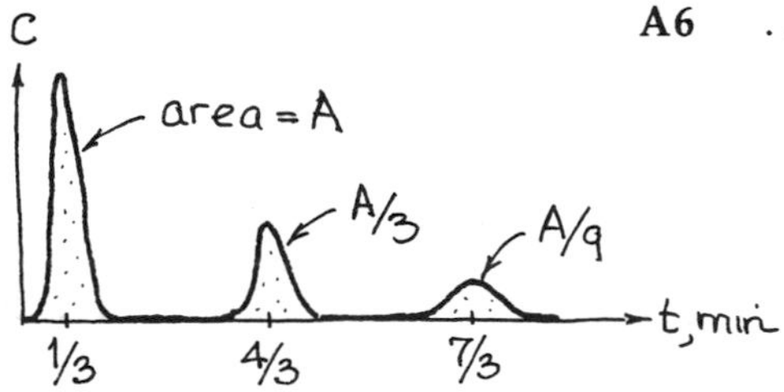

A6 . . .

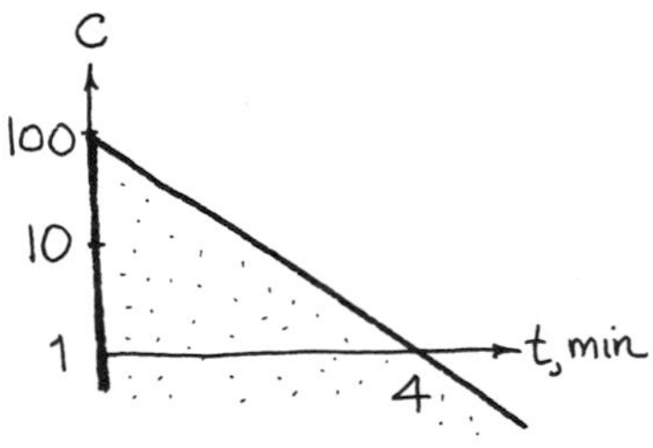

A7 . . .

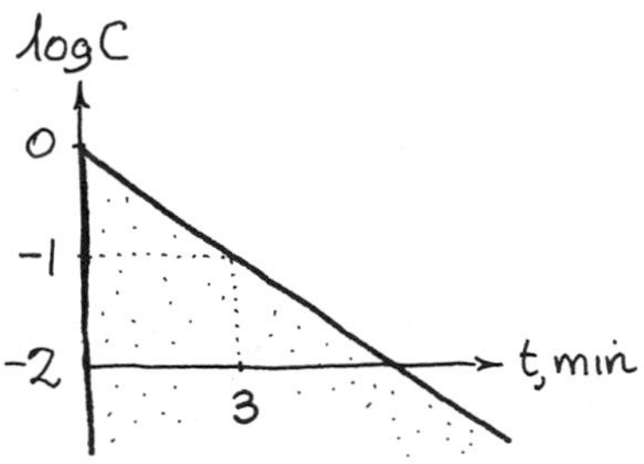

A8 . . .

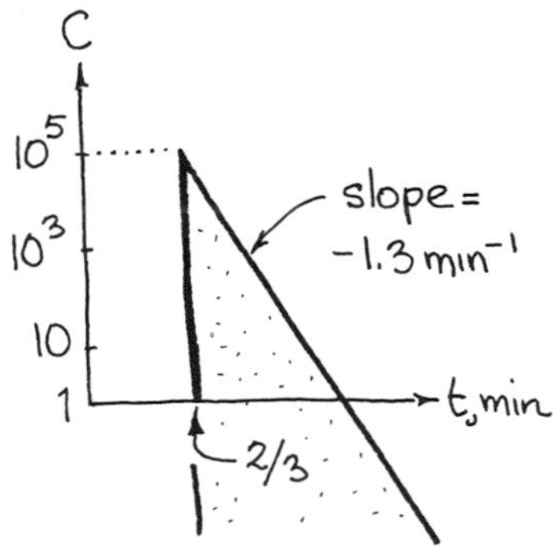

A step input tracer test (switching from tap water to salt water, measuring the conductivity of fluid leaving the vessel) is used to explore the flow pattern of fluid through the vessel ($V = 1\ m^3$, $v = 1\ m^3/min$). Devise a flow model to represent the vessel from the following data.

B9 . . .

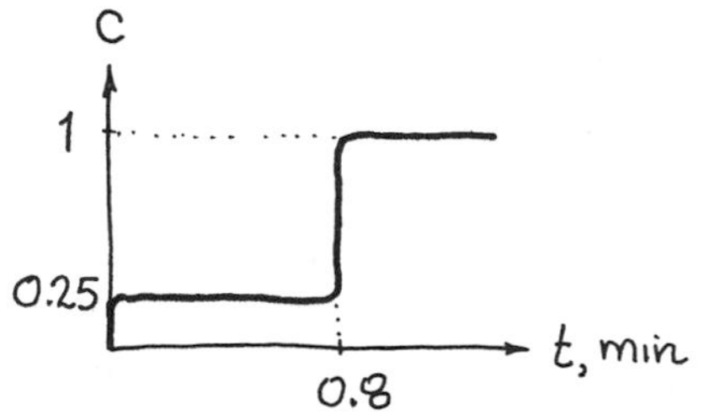

B10 . . .

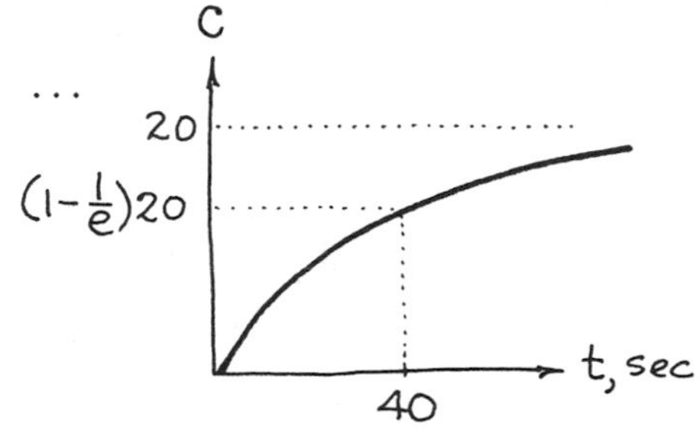

B11 . . .

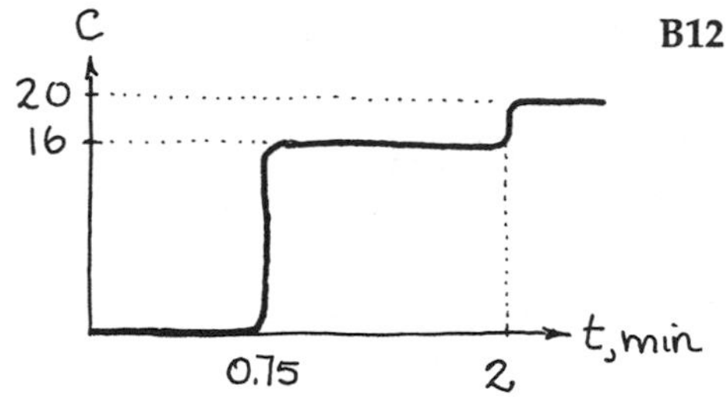

B12 . . .

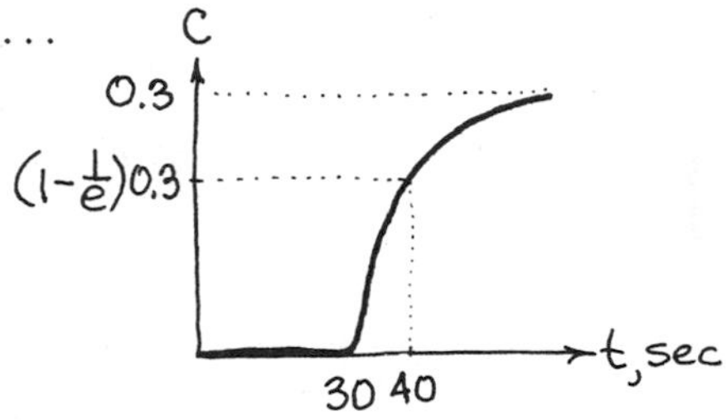

B13 . . .

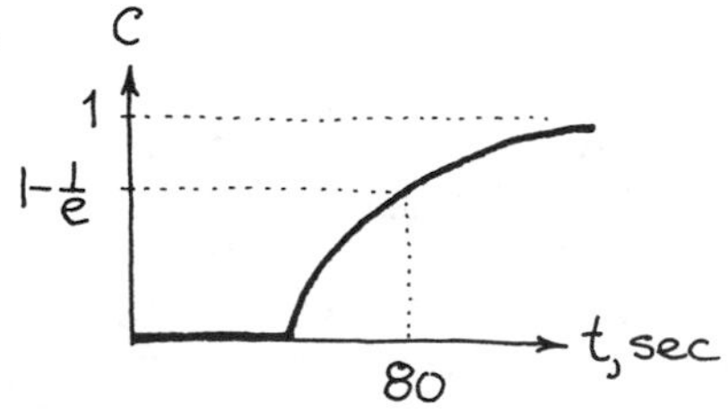

B14 . . .

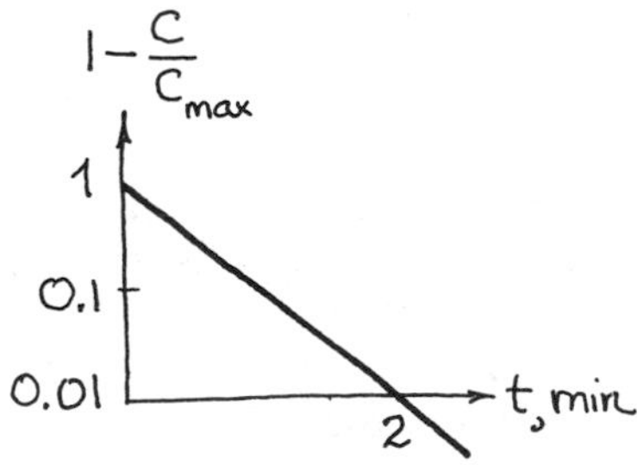

B15 . . .

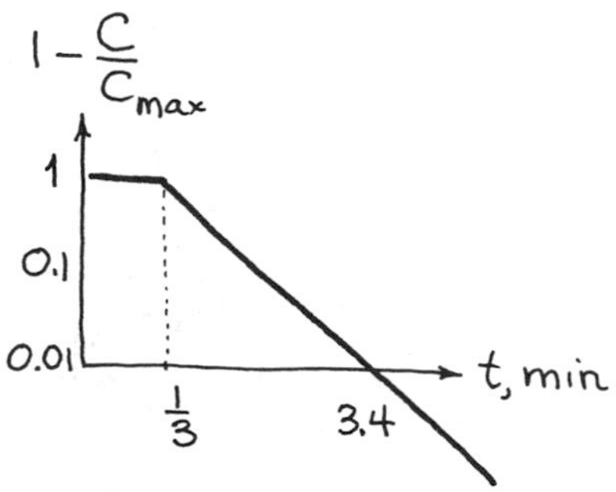

B16 . . .

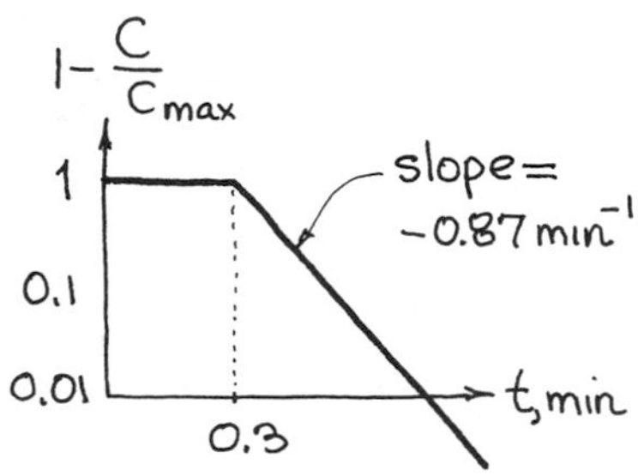

Chapter 62 Problems

At present our 6 m^3 tank reactor gives 75% conversion for the first order reaction $A \rightarrow R$. However, since the reactor is stirred with an underpowered paddle turbine we suspect incomplete mixing and poor flow patterns in the vessel. A pulse tracer shows that this is so, and gives the flow model sketched below. What conversion can we expect if we replace the stirrer with one powerful enough to ensure mixed flow?

C17 . . .

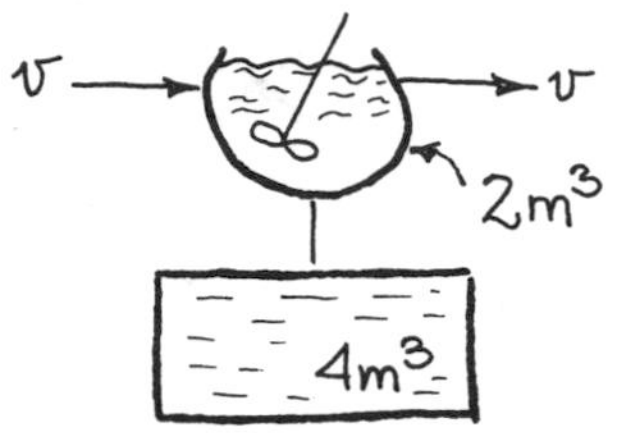

C18 . . .

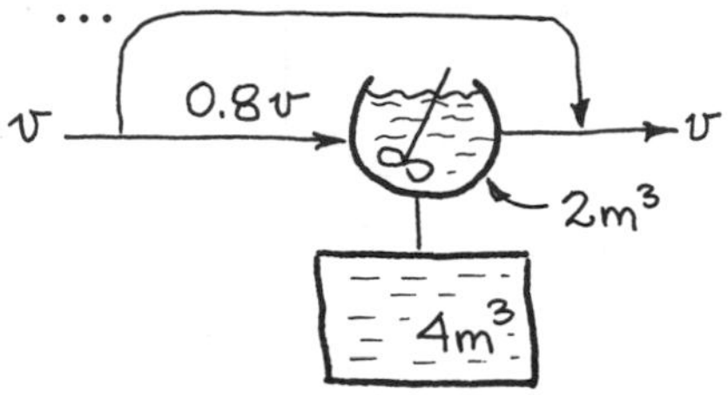

Suppose we decide to scrap our large tank reactor (see above problems) and replace it with a well stirred reactor of equal performance (75% conversion). How large should it be

C19 . . . for the data of problem 17

C20 . . . for the data of problem 18

The second order aqueous reaction $A + B \rightarrow R + S$ is run in a large tank reactor ($V = 24$ m^3) and for an equimolar feed stream ($C_{A0} = C_{B0}$) conversion of reactants is 60%. Unfortunately, agitation in our reactor is rather inadequate and tracer tests of the flow within the reactor give the flow model sketched below. What size of mixed flow reactor will equal the performance of our present unit?

C21 . . .

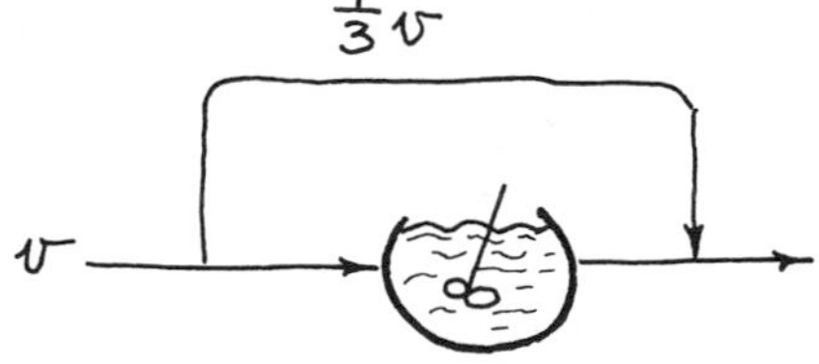

C22 . . .

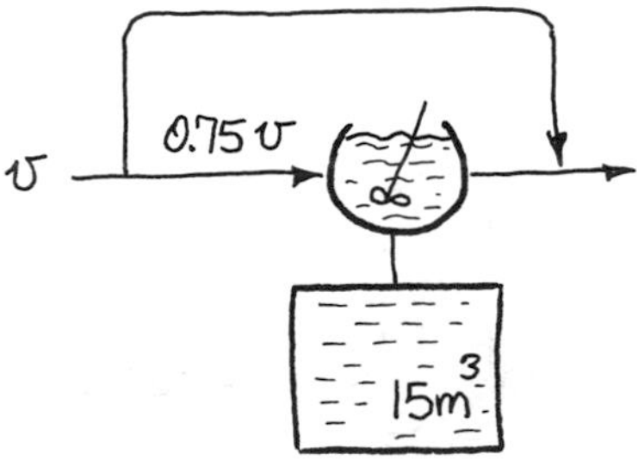

Chapter 62 Problems

D23* Our long narrow tank reactor with double turbine on one shaft isn't behaving as it should, and I suspect that it isn't following mixed flow. Let us check this by a pulse experiment using 1 m^3/min of flowing fluid. Find a flow model to fit the obtained response data, shown below.

t, min	0.5	2.0	4.0	7.5	9.0	12.5	18.5	22	28	35.5
E_t, min^{-1}	0.28	0.16	0.076	0.024	0.016	0.008	0.004	0.003	0.002	0.0012

D24 The flow pattern in a jet reactor (V = 161 cm^3) was studied by passing air and radioactive Kr-85 through the reactor (v = 10.4 cm^3/s), then switching to pure air and monitoring the K-85 at the exit of the reactor. From the data below develop a model to represent the flow in the reactor.

t, sec	8	16	24	32	40
C/C_0	0.68	0.35	0.18	0.09	0.05

Data reconstructed from Bartok *et al* AIChE J **6** 685 (1960).

Wolf and Resnick, IECF **4** 77 (1965) propose the following equation to represent the flow of solids through fluidized beds

$$F(t) = 1 - \exp\left[\frac{-A(t-B)}{\bar{t}}\right] \qquad \text{for } t \geq B$$

$$F(t) = 0 \qquad \text{for } 0 < t < B$$

Some of their 31 reported experimental runs (see document 8217 ADI) can be summarized as follows

	$B/\bar{t}$	A
Run 27 (typical of 2 runs)	0.10	1.14
Run 31 (typical of 22 runs)	0.10	0.90

Sketch the flow model giving volume fraction of regions and the flow split which represents

D25 . . . run 27

D26 . . . run 31

Chapter 63. THE MEAN AND VARIANCE OF A TRACER CURVE.

Here we define the mean $\bar{t}$ and variance σ^2 of a pulse response curve, and show how to evaluate these quantities from pulse and step experiments. These quantities $\bar{t}$ and σ^2 are widely used in tracer work, are simple to evaluate, but are even simpler to evaluate incorrectly — especially for discrete data. Hence this presentation.

I $\bar{t}$ and σ^2 from Experimental Pulse-Response Data.

The two most useful measures for describing tracer curves, measures used in all areas of tracer experimentation, are

the mean, $\bar{t}$: tells when a curve passes a measuring point, locates its center of gravity in time.

the variance, σ^2: tells how spread out in time, how "fat" the curve is.

Given a smooth continuous pulse-response curve C

the area under the curve: $$= \int_0^\infty C\,dt$$

the mean: $$\bar{t} = \mu = \frac{\int_0^\infty tC\,dt}{\int_0^\infty C\,dt}$$

the variance: $$\sigma^2 = \frac{\int_0^\infty t^2 C\,dt}{\int_0^\infty C\,dt} - \bar{t}^2$$

Here are some quick estimates of the variance if the curve looks roughly rectangular, triangular, or nicely symmetrically bell shaped.

$$\sigma^2 = \frac{a^2}{12}$$

$$\sigma^2 = \frac{a^2}{24}$$

$$\sigma^2 = \frac{a^2 + ab + b^2}{18}$$

$$\text{mean} = x_0 + \frac{2a+b}{3}$$

the gaussian or normal curve: (a very special bell-shaped curve)

C_{max} 68% of area $0.61 C_{max}$ $\leftarrow 2\sigma \rightarrow$

C_{max} 76% of area $0.5 C_{max}$ $\leftarrow 2.36\sigma \rightarrow$

38.3% of area 95.4% $\rightarrow \sigma \leftarrow$ $\leftarrow 4\sigma \rightarrow$

95% of area -1.96σ 0 $+1.96\sigma$

90% of area 99% -2.58σ -1.64σ $+1.64\sigma$ -2.58σ

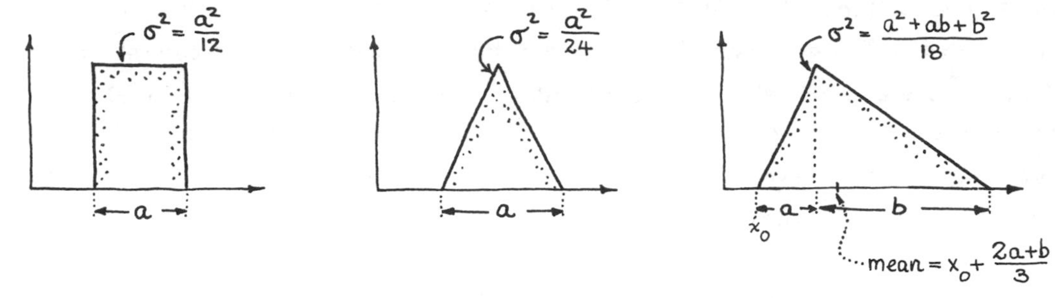

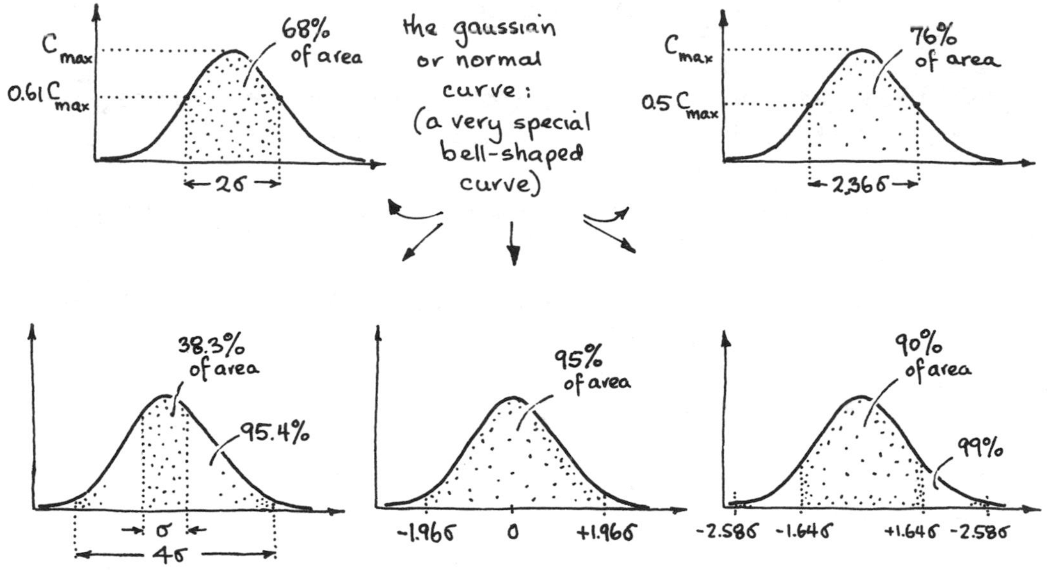

Usually you want to find $\bar{t}$ and σ^2 from a set of discrete data

c	- - - - -
t	- - - - -

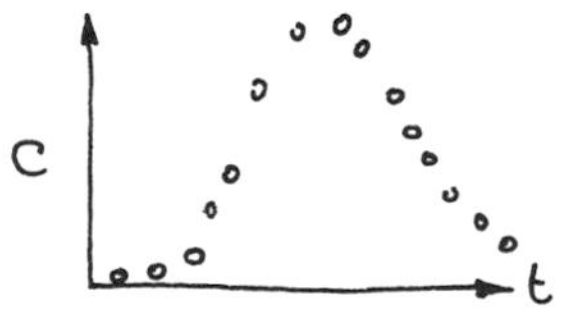

How you proceed depends on how much data and what kind of data are available. In essense we can use one of three approaches.

1. **Analysis of abundant data.** If the data points are numerous and all closely spaced we can estimate $\bar{t}$ and σ^2 by

$$\bar{t} = \frac{\sum_i t_i C_i \Delta t_i}{\sum C_i \Delta t_i} \;\underset{\Delta t_i}{\overset{\text{for equal time intervals}}{=\!=}}\; \frac{\sum_i t_i C_i}{\sum C_i}$$

$$\sigma^2 = \frac{\sum t_i^2 C_i \Delta t_i}{\sum C_i \Delta t_i} - \bar{t}^2 \;\underset{\Delta t_i}{\overset{\text{for equal}}{=\!=}}\; \frac{\sum t_i^2 C_i}{\sum C_i} - \bar{t}^2$$

2. **Analysis by linear interpolation.** If the data are not that numerous, say 10 ~ 20 points, then linear interpolation between points may be satisfactory. But we must be careful because there are two different ways of taking a set of C vs t data, and the proper procedure for calculating $\bar{t}$ and σ^2 will depend on how the discrete set of data is taken.

(a) **Collecting data by instantaneous readings.** Here you read the tracer concentration at the vessel exit at various times, for example

t, sec	C, mol/lit
2	0
5	3
6	15
8	24
12	9
⋮	⋮

or

t	C
t_1	C_1
t_2	C_2
t_3	C_3
⋮	⋮
t_n	C_n

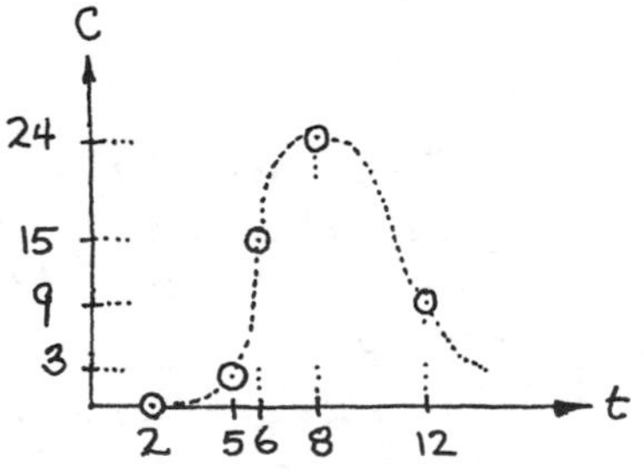

Then for a set of n C vs t readings the mean is calculated by

$$\bar{t} = \frac{\sum_{i=1}^{n-1} (t_{i+1}+t_i)(C_{i+1}+C_i)(t_{i+1}-t_i)}{2\sum_{i=1}^{n-1} (C_{i+1}+C_i)(t_{i+1}-t_i)} = \frac{1}{2}\left[\frac{(2+5)(0+3)3 + (5+6)(3+15)1 + \cdots}{(0+3)3 + (3+15)1 + \cdots}\right]$$

The variance is calculated by

$$\sigma^2 = \frac{\sum_{i=1}^{n-1}(t_i+t_{i+1})^2(C_i+C_{i+1})(t_{i+1}-t_i)}{4\sum_{i=1}^{n-1}(C_i+C_{i+1})(t_{i+1}-t_i)} - \bar{t}^2$$

$$= \frac{1}{4}\left[\frac{(2+5)^2(0+3)3+(5+6)^2(3+15)1+\cdots}{(0+3)3+(3+15)1+\cdots}\right] - \bar{t}^2$$

For **equidistant points** the expressions simplify to give

$$\bar{t} = \frac{\sum_{i=1}^{n-1}(t_i+t_{i+1})(C_i+C_{i+1})}{2\sum_{i=1}^{n-1}(C_i+C_{i+1})}$$

$$\sigma^2 = \frac{\sum_{i=1}^{n-1}(t_i+t_{i+1})^2(C_i+C_{i+1})}{4\sum_{i=1}^{n-1}(C_i+C_{i+1})} - \bar{t}^2$$

(b) **Collecting data by mixing cup readings.** For various time intervals collect the fluid which is leaving the vessel in little "cups", stir to make uniform, and then analyse, for example

time interval Δt	average time in interval t	C
0 – 2	1	0
2 – 5	3.5	1
5 – 6	5.5	9
6 – 8	7.0	22
8 – 12	10	16
⋮	⋮	⋮

(tabulate this column — average time in interval)

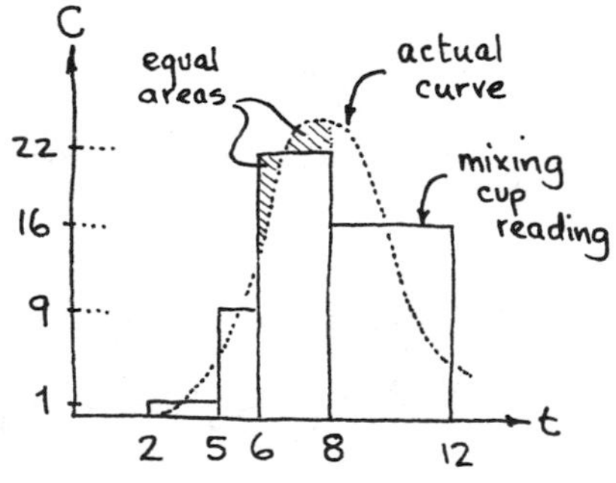

For a set of readings of this type

$$\bar{t} = \frac{\sum_{i=1}^{n} t_i C_i \Delta t_i}{\sum_{i=1}^{n} C_i \Delta t_i} = \frac{1(0)(2-0) + 3.5(1)(5-2) + 5.5(9)(6-5) + \cdots}{0(2-0) + 1(5-2) + 9(6-5) + \cdots}$$

$$\sigma^2 = \frac{\sum_{i=1}^{n} t_i^2 C_i \Delta t_i}{\sum_{i=1}^{n} C_i \Delta t_i} - \bar{t}^2 = \frac{1^2(0)(2-0) + (3.5)^2(1)(5-2) + (5.5)^2(9)(6-5) + \cdots}{0(2-0) + 1(5-2) + 9(6-5) + \cdots} - \bar{t}^2$$

For **equal time increments** the expressions simplify to

$$\bar{t} = \frac{\sum_{i=1}^{n} t_i C_i}{\sum_{i=1}^{n} C_i}$$

$$\sigma^2 = \frac{\sum_{i=1}^{n} t_i^2 C_i}{\sum_{i=1}^{n} C_i} - \bar{t}^2$$

(c) **Comments.** When the data points are numerous then these two calculation methods approach each other. The maximum difference in calculated $\bar{t}$ values obtained by these two methods is about $\Delta t/2$.

3. Analysis of meager or scattered data. Here it is best to sketch a reasonable concentration curve through the data, read off many C vs t values from this curve using equal time intervals, and then calculate $\bar{t}$ and σ^2 using the simple formulae

$$\bar{t} = \frac{\sum_i (t_i C_i)}{\sum_i C_i} \quad \ldots \text{and} \ldots \quad \sigma^2 = \frac{\sum_i (t_i^2 C_i)}{\sum_i C_i} - \bar{t}^2$$

The crucial step in this procedure is sketching a good response curve. Do this with care, and remember, how you draw the curve depends on whether the data comes from instantaneous or mixing cup readings.

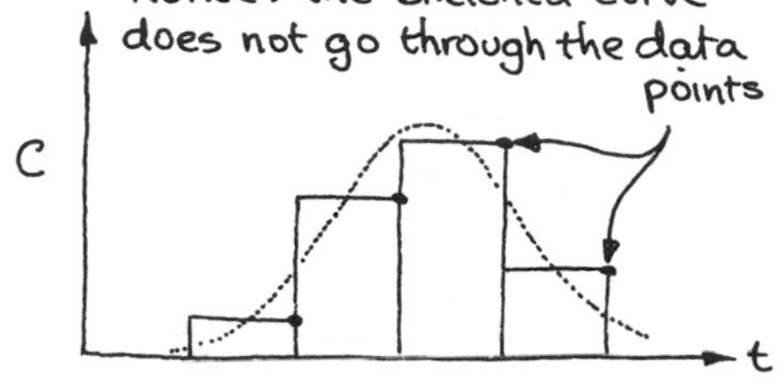
Mixing cup readings
Notice: the sketched curve does not go through the data points
C
t

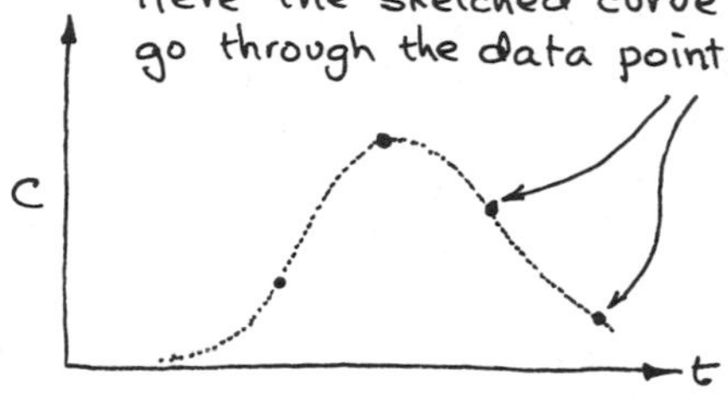
Instantaneous readings
Here the sketched curve does go through the data points
C
t

In sketching these curves also keep in mind what tracer response curves are likely to look like,

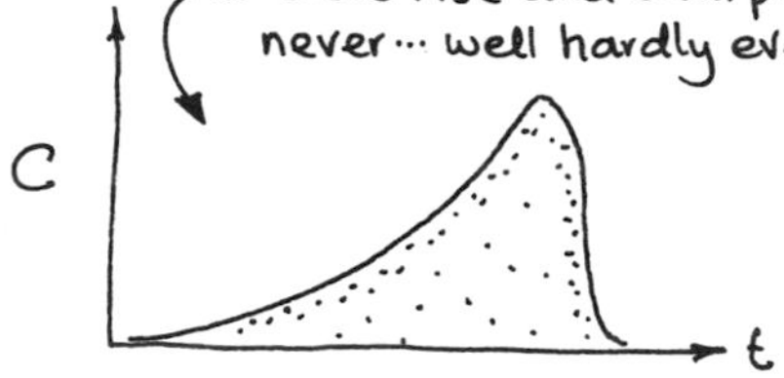
a slow rise and sharp drop: never ... well hardly ever.
C
t

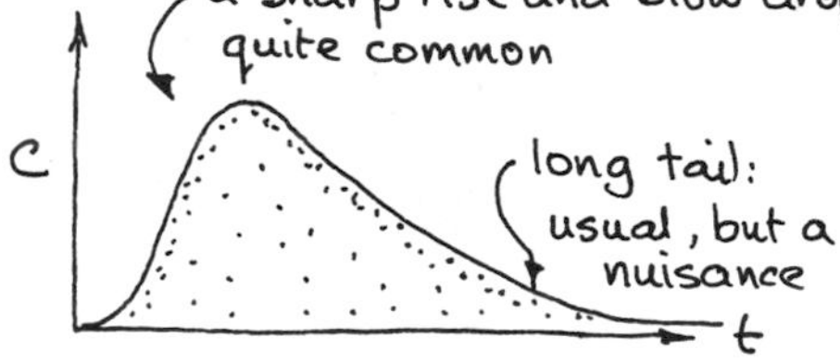
a sharp rise and slow drop: quite common
long tail: usual, but a nuisance
C
t

II $\bar{t}$ and σ^2 of RTD's from Step Response Data.

The pulse-mean and the pulse-variance is found from the corresponding step response curve in either of two ways

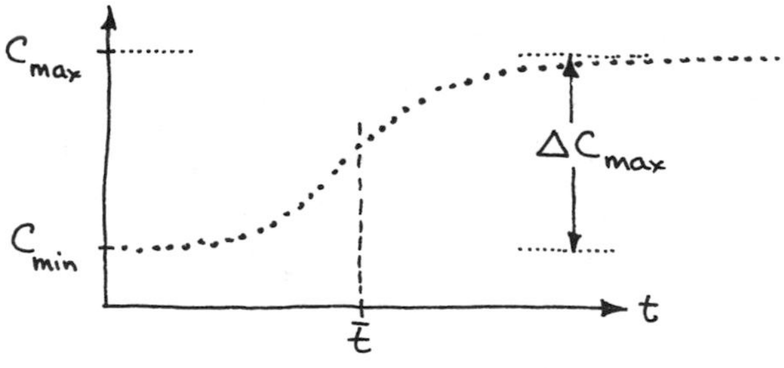
C_{max}
C_{min}
ΔC_{max}
t
$\bar{t}$

$$\bar{t} = \frac{\int_0^\infty (C_{max} - C)\,dt}{\Delta C_{max}} = \frac{\int_{C_{min}}^{C_{max}} t\,dC}{\Delta C_{max}}$$

and

$$\sigma^2 = \frac{2\int_0^\infty t(C_{max} - C)\,dt}{\Delta C_{max}} - \bar{t}^2 = \frac{\int_{C_{min}}^{C_{max}} t^2\,dC}{\Delta C_{max}} - \bar{t}^2$$

A smooth S-shaped step-response curve could correspond to a gaussian pulse-response curve. A plot of this S-shaped curve on probability paper will tell

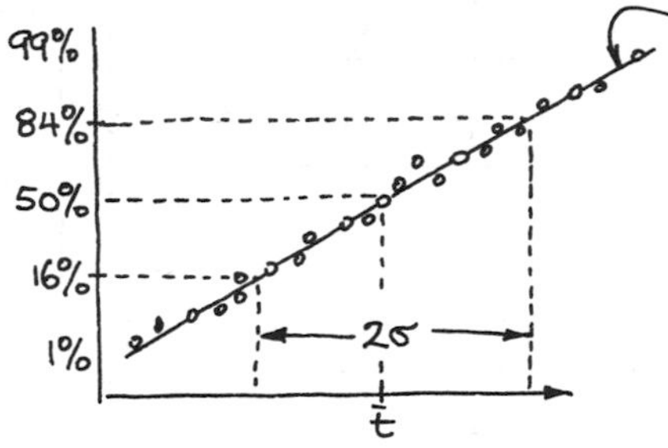

a straight line on this graph guarantees a gaussian pulse-response curve. Thus $\bar{t}$ and σ^2 can be found directly.

The next page is a sample of this special graph paper.

For all other shapes of step response curves we calculate $\bar{t}$ and σ^2 from discrete data which is of the form.

C	- - - -
t	- - - -

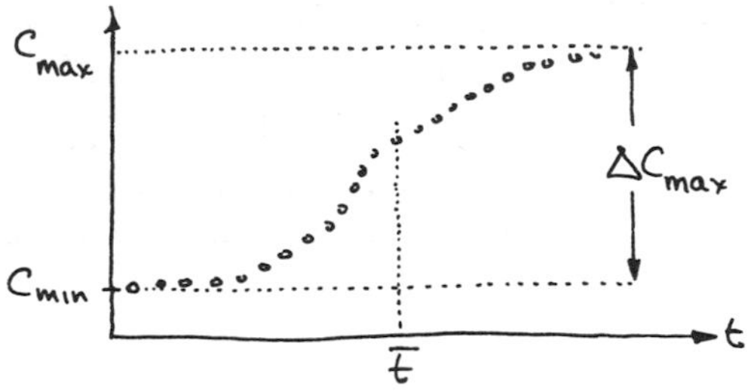

Here we again have three approaches, depending on the amount of and the type of data available, and how good it is.

Probability graph paper.

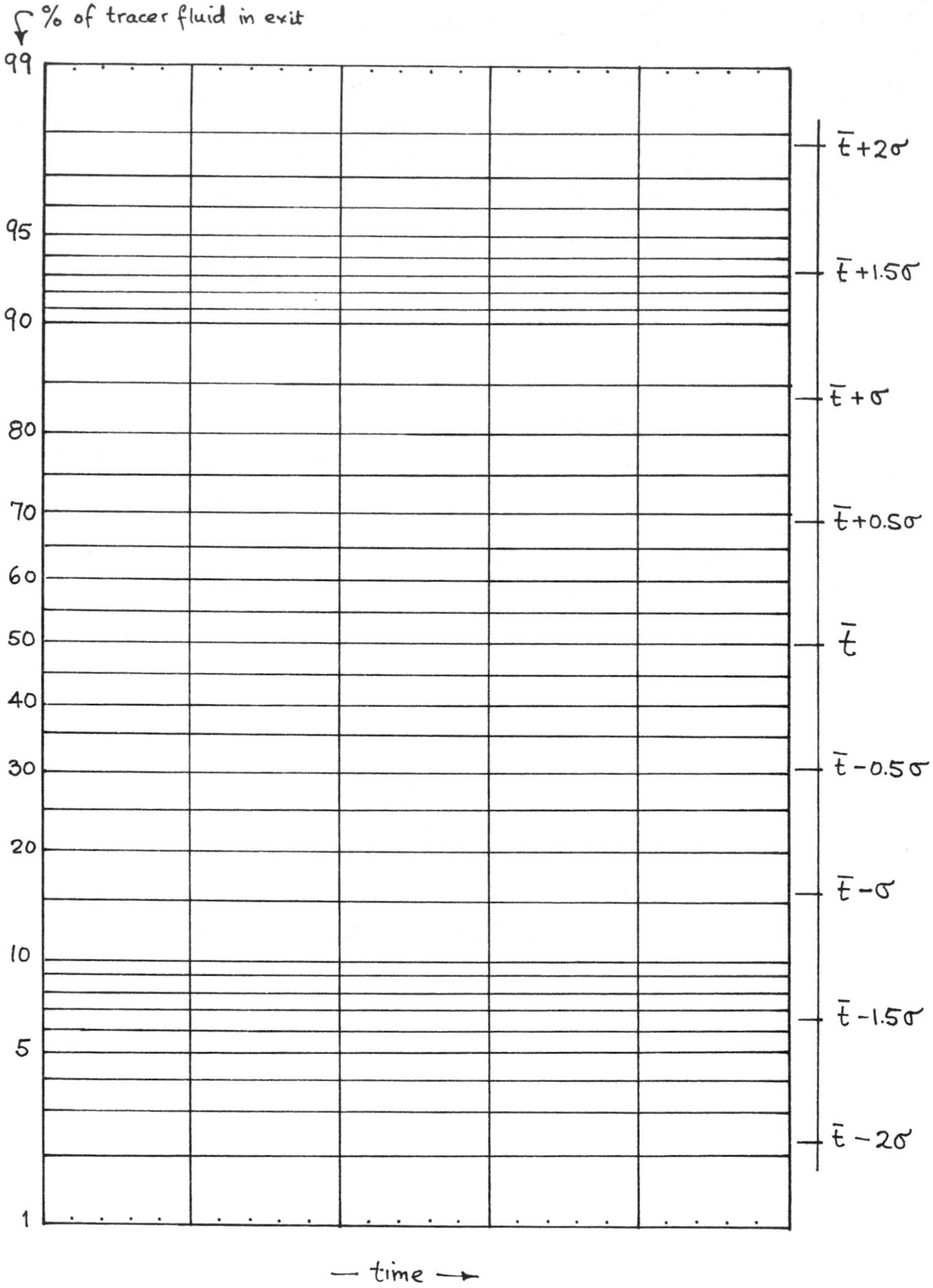

1. **Analysis of abundant data**. With numerous closely spaced points having little experimental error we can write

$$\bar{t} = \frac{\sum_{i=1}^{n} (C_{max} - C_i)\Delta t_i}{\Delta C_{max}} \;\underline{\underline{\text{or}}}\; \frac{\sum_{i=1}^{n} t_i \Delta C_i}{\Delta C_{max}} \qquad \Delta C_i = C_i - C_{i-1}$$

and

$$\sigma^2 = \frac{2\sum_{i=1}^{n} t_i (C_{max} - C_i)\Delta t_i}{\Delta C_{max}} - \bar{t}^2 \;\underline{\underline{\text{or}}}\; \frac{\sum_{i=1}^{n} t_i^2 \Delta C_i}{\Delta C_{max}} - \bar{t}^2$$

2. **Analysis by linear interpolation**. Again, as with pulse measurements, we take two types of measurements, either instantaneous concentration readings at the exit of the vessel, or mixing cup measurements. Let us see how to calculate $\bar{t}$ and σ^2 from each of these.

(a) **Collecting data by instantaneous readings**. Suppose the tracer concentration at the vessel exit is as follows

t	C
0	0
1	0
4	2
5	6
7	9
⋮	⋮
25 ~ ∞	14

← be sure to include this initial reading

... or ...

t	C
t_0	C_0
t_1	C_1
t_2	C_2
⋮	⋮
t_n	C_n

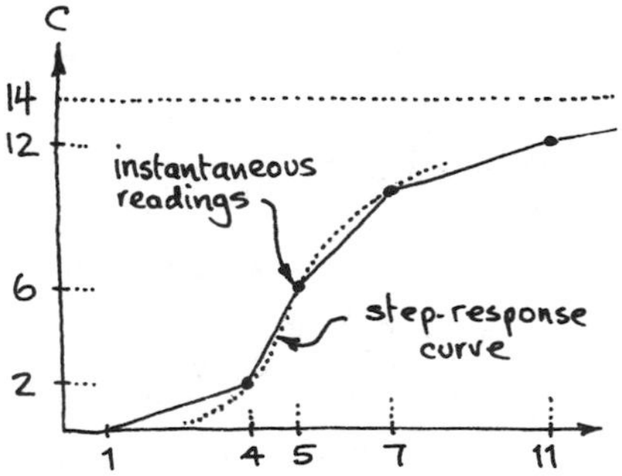

then

$$\bar{t} = \frac{\sum_{i=1}^{n} (2\Delta C_{max} - C_{i-1} - C_i)(t_i - t_{i-1})}{2\,\Delta C_{max}} = \frac{(28-0-0)(1-0) + (28-0-2)(4-1) + \cdots}{2(14)}$$

and

$$\sigma^2 = \frac{\sum_{i=1}^{n} (t_{i-1}+t_i)(2\Delta C_{max} - C_{i-1} - C_i)(t_i - t_{i-1})}{2\,\Delta C_{max}} - \bar{t}^2$$

$$= \frac{(0+1)(28-0-0)(1-0) + (1+4)(28-0-2)(4-1) + \cdots}{2(14)} - \bar{t}^2$$

If you suspect that the pulse-response is gaussian plot C_1, t_1, C_2, t_2 … directly on probability paper. If you get a straight line read $\bar{t}$ and σ^2 directly from the graph.

(b) Collecting data by mixing cup readings. For discrete data such as

time interval Δt	average time in interval t	average conc. in mixing cup C
0~2	1	0
2~5	3.5	1
5~6	5.5	4
6~8	7	8
⋮	⋮	⋮
25~∞		14

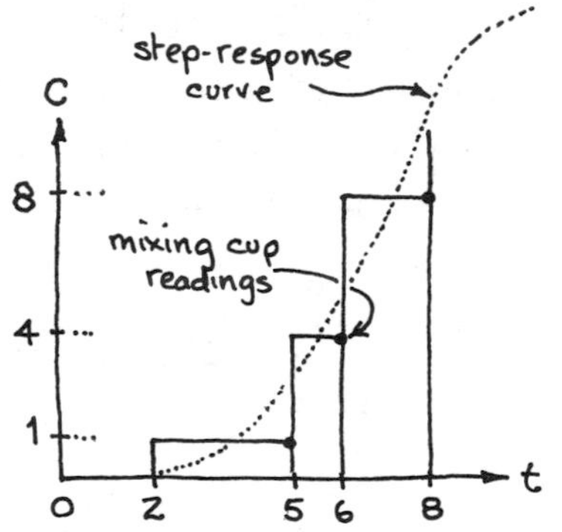

we have

$$\bar{t} = \frac{\sum_{i=1}^{n} (C_{max} - C_i)\Delta t_i}{\Delta C_{max}} = \frac{(14-0)(2-0) + (14-1)(5-2) + \cdots}{14}$$

and

$$\sigma^2 = \frac{2\sum_{i=1}^{n} t_i (C_{max} - C_i)\Delta t_i}{\Delta C_{max}} - \bar{t}^2 = \frac{2\left[1(14-0)(2-0) + 3(14-1)(5-2) + \cdots\right]}{14} - \bar{t}^2$$

Do not use probability paper with mixing cup measurements. It leads to error, and you do not get a straight line with gaussian curves.

(c) **Comments.** Using the method of linear interpolation the error in estimate of $\bar{t}$ is of the order of $\Delta t/2$, the error in estimate of σ is greater. Actually the data used in the above illustrations are too few and far apart to use the linear interpolation procedure. One should use the next method.

Again, if the data points are numerous and all closely spaced then both instantaneous and mixing cup methods give the same value for $\bar{t}$ and σ^2.

3. <u>Analysis of meager or scattered data.</u> Here it is best to sketch a smooth curve through the data, read of many C vs t values from the curve using equal concentration intervals from C_{min} to C_{max} and then apply the simple formulae:

$$\bar{t} = \frac{1}{n}\sum_{i=1}^{n} t_i \quad \text{...and...} \quad \sigma^2 = \frac{1}{n}\sum_{i=1}^{n} t_i^2 - \bar{t}^2$$

It is imperative to draw the step-response curve properly through the data. How this is done depends on whether you are dealing with mixing cup or instantaneous readings, as shown.

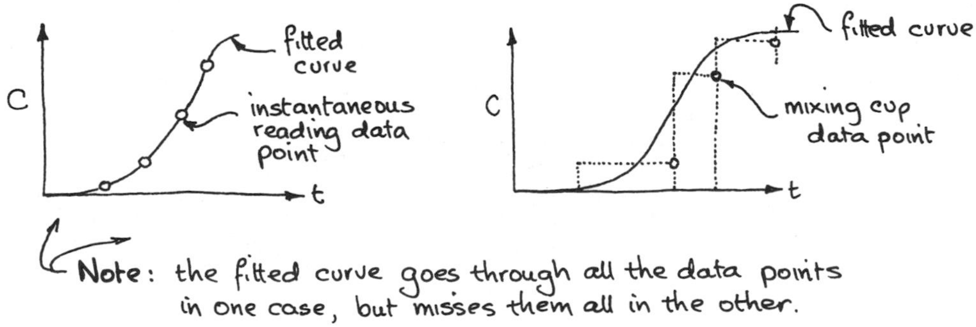
C
t
fitted curve
instantaneous reading data point
C
t
fitted curve
mixing cup data point
Note: the fitted curve goes through all the data points in one case, but misses them all in the other.

This is a simple general procedure which can safely be used for meager, or abundant, or good or bad data.

Comment. No problems are presented in this chapter. However there are many exercises in calculating $\bar{t}$ and σ^2 in the chapters which follow.

Chapter 64 THE DISPERSION MODEL.

Models are useful for representing flow in real vessels, for scale up, for diagnosing poor flow. We have different kinds of models depending on whether flow is close to plug, mixed, or intermediate.

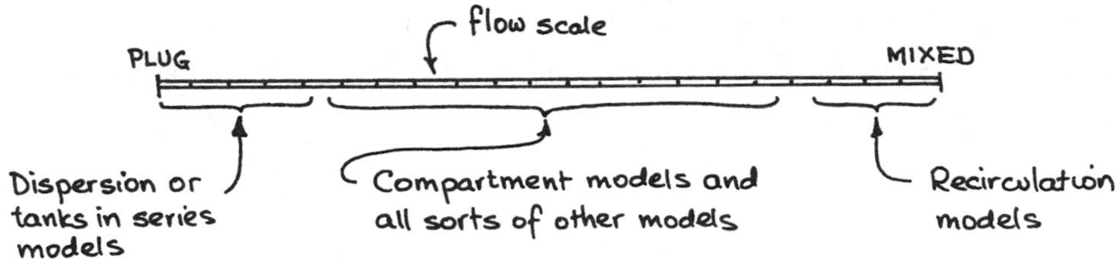

Chapters 64~67 deal primarily with small deviations from plug flow. There are two models for this: the **dispersion model** and the **tanks in series** model. Use the one which is comfortable for you. They are roughly equivalent. These models apply to turbulent flow in pipes, laminar flow in long tubes, packed beds, shaft kilns, long channels, etc.

For laminar flow in short tubes or laminar flow of viscous materials these models may not apply, and it may be that the parabolic velocity profile is the main cause of deviation from plug flow. We treat this situation, called the **pure convection model** in chapters 68~69.

If you are unsure which model to use go to the chart at the beginning of chapter 68. It will tell you which model should be fitted to your set up.

I. Dispersion Model.

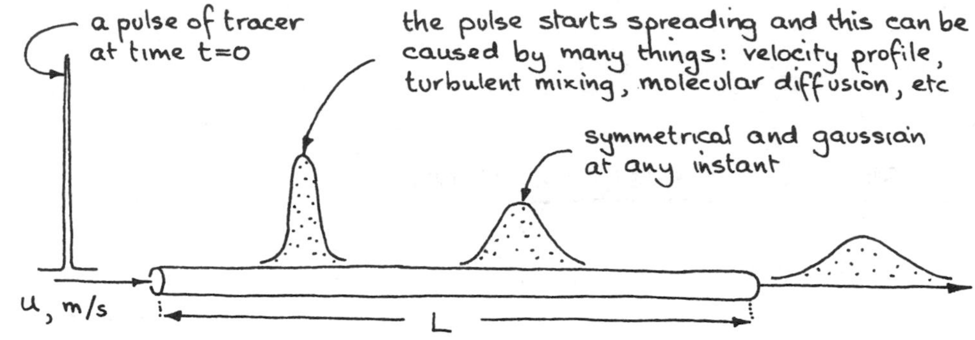
a pulse of tracer at time t=0
the pulse starts spreading and this can be caused by many things: velocity profile, turbulent mixing, molecular diffusion, etc
symmetrical and gaussian at any instant
u, m/s
L

To characterize the spreading we assume a diffusion-like process superimposed on plug flow. We call this **dispersion** or longitudinal dispersion to distinguish it from molecular diffusion. The **dispersion coefficient D** (m^2/s) represents this spreading process. Thus

- large D means rapid spreading of the tracer curve
- small D means slow spreading
- D=0 means no spreading hence plug flow

Also

$\left(\frac{D}{uL}\right)$ is the dimensionless group characterizing the spreading rate for the vessel.

We evaluate D or D/uL by recording the shape of the tracer curve as it passes the exit of the vessel. In particular, we measure

$\bar{t}$ = mean time of passage, or when the curve passes by

σ^2 = variance, or [how long]^2 it takes for the curve to pass by.

These measures, $\bar{t}$ and σ^2, are directly linked by theory to D and D/uL. On solving the mathematics we find a simple solution for slow spreading of tracer, but a messier solution for rapid spreading. Let us look at these solutions in turn.

II. Small Deviation from Plug Flow, $\frac{D}{uL} < 0.01$

Here the tracer curve is narrow so it passes the measuring point quickly compared to $\bar{t}$. As a result we assume that the measured curve **doesn't change shape** as it is being measured, thus it is symmetrical and gaussian. Its spread then depends on D/uL, and its characteristics, properties and equation are as follows

$E_{\theta,max} = \frac{1}{\sqrt{4\pi\cdot\frac{D}{uL}}}$

eq. 1

shaded area = 0.68

point of inflection

total area = 1

$0.61\,E_{\theta,max}$

$2\sqrt{2\frac{D}{uL}}$

$1-\sigma_\theta$ 1 $1+\sigma_\theta$

$= 1+\sqrt{2\frac{D}{uL}}$

$\frac{D}{uL} = 0.00005$

$= 0.0002$

$= 0.0008$

$= 0.0032$

$\frac{D}{uL} = 0.0128$

At this value of D/uL the tracer curve is becoming non symmetrical. This should be the upper limit for the use of the "small deviation" assumption

$\theta = \frac{t}{\bar{t}} = \frac{t\upsilon}{V}$

0.9   1.0   1.1

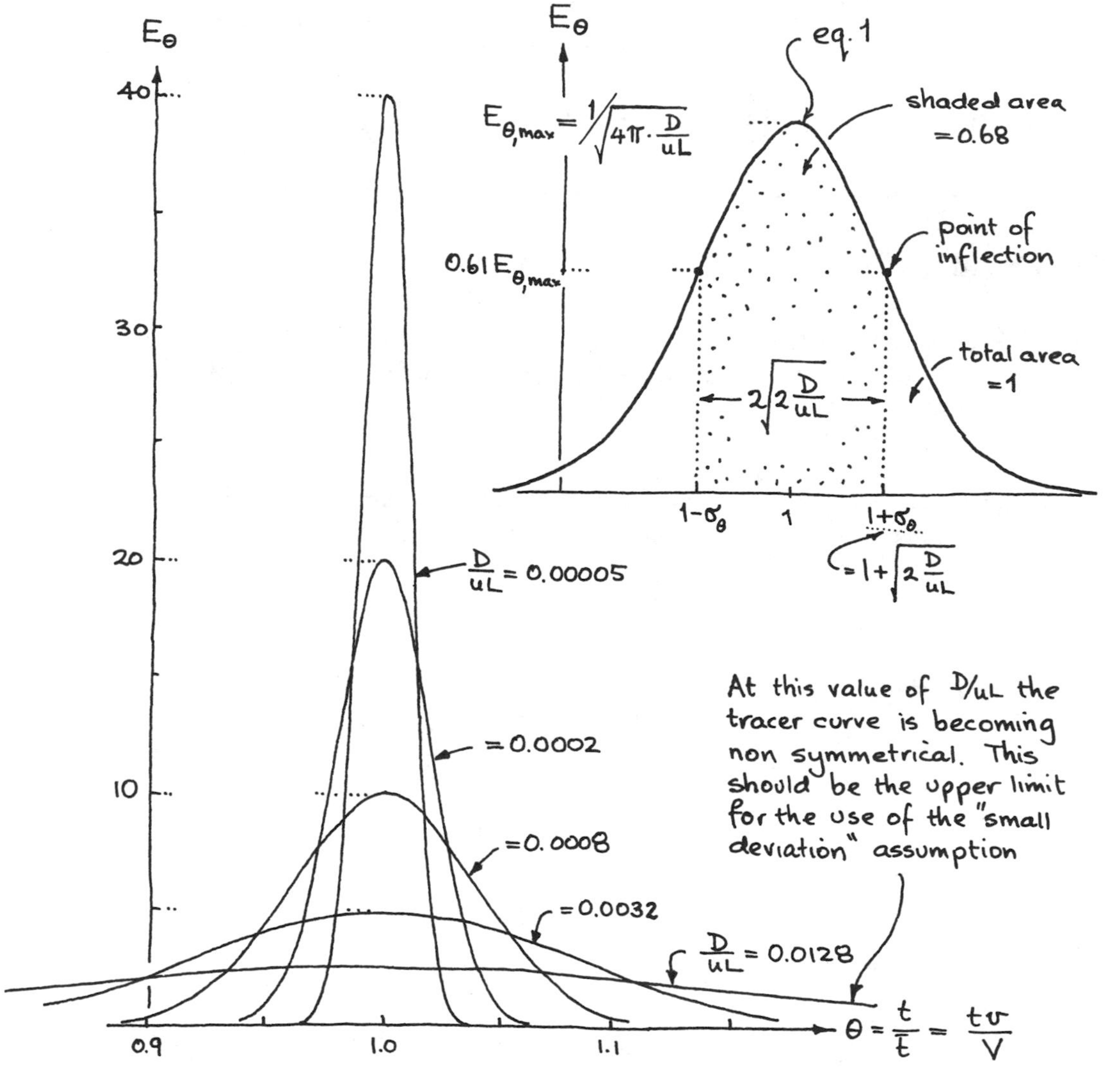

$$E_\theta = \bar{t} \cdot E_t = \frac{1}{\sqrt{4\pi (D/uL)}} \exp\left[-\frac{(1-\theta)^2}{4(D/uL)} \right]$$

$$E_t = \sqrt{\frac{u^3}{4\pi DL}} \exp\left[-\frac{(L-ut)^2}{4DL/u} \right] \qquad \cdots (1)$$

$$\bar{t}_E = \frac{V}{v} = \frac{L}{u} \quad \text{or} \quad \bar{\theta}_E = 1$$

(mean of E curve)

$$\sigma_\theta^2 = \frac{\sigma_t^2}{\bar{t}^2} = 2\left(\frac{D}{uL}\right) \quad \text{or} \quad \sigma_t^2 = 2\left(\frac{DL}{u^3}\right)$$

Comments

(a) To evaluate D/uL use any of the properties of the pulse-response curve, either σ_t^2, maximum height, or width at 61% maximum height.

(b) Note how the tracer curve spreads as it moves down the vessel. From the variance expression of eq 1 we find

$$\sigma_t^2 \propto L \quad \text{or} \quad \left(\begin{matrix}\text{width of tracer}\\ \text{curve}\end{matrix}\right)^2 \propto L$$

(c) For a sloppy input of tracer we have

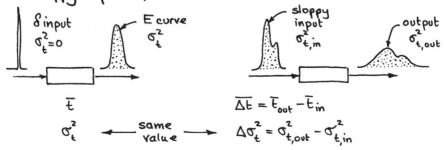

$\bar{t}$ $\qquad\qquad\qquad$ $\overline{\Delta t} = \bar{t}_{out} - \bar{t}_{in}$

σ_t^2 ← same value → $\Delta\sigma_t^2 = \sigma_{t,out}^2 - \sigma_{t,in}^2$

Since $\Delta\sigma_t^2$ (sloppy input) $= \sigma_t^2$ (pulse input) it can be used directly in place of σ_t^2 to evaluate D/uL.

(d) **For a series of vessels** certain properties are additive, thus

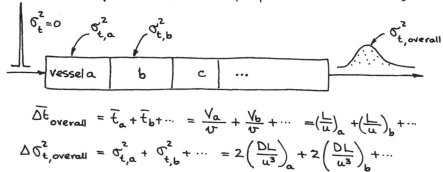

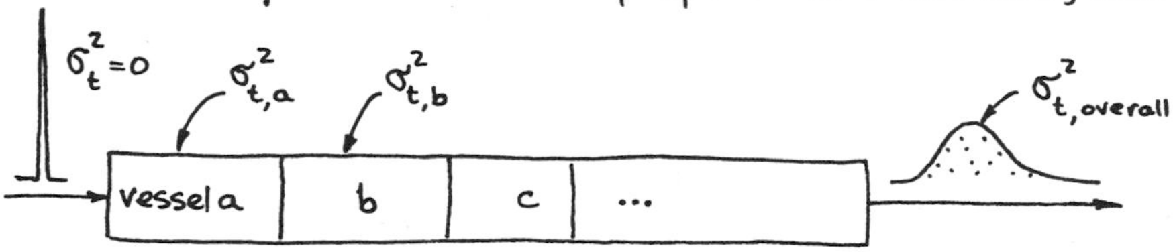

$$\Delta \bar{t}_{overall} = \bar{t}_a + \bar{t}_b + \cdots = \frac{V_a}{v} + \frac{V_b}{v} + \cdots = \left(\frac{L}{u}\right)_a + \left(\frac{L}{u}\right)_b + \cdots$$

$$\Delta \sigma^2_{t,overall} = \sigma^2_{t,a} + \sigma^2_{t,b} + \cdots = 2\left(\frac{DL}{u^3}\right)_a + 2\left(\frac{DL}{u^3}\right)_b + \cdots$$

The additivity of times is expected, but the additivity of variance is not generally expected. This is a useful property since it allows us to subtract for the distortion of the measured curve caused by input lines, long measuring leads, etc.

(e) **Small deviation from plug flow** can reasonably be assumed when $D/uL < 0.01$. Under these conditions any error in estimate of D/uL from a curve is less than 5%.

III Large Deviation from Plug Flow, $\frac{D}{uL} > 0.01$

Here the pulse response is broad and it passes the measurement point slowly enough that it changes shape — it spreads — as it is being measured. This gives a non symmetrical E curve.

An additional complication enters the picture for large D/uL: what happens right at the entrance and exit of the vessel strongly affects the shape of the tracer curve as well as the relationship between the parameters of the curve and D/uL.

Let us consider two types of boundary conditions: either the flow is undisturbed as it passes the boundary (we call this the open b.c.), or you have plug flow outside the vessel up to the boundary (we call this the closed b.c.). This leads to four combinations of boundary conditions, each with its response curve.

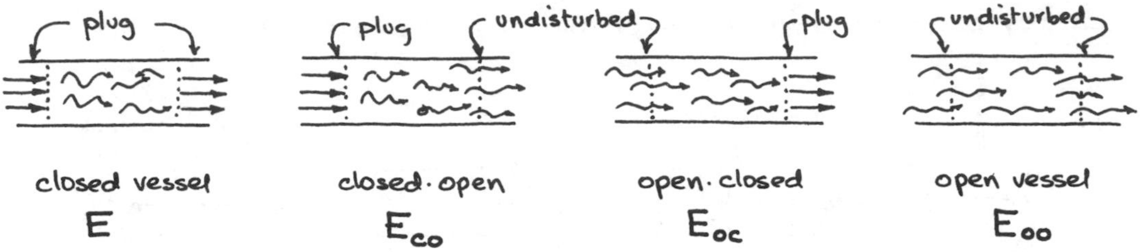

- If the fluid enters and leaves the vessel in small pipes in turbulent flow then you have a closed vessel.

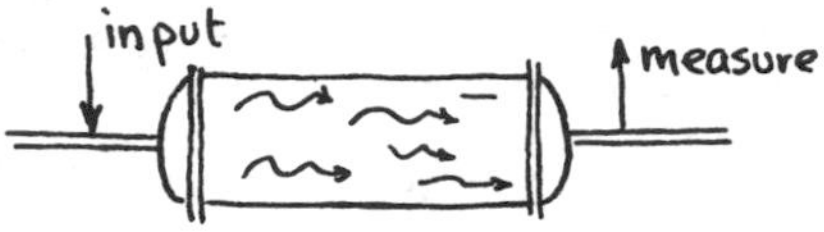

- Measuring the dispersion in a section of a larger vessel, or in a section of long pipe represents an open vessel.

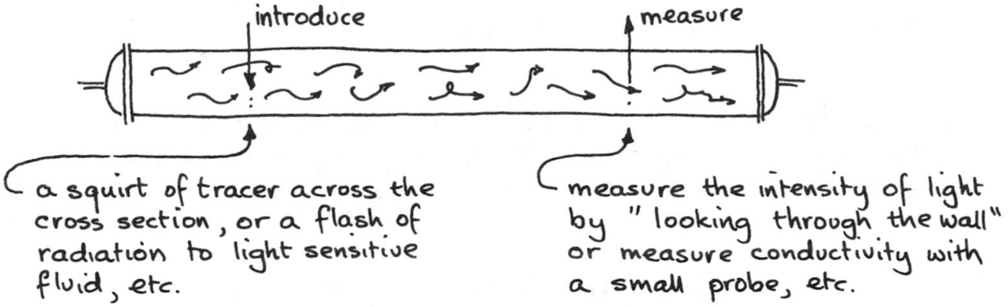

- Switching from one fluid to another (in step experiments) represents a closed input.

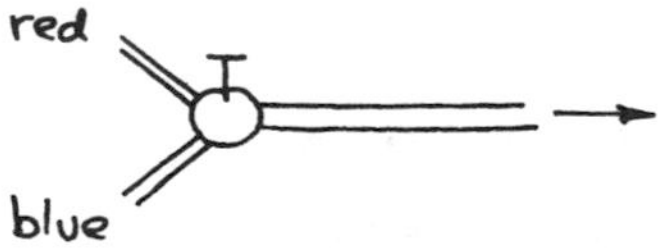

- Taking a mixing cup measurement at the exit represents a closed output.

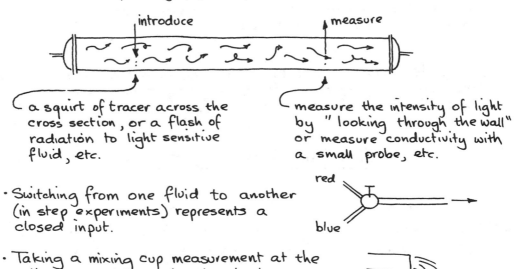

Now only one boundary condition gives a tracer curve which is identical to the E function and which fits all the mathematics of chapter 61, and that is the closed vessel. For all other boundary conditions you do not get a proper RTD, and $\bar{t} > \frac{V}{v}$. To distinguish between these curves we use indicating subscripts, thus E, E_{oc}, E_{co}, E_{oo}.

In all cases you can evaluate D/uL from the parameters of the tracer curves, however each curve has its own mathematics.

1. **Closed vessel.** Here an analytic expression for the E curve is not available. However we can construct the curve by numerical methods, and evaluate its mean and variance exactly. Thus

$$\bar{t}_E = \bar{t} = \frac{V}{v} \quad \cdots \text{or} \cdots \quad \bar{\theta}_E = \frac{\bar{t}_E}{\bar{t}} = \frac{\bar{t}_E v}{V} = 1 \qquad \text{(of measured curve)}$$

$$\sigma_\theta^2 = \frac{\sigma_t^2}{\bar{t}^2} = 2\left(\frac{D}{uL}\right) - 2\left(\frac{D}{uL}\right)^2\left[1 - e^{-uL/D}\right] \quad \cdots (2)$$

van der Laan CES 7 187 (1958)

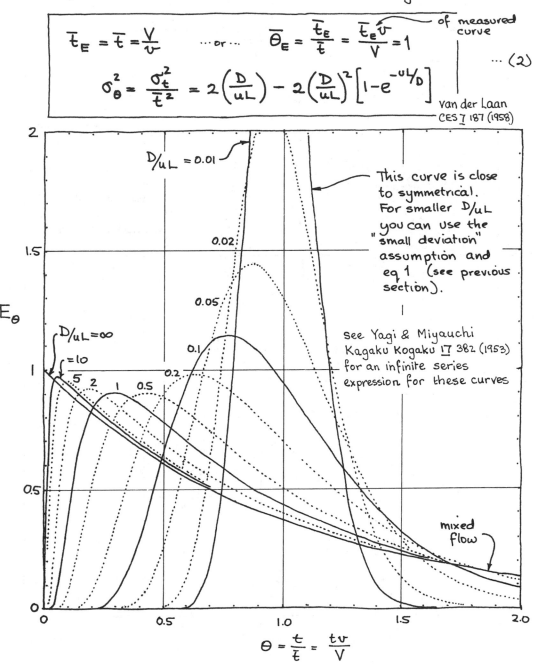

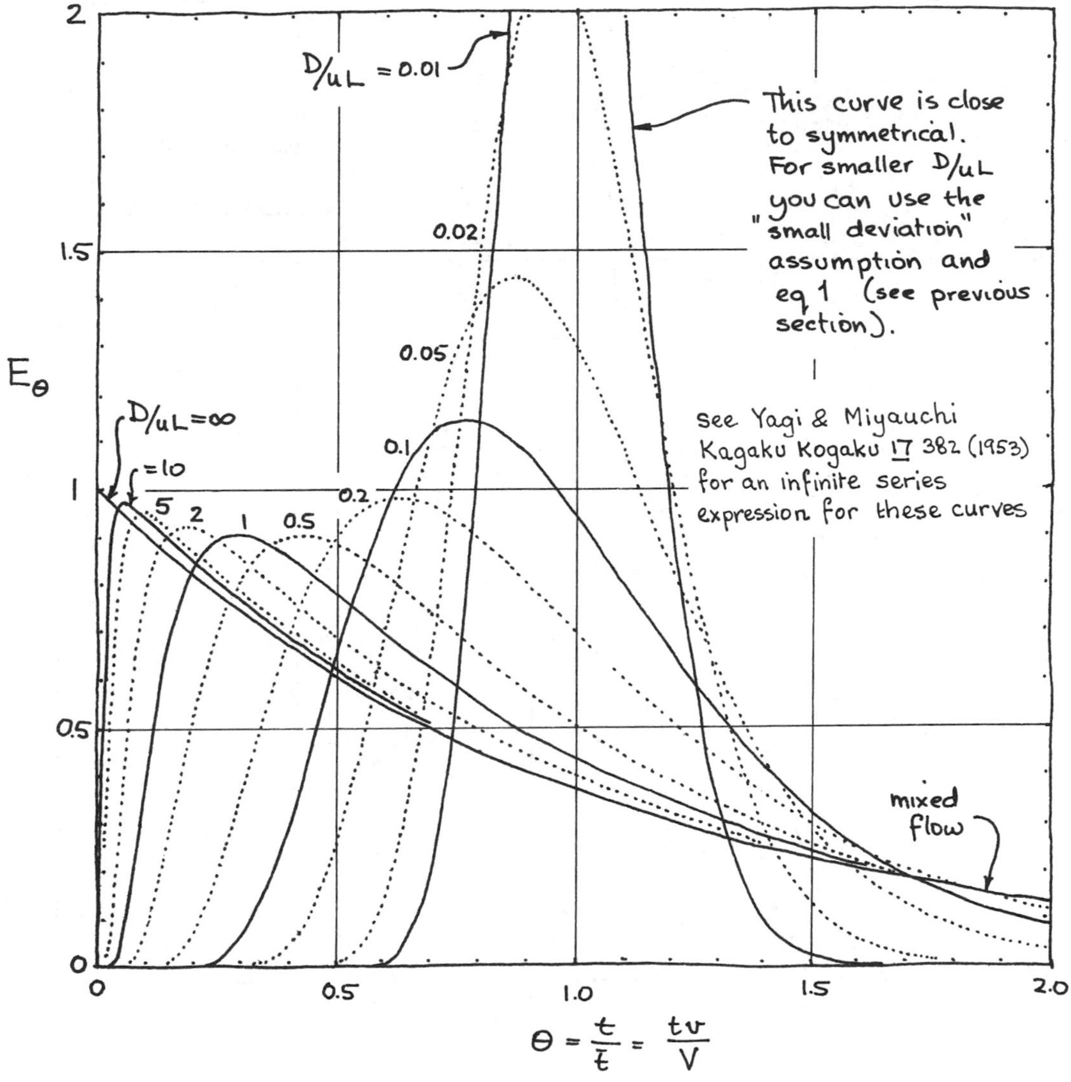

2. Open-closed and closed-open vessels. Again we cannot derive the equation for, but we can construct the tracer curves and evaluate their mean and variance in terms of D/uL. Thus

$$\bar{\theta}_{E_{oc}} = \bar{\theta}_{E_{co}} = 1 + \frac{D}{uL} \quad \text{...or} \quad \bar{t}_{E_{oc}} = \bar{t}_{E_{co}} = \frac{V}{v}\left(1 + \frac{D}{uL}\right)$$

$$\sigma^2_{\theta oc} = \sigma^2_{\theta co} = \frac{\sigma^2_{t,oc}}{\bar{t}^2} = \frac{\sigma^2_{t,oc}}{(V/v)^2} = 2\left(\frac{D}{uL}\right) + 3\left(\frac{D}{uL}\right)^2 \quad \cdots (3)$$

Van der Laan CES 7 187 (1958)

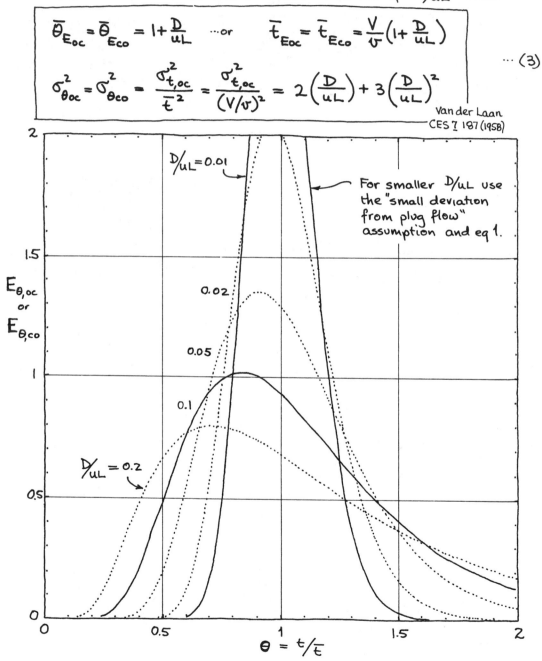

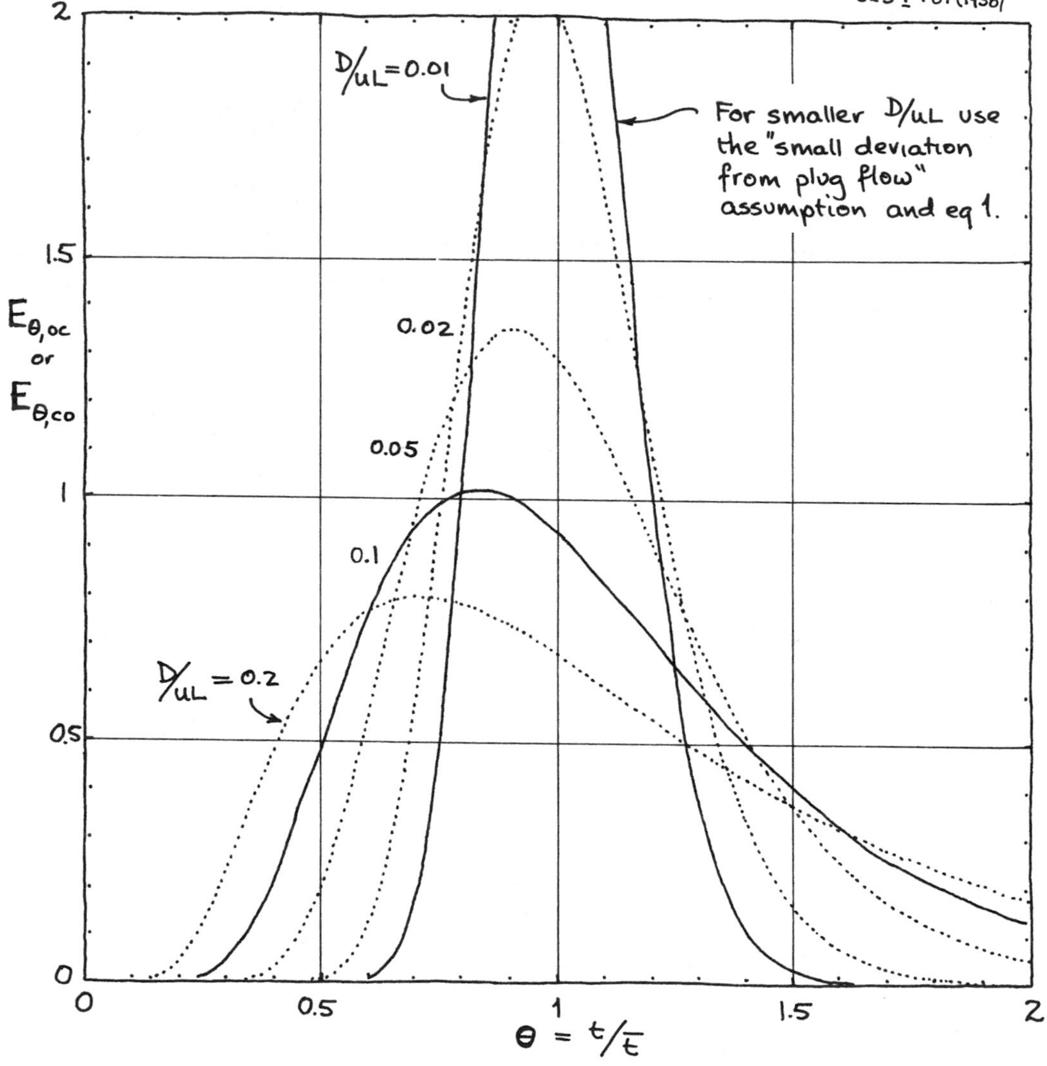

3. Open vessel. This represents a convenient and commonly used experimental device, the section of long pipe. It also happens to be the only physical situation (besides small D/uL) where the analytical expression for the E curve is not too complex. We thus find the following response curve and equations.

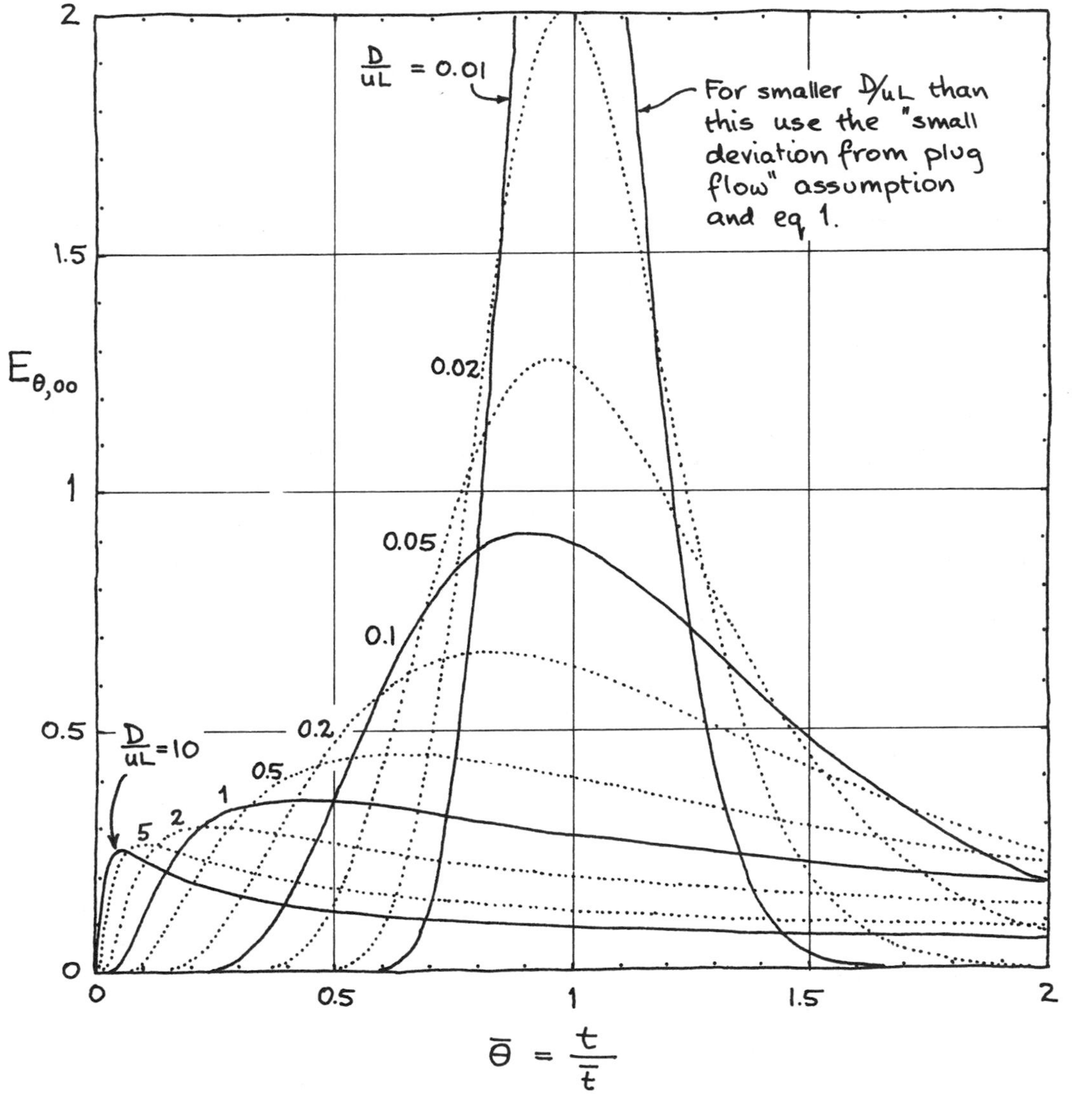

$$E_{\theta,oo} = \frac{1}{\sqrt{4\pi (D/uL)\theta}} \exp\left[-\frac{(1-\theta)^2}{4\theta(D/uL)}\right]$$

$$E_{t,oo} = \frac{u}{\sqrt{4\pi Dt}} \exp\left[-\frac{(L-ut)^2}{4Dt}\right]$$

$$\bar{\theta}_{E_{oo}} = \frac{\bar{t}_{E_{oo}}}{\bar{t}} = 1 + 2\left(\frac{D}{uL}\right) \quad \text{...or} \quad \bar{t}_{E_{oo}} = \frac{V}{v}\left(1 + 2\frac{D}{uL}\right) \qquad \text{... (4)}$$

open.open vessel

$$\sigma^2_{\theta,oo} = \frac{\sigma^2_{t,oo}}{\bar{t}^2} = 2\frac{D}{uL} + 8\left(\frac{D}{uL}\right)^2$$

Levenspiel & Smith
CES 6 227 (1957)

Comments

(a) For small D/uL the curves for the different boundary conditions all approach the "small deviation" curve of eq 1. At larger D/uL the curves differ more and more from each other

(b) To evaluate D/uL either match the measured tracer curve or σ^2 to theory. Matching σ^2 is simplest, though not necessarily best, so it is often used. But be sure to use the right boundary conditions.

(c) If the flow deviates greatly from plug (D/uL large) chances are that the real vessel doesn't meet the assumption of the model (a lot of independent random fluctuations). Here it becomes questionable whether the model should even be used. I hesitate when D/uL > 1.

(d) You must always ask whether the model should be used. You can always match σ^2 values, but if the shape looks wrong dont use this model, use some other model. For example

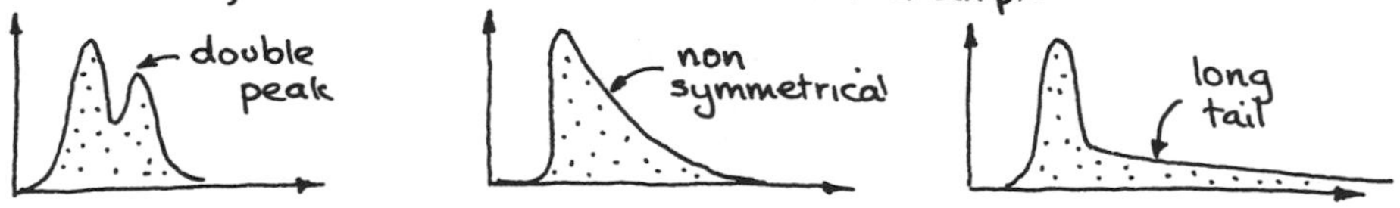

IV. Step Input of Tracer.

Here the output F curve is S-shaped

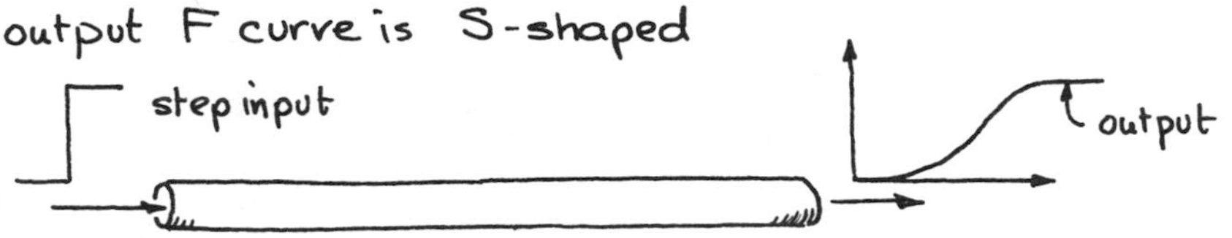

and it is obtained by integrating the corresponding E curve. Thus at any time t or θ

$$F = \int_0^{\theta} E_{\theta}\, d\theta = \int_0^{t} E_t\, dt \qquad (5)$$

The shape of the F curve depends on D/uL and the boundary conditions for the vessel. Analytical expressions are not available for any of the F curves however their graphs can be constructed, and these are shown below.

1. Small deviation from plug flow, $\frac{D}{uL} < 0.01$. From eq 1 and 5 we find

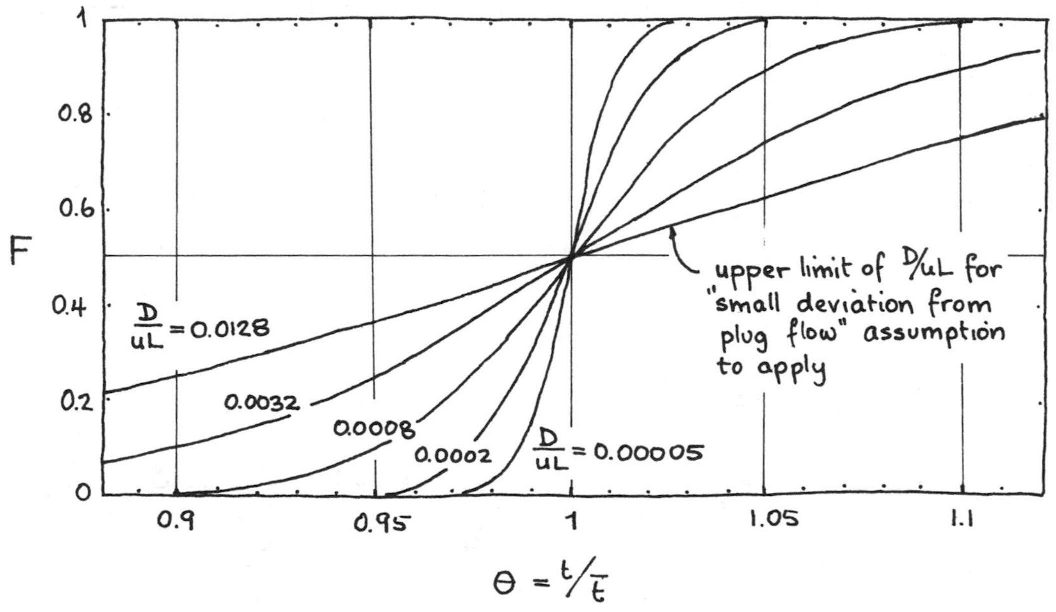

2. Closed vessel with large dispersion, $D/uL > 0.01$. This is the "proper" F curve, the one which gives the "proper" E curve on differentiating. Chapter 61 deals with this F curve.

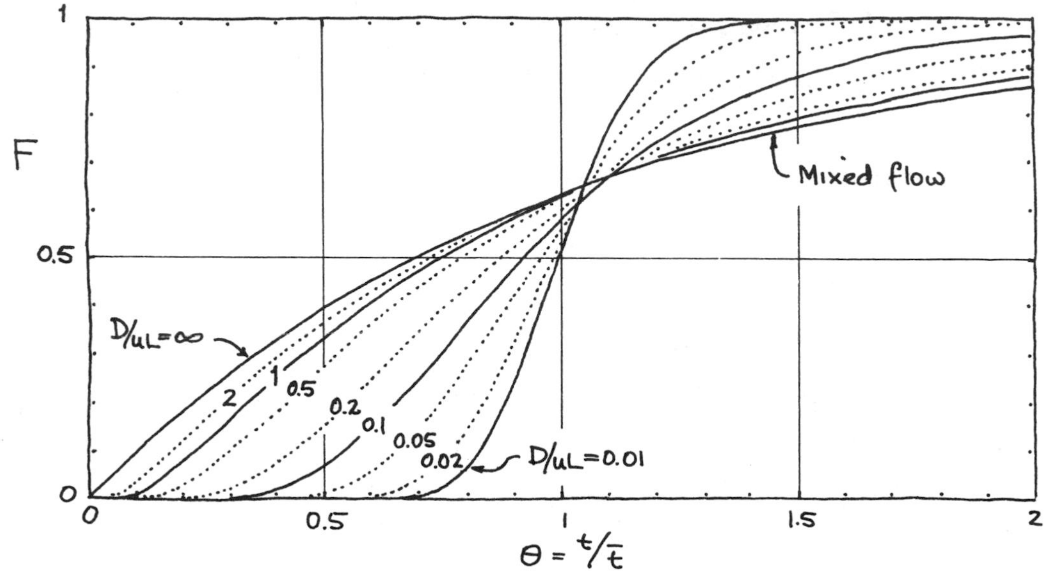

3. Closed-open and open-closed vessels with large dispersion, $D/uL > 0.01$. The curves are identical for these two cases.

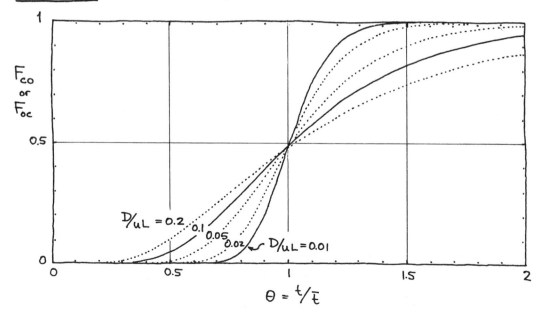

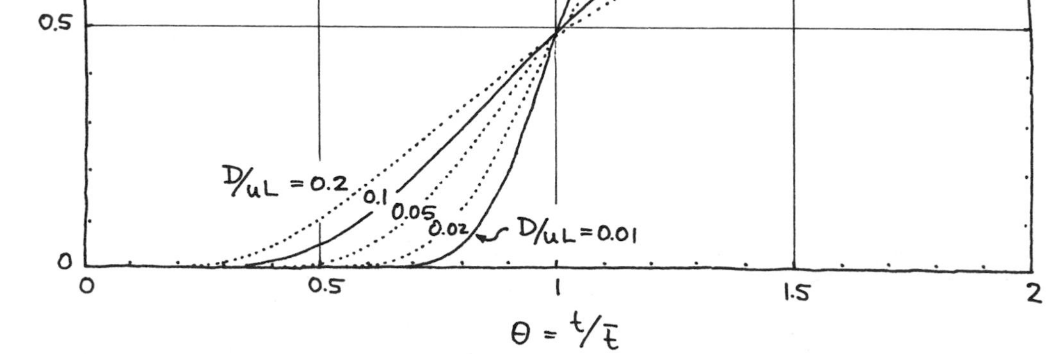

4. Open vessel with large dispersion, $D/uL > 0.01$. Integration of eq 4 gives the following F_{oo} curve

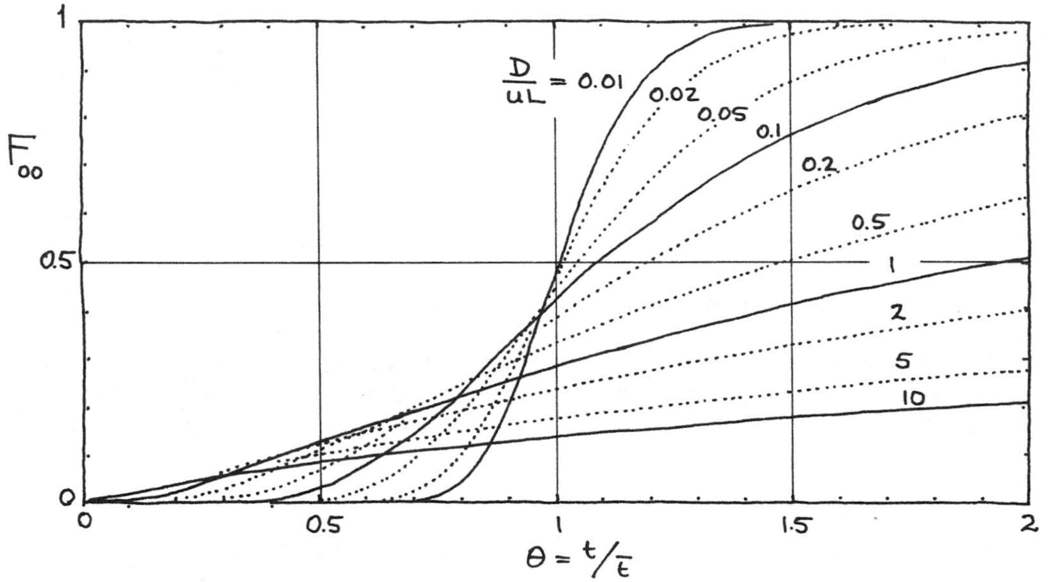

Comments

(a) To evaluate D/uL from the F curve either

- Match the experimental F curve to one of the family of curves displayed above.
- From the data calculate $\bar{t}$ and σ^2 for the corresponding pulse response curve, and use that to evaluate D/uL. See chapter 63 for the calculation procedure.
- For small enough deviation from plug flow ($D/uL < 0.01$) plot the F curve directly on probability paper. Again see chapter 63.

(b) One direct commercial application is to find the zone of intermixing — the contaminated width — between two fluids of somewhat similar properties flowing one after the other in a long pipeline. Given D/uL we find this directly by plotting the expected F curve on probability paper. Thus

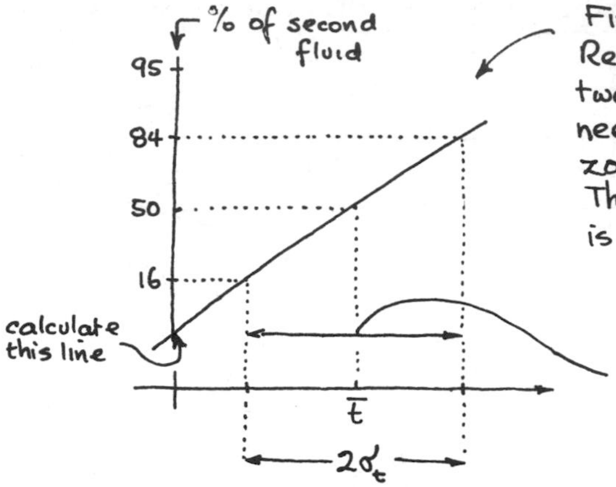

First construct the line on this graph. Reading the time interval between any two percentage values gives the time needed Δt for this contaminated zone to pass the measuring point. Thus the width of contaminated zone is

$$\Delta L = u \cdot \Delta t$$

From $\sigma_\theta^2 = 2\frac{D}{uL}$ we find $2\sigma_t = \sqrt{\frac{8DL}{u^3}}$

In designing a pipeline for minimum contamination use turbulent flow throughout and have no side loops or holding tanks anywhere along the line.

(c) Should you use a pulse or step injection experiment? Sometimes one type of experiment is naturally more convenient for one of many reasons. In such a situation this question does not arise. But when you do have a choice then the pulse experiment is preferred because it gives a more "honest" result. The reason is that the F curve integrates effects, it gives a smooth good-looking curve which could well hide real effects. For example the sketches below show the corresponding E and F curves for a given vessel.

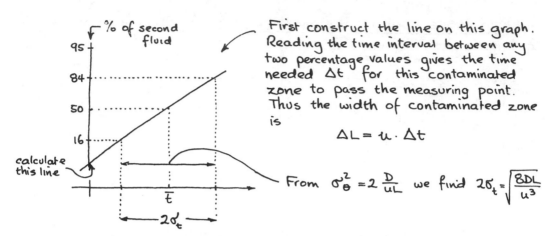

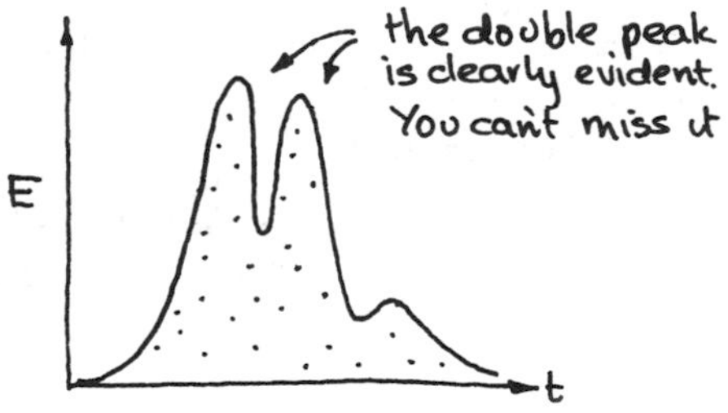

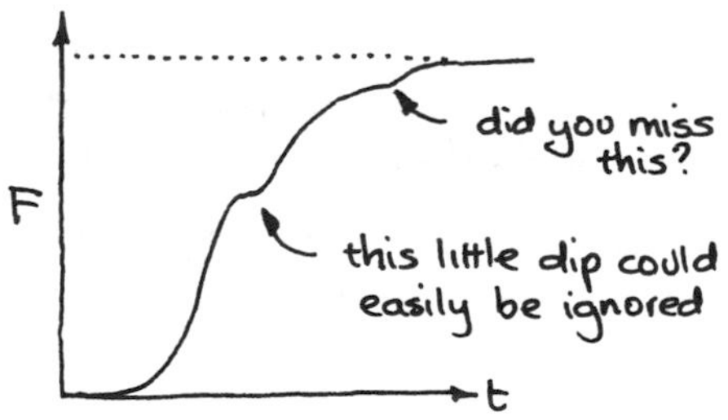

V. Correlations for Axial Dispersion.

The vessel dispersion number:

$$\frac{D}{uL} = \binom{\text{intensity of}}{\text{dispersion}}\binom{\text{geometric}}{\text{factor}} = \frac{D}{ud} \cdot \frac{d}{L} \qquad \cdots (6)$$

this characterizes the vessel as a chemical reactor

$$\frac{D}{ud} = f\binom{\text{fluid}}{\text{properties}}, \frac{\text{flow}}{\text{dynamics}}$$

Schmidt no.   Reynolds no.

characteristic length: d_t or d_p

Theory and experiment give $\frac{D}{ud}$ for various situations. We summarize these findings below

For lamnar flow we get a different line for each Schmidt no.

For all these lines

$$D = \mathcal{D} + \frac{u^2 d_t^2}{192 \mathcal{D}}$$

or

$$\frac{D}{uL} = \frac{1}{Re \cdot Sc} + \frac{Re \cdot Sc}{192}$$

$$Re = \frac{d_t u \rho}{\mu}$$

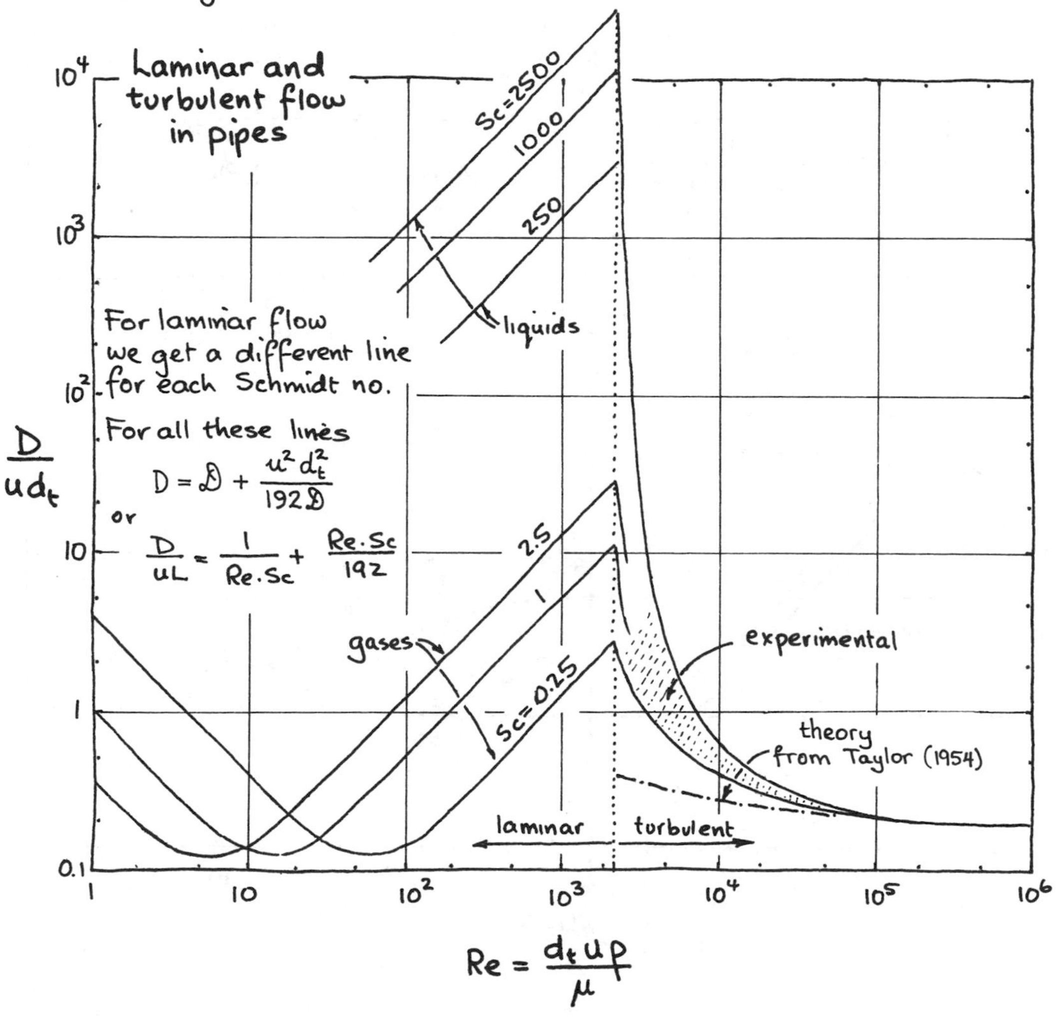

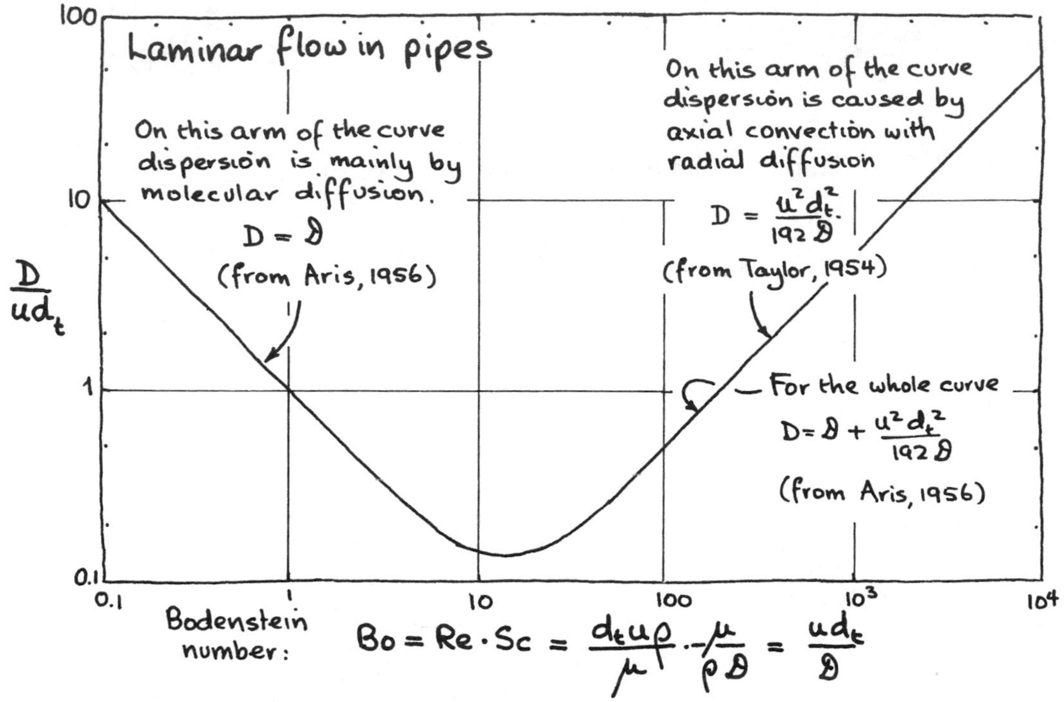
Laminar flow in pipes
On this arm of the curve dispersion is mainly by molecular diffusion.
$D = \mathcal{D}$
(from Aris, 1956)
On this arm of the curve dispersion is caused by axial convection with radial diffusion
$D = \frac{u^2 d_t^2}{192 \mathcal{D}}$
(from Taylor, 1954)
For the whole curve
$D = \mathcal{D} + \frac{u^2 d_t^2}{192 \mathcal{D}}$
(from Aris, 1956)
$\frac{D}{u d_t}$
100
10
1
0.1
0.1
1
10
100
10^3
10^4
Bodenstein number:
$Bo = Re \cdot Sc = \frac{d_t u \rho}{\mu} \cdot \frac{\mu}{\rho \mathcal{D}} = \frac{u d_t}{\mathcal{D}}$

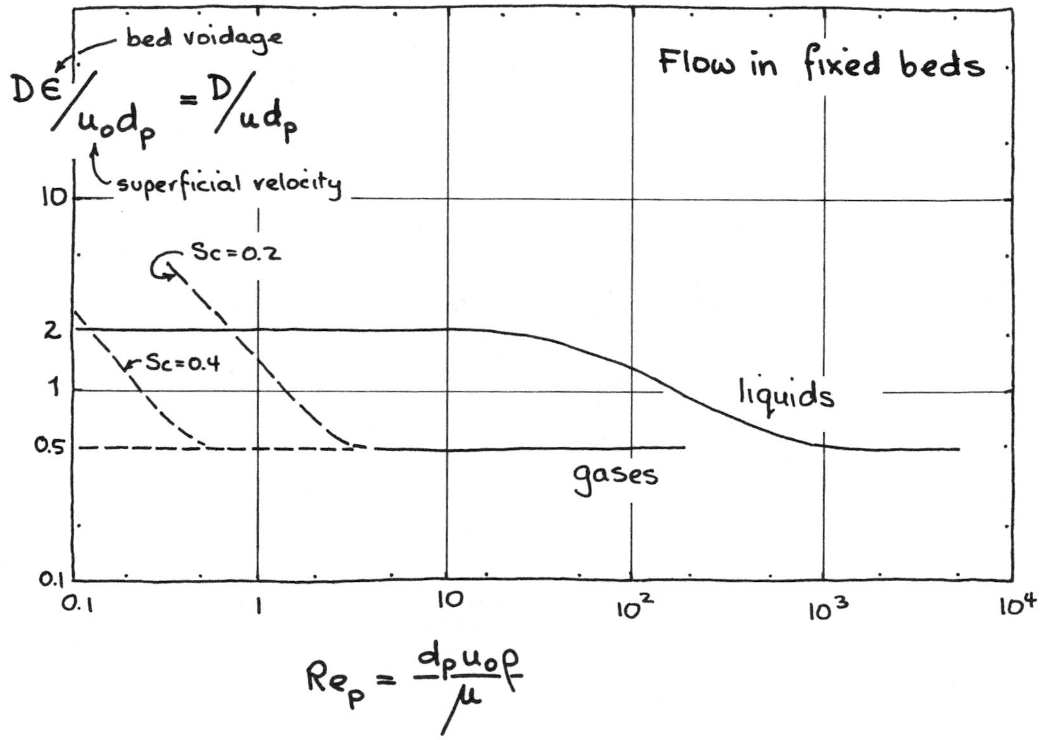
bed voidage
$D\epsilon / u_o d_p = D / u d_p$
superficial velocity
Flow in fixed beds
Sc=0.2
Sc=0.4
liquids
gases
10
2
1
0.5
0.1
0.1
1
10
10^2
10^3
10^4
$Re_p = \frac{d_p u_o \rho}{\mu}$

Extensions and comments.

(a) As a rule of thumb for experimentation, we get a gaussian RTD curve if:

$$\frac{D}{uL} < 0.01 \quad \text{... and ...} \quad V_{\text{injected sample}} < 0.01\, V_{\text{vessel}}$$

(b) In laminar flow of newtonians

- if $Bo < 3$ use $D = \mathscr{D}$. In this regime axial dispersion is caused by molecular diffusion alone
- if $Bo > 50$ use $D = u^2 d_t^2 / 192\,\mathscr{D}$. In this regime axial dispersion is a result of the interaction of velocity variations with lateral molecular diffusion.
- if $3 < Bo < 50$ use $D = \mathscr{D} + u^2 d_t^2 / 192\,\mathscr{D}$. This is the intermediate regime where all mechanisms play in the symphony.

The charts verify these conclusions. These relationships were derived theoretically by

Taylor, Proc. Roy. Soc. 219A 186 (1953); 225A 473 (1954).
Aris, Proc. Roy. Soc. 235A 67 (1956).

(c) Finding $\mathscr{D}$ of fluids by experiment. Measuring the axial dispersion in laminar flow is a neat, quick, simple and accurate way for finding the molecular diffusion coefficient of fluids. However, in solving the quadratic expression you will come up with two $\mathscr{D}$ values. In other words two $\mathscr{D}$ values will give the same extent of axial dispersion.

D/ud_t
the larger 𝒟 value is on this arm of the curve. Here:
D is independent of u and d_t
the smaller 𝒟 value is on this arm of the curve. Here:
D ∝ u² d_t²
Bo = ud_t/𝒟

If you know which arm of the curve you're on (a rough estimate of the Bodenstein number may help) you can find the correct value for $\mathscr{D}$; if not then you cannot tell, and you need at least two runs at different velocities or in different size pipes.

(d) **Laminar flow in all shapes of channels and conduits** give closely similar results

Circular tubes, Newtonians $$D = \mathcal{D} + \frac{u^2 d_t^2}{192\mathcal{D}}$$ ... Aris, Proc. Roy. Soc. 235A 67 (1956)

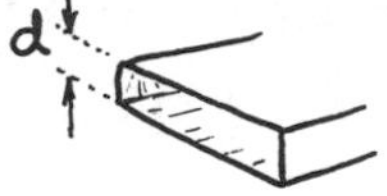

Parallel slots, Newtonians $$D = \mathcal{D} + \frac{u^2 d^2}{210\mathcal{D}}$$ ... Aris, Proc. Roy. Soc. 252A 538 (1959)

Elliptical channels, Newtonians $$D = \mathcal{D} + \frac{24 - 24e^2 + 5e^4}{24 - 12e^2}\,\frac{u^2 a^2}{192\mathcal{D}}$$

where $e^2 = \dfrac{a^2 - b^2}{a^2}$

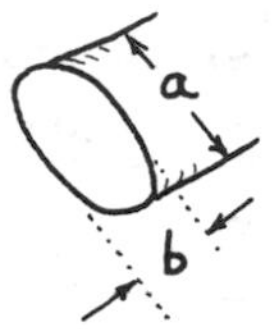

Circular tubes, power law fluids $$D = \mathcal{D} + \frac{u^2 d_t^2}{8(n+3)(n+5)\mathcal{D}}$$ ... Fan and Hwang, Proc. Roy. Soc. 283A 576 (1965)

Parallel slots, power law fluids $$D = \mathcal{D} + \frac{u^2 d^2}{6(n+4)(2n+5)\mathcal{D}}$$

Circular tubes, Bingham plastics: see eq 17 in the reference (rather long)

... Fan and Wong Proc. Roy. Soc 292A 203 (1966)

(e) **For time variable flow** say in an estuary or an artery use a time average D, see Bischoff, CES 19 989 (1964)

(f) **Newtonians in coiled tubes.** In certain flow regimes dispersion is higher than in straight pipe, in other regimes it is lower

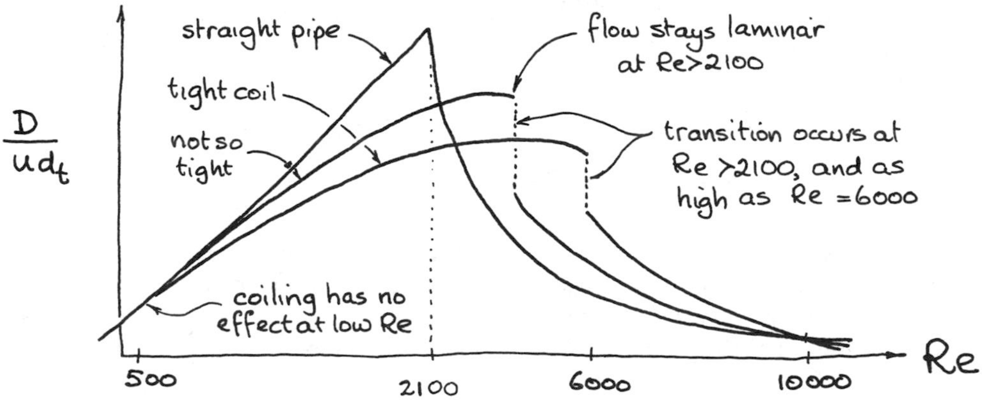

(g) Adsorbing porous-walled tubes, and a tube model for packed beds of porous adsorbing particles

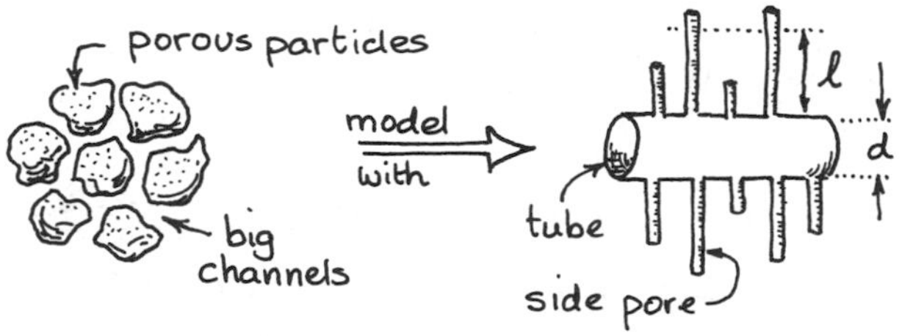

$$\beta = \frac{V_{pore}}{V_{tube}}$$

$$\gamma = \frac{V_{\text{adsorption on side wall of pore}}}{V_{pore}} = \frac{2}{k\ell}$$

$$\delta = \frac{V_{\text{adsorbed on tube wall \& bottom of pore}}}{V_{tube}} = \frac{4}{kd}$$

$$\varepsilon = 1+\gamma$$

For adsorbing component ... $C_{\text{in fluid}} = k\,W_{\text{on surface}}$ (k = adsorption coef, m^{-1})

$$\theta = \frac{u}{u_{eff}} = \frac{\bar{t}_{eff}}{\bar{t}} = \frac{V_{eff}}{V_{tube}} = 1+\beta\varepsilon+\delta$$

(u, $\bar{t}$: in tube alone with no adsorption; u_{eff}: actual, for adsorbing component)

$$\sigma^2_{pulse} = \bar{t}^2_{eff}\left(\frac{2D}{u_{eff}L}\right)$$

General expression ... $D = f$ [velocity profile, pore length distribution, molecular diffusion, adsorption coefficient]

See Dayan, PhD thesis IIT Chicago 1968

↓ one size pore, laminar flow

Dayan & Levenspiel CES 23 1327 (1968)

$$D = \mathscr{D} + \left[1+6\beta\varepsilon+6\delta+22\beta\delta\varepsilon+11\beta^2\varepsilon^2+11\delta^2+24(\beta\delta\varepsilon+2\delta^2)\frac{\ell}{d}+32(2\beta\varepsilon+3\delta)\left(\frac{\ell}{d}\right)^2\right]\frac{u_{eff}^2 d^2}{192\mathscr{D}}$$

Porous but no adsorption: $k=\infty$, $\gamma=\delta=0$, $\theta=1+\beta$

Aris CES 11 194 (1958)

$$D = \mathscr{D} + \left[1+6\beta+11\beta^2+64\left(\frac{\ell}{d}\right)^2\right]\frac{u_{eff}^2 d^2}{192\mathscr{D}}$$

Adsorption on smooth tubes: $\ell=0$, $\beta=\gamma=0$, $\theta=1+\delta$

Dayan & Levenspiel IECF 8 840 (1969)

$$D = \mathscr{D} + \left[1+6\delta+11\delta^2\right]\frac{u_{eff}^2 d^2}{192\mathscr{D}}$$

Pore length = 0, $\beta=0$, $\ell=0$ — Negligible adsorption, $\delta=0$:

$$D = \mathscr{D} + \frac{u^2 d^2}{192\mathscr{D}}$$

Aris Proc. Roy. Soc. A235 67 (1956)

Aris Taylor expression for straight tubes with no adsorption

Long pores, $\beta\to\infty$ — High adsorption, $\delta\to\infty$:

$$D = \mathscr{D} + \frac{11u^2 d^2}{192\mathscr{D}}$$

Westhaver IEC 34 126 (1942)

high adsorption or long pores in straight tubes

VI Chemical Conversion.

When the flow of fluid can be represented by axial dispersion superimposed on plug flow the reactor behaves as follows:

1. **First order reaction** for both micro and macrofluids, $\varepsilon_A = 0$:
An analytical solution to the governing equation gives, for any D/uL:

$$\frac{C_A}{C_{A0}} = 1 - X_A = \frac{4a \exp\left[\frac{1}{2}\frac{uL}{D}\right]}{(1+a)^2 \exp\left[\frac{a}{2}\frac{uL}{D}\right] - (1-a)^2 \exp\left[-\frac{a}{2}\frac{uL}{D}\right]} \qquad \cdots (7)$$

with $a = \sqrt{1 + 4k\tau\left(\frac{D}{uL}\right)}$

Langmuir JACS 30 1742 (1908)
Danckwerts CES 2 1 (1953)
Wehner & Wilhelm CES 6 89 (1956)

A graphical comparison with plug flow gives

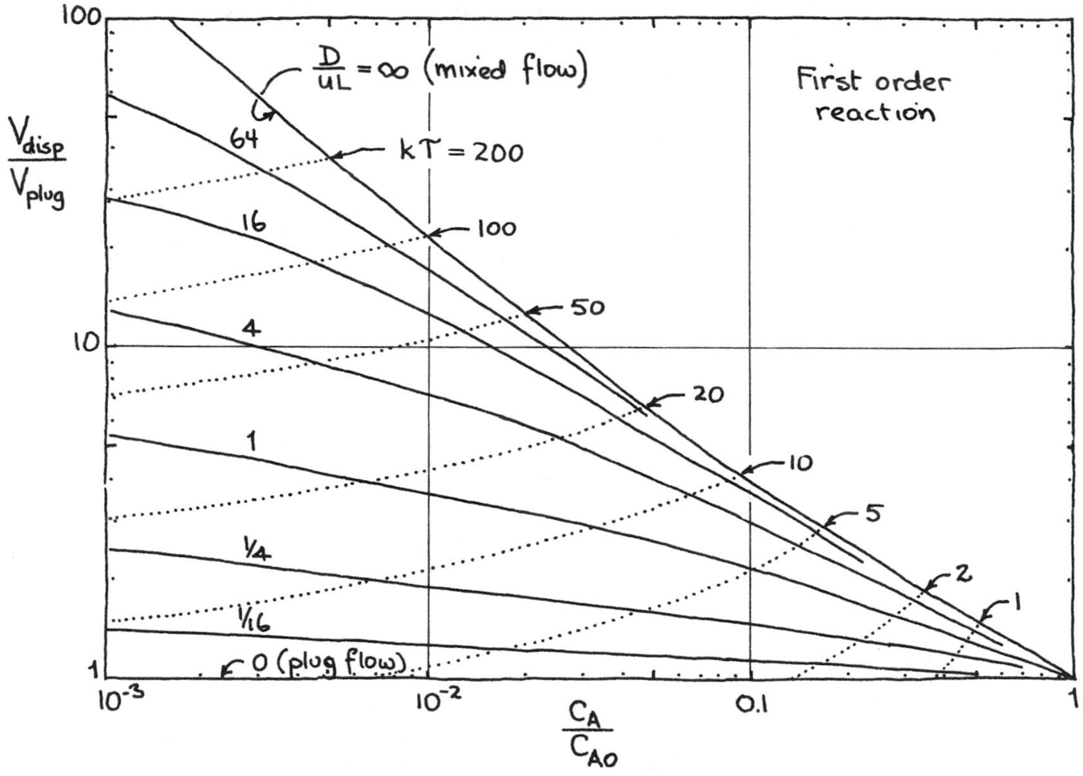

For $\frac{D}{uL} \ll 1$ and $\frac{D}{uL} \cdot k\tau \ll 1$ (small dispersion, especially for $X_A \to 1$).

$$\frac{C_A}{C_{A0}} = \exp\left[-k\tau + (k\tau)^2 \frac{D}{uL}\right] = \exp\left[-k\tau + \frac{k^2\sigma^2}{2}\right] \quad \cdots (8)$$

- $-k\tau$: plug flow term
- $(k\tau)^2 \frac{D}{uL}$: contribution of axial dispersion
- $-k\tau + \frac{k^2\sigma^2}{2}$: this expression can be used for any narrow close to symmetrical distribution. Just use σ^2 for the E curve of that distribution.

Comparing with plug flow gives

$$\frac{L_{actual}}{L_{plug}} = \frac{k_{measured}}{k_{true}} = 1 + k\tau \cdot \left(\frac{D}{uL}\right) \quad \cdots (9)$$

2. **Second order reaction.** $\left.\begin{array}{l} A+B \to \text{products}, \ C_{A0} = C_{B0} \\ 2A \to \text{products} \end{array}\right\}$, microfluid, not early or late mixing, but uniform intensity of mixing along the reactor such as viewed by the dispersion model. No analytical solution is available, however a numerical comparison with plug flow gives:

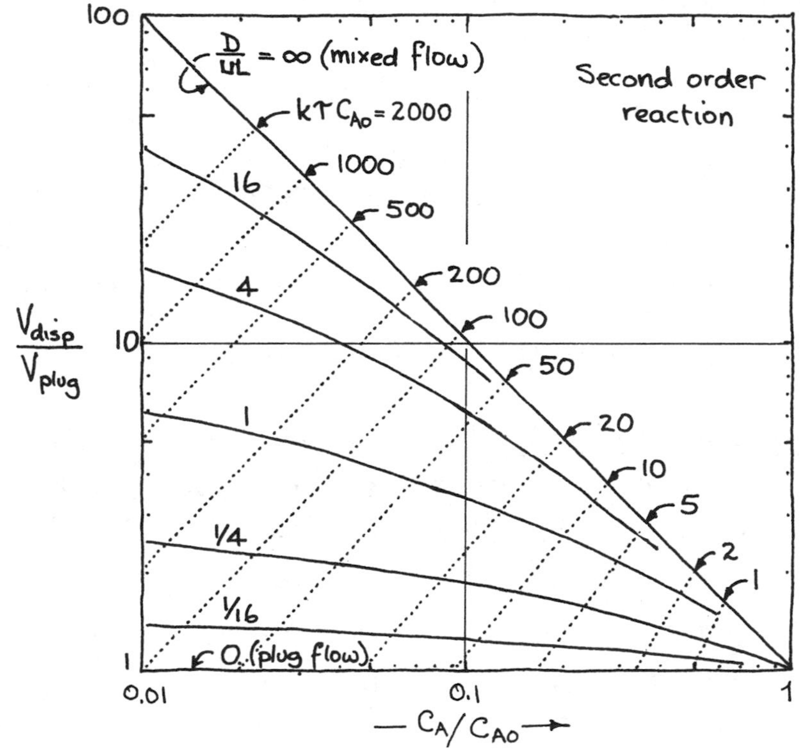

For small deviation from plug flow

$$\frac{L_{actual}}{L_{plug}} = \frac{k_{measured}}{k_{true}} = \frac{1+2+2\left(\frac{D}{uL}\right)R\ln(1+R)}{1+R-2\left(\frac{D}{uL}\right)\ln(1+R)}, \quad R = kC_{A0}\tau \qquad \cdots(10)$$

or

$$\frac{C_A}{C_{A0}} = \left[1 + \frac{2\left(\frac{D}{uL}\right)R\ln(1+R)}{1+R}\right]\underbrace{\left(\frac{1}{1+R}\right)}_{\text{for plug flow alone}}, \quad R = kC_{A0}\tau \qquad \cdots(11)$$

3. Any order reaction, for a microfluid, small $\frac{D}{uL}$

$$\frac{C_A}{C_{Ap}} = 1 + \frac{n\left(\frac{D}{uL}\right)\left(kC_{A0}^{n-1}\tau\right)\ln\frac{C_{A0}}{C_{Ap}}}{1+(n-1)kC_{A0}^{n-1}\tau} \qquad \cdots(12)$$

4. Any rate form, for a microfluid, small $\frac{D}{uL}$

$$C_A - C_{Ap} = \frac{D}{uL}\left(-r_{Ap}\right)\tau\ln\frac{r_{A0}}{r_{Ap}} \qquad \cdots(13)$$

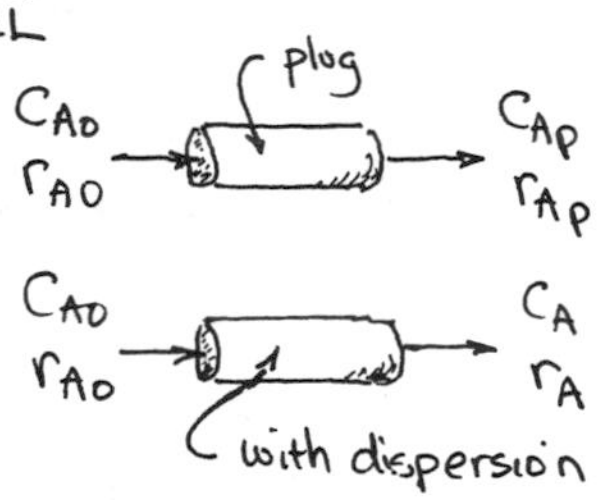

from Pasquon & Dente, J. Cat., 1 508 (1962)

5. For molar expansion, $\varepsilon_A \neq 0$, first order reaction,

see Douglas & Bischoff, IEC/PDD 3 130 (1964).

6. For reactions in series. For small deviations from plug flow, or $\frac{D}{uL} < 0.05$, the fractional decrease in $C_{R,max}$ for $A \rightarrow R \rightarrow S$ is given roughly by the $\frac{D}{uL}$ value; see Tichacek, AIChE J. 9 394 (1963).

7. For other kinetics we cannot solve the mathematics of the dispersion model. In these cases use the tanks in series model whose mathematics is relatively simple. The results are closely similar.

Chapter 64 Problems

A1 The flow pattern of gas through blast furnaces was studied by VDEh (Veren Deutscher Eisenhüttenleute Betriebsforschungsinstitut) by injecting Kr-85 into the air stream entering the tuyeres of the 688 m^3 furnace. A sketch and listing of pertinent quantities for run 10.5 of 9.12.1969 is as follows

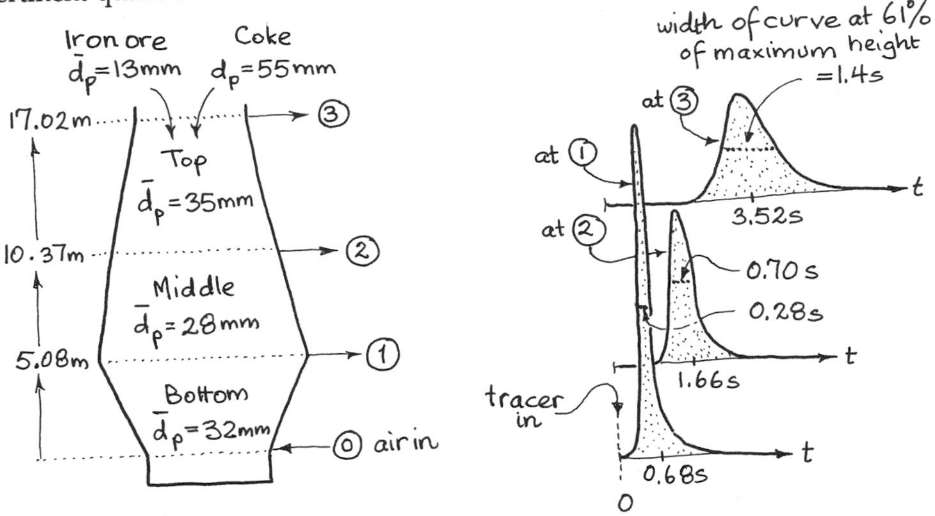

Assuming that the axial dispersion model applies to the flow of gas in the blast furnace, compare D/ud for the bottom, middle and top sections of the blast furnace with that expected in an ordinary packed bed. Any comments?

From Standish and Polthier, pg 99 *Blast Furnace Aerodynamics* N. Standish, ed., Australian I. M. M. Symp., Wollongong, 1975.

A2 Denmark's longest and greatest river, the Gudenaa certainly deserves study, so pulse tracer tests were run on various stretches of the river using radioactive Br-82. Find the axial dispersion coefficient in the upper stretch of the river, between Tørring and Udlum, 8.7 km apart, from the following reported measurements

t, hr	C, arbitrary	t, hr	C, arbitrary
3.5	0	5.75	440
3.75	3	6	250
4	25	6.25	122
4.25	102	6.5	51
4.5	281	6.75	20
4.75	535	7	9
5	740	7.25	3
5.25	780	7.5	0
5.5	650		

Data from Danish Isotope Center, report of Nov. 1976.

Chapter 64 Problems

A3 RTD studies were carried out by Jagadeesh and Satyanarayana IEC/PDD **11** 520 (1972) in a tubular reactor (L = 1.21 m, 35 mm ID). A squirt of NaCl solution (5 N) was rapidly injected at the reactor entrance, and mixing cup measurements were taken at the exit. From the following results calculate the vessel dispersion number; also the fraction of reactor volume taken up by the baffles.

t, sec	NaCl in Sample	
0 - 20	0	
20 - 25	60	
25 - 30	210	
30 - 35	170	
35 - 40	75	(v = 1300 ml/min)
40 - 45	35	
45 - 50	10	
50 - 55	5	
55 - 70	0	

B4 A pulse of radioactive Ba-140 was injected into a 10 inch pipeline (25.5 cm ID) 293 km long used for pumping petroleum products (u = 81.7 cm/s, Re = 24000) from Rangely Colorado to Salt Lake City, Utah. Estimate the time of passage of fluid having more than 1/2 Cmax of tracer and compare the value you find with the reported time of passage of 895 sec averaged over 5 runs.

Data from Hull and Kent, IEC **44** 2745 (1952)

B5 An injected slug of tracer material flows with its carrier fluid down a long straight pipe in dispersed plug flow. At point A in the pipe the spread of tracer is 16 m. At point B one kilometer downstream from A its spread is 32 m. What do you estimate its spread to be at point C two kilometers downstream from point A?

B6 At present we are processing a liquid stream in a tubular reactor. We plan to quadruple the processing rate keeping $\bar{t}$ fixed, and for this we have two alternatives:

- quadruple the length of reactor leaving the pipe diameter unchanged
- double the pipe diameter keeping the length unchanged

Compare the deviation from plug flow of these proposed larger units with that of the present unit. Assume that the reactors are long enough for the dispersion model to apply and that

(a) highly turbulent flow prevails throughout

(b) laminar flow prevails throughout

Chapter **64** Problems

B7 Kerosene and gasoline are pumped successively at 1.1 m/s through a 10 inch (25.5 cm ID) pipeline 1000 km long. Calculate the 5/95% to 95/5% contaminated width at the exit of the pipe given that the kinematic viscosity for the 50/50% mixture is

$$\mu/\rho = 0.9 \times 10^{-6}\ \mathrm{m^2/s}$$

Data and problem from Sjenitzer, Pipeline Engineer, Dec. 1958.

A refinery pumps products A and B successively to receiving stations up to 100 km away through a 10 cm ID pipeline. The average properties of A and B are $\rho = 850\ \mathrm{kg/m^3}$, $\mu = 1.7 \times 10^{-3}\ \mathrm{kg/m{\cdot}s}$, $\mathcal{D} = 10^{-9}\ \mathrm{m^2/s}$, the fluid flows at u = 20 cm/s, and there are no reservoirs, holding tanks or pipe loops in the line; just a few bends.

B8 . . . Estimate the 1% - 90% contaminated width 100 km away.

B9 . . . If the flow is speeded to Re = 100000 what would this do to a contaminated width 100 km away?

B10 . . . If the flow is slowed to Re = 1000 what would this do to a contaminated width 100 km away? Before trying to solve this problem be sure to check pages 1, 2 and 3 of chapter 68.

Adapted from Petroleum Refiner **37** 191 (March 1958); Pipe Line Industry, pg 51 (May 1958).

We wish to design an experimental set up to evaluate the molecular diffusivity of solute A in solvent B using a 1 mm tube. To guarantee that the experiment will be run in the regime where dispersion theory applies

C11 . . . how long a tube must we use for a flow rate of 10 cm/s, where A/B are liquids?

C12 . . . how long a tube must we use for a flow rate of 10 cm/s, where A/B are gases?

C13 . . . what velocity must we use in a 20 m long tube, where A/B are liquids?

For liquids take $\rho = 1000\ \mathrm{kg/m^3}$, $\mu = 10^{-3}\ \mathrm{kg/m{\cdot}s}$, $\mathcal{D} \approx 10^{-9}\ \mathrm{m^2/s}$
For gases take $\rho = 1\ \mathrm{kg/m^3}$, $\mu = 10^{-5}\ \mathrm{kg/m{\cdot}s}$, $\mathcal{D} \approx 10^{-5}\ \mathrm{m^2/s}$

<u>Note:</u> Only attempt these problems after having digested pages 1, 2 and 3 in chapter 68.

Chapter 64 Problems

C14* 1 **N** ammonium chloride flows at constant velocity through a straight tube 0.0271 cm ID. At time t = 0 we switch to 3 **N** solution and we monitor the concentration of NH_4Cl 101 cm downstream with the following results

% Second Fluid	5	10	40	80	97
Time, s	5805	5840	5940	6050	6150

At the temperature of the experiment (23 °C) 1 **N** to 3 **N** NH_4Cl have the following properties

$$\mu = 9.2 \times 10^{-4}\ \text{kg/m·s}, \quad \rho = 1020\ \text{kg/m}^3$$

From this experiment calculate the molecular diffusion coefficient for NH_4Cl in water in this concentration range. How does it compare with the reported value of $\mathcal{D} = 18 \times 10^{-10}\ \text{m}^2/\text{s}$?

Data from Blackwell, Local AIChE meeting, Galveston TX, Oct 18, 1957.

C15* Diffusivity of dissolved gases in liquids. Deaerated distilled water flows by gravity through a 1.63 mm tube wound in a 0.3 m diameter coil and immersed in a water bath kept at 17 °C. A small amount of water saturated with dissolved CO_2 is pulsed into the tube and the concentration of CO_2 is monitored by a refractometer 7.544 m downstream. At each flow rate a bell shaped curve is recorded. The data is as follows

Flow Velocity u, mm/s	Variance of Bell Shaped Curve σ_t^2, s^2
8.6	10700
13.7	4700
17.1	2700

Calculate the diffusion coefficient of dissolved CO_2 in water. Any comments?

Data extracted from Pratt *et al* CES **28** 1901 (1973).

C16* A strongly colored 1% solution of $KMnO_4$ flows slowly through a 0.504 mm ID glass tube, and at time t = 0 the flow is switched to pure water. The spreading front between fluids is measured 31 cm downstream by comparing the color with standardized sample tubes of diluted $KMnO_4$ solution, with results shown below. From this information calculate the molecular diffusion coefficient of $KMnO_4$ in water in this concentration range. Compare your results with literature values of

$$\mathcal{D} = 4.35 \times 10^{-10}\ \text{m}^2/\text{s} \ \text{to}\ 15 \times 10^{-10}\ \text{m}^2/\text{s}$$

$1-C/C_{initial}$	t, sec	$1-C/C_{initial}$	t, sec
0.01	10300	0.4	11047
0.02	10405	0.5	11291
0.04	10527	0.6	11399
0.1	10636	0.7	11435
0.2	10846	0.8	11621
0.3	10996	0.9	11931

The data for this problem comes from Taylor's classic experiment, reported in Proc. Roy. Soc. **219A** 186 (1953).

D17 Calculations show that a plug flow reactor would give 99.9% conversion of reactant which is in aqueous solution. However our reactor has an RTD somewhat as shown below

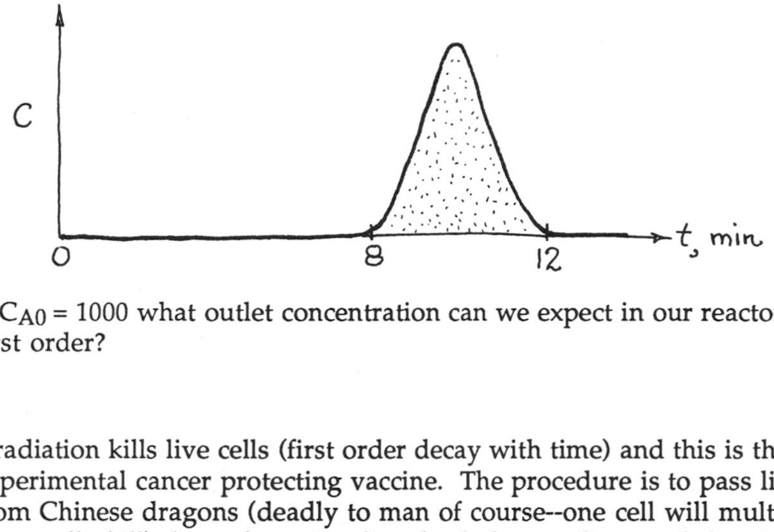

If $C_{A0} = 1000$ what outlet concentration can we expect in our reactor if reaction is first order?

D18 γ-radiation kills live cells (first order decay with time) and this is the basis of a new experimental cancer protecting vaccine. The procedure is to pass live cancer cells from Chinese dragons (deadly to man of course--one cell will multiply and eventually kill) through a γ-irradiated tubular sterilizer and then inject the debris into the person to be protected.

An injection dose starts with 1 μmol of live active dragon cancer cells in 10 ml of saline solution. This is irradiated in the flow tube, and based on the plug flow assumption we calculate that after sterilization the chance of finding a single live cell in the dose is 10^{-9}, an extremely small value. However the flow in our sterilizer deviates slightly from plug flow and tracer tests show that $\bar{t} = 100$ s, $\sigma^2 = 100\ s^2$. What does this deviation do to our calculated chances of being injected with a deadly live cancer cell?

Chapter 64 Problems

D19 Tubular reactors for thermal cracking are designed on the assumption of plug flow. On the suspicion that nonideal flow may be an important factor now being ignored, let us make a rough estimate of its role. For this assume isothermal operations in a 2.5 cm ID tubular reactor, using a Reynolds number of 10,000 for flowing fluid. The cracking reaction is approximately first order. If calculations show that 99% decomposition can be obtained in a plug flow reactor 3 m long, how much longer must the reactor be if nonideal flow is taken into account?

Chapter 66 The Tanks in Series Model.

This model can be used whenever the dispersion model is used; and for not too large a deviation from plug flow both models give identical results, for all practical purposes. Which model you use depends on your mood and juices.

The dispersion model has the advantage in that all correlations for flow in real reactors invariably use this model. On the other hand the tanks in series model is simple, can be used with any kinetics, and it can be extended without too much difficulty to any arrangement of compartments, with or without recycle.

I Pulse Response Experiments and the RTD.

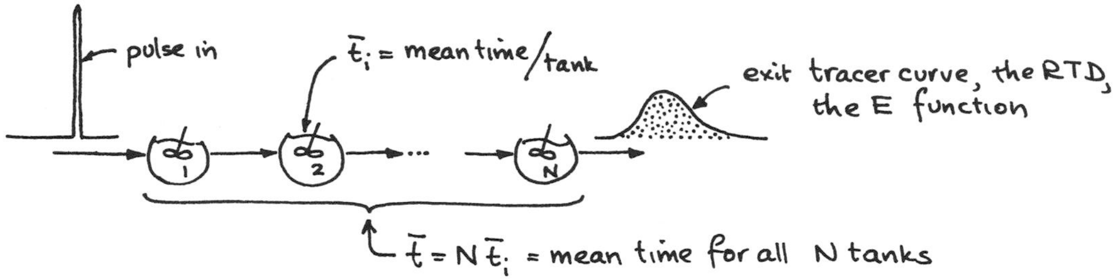

Also define

$$\theta_i = \frac{t}{\bar{t}_i} = \text{dimensionless time based on the time per tank } \bar{t}_i$$

$$\theta = \frac{t}{\bar{t}} = \text{dimensionless time based on the time for all N tanks, } \bar{t}.$$

Then

$$\theta_i = N\theta \quad \cdots\text{and}\cdots \quad \bar{\theta}_i = 1\ , \quad \bar{\theta} = 1$$

The RTD is found to be

for N=1 ... $\bar{t}_i E_t = e^{-t/\bar{t}_i}$

for N=2 ... $\bar{t}_i E_t = \frac{t}{\bar{t}_i} e^{-t/\bar{t}_i}$

for N=3 ... $\bar{t}_i E_t = \frac{1}{2}\left(\frac{t}{\bar{t}_i}\right)^2 e^{-t/\bar{t}_i}$ ... and so on.

For any number of tanks the RTD, mean and variance for this model are :

$$\bar{t}\,E_t = \left(\frac{t}{\bar{t}}\right)^{N-1}\frac{N^N}{(N-1)!}\,e^{-tN/\bar{t}} \quad \cdots \quad \bar{t} = N\bar{t}_i \quad \cdots \quad \sigma_t^2 = \frac{\bar{t}^2}{N}$$

$$\bar{t}_i E_t = \left(\frac{t}{\bar{t}_i}\right)^{N-1}\frac{1}{(N-1)!}\,e^{-t/\bar{t}_i} \quad \cdots \quad \bar{t}_i = \frac{\bar{t}}{N} \quad \cdots \quad \sigma_t^2 = N\bar{t}_i^2 = \frac{\bar{t}^2}{N}$$

$$E_{\theta_i} = \bar{t}_i E_t = \frac{\theta_i^{N-1}}{(N-1)!}\,e^{-\theta_i} \quad \cdots \quad \bar{t}_{\theta_i} = N \quad \cdots \quad \sigma_{\theta_i}^2 = N \qquad \cdots (1)$$

$$E_\theta = (N\bar{t}_i)\,E_t = \frac{N(N\theta)^{N-1}}{(N-1)!}\,e^{-N\theta} \quad \cdots \quad \bar{t}_\theta = 1 \quad \cdots \quad \sigma_\theta^2 = \frac{1}{N}$$

MacMullin & Weber Trans. AIChE 31 409 (1935)

Graphically:

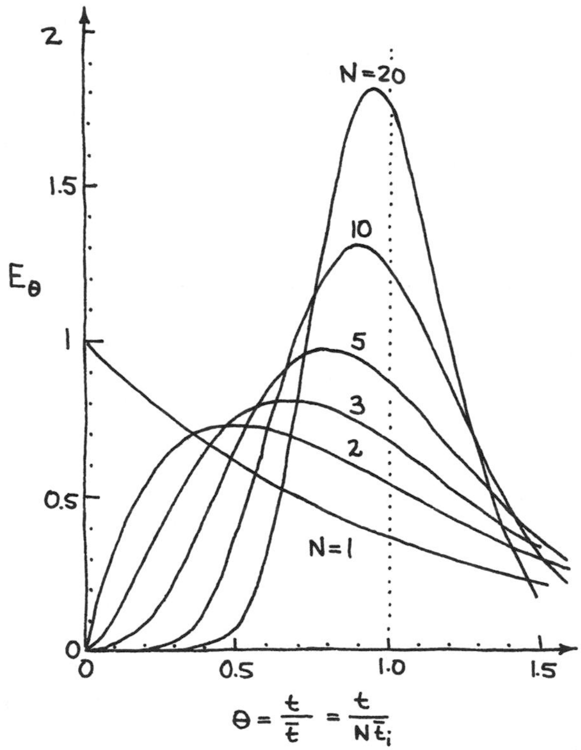

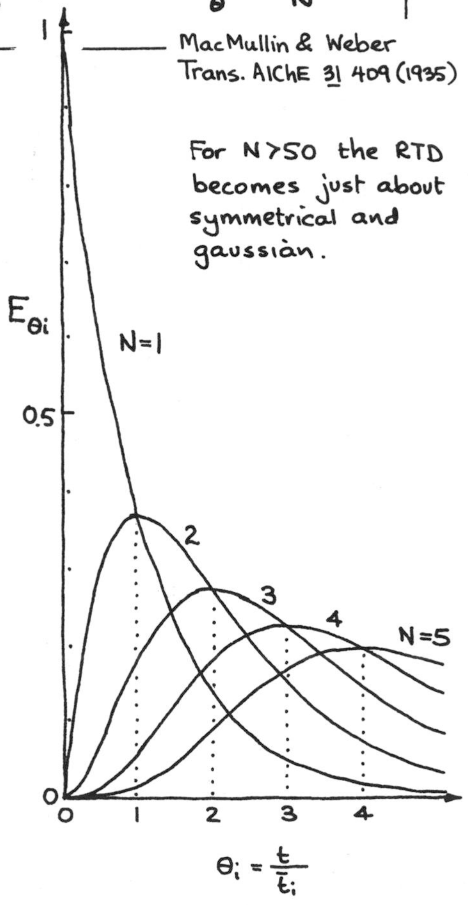

For N > 50 the RTD becomes just about symmetrical and gaussian.

The properties of the RTD curves are sketched below:

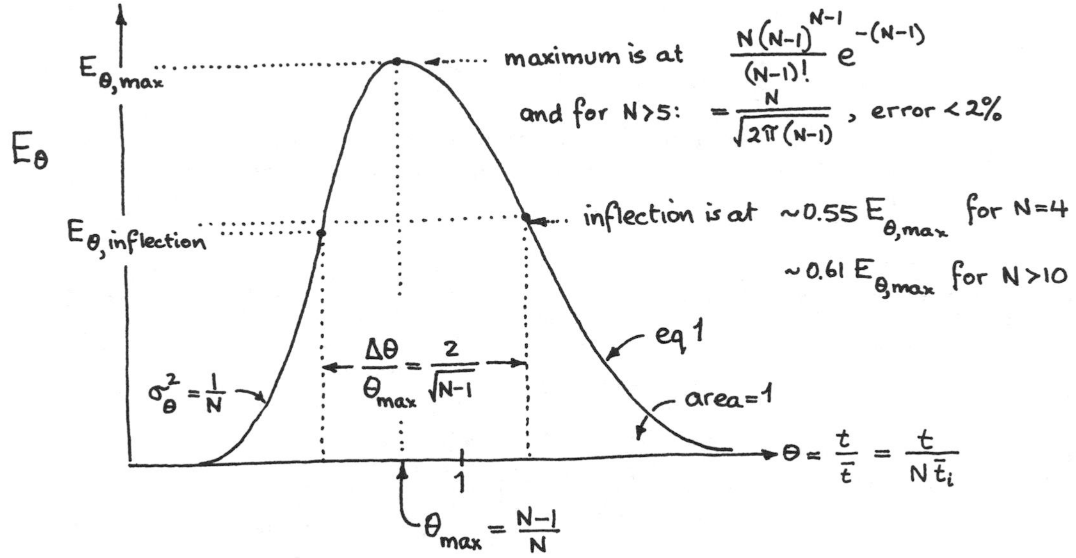

Comments

(a) For small deviation from plug flow, N>50, the RTD becomes symmetrical and gaussian. Thus eq 1 can be approximated by

$$E_\theta = \frac{1}{\sqrt{2\pi\sigma^2}} \exp\left[-\frac{(1-\theta)^2}{2\sigma^2}\right] \quad \text{... the gaussian distribution}$$

$$= \sqrt{\frac{N}{2\pi}} \exp\left[-\frac{(1-\theta)^2}{2/N}\right] = \sqrt{\frac{N}{2\pi}} \exp\left[-\frac{(1-t/\bar{t})^2}{2/N}\right] \quad \text{... (2)}$$

The figure on page 64.3 with $N = 1/2\left(\frac{D}{uL}\right)$ shows this equation. The five curves in that figure are for N = 39, 156, 625, 2500 and 10^4.

(b) How to find N which fits an experimental curve

- draw the RTD curves for various N and see which matches the experimental curve most closely
- calculate σ^2 from experiment and compare with theory
- evaluate the width of the curve at 61% of maximum height
- match the maximum height.

(decreasing reliability ↓)

... and there are many other ways

(c) **Independence.** If M tanks are connected to N more tanks (all of same size) then the individual means and variances (in ordinary time units) are additive, or

$$\bar{t}_{M+N} = \bar{t}_M + \bar{t}_N \quad \cdots \text{and} \cdots \quad \sigma^2_{t,M+N} = \sigma^2_{t,M} + \sigma^2_{t,N} \qquad \cdots (3)$$

Because of this property we can join streams and recycle streams. Thus this model becomes useful for treating recirculating systems.

(d) From the above variance expression, eq 3, we see that in adding tanks we get

$$\sigma^2_t \propto N, \quad \cdots \text{or} \quad \sigma^2_t \propto L, \quad \cdots \text{or} \quad \begin{pmatrix}\text{spread}\\ \text{of curve}\end{pmatrix} \propto \sqrt{L} \qquad (4)$$

(e) For any one shot tracer input

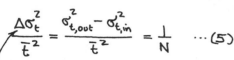

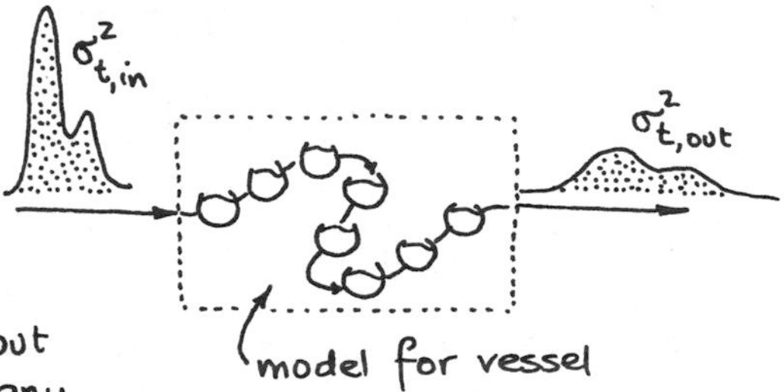

$$\frac{\Delta\sigma^2_t}{\bar{t}^2} = \frac{\sigma^2_{t,out} - \sigma^2_{t,in}}{\bar{t}^2} = \frac{1}{N} \qquad \cdots (5)$$

the increase in variance between input and output points is the same for any kind of input, whether pulse, double peaked, etc.

(f) **Relationship between dispersion and tanks in series model.** For small deviation from plug flow

$$\left.\begin{array}{ll}\text{Dispersion model:} & \sigma^2_\theta = 2\left(\frac{D}{uL}\right) \\ \text{Tanks-in-series:} & \sigma^2_\theta = \frac{1}{N}\end{array}\right\} \quad \text{thus} \quad \frac{1}{N} = 2\left(\frac{D}{uL}\right) \qquad \cdots (6)$$

For large deviation from plug flow see CES 17 576 (1962)

(g) **Value of N for flow of gases in fixed beds.** From the fixed bed graph of chapter 64 we find

$$\frac{D\epsilon}{u_o d_p} = \frac{D}{u d_p} = \frac{D}{u(L/n_{particles})} \cong \frac{1}{2} \quad \cdots \text{or} \quad \frac{D}{uL} = \frac{1}{2\, n_{particles}} \qquad \cdots (7)$$

Comparing eqs 6 and 7 then gives

$$N_{tanks} \cong n_{particles} \qquad (8)$$

Thus each particle acts as one stirred tank, and a bed many particles deep very closely approaches plug flow.

(h) **Value of N for flow of liquids in fixed beds.** From the fixed bed graph of chapter 64 we find

$$\frac{D\epsilon}{u_o d_p} = \frac{D}{u d_p} \cong 2$$

So by arguments similar to the case of gases we find that

$$N_{tanks} \cong \left(\frac{1}{4} \sim 1\right) n_{particles} \qquad \cdots (9)$$

or each 4 particles in succession act as one stirred tank (ideal).

(i) **The boundary conditions.** Here we have no problem as with the dispersion model. The entrance and exit are usually well approximated by the closed vessel boundary conditions so the measured E and F curves are in fact the proper E and F curves of chapter 61.

Whatever the boundary conditions, we must still take note of how the measurements are taken... either instantaneously or by "mixing cup".

If you do have backmixing or dispersion at inlet and outlet, and also between tanks, then you get a different model which we do not consider here

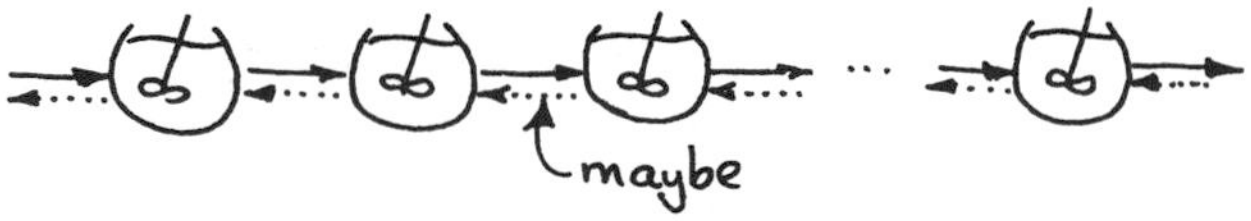

(j) Before deciding to use this model be sure to check the shape of the experimental curve to see if the model really applies. Do not use the model indiscriminately.

II. Step Response Experiments and the F Curve.

The output F curve from a series of N ideal stirred tanks is, in its various forms

$$F = 1 - e^{-N\theta}\left[1 + N\theta + \frac{(N\theta)^2}{2!} + \cdots + \frac{(N\theta)^{N-1}}{(N-1)!}\right] \qquad \theta = \frac{t}{\bar{t}}$$

$$F = 1 - e^{-\theta_i}\left[1 + \theta_i + \frac{\theta_i^2}{2!} + \cdots + \frac{\theta_i^{N-1}}{(N-1)!}\right] \qquad \theta_i = \frac{t}{\bar{t}_i} \qquad \cdots (10)$$

MacMullin & Weber
Trans. AIChE 31 409 (1935)

In graphical form:

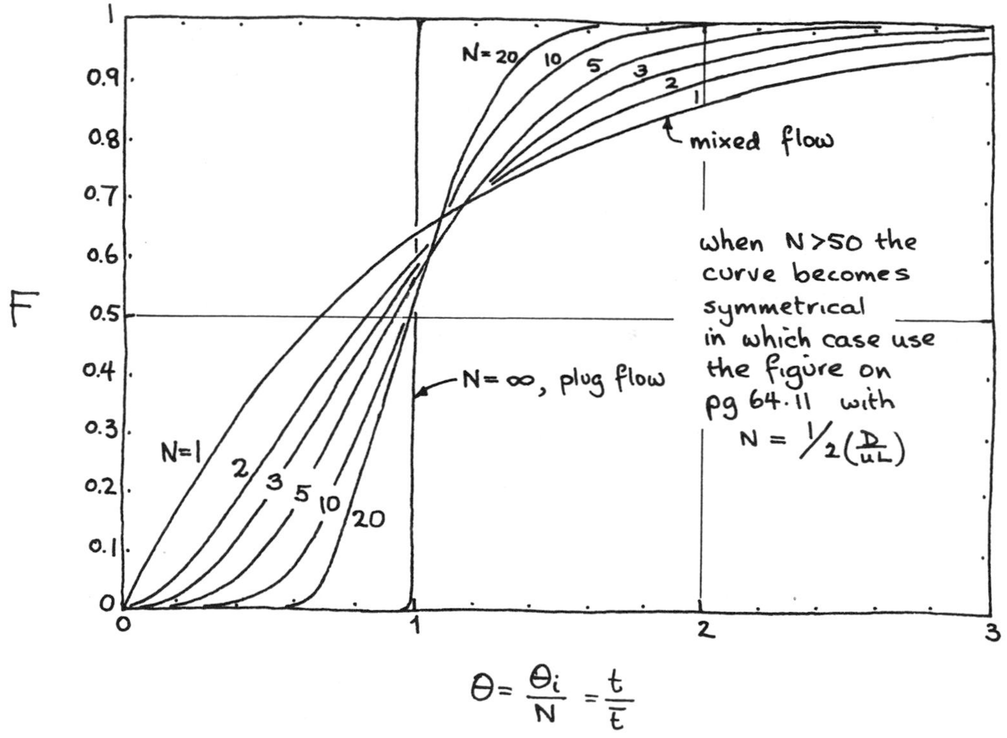

III Chemical Conversion.

1. First order reaction of either micro- or macrofluids.

Writing the performance equation for each of the tanks and eliminating intermediate concentrations gives

$$\frac{C_A}{C_{A0}} = \frac{1}{(1+k\bar{t}_i)^N} = \frac{1}{\left(1+\frac{k\bar{t}}{N}\right)^N}$$

A comparison with plug flow gives the following graph

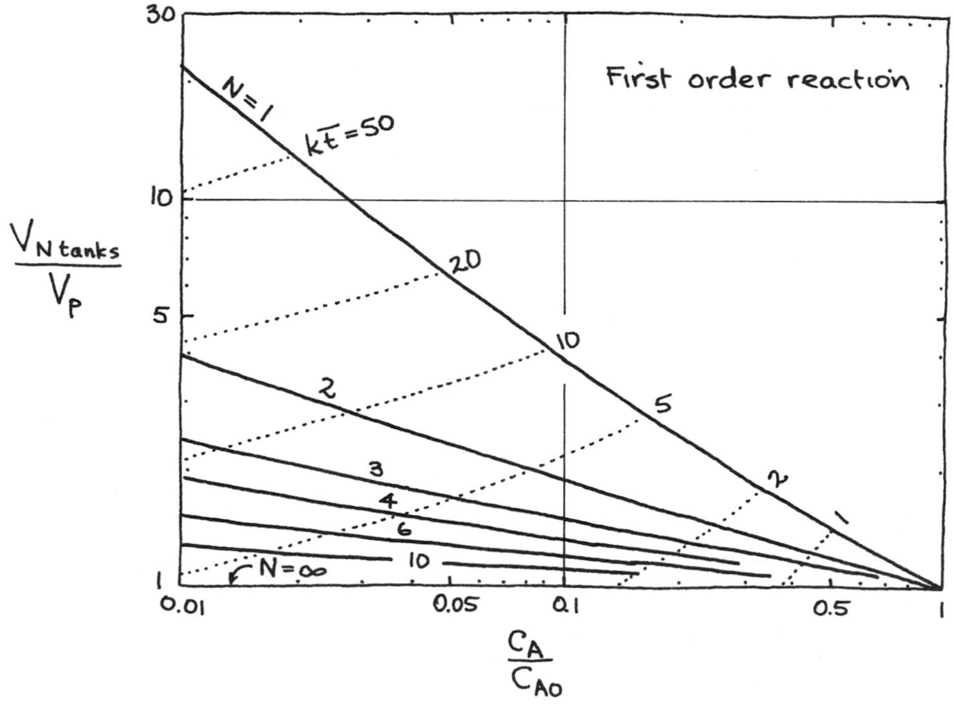

For small deviations from plug flow (large N) comparison with plug flow gives

for same $C_{A\,final}$: $\frac{V_{N\,tanks}}{V_p} = 1 + k\bar{t}_i = 1 + \frac{k\bar{t}}{2N}$

for same volume V : $\frac{C_{A,N\,tanks}}{C_{Ap}} = 1 + \frac{(k\bar{t})^2}{2N}$

2. Second order reaction, $A \rightarrow R$ or $A+B \rightarrow R$ with $C_{A0}=C_{B0}$.

For a microfluid flowing through N tanks in series we have

$$\frac{C_A}{C_{A0}} = \frac{1}{4C_{A0}k\bar{t}_i}\left(-2+2\sqrt{-1+2\sqrt{-1+\cdots\sqrt{+1+4C_{A0}k\bar{t}_i}}}\right) \quad \text{N square roots}$$

For a macrofluid flowing through N tanks in series we have

$$\frac{C_A}{C_{A0}} = \int_0^\infty \frac{E_t}{1+kC_{A0}t}\,dt = \left(\frac{N}{\bar{t}}\right)^N \frac{1}{(N-1)!}\int_0^\infty \frac{t^{N-1}}{1+kC_{A0}t}\, e^{-\frac{Nt}{\bar{t}}}\,dt$$

Comparing with plug flow gives

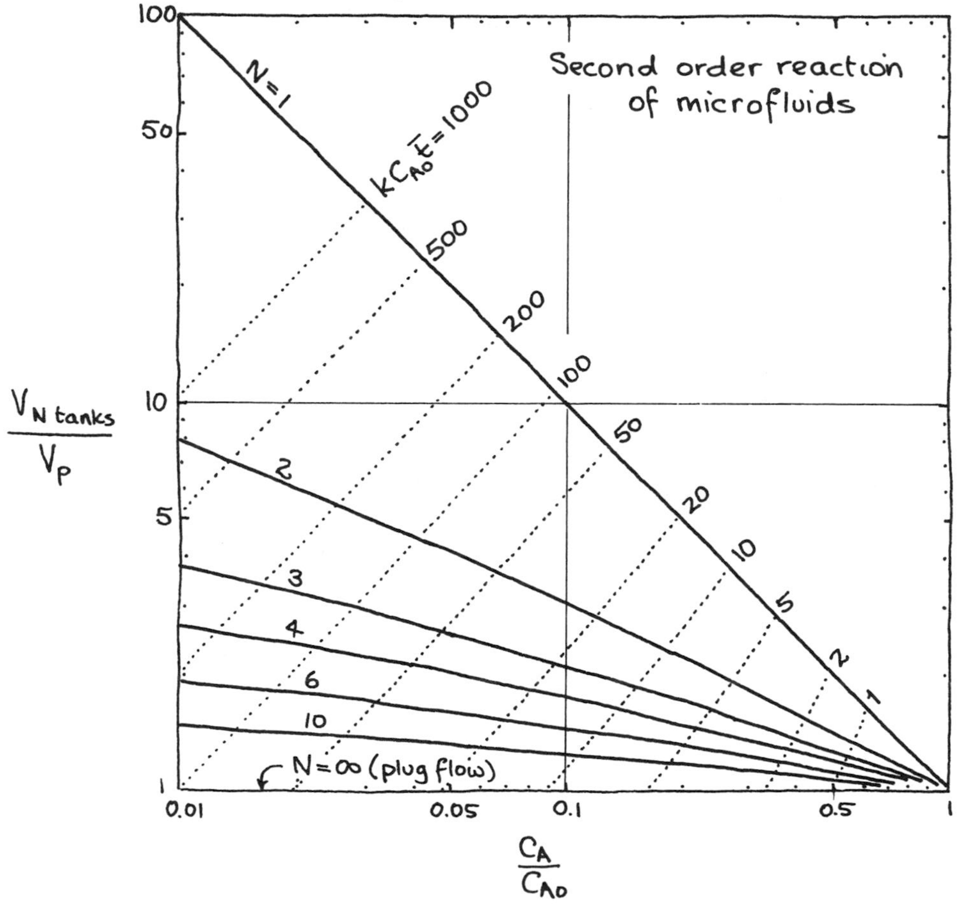

3. **For microfluids and all other reaction kinetics** either solve the mixed flow equation for tank after tank

$$\tau = \frac{C_{i-1} - C_i}{-r_i} \qquad \ldots \text{ with } \quad C_{i-1} \rightarrow (\tau) \rightarrow C_i$$

a tedious procedure, but no problem today with our handy slave, the pocket calculator, or else use the graphical procedure

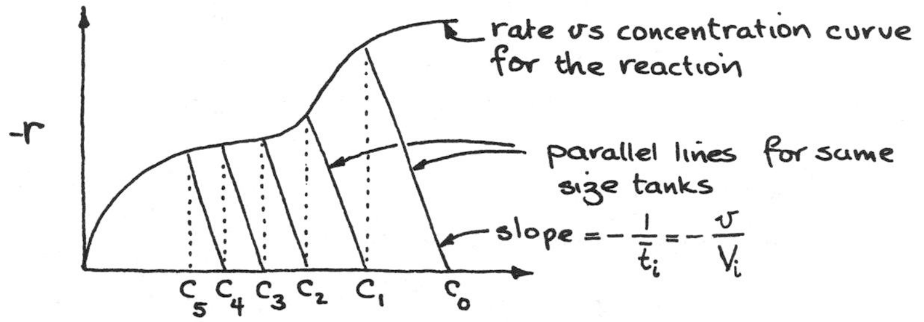

4. **For macrofluids and any kinetics** just solve the general conversion expression

$$\frac{C}{C_0} = \int_0^\infty \left(\frac{C}{C_0}\right)_{\text{for an element}} \cdot E_t \, dt$$

insert the proper kinetic expression (for $\left(\frac{C}{C_0}\right)_{\text{for an element}}$)

insert the proper RTD expression from eq 1 (for E_t)

Chapter 66 Problems

A1 Fit the tanks in series model to the following output data to a pulse input

(a) Use linear interpolation between the data points.

(b) Use something better than linear interpolation.

t	0	2	4	6	8	10	12
C	0	2	10	8	4	2	0

The concentrations are instantaneous readings taken at the exit of the vessel.

A2 Fit the tanks in series model to the following mixing cup output data to a pulse input.

(a) Use linear interpolation between the data points.

(b) Use something better than linear interpolation.

t	0 - 2	2 - 4	4 - 6	6 - 8	8 - 10	10 - 12
C	2	10	8	4	2	0

A3 Denmark has a factory which extracts agar from seaweed using a seven tank extraction unit. In flowing through the system the viscosity of the fluid changes over 10 fold and the engineers are worried that the seven tanks may not be behaving ideally. To put this worry to rest the RTD of the unit is measured using as tracer 200 millicuries of radioactive Br-82 in the form of NH_4Br dissolved in 1 liter of water. The tracer is dumped into the first tank at time zero and the output tracer concentration from the last tank is recorded. How many ideal stirred tanks in series represents the real system?

t, min	C, arbitrary	t, min	C, arbitrary
180	0	1006	242
206	4	1126	214
266	12	1360	118
296	42	1600	78
416	88	1836	42
534	160	2070	18
650	216	2540	10
770	244	3000	(0)
890	254		

Data from the Danish Isotope Center, report of May 1977.

Chapter 66 Problems

B5 Fluid flows at a steady rate through 10 tanks in series. A pulse of tracer is introduced into the first tank, and the time this tracer leaves the system is measured giving

maximum concentration = 100 mmol/liter
tracer spread = 1 min

If 10 more tanks are connected in series with the original 10 tanks what would be

(a) the maximum concentration of leaving tracer?

(b) the tracer spread?

(c) How does the relative spread change with number of tanks?

B6 A small diameter pipe 32 m long runs from the fermentation room of a winery to the bottle filling cellar. Sometimes red wine is pumped through the pipe, sometimes white, and whenever the switch is made from one to the other a small amount of "house blend" rosé is produced (8 bottles). Because of some construction in the winery the pipeline length will have to be increased to 50 m. For the same flow rate of wine how many bottles of rosé may we now expect to get each time we switch the flow?

Our 16 stirred tank system (1 m^3 each) is contaminated, consequently we've got to flush it with fresh water (1 m^3/min) so that nowhere in the system is the concentration of contaminant more than 0.1% its present value. How long must we flush

B7 . . . if each tank is fed fresh water and discharges its own waste?

B8 . . . if the tanks are connected in series, the first tank is fed fresh water, and only the last tank discharges waste?

B9 From the New York Times Magazine, December 25, 1955, we read: "The United States Treasury reported that it costs eight-tenths of a cent to print dollar bills, and that of the billion and a quarter now in circulation, a billion have to be replaced annually." Assume that the bills are put into circulation at a constant rate and continuously, and that they are withdrawn from circulation without regard to their condition, in a random manner.

Suppose that a new series of dollar bills is put in circulation at a given instant in place of the original bills.

(a) How many new bills will be in circulation at any time?

(b) After 21 years how many old bills will still be in circulation?

Chapter 66 Problems

A4 In physiological studies the tracer injection and sampling system (ISS) may not be small compared to the organism being studied, for example for hummingbirds. In such situations may be important to correct for the time delay and distortion introduced by imperfect pulse injection and by the lines leading to and from the ISS.

In one such study, with indocyanine green dye in blood (0.038 mg/ml) as flow tracer, we connect the injection needle directly to the mouth of the sampling line, we introduce a standard pulse at t = 0, and we record its response (curve A). We then repeat this procedure with the injection needle and sampling probe in the organism to be studied (curve B). Results of a typical run are as follows

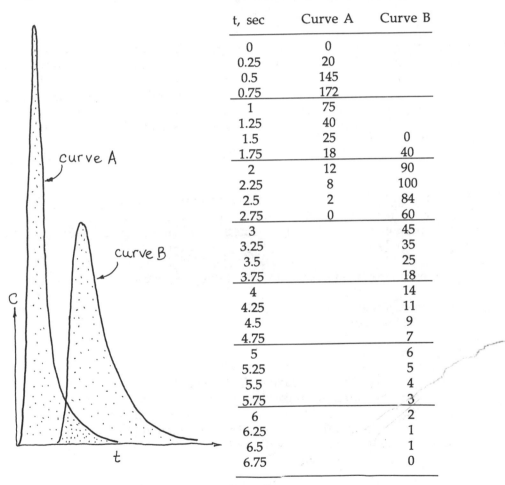

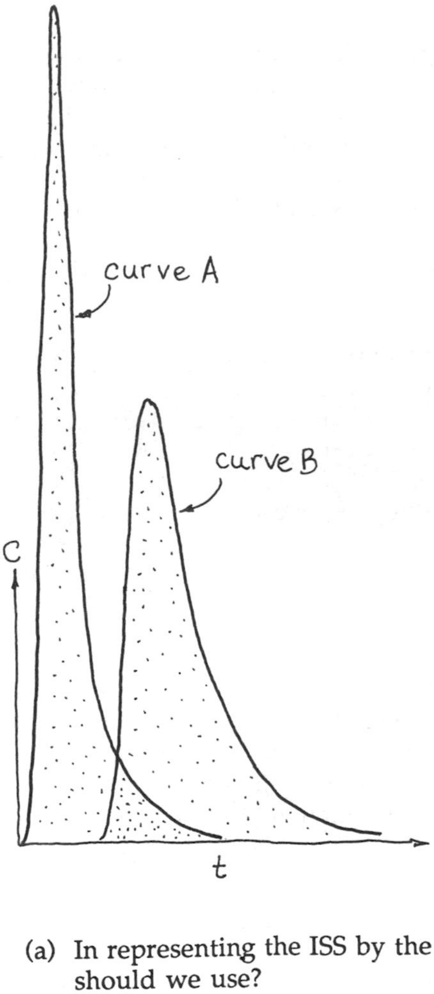

t, sec	Curve A	Curve B
0	0	
0.25	20	
0.5	145	
0.75	172	
1	75	
1.25	40	
1.5	25	0
1.75	18	40
2	12	90
2.25	8	100
2.5	2	84
2.75	0	60
3		45
3.25		35
3.5		25
3.75		18
4		14
4.25		11
4.5		9
4.75		7
5		6
5.25		5
5.5		4
5.75		3
6		2
6.25		1
6.5		1
6.75		0

(a) In representing the ISS by the tanks in series model what values of parameters should we use?

(b) What flow model would you use for the organism?

Data from Oleksy *et al* J. App. Physiology **26** 227 (1969).

Chapter 66 Problems

B10 Referring to the previous problem, suppose that during a working day a gang of counterfeiters put into circulation one million dollars in fake one-dollar bills.

(a) If not detected, what will be the number in circulation as a function of time?

(b) After 10 years, how many of these bills would still be in circulation?

C11 Repeat problem 64.17, but solve using the tanks in series model instead of the dispersion model.

C12 A stream of fully suspended fine solids ($v = 1\ m^3/min$) passes through two mixed flow reactors in series, each containing $1\ m^3$ of slurry. As soon as a particle enters the reactors conversion to product begins, proceeds at a constant rate, and is complete after two minutes in the reactors. When a particle leaves the reactors reaction stops.

(a) What fraction of particles is completely converted to product in this system?

(b) Write the expression for the fractional conversion of reactant to product in the exit stream. Do not solve.

C13* Here's the latest brainchild of our process development department--a commercial type popcorn popper--and it works like this. Cold popping corn is fed continuously to a chamber containing hot fluidized corn which is being popped. Each kernel of corn heats up and after exactly 0.5 min pops and expands to 33 times its original volume but with no change in mass. If we feed the popper $0.1\ m^3/min$ of unpopped corn, and if the volume of the swirling mass of well mixed popped and unpopped corn is $0.5\ m^3$, what fraction of the exit stream from the popper will leave unpopped. Assume the same voidage everywhere.

C14* A 1 N NaOH solution is slowly poured into a $1\ m^3$ vat filled to the brim with 1 N HCl. The vat is stirred continuously, its contents are well mixed, neutralization is practically instantaneous, and fluid overflows into a collection tank such that the volume of the vat remains $1\ m^3$ at all times.

(a) How much NaOH solution must be added to neutralize the acid in the vat?

(b) What is the concentration of HCl in the collection tank at this moment?

(c) What is the concentration of acid or base in the vat after $1\ m^3$ of NaOH has been added to the vat?

This problem was suggested by E.J. Stamhuis of the University of Groningen.

Chapter 66 Problems

C15* At time t = 0 a solution with base B (C_{B0} = 200 mol/m^3) is added (v = 10^{-3} m^3/s) to a reactor (v = 6 m^3) containing acid A (C_{A0} = 100 mol/m^3). The reactor is well mixed and of constant volume hence there is an outflow equal to the inflow, and the reaction between acid and base, A + B → salt + H_2O, is instantaneous. At what time will the contents of the reactor be neutralized?

D16 Gas and liquid pass cocurrently upward through a vertical reactor packed with catalyst (V_{total} = 5m^3, fraction solids = 0.64). A pulse test on the liquid (v_ℓ = 200 lit/min) gives the tracer curve shown below.

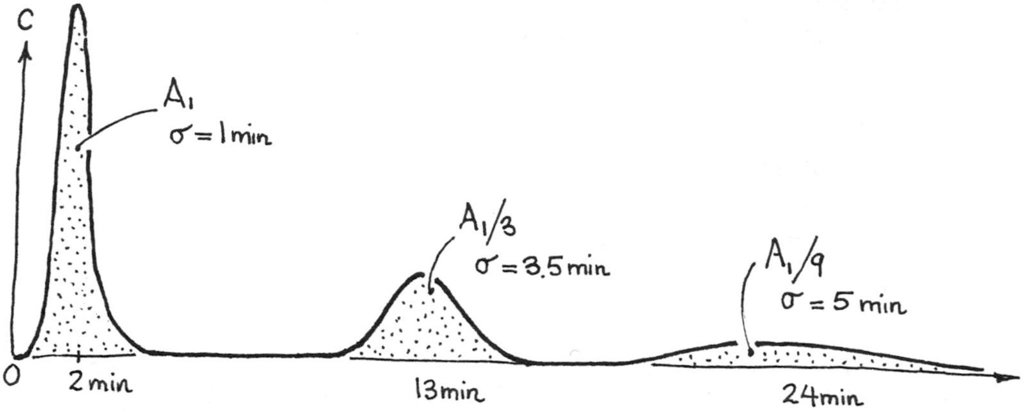

(a) Develop a tank in series flow model to represent the flow of liquid through the column.

(b) What do you think is the state of the column -- liquid trickling over the particles? Gas bubbling through a liquid filled column? etc.

D17 A reactor with central dividing baffle is to be used to run the reaction

$$A \rightarrow R \qquad \text{with} \qquad -r_A = 0.05\, C_A \text{ mol/lit·min}$$

A pulse tracer test gives the following result

Concentration reading	0	10	20	30	40	50	60	70
time, min	35	38	40	40	39	37	36	35

(a) Find the area under the C vs t curve.

(b) Find the E_t vs t curve.

(c) Calculate the variance of the E_t curve.

(d) How many tanks in series is this vessel equivalent to?

(e) Calculate X_A assuming plug flow.

(f) Calculate X_A assuming mixed flow.

(g) Calculate X_A assuming the tanks in series model.

(h) Calculate X_A directly from the data.

Chapter 68. CONVECTION MODEL FOR LAMINAR FLOW.

When a vessel is long enough then the dispersion or tanks·in·series model well describes its flow behavior. But how long is "long enough"? For packed beds and for turbulent flow in pipes just about any vessel length is long enough, however for laminar flow in pipes we may be in other flow regimes, in particular, that of the pure convection model. But first let us look at the extremes for laminar flow

- If the tube is long enough then molecular diffusion in the lateral direction will have enough time to distort the parabolic velocity profile so that the **dispersion model** applies.

- If the tube is short enough and the flow rate is high then molecular diffusion has not enough time to act so all we need to consider as causing a spread in residence time of fluid is the velocity profile. We are in the **pure convection** regime.

- If flow is so slow that the main movement of fluid is by molecular diffusion, not by bulk flow, then we enter the **pure diffusion** regime. We rarely meet this situation outside of reservoir engineering.

Here are RTD curves typical of these regimes.

Pure diffusion gives a pulse output at $t = 0$ (open-open vessel)

Pure convection gives

$$E = \frac{1}{2\theta^3} \ldots \theta > \tfrac{1}{2},$$

the same curve for all velocities

The dispersion model gives a more or less distorted bell shaped curve whose spread depends on the flow conditions

$$\theta = \frac{t}{\bar{t}} = \frac{t}{V/v}$$

tracer in at time zero

mean for all three curves

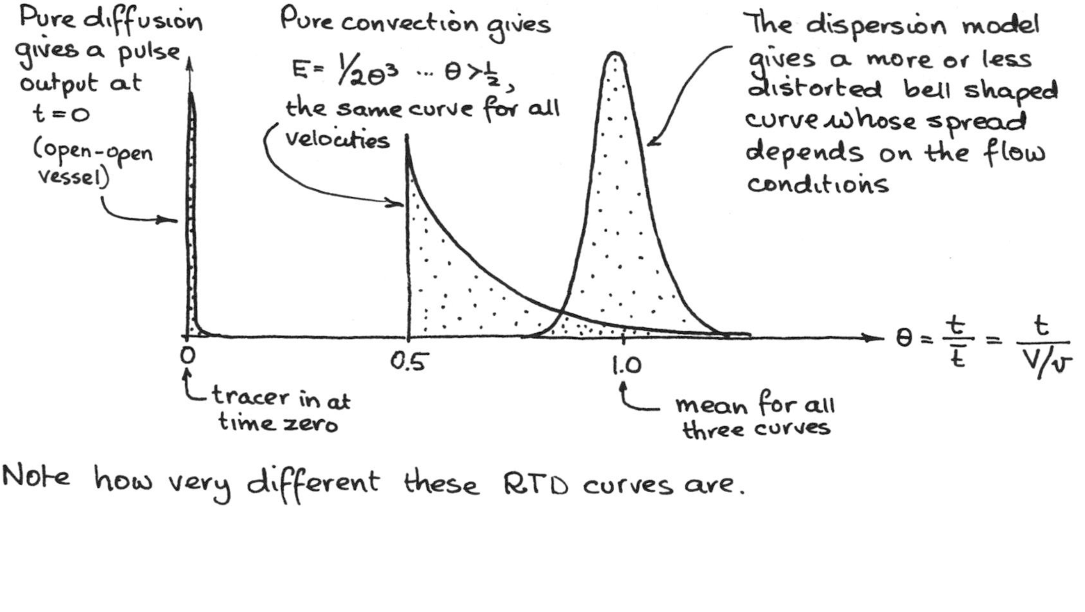

Note how very different these RTD curves are.

The following chart tells what regime you're in and which model to use. Just locate the point on the chart which corresponds to the fluid being used (Schmidt no.), the flow conditions (Reynolds no.) and vessel geometry (L/d_t). But be sure to check that you are not in turbulent flow. This chart only has meaning if you have laminar flow.

$\mathscr{D}/u d_t$
is the reciprocal of the **Bodenstein number**.
It measures the flow contribution made by molecular diffusion.
It is **NOT** the axial dispersion number, D/ud_t except in the pure diffusion regime.

$$Bo = Re \cdot Sc = \frac{d_t u \rho}{\mu} \cdot \frac{\mu}{\rho \mathscr{D}} = \frac{u d_t}{\mathscr{D}}$$

This chart is adapted from Ananthakrishnan et al, AIChE J <u>11</u> 1063 (1965). See there for approximate and for numerical solutions for the intermediate regimes

this is not a very interesting regime because it represents very very slow flow

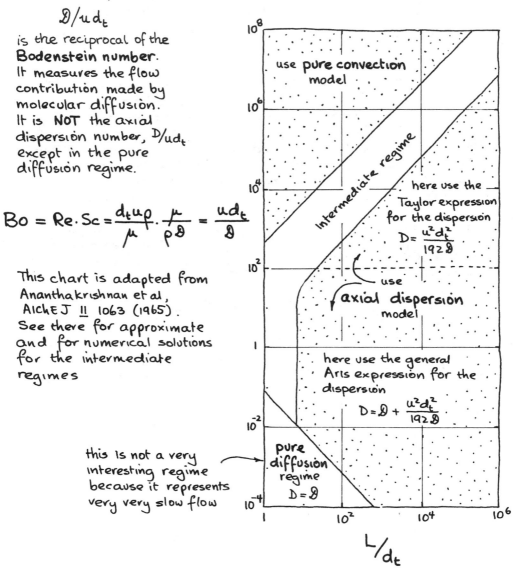

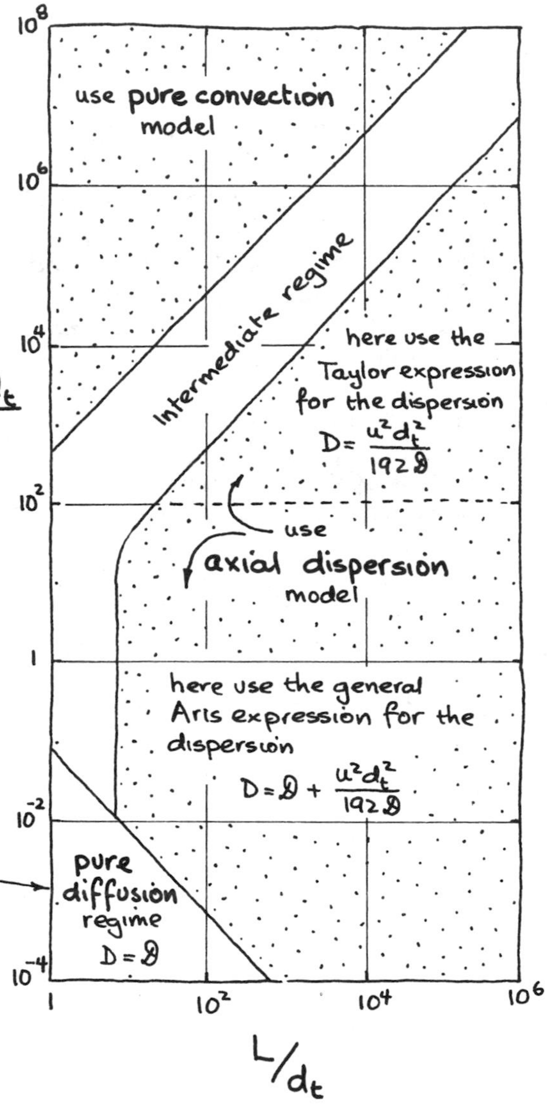

Gases are likely to be in the dispersion regime, not the pure convection regime. Liquids can well be in one regime or other. Very viscous liquids such as polymers are likely to be in the pure convection regime. If your system falls in the no-man's-land between regimes calculate the reactor behavior based on the two bounding regimes and then try averaging. The numerical solution is impractically complex to use.

The pure convection model assumes that each element of fluid slides past its neighbor with no interaction by molecular diffusion. Thus the spread in residence times is caused only be velocity variations.

fluid close to the wall moves slowly
fastest flowing fluid element is in the center
tube wall

This chapter deals with this model.

I. Pulse Response Experiment and the E Curve.

The shape of the response curve is extremely influenced by the way tracer is introduced into the flowing fluid, and how it is measured. You may inject in two main ways

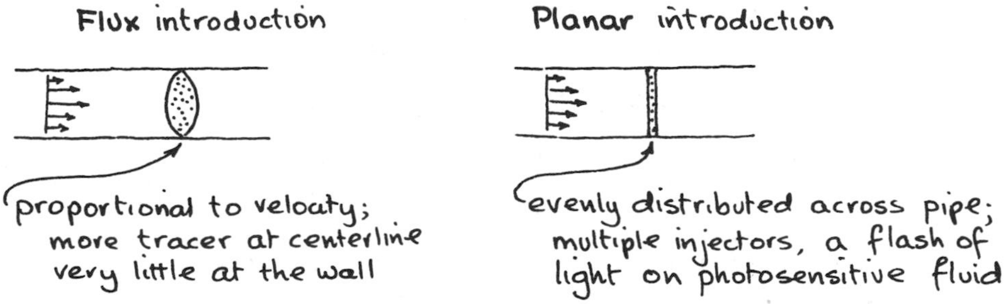
Flux introduction
Planar introduction
proportional to velocity; more tracer at centerline very little at the wall
evenly distributed across pipe; multiple injectors, a flash of light on photosensitive fluid

Flux measurement

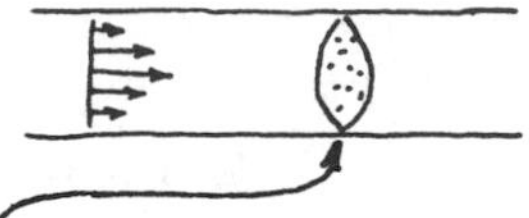

mixing cup measurement; catch all the exit fluid. In essense this measures $\overline{v \cdot C}$

Planar measurement

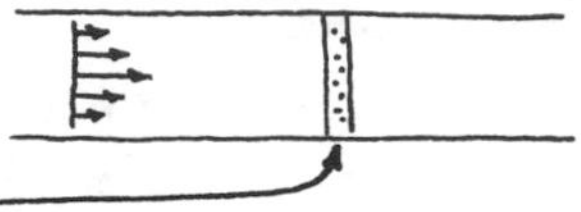

this could be a through-the-wall measurement such as with a light meter or radioactivity counter; also a series of probes (for example conductivity) across the tube. This measures $\bar{C}$ at an instant

We therefore have four combinations of boundary conditions, each with its own particular E curve

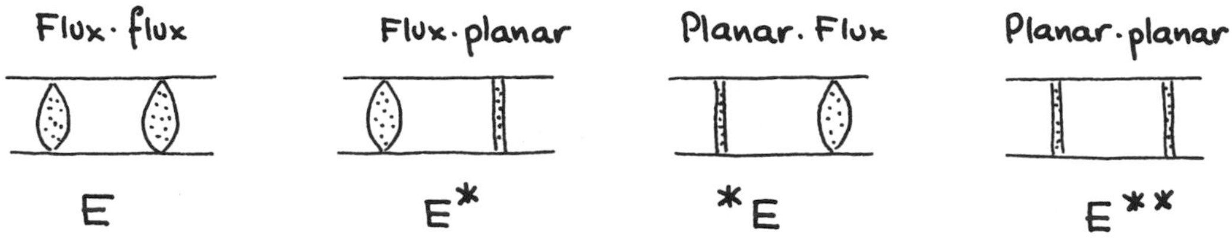

It can be shown that

- E is the proper response curve for reactor purposes, it is the curve treated in chapter 61, it represents the RTD in the vessel.
- E^* and $^*E$ are identical always, so we will call them E^* from now on. One correction for the planar b.c. will bring or transform this to the proper RTD.
- E^{**} requires two corrections, one for entrance, one for exit to transform it to a proper RTD.

It may be simpler to determine E^* or E^{**} rather than E. This is perfectly alright. However remember to transform these measured tracer curves to the E curve before calling it the RTD.

For pipes and tubes with their parabolic velocity profile the various pulse response curves are found to be as follows:

$$E_t = \frac{\bar{t}^2}{2t^3} \quad \text{for } t \geq \frac{\bar{t}}{2} \quad \text{and} \quad \mu_t = \bar{t} = \frac{V}{v}$$

$$E_\theta = \frac{1}{2\theta^3} \quad \text{for } \theta \geq \frac{1}{2} \quad \text{and} \quad \mu_\theta = 1$$

$$E_t^* = \frac{\bar{t}}{2t^2} \quad \text{for } t \geq \frac{\bar{t}}{2}$$

$$E_\theta^* = \frac{1}{2\theta^2} \quad \text{for } \theta \geq \frac{1}{2} \quad \text{and} \quad \mu^* = \infty \qquad \cdots (1)$$

$$E_t^{**} = \frac{1}{2t} \quad \text{for } t \geq \frac{\bar{t}}{2}$$

$$E_\theta^{**} = \frac{1}{2\theta} \quad \text{for } \theta \geq \frac{1}{2} \quad \text{and} \quad \mu^{**} = \infty$$

Note the simple relationship between E E^* and E^{**}. Thus at any time we can write

$$E_\theta^{**} = \theta E_\theta^* = \theta^2 E_\theta$$

or

$$E_t^{**} = \frac{t}{\bar{t}} E_t^* = \frac{t^2}{\bar{t}^2} E_t \qquad \cdots (2)$$

$\bar{t} = V/v$

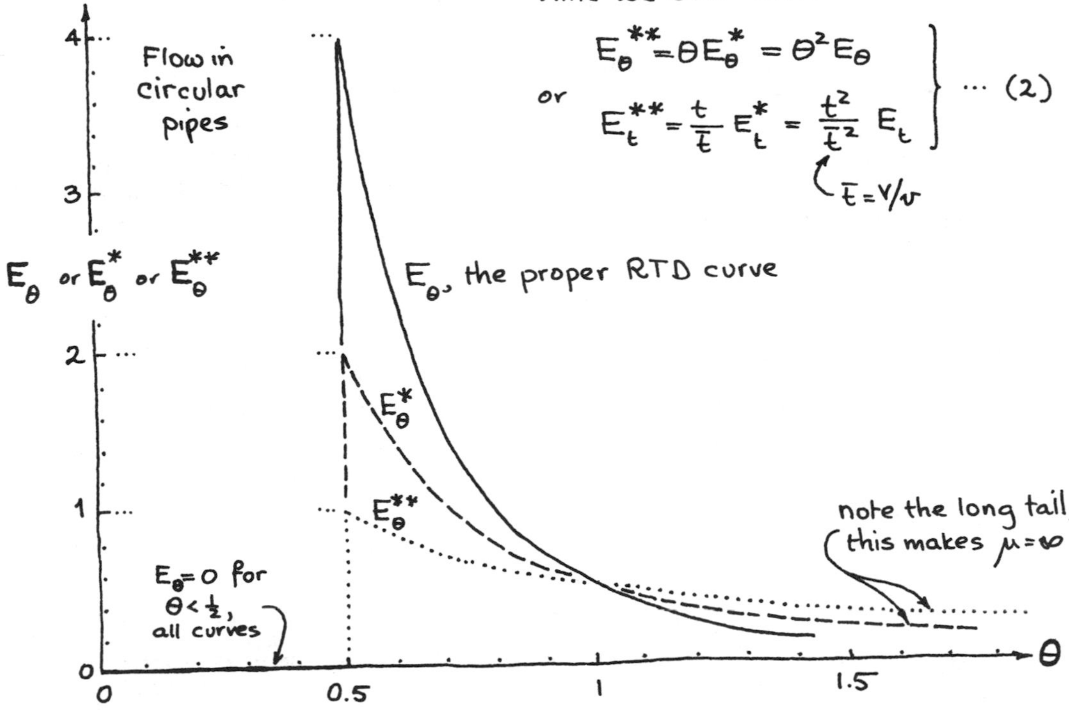

II Step Response Experiment and the F Curve.

The way tracer is introduced and the way it is measured will determine the shape of the resulting curve. Again we have two main ways of introducing tracer

Flux introduction

a switch from one fluid to another. More of the second fluid flows down the centerline than near the wall

Planar introduction

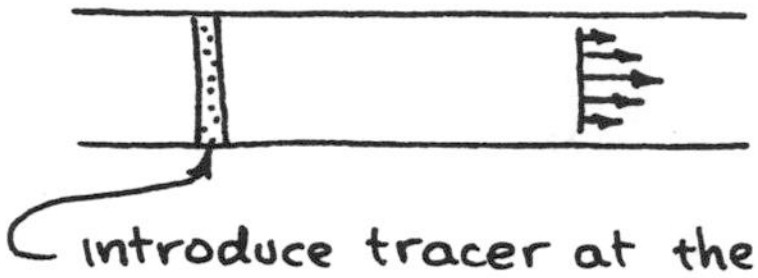

introduce tracer at the same rate across the cross section. Thus fluid at center has a lower tracer concentration than at walls

and we can measure it in two main ways

Flux measurement

this represents a mixing cup measurement, for example collect all exit fluid.

Planar measurement

through the wall scanner (light meter) or a series of probes across the exit plane

Thus again we have four combinations of boundary condition with their corresponding F curves.

Flux · flux

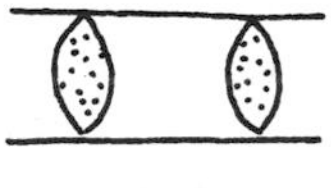

F

Flux · planar

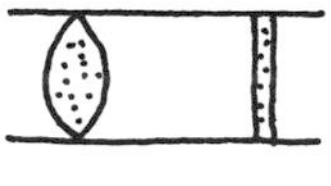

F^*

Planar · flux

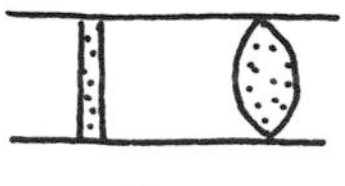

$^*F$

Planar · planar

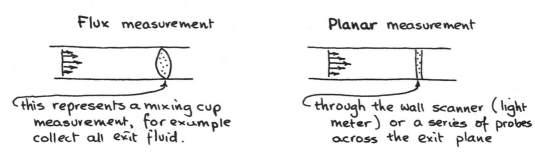

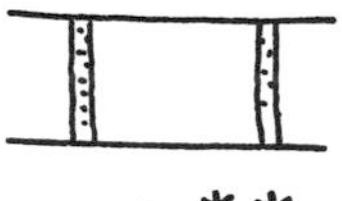

F^{**}

Again $F^* = {}^*F$, and F is the proper step response function of chapter 61. The equations shapes and relationships between these F curves are as follows.

$$F = 1 - \frac{1}{4\theta^2} \quad \text{for } \theta \geq \frac{1}{2}$$

$$F^* = 1 - \frac{1}{2\theta} \quad \text{for } \theta \geq \frac{1}{2} \qquad \cdots (3)$$

$$F^{**} = \frac{1}{2} \ln 2\theta \quad \text{for } \theta \geq \frac{1}{2}$$

for flow in circular pipes

Graphically

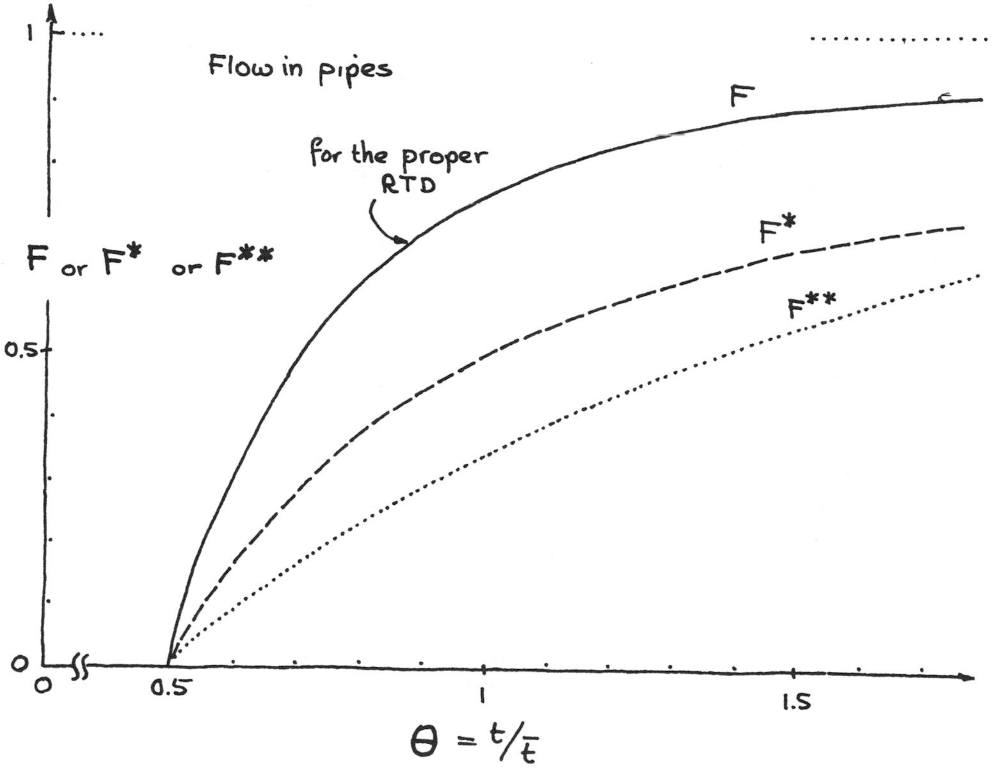

Also each F curve is related to its corresponding E curve. Thus at any time t_1 or θ_1

$$F^* = \int_0^{t_1} E_t^* \, dt = \int_0^{\theta_1} E_\theta^* \, d\theta \quad \cdots \text{and} \quad E_t^* = \left.\frac{dF^*}{dt}\right|_{t_1} \quad \text{or} \quad E_\theta^* = \left.\frac{dF^*}{d\theta}\right|_{\theta_1} \cdots (4)$$

Similarly for the relationship between E^{**} and F^{**}, and between E and F.

III Tracer Curves for Non Newtonians and for Non Circular Channels.

1. Power law fluids in pipes.

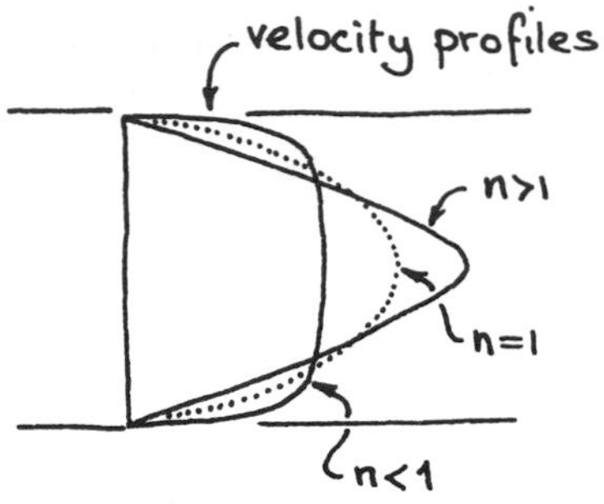

The shear force vs velocity gradient relationship and the resulting velocity profile for power law fluids are

$$\tau = \frac{K}{g_c}\left(\frac{du}{dy}\right)^n$$

- τ — shear stress, N/m^2
- K/g_c — consistency index, $N\cdot s^n/m^2$
- du/dy — velocity gradient, s^{-n}
- n — behavior index
  - $n \cong 0.4 \sim 0.6$ for many foods: soups, sauces, tomato juice
  - $n \cong 0.1 \sim 0.2$ for slurries of fine solids in water: lime water, cement rock in water, clay in water

Solving the equations for the pulse response curve gives

$$\left.\begin{aligned} E_\theta &= \frac{2n}{3n+1}\,\frac{1}{\theta^3}\left[1-\frac{n+1}{3n+1}\,\frac{1}{\theta}\right]^{n-1/n+1} \quad \text{for } \theta \geqslant \frac{n+1}{3n+1} \\ E^*_\theta &= \theta\cdot E_\theta \quad \text{and} \quad E^{**}_\theta = \theta^2\cdot E_\theta \end{aligned}\right\} \quad \cdots (5)$$

and for the step response, following eq 4,

$$\left.\begin{aligned} F &= \left[1-\frac{n+1}{3n+1}\cdot\frac{1}{\theta}\right]^{\frac{2n}{n+1}}\left[1+\frac{2n}{3n+1}\cdot\frac{1}{\theta}\right] \quad \text{for } \theta \geqslant \frac{n+1}{3n+1} \\ F^* &= \left[1-\frac{n+1}{3n+1}\cdot\frac{1}{\theta}\right]^{\frac{2n}{n+1}} \quad \text{for } \theta \geqslant \frac{n+1}{3n+1} \end{aligned}\right\} \quad \cdots (6)$$

F^{**} gives an awkward expression

Note that eq 4 relates each E to its corresponding F expression.

Here is the graphical representation for various n values

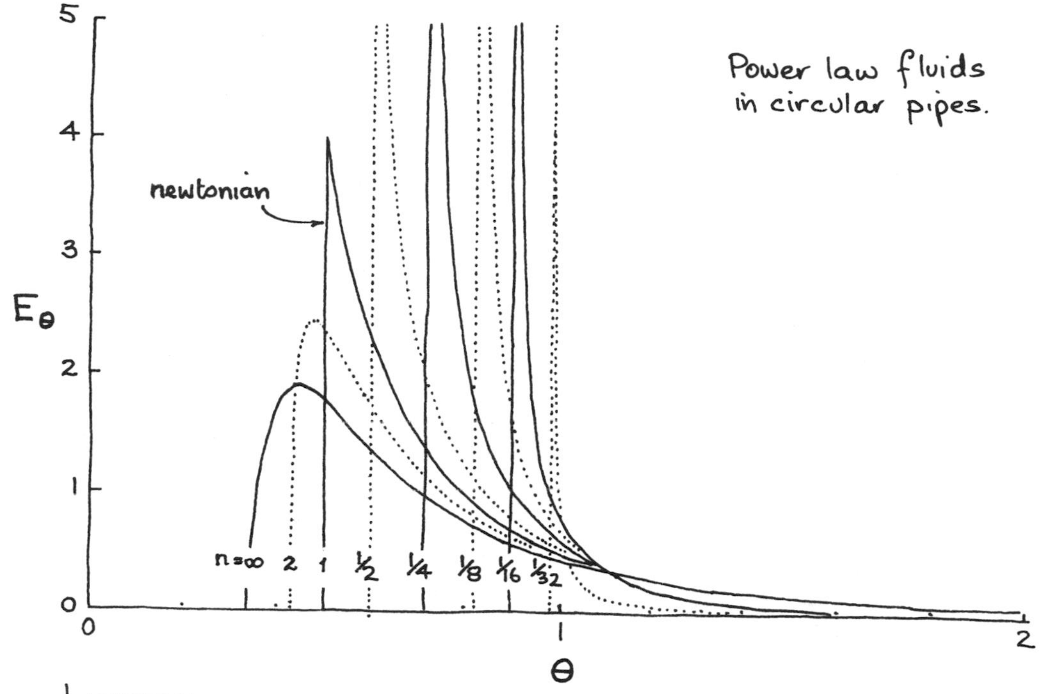

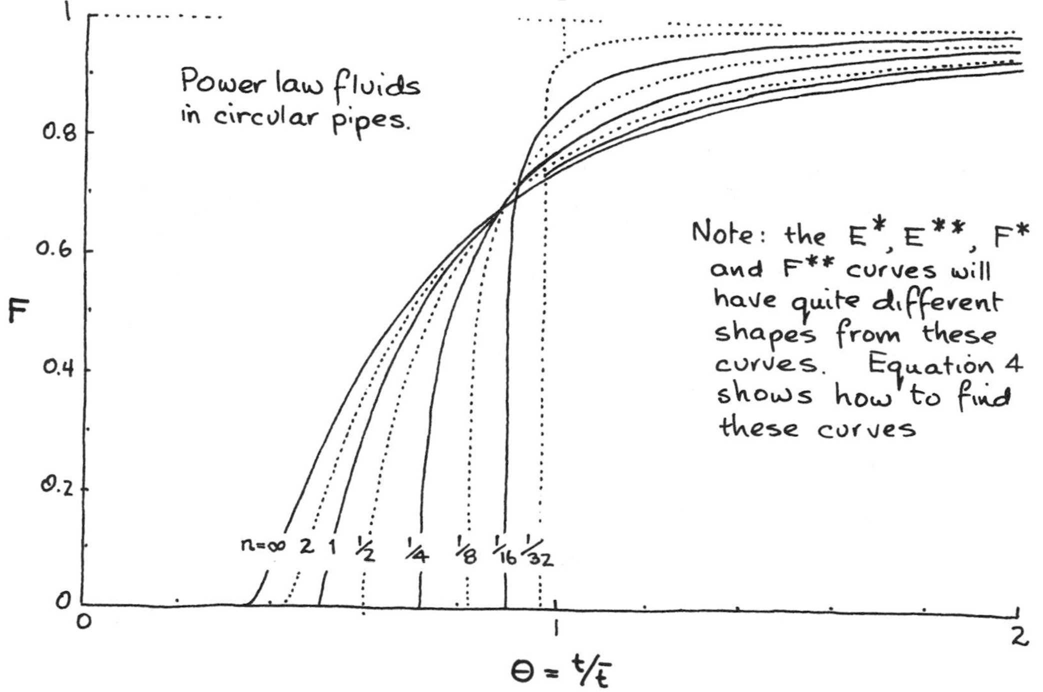

Note: the E^*, E^{**}, F^* and F^{**} curves will have quite different shapes from these curves. Equation 4 shows how to find these curves

2. Bingham plastics in pipes

The shear stress vs velocity gradient relationship is

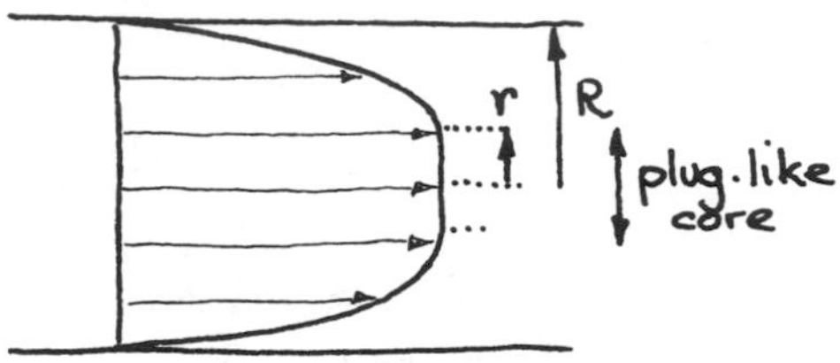

$$\tau = \tau_0 + \frac{\eta}{g_c}\left(\frac{du}{dy}\right)$$

(τ_0: yield stress; η: plastic viscosity)

- for butter just out of the refrigerator: $\tau_0 = 100 \sim 200 \ N/m^2$
- for warm just ready to melt butter: $\tau_0 = 10 \sim 20 \ N/m^2$

Going through the necessary mathematics we find the following expressions for the pulse and step responses

$$E_\theta = \frac{(1-m)\,\theta_0}{\theta^3}\left[1-m+\frac{m}{\sqrt{1-\theta_0/\theta}}\right] \quad \cdots \text{for } \theta \geq \theta_0$$

$$E^*_\theta = \theta \cdot E_\theta \quad \text{and} \quad E^{**}_\theta = \theta^2 \cdot E_\theta \qquad \cdots (7)$$

$$F = \frac{m^2}{\theta_0} + \frac{2(1-m)}{\theta_0}\left\{\frac{m}{3}\left(1-\frac{\theta_0}{\theta}\right)^{1/2}\left(2+\frac{\theta_0}{\theta}\right) + \frac{1-m}{4}\left[1-\left(\frac{\theta_0}{\theta}\right)^2\right]\right\}$$

$$F^* = \left[m + (1-m)\left(1-\frac{\theta_0}{\theta}\right)^{1/2}\right]^2 \qquad \cdots (8)$$

F^{**} = very complicated

where

$$m = \frac{r}{R_0} = \frac{\tau_0}{\tau_{wall}} = \frac{4\tau_0 L}{(\Delta p_{loss})\,d_t}$$

$$\theta_0 = \left(\begin{matrix}\text{residence time of the central}\\ \text{plug of fast moving fluid}\end{matrix}\right) = \frac{m^2+2m+3}{6}$$

Graphically

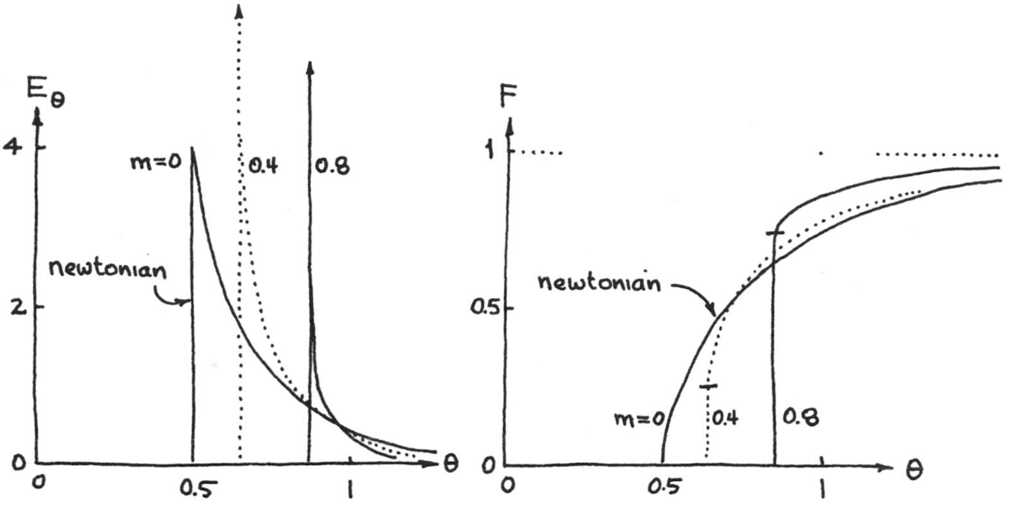

3. Falling film flow or flow between parallel plates.

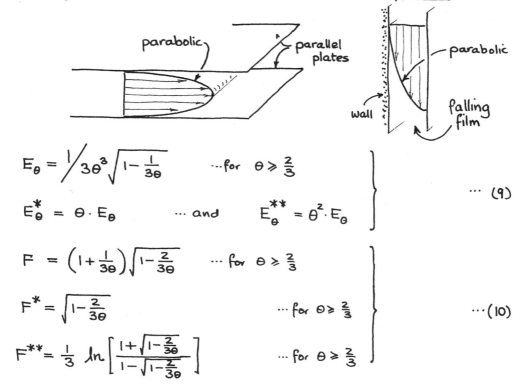

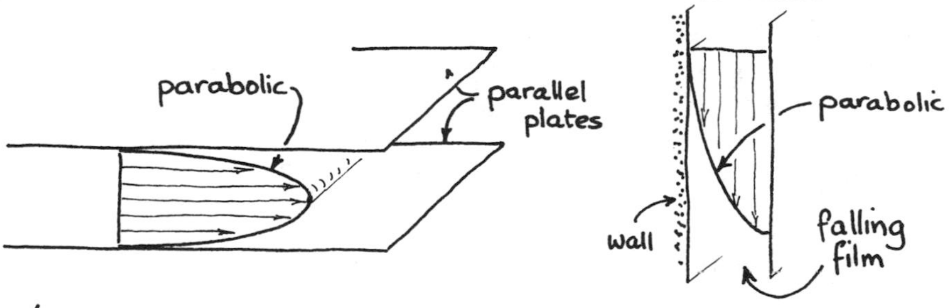

$$E_\theta = 1\Big/3\theta^3\sqrt{1-\frac{1}{3\theta}} \quad \cdots \text{for } \theta \geq \frac{2}{3}$$

$$E^*_\theta = \theta \cdot E_\theta \quad \cdots \text{and} \quad E^{**}_\theta = \theta^2 \cdot E_\theta \qquad \cdots (9)$$

$$F = \left(1+\frac{1}{3\theta}\right)\sqrt{1-\frac{2}{3\theta}} \quad \cdots \text{for } \theta \geq \frac{2}{3}$$

$$F^* = \sqrt{1-\frac{2}{3\theta}} \quad \cdots \text{for } \theta \geq \frac{2}{3} \qquad \cdots (10)$$

$$F^{**} = \frac{1}{3}\ln\left[\frac{1+\sqrt{1-\frac{2}{3\theta}}}{1-\sqrt{1-\frac{2}{3\theta}}}\right] \quad \cdots \text{for } \theta \geq \frac{2}{3}$$

IV Response Curves Taken with Line Measurements.

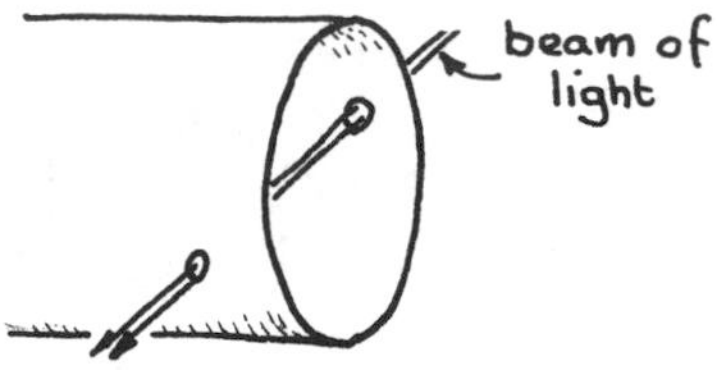

So far we have considered planar and flux measurements at the vessel exit. However, tracer concentration is often measured along a line (usually going through the center of the pipe). For this type of measurement the E and F curves and their various relationships are

In general

$$E_\theta^{*\ell} = \theta \cdot E^\ell, \qquad E_\theta^\ell = \frac{dF^\ell}{d\theta}, \qquad E_\theta^{*\ell} = \frac{dF^{*\ell}}{d\theta} \qquad \cdots (11)$$

For a newtonian in a circular pipe

$$\left.\begin{aligned} E_\theta^\ell &= 1/4\theta^2\sqrt{1-\frac{1}{2\theta}} \qquad \cdots \text{ with } \theta > \tfrac{1}{2} \\ F^\ell &= \sqrt{1-\frac{1}{2\theta}} \\ F^{*\ell} &= \frac{1}{4}\ln\left\{2\theta\left[1+\sqrt{1-\frac{1}{2\theta}}\,\right]^2\right\} \end{aligned}\right\} \qquad \cdots (12)$$

For a power law fluid in a circular pipe

$$\left.\begin{aligned} E_\theta^\ell &= \frac{n}{(3n+1)\theta^2}\left[1-\frac{\theta_0}{\theta}\right]^{-1/n+1} \qquad \cdots \text{ with } \theta > \theta_0 = \frac{n+1}{3n+1} \\ F^\ell &= \left(1-\frac{\theta_0}{\theta}\right)^{\frac{n}{n+1}} \end{aligned}\right\} \qquad \cdots (13)$$

For a Bingham plastic in a circular pipe

$$\left.\begin{aligned} E_\theta^\ell &= \frac{(1-m)\theta_0}{2\theta^2\sqrt{1-\frac{\theta_0}{\theta}}} \qquad \text{with } \theta \geqslant \theta_0 = \frac{m^2+2m+3}{6}, \quad m = \frac{r_{plug}}{R} \\ F^\ell &= m + (1-m)\sqrt{1-\frac{\theta_0}{\theta}} \end{aligned}\right\} \qquad \cdots (14)$$

For falling films or flow between parallel plates, with newtonians

$$E^\ell = E^*, \qquad E^{*\ell} = E^{**}, \qquad F^\ell = F^*, \qquad F^{*\ell} = F^{**} \qquad \cdots (15)$$

V. Chemical Conversion for Pure Convection Reactors.

In the pure convection regime (negligible molecular diffusion) each element of fluid follows its own streamline with no intermixing with neighboring elements. In essense this gives macrofluid behavior even though you may have a microfluid. From chapter 61 the conversion expression is then

$$\frac{C_A}{C_{A0}} = \int_0^{\infty} \left(\frac{C_A}{C_{A0}}\right)_{\text{element of fluid}} \cdot E_t \, dt$$

for zero order reaction: $\frac{C_A}{C_{A0}} = 1 - \frac{kt}{C_{A0}}$ for $t \leq \frac{C_{A0}}{k}$

for first order reaction: $\frac{C_A}{C_{A0}} = e^{-kt}$

for second order reaction: $\frac{C_A}{C_{A0}} = \frac{1}{1+kC_{A0}t}$

if you have E^*, E^{**}, E^{ℓ} or $E^{*\ell}$, or else F^*, F^{**}, F^{ℓ} or $F^{*\ell}$ first transform to E and then insert above

etc. for other kinetics, reaction of particles ...; and for non-newtonians see Sawinski CES 43 1209 (1988).

For zero order reaction of a newtonian in a pipe integration gives:

$$\frac{C_A}{C_{A0}} = \left(1 - \frac{k\bar{t}}{2C_{A0}}\right)^2 \qquad \cdots (16)$$

For first order reaction of a newtonian in a pipe:

$$\frac{C_A}{C_{A0}} = \frac{\bar{t}^2}{2} \int_{\bar{t}/2}^{\infty} \frac{e^{-kt}}{t^3} dt = y^2 \, ei(y) + (1-y)e^{-y}, \quad y = \frac{k\bar{t}}{2} \qquad \cdots (17)$$

(ei: exponential integral, see pg. 32·6)

For second order reaction of a newtonian in a pipe:

$$\frac{C_A}{C_{A0}} = 1 - kC_{A0}\bar{t}\left[1 - \frac{kC_{A0}\bar{t}}{2} \ln\left(1 + \frac{2}{kC_{A0}\bar{t}}\right)\right] \qquad \cdots (18)$$

For other kinetics, channel shapes or types of fluids insert the proper terms in the general performance expression and integrate.

VI Comments.

(a) **Test for an RTD curve.** Proper RTD curves must satisfy the material balance checks (zero and first moment)

$$\int_0^\infty E_\theta \, d\theta = 1 \qquad \text{and} \qquad \int_0^\infty \theta E_\theta \, d\theta = 1$$

The E curves of this chapter, for non newtonians and all shapes of channels, all meet this requirement. All the E* and E** curves of this chapter do not, however their transforms to E do.

(b) **RTD curves from experiment.** If you wish to represent data by an empirical E curve be sure that the empirical equation satisfies the above two conditions. For example, in the literature we sometimes find the following equation form to represent coiled tubes, screw extruders and the like

$$E_\theta \begin{cases} = \dfrac{AB}{\theta^{B+1}} \\ = 0 \end{cases} \quad \text{or} \quad F \begin{cases} = 1 - \dfrac{A}{\theta^B} & \cdots \text{ for } \theta \geq \theta_0 \\ = 0 & \cdots \text{ for } \theta < \theta_0 \end{cases}$$

In satisfying the above two conditions we find that the three constants of the above expression are interrelated to give just one independent parameter. Thus if we take the breakthrough time θ_0 as the independent measure then

$$A = \theta_0^{1/1-\theta_0} \; ; \qquad B = \frac{1}{1-\theta_0} \; ; \qquad A = \left(\frac{B-1}{B}\right)^B$$

and

$$\left.\begin{aligned} E_\theta &= \frac{1}{1-\theta_0} \, \frac{1}{\theta} \left(\frac{\theta_0}{\theta}\right)^{1/1-\theta_0} \\ F &= 1 - \left(\frac{\theta_0}{\theta}\right)^{1/1-\theta_0} \end{aligned}\right\} \quad \cdots \text{ for } \theta > \theta_0$$

The same sort of argument holds for other types of RTD curves. The parameters can not all be independently chosen.

(c) The variance and other RTD descriptors. The variance of all the E curves of this chapter is finite; but it is infinite for all the E* and E** curves. So be sure you know which curve you are dealing with.

In general the convection model E curve has a long tail. This makes the measurement of its variance unreliable. Thus σ^2 is not a useful parameter for convection models and is not presented here.

The breakthrough time θ_0 is probably the most reliably measured and most useful descriptive parameter for convection models, so it is widely used.

(d) Comparison with plug flow for n^{th} order reaction

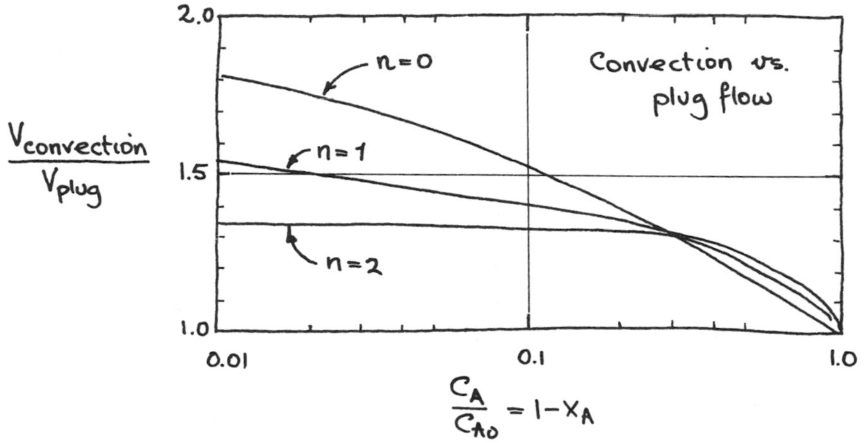

This graph shows that even at high X_A convective flow does not drastically lower reactor performance. This result differs from the dispersion and tanks-in-series models (see chapters 64, 66.)

(e) References for derivations and extensions

Osborne CES 30 159 (1975): series reactions of power law fluids
Wen and Fan: E, E*, F, F* for power law fluids
Novosad and Ulbrecht CES 21 405 (1966): reaction of power law fluids.
Kim and Harris CES 28 1653 (1973): line measurements of newtonians
Dalkeun Park PhD thesis OSU 1980: equations for E**, F** and for Bingham plastics.
Lin CES 35 1477 (1980): power law fluids in annuli

Chapter 68 Problems

A viscous liquid is to react while passing through a tubular reactor in which flow is expected to follow the convection model. What conversion can we expect in this reactor if plug flow in the reactor will give 80% conversion?

A1 ... Reaction follows zero order kinetics.

A2 ... Reaction is second order.

A3 Assuming plug flow we calculate that a tubular reactor 12 m long would give 96% conversion of A for the second order reaction $A \rightarrow R$. However, the fluid is very viscous, and flow will be strongly laminar, thus we expect the convection model, not the plug flow model, to closely represent the flow. How long should we make the reactor to insure 96% conversion of A?

A4 Aqueous A (C_{A0} = 1 mol/lit) with physical properties close to water (ρ = 1000 kg/m^3, $\mathcal{D} = 10^{-9}$ m^2/s) reacts by a first order homogeneous reaction ($A \rightarrow R$, $k = 0.2$ s^{-1}) as it flows at 100 mm/s through a tubular reactor (d_t = 50 mm, L = 5 m). Find the conversion of A in the fluid leaving this reactor.

A5 Aqueous A (C_{A0} = 50 mol/m^3) with physical properties close to water (ρ = 1000 kg/m^3, $\mathcal{D} = 10^{-9}$ m^2/s) reacts by a second order reaction ($k = 10^{-3}$ m^3/mol·s) as it flows at 10 mm/s through a tubular reactor (d_t = 10 mm, L = 20 m). Find the conversion of reactant A from this reactor.

B6 We want to model the flow of fluid in a flow channel. For this we locate three measuring points A, B, and C, 100 m apart along the flow channel. We inject tracer upstream of point A, fluid flows past points A, B, and C with the following results

At A the tracer width is 2 m

At B the tracer width is 10 m

At C the tracer width is 14 m

What type of flow model would you try to use to represent this flow: dispersion, convective, tanks in series, or none of these? Give a reason for your answer.

Chapter 81. ENZYME FERMENTATION.

The term "fermentation" can be used in its original strict meaning (to produce alcohol from sugar — nothing else) or it can be used more or less broadly. We will use the modern broad definition:

> From the simplest to the most complex, biological processes may be classed as **fermentations, elementary physiological processes** and the **action of living entities**. Further, fermentations can be divided into two broad groups: those promoted and catalysed by microorganisms or microbes (yeasts, bacteria, algae, molds, protozoa) and those promoted by enzymes (chemicals produced by microorganisms). In general then fermentations are reactions wherein a raw organic feed is converted into product by the action of microbes or by the action of enzymes.

Enzyme fermentations can be represented by

$$(\text{organic feed, A}) \xrightarrow[\text{acting as catalyst}]{\text{enzyme E}} (\text{product chemicals, R})$$

Microbial fermentations can be represented by

$$(\text{organic feed, A}) \xrightarrow[\text{which acts as catalyst}]{\text{microbe C}} (\text{product, R}) + (\text{more cells, C})$$

The key distinction between these two types of fermentation is that in enzyme fermentation the catalytic agent, the enzyme, does not reproduce itself, it acts as an ordinary chemical, while in microbial fermentation the catalytic agent, the cell or microbe, reproduces itself. Within the cells the enzyme catalyses the reaction, just as in enzyme fermentation, however, in reproducing itself the cell manufactures its own enzyme.

In this chapter we introduce enzyme fermentations, in the following chapters we take up microbial fermentations.

I Michaelis - Menten Kinetics.

In a sympathetic environment, with just the right enzyme for catalyst, organic A will react to product R. Observations show the following behavior

$$A \xrightarrow{E} R$$

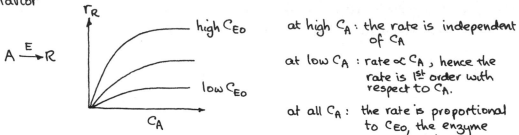

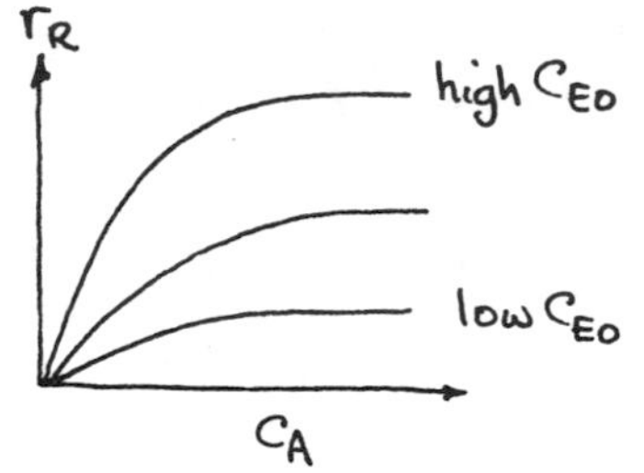

at high C_A: the rate is independent of C_A

at low C_A : rate $\propto C_A$, hence the rate is 1st order with respect to C_A.

at all C_A: the rate is proportional to C_{EO}, the enzyme concentration

A simple expression which accounts for this behavior is

$$-r_A = r_R = k \frac{C_{EO} C_A}{C_M + C_A}$$

(C_{EO}: total enzyme; C_M: a constant)

In searching for the simplest mechanism to explain these observations and this rate form consider the two step elementary reaction

$$A + E \underset{2}{\overset{1}{\rightleftharpoons}} X \xrightarrow{3} R + E \qquad \text{... and ...} \qquad C_{EO} = C_E + C_X$$

(X: intermediate (A·E); C_{EO}: total enzyme; C_E: free enzyme; C_X: enzyme attached to reactant)

In eliminating the concentration of intermediate from the final rate expression we have a number of choices

either

- Assumption 1 : $C_X \cong 0$, or most of the enzyme is in free form, or $C_E \cong C_{EO}$
- Assumption 2 : $C_X \neq 0$, or a significant fraction of the enzyme can be bound as X, or $C_{EO} = C_E + C_X$.

and

either
- Assumption 3 : use the concept of rate determining steps, thus the slow step determines the rate, all others are at equilibrium. Here this means that

$$K = \frac{C_X}{C_A C_E} = \frac{k_1}{k_2}$$

This assumption is much used in heterogeneous catalysis.

- Assumption 4: use the steady state approximation for intermediate, or

$$\frac{dC_X}{dt} = 0$$

This assumption is commonly used in developing rate expressions in homogeneous catalysis.

With assumptions 1 and 3 we get ... $r_R = \frac{k_1 k_3}{k_2} C_A C_{EO}$

With assumptions 1 and 4 we get ... $r_R = \frac{k_1 k_3}{k_2 + k_3} C_A C_{EO}$

} No good, doesn't give 0 and 1st order kinetics with respect to A.

With assumptions 2 and 3 we get ... $r_R = \frac{k_3 C_A C_{EO}}{k_2/k_1 + C_A}$

With assumptions 2 and 4 we get ... $r_R = \frac{k_3 C_A C_{EO}}{\frac{k_2 + k_3}{k_1} + C_A}$

} Both these fit the data, and are thus possible mechanisms

Michaelis-Menten in Biochem Z. 49 333 (1913) chose this.

Briggs-Haldane in Biochem J. 19 338 (1925) chose this.

By careful analysis of careful experiments Chance, in J. Biol. Chem. 151 553 (1943) favors the Briggs-Haldane mechanism. Later evidence reinforces this choice. Thus we end up today with the so called **Michaelis-Menten** equation although it is in fact the Briggs-Haldane modification of the M-M equation.

$$A + E \underset{k_2}{\overset{k_1}{\rightleftharpoons}} X \xrightarrow{k_3} R + E \qquad \cdots r_R = \frac{k_3 C_{E0} C_A}{C_M + C_A}$$

$$C_{E0} = C_E + C_x$$

Steady state approximation: $\frac{dC_x}{dt} = 0$

$C_M = \frac{k_2 + k_3}{k_1}$: the Michaelis-Menten constant

The meaning of C_M

From $\left.\begin{array}{l} \frac{dC_x}{dt} = 0 = k_1 C_A C_E - (k_2 + k_3) C_x \\ \text{and } C_{E0} = C_E + C_x \end{array}\right\}$ we find ... $\frac{C_x}{C_E} = \frac{C_A}{C_M} = \frac{(\text{enzyme in combined form})}{(\text{enzyme in free state})}$

As a consequence

- when $C_A = C_M$ half the enzyme is in free form, the other half combined.
- when $C_A \gg C_M$ most of the enzyme is tied up as complex X.
- when $C_A \ll C_M$ most of the enzyme is in free form.

Graphically we show this equation as follows.

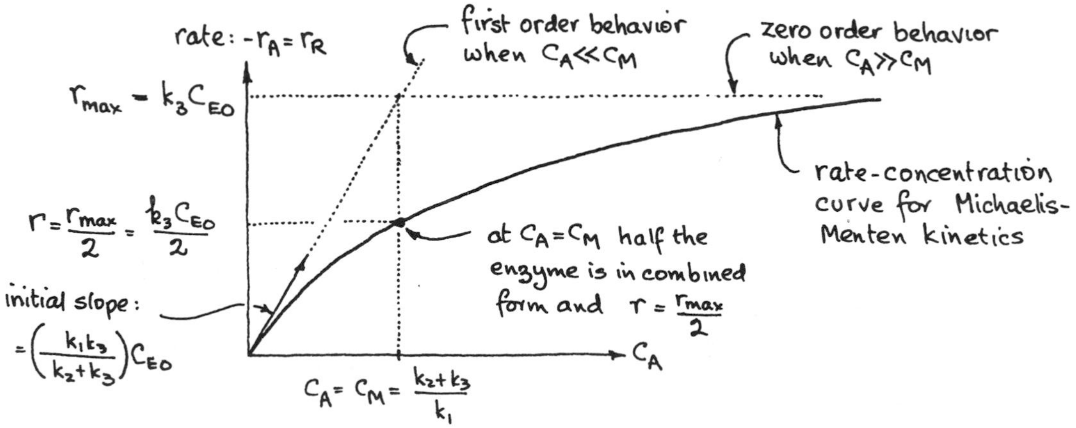

A. Batch or plug flow fermentor.

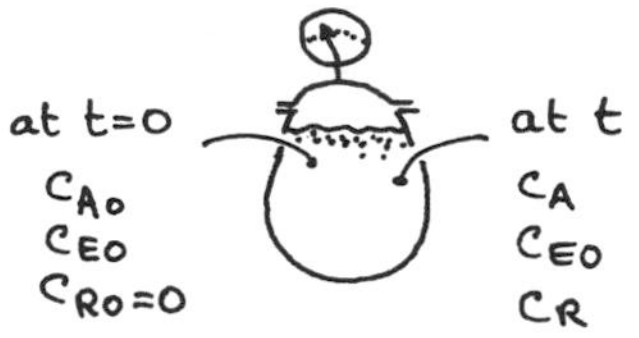

For this system integration of the M-M equation gives (see chapter 3 or see Michaelis and Menten 1913)

at t=0   at t
C_{AO} C_A
C_{EO} C_{EO}
$C_{RO}=0$ C_R

$$C_M \ln \frac{C_{AO}}{C_A} + (C_{AO}-C_A) = k_3 C_{EO} t$$

$\nwarrow$ first order term $\nwarrow$ zero order term

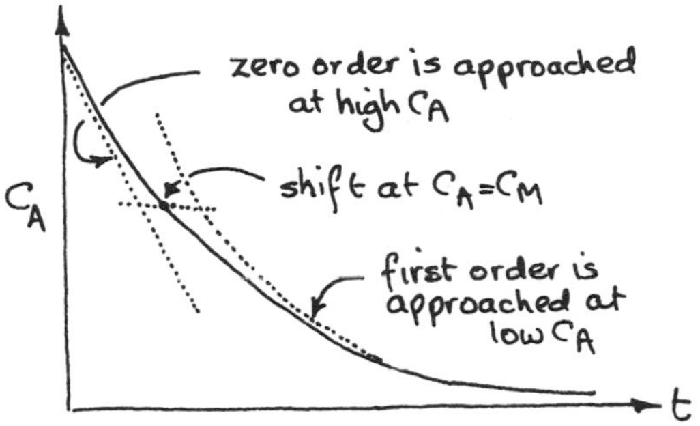

This behavior is shown on the accompanying C vs t diagram

zero order is approached at high C_A

shift at $C_A = C_M$

first order is approached at low C_A

C_A t

Unfortunately this equation can not be plotted directly to find the values of the constants k_3 and C_M. However, by manipulation we find the following useful form which can be plotted.

$$\frac{C_{AO}-C_A}{\ln ^{C_{AO}}/C_A} = -C_M + k_3 C_{EO} \cdot \frac{t}{\ln ^{C_{AO}}/C_A}$$

zero order regime here (high C_A)

C_{AO}

$\dfrac{C_{AO}-C_A}{\ln ^{C_{AO}}/C_A}$

first order here

time

slope = k_3

$\dfrac{C_{EO}t}{\ln ^{C_{AO}}/C_A}$

O $\dfrac{C_M}{k_3}$ $\dfrac{C_M+C_{AO}}{k_3}$

$-C_M$

this plot gives one line for all C_{EO}

for high C_{EO} for low C_{EO}

C_{AO}

$\dfrac{C_{AO}-C_A}{\ln ^{C_{AO}}/C_A}$

slope = $k_3 C_{EO}$

$\dfrac{t}{\ln ^{C_{AO}}/C_A}$

O $\dfrac{C_M}{k_3 C_{EO}}$ C

$-C_M$

$\dfrac{C_M+C_{AO}}{k_3 C_{EO}}$

separate line for each C_{EO}

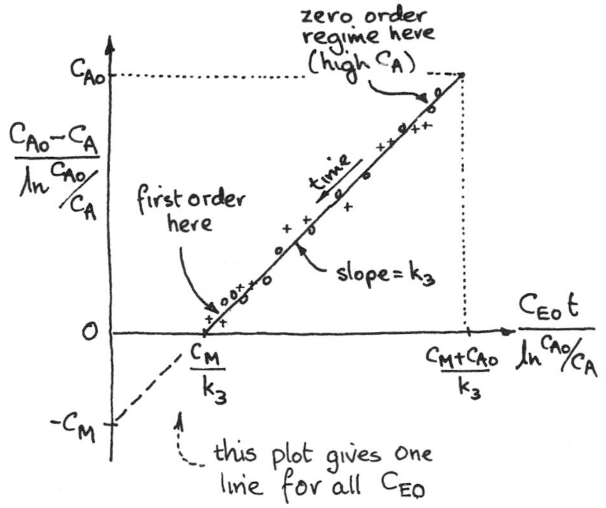

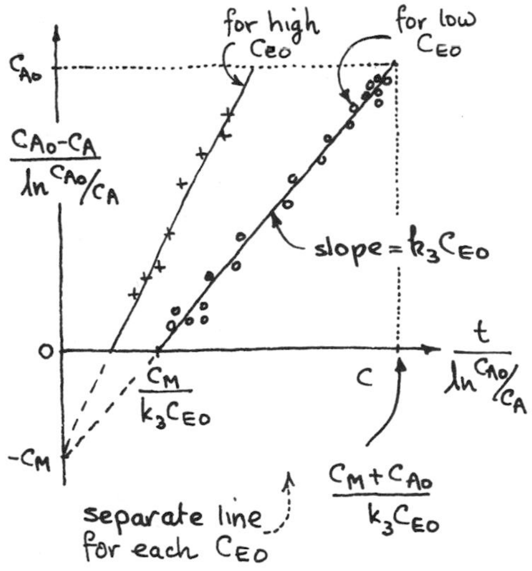

... either plot will do ...

B. Mixed flow fermentor.

Inserting the M-M equation into the mixed flow performance expression gives

$$\tau = \frac{C_{A0}-C_A}{-r_A} = \frac{(C_{A0}-C_A)(C_M+C_A)}{k_3 C_{E0} C_A} \quad \ldots \text{ or } \quad k_3 C_{E0}\tau = \frac{(C_{A0}-C_A)(C_M+C_A)}{C_A}$$

Unfortunately we cannot devise a plot of this equation to give k_3 and C_M. However, on rearrangement we find an equation form which does allow a direct evaluation of k_3 and C_M, or

$$C_A = -C_M + k_3\left(\frac{C_{E0}C_A\tau}{C_{A0}-C_A}\right)$$

In graphical form this gives

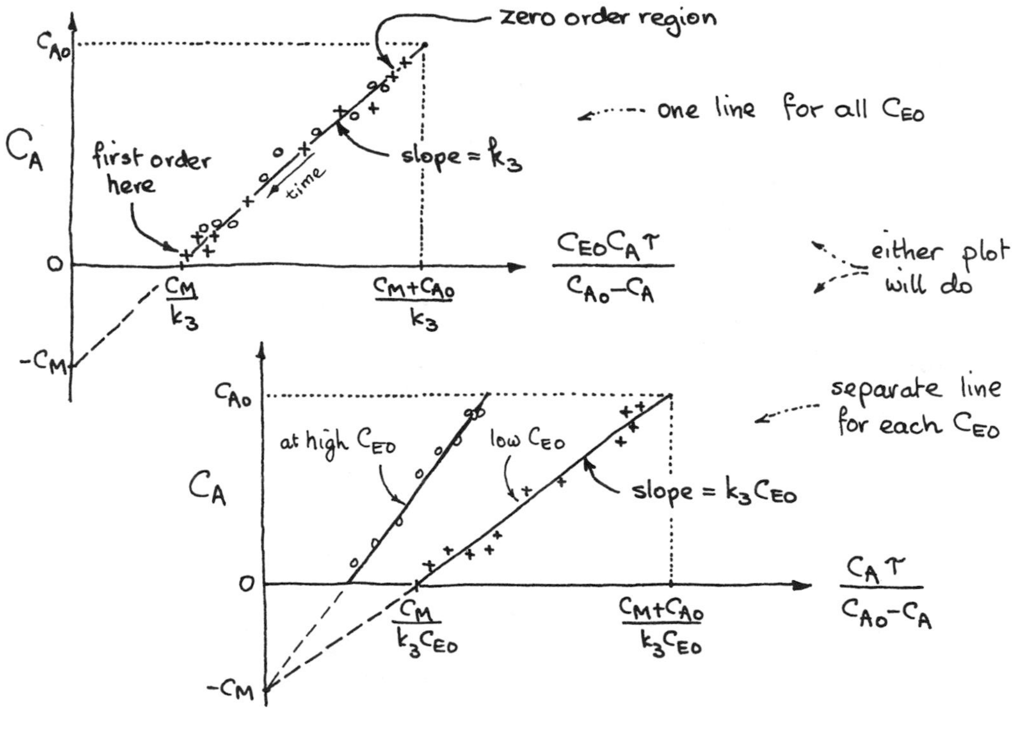

C. Direct fit of the M-M equation with rate-concentration data.

We must first obtain r vs C data from experiment.

- for mixed flow $r_R = \frac{C_{A0}-C_A}{\tau}$ … and each data point gives one value for r.
- for batch or plug flow $+r_R = -\frac{dC_A}{dt}$ … and we must evaluate slopes to find r.

We next have three ways of plotting r vs C data to find k_3 and C_M

- $-r_A$ vs $\frac{-r_A}{C_A}$ … the Eadie or the Eadie-Hofstee plot
- $\frac{1}{-r_A}$ vs $\frac{1}{C_A}$ … the Lineweaver or the Lineweaver-Burk plot.
- $\frac{C_A}{-r_A}$ vs C_A … the no-name plot.

1. The Eadie plot.

Rearranging the M-M equation gives

$$\frac{-r_A}{C_{E0}} = k_3 - C_M\left(\frac{-r_A}{C_{E0}C_A}\right)$$

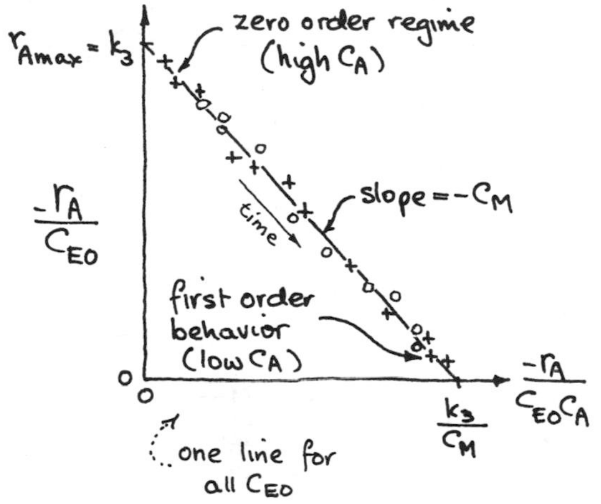

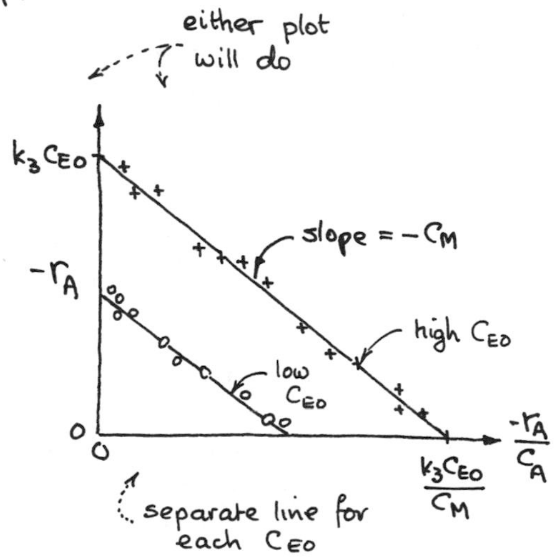

2. <u>The Lineweaver plot</u>. In another arrangement the M-M equation gives

$$\frac{C_{E0}}{-r_A} = \frac{C_M}{k_3} \cdot \frac{1}{C_A} + \frac{1}{k_3} \quad \cdots \text{or} \cdots \quad \frac{1}{-r_A} = \frac{C_M}{k_3 C_{E0}} \cdot \frac{1}{C_A} + \frac{1}{k_3 C_{E0}}$$

and in graphical form

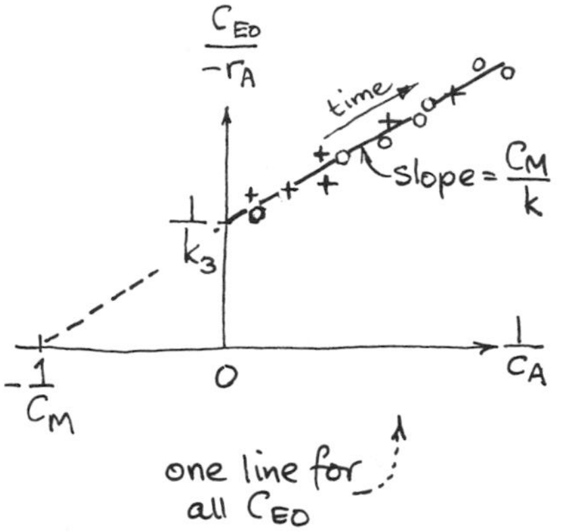

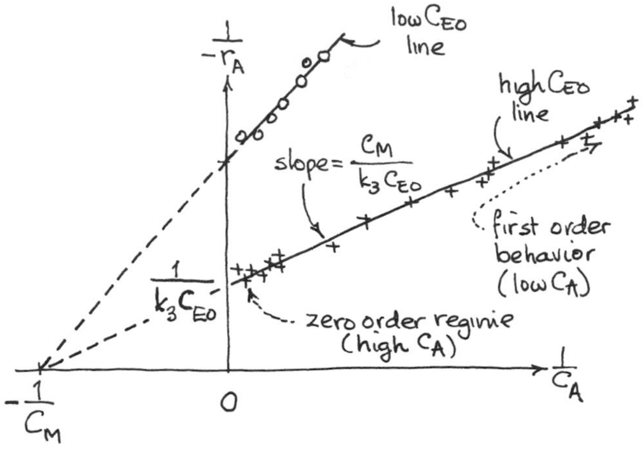

3. <u>The no-name plot</u>. There is no particular advantage to this plot so let us forget it

Comments

(a) In interpreting the r vs C data which plot should we use, the Eadie or the Lineweaver? Here are some facts to consider:

- The Lineweaver plot goes to ∞ at low C_A thus curve fitting in this region can lead to much distortion. Au contraire, the Eadie plot gives a rather even weighting of data.
- For highly scattered data the Lineweaver plot gives a less scattered more easily interpreted graph than the Eadie plot.
- With inhibition, to be considered next, the Eadie plot gives a sharper distinction between mechanisms

To sum up: except for very scattered data the Eadie plot is preferred. It will be used from now on. Many authors do not agree with these recommendations; for example, see Dixon and Webb pg 70.

(b) Since good interpretable data can only come from batch, plug flow or mixed flow reactors it is best to use the direct fit of raw data from these reactors rather than evaluate the rate at each point and then fit the r vs C data. The two step procedure compounds errors, is less reliable, and is more liable to fiddling. Thus in most situations we should not be getting data in the form where the Eadie or Lineweaver plot can be used.

II Inhibition by a Foreign Substance – Competitive and Non-Competitive Inhibition.

When the presence of substance B causes the slowdown of the enzyme-substrate reaction then B is called an inhibitor. We have various kinds of inhibitor action, the simplest models being called competitive and non competitive. We have **competitive inhibition** when A and B attack the same site on the enzyme. We have **non competitive inhibition** when B attacks a different site on the enzyme, but in doing so stops the action of A. In simple pictures:

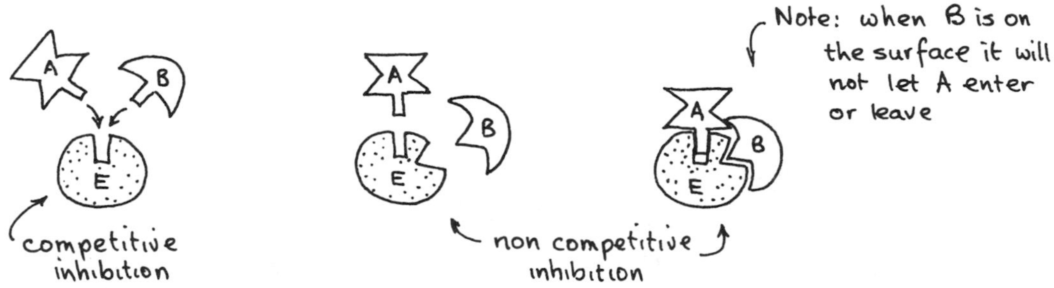

Pharmacological significance: the study of enzymes and inhibition is one of the major methods in determining the action of existing drugs and in developing new drugs. This approach has changed the whole direction of pharmacological research in recent years. The main thrust today is

- to study the disease biochemically, then
- synthesize a chemical to block the action of a crucial enzyme.

Let us develop kinetic expressions for these two types of inhibition.

A. Kinetics of Competitive Inhibition.

With A and B competing for the same site on the enzyme we have

$$A + E \underset{2}{\overset{1}{\rightleftharpoons}} X \xrightarrow{3} R + E \qquad (1)$$

$$B + E \underset{5}{\overset{4}{\rightleftharpoons}} Y \qquad (2)$$

and the rate of reaction (formation of R) is

$$r_R = \frac{dC_R}{dt} = k_3 C_X \qquad (3)$$

Making the Briggs-Haldane assumption for eqs 1 and 2

$$\frac{dC_X}{dt} = 0 = k_1 C_A C_E - (k_2 + k_3) C_X \qquad (4)$$

$$\frac{dC_Y}{dt} = 0 = k_4 C_B C_E - k_5 C_Y \qquad (5)$$

and an accounting for the enzyme in its various forms gives

$$C_{E0} = C_E + C_X + C_Y \qquad (6)$$

... where C_X and C_Y are not necessarily small

Finally assume

$$\left. \begin{array}{l} C_{B0} = C_B + \cancel{C_Y}^{=0}, \quad \text{or } C_{B0} \cong C_B, \quad \text{or } C_{B0} \gg C_Y, \quad \text{or } \frac{k_4}{k_5} \to 0 \\ \text{or best of all } C_{B0} \gg C_{E0} \end{array} \right\} \qquad (7)$$

these assumptions are all equivalent, I think. We have to include one of these otherwise we get a messy unsolvable set of equations

Combine eqs 3 to 7 to eliminate C_E, C_X and C_Y. This gives

$$r_R = \frac{k_3 C_{E0} C_A}{C_M + C_A + N C_{B0} C_M} = \frac{k_3 C_{E0} C_A}{C_M (1 + N C_{B0}) + C_A}$$

... where $C_M = \dfrac{k_2 + k_3}{k_1}, \ \dfrac{\text{mol}}{\text{m}^3}$; $N = \dfrac{k_4}{k_5}, \ \dfrac{\text{m}^3}{\text{mol}}$

compared to systems without inhibition where $r_R = k_3 C_{E0} C_A / C_M + C_A$ we see that all we need do here is modify C_M, or ... replace C_M by $C_M (1 + N C_{B0})$.

B. Kinetics of non competitive inhibition.

Here A attacks one site on the enzyme, B attacks a different site, but in doing so stops the action of A.

$$A + E \underset{2}{\overset{1}{\rightleftharpoons}} X \xrightarrow{3} R + E \qquad (1)$$

$$B + E \underset{5}{\overset{4}{\rightleftharpoons}} Y \qquad (2)$$

$$B + X \underset{7}{\overset{6}{\rightleftharpoons}} Z \qquad (3)$$

note that B attacks the enzyme irrespective of whether A is attached to it or not

The rate of reaction is

$$r_R = \frac{dC_R}{dt} = k_3 C_X \qquad (4)$$

and for the intermediates make the Briggs-Haldane assumptions, or

$$\frac{dC_X}{dt} = 0 = k_1 C_A C_E + k_7 C_Z - (k_2 + k_3) C_X - k_6 C_B C_X \qquad (5)$$

$$\frac{dC_Y}{dt} = 0 = k_4 C_B C_E - k_5 C_Y \qquad (6)$$

$$\frac{dC_Z}{dt} = 0 = k_6 C_B C_X - k_7 C_Z \qquad (7)$$

An accounting for the enzyme in its various forms gives

$$C_{E0} = C_E + C_X + C_Y + C_Z \qquad (8)$$

Finally, to avoid horrible mathematics assume

$$C_{B0} \gg C_{E0} \quad \text{...and...} \quad C_{A0} \gg C_{E0} \qquad (9)$$

Combining eqs 4 to 9 so as to eliminate C_E C_X C_Y and C_Z then gives

$$r_R = \frac{k_3 C_{E0} C_A}{C_M + C_A + N C_M C_{B0} + L C_A C_{B0}} = \frac{\dfrac{k_3}{(1 + L C_{B0})} \cdot C_{E0} C_A}{C_M \left(\dfrac{1 + N C_{B0}}{1 + L C_{B0}} \right) + C_A} \quad \text{...where} \begin{cases} C_M = \dfrac{k_2 + k_3}{k_1} \\ N = \dfrac{k_4}{k_5} \\ L = \dfrac{k_6}{k_7} \end{cases}$$

Compared to enzyme reactions without inhibition where

$$r_R = \frac{k_3 C_{E0} C_A}{C_M + C_A}$$

we see that both k_3 and C_M are modified here. Thus for non competitive inhibition

- replace k_3 by $\frac{k_3}{1+LC_{B0}}$
- replace C_M by $C_M\left(\frac{1+NC_{B0}}{1+LC_{B0}}\right)$

C. How to tell between competitive and non competitive inhibition from experiment.

With C vs t data obtained from either batch, mixed or plug flow runs, or r vs C data make one of the recommended plots for inhibition-free systems (see section IA, IB and IC). With inhibition these plots are modified as follows

1. Batch or plug flow data.

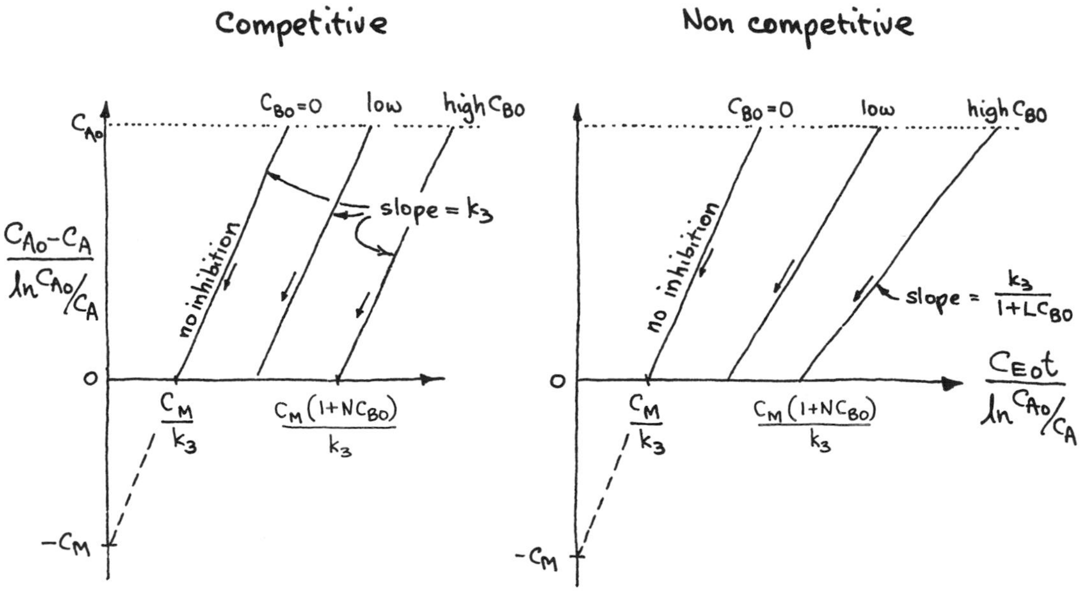

2. Mixed flow data.

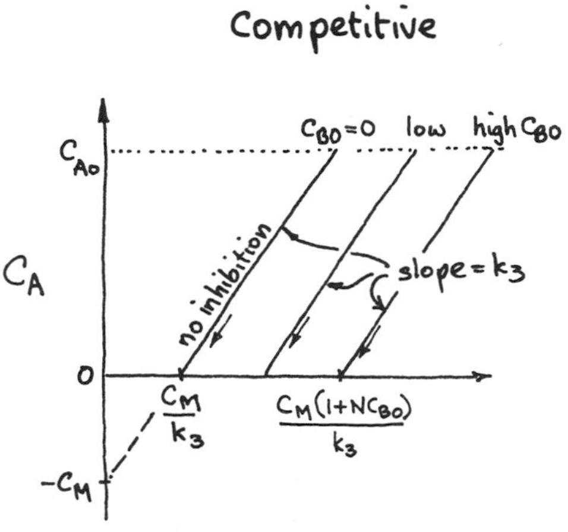

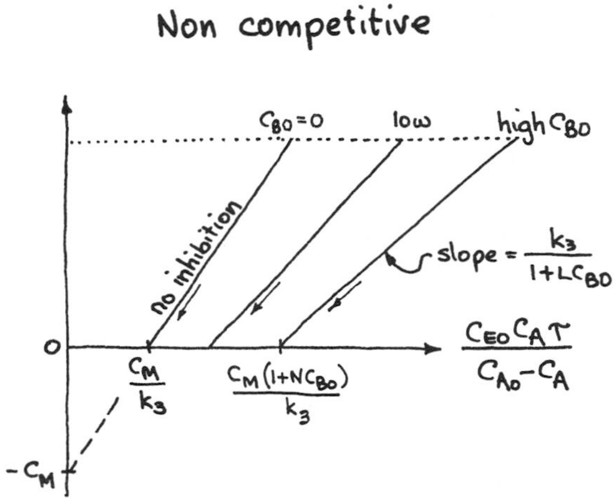

3. Rate vs concentration data. Here the Eadie plot becomes

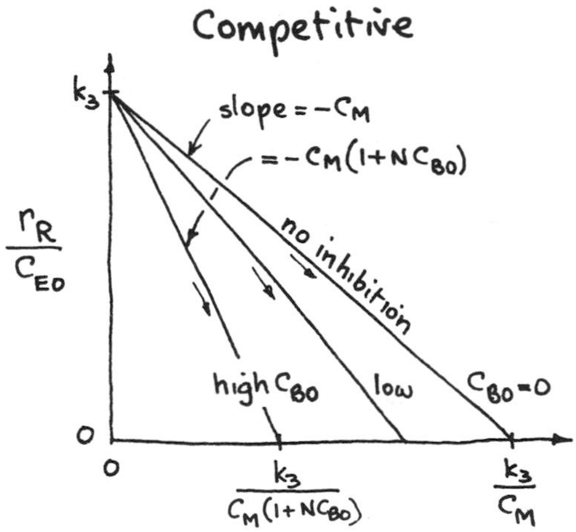

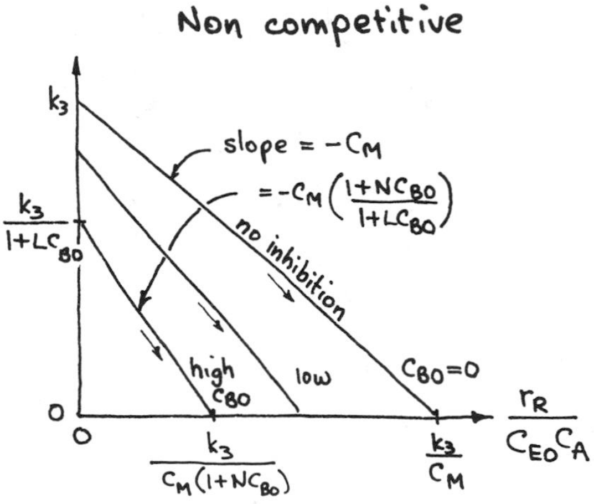

Comments

(a) For batch data use the batch plot. Do not take slopes and then use the Eadie plot. For mixed flow use either the mixed flow plot or the Eadie plot.

(b) These two models of inhibition are the simplest imaginable. Others are more complex mathematically, so always try these first.

III. Substrate Inhibition.

Sometimes excess substrate can cause interference at the active sites of the enzyme, and lower the rate of reaction. The simplest model for this is

$$A + E \underset{2}{\overset{1}{\rightleftharpoons}} X \xrightarrow{3} R + E \qquad (1)$$

$$A + X \underset{5}{\overset{4}{\rightleftharpoons}} Y \qquad (2)$$

The rate of reaction is

$$r_R = \frac{dC_R}{dt} = k_3 C_X \qquad (3)$$

The Briggs-Haldane assumptions for eqs 1 and 2 are

$$\frac{dC_X}{dt} = 0 = k_1 C_A C_E + k_5 C_Y - (k_2 + k_3) C_X - k_4 C_A C_X \qquad (4)$$

$$\frac{dC_Y}{dt} = 0 = k_4 C_A C_X - k_5 C_Y \qquad (5)$$

An accounting for enzyme in its various forms gives

$$C_{EO} = C_E + C_X + C_Y \qquad (6)$$

Combining eqs 3 to 6 allows us to eliminate C_E C_X and C_Y. Thus the rate becomes

$$r_R = \frac{k_3 C_A C_{EO}}{C_M + C_A + N C_A^2} \qquad \text{... where } N = \frac{k_4}{k_5}$$

N measures the strength of self inhibition. Large N means strong self inhibition

A. Graphical representation.

Let us see how self inhibition modifies the inhibition free plots.

1. Batch or plug flow plot.

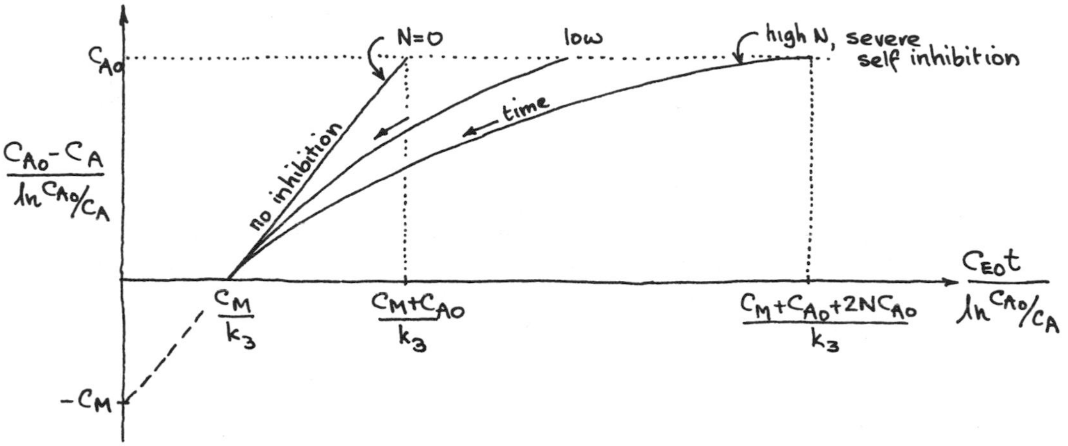

2. Mixed flow plot.

Here you get a plot very much like the plug flow plot. Neither is particularly useful (how do you fit a curve?). Better still find the rate at various concentrations and then make the Eadie plot, shown next.

3. Rate vs concentration plot.

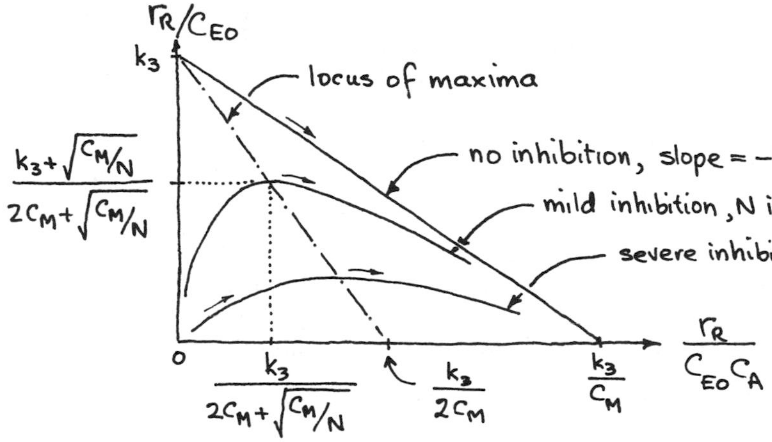

Chapter 81 Problems

A1 Substrate and enzyme flow through a mixed flow reactor (V = 6 lit). From the entering and leaving concentrations and flow rate find a rate equation to represent the action of enzyme on substrate.

C_{E0}, mol/lit	C_{A0}, mol/lit	C_A, mol/lit	v, lit/hr
0.02	0.2	0.04	3.0
0.01	0.3	0.15	4.0
0.001	0.69	0.60	1.2

A2 At room temperature sucrose is hydrolized by the enzyme sucrase as follows

$$\text{sucrose} \xrightarrow{\text{sucrase}} \text{products}$$

Starting with sucrose (C_{A0} = 1 mol/m^3) and sucrase (C_{E0} = 0.01 mol/m^3) the following data are obtained in a batch reactor (concentrations are calculated from optical rotation measurements)

C_A, mol/m^3	0.68	0.16	0.006
t, hr	2	6	10

Find a rate equation to represent the kinetics of this reaction

A3 In a number of separate runs different concentrations of substrate and enzyme are introduced into a batch reactor and allowed to react. After a certain time the reaction is quenched and the vessel contents analyzed. From the results found below find a rate equation to represent the action of enzyme on substrate.

Run	C_{E0}, mol/m^3	C_{A0}, mol/m^3	C_A, mol/m^3	t, hr
1	3	400	10	1
2	2	200	5	1
3	1	20	1	1

B4 Carbohydrate A decomposes in the presence of enzyme E. We also suspect that carbohydrate B in some way influences this decomposition. To study this phenomenon various concentrations of A, B and E flow into and out of a mixed flow reactor (V = 240 cm^3).

(a) From the following data find a rate equation for the decomposition.

(b) What can you say about the role of B in the decomposition?

(c) Can you suggest a mechanism for this reaction?

C_{A0}, mol/m^3	C_A, mol/m^3	C_{B0}, mol/m^3	C_{E0}, mol/m^3	v, cm^3/min
200	50	0	12.5	80
900	300	0	5	24
1200	800	0	5	48
700	33.3	33.3	33.3	24
200	80	33.3	10	80
900	500	33.3	20	120

B5 Enzyme E catalyses the decomposition of substrate A. To see whether substance B acts as inhibitor we make two kinetic runs in a batch reactor, one with B present, the other without B. From the data recorded below

(a) find a rate equation to represent the decomposition of A.

(b) What is the role of B in this decomposition?

(c) Suggest a mechanism for the reaction.

Run 1. $C_{A0} = 600$ mol/m^3, $C_{E0} = 8$ gm/m^3, no B present

C_A	350	160	40	10
t, hr	1	2	3	4

Run 2. $C_{A0} = 800$ mol/m^3, $C_{E0} = 8$ gm/m^3, $C_{B0} = C_B = 100$ mol/m^3

C_A	560	340	180	80	30
t, hr	1	2	3	4	5

Cellulose can be converted to sugar by the following enzymatic attack

$$\text{cellulose} \xrightarrow{\text{cellulase}} \text{sugar}$$

and both cellubiose and glucose act to inhibit the breakdown. To study the kinetics of this reaction a number of runs are made in a mixed flow reactor kept at 50 °C and using a feed of finely shredded cellulose ($C_{A0} = 25$ kg/m^3), enzyme (C_{E0}, same for all runs) and various inhibitors. The results are as follows

Run	exit stream C_A, kg/m^3	Series 1 *no inhibitor* τ, min	Series 2 *with cellubiose* $C_{B0} = 5$ kg/m^3 τ, min	Series 3 *with glucose* $C_{G0} = 10$ kg/m^3 τ, min
1	1.5	587	691	810
2	4.5	279	306	363
3	9.0	171	182	224
4	21.0	36	38	45

Chapter 81 Problems

A6 ... Find a rate equation to represent the breakdown of cellulose by cellulase in the absence of inhibitor.

B7 ... What is the role of cellubiose in the breakdown of cellulose (find the type of inhibition, and rate equation).

B8 ... What is the role of glucose in the breakdown of cellulose (find the type of inhibition, and the rate equation).

The rate data from these problems come from Ghose and Das, Advances in Biochemical Engineering **1** 66 (1971).

D9 A feed stream ($v = 0.01\ m^3/min$, $C_{A0} = 100\ mol/m^3$, $C_{E0} = 1\ mol/m^3$) is to be processed to 95% conversion ($C_A = 5\ mol/m^3$). The enzyme catalysed reaction

$$A \xrightarrow{E} R$$

follows substrate inhibiting Michaelis - Menten kinetics with $C_M = 100\ mol/m^3$, $k = 1.0\ min^{-1}$ and $N = 0.25\ m^3/mol$ (see pg 81.14).

Determine the reactor system which will require the smallest volume for this operation. You may use plug flow, mixed flow or any combination of these that you wish. Then sketch your recommended reactor set-up and on it show the volume of reactor or reactors.

Chapter 82. MICROBIAL FERMENTATION. INTRODUCTION AND OVERALL PICTURE.

Consider the simplest of situations

- one type of microbe C. We sometimes call this the cell or bug.
- one type of needed food A. This is called the substrate by life science workers.

If the food is right the bugs eat it, they multiply and in the process produce waste material R. In symbols

$$A \xrightarrow{C} C + R$$

In some cases the presence of product R inhibits the action of the cells, no matter how much food is available and we have what is called poisoning by product, or **product poisoning**. Wine making is an example of this

$$\begin{pmatrix}\text{squished grapes, fruit,}\\ \text{cereals, potatoes, etc.}\end{pmatrix} \xrightarrow{\text{bugs}} \begin{pmatrix}\text{more}\\ \text{bugs}\end{pmatrix} + \text{alcohol}$$

As the concentration of alcohol rises the cells multiply more slowly, and at about 12% alcohol the bugs quit. Alcohol is the poison here.

Activated sludge treatment of waste water is an example of a fermentation which is free of product poisoning

$$\begin{pmatrix}\text{organic waste}\\ \text{material}\end{pmatrix} \xrightarrow{\text{bugs}} \begin{pmatrix}\text{more}\\ \text{bugs}\end{pmatrix} + \begin{pmatrix}\text{breakdown products,}\\ CO_2,\ H_2O, \dots\end{pmatrix}$$

Sometimes we are interested in the breakdown of A, as in waste water treatment. In other situations we are interested in producing cells C, as in growing single cell protein for food. In still others we want the cell's waste material R, as in the production of penicillin and other antibiotics.

Let us see what typically happens with a single type of bug and single food.

A. Constant environment fermentation, qualitative.

What happens when we introduce a batch of microbes into a friendly constant composition medium having food of concentration C_A? First the microbes take some time to adapt to their new environment, then they grow exponentially. Thus

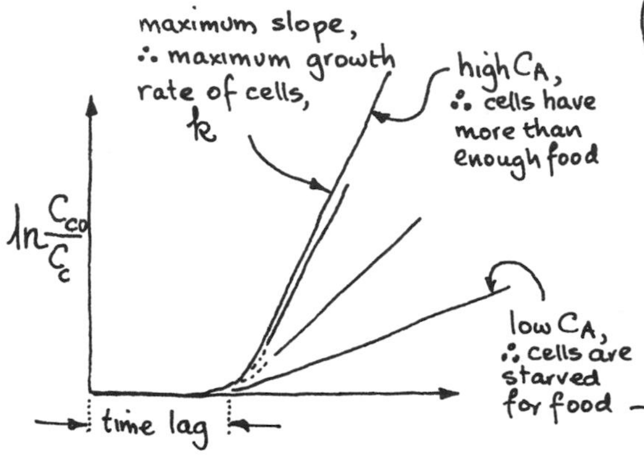

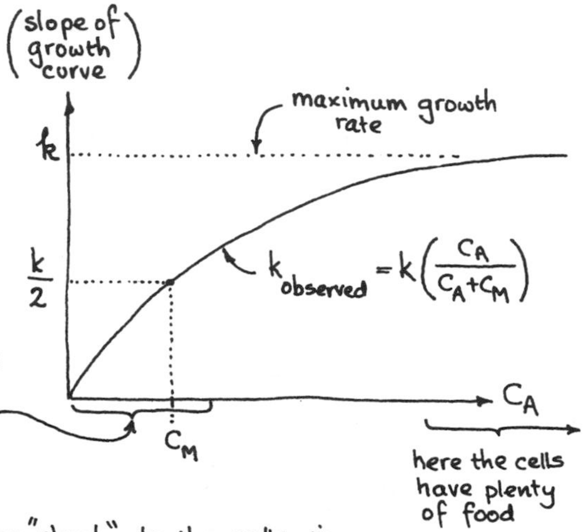

Roughly • the time lag is a result of the "shock" to the cells in finding themselves in these new surroundings

• the growth rate of cells (after the time lag) is given by Monod as

$$r_c = \frac{k C_A C_c}{C_A + C_M}$$

← C_M: the concentration of A where the cells reproduce at ½ their maximum rate

B. Batch fermentor, qualitative.

Here cells reproduce, the composition of the substrate changes, and product which can be toxic to the cells forms. Typically we see

- an induction period (time lag)
- a growth period
- a stationary period and
- a dying of cells

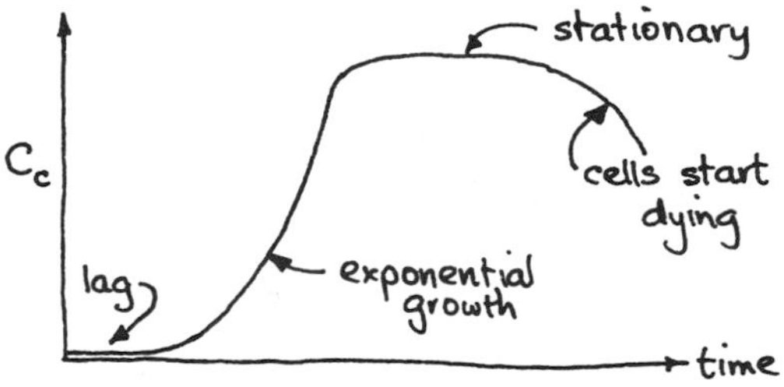

A few words about these regimes

82.3

(a) **Lag**. As the cells in a container use up their food they stop multiplying, their enzyme activity decreases, low molecular weight chemicals diffuse out, and the cells change character. They age. So when they are introduced into a new environment a lag is observed as the cells remanufacture the chemicals needed for growth and reproduction. In general any change in environment results in an induction period as the cells adjust. We find

Usual form of lag curve

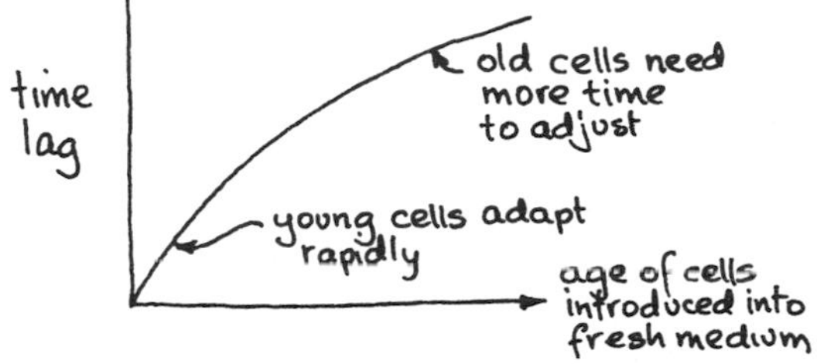

Other forms of lag curves are sometimes observed, for example

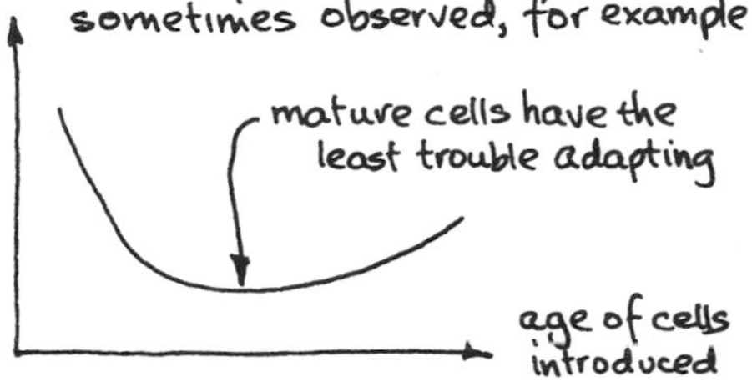

(b) **Grow and stationary phase**. Cells grow exponentially in a uniform environment, but in a batch system the medium changes so growth rate changes. The eventual drop in cell growth is governed either by

- depletion of food or
- accumulation of toxic materials (toxic to the cell).

Graphically we summarize this by the following sketches

Substrate limiting
(product does not affect the rate)

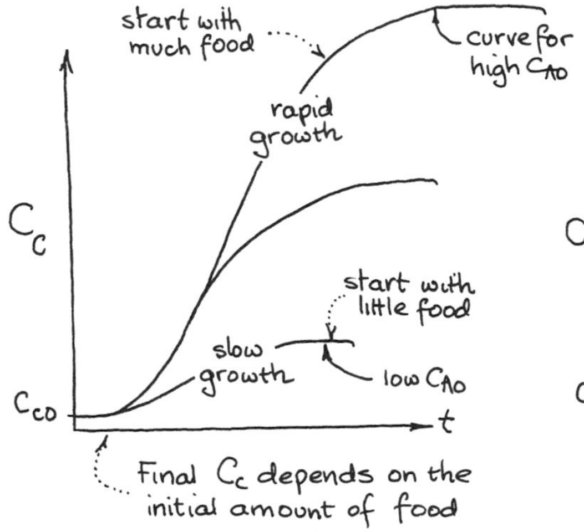

Poison limiting
(product slows and then stops the reaction in a batch reactor)

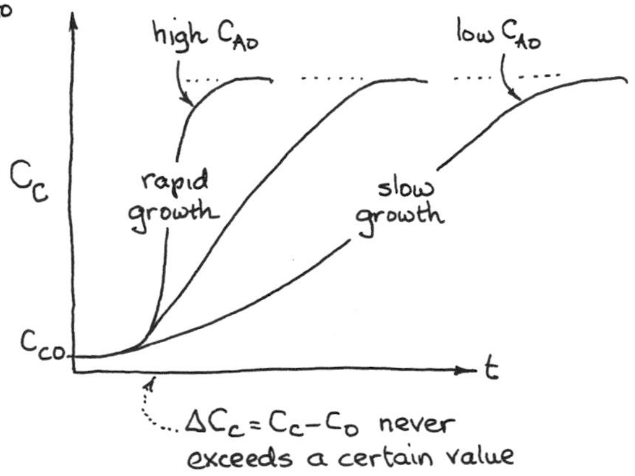

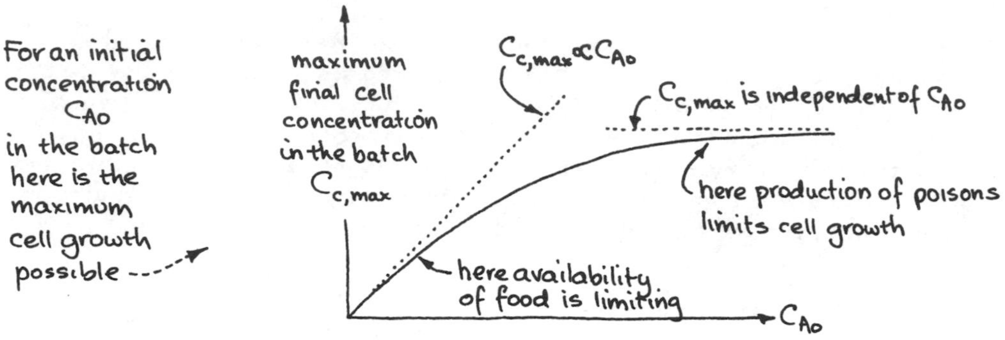

C. Mixed flow fermentor.

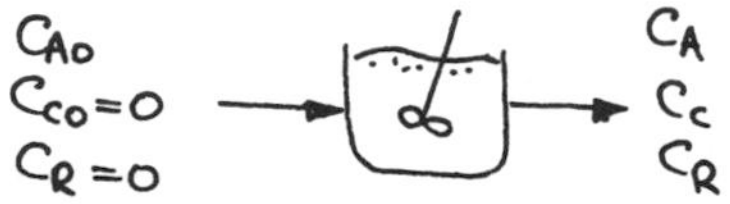

Here the cells are in a uniform environment. No adaptation is needed and cell multiplication proceeds at a constant rate determined by the composition of the fluid in the vessel. This is frequently represented by a Monod-type equation

$$-r_A = \frac{k C_A C_c}{C_A + C_M}$$

(the k value depends on all sorts of things, temperature, presence of trace elements, vitamins, toxic substances, light intensity, etc.)

D. Product distribution and fractional yields.

Look again at the stoichiometry

$$A \xrightarrow{C} cC + rR$$

(c, r: it is possible to get fractional and/or changing values as reaction proceeds)

and let us define

$$\text{(C/A)} = \varphi(C/A) = \frac{d(C\text{ formed})}{d(A\text{ used})}$$

$$\text{(R/A)} = \varphi(R/A) = \frac{d(R\text{ formed})}{d(A\text{ used})}$$

$$\text{(R/C)} = \varphi(R/C) = \frac{d(R\text{ formed})}{d(C\text{ formed})}$$

(circled symbols ← shorthand notation; always positive; treat as fractions)

then

$$\text{(R/A)} = \text{(R/C)} \cdot \text{(C/A)}$$

$$\text{(A/C)} = 1/\text{(C/A)}$$

$$r_C = (-r_A)\,\text{(C/A)}$$

$$r_R = (-r_A)\,\text{(R/A)}$$

$$r_R = (r_C)\,\text{(R/C)}$$

In general the stoichiometry can be messy with fractional yields changing with composition. Treatment of this case can be difficult. We'd like therefore to make the simplification that all ϕ values remain constant at all compositions, or that $\Delta C_A \propto \Delta C_R \propto \Delta C_c$ throughout the reaction. This assumption may be reasonable for mixed flow, or for the exponential growth period of batch reactors, otherwise it is questionable.

Let us make this assumption anyway ... all ϕ values stay constant. In this case for any change we can write

$$C_c - C_{co} = \phi(C/A)(C_{Ao} - C_A) \quad \text{... or ...} \quad C_c = C_{co} + \phi(C/A)(C_{Ao} - C_A)$$

$$C_R - C_{Ro} = \phi(R/A)(C_{Ao} - C_A) \quad \text{... or ...} \quad C_R = C_{Ro} + \phi(R/A)(C_{Ao} - C_A)$$

$$C_R - C_{Ro} = \phi(R/C)(C_c - C_{co}) \quad \text{... or ...} \quad C_R = C_{Ro} + \phi(R/C)(C_c - C_{co}) \quad \text{... etc.}$$

E. Kinetic expressions

The rate of cell multiplication depends in general on the availability of food and on the build up of wastes which interfere with cell multiplication.

1. **Availability of food.** For a reasonable quantitative expression make the analogy with enzyme kinetics

For enzymes:

$$A + E \rightleftharpoons X$$
$$X \rightarrow R + E$$
$$\text{and } C_{EO} = C_E + C_X$$

at high C_A ... $r_R = kC_{EO}$

at low C_A ... $r_R = kC_{EO}C_A/C_M$

at all C_A ... $r_R = \dfrac{kC_{EO}C_A}{C_A + C_M}$ ← Michaelis-Menten equation; C_M = Michaelis constant

For microbes:

$$A + C_{resting} \rightleftharpoons C_{pregnant}$$
$$C_{pregnant} \rightarrow 2C_{resting} + R$$
$$\text{and } C_{c,total} = C_{c,preg.} + C_{c,rest.}$$

at high C_A ... $r_R = kC_c$

at low C_A ... $r_R = kC_cC_A/C_M$

at all C_A ... $r_R = \dfrac{kC_cC_A}{C_A + C_M}$ ← Monod equation; C_M = Monod constant

Many other kinetic forms have been proposed and have been used in the past, however they have all been forgotten since Monod came out with his expression. Its simplicity won the day. So we will use this type of expression throughout to relate the rate of cell growth to substrate concentration.

2. Effect of harmful wastes. As wastes R build up they interfere with cell multiplication. Thus the observed Monod rate constant k_{obs} decreases with C_R. A simple form of this relationship is

$$k_{obs} = k\left(1 - \frac{C_R}{C_R^*}\right)^n$$

order of product poisoning (n)

rate constant in the absence of harmful waste material (k)

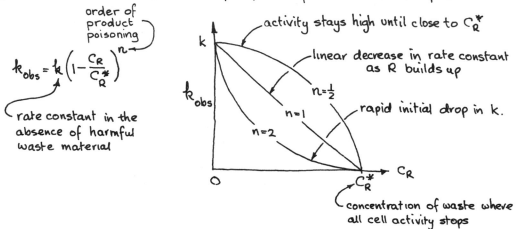

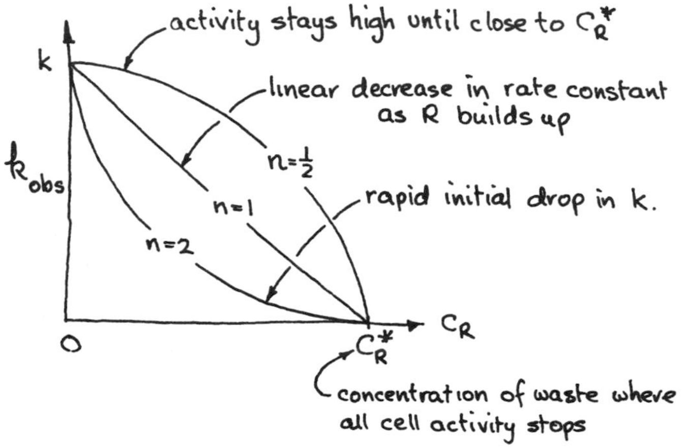

3. General kinetic expression. The simplest expression of the Monod type which can account for both factors in microbial fermentation is

$$-r_A\,(C/A) = r_R\,(C/R) = r_C = k_{obs}\frac{C_A C_C}{C_A + C_M} \quad \cdots\text{where}\cdots \quad k_{obs} = k\left(1 - \frac{C_R}{C_R^*}\right)^n$$

generalized Monod equation — k_{obs} decreases as C_R rises — concentration where all reaction stops (C_R^*)

In general, then, reaction and cell multiplication will slow down either by depletion of A (famine) or by build up of R (environmental pollution).

F. Planned treatment of the subject.

The next two chapters treat in turn the performance expressions and design consequences for:

- poison-free Monod kinetics. Here food limitation alone affects the growth rate of cells.
- product poisoning kinetics. Here some product formed during fermentation slows the rate.

We also assume in these chapters a constant fractional yield throughout, and since everything is liquid we take $\varepsilon_A = 0$, and we will use concentrations throughout.

More generally, an excess of either substrate or cells in the broth can also slow the rate of fermentation. In these situations the Monod equation should be suitably modified, see Han & Levenspiel, Biotech. and Bioeng. 32 430 (1988), for a discussion and general treatment for all these forms of inhibition.

Chapter 83. MICROBIAL FERMENTATION. SUBSTRATE LIMITING, POISON-FREE MONOD KINETICS.

If we assume a constant fractional yield and no slowing of the rate as a result of product poisoning or increase in cell density then the general rate equation of the previous chapter reduces to the well known Monod equation

$$r_C = (C/A)(-r_A) = \frac{k C_A C_C}{C_A + C_M} \quad \text{... where } C_C - C_{C0} = (C/A)(C_{A0} - C_A) \quad \text{... (1)}$$

where C_{A0} and C_{C0} are the feed or starting compositions. By differentiating the maximum rate is found to occur at

$$C_{A,\,\text{max rate}} = \sqrt{C_M^2 + C_M\left(C_{A0} + (A/C)\, C_{C0}\right)} - C_M \quad \text{... (2)}$$

Graphically we represent the changing rate with composition as

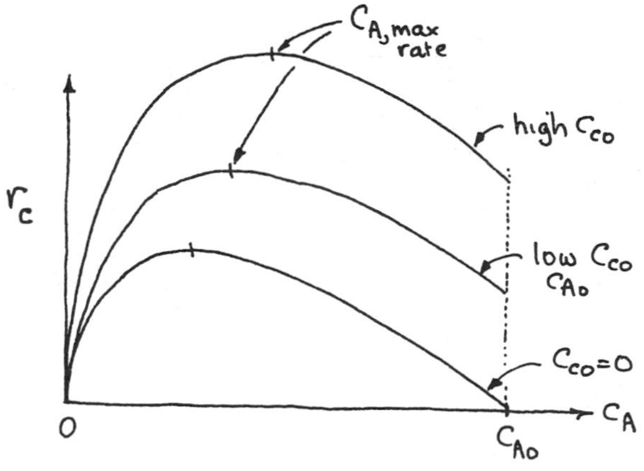

The maximum rate is found by combining eqs 1 and 2.

With a feed C_{A0}, C_{C0} to any system the key to proper design is to use mixed flow to reach $C_{A,\text{max rate}}$ ... all in one step. Then use plug flow beyond this point. Thus it is always important to know $C_{A,\text{max rate}}$.

A. Batch or plug flow fermentor.

Applying the batch or plug flow performance equations we find

$$t_b = \tau_p = \int_{C_{C0}}^{C_C} \frac{dC_C}{r_C} = \frac{1}{k}\int_{C_{C0}}^{C_C} \frac{C_A + C_M}{C_C C_A}\, dC_C = \int_{C_A}^{C_{A0}} \frac{dC_A}{(A/C)\, r_C} = \frac{1}{k}\int_{C_A}^{C_{A0}} \frac{C_A + C_M}{(A/C)\, C_C C_A}\, dC_A$$

where $C_A = C_{A0} - (A/C)(C_C - C_{C0})$ and $C_C = C_{C0} + (C/A)(C_{A0} - C_A)$.

Integration then gives

$$k t_b = k\tau_p = \left(\frac{C_M}{C_{A0} + (A/C)\, C_{C0}} + 1\right) \ln \frac{C_C}{C_{C0}} - \left(\frac{C_M}{C_{A0} + (A/C)\, C_{C0}}\right) \ln \frac{C_A}{C_{A0}} \qquad \ldots(3)$$

$$\ldots \text{ with } C_C - C_{C0} = (C/A)(C_{A0} - C_A)$$

with a time lag just add t_ℓ to the above time to find t_{total}.

If we wish we can write the performance equation in terms of C_R instead of C_A and C_C. Just remember that

$$C_R = C_{R0} + (R/C)(C_C - C_{C0}) = C_{R0} + (R/A)(C_{A0} - C_A)$$

The following sketches show the main properties of this performance equation.

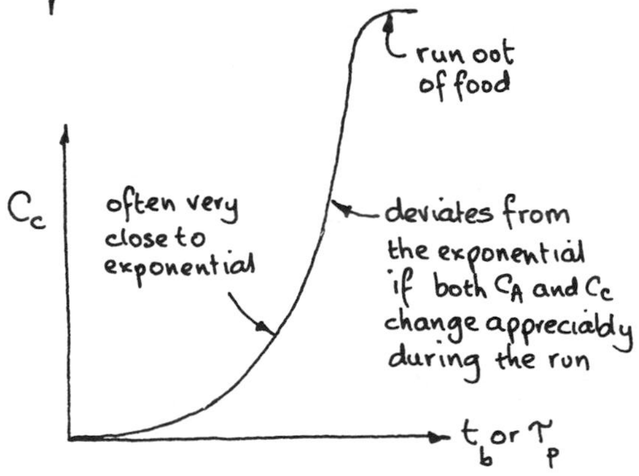

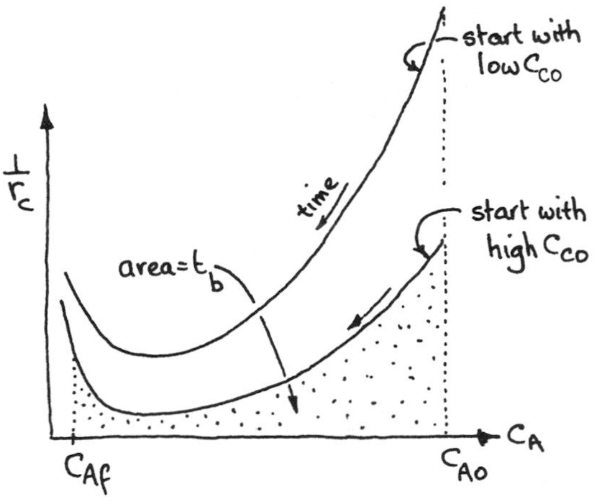

How to find the Monod constants from experiment.

Method (a) Rearrange eq 3 to give

$$\frac{t_b}{\ln C_C/C_{C0}} = \frac{M+1}{k} + \frac{M}{k}\cdot\frac{\ln C_{A0}/C_A}{\ln C_C/C_{C0}} \quad \cdots \text{ with } \quad M = \frac{C_M}{C_{A0} + (A/C)\, C_{C0}}$$

Then plot as shown to find k and C_M ····>

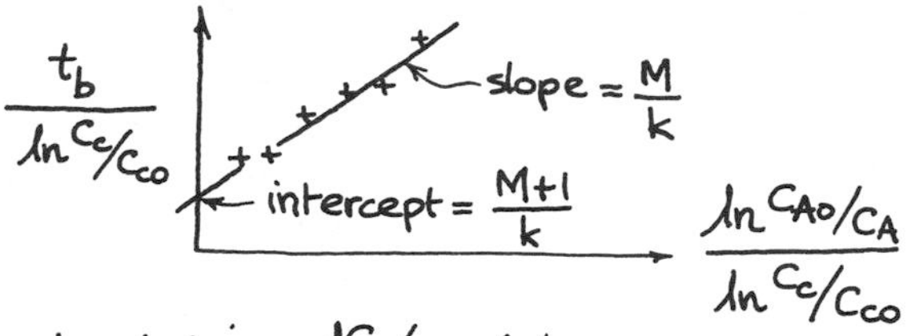

Method (b) First find r_C by taking dC_C/dt data, then rearrange the Monod equation to give

$$\frac{C_C}{r_C} = \frac{1}{k} + \frac{C_M}{k}\cdot\frac{1}{C_A}$$

Then plot to find k and C_M ····>

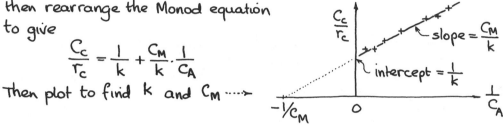

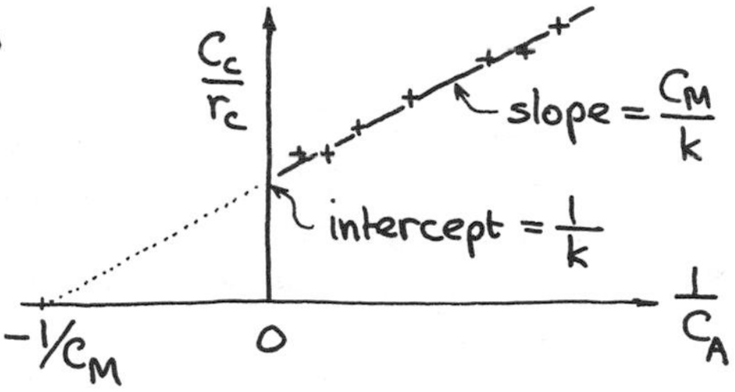

Method (c) Differentiate the Monod equation with respect to C_A and set to zero, thus $dr_C/dC_A = 0$. This gives

$$C_{A,\text{at max rate}} = \sqrt{C_M^2 + C_M\left(C_{A0} + (A/C)\,C_{C0}\right)} - C_M \quad \cdots\text{or}\cdots \quad C_M = \left(\frac{C_A^2}{C_{A0} - 2C_A + (A/C)\,C_{C0}}\right)_{\text{at max rate}}$$

From experiment locate r_C and C_A at the maximum rate ⟹ Then find C_M from the above equation ⟹ and k from eq 1.

Evaluate these 3 methods

- Method (a) uses all the data directly and presents it as a linear plot. This method is probably the best, all round.
- Method (b) requires taking derivatives or slopes from experimental data, is more tedious, and is probably less reliable
- Method (c) only uses data in the region of the maximum rate, and so is the poorest of the three.

Comments and Extensions

(a) **For high C_A**, thus $C_A \gg C_M$, put $C_M = 0$ in the Monod equation. This gives $r_C = kC_C$, in which case the performance expression, eq 3, simplifies to

$$k\tau_p = \ln \frac{C_C}{C_{C0}} \quad \text{... an exponential growth curve}$$

(b) **For low C_A**, thus $C_A \ll C_M$, the Monod equation becomes simple autocatalytic, and the performance expression, eq 3, reduces to

$$k\tau_p = \frac{C_M}{C_{A0} + (A/C)\, C_{C0}} \ln \frac{C_{A0} C_C}{C_A C_{C0}} \quad \text{...}$$

S-shaped growth curve. See the autocatalytic equation in chapter 2.

(c) **For very high C_C** the poison-free Monod equation just can't apply, for even if there is plenty enough food the cells will crowd each other out, and growth will slow down and eventually stop. So for very high cell concentration we must go to product poison kinetics

(d) **For $C_{C0} = 0$** no cells enter the reactor, nothing happens, no reaction, no spontaneous generation of life, so no cells leave.

(e) **For plug flow with recycle, $C_{C0} \neq 0$** the performance expression is

$$\tau = (R+1) \int_{C_{Af}}^{\frac{C_{A0}+RC_{Af}}{R+1}} \frac{C_A + C_M}{(A/C)\, k C_A C_C}\, dC_A$$

where $C_C = C_{C0} + (C/A)(C_{A0} - C_A)$

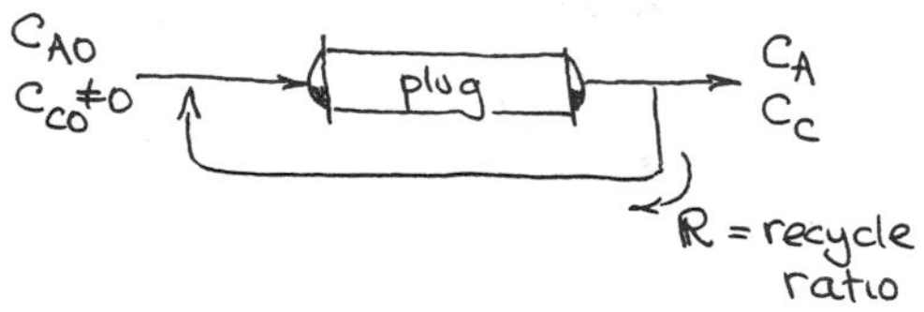

which gives, on integration,

$$k\tau = (R+1)\left[\frac{C_M}{C_{A0} + (A/C)\, C_{C0}} \ln \frac{C_C (C_{A0} + RC_A)}{C_A (C_{C0} + RC_C)} + \ln \frac{C_C (R+1)}{C_{C0} + RC_C}\right] \quad \text{...} \quad (4)$$

(f) For plug flow with recycle and $C_{C0}=0$ the general recycle equation simplifies to

$$k\tau_p = (R+1)\left[\frac{C_M}{C_{A0}} \ln \frac{C_{A0}+RC_A}{RC_A} + \ln \frac{R+1}{R}\right] \quad \cdots(5)$$

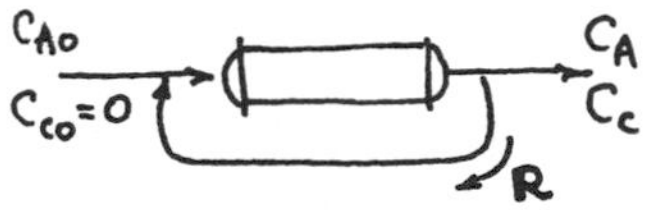

(g) The optimum recycle ratio with $C_{C0}=0$, in the sense that it produces most cells, is found by putting $(\partial C_C/\partial R)_T = 0$. This gives the following condition

$$\frac{C_M}{C_{A0}} \ln \frac{C_{A0}+RC_A}{RC_A} + \ln \frac{R+1}{R} = \frac{R+1}{R}\cdot\frac{C_M}{C_{A0}+RC_A} + \frac{1}{R} \quad \cdots(6)$$

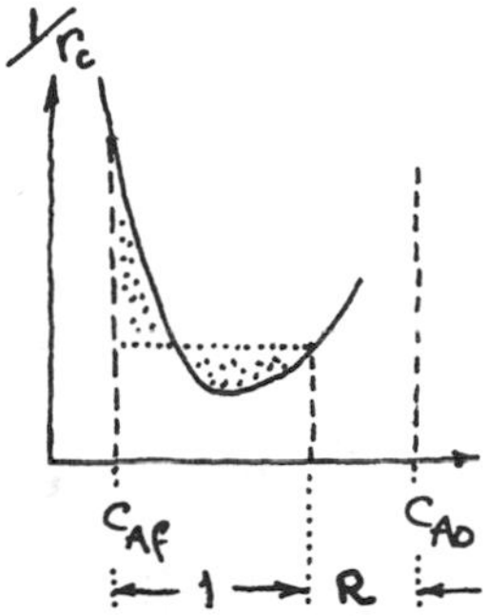

which is solved by trial and error. The optimum R is found to be a function of C_M/C_{A0} and C_A/C_{A0}. This is displayed below.

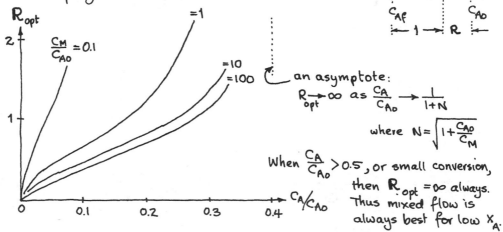

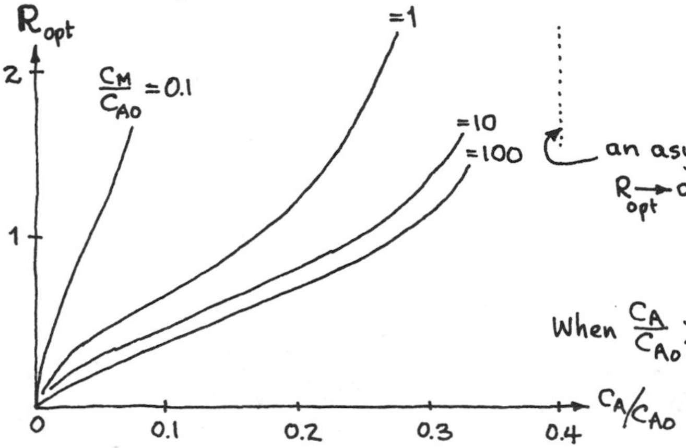

an asymptote: $R_{opt} \to \infty$ as $\frac{C_A}{C_{A0}} \to \frac{1}{1+N}$

where $N = \sqrt{1+\frac{C_{A0}}{C_M}}$

When $\frac{C_A}{C_{A0}} > 0.5$, or small conversion, then $R_{opt} = \infty$ always. Thus mixed flow is always best for low X_A.

(h) On optimum operations with plug flow reactors. Although eq 6 gives the best possible recycle ratio, we can do even better still by operating at the maximum rate whenever possible ... thus by putting infinite recycle at the appropriate place within the reactor. See a few pages further on for a discussion on this point.

(i) It is awkward to try to evaluate the rate constants of the Monod equation from batch or plug flow data. Mixed flow data are so much simpler to interpret, as we shall see.

B. Mixed flow fermentor with $C_{co}=0$.

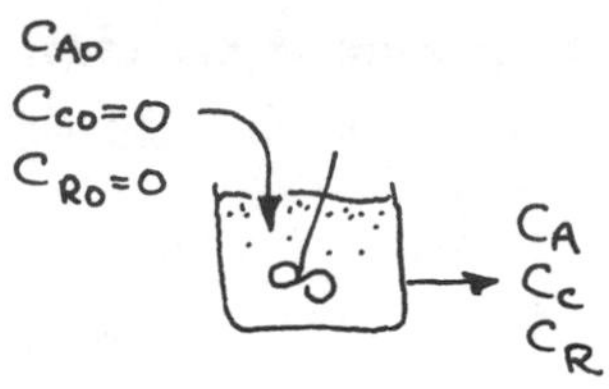

Assume Monod kinetics (no product poisoning), constant fractional yields φ, and no cells entering in the feed stream.
Then the mixed flow performance equation becomes

$$\tau_m = \frac{\Delta C_i}{r_i} \qquad \text{where } i = A, C \text{ or } R.$$

Replacing r_i gives:

In terms of C_A

$$k\tau_m = \frac{C_M + C_A}{C_A} \quad \cdots \text{or} \quad C_A = \frac{C_M}{k\tau_m - 1} \quad \cdots \text{for } k\tau_m > 1$$

In terms of C_c

$$k\tau_m = \frac{(C/A)(C_{A0}+C_M) - C_c}{(C/A)C_{A0} - C_c} \quad \cdots \text{or} \quad C_c = (C/A)\left(C_{A0} - \frac{C_M}{k\tau_m - 1}\right) \quad \cdots \text{for } k\tau_m > 1 \quad \cdots (7)$$

In terms of C_R

$$k\tau_m = \frac{(R/A)(C_{A0}+C_M) - C_R}{(R/A)C_{A0} - C_R} \quad \cdots \text{or} \quad C_R = (R/A)\left(C_{A0} - \frac{C_M}{k\tau_m - 1}\right) \quad \cdots \text{for } k\tau_m > 1$$

no solution possible if $k\tau_m < 1$

This intriguing expression was first developed by Monod, Annales de l'Institut Pasteur 79 390 (1950), and independently at about the same time by Novick and Szilard, Proc. N.A.S. Washington 36 708 (1950).

To evaluate the kinetic constants from a set of mixed flow runs rearrange eq 7 to give

$$\frac{1}{C_A} = \frac{k}{C_M} \tau_m - \frac{1}{C_M} \qquad \cdots (8)$$

and then plot as shown ----→

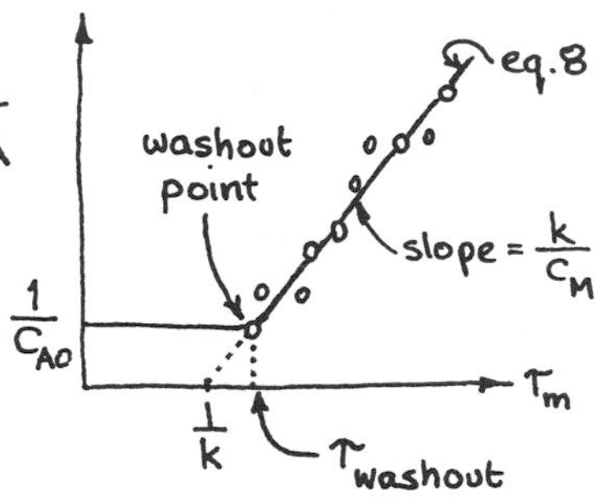

The characteristics of eq 7, the mixed flow performance equation are displayed and summarized in the following figures:

Shape of curve

when $C_A \ll C_M$ the curve is symmetrical

$C_A > C_M$

Maximum rate: there always is one

$\uparrow$ at $-r_{A, max}$

Minimum τ_m possible: if τ is any smaller than that shown no reaction will occur and all cells will wash out

τ_{min}

slope = $\begin{pmatrix} \text{rate of} \\ \text{formation} \\ \text{of cells} \end{pmatrix} = r_c = \frac{C_c}{\tau_m}, \left[\frac{cells}{s \cdot m^3} \right]$

points X and Y on this line have the same production rate of cells

production rate line $F_c = \upsilon \cdot C_c, \left[\frac{cells}{s} \right]$

$\tau_m = \bar{t} = \frac{V}{\upsilon}, [sec]$

Concentration

maximum production rate

washout point

maximum production rate of cells

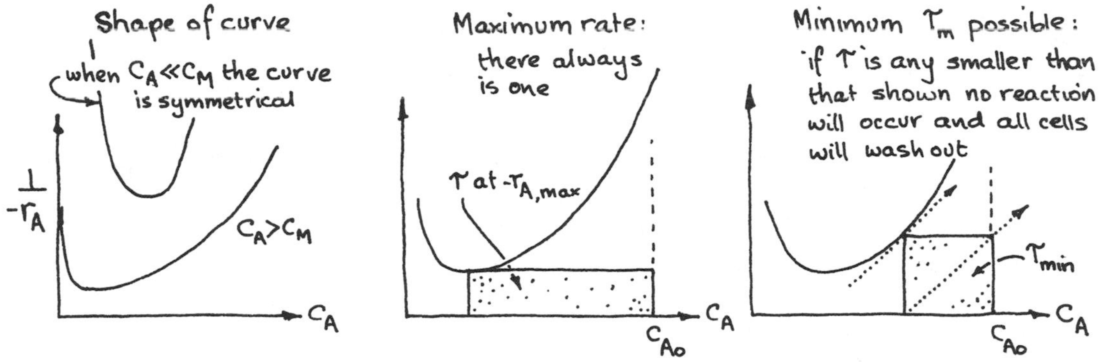

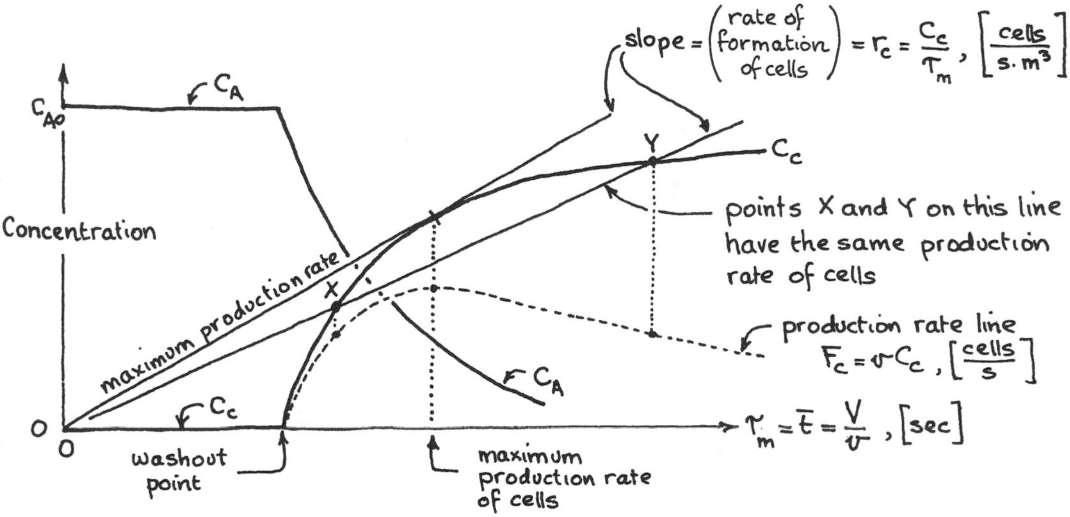

The performance equation shows that everything — washout, optimum cell concentration, maximum production rate — depends on C_M and C_{AO} (there is no other parameter in this equation), so let us develop in more detail the properties of this equation

$$C_{c,optimum} = \frac{\textcircled{C/A}\, C_{AO}\, N}{N+1}$$

$$\frac{C_{c,optimum}}{C_{c,max.possible}} = \frac{N}{N+1} \Bigg\} \text{ where } N = \sqrt{1 + \frac{C_{AO}}{C_M}}$$

$$F_{c,max} = (\upsilon C_c)_{opt} = k V \textcircled{C/A}\, C_{AO} \left(\frac{N-1}{N+1}\right), \left[\frac{cells}{s}\right]$$

$C_{c,max\ possible}$

$C_{c,optimum}$

C_c

Highest production rate of cells: $r_{c,opt} = \left(C_c/\tau\right)_{opt}$

Maximum consumption rate of A
$$X_{A,opt} = \frac{N}{N+1}$$
$$\frac{C_{A,opt}}{C_{AO}} = \frac{1}{N+1}$$

C_A

$k\,\tau_m$

if $C_{AO} = \infty$ then washout occurs here

$$\frac{C_{AO} + C_M}{C_{AO}} = \frac{N^2}{N^2 - 1}$$

Washout occurs here.

$$\frac{C_{AO} + C_M}{C_{AO}} \cdot \left(\frac{N+1}{N}\right) = \frac{N}{N-1}$$

Maximum production rate of cells (maximum rate of everything) occurs here.

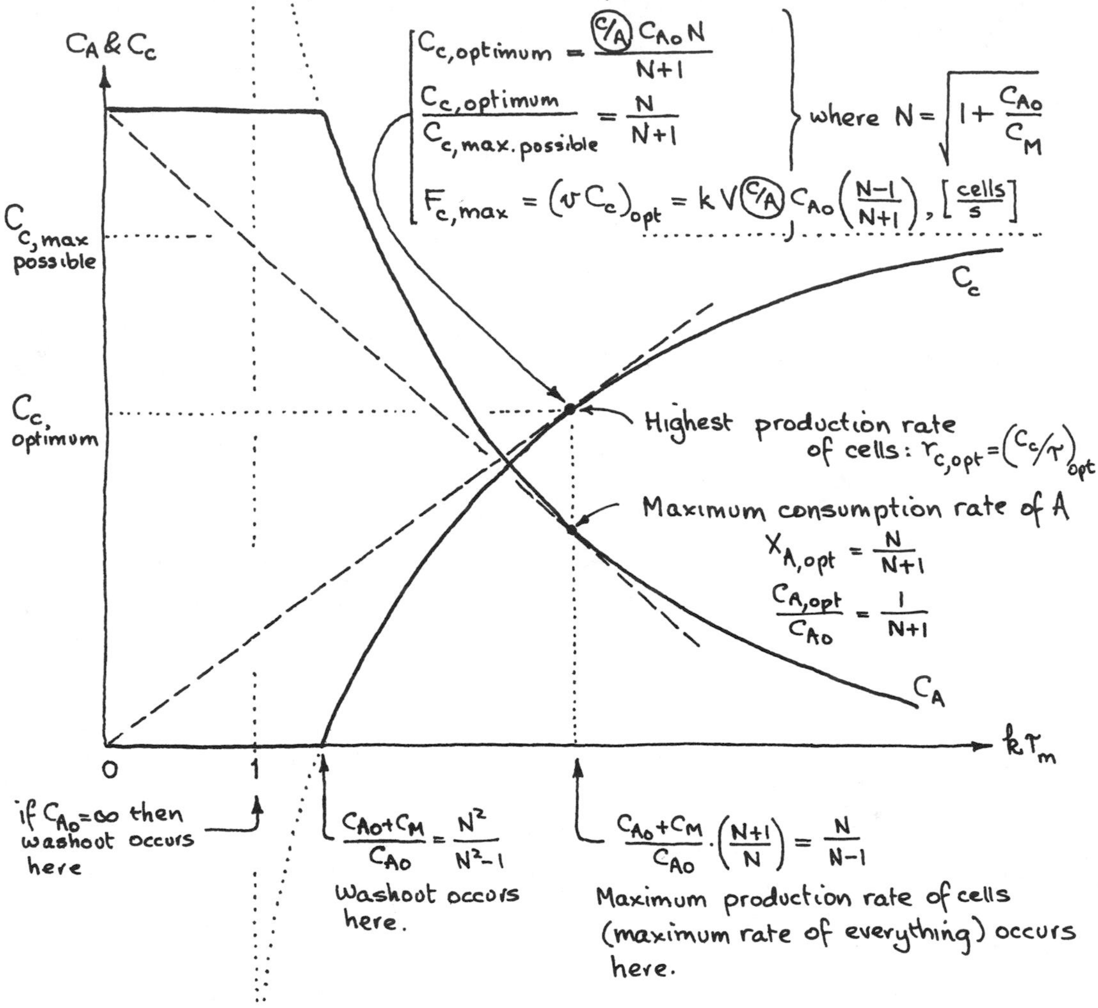

Note: Optimum operations in a mixed flow reactor occurs where

$$\frac{C_A}{C_{AO}} = \frac{1}{N+1}, \quad \frac{C_c}{C_{c,max\ possible}} = \frac{N}{N+1}, \quad k\,\tau_{m,optimum} = \frac{N}{N-1} \quad \dots \text{where } N = \sqrt{1 + \frac{C_{AO}}{C_M}}$$

C. Mixed flow fermentor, $C_{C0} \neq 0$.

Assume Monod kinetics, no product poisoning, constant φ, but with cells entering in the feed. Then the mixed flow equation gives

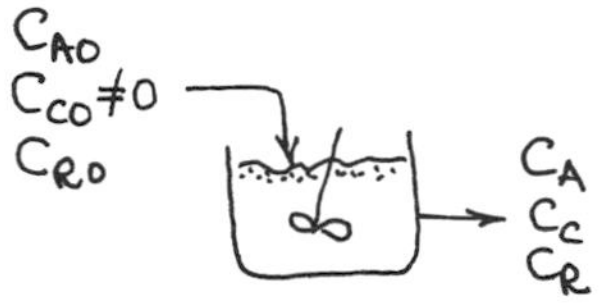

$$k\tau_m = \frac{(C_{A0}-C_A)(C_A+C_M)}{\left(\frac{A}{C}\right)C_{C0}C_A + C_A(C_{A0}-C_A)} = \frac{(C_C-C_{C0})\left[\left(\frac{C}{A}\right)(C_{A0}+C_M)-(C_C-C_{C0})\right]}{\left(\frac{C}{A}\right)C_{A0}C_C - C_C(C_C-C_{C0})} \quad \cdots (9)$$

Since $C_{C0} \neq 0$ there is no washout, no restriction on τ_m, and there are always cells within the reactor

The highest production rate occurs where $r_C = \dfrac{C_C - C_{C0}}{\tau_m} = \text{maximum}$, or when

$$k\tau_{m,opt} = \frac{N}{N-1}\left[\frac{C_{A0}-(N-1)C_M}{C_{A0}+\left(\frac{A}{C}\right)C_{C0}-(N-1)C_M}\right] \quad \cdots \text{where } N = \sqrt{1+\frac{C_{A0}+\left(\frac{A}{C}\right)C_{C0}}{C_M}} \quad \cdots (10)$$

If we define C'_{A0} as that fictitious concentration of entering A at which no cells would have existed then

$$C'_{A0} = C_{A0} + \left(\frac{A}{C}\right) C_{C0}$$

and we can graphically represent eq 10 by the following sketch

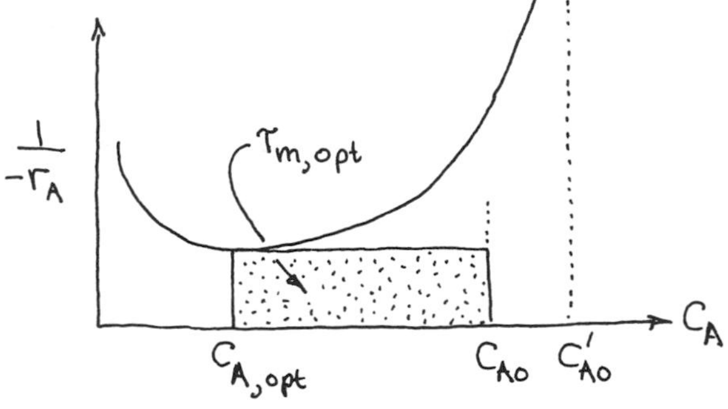

$C_{A,opt}$ is found by combining eqs 9 and 10

D. Optimum operations of fermentors.

With poison-free Monod kinetics and a given feed we have a U shaped $1/r$ vs C curve. Here

- to reach any point between A and B run part of the feed at A in mixed flow and mix with the rest.
- to reach any point between O and A go directly to A in mixed flow and then use plug flow beyond A.

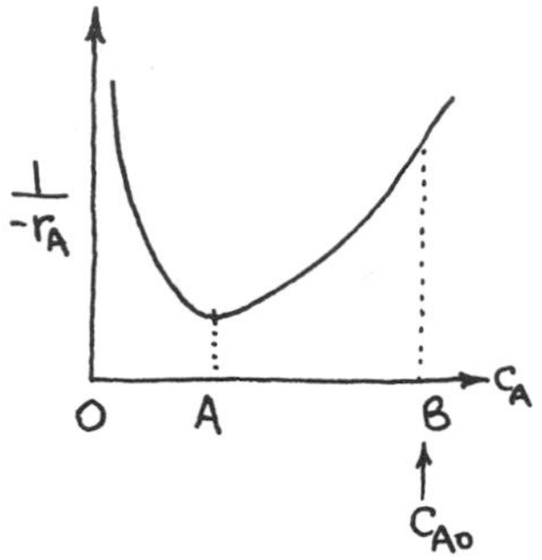

Let us illustrate this important principle by showing how to best operate various combinations of reactors. For this suppose

$$k = 2, \quad \frac{C_{A0}}{C_M} = 3 \quad \text{and} \quad V_m = 1 \quad \text{for each reactor}$$

Then from the figure on pg 83·8 we find for mixed flow that

$$N = 2, \quad \tau_{m,opt} = 1, \quad v_{opt} = 1, \quad \tau_{m,washout} = \frac{2}{3}, \quad v_{washout} = 1.5$$

(a) Single mixed flow fermentor

High feed rate ($v = 3$)

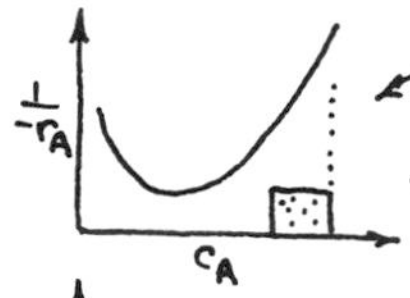

← won't work

… poor scheme; since $\tau = \frac{1}{3}$ which is less than $\frac{2}{3}$ we get washout.

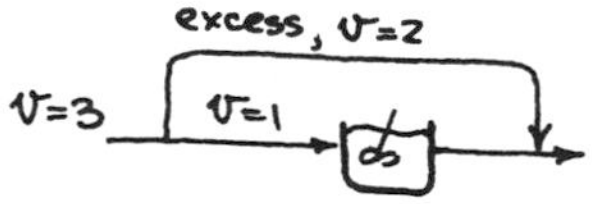

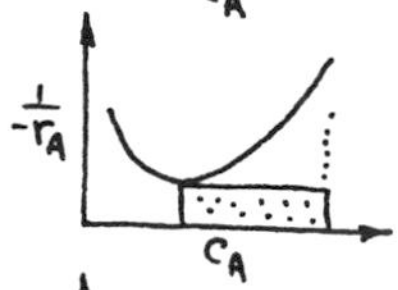

… best scheme uses bypass of excess feed.

Optimum feed rate ($v = 1$)

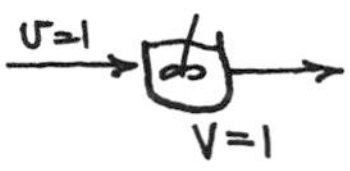

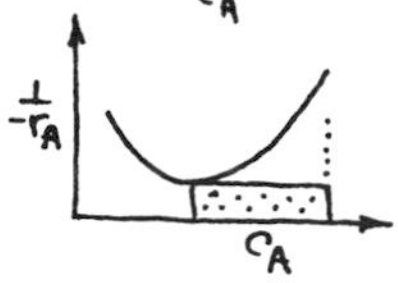

… highest rate of reaction. Just perfect.

Low feed rate ($v = \frac{1}{3}$)

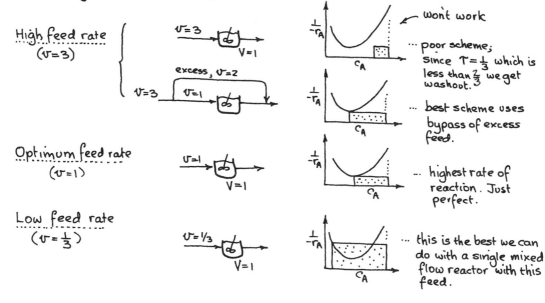

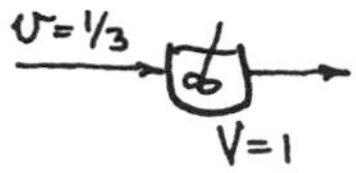

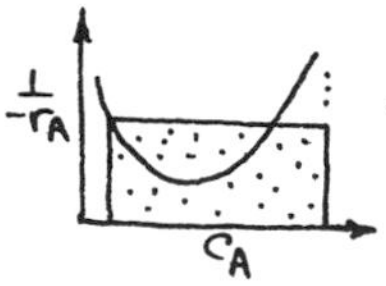

… this is the best we can do with a single mixed flow reactor with this feed.

(b) Two mixed flow fermentors

Very high feed rate
($v > 2$, say 3)

excess, $v=1$

$v=1$

$v=1$

...or...

excess $v=1$

$v=1$ $v=1$

$V=1$ $V=1$

... equally good schemes

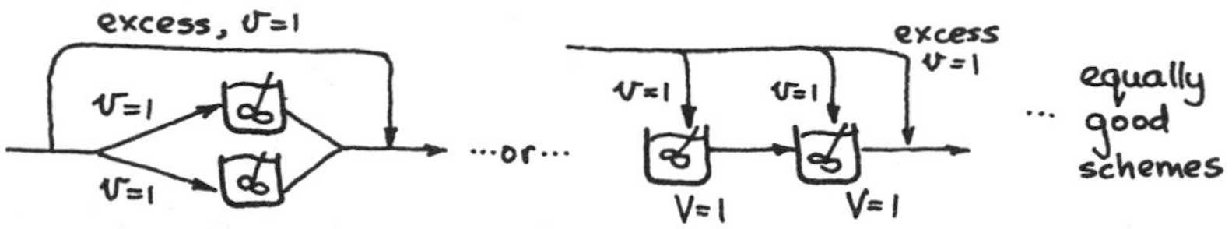

Optimum feed rate
($v=2$)

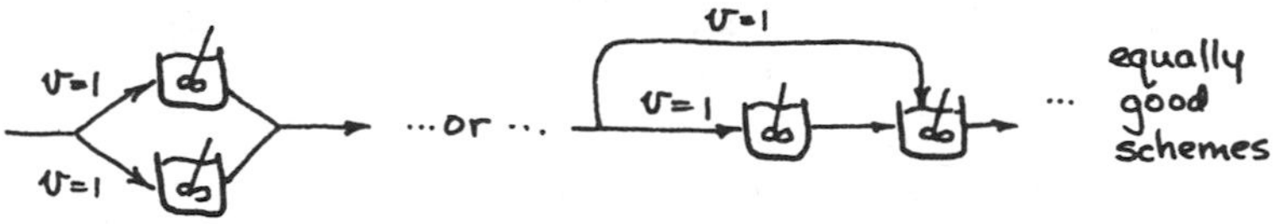

$v=1$

$v=1$

...or...

$v=1$

$v=1$ $v=1$

equally good schemes

Intermediate feed rate
($v = 1$ to 2, say 1.5)

$v=\frac{1}{2}$

$v=1$

keep at optimum

$\frac{1}{-r_A}$ $\frac{2}{3}$ $\tau=1$ c_A

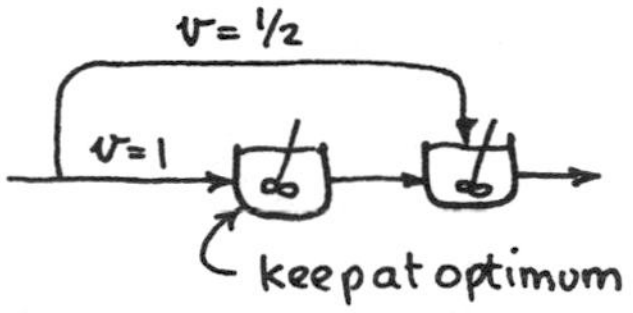

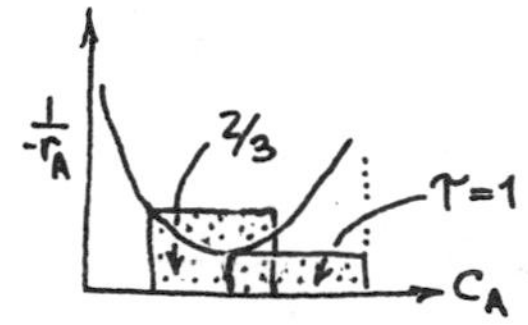

Low feed rate
($v < 1$, say $\frac{1}{2}$)

$v=\frac{1}{2}$

$V=1$ $V=1$

$\frac{1}{-r_A}$ $\tau=2$ $\tau=2$ c_A

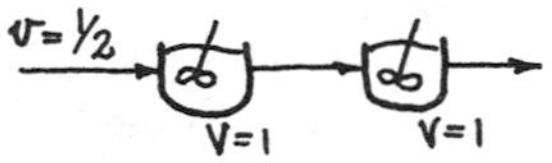

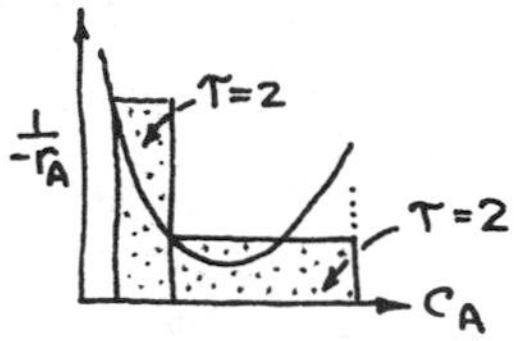

(c) N mixed flow fermentors, say $N=5$

High feed rate
($v > 5$, say 7)

$v=1$

excess, $v=2$

excess $v=2$

equally good schemes. Keep each vessel at the optimum, $\tau=1$, and bypass the rest of the fluid

Intermediate feed rate
($v = 1$ to 5, say 2.6)

excess, $v=0.6$

beyond the optimum

excess, $v=0.6$

beyond the optimum

$\frac{1}{-r_A}$ $\tau_3 = \tau_4 = \tau_5 = 1/2.6$ $\tau_1 = \tau_2 = 1$ c_A

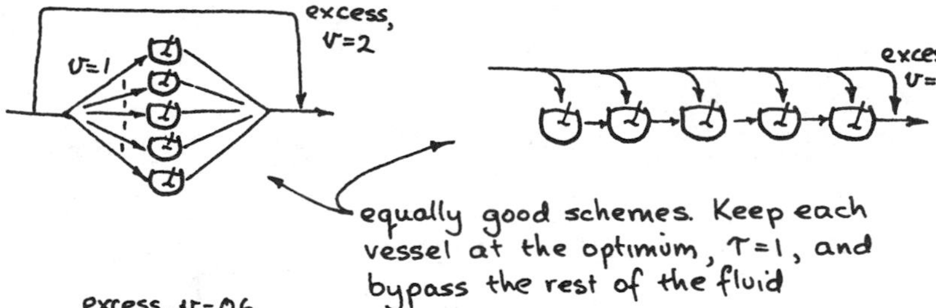

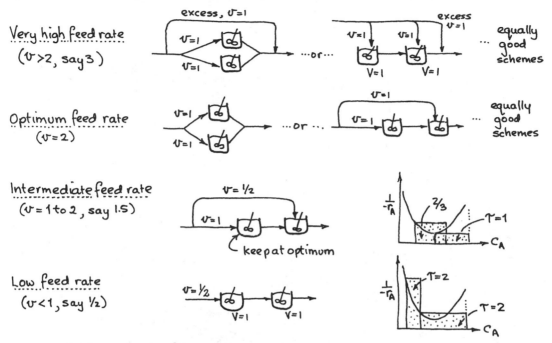

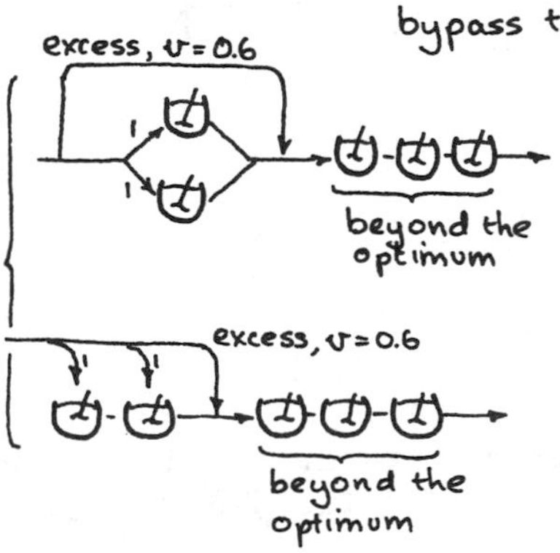

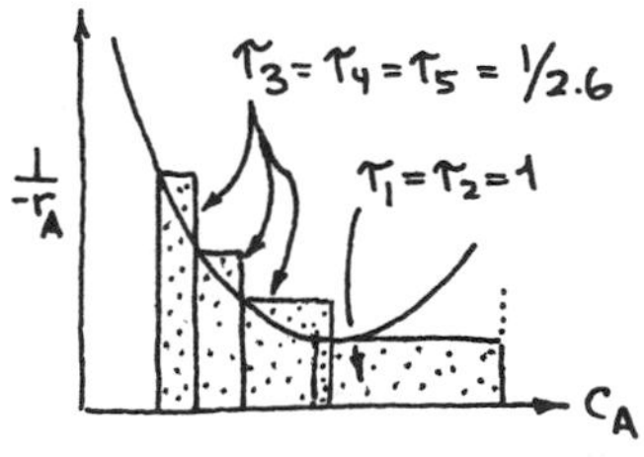

Very low feed rate
($v < 1$, say ½)

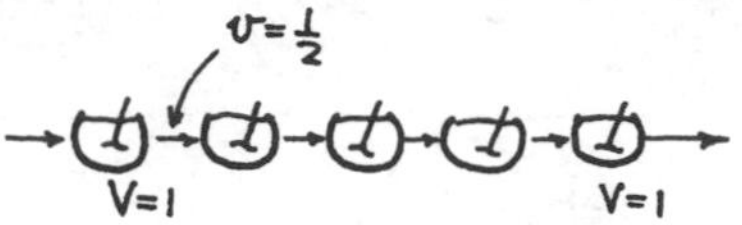

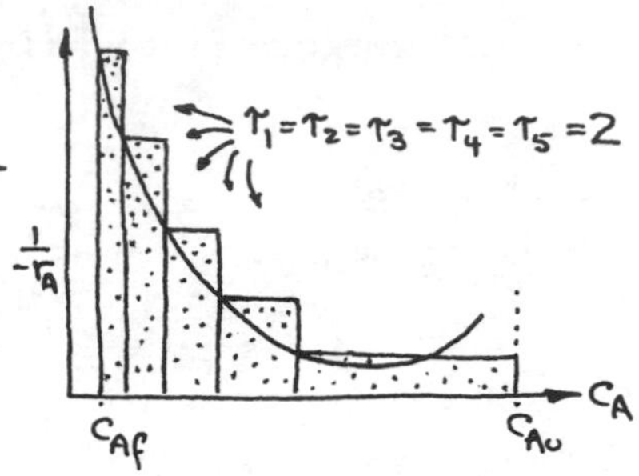

(d) Plug flow fermentors.

at high conversion
(or low feed rate)

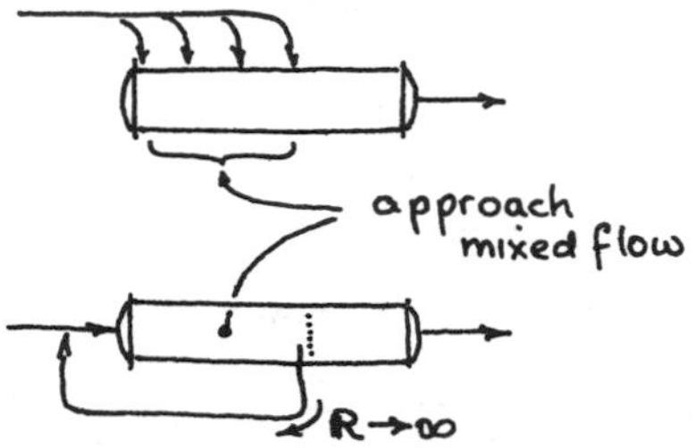

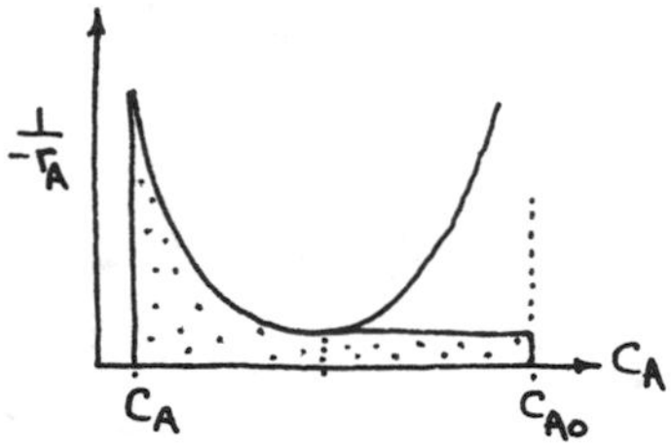

at low conversion
(or high feed rate)

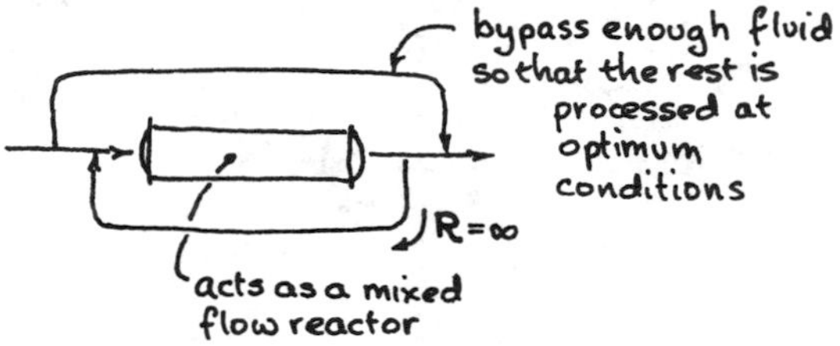

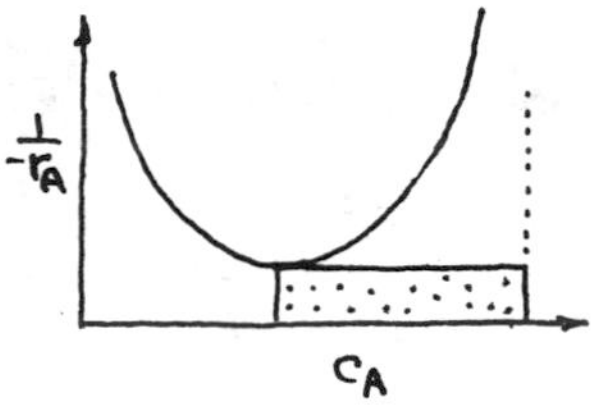

(e) Mixed flow and plug flow combination

High feed rate.

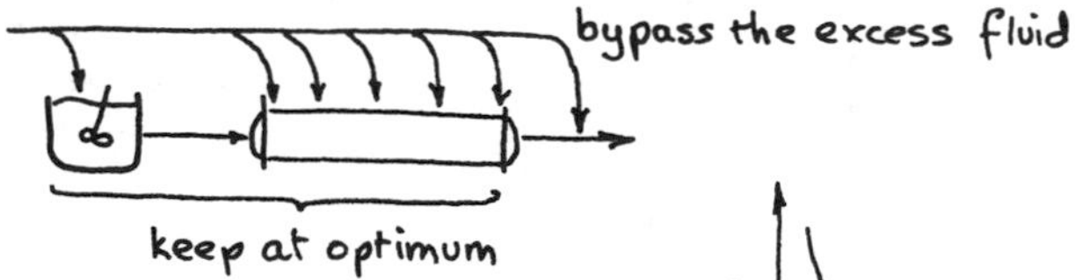

Low feed rate

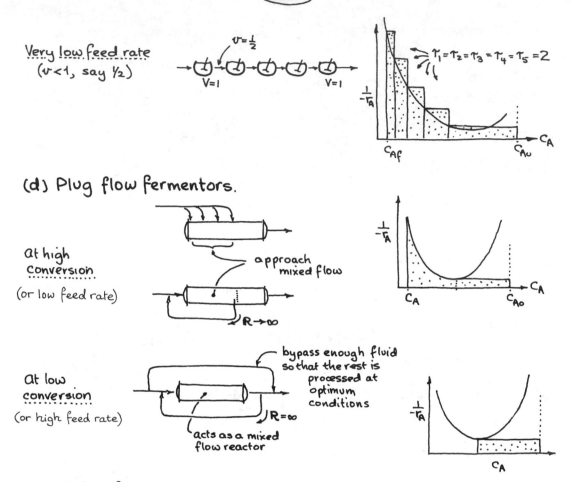

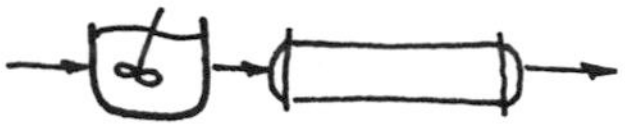

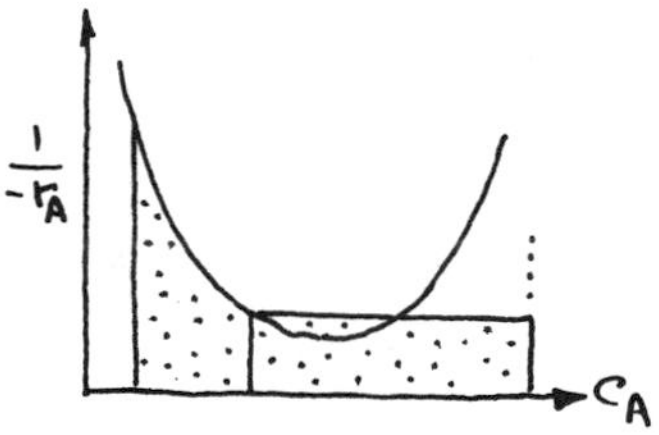

(f) General rule. Always put the biggest mixed flow reactor first, then follow with smaller ones. Put the plug flow unit at the tail end.

E. Operations using concentration and recycle of cells.

In some cases the exit stream from a fermentor can conveniently be treated (by centrifuge, by filter, by sedimentation) so that the cells are concentrated in one stream which is then returned to the fermentor. This can give improved performance — higher treatment rate, smaller vessel size, higher conversion.

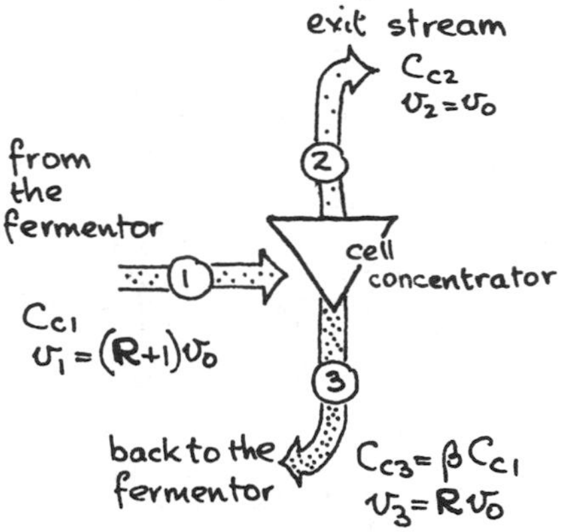

Define the **concentration factor**: $\beta = \frac{C_{C3}}{C_{C1}} > 1$; and let the **recycle ratio**: $R = \frac{v_3}{v_2}$, and as a reasonable approximation assume that C_A and C_R are the same in all streams entering and leaving the cell concentrator. Then a material balance about the concentrator gives

$$\frac{C_{C3}}{C_{C1}} = \beta; \qquad \frac{C_{C2}}{C_{C1}} = 1-(\beta-1)R; \qquad \frac{C_{C3}}{C_{C2}} = \frac{\beta}{1-(\beta-1)R}$$

and the fraction of cells recycled is

$$\frac{C_{C3}v_3}{C_{C1}v_1} = \frac{\beta R}{R+1}$$

We are now ready to develop the performance expressions for such systems.

1. Mixed flow fermentor with cell concentration and recycle, $C_{C0}=0$.

a sketch of the system gives ---→

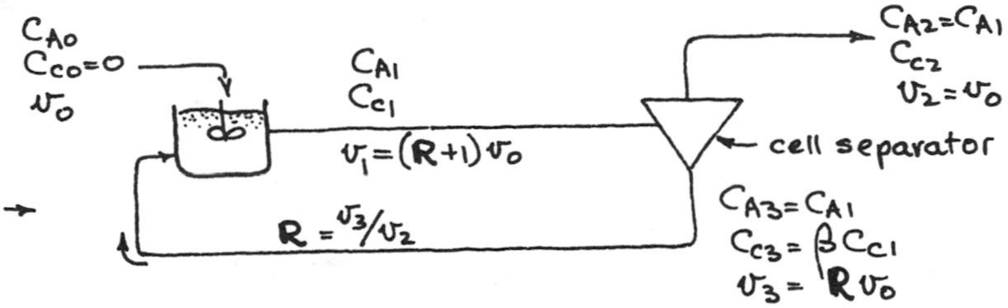

For poison-free Monod kinetics, no time lag and $C_{C0}=0$ the performance equation for the reactor-concentrator set up as a whole gives

$$\tau = \frac{C_{C2}-\cancel{C_{C0}}^{\,0}}{r_{C1}} = \frac{C_{C2}}{kC_{A1}C_{C1}/(C_{A1}+C_M)} \qquad C_{C2} = C_{C1}[1-(\beta-1)R]$$

or

$$\tau\left(\frac{1}{1-(\beta-1)R}\right) = \frac{C_{A1}+C_M}{kC_{A1}}$$

... comparing with eq. 7 for straight mixed flow we see that there is one correction factor here $\left(\frac{1}{1-(\beta-1)R}\right)$, and this >1

Thus a comparison gives

$$\left(\frac{\tau_{\text{with cell concentration}}}{\tau_{\text{without cell concentration}}}\right)_{\text{at washout}} = \left(\frac{\tau_{\text{with}}}{\tau_{\text{without}}}\right)_{\text{at optimum}} = \frac{v_{\text{without}}}{v_{\text{with}}} = \frac{F_{\text{without}}}{F_{\text{with}}} = \underbrace{1-(\beta-1)R}_{\text{always}<1} = \frac{k}{k_{\text{eff}}}$$

(k_{eff} ... with cell concentration)

Cell concentration gives improved performance in that smaller τ is needed. All depends on the factor $1-(\beta-1)\mathbf{R}$. For optimum operations make β and $\mathbf{R}$ as large as possible.

A simple way to treat such systems is to replace k by k_{eff} and then consider the system as an ordinary mixed flow reactor.

2. Plug flow fermentor with cell concentration and recycle, $C_{C0}=0$

Here it is best to operate the reactor at its highest rate (approach mixed flow by making $R_1 \to \infty$) and adjust the performance level by changing the cell concentration factor β and overall recycle $\mathbf{R}_2$.

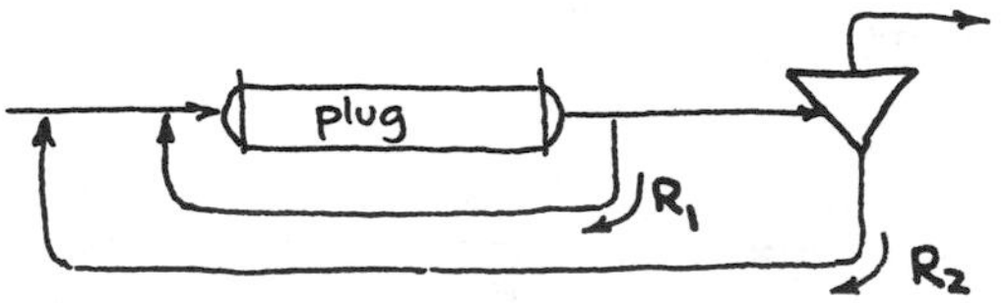

... operate as a mixed flow reactor.

There is no need to consider operations such as

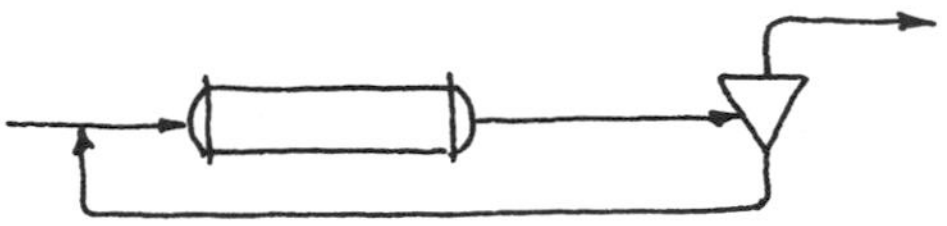

F. Comments

(a) In microbiology they use the terms

- **substrate** for the feed
- **dilution rate** for $1/\tau$. In chemical engineering we call this the space velocity. Here we use neither term. We use **space time** τ.
- **chemostat**, **turbidostat** for mixed flow reactor.

We should be aware of the difference in language.

(b) In the literature on continuous fermentation much effort is spent calculating what happens in this or that set up. Most of the schemes are nowhere near optimum so we do not consider them.

(c) When the φ values are constant throughout, at high and low conversions, then we have just one independent variable as composition changes with time or position. Thus we can use any one concentration, C_A, C_R or C_C in the performance expression. We can compare performance of various reactor types, plug flow, mixed flow, etc. with no difficulty. This is what we have done here.

In general, however $\varphi = f(C_A, C_R, C_C)$. And when φ varies with composition then things get more difficult and we cannot directly compare reactor types.

(d) In 1939, as part of his thesis, Jacques Monod proposed the equation which we use here. The thesis was published as a book (see book list), and was later condensed and translated into English in the Annual Rev. Microbiol. 3 371 (1949).

Chapter 83 Problems

In his thesis which was published as a book Monod first proposed the celebrated equation which bears his name. As experimental support for this equation form he presented results from four batch reactor runs on the growth of a pure bacterial culture in a lactose solution, Monod, pg 74. Here are the reported data for two of his runs.

	For Run 1			For Run 2		
Time Interval Number	Δt, hr	$\bar{C}_A$	C_C	Δt, hr	$\bar{C}_A$	C_C
1	0.54	137	15.5 to 23.0	0.52	158	15.8 to 22.8
2	0.36	114	23.0 to 30.0	0.38	124	22.8 to 29.2
3	0.33	90	30.0 to 38.8	0.32	114	29.2 to 37.8
4	0.35	43	38.8 to 48.5	0.37	94	37.8 to 48.5
5	0.37	29	48.5 to 58.3	0.36	25	48.5 to 59.6
6	0.38	9	58.3 to 61.3	0.37	19	59.6 to 66.5
7	0.37	2	61.3 to 62.5	0.38	2	66.5 to 67.8

Fit the Monod equation to the data of

A1 . . . run 1

A2 . . . run 2.

Note: It would be interesting to compare the fit obtained by the different methods of this chapter as well as that used by Monod. You will notice enormous differences between the results of all these methods.

A3 A culture of *E. coli* was grown on lactose in a mixed flow reactor (V = 1 lit) using various flow rates of a C_{A0} = 160 mg lactose/lit feed. The following results were obtained

v, lit/hr	C_A, mg/lit	Cell Concentration, arbitrary
0.2	4	15.6
0.4	10	15
0.8	40	12
1.0	100	6

Find a rate equation to represent this growth.

Chapter 83 Problems

E. coli lives and grows on mannitol with the following kinetics

$$r_C = \frac{1.2\, C_A C_C}{C_A + 2}, \quad C_A = \text{gm mannitol/m}^3, \quad (C/A) = 0.1 \text{ gm cells/gm mannitol}$$

Find the outlet concentration of cells from the reactor when 1 m^3/hr of mannitol solution (C_{A0} = 6 gm/m^3) is fed directly to a mixed flow reactor of volume

B4 . . . V = 5 m^3

B5 . . . V = 1 m^3.

Can you do better and produce more cells (if so find C_C) by proper bypass or recycle of fluid from the reactor for the system of

C6 . . . of problem 4.

C7 . . . of problem 5.

C8 How curious--two different flow rates of a C_{A0} = 500 mol/m^3 feed to our 1 m^3 mixed flow reactor produces the same 100 gm/hr of yeast cells in the exit stream, namely

- at 0.5 m^3/hr of feed for which we find C_A = 100 mol/m^3
- at 1 m^3/hr of feed for which we find C_A = 300 mol/m^3

Substrate limiting Monod kinetics should well represent yeast formation. From this information find

(a) the fractional yield of yeast,

(b) the kinetic equation for yeast formation,

(c) the flow rate for maximum yeast production,

(d) the maximum production rate of yeast.

C9 The *E. coli* microbe grows contentedly on glucose according to Monod kinetics as follows

$$r_C = \frac{1.333\, C_A C_C}{C_A + 4} \; \frac{\text{gm cells}}{\text{m}^3\cdot\text{hr}} \quad \text{with} \quad \begin{cases} (C/A) = 0.1 \\ C_A = [\frac{\text{gm glucocse}}{\text{m}^3}] \end{cases}$$

Chapter 83 Problems

What feed rate of glucose solution (C_{A0} = 60 gm/m^3) to a mixed flow reactor (V = 1 m^3) would give the maximum consumption rate of glucose, hence maximum production rate of cells? Find this production rate.

A stream of reactant A ($C_{A0} = 3$, $C_{R0} = 0$, $C_{C0} = 0$), is to be decomposed by the following microbial fermentation

$$A \rightarrow R + C, \quad r_C = \frac{kC_AC_C}{C_A + C_M} \quad \text{with} \quad \begin{cases} k = 2 \\ C_M = 1 \\ (C/A) = 0.5 \end{cases}$$

In the following problems sketch your recommended reactor set-up with recycle, bypass, etc., and on it indicate pertinent quantities.

What is the lowest C_A which can be obtained in a single mixed flow reactor of size V = 1 for a feed rate of

D10 . . . v = 1

D11 . . . v = 1/3

D12 . . . v = 3

What is the lowest C_A which can be obtained with 2 properly connected mixed flow reactors, each of volume V = 1, for a feed rate

D13 . . . v = 2

D14 . . . v = 1

What is the lowest C_A which can be obtained with 3 wisely connected mixed flow reactors, each of volume V = 1, for a feed rate

D15 . . . v = 6

D16 . . . v = 2

For a feed rate v = 3 what is the smallest size of plug flow reactor with appropriate piping (bypass or recycle or side taps on the reactor) which will give

E17 . . . $C_C = 0.5$, side tap allowed

E18 . . . $C_C = 1.25$, side tap not allowed

E19 . . . $C_C = 1.44$, side tap allowed

Chapter 83 Problems

Find the lowest C_A obtainable from a plug flow reactor of volume V = 4 (bypass, recycle and/or side taps are all allowed) for a feed rate

E20 . . . v = 6

E21 . . . v = 3

What combination of plug and mixed flow reactors gives the minimum total volume for treating v = 3 of feed to a final concentration of

F22 . . . $C_C = 0.5$

F23 . . . $C_A = 0.12$

For the system of the above problems we now add a centrifugal cell separator. This gives one leaving stream having half the flow rate and four times the cell concentration of the other leaving stream. With this addition what do we find for C_A and C_C for the situation of

G24 . . . problem 10.

G25 . . . problem 12.

G26 . . . problem 15.

Chapter 84. MICROBIAL FERMENTATION. PRODUCT POISONING SYSTEMS.

With sufficient food and harmonious environment cells multiply freely. However, no matter how much food is available there always comes a point where either cells crowd each other out, or their waste products inhibit their growth. We call this **product poisoning**. Hence Monod kinetics always is a special case of a more general rate form which includes product poisoning. A simple equation of the general rate form is

$$r_C = \left(C/R\right) r_R = k \left(1 - \frac{C_R}{C_R^*}\right)^n \frac{C_A C_C}{C_A + C_M} \quad \cdots (1)$$

(n: order of product poisoning; k: rate constant in the a poison free environment; $k\left(1 - \frac{C_R}{C_R^*}\right)^n = k_{obs}$ decreases as product builds up.)

In the special case of sufficient food, or $C_A \gg C_M$, and $n=1$, the above equation reduces to the simplest expression for **product poison control**

$$\boxed{r_C = \left(C/R\right) r_R = k \left(1 - \frac{C_R}{C_R^*}\right) C_C} \quad \cdots (2)$$

(reaction stops when C_R reaches C_R^*)

We start with the rate form of eq 2, then we extend the treatment to systems where $n \neq 1$, or eq 1. Let us also develop everything in terms of C_R, in which case eq 2 becomes

$$r_R = \left(R/C\right) r_C = \left(R/C\right) k \left(1 - \frac{C_R}{C_R^*}\right) C_C = k \left(1 - \frac{C_R}{C_R^*}\right)\left(C_R - C_{R0} + \left(R/C\right) C_{C0}\right) \quad \cdots (3)$$

The maximum rate then occurs where $\frac{dr_R}{dC_R} = 0$. Solving gives

$$C_{R,\,\text{max rate}} = \frac{1}{2}\left(C_{R0} + C_R^* - \left(R/C\right) C_{C0}\right) \quad \cdots (4)$$

Displayed graphically, eq 2 and 3 give

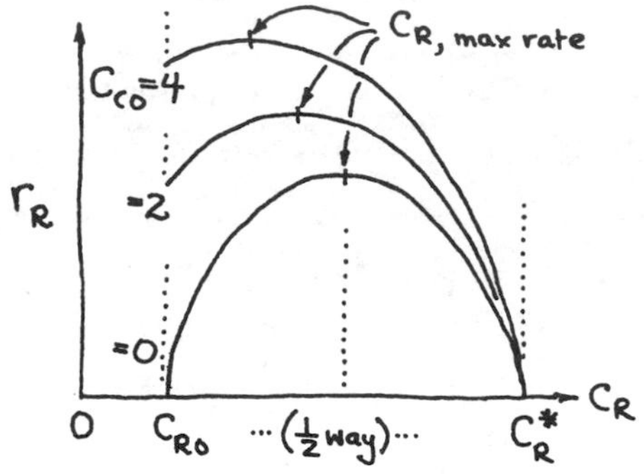

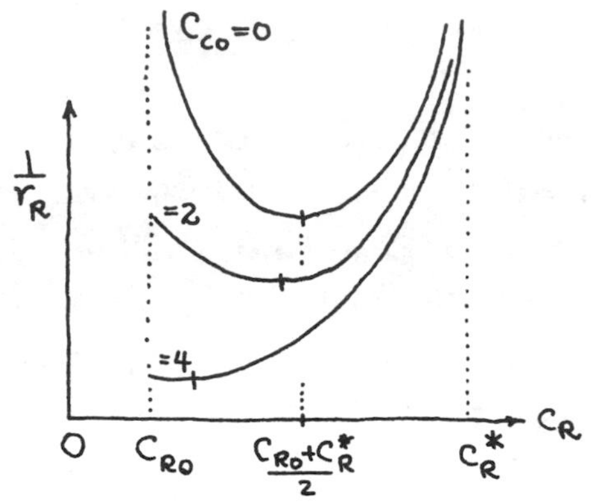

A. Batch or plug flow fermentor for n=1 poison limiting kinetics.

To find the time needed to reach a given C_R we integrate the performance equation

$$\tau_p = t_b = \int_{C_{Ro}}^{C_R} \frac{dC_R}{r_R}$$

where $r_R = k\left(1-\frac{C_R}{C_R^*}\right)\left(C_R - C_{Ro} + (R/C)\,C_{co}\right)$

or

$$k\tau_p = k t_b = \frac{C_R^*}{C_R^* - C_{Ro} + (R/C)\,C_{co}} \ln \frac{C_c\,(C_R^* - C_{Ro})}{C_{co}\,(C_R^* - C_R)} \qquad \cdots (5)$$

where $C_c = C_{co} + (C/R)(C_R - C_{Ro})$

Graphically

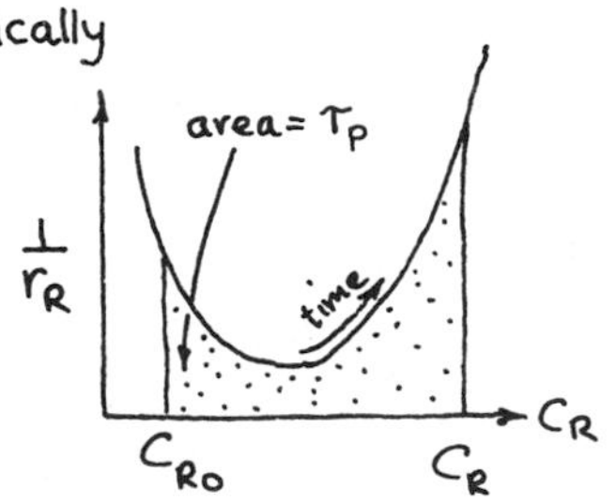

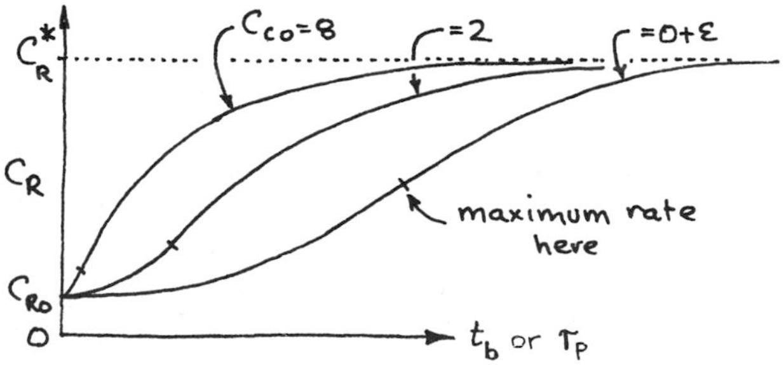

Comments and Extensions

(a) Shape of conversion-time curve. At the start of a run low C_C is responsible for the low rate; at the end of a run the approach to C_R^* slows the rate. Consequently we observe autocatalytic type behavior, superficially somewhat like poison free Monod kinetics (see sketch on previous page).

(b) For $C_{C0}=0$ no cells enter the reactor hence there is no reaction.

(c) For $C_{C0}=0+\varepsilon$ the maximum rate occurs at $\frac{C_R^*+C_{R0}}{2}$, or half way to the maximum cell concentration.

(d) For plug flow with recycle and $C_{C0}\neq 0$ the performance equation is

$$\tau=(R+1)\int_{\frac{C_{R0}+RC_{Rf}}{R+1}}^{C_{Rf}}\frac{dC_R}{r_R} \qquad r_R = k\left(1-\frac{C_R}{C_R^*}\right)\left(C_R-C_{R0}+(R/C)\,C_{C0}\right)$$

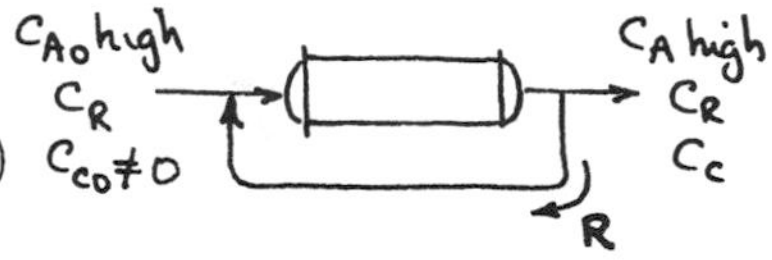

Integration gives

$$k\tau=\frac{(R+1)\,C_R^*}{C_R^*-C_{R0}+(R/C)\,C_{C0}}\ln\left[\frac{C_C}{RC_C+C_{C0}}\left(R+\frac{C_R^*-C_{R0}}{C_R^*-C_R}\right)\right] \qquad \cdots (6)$$

where $C_C = C_{C0}+(C/R)\,(C_R-C_{R0})$

(e) For plug flow with recycle and $C_{R0}=C_{C0}=0$ eq 6 reduces to

$$k\tau=(R+1)\ln\left[1+\frac{1}{R\left(1-C_R/C_R^*\right)}\right] \qquad \cdots (7)$$

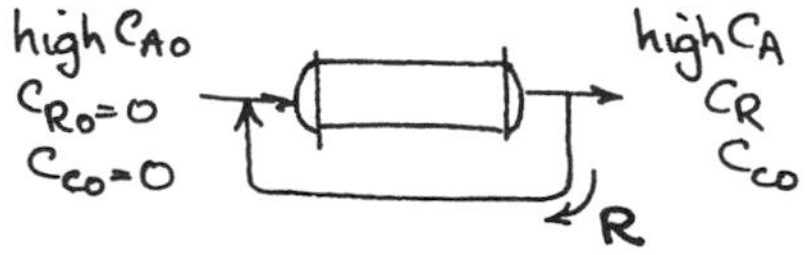

We find the optimum recycle ratio by taking $(\partial\tau/\partial R)_{C_R}=0$, thus the following condition which must be evaluated numerically.

$$\ln\left[1+\frac{1}{R\left(1-C_R/C_R^*\right)}\right]=\frac{R+1}{R}\left[\frac{1}{1+R\left(1-C_R/C_R^*\right)}\right] \qquad \cdots (8)$$

The sketch below shows the features of this equation

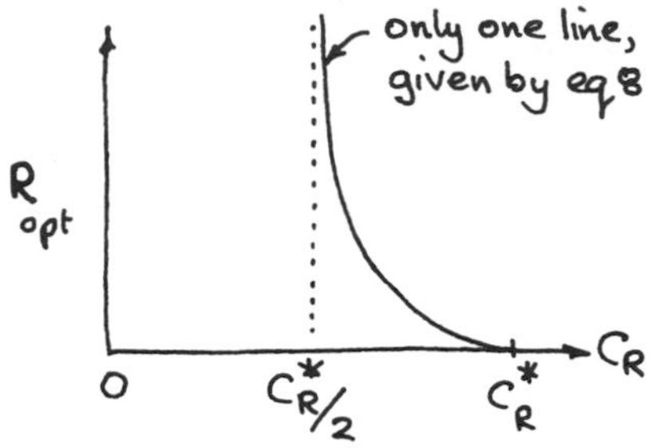

- For low C_R, up to $C_R^*/2$ the optimum recycle ratio is ∞.
- Beyond $C_R^*/2$ the optimum recycle ratio falls progressively
- At high C_R, approaching C_R^*, the optimum recycle ratio → 0.

(f) **The best way of operating a plug flow reactor.** We can do better than optimum recycle if we operate as much as possible at conditions of maximum rate. This requires proper feed introduction, recycle, bypass and so on. For example, the sketches below show optimum operations when C_{C0} and C_{R0} are both zero.

At high conversion
$\left(C_R/C_R^* > \frac{1}{2}\right)$

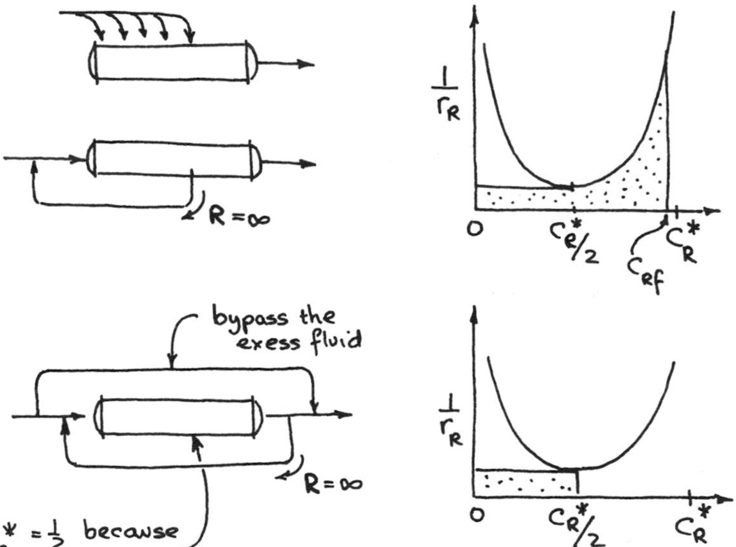

At low conversion
$\left(C_R/C_R^* < \frac{1}{2}\right)$

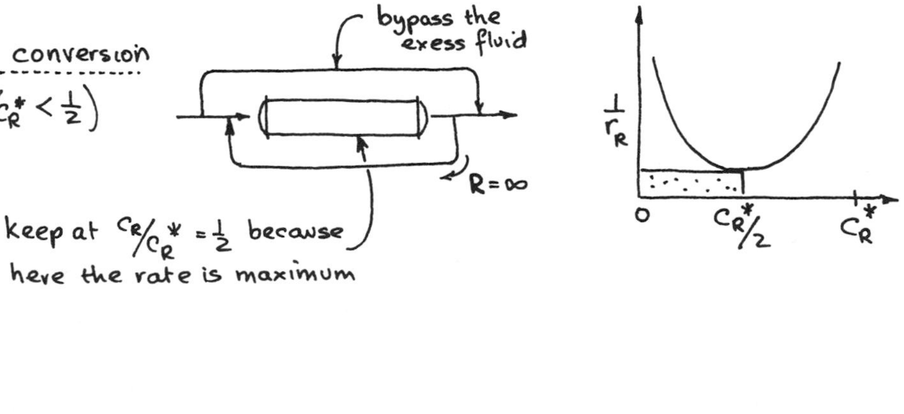

B. Mixed flow fermentor for n=1 poison limiting kinetics.

For the case of negligible time lag for feed cells which enter their new environment we have

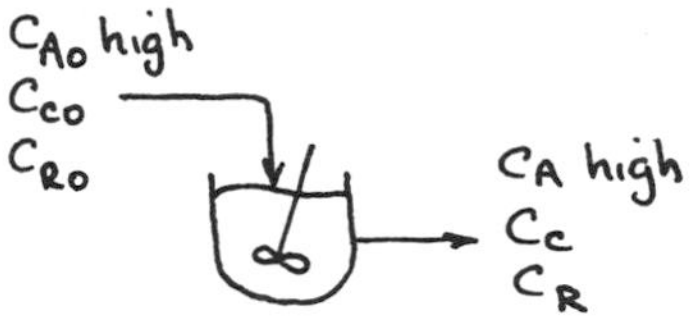

$$\tau_m = \frac{C_R - C_{Ro}}{r_R} = \frac{C_R - C_{Ro}}{k\left(1-\frac{C_R}{C_R^*}\right)\left(C_R - C_{Ro} + (R/C)\, C_{co}\right)} \quad \cdots (9)$$

For the special case where $C_{co}=0$ and $C_{Ro}=0$ the above general expression simplifies to

$$k\tau_m = \frac{C_R^*}{C_R^* - C_R} = \frac{1}{1 - C_R/C_R^*} \qquad \text{for } k\tau_m > 1 \quad \cdots (10)$$

where $(R/C)\, C_c = (R/A)(C_{Ao} - C_A)$, for $C_{co} = C_{Ro} = 0$

To evaluate the kinetic constants from mixed flow experiments rearrange eq 10 as follows and plot

$$C_R = C_R^* - \frac{C_R^*}{k} \cdot \frac{1}{\tau_m} \quad \cdots (10a)$$

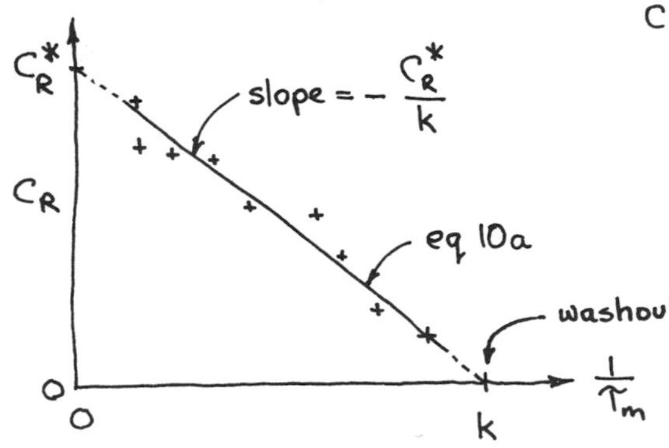

The properties of eq 10 are displayed below

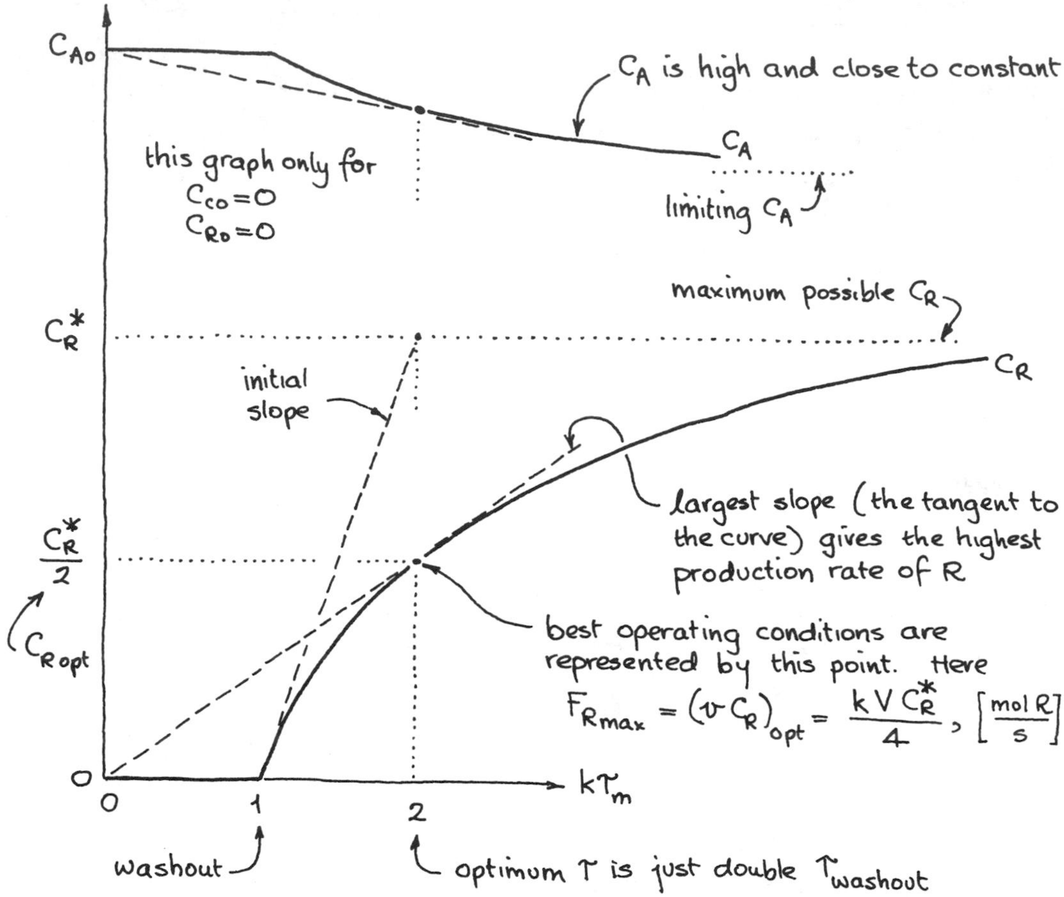

Comments and extensions

(a) For mixed flow with $C_{C0}=0$, $C_{R0}=0$ and any high C_{A0}.

- washout occurs at $k\tau_m=1$ for any feed concentration
- maximum production rate of cells and product R is obtained at
  $k\tau_m=2$ ··· and ··· $C_R = C_R^*/2$
- maximum production rate of cells and product is found to be
  $F_{R\,max} = (R/C)\,F_{C,max} = kVC_R^*/4$
- the C_C curve is similar in shape to the C_R curve and is proportional to it. Thus it rises from 0 to $(C/R)\,C_R^*$.

(b) With cell concentration the same sort of relationships are found as for systems which follow Monod kinetics. Thus for poison limiting kinetics

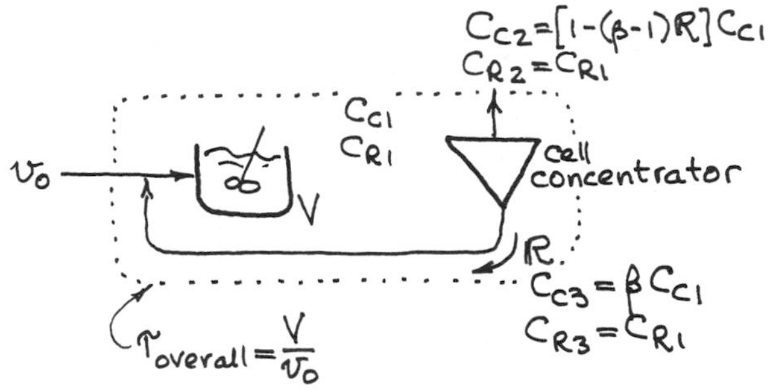

$$\frac{k_{eff}}{k} = \frac{k_{\text{with cell concentration}}}{k_{\text{without}}} = \frac{1}{1-(\beta-1)R} > 1 \qquad \cdots (11)$$

($\beta > 1$)

Just treat the system as a single mixed flow reactor, with k_{eff} and τ_{eff}, in place of k and $\tau_{overall}$.

(c) Optimum operations for multistage systems. follow the same pattern as for poison-free systems. The general rule is to use mixed flow to reach $C_R^*/2$ in one step. Proceed beyond this with plug flow

only if $C_{C0}=0$ and $C_{R0}=0$. In the general case $C_{R\,opt}$ is given by eq 4.

C. Fermentation with $n \neq 1$ poison limiting kinetics

For n^{th} order product poisoning kinetics we have

$$r_R = k\left(1-\frac{C_R}{C_R^*}\right)^n C_C \qquad \cdots (12)$$

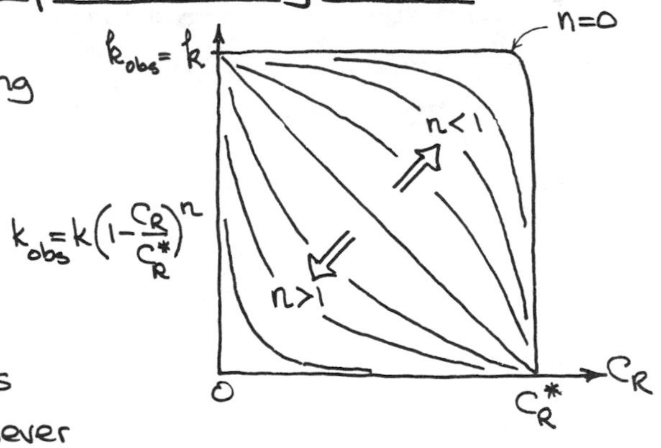

The performance equations for plug flow are messy, however for mixed flow the equations can be obtained directly. Thus in general, for $C_{C0}\neq 0$ and $C_{R0}\neq 0$ we have

$$k\tau_m = \frac{C_R - C_{R0}}{\left(C_R - C_{R0} + (R/C)\, C_{C0}\right)\left(1 - \frac{C_R}{C_R^*}\right)^n} \qquad \cdots (13)$$

and for the special case where $C_{C0} = 0$ and $C_{R0} = 0$

$$k\tau_m = \frac{1}{\left(1 - \frac{C_R}{C_R^*}\right)^n} \quad \cdots \text{when } k\tau_m > 1 \qquad \cdots (14)$$

The properties of this equation, washout, maximum production, etc., are displayed in the sketch below

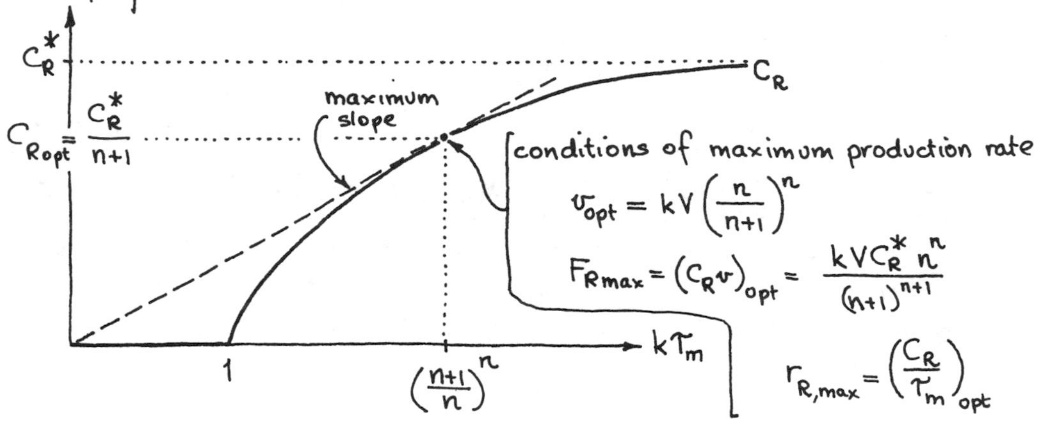

To find the kinetic constants C_R^*, k and n from experiment first evaluate C_R^* in a batch run using an excess of reactant A and $t \to \infty$. Then rearrange the mixed flow equation, eq 14, and plot as follows

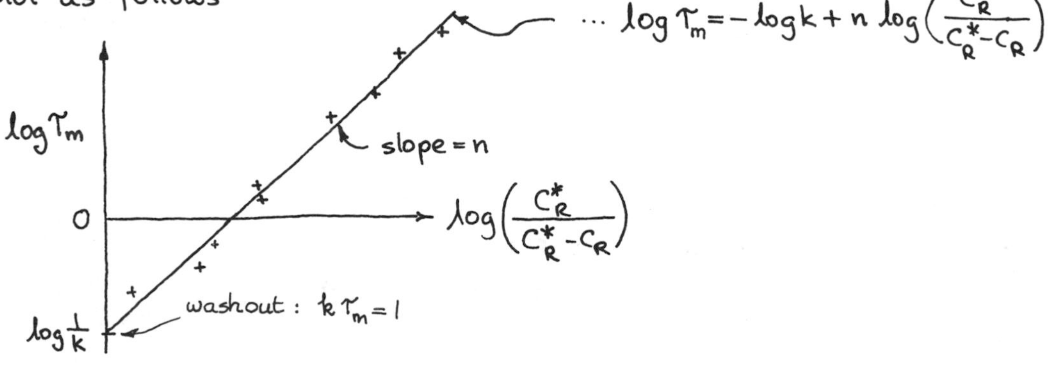

Optimum operations for any reactor system follows the same strategy as for other kinetics: go to the point of maximum rate in a mixed flow reactor, then approach plug flow as closely as possible.

Extension of these findings to the case where $C_{Ro} \neq 0$ and $C_{co} = 0$ is straightforward but leads to messier equations.

D. Discussion.

The similarity in shape of the mixed flow graphs for product limiting and substrate limiting (Monod) kinetics has led many investigators to fit product poisoning systems with the simple Monod equation. The fit will be good ... but don't try to use the fitted equation for different feed conditions. Your predictions are likely to be way off because the logic of the extension is wrong.

You must first find which of these two factors is rate limiting. This is easy to do so there is no excuse for using the wrong expression. In one case the final extent of reaction is dependent on C_{Ao} and not on C_{Ro}; in the other case just the opposite holds. The discussion and sketches of chapter 82 show this.

E. Situations where both substrate and product affect the kinetics.

Chapter 83 treated substrate limiting kinetics acting alone, while this chapter so far has only considered product poison limiting kinetics. But often a system is run under conditions where both factors influence the rate. For example, in making a dry wine we want to run out of sugar just as we reach the maximum alcohol concentration. In such situations we must use the generalized Monod equation, see chapter 82,

$$-r_A \; (C/A) = +r_R \; (C/R) = r_C = k\left(1-\frac{C_R}{C_R^*}\right)^n \frac{C_A C_C}{C_A + C_M}$$

The kinetic constants of this expression k, C_R^*, n, and C_M are best found in a mixed flow reactor. It would be impractical to try to unravel the interacting effects of these factors in a batch reactor.

Suppose we make a series of runs, each at different $C_{R\,out}$ in a mixed flow reactor using a cell-free feed. From the reactor composition we find all concentrations, rates and τ. Then on rearranging, the performance expression becomes

$$\frac{1}{\tau_m} = \frac{r_C}{C_C} = k_{obs}\left(\frac{C_A}{C_A+C_M}\right) \quad \cdots \text{with} \quad k_{obs} = k\left(1-\frac{C_R}{C_R^*}\right)^n \quad \cdots (15)$$

$\frac{r_C}{C_C}$: called the specific growth rate by the biochemist with symbol μ, [s^{-1}]

$k = \mu_0$: called the maximum specific growth rate. Occurs when $C_A \to \infty$, $C_R \to 0$

or in the language of the biochemist

$$\mu = \mu_0\left(1-\frac{C_R}{C_R^*}\right)^n\left(\frac{C_A}{C_A+C_M}\right)$$

But let us stay with our own more general language.

Inverting eq 15 gives

$$\tau_m = \frac{1}{k_{obs}} + \frac{C_M}{k_{obs}} \cdot \frac{1}{C_A}$$

which can then be plotted to find the rate constants. Thus

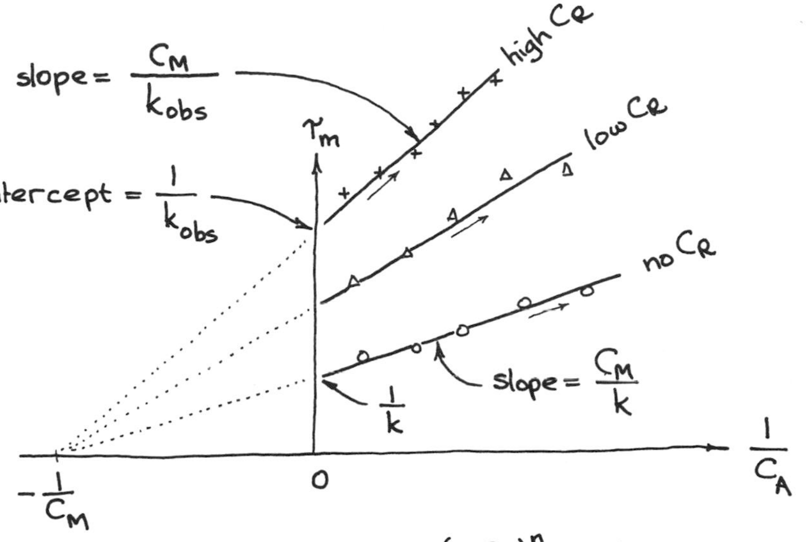

This graph gives C_M, k and $k_{obs} = \left(1-\frac{C_R}{C_R^*}\right)^n$. Then knowing C_R^* (this is usually easily found beforehand) we can find n from the following plot

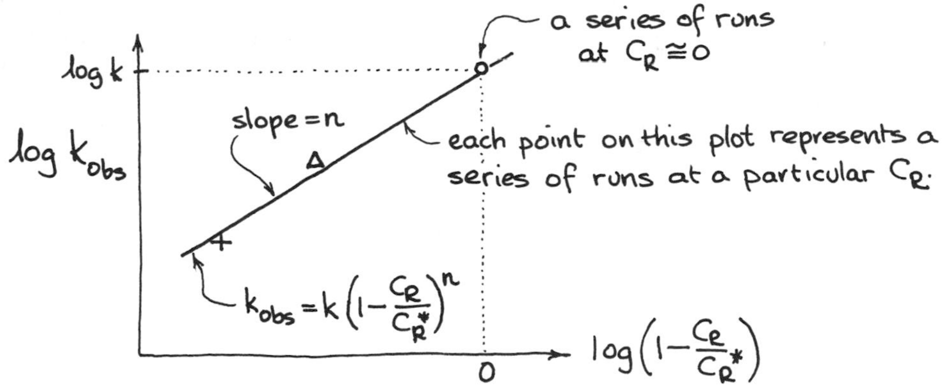

or if C_R^* is unknown guess C_R^* until you do get a straight line

F. Behavior of reactors in the intermediate regime.

Since mixed flow reactors in either the pure substrate limiting or the pure poison limiting regime give similar looking C vs τ curves, both with washout, maximum rate, etc., we would not expect different behavior when both factors influence the rate.

For plug flow or batch operations S-shaped curves are obtained for both regimes, hence when both factors act simultaneously we again expect S-shaped curves in the intermediate regime. Evaluation of the kinetic constants from batch experiments would be awkward.

Chapter 84 Problems

Material R is to be produced from the following microbial fermentation, using a feed stream $C_{A0} = 10^6$, $C_{R0} = 0$, $C_{C0} = 0$

$$A \xrightarrow{C} R + C$$

$$r_C = k\left(1 - \frac{C_R}{C_R^*}\right)\frac{C_A C_C}{C_A + C_M} \quad \text{with} \quad \begin{cases} k = 2 \\ C_M = 50 \\ C_R^* = 12 \\ (R/A) = 0.1 \\ (C/A) = 0.01 \end{cases}$$

In each of the following problems sketch your recommended reactor set-up and on the sketch indicate pertinent quantities.

What C_R is obtainable in a single mixed flow reactor of size V = 1 for a feed rate

A1 . . . v = 1

A2 . . . v = 4

What C_R is obtainable using two mixed flow reactors, each of volume V = 1, for a feed rate

A3 . . . v = 1

A4 . . . v = 3

For a feed rate v = 3 what size of plug flow reactor with appropriate piping, recycle, bypass or anything you want to use is needed to give

B5 . . . $C_R = 6$, side tap allowed

B6 . . . $C_R = 4$, side tap allowed

B7 . . . $C_R = 9$, no side tap allowed

B8 . . . $C_R = 9$, side tap allowed

What combination of plug and mixed flow reactors gives minimum total volume for treating v = 3 of feed to

C9 . . . $C_R = 10.8$

Chapter 84 Problems

For the system of the above problems we now add a centrifugal cell separator. This gives an equal flow split but with one stream having three times the cell concentration as other. With this new addition what do we find for

D10 ... problem 1

D11 ... problem 2

D12* ... problem 3

E13 The microbial fermentation of A produces R as follows

$$10A + Cell \rightarrow 18R + 2\ Cells$$

and experiments in a mixed flow reactor with $C_{A0} = 250\ mol/m^3$ show that

$$C_R = 24\ mol/m^3 \text{ when } \tau = 1.5\ hr$$
$$C_R = 30\ mol/m^3 \text{ when } \tau = 3.0\ hr$$

In addition, there seems to be a limiting upper value for C_R at 36 mol/m^3 for any t, C_A or C_C.

From this information determine how to maximize the production rate of R from a feed stream of 10 m^3/hr of $C_{A0} = 350\ mol/m^3$. Cell or product separation and recycle is not practical in this system so only consider a once-through system. Present your answer as a sketch showing reactor type, reactor volume, C_R in exit stream, and mols of R produced/hr.

Frushed fruit flies (A) ferment in alcohol (R) with product limiting kinetics estimated to be

$$A \xrightarrow{C} R + C$$

$$r_R = k\left[1 - \frac{C_R}{C_R^*}\right]^n C_C \quad \text{where} \begin{cases} k = \sqrt{3}\ hr^{-1} \\ n = 0.5 \text{ in summer} \\ n = 1 \text{ in spring and fall} \\ n = 2 \text{ in winter} \\ C_R^* = 0.12 \text{ gm alcohol/gm solution} \\ \rho = 1000\ kg/m^3 \end{cases}$$

What is the most alcohol you can produce (kg/day) in a commercial sized mixed flow reactor ($V = 30\ m^3$) using any flow rate you wish of fragrant fresh frappèed fluit fries.

E14 ... in spring

E15 ... in summer

E16 ... in winter

Chapter 84 Problems

E17 Shredded chemical reactor textbooks are degraded to glucose in a pilot plant well stirred fermenter (V = 50 lit) under the action of a word gobbling bug. With a large excess of these shredded incomprehensible words the presence of glucose becomes the rate limiting factor. We summarize the findings as follows

when v = 16 lit/hr	C_R = 54 μmol/lit
when v = 4 lit/hr	C_R = 75 μmol/lit
when $v \to 0$	$C_R \to$ 90 μmol/lit

Determine the flow rate which maximizes glucose production, and find this production rate.

E18 Professor Microbe has submitted a paper for publication in which he studied the growth of a new strain of bug in a mixed flow fermenter (V = 46.4) using a pure substrate feed ($C_{A0} = 150$, $C_{R0} = C_{C0} = 0$). His raw data is as follows

v	C_A
4.64	5
20.0	125
22.0	150 (washout)

with $(R/A) = 0.5$

He asserts without giving details that this data clearly represents poison-limiting kinetics with rate constants

$$k = 0.50, \quad C_R^* = 90.6, \quad n = 1.0$$

The reviewer of the paper, Dr. Ferment, counters that Microbe is quite wrong, that the data in fact represents substrate limiting Monod kinetics with

$$C_M = 20, \quad k = 0.50$$

But out of orneriness he didn't present the details of his calculations either.

The editor can't determine who is right (this is not his field) so he sends the paper and the review to duWayne Zuelhsdorff. What is duWayne's answer?

- Is Microbe, or Ferment, or both, or neither, right?

F19* Consider the fermentation of glucose which is catalysed by a yeast

$$\text{glucose (A)} \xrightarrow{\text{yeast}} \text{alcohol (R) + more yeast (C)}$$

The reaction was run in a mixed flow reactor with the following results

for $C_{C0} = 0$ and $C_R = 0$	
C_A, gm/lit	τ_m, hr
0.25	4
0.19	5
0.14	6
0.10	8
0.075	10

for $C_{C0} = 0$ and $C_R \approx 20$ gm/lit	
C_A, gm/lit	τ_m, hr
0.7	4
0.4	5
0.3	6
0.2	8
0.15	10

Knowing that $C_R^* = 120$ gm/lit find the complete rate equation for this reaction, one that includes the effect of alcohol build up and of glucose depletion. Also assume a constant fractional yield in all these runs.

Note: Other substances affected the rate, however their concentrations were kept the same in all runs so their effects were ignored

F20* Bazua and Wilke, in Biotech. and Bioeng. Symp. **7**, 105 (1977) reported on the effect of product poisoning during ethanol production in a mixed flow fermenter using a glucose feed (A) and a particular yeast *Saccharomyces cerevisiae* (C). Their experimental results are as follows

τ_m, hr	C_{A0}	C_A	C_{R0}	$\bar{C}_R$	
13.88	9.4	0.048	0	4.37	For all runs
5.21		0.230			
3.79		0.375			$(R/C) = 3.90$
3.70		0.400			
2.38		4.500			
16.67	9.05	0.045	26.22	29.19	
7.58		0.122			
3.97		0.477			
3.21		5.340			
2.66		6.760			
13.66	8.35	0.087	58.54	61.29	
7.25		0.270			
4.96		0.470			
3.88		5.100			
26.04	9.10	0.083	78.40	81.30	
14.37		0.230			
13.44		0.270			
10.42		0.480			
9.92		0.480			
7.25		6.000			

Develop a rate equation, r_R, for ethanol production which accounts for substrate concentration and the hindering effect of the alcohol itself.

Chapter 100. MISCELLANY: Dimensions, Units, Conversions and the Order of Magnitude of This and That

A. Newton's Law.

$$F = \frac{ma}{g_c}$$

at earth's surface $a = g = 9.806$ m/s

$$\ldots \quad 1 \cdot N = \frac{(1\,kg)(1\,m/s)}{(1\,kg \cdot m/s^2 \cdot N)}$$

conversion factor: $g_c = \frac{1\,kg \cdot m}{s^2 \cdot N}$

B. Length

10^{10}	10^6	39.37	3.28083	1	0.0006214
angstrom	micron	inch	foot	**meter**	mile

C. Volume.

61023	1000	264.2	220.2	35.318	6.29	4.80	1
in^3	lit	US gal	Imp. gal	ft^3	bbl (oil)	drum	**m^3**
					42 US gal	55 US gal	

... also wine barrel, beer barrel, etc.

D. Mass.

35.27	2.205	1	0.0011025	0.001	0.0009842
oz	lb	**kg**	short ton	metric ton	long ton
			2000 lb	or 'tonne'	2240 lb

E. Pressure.

the Pascal: $1\,Pa = 1\,\frac{N}{m^2} = 1\,\frac{kg}{m \cdot s^2} = 10\,\frac{dyne}{cm^2}$

1 atm = 760 mm Hg = $14.696\,\frac{\#f}{in^2}$ = 29.92 in Hg = 33.93 ft H_2O = 101325 Pa

1 bar = 10^5 Pa ... close to 1 atm, sometimes called a technical atm.

1 inch H_2O = 248.86 Pa $\cong$ 250 Pa

F. Work, Energy and Heat.
the joule: $1\,J = 1\,N\cdot m = 1\,\frac{kg\cdot m^2}{s^2}$

10^{13}	10^{6}	737562	238846	101972	9869	947.8	238.85	0.37251	0.277778
erg	J	ft·lb$_f$	cal	kg$_f$·m	lit·atm	Btu	kcal	Hp·hr	kW·hr

Btu ← 778 ft·lb$_f$

G. Molecular weight.

In SI units: $(mw)_{O_2} = 0.032\,\frac{kg}{mol}$

$(mw)_{air} = 0.0289\,\frac{kg}{mol}$ ... etc.

H. Ideal Gas.

$pV = nRT$ ... or $\frac{p}{\rho} = \frac{RT}{(mw)}$ ... or $C_A = \frac{N_A}{V} = \frac{p_A}{RT}$

R ← the gas constant; ρ ← kg/m³; V ← m³/mol

$$R = \boxed{8.314\,\frac{J}{mol\cdot K}} = 1.987\,\frac{cal}{mol\cdot K} = 0.729\,\frac{ft^3\cdot atm}{lb\,mol\cdot {}^\circ R}$$

$$= 0.08206\,\frac{lit\cdot atm}{mol\cdot K} = 1.987\,\frac{Btu}{lb\,mol\cdot {}^\circ R} = 82.06\times10^{-6}\,\frac{m^3\cdot atm}{mol\cdot K}$$

$$= \boxed{8.314\,\frac{Pa\cdot m^3}{mol\cdot K}} = 8314\,\frac{Pa\cdot liter}{mol\cdot K}$$

I. Viscosity (μ).
the poiseuille: $1\,P\ell = 1\,\frac{kg}{m\cdot s}$

$$\boxed{1\,P\ell = 1\,\frac{kg}{m\cdot s}} = 10\text{ poise} = 1000\text{ cp} = 0.672\,\frac{lbm}{ft\cdot s} = 2420\,\frac{lbm}{ft\cdot hr}$$

poise ← 1 gm/cm·s; cp ← centipoise

for water: $\mu_{20°C} = 10^{-3}\,P\ell$

for gases: $\mu \cong 10^{-5}\,P\ell$

for air: $\mu_{20°C} = 1.8\times10^{-5}\,P\ell$

J. Density. $\rho = \left[\frac{kg}{m^3}\right]$

for water: $\rho \cong 1000 \frac{kg}{m^3}$

for ideal gas: $\rho = \frac{p(mw)}{RT} \underset{20°C}{\overset{air}{=}} \frac{(101325)(0.0289)}{(8.314)(293)} = 1.20 \frac{kg}{m^3}$

K. Diffusivity. $\mathcal{D}$ and $\mathcal{D}_{eff} = \frac{m^2}{s} = 3.875 \times 10^4 \frac{ft^2}{hr}$

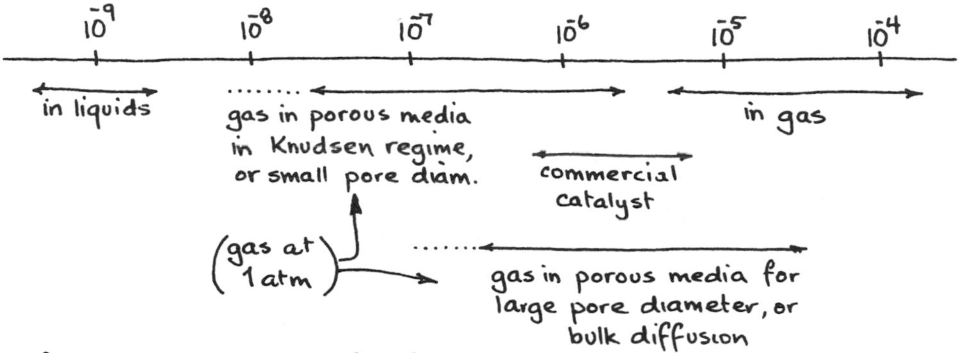

$\mathcal{D}$ independent of π ... for liquids

$\mathcal{D} \propto T^{3/2}$, $\mathcal{D} \propto \frac{1}{\pi}$ ... for bulk diffusion of gases

$\mathcal{D} \propto T^{1/2}$, $\mathcal{D}$ independent of π ... for Knudsen diffusion of gases

In a tube of diameter d Knudsen diffusion occurs when $\pi d < 0.01$, Pa·m.
In this situation

$$\mathcal{D} = 1.534\, d \sqrt{T/(mw)}$$

Dimensions

In gas or any fluid: $\mathcal{D} = \left[\frac{m^2\ fluid}{s}\right]$

In a porous structure: $\mathcal{D} = \left[\frac{m^3\ fluid}{m\ solid \cdot s}\right]$

L. Concentration. $C_A = \frac{mol}{m^3\ fluid} = 6.24 \times 10^{-5} \frac{lb\ mol}{ft^3}$

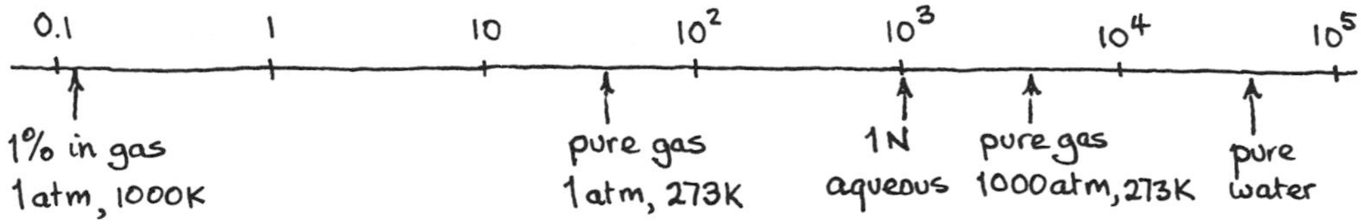

M. Thermal conductivity. k and $k_{eff} = \frac{W}{m \cdot K}$

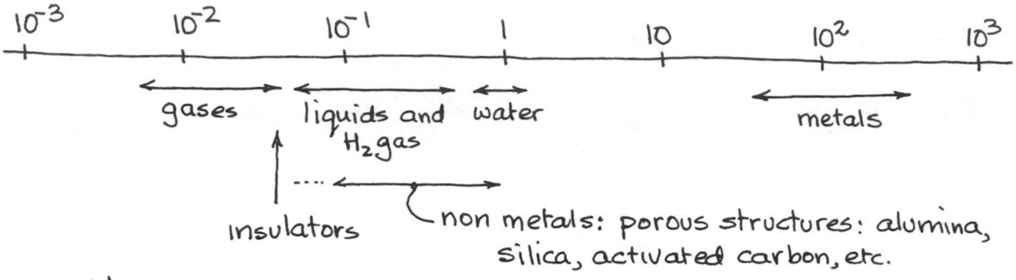

$$1 \frac{W}{m \cdot K} = 0.239 \frac{cal}{m \cdot K \cdot s} = 0.578 \frac{Btu}{hr \cdot ft \cdot {}^\circ F}$$

k and k_{eff} are independent of π

Dimensions: in gas or liquid ... $k = \left[\frac{W}{m\ fluid \cdot K}\right]$

in porous structures ... $k_{eff} = \left[\frac{W}{m\ structure \cdot K}\right]$

N. Heat transfer coefficient. $h = \frac{W}{m^2 \cdot K}$

$$1 \frac{W}{m^2 \cdot K} = 0.239 \frac{cal}{m^2 \cdot K \cdot s} = 0.176 \frac{Btu}{hr \cdot ft^2 \cdot {}^\circ F}$$

Gas to particle: $h = 8 - 1200$

Gas to fine entrained particles (fast fluidized systems, FCC, etc: $h \cong 1000 - 1200$

Liquid to particle: $h = 80 \sim 1200$

In packed beds: $Nu = \frac{h d_p}{k} = 2 + 1.8 (Re_p)^{1/2} (Pr)^{1/3}$ ... $Re_p > 100$

(Pr: $\cong 1$ for gases; $\cong 10$ for liquids)

O. Mass transfer coefficient. $k_g = \frac{m^3\ gas}{m^2\ surface \cdot s}$

Gas to particle: $k_g = 0.02 - 2$

Liquid to particle: $k_g = 2 \times 10^{-7} - 2 \times 10^{-5}$

In packed beds: $Sh = \frac{k_g d_p}{\mathcal{D}} = 2 + 1.8 (Re_p)^{1/2} (Sc)^{1/3}$ ... $Re_p > 80$

(Sc: $\cong 1$ for gases; $\cong 1000$ for liquids)

For gases: $k_g \propto 1/\pi$

P. Rate of reaction.

$$-r_A''' = \frac{\text{moles of A disappearing}}{\text{m}^3 \text{ of thing} \cdot \text{s}}$$

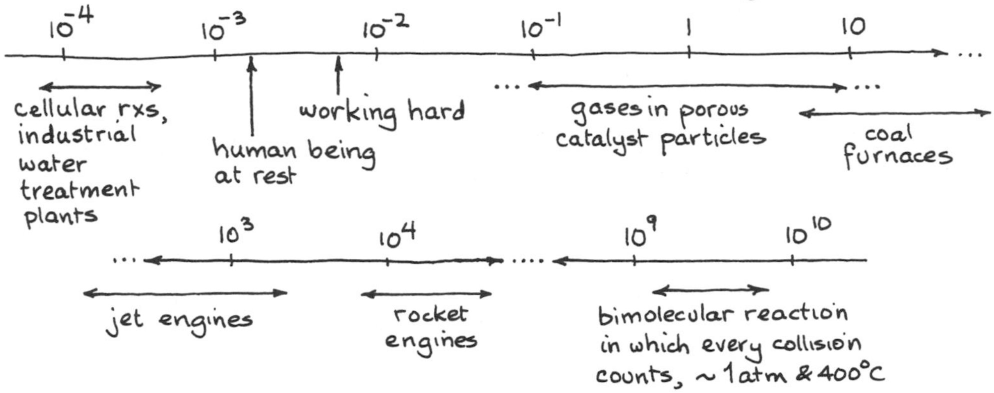

Q. Dimensionless groups.

$$\boxed{Sc} = \frac{\mu}{\rho \mathcal{D}} = \frac{\text{molecular momentum transfer}}{\text{molecular mass transfer}} \quad \cdots \text{ Schmidt number}$$

(numerator: viscous effects; denominator: diffusion effects)

$$\cong \frac{10^{-5}}{(1)(10^{-5})} = 1 \quad \cdots \text{ for gases}$$

$$\cong \frac{10^{-3}}{(10^{3})(10^{-9})} = 10^{3} \quad \cdots \text{ for liquids}$$

$$\boxed{Pr} = \frac{C_p \mu}{k} = \frac{\text{molecular momentum transfer}}{\text{molecular heat transfer}} \quad \cdots \text{ Prandtl number}$$

(numerator: viscous effects; denominator: heat conduction)

$\cong 0.66 \sim 0.75$ for air, A, CO_2, CH_4 CO H_2 He N_2 and other common gases

$\cong 1.06$ for steam

$= 10 \sim 1000$ for most liquids

$= 0.006 \sim 0.03$ for most liquid metals

$$\boxed{Re} = \frac{du\rho}{\mu} = \frac{\text{total momentum transfer}}{\text{molecular momentum transfer}} \quad \cdots \text{ Reynolds number}$$

(numerator: inertial effects; denominator: viscous effects)

$$\boxed{Nu} = \frac{hd}{k} = \frac{\text{total heat transfer}}{\text{molecular heat transfer}}$$ ... **Nusselt number**

(total heat transfer: turbulent and laminar, conduction and convection; molecular heat transfer: heat conduction alone)

$$\boxed{Sh} = \frac{k_g d}{\mathscr{D}} = \frac{\text{total mass transfer}}{\text{molecular mass transfer}}$$ ... **Sherwood number**

$$\boxed{Pe} = \frac{du\rho C_p}{k} = (Re)(Pr) = \frac{\text{total momentum transfer}}{\text{molecular heat transfer}}$$ ... **Peclet no.**

$$\boxed{Bo} = \frac{ud}{\mathscr{D}} = (Re)(Sc) = \frac{\text{total momentum transfer}}{\text{molecular mass transfer}}$$ ... **Bodenstein no.**

$$\boxed{\frac{D}{ud} \text{ and } \frac{D}{uL}} = \frac{\text{movement by longitudinal dispersion}}{\text{movement by bulk flow}}$$ ... **dispersion groups**

(movement by longitudinal dispersion: fluid overtaking caused by molecular diffusion, velocity differences, turbulent eddies, etc)

This is a new and different type of dimensionless group introduced by workers in chemical reaction engineering. Unfortunately someone started calling the reciprocal of this group the Peclet number. This is wrong. It is neither the Peclet number nor its mass transfer analog, which is widely called the Bodenstein number in Europe. The difference rests in the use of D in place of $\mathscr{D}$, hence these groups have completely different meanings.

A name is needed for this group. Until one is chosen let us use:

$\frac{D}{ud}$ ... intensity of axial dispersion

$\frac{D}{uL}$ ... vessel dispersion number.

References for this chapter

Weisz CEP Symp. Series no 25 55 29 (1959); Perry 3rd ed; Satterfield 170; McAdams, appendix; Kunii and Levenspiel 324.

ANSWERS TO SELECTED PROBLEMS

(Prepared by ZHANG GUO TAI)

Chapter 1

A2 For $2NO_2 + 0.5\,O_2 \rightarrow N_2O_5$, $r_{N_2O_5} = -2\,r_{O_2} = -0.5\,r_{NO_2}$

B10 $E = 274.35$ kJ

C20 $n = 0.5$

D24 $X_B = 0.4$, $C_A = 20$, $C_B = 120$

E30 $X_A = 0.82$, $X_B = 0.41$, $C_B = 129.6$

Chapter 2

A2 $-r_A = (6.52 \times 10^{-5}\ \text{lit/mol} \cdot \text{hr})(C_A\ \text{mol/lit})^2$, where $A = NH_2 - CO - NH_2$

B6 $-r_A = 0.08$ mol/lit · min

C8 $t = 11.2$ min

D10 $-r = (0.1\ \text{lit}^{0.38}/\text{mmol}^{0.38} \cdot \text{hr})\, C_A^{1.38}$

E14 1 hr

F18 $X_A = 90.9\ \%$, $C_A = 0.909$ mol/lit

G24 $C_A = 3$ mol/lit

Chapter 3

A2 $-r_A = 10$ mmol/lit · s

B6 $V = 36$ lit

C8 $-r_A = 10\ (\text{mmol/lit} \cdot s^2)^{1/2}\, (C_A\ \text{mmol/lit})^{1/2}$

D10 $C_A = 0.077$ mol/lit

E20 Four times as large

F26 2 mol/lit

G28 $-r_A = (8.44 \times 10^{11}\, e^{-53500/RT}\, s^{-1})\, C_A$

H30 $X_{Ae} = 0.75$, $V = 5\ m^3$

Chapter 4

A2 $-r_A = 0.025$ mol/lit · min, $r_S = 0.005$ mol/lit · min, $\bar{t} = 10$ min, $\tau = 6.67$ min

B4 $X_{Ae} = 0.8$, $C_A = 60$ mmol/lit

C10 $v_2 / v_1 = 0.333$

D12 $v = 62.5$ lit/min

Answers to selected problems

E14 $-r_A = (24\ \text{min}^{-1})\, C_A$

F22 $F_{A0} = 1.75 \times 10^5\ \text{mol/min}$

G26 $-r_A = (10^{10} \times e^{-E/RT}\ \text{lit/mol} \cdot \text{min})\, C_A^2$

Chapter 5

A2 It would help. The activity of the exit stream is 1/16 of the entering stream.

B22 $V = 1500\ \text{lit}$, $X_A = 0.667$, $\$_R = \$\,0.9/\text{mol R}$

Chapter 6

A2 Plug flow, rising T

B22 Same fixed ratio of A to B

Chapter 7

A2 $k_2/k_1 = 5$

B22 $V = 153\ \text{lit}$

C32 Mixed flow reactor with $V = 4\ \text{m}^3$

D34 $V = 600\ \text{lit}$, $X_A = 0.667$, Profit = \$ 90/hr

Chapter 8

A2 Mix the streams (ratio of A to R doesn't change) and then pass through reactor

$C_A = 5/12$, $C_R = 5/6$, $X_A = 0.75$

B4 Minimum cost of R = \$ 26/mol R formed

C10 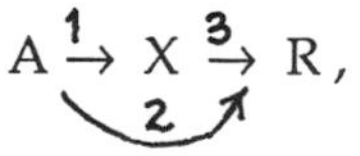 , $k_1 = 0.28\ \text{min}^{-1}$, $k_2 = 0.14\ \text{min}^{-1}$, $k_3 = 0.0715\ \text{min}^{-1}$

D16 $A \xrightarrow{1} R \xrightarrow{2} S$, $k_1/k_2 = 2$

Chapter 21

A2 $-r_A' = (0.567\ \text{m}^3/\text{kg cat} \cdot \text{hr})\,(C_A\ \text{mol/m}^3)$

B10 $-r_A' = 1.5\ \text{mol/gm cat} \cdot \text{hr}$

C18 $W = 13\ \text{kg}$

D24 $W = 80\ \text{kg}$

E32 $-r_A = 10\, C_A$, $\text{mol/m}^3 \cdot \text{s}$

F35 $\pi = 1\ \text{atm}$, $X_A = 1$, $W = 500\ \text{kg}$, cost of R = \$ 0.167/mol

Answers to selected problems

Chapter 22

A2 Only film ΔT influences the observed rate.
$\mathcal{E}_{500} = 674$, $k'''_{500} = 0.0015$ m³ fluid/m³ solid · s

B14 $\mathcal{E} = 1$, $T_g = T_s = T_{center} = 500$ K

Chapter 23

A2 $\mathcal{E} = 0.236$

B8 No pore diffusion

C12 $X_A = 0.393$

D18 E = 219 kJ/mol

E26 $C_{R,max}/C_{A0} = 0.83$, small enough d_p, plug flow, $k_2/k_1 = 1/16$

F34 Saving of platinum = 70 %

Chapter 24

A2

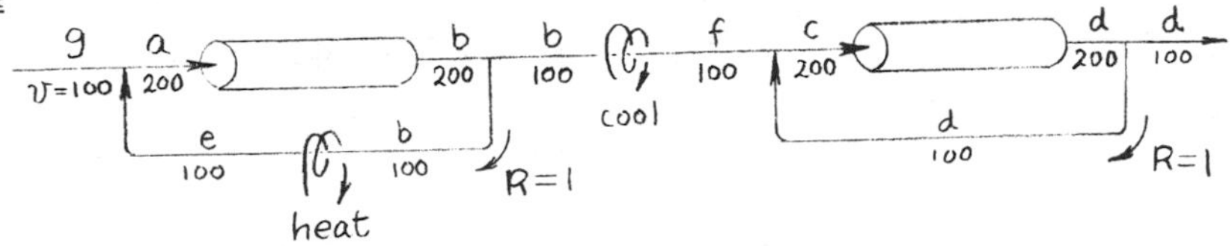

B14

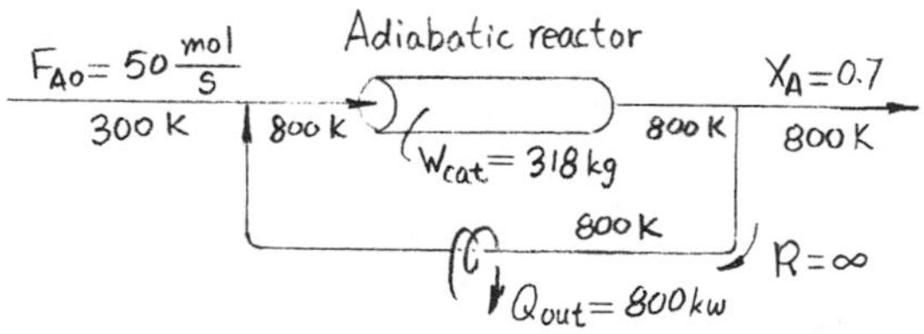

C18

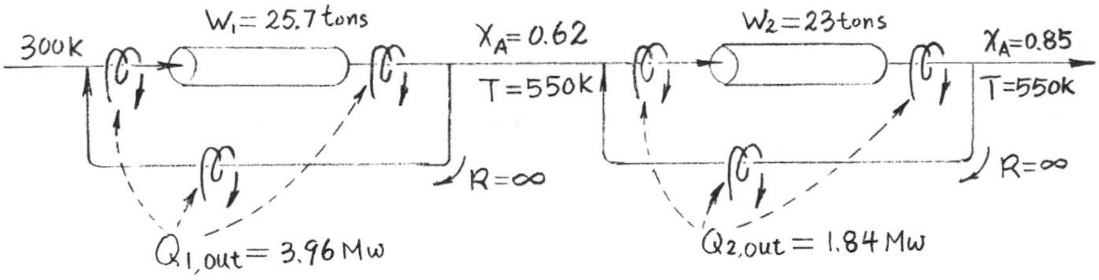

D23

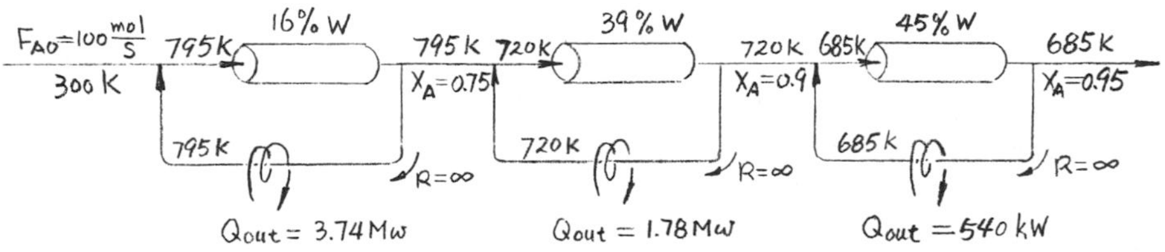

Answers to selected problems

$$T_{10\%} = 898\ K,\ T_{20\%} = 840\ K,\ T_{30\%} = 825\ K, \cdots$$

Heat removed: $Q_{10\%} = 3.37$ MW, $Q_{20\%} = 1.50$ MW, $Q_{30\%} = 0.85$ MW, $\cdots$

Heat added before reactor: $Q = 2.4$ MW

Chapter 25

A2 $X_A = \sim 79.1\%$

B10 $W_{cat} = 15.4$ tons, $(C_R/C_{A0})_{max} = 0.62$

Chapter 26

A2 $-r_A'' = 200\ C_A$, mol/m$^2\cdot$hr ; $X_A = 50\ \%$, $-r_A'' = 300\ C_A$, mol/m$^2\cdot$hr

B4 (a) $L = 7$ m, (b) $L = 14$ m

Chapter 31

A2 $-r_A' = (90\ m^6/kg\ cat \cdot mol \cdot min)\ C_A^2\ a$, $-da/dt = (0.1\ hr^{-1})\ a$

B6 $-r_A' = C_A^2\ a$, mol/gm cat $\cdot$ min, $-da/dt = C_A^{0.5}\ a$, hr^{-1}

C8 $-r_A' = 2.02\ C_A a$, mol/kg cat $\cdot$ hr, $-da/dt = 0.4082\ a$, hr^{-1}

D14 383 days

Chapter 32

A2 $X_A = 0.73$

B12 $t_{run} = 477$ days

C16 $W = 200$ kg, $t = 811$ days

Chapter 33

A2 $k' = 2.75 \times 10^{-4}\ m^3/kg\ cat \cdot s$, $k_d = 0.1\ s^{-1}$

B14 $X_A = 0.67$

Chapter 34

A2 $X_B = 0.42$

A6 $t = 13$ hr

Chapter 41

A2 (a) $-r_A'''' = 5\ mol/hr \cdot m^3$, (b) Resistance: 50 % gas film, 50 % liquid film, reaction in liquid film ; pseudo first order reaction

A14 $-r_A'''' = 4.96 \times 10^{-2}\ mol/m^3 \cdot s$

Chapter 42

Answers to selected problems

Chapter 42

A2 $V_r = 28.8\ m^3$, gas film resistance control

B20 $h = 6.9$ m

C22 (a) $t = 9.53$ hr, (b) A unreacted = 6.58 %

Chapter 51

A2 Film diffusion control

B8 $t/\tau = 0.5\,[1-3\,(1-X_B)^{2/3} + 2\,(1-X_B)] + 0.5\,[1-(1-X_B)^{1/3}]$

C12 Ash diffusion contributes 50% to the overall resistance for a particle of size R.

Chapter 52

A2 $\bar{X}_B = 0.89$

B8 22.4 times the original feed rate

C10 $\bar{\bar{X}}_B = 0.98$

D24 Entrained solids: A = 500 kg, B = 200 kg, total = 700 kg

E30 $\bar{X}_B = 0.84$

Chapter 53

A2 W = 3.05 tons

B16 Actual $\tau = 2$ hr. If mixed flow gas in reactor then in entering gas environment ††t = 1.2 min, if plug flow then t = 25.8 min.

Chapter 54

A2 10000 hr

B12 40% of carbon particles escapes unburned.

Chapter 55

A2 $W_{needed} = 15.69$ tons

B6 τ_1 slow, τ_2 fast, τ_3 fast

C14 Below $X_B = 0.33$: $X_B = t/300$

Above $X_B = 0.33$: $(t-100)/260 = 1-(3X_B/2 - 1/2)^{1/3}$

First step ---- migration of O_2 to the surface of particles

Second step ---- GPM--reaction control (diffusion of H_2 is so great that diffusion resistance can be ignored).

Answers to selected problems

Chapter 61

A2 $V = 8$ lit , consistent

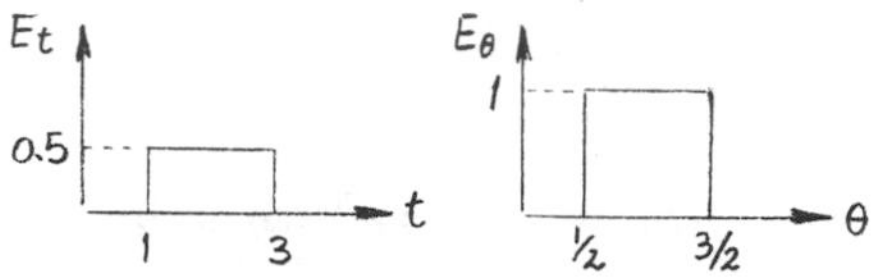

B18 $X_A = 2/3$

C36 Fraction of A which has decomposed = 0.568

Chapter 62

A2

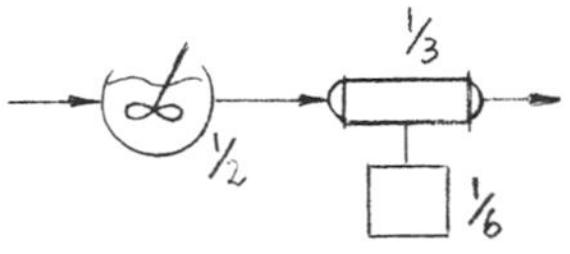

B10

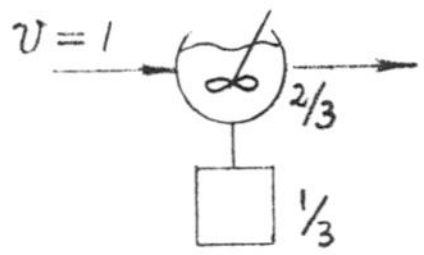

C18 $X_A = 0.973$

D24

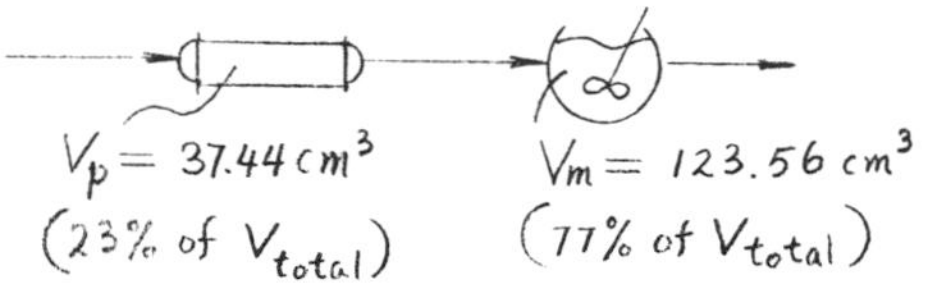

Chapter 64

A2 $D = 0.06927\ \text{km}^2/\text{hr}$

B4 $t = 661$ s

C12 Can not be done , $Re > 2000$, turbulent

D18 Instead of 1 in 10^9 the chance is 1 in 5124, or 200,000 times as likely.

Chapter 66

A2 (a) $n = 4.04$ (b) $n = 5.13$

B6 10 bottles of house blend

C12 (a) Conversion = 40.6 % (b) $X_A = 0.5\int_0^2 t^2 e^{-t}\,dt + \int_2^\infty te^{-t}\,dt$

Chapter 68

A2 $X_A = 0.76$

B6 The difference does not seem serious, however the significance of this finding is that this theoretical equation is incorrect.

Chapter 81

A2 $-r_A = 20\,C_A C_B/(C_A+0.2)$

Answers to selected problems

B4 (a) $-r_A = 20\, C_{E0} C_A / [200 + C_A + 0.01287\,(200 + C_A)\, C_B]$

(b) Non competitive inhibition

(c) $A + E \underset{2}{\overset{1}{\rightleftharpoons}} X \xrightarrow{3} R + E$

$B + E \underset{5}{\overset{4}{\rightleftharpoons}} Y$

$B + X \underset{7}{\overset{6}{\rightleftharpoons}} Z$

Independent attack, $k_4/k_5 = k_6/k_7$

C9

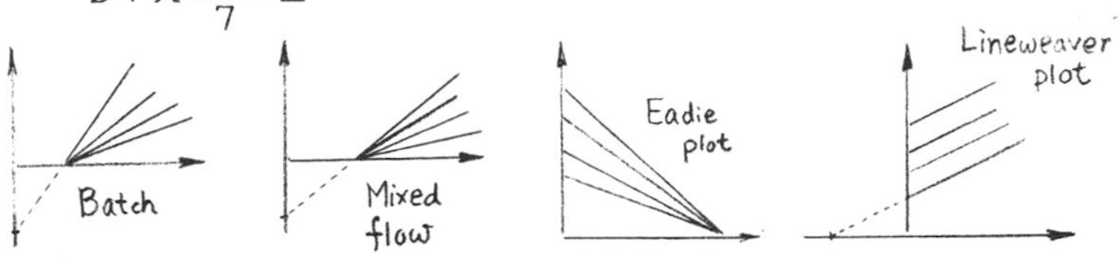

Chapter 83

A2 $r_C = 0.97\, C_A C_C/(C_A + 36)$ The answer will strongly depend on the method used to analyze the data.

B4 $C_C = 0.56\ \text{gm/m}^3$

C6 Can not do any better than original

D10 Lowest concentration is $C_A = 1$

E18 $V_m = 4.5$, V_p (with **R** = 2) = 3.9

F22

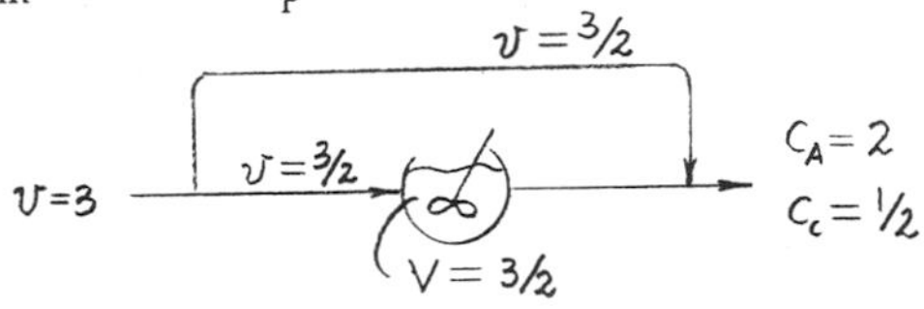

G24 $C_A = 1/3$, $C_C = 4/3$

Chapter 84

A2 $C_R = 1.5$

B8

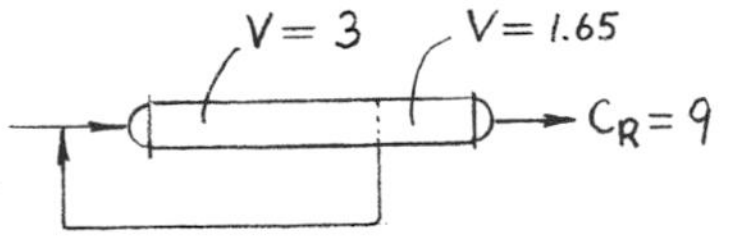

C9

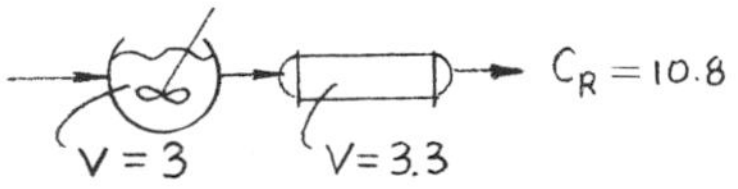

D10 $C_R = 9$

E14 37.44 ton/day

F20 $r_C = (C/R)\, r_R = 0.52\,(1 - C_R/120)^{0.95} \cdot C_A C_C/(C_A + 0.29)$

$\cong 0.5(1 - C_R/120) \cdot C_A C_C/(C_A + 0.27)$

AUTHOR INDEX

Abbas, S.A., 32.P23 - P26
Aris, R., 64.16-19
Ananthakrishan, V., 68.2
Arrhenius, S., 1.4
Avrami, M., 55.18

Baldi, G., 41.4
Barnett, L.G., 21.P16
Bartok, W., 62.P24
Bazua, C.D., 84.P20
Binns, D.T., 6.P1
Bischoff, K.B., 64.18, 64.21
Blackwell, R.J., 64.P14
Bodenstein, M., 3.P19
Brahme, P.H., 34.P3
Briggs, G.E., 81.3
Broucek, R., 21.6
Butt, W.M., 2.P2, 32.P23 - P26

Cates, D. L., 8.P24
Chance, B., 81.3
Chaudhari, R.V., 34.13
Chien, J. Y., 8.24
Chu, C., 55.12
Colakyan, M., 1.P34
Comroe, J.H., *see* book index
Corcoran, W.H., *see* book index
Coughlin, R.W., 55.12
Crowe, C.M., 32.14
Cunningham, R.E., 22.P13

Danckwerts, P.V., 42.P19, 64.20, *see* book index
Das, K., 81.P6
Davidson, J.F., *see* book index
Dayan, J., 64.19
Denbigh, K.G., *see* book index
Dente, M., 64.21
Dixon, M., *see* book index
Dolbear, A.E., 1.P17
Doraiswamy, L.K., 34.P3
Douglas, J.M., 64.21

Eliezer, K.F., 21.P15

Fabre, H., 1.P11
Fan, L.T., 64.18, *see* book index
Fane, A.G.. 55.24, 55.P14
Froessling, N., 54.25

Gangiah, K., *see* book index
Ghose, T.K., 81.P6
Gillham, A.J., 42.P19
Golike, G., 41.P20
Gorring, R.L., 23.6
Goto, S., 22.P12
Govindarao, V.M.H., 34.P5
Grace, J.R., 25.18
Grey, H., *see* book index

Haldane, J.B.S., 81.3
Han, K., 82.7
Harris, T.R., 68.15
Harrison, D., *see* book index
Hartman, M., 55.12
Havewala, N.B., 31.P11
Hegedus, L. L., 31.P7
Hicks, J.S., 22.6
Hill, C.G., Jr., *see* book index
Hoftijzer, P., 41.4
Horn, F., 24.8
Hull, D.E., 64.P4
Husain, A., *see* book index
Hwang, W.S., 64.18
Horvath, C., 26.4

Ishida, M., 55.6

Jagadeesh, V., 64.P3

Kabel, R.L., 54.P4
Kayihan, F., 54.12, 54.17
Kelly, B., 42.P19
Kent, J.W., 64.P4
Khang, S.J. 31.18
Kim, B.M., 68.15
Kimura, S., 24.20, 53.8
Kittrell, J.R., 31.18, 31.P17
Konoki, K.K., 24.8 - 10
Koestenblatt, S., 31.P10
Krishnaswamy, S., 31.18, 31.P17
Kumar, S., 52.8
Kunii, D., 51.P11, 52.1, 61.P16, *see* book index
Kunugita, E., 31.P8
Kunzru, D., 3.P28

Lacey, W.N., *see* book index
Langmuir, I., 64.20
Lee, H. H., 55.12
LePage, A.H., 55.24, 55.P14
Levenspiel, O., 24.20, 25.14, 31.18, 32.12, 55.8, 64.10, 64.19, 82.7,*see* book index

Author index

Levich, B.G., *see* book index
Lin, S.H., 68.15
Lo, S.N., 24.P100

MacMullin, R.B., 66.2, 66.6
Mathis, J.F., 25.P9
McAdams, W.H., *see* book index
McGreavy, C., 22.P14
Menten, M.L., 81.3
Michaelis, L., 81.3
Miyauchi, T., 64.7
Monod, J., 83.6, 83.15, *see* book index
Morita, N., 22.P12
Murhammer, D., 52.16
Murthy, K.V.R., 34.P5

Nevo, A.C., 23.P4
Novick, L., 83.6
Novosad, Z., 68.15

Oleksy, S.J., 66.P4
Osborne, F.T., 68.15
Overturf, B.W., 54.12, 54.17

Park, D., 68.15
Park, J. Y., 32.12, 55.8
Pasquon, I., 64.21
Perry, J.H., *see* book index
Pigford, R.L., 55.6
Pitcher, H.W., Jr., 31.P11
Polthier, K., 64.P1
Pratt, K.C., 64.P15
Prout, E.G., 55.16
Pye, E.K., *see* book index

Ramachandran, P.A., 34.13, 55.12
Ratcliffe, J.S., 7.P30
Resnick, W., 62.P25
Rikmenspoel, R., 23.P4

Sato, Y., 34.P1
Satterfield, C.N., *see* book index
Satyanarayan, M., 64.P3
Sawinsky, J., 68.13
Shankar, S., 31.P9
Sherwood, T.K., *see* book index
Sicardi, S., 41.4
Sjenitzer, F., 64.P7
Sliger, G., 55.6
Smith, J.M., 55.12, *see* book index
Smith, T.G., 22.12,
Smith, W.K., 64.10
Sohn, H.Y., 55.6
Stamhuis, E. J., 66.P14
Standish, N., 64.P1
Stephanakis, A., 31.18
Subramanian, P., 1.P34
Summers, J. C., 31.P7
Szekely, J., 55.6
Szilard, L., 83.6

Tarhan, M.O., *see* book index
Taylor, G.I., 64.15, 64.16, 64.17, 64.P16
Thornton, J.M., 22.P14
Tichacek, L.J., 64.22
Tien, C., 55.6
Timberlake, D., 31.P7
Tompkins, F.C., 55.16
Tsay, Q.T., 55.20
Turkdogen, E.T., 55.6
Turner, J.C.R., *see* book index

Ulbrecht, J., 68.15

van der Laan, E.T., 64.7, 64.8
van Hooren, C.J., 41.P18
van Krevelen, D.W., 41.4, 41.P18
Villadsen, J., 21.6

Watson, K.M., 25.P9
Wadel, S., 21.6
Webb, E.C., *see* book index
Weber Jr., M., 66.2, 66.6
Weekman, V.W., Jr., 23.6
Wehner, J.F., 64.20
Weisz, P.B., 22.6, 23.P3, 23.P5, 100.6
Wen, C.Y., 55.6, *see* book index
Westhaver, J.W., 64.19
Wheeler, A., 23.7
Wilhelm, R.H., 64.20
Wilke, C.R., 84.P20
Wingard, L.B., *see* book index
Wolf, D., 62.P25
Wong, C.B., 64.18
Wood, T., 5.9

Yagi, S., 51.P11, 52.1, 64.7, *see* book index
Yoshida, K., 61.P16

Ziegler, E.N., 31.P10
Zuelhsdorff, DuW., 41.P18, 84.P18

BOOK INDEX

J.H. Comroe *Physiology of Respiration* 2nd ed., Year Book Medical Publishers, 1974: 41.P20

W.H. Corcoran and W. N. Lacey *Introduction to Chemical Engineering Problems* McGraw-Hill, 1970: 3.P17

P.V. Danckwerts *Gas-Liquid Reactions* McGraw-Hill, 1970: 41.P13, 41P17

J.F. Davidson and D. Harrison *Fluidized Particles* Cambridge Univ. Press, 1963: 25.2

K.G. Denbigh and J.C.R. Turner *Chemical Reactor Theory; an Introduction* 2nd ed., Cambridge Univ. Press, 1971: 3.P19

M. Dixon and E.C. Webb *Enzymes* 2nd ed., Academic Press, 1964: 81.8

L.T. Fan *The Continuous Maximum Principle; a Study of Complex Systems Optimization"* Wiley, 1966: 6.7

H. Grey *Anatomy of the Human Body* C.M. Gross ed., 29th American ed. Lea and Febiger, 1973: 41.P20

C.G. Hill, Jr. *An Introduction to Chemical Engineering Kinetics and Reactor Design* Wiley, 1977: 22.P13

A. Husain and K. Gangiah *Optimization Techniques for Chemical Engineers* Macmillan of India, Delhi, 1976: 6.6, 6.7, 6.P1, 6.P19

D.Kunii and O. Levenspiel *Fluidized Engineering* 2nd ed., Butterworth-Heinemann, 1991: 25.1, 25.4, 54.17, 100.6

O. Levenspiel *Chemical Reaction Engineering* 2nd ed., Wiley, 1972: 2.4, 2.5, 2.8, 5.3, 5.4, 5.5

B. G. Levich *Physiochemical Hydrodynamics* Prentice Hall, 1962: 54.24

W. H. McAdams *Heat Transmission* 3rd ed., McGraw-Hill, 1954: 100.6

J. Monod *Recherches sur la Croissance des Cultures Bacteriennes* 2nd ed., Herman, Paris, 1958: 83.P1

J.H. Perry *Chemical Engineers' Handbook* McGraw-Hill; 3rd ed., 1950; 5th ed., 1973: 41.P20, 100.6

E.K. Pye and L.B. Wingard, eds. *Enzyme Engineering* Vol. 2, Plenum, 1974: 26.4, 31.P11

C.N. Satterfield *Mass Transfer in Heterogeneous Catalysis* M.I.T. Press, 1970: 21.P7, 22.P10, 100.6

T.K. Sherwood, R.L. Pigford and C.R. Wilke *Mass Transfer* McGraw-Hill, 1975: 41.P20

J.M. Smith *Chemical Engineering Kinetics* 2nd ed., McGraw-Hill, 1970: 55.12

M.O. Tarhan *Catalytic Reactor Design* McGraw-Hill, 1983: 21.P8

C.Y. Wen and L.T. Fan *Models for Flow Systems and Chemical Reactors* Dekker, 1971: 68.15

S. Yagi and D. Kunii *Fifth (International) Symposium on Combustion* pg. 231, Reinhold, 1955: 51.1, 52.1, 55.3

SUBJECT INDEX

Absorption (no reaction),
  kinetics, 41.1
  design, 42.6 - 12
Absorption with reaction
  kinetics, 41.3 - 10
  design, 42.13 - 18
Activation energy, 1.4
  apparent under strong pore diffusion, 23.2
Active flow, 62.1
Adiabatic packed beds, 24. -
  cold inert injection, 24.11
  cold shot cooling, 24.10
  endothermic reaction, 24.14
  energy balance line, 24.2
  hot spots, 24.15
  multistage design, 24.7
  single reactor design, 24.3
  temperature excursions, 24.15
  unstable operating regimes, 24.19
Age distribution, *see* E curve
Agitated tanks, 42.1
Analysis of data,
  differential and integral, 2.2
  by tracer curves, 63. -
Apparent activation energy, 23.2, 31.17
Arbitrary E curve, conversion with, 61.6
Aris-Taylor expression, 64.19
Arrhenius activation energy, *see* Activation energy
Ash diffusion control,
  for multistage operations, 52.15
  kinetics for SCM, 51.2, 51.5
  for single fluidized reactors, 52.3
Attrition in reactors, 52.12
Autocatalytic reactions, 2.6, 5.3
Avrami model, 55.18
Axial dispersion coefficient, *see* Dispersion coefficient
Axial dispersion in flow, *see* Dispersion

Backmix, *see* Mixed flow
Basket reactor, 21.5
  for deactivation studies, 31.2
Batch reactors,
  basic equations, 2.1
  constant volume, 2.2
  differential method, 2.2
  for catalytic reactions, 21.5, 21.P13, 21.P14
  for enzyme fermentations, 81.12, 81.15
  for G/L reactions, 42.11, 42.17
  for G/S reactions, 52.2
  for microbial fermentations, 82.2, 83.2, 84.2
  integrated forms, 2.2, 3.2
  variable volume, 2.7
Bingham plastics, tracer curve, 68.10
Bodenstein number, 68.2, 100.6
Briggs-Haldane mechanism, 81.3
Brownian motion, 54.22
Boundary conditions, *see* Vessel
Bubble tank, 42.1
Bubble tower, 42.1
Bubbling fluidized bed, 25. -
Bubbling bed model, *see* K· L model
Bypass flow, 62.1, 62.6

Carryover from fluidized beds, *see* Elutriation
Catalyst, *also see* Solid catalysed reaction
  deactivation 31.1
  effective pellet size, 22.2, 23.1
  enzymes, 81. -
  macro-micro structure, 23.9
  microbes, 82. -
  pore diffusion resistance, 22.3, 23. -
  regeneration, 33.1
  test for mass transfer effects, 22.12
Catalytic reactors
  basic equations 21.3
  choice in practice, 21.7
  circulation systems, 33.2
  enzyme, 81. -
  experimental, 21.5
  fixed beds, 24. -
  fluidized beds, 25. -
  microbial, 82.-, 83.-, 84.-
  monolith, 26. -
  parallel plate, 26. -
  porous wall, 26. -
  product distribution, 23.7
  slurry, 34. -
  three phase fluidized, 34. -
  trickle bed, 34. -
  tube wall, 21.1, 23.P37, 26. -
  with deactivating catalyst, 31. -, 32. -, 33. -
CCM, 55.6
CCM for multistep reactions, 55.22
Changing voidage models, 55.8
Chart of X_A *vs* T, 24.P13
Chemical tracers, 61.11, 61.17, 62.7
Chemostat, 83.15
Circulation system,
  for growing and shrinking solids, 54.20
  for SCM, 53.5
Closed-open vessel B.C., 64.8
Closed vessel B.C., 64.7
Cloud phase, 25.3
Coagulation of particles, 54.22
Coalescence of particles, 54.22
Cold inert injection, 24.11

Subject index

Cold shot operations, 24.10
Combining rates, 11.12, 51.3
Comparison of reactors, 5.4
Compartment flow models, 62. -
  listing, 62.2
Competing reactions, *see* Parallel reactions
Competitive inhibition, 81.9
  experimental fit, 81.12
Concentration to conversion, 1.7
Condensation onto particles, 54.23
Consecutive-competitive reactions, *see* Series-parallel reactions
Convection flow model, 68. -
  and reaction, 68.13
  for falling films, 68.11
  for non newtonians, 68.8
  line measurement, 68.12
  pulse response, 68.3
  step response, 68.6
Conversion to concentration, 1.7
Crackling core model, 55.6
CSTR, *see* Mixed flow reactor
CVM, 55.8 - 12

Davidson bubble, 25.3
Deactivation,
  example, 31.19
  experimental devices, 31.2
  experimental search, 31.4
  flowing solids, 33. -
  in fluidized reactors, 33. -
  in reactor/regenerators, 33. -
  in raining solids reactors, 33.P17
  in transfer line reactors, 33.P18
  once through reactors, 32.2
  order, 31.3
  product poisoning, 82.6, 84. -
  rate forms, 31.1
  recirculating reactors, 32.15
  slow, 32. -
  with pore diffusion, 31.16
Dead regions in reactors, 62.1, 62.6
Deadwater, 62.1, 62.6
Decaying catalysts, *see* Deactivation
Decoupling rate phenomena, 31.10
Degrees of freedom,
  in S/S reactions, 55.14
Delta function, 61.12
Denbigh reaction scheme, 8.21
  illustrative example, 25.15
  in fluidized beds, 25.12
Differential reactors, for catalytic reactions, 21.5
Diffusion in product layer, *see* Ash diffusion
Diffusivity, units, 100.3
  from dispersion experiments, 64.17, 64.P14 - P16
Dilution, 83.15
Dimensionless groups, listing, 100.5
Dirac d-function, 61.12
Dispersion and reaction,
  first order, 64.20
  n th order, 64.21
  other reactions, 64.22
Dispersion coefficient, 64.2
Dispersion equations and charts,
  far from plug flow, 64.5, 64.12
  near plug flow, 64.3, 64.11
Dispersion in laminar flow
  adsorbing surfaces, 64.19
  coiled tubes, 64.18
  newtonians, 64.18
  non newtonians, 64.18
  porous particles, 64.18
  porous vessel walls, 64.19
  various channel shapes, 64.18
Dispersion model, 64. -
  and reaction, 64.19
  pulse experiments, 64.2
  step experiments, 64.11
  vs tanks in series, 66.4
Dispersion number, dimensionless,
  intensity measure, 64.15, 100.6
  overall, for vessel, 64.2, 64.15, 100.6
Dispersion number, experimental,
  in packed beds, 64.16
  in tubes and pipes, 64.15
  restrictions, 64.17

Eadie plot, 81.7
Early and late mixing, 61.4
E curve, 61.2
  for compartment models, 62.2
  for convection model, 68.3, 68.8
  for dispersion model, 64.3
  for mixed flow, 61.16, 62.2
  for plug flow, 61.16, 62.2
  for tanks in series model, 66.2
  from chemical experiments, 61.17
  from pulse experiments, 61.9, 61.15
  relation to F curve, 61.15
Economic problems, 5.14
Effectiveness factor, 22.3, 23.1
Effective particle size, 23.1
Elutriation,
  definition of constant, 52.6
  effect on $\bar{t}$, 52.9
  experimental evaluation, 52.7
Elutriation constant,
  from batch experiments, 52.7

Subject index

from circulation systems, 52.8
Emulsion phase, 25.3
Endothermic reactions,
best reactor type, 24.5
equilibrium shift with temperature, 24.2
Energy, units, 100.2
Energy balance,
adiabatic operations, 24.2
non-adiabatic operations, 24.5
Enhancement factor, 41.3
design chart, 41.3
Entrainment, *see* Elutriation
Enzyme fermentation, 81.1
batch or plug flow 81.5
mechanism of action, 81.2
Michaelis-Menten, 81.2
mixed flow, 81.6
vs microbial fermentation, 81.1, 82.5
with inhibition, 81.9
Enzyme inhibition, 81.9
competitive, 81.9 - 13
non-competitive, 81.9 - 13
substrate, 81.14 - 15
uncompetitive, 81.P9
Equations for batch reactors
autocatalytic, 2.6
constant volume, 2.2 - 2.6
deactivating catalysts, 31.13 - 15
enzyme reactions, 81.5
enzymes with inhibition, 81.12 - 81.15
first order, 2.2
homogeneous catalysed, 2.6
macrofluids, 51.5, 61.7, 68.13
microbial, 83.2, 84.12
Michaelis-Menten, 81.5
Monod, 83.2
multiple reactions, 8.-
n th order, 2.4
parallel, 7.2
reversible first order, 2.3
reversible second order, 2.3
second order, 2.3
series reactions, 2.5, 8.1
shifting order, 2.5
solid catalysed, 21.3
third order, 2.4
variable volume, 2.7
zero order, 2.2
Examples, *see* Illustrative examples
Exit age distribution, *see* E curve
Expansion factor, 1.6, 1.P34
Experimental catalytic reactors, 21.5
Exponential integral, 32.6
F curve, 61.14
for compartment model, 62.2
for convection model, 68.6
for dispersion model, 64.11
for mixed flow, 61.16, 62.2
for plug flow, 61.16, 62.2
from step experiments, 61.14
for tanks in series model, 61.1
relation to E curve, 61.15
Falling film flow, tracer curve, 68.11
Fast bubble, 25.3
Fast fluidized bed, 25.1
Fermentation, definition, 81.1
Film conversion parameter, 41.4
Film diffusion control
for SCM, 51.2, 51.5
in multistage operations, 52.15
Film heat transfer, around catalysts, 22.8
Film mass transfer
around catalysts, 22.10
at a surface, 11.3
in G/L systems, 41.2
in G/S systems 51.1
rate equations, 54.25
Film ΔT, 22.9
First order reaction,
in batch reactors, 2.2
in dispersed plug flow, 64.19
in fluidized beds, 25.7
in laminar flow 68.13
in mixed flow, 4.2
in plug flow 3.2
in recycle reactors, 5.2
in tanks in series, 5.5
with tracer curves, 61.1
Fixed bed reactors, *see* Adiabatic packed beds,
dispersion within, 64.16
Flow boundary conditions,
closed-open vessel, 64.8, 64.12
closed vessel, 64.7, 64.12
near plug flow, 64.3, 64.11
open-closed vessel, 64.8, 64.12
open vessel, 64.9, 64.12
Flow model,
choice between, 64.1, 68.1
comparison, 64.1, 66.4, 68.1
compartment, 62. -
convection, 68. -
dispersion, 64. -
fluidized bed, 25.4
pure diffusion, 68.1
tanks in series, 66. -
Fluidized reactors,
for catalytic reactions, 25. -

Subject index

for deactivating catalysts, 33.1
for G/S reactions, 52. -, 53. -
for three phase systems, 34. -
$\bar{t}$ for solids, 52.9
Fluid solid reactions, *see* G/S reactions
Flux input and output, 68.4
Fractional conversion, *see* Conversion
Fractional life, 2.9
Fractional yield, 7.1
effect of pore diffusion, 23.7 - 8
in macro-micro pores, 23.11
in microbial fermentations, 82.4
in mixed flow, 7.2
in plug flow, 7.2

Gas constant, 100.2
G/L kinetics,
special cases, 41.6
straight absorption 41.2
use of equations, 41.9
with reaction, 41.3
G/L reactors,
agitated tanks, 42.15
batch of liquid, 42.17
bubble tanks, 42.16
static mixers, 42.14
towers, design 42.13
types and features, 42.2
GPM, 55.4
GPM for multistep reactions, 55.21
Grainy pellet model, 55.4
Growing particles,
from seed, 54.13, 54.15
mechanisms of growth, 54.22
mixed flow, basics, 54.5
numerical calculations, 54.16
one size feed, 54.14
plug flow, 54.4
rate equations, 54.1
G/S reactions,
changing gas environment, 53. -
growing particles, 54. -
in fluidized beds, examples, 51.9, 51.13
kinetic models, 51. -. 55.1
models for constant size, 51. -. 55.1
multistep reactions, 55.20
recirculation systems, 53.2
shrinking particles, 54. -
G/S reactions, kinetic models,
Avrami, 55.18
CCM, 55.6
CCM for multistep reactions, 55.22
changing voidage, 55.8
CVM, 55.8
GPM, 55.4
GPM for multistep reactions, 55.21
grainy pellet, 55.4
growing particles, 54.1
n th order form, 51.6
PCM, 55.16
Prout-Tompkins, 55.16
SCM, 51. -, 55.2
SCM for multistep reactions, 55.20
shrinking core, 51. -, 55.2
shrinking particles, 54.1
TDM, 55.13
thermal decomposition, 55.13
uniform conversion, 55.3
G/S reactors, design equations,
charts, 52.17
choice in practice, 52.19
for changing particles size, 54. -
for elutriating solids, 52.5
for fluidized beds, 52.3
for grower-shrinker, 54.20
for multistage fluidized beds, 52.14
for shaft kilns, 52.2
for size mixtures, 52.3
for wide size distribution, 52.16

Half life of a reaction, 2.4
Hatta modulus, 41.4
Heat effects in catalyst pellets, 22.5
Heat transfer coefficient units, 100.4
Henry's law, 23.P5, 41.2
Holding time, *see* Mean residence time
Homogeneous reactions,
batch operations, 2. -
batch recirculation, 5.13
economic considerations, 5.14
mixed flow, 4. -
multistage operations, 5.5
optimum set up, 5.6
plug flow, 3. -
recycle flow, 5.1
side entry, 5.10, 6.3, 6.5
Hot spots, 24.15
H_2S removal from gas, 53.2

Ideal gas, 100.2
Ideal stirred tank, *see* Mixed flow
Ideal tubular reactor, *see* Plug flow
Illustrative examples,
3 phase bubble column, 34.14
deactivation and pore resistance, 31.19
fluidized beds, catalytic, 25.9, 25.15
G/S reactions, 53.9, 53.13

Subject index

homogeneous reactions, 1.9, 2.9, 3.5
multiphase reactors, 11.1, 11.2, 11.4
parallel reactions, 7.2
product distribution, 6.5
slurry reactors, 34.16
tube wall reactor, 26.5
Induction period, 82.2
Inhibition in enzyme systems, 81.9
in microbial systems, *see* Product poisoning
Inlet of vessel, *see* Vessel
Impaction onto particles, 54.23
Instantaneous fractional yield, 7.1
Independent deactivation, 31.2
Integral analysis, 2.2
Integrated rate expressions, *see* Equations for
Intercooling between staged packed beds, 24.13
Internal diffusion in porous catalysts, *see* Pore diffusion
Irreversible adiabatic reaction, 24.2
Irrigated packed bed, 42.1

K·L model,
Denbigh reaction example, 25.15
development, 25.4
first order example, 25.9
for catalytic reactions, 25.7
for deactivating catalysts, 33.6
for Denbigh reactions, 25.11
for G/S reactions, 53.5
G/S examples, 53.9, 53.13
Knudsen diffusion, 100.3

Laminar flow,
convection model, 68. -
dispersion, *see* Dispersion in laminar flow
conversion, 68.13
Langmuir kinetics, 23.6
Large particle fluidized beds, 25.19
Linearizing the rate equations, 11.3
Line tracer measurement, 68.12
Lineweaver plot, 81.8

Macrofluid, 61.2
conversion, 61.7
Macro-micro pores, 23.10
Mass, units, 100.1
Mass transfer coefficient, units, 100.4
Maximization of rectangles, 5.6
Mean residence time, 1.6
from pulse experiments, 63.3
from step experiments, 63.7
in porous adsorbing systems, 64.19
of solids, 33.2
Mean size of solids, 54.3
Mechanism,
of deactivation, 31.1, 31.3
of enzyme action, 81.2
of enzyme inhibition, 81.9
of microbial fermentation, 82.2, 82.5
of multistep reactions of solids, 55. -
of particle growth, 54.22
of particle reaction, 51.1, 55. -
of particle shrinkage, 54.24
Michaelis constant, 81.4
Michaelis-Menten kinetics, 81.2
batch or plug flow, 81.5
contrast with Monod equation, 82.5
experimental fit, 81.7
mechanism, 81.2
mixed flow, 81.6
Microbial fermentation,
general discussion, 82. -
general kinetic equation, 82.6, 84.1
Monod equation, 82.5
poison limiting equation, 82.6
Microfluid, 61.2
conversion equations, 61.7
Minimum fluidizing velocity, 25.4
Mixed fermentors,
optimum operations, 83.8, 84.6, 84.8
washout, 83.8, 84.6, 84.8
with cell recycle, 83.13, 84.7
Mixed flow reactors,
basic equation, 4.1
changing particle size, 54.5
constant particle size, 52.3
for catalytic reactions, 21.5
for macrofluids, 61.7
for G/S reactions, 52.3
for microbial fermentations, 83.6, 84.5
for various kinetics, 4.2
in series, 5.5
optimum size ratio, 5.6
RTD, 61.16, 62.2
vs plug flow, 5.4
Mixing cup measure, *see* Flux
Molecular weight, units, 100.2
Monod constant, 82.5
Monod kinetics,
contrast with Michaelis-Menten, 82.5
experimental fit, 83.3
generalized, 82.6, 84.10
in batch or plug flow, 83.2
in mixed flow 83.6
Monolith reactors, 21.1, 26. -
Moving bed reactors, 52.1
Multiple reactions,

Denbigh system, 8.21
examples, qualitative, 6.5
fractional yield, 7.1
general discussion, 6.1, 7.1
on porous catalysts, 23.7
optimum temperatures, 6.2, 6.6
parallel, 7.1, 23.7
qualitative, 6. -
rules for operations, 6.2
series, 6.3, 8.1, 23.8
series-parallel, 8.12
side by side, 7.1, 23.7
Multiphase reactors,
flow models, 11.7, 11.P100
general discussion, 11. -
types, 32.1, 34.1, 42.1, 52.1, 53.1
Multistage adiabatic reactors, 24.7
best reactor type, 24.12
cold inert injection, 24.11
cold shot cooling, 24.10
location of heat exchangers, 24.13
mixed flow, 24.9
plug flow, 24.7
recycle, 24.9
Multistage reactors,
for fixed bed catalytic, 24.7
for G/S systems, 52.14
for homogeneous reactions, 5.5
for microbial fermentations, 83.10

Non adiabatic fixed beds, 24.3, 24.5
Non competitive inhibition, 81.9
experimental fit, 81.12
Non-ideal flow, 61. - to 68. -
compartment models, 62. -
convection model, 68. -
dispersion model, 64. -
experimental methods, 61.8
tanks in series model, 66. -
n th order reactions,
apparent, in catalysts, 23.5
half life, 2.4
in batch reactors, 2.4
in dispersed plug flow, 64.20
in macrofluids, 61.7
in mixed flow, 4.3
in plug flow, 2.4, 61.7
in strong pore diffusion regime, 23.5
Nusselt number, 100.6

Observed activation energy, 23.5
Observed reaction order, 23.5
Open-closed vessel, B.C., 64.8
Optimum reactor combination, 5.7
adiabatic packed beds, 24.4, 24.7
microbial fermentations, 83.10, 84.7
Optimum recycle ratio, 5.3, 24.9
Optimum size ratio,
adiabatic packed beds, 24.9
flowing catalyst, 33.7
flowing reacting solids, 53.5
mixed flow reactors, 5.6
Optimum temperature,
for multiple reactions, 6.6, 7.6
in adiabatic packed beds, 24.2
Optimum temperature progression,
in deactivating systems, 32.9
in fixed bed reactors, 24.5
Order,
observed for catalysts, 23.5
of deactivation, 31.3
of product poisoning, 82.6, 84.1, 84.7
of reaction, 1.3

Packed beds, intensity of dispersion, 64.16
Parallel deactivation, 31.1
Parallel reactions,
best reactor type 7.3
in porous catalysts, 23.7
optimum temperature, 7.7
qualitative, 6.2
qualitative examples, 6.5
quantitative, 7. -
temperature effects, 7.6
Partial emptying batch reactor, 5.8
Particle growth, *see* Growing particles
Particle shrinkage, *see* Shrinking particles
Pathological flow in vessels, 62.6
PCM, 55.16
Peclet number, 100.6
PEBR, 5.8
Performance equations,
batch reactors, 2.1
catalytic reactors, 21.3
deactivating catalysts, 31. -
enzyme reactors, 81.5
fluidized reactors, 25.8, 25.23
microbial reactors, 83.2, 84.2
mixed flow reactors, 4.1
plug flow reactors, 3.1
recycle reactors, 5.1
PFR *see* plug flow reactor
Phase change models, 55.16
Planar input and output, 68.4
Plate tower, 42.1
Plug flow reactors,
basic equation, 3.1
for catalytic reactions, 21.3

Subject index

for enzyme reactions, 81.5
for microbial reactions, 83.2, 84.2
integrated forms, 3.2
non isothermal, 3.4
vs mixed flow reactors, 5.4
Pore diffusion resistance, 23. -
effectiveness factor, 23.1
with deactivation, 31.16
Porous catalyst pellet,
film ΔT, 22.9
film mass transfer, 22.10
interpreting experiments, 22.12
pore diffusion, 22.3
surface kinetics, 22.2
temperature gradients, 22.5
with deactivation, 31.16
with multiple reactions 23.7
Porous wall reactor, 26.1 -
Power law fluid,
tracer curve, 68.8
Prandtl number, 100.5
Pressure, units, 100.1
Probability paper, 63.8
use with dispersion model, 64.14
Product distribution
in microbial fermentations, 82.4
in multiple reactions, 6. -, 7. -, 8. -
in strong pore diffusion, 23.7
Product poisoning fermentors, 84. -
batch or plug flow, 82.3, 84.2
kinetic equation, 82.6, 84.1, 84.7
mixed flow, 84.5
optimum operations, 84.4, 84.8
recycle reactor, 84.3
with cell recycle, 84.7
Product poisoning plus substrate depletion, 84.10
Prout-Tompkins model, 55.16
Pipe flow, intensity of dispersion, 64.15 - 16
Pulse tracer experiment, 61.9

Raining solids reactor, 33.P17
Rate equations, 1.3
concentration dependent term, 1.4
for catalytic reactions, 21.2
for catalyst regeneration, 33.1
for deactivating catalysts, 31.1
for enzyme reactions, 81. -
for G/L reactions, 41.3
for growing particles, 54. -
for G/S, constant particle size, 51. -, 55. -
for microbial reactions, 83. -, 84. -
for porous catalysts, 22.1
for shrinking particles, 54. -
for slurry reactors, 34.2
for S/S reactions, 55.14
for straight absorption, 41.2
for three phase systems, 34.2
for trickle beds, 34.2
magnitude, 100.5
Rate of reactions, *see* Rate equations
Reaction order, 1.3
observed or apparent, 23.5
Reactions in series,
$A \rightarrow R \rightarrow S$, 8.1
$A \rightarrow R \rightarrow S \rightarrow T$, 8.8
mixed orders, 8.6
Reactor-regenerator,
for deactivating catalyst, 33. -
for growing and shrinking solids, 54.20
for G/S reactions, 53.5
Recirculating flow, *see* Recycle reactors,
Recycle reactors,
basic equation, 5.1
for catalytic reactions, 21.6
for microbial fermentations, 83.4, 84.3
integrated forms, 5.2
optimum recycle in fermentors, 83.5
optimum recycle ratio, 5.3
tracer curves, 62.3, 62.4, 62.6
warnings on use of, 21.6
with cell recycle, 83.14
with Monod kinetics, 83.4
with product poison fermentation, 84.3
Regeneration equations, 33.1
Residence time distribution, 61.2
Reynolds number, 100.5
RTD, *see* E curve

Schmidt number, 100.5
SCM, 51. -, 55.2
ash diffusion control, 51.2
combined resistance, 51.3
conversion equations, 51.5
film control, 51.2
finding the rate controlling step, 51.4
for multistep reactions, 55.20
reaction control, 51.2
Second order reaction,
in batch reactors, 2.3
in dispersed plug flow, 64.21
in laminar flow, 68.13
in macrofluids, 61.7
in mixed flow, 4.2
in plug flow, 3.2
in recycle reactors, 5.2
in series of tanks, 5.5
Sedimentation in reactors, 52.10
Segregated flow, 61.2

Subject index

Series deactivation, 31.2
Series-parallel reactions,
two step, 8.12
three step, 8.18
Denbigh, 8.21
Series reactions,
qualitative, 6.3
qualitative examples, 6.5
quantitative, 8.1
in porous catalysts, 23.8
Shaft kilns, 52.1
with SCM, 52.2
Sherwood number, 100.6
Shifting order reactions, 2.5, 81.4
with strong pore diffusion, 23.6
Shortcircuiting in reactors, 24.16, 62.6
Shrinking core model, *see* SCM
Shrinking particles,
mechanisms of shrinkage, 54.22
mixed flow, basics, 54.5
numerical calculations, 54.11
one size feed, 54.7
plug flow reactor, 54.4
rate equation, 54.1
Side-by-side deactivation, 31.2
Side-by-side reactions, 7.1
in porous catalysts, 23.7
Side entry reactor, 5.10
Side feed reactor, 5.10
Single phase reactions, *see* Homogeneous reactions
Size distribution of solids, 52.1, 54.2
Slow bubble, 25.3
Slow deactivation, 32. -
changing flow, 32.7
changing temperatures, 32.9
constant flow, 32.2
with product separation and recycle, 32.15
Slow reaction in G/L systems, 41.8
Slugging fluidized beds, 25.1
Slurry reactors, 21.1, 34. -
general rate equation, 34.2
performance equation, 34.6
vs trickle beds, 34.11
example, 34.16
Solid catalysed reaction,
effectiveness factor, 22.3, 23.1
film resistance, 22.10
heat effects, 22.5
kinetic regimes, 22.1
pore diffusion, 22.3, 23.1
product distribution, 23.7
rate controlling regimes, 22.1
rate with deactivation, 31.1
rate with no deactivation, 21. -, 22. -, 23. -
regeneration, 33.1
Solids, size distribution, 52.1, 54.2
Space-time, 1.6, 21.4
Spherical particles, *see* G/S reactions
Spray tower, 42.1
S/S reactions, 55.14
Staged bubble tower, 42.1
Stagnant regions in reactors, 62.1, 62.6
State of aggregation, 61.2
Static mixer, 42.1
Staged reactors,
homogeneous reaction, 5.5
fixed bed catalytic, *see* Multistage
microbial reaction, 83.10
Step response, *see* F curve
Step tracer experiment, 61.13
Substrate inhibition, 81.14, 82.7
experimental fit, 81.15
Substrate limiting microbial fermentation, 83. -
in batch or plug flow, 83.2
in mixed flow, 83.6
in recycle reactor, 83.4
optimum operations, 83.10
with cell recycle, 83.13
Successive reaction, *see* Reactions in series
Surface reaction control,
conversion equations, 11.3
for SCM, 51.2, 51.5
in multistage operations, 52.15
Surface-time, 21.4

$\bar{t}$ of solids in reactors, 52.3
in multistage operations, 52.14
with attrition and elutriation, 52.12
with elutriation, 52.19
with sedimentation, 52.11
Tanks in series model, 66. -
and reaction, 66.7
near plug flow, 66.3
pulse experiment, 66.1
step experiment, 61.6
vs dispersion model, 66.4
TDM, 55.13
Temperature and reaction rate, 1.3, 24.1
Temperature gradients,
across the film, 22.9
within the pellet, 22.5
Temperature progression, optimum in fixed bed reactors, 24.5
Temperature runaway, 24.15
Terminology,
for batch reactors, 1.5
for flow reactors, 1.6

for biochemical reactions, 83.15
Thermal conductivity, units, 100.4
Thermal decomposition model, 55.13
Thiele modulus, 22.3, 23. -
for first order reaction, 22.3, 23.1
for first order reversible, 23.4
for macro-micro particles, 23.10
for *n* th order reaction, 23.4
for shifting order, 23.6
with deactivation, 31.16
with multiple reactions, 23.7
Three phase fluidized beds, 34. -
general rate equation, 34.2
performance equation, 34.2
vs slurry reactors, 34.11
vs trickle beds, 34.11
Through the wall measure, *see* Planar
Time
mixing *vs* others, 61.3
reaction *vs* others, 61.3, 61.5
residence *vs* others, 61.5
space-time, 1.6
weight-time, 21.3
Time lag fermentation, 82.3
Tracer curves for flow,
as diagnostic tools, 62.6
mean of, 63.1
variance of, 63.1
also see E curves and F curves
Tracer methods, 61.8
Transfer line reactor, 33.P34
Trickle bed reactor, 21.1, 34. -
general rate equation, 34.2
performance equation, 34.6
vs slurry reactors, 34.11
Turbidostat, 83.15
Two film theory, 34.3, 41.2
Two step reactions,
first order, 8.1
mixed order, 8.8
series-parallel, 8.12

UCM, 55.3
Uncompetitive inhibition, 81.P9
Uniform conversion model, 55.3

Variance of tracer curve, 63.1
and dispersion, 64.4 - 10
and number of tanks, 66.2
from pulse experiments, 63.3
from step experiments, 63.7
Vessel, inlet and outlet,
closed, 64.8
flux, 68.4
open, 64.8
planar, 68.4
Viscosity, units, 100.2

Wagner-Weisz-Wheeler modulus, 22.3
Wake, 25.2
Washout in fermentors, 83.8
with cell recycle, 83.14
Weight-time, 21.3
Weisz-Wagner-Wheeler modulus, 22.3
Wheeler-Wagner-Weisz modulus, 22.3

Zero order reaction,
in batch reactors, 2.2
in dispersed plug flow, 64.20
in laminar flow, 68.13
in macrofluids, 61.7
in mixed flow, 4.2
in plug flow, 3.2
in series of tanks, macrofluid, 52.15